MODERN ALGEBRAIC TOPOLOGY

D. G. BOURGIN

Professor of Mathematics, University of Illinois

ALGEBRAIC

MODERN TOPOLOGY

THE MACMILLAN COMPANY, NEW YORK

COLLIER-MACMILLAN LIMITED, LONDON

First Printing

Library of Congress catalog card number: 63-7395

THE MACMILLAN COMPANY, NEW YORK
COLLIER-MACMILLAN CANADA, LTD., TORONTO, ONTARIO

Printed in the United States of America

To my family

PREFACE

This book came into being as a foundations preface to a projected monograph on fixed point theory. The foundations finally engulfed the structure, though the original intention persists in vestigial traces. The book is planned to provide basic understanding of various aspects of modern algebraic topology. The material has been taken from the author's lectures at the University of Illinois in recent years.

Many excellent suggestions have not been adopted either because of equally excellent counter suggestions, or because in a state of euphoria the author planned on their later incorporation. Eventually with the horizon of algebraic topology receding faster than the rate at which new additions could be made, the writer stopped. Not that the book had been finished; no such book can be, probably, but there was a halt to the writing. Accordingly the list of topics omitted looms large. With a wide interpretation, the choice of material for inclusion has more often than not been decided by its possible bearing on maps.

The book opens with the definition of a group and ends with spectral sequence applications of sheaf theory. It is intended for formal class or self study by the neophyte or more advanced student, for the mathematician interested in apprehending topological methods, as well as for the bookshelf of the serious practitioner in the field.

Effort has been taken to make the explanations clear and complete. The exposition is fortified with numerous examples and remarks culled from the recent literature, from results obtained by the author, and from his students' theses. Proofs are almost invariably given in all detail, except when the argument is really transparent. Very few steps have been left to the reader. There is no art for art's sake; all the concepts introduced find eventual use. The problems are not slabs of unprocessed research literature, but are fair and serve as illustrations and tests of comprehension. They are generally of not too great difficulty and sometimes announce novel results. Hints are frequently provided.

The reader who starts with Chapter 1 should be acquainted with the rudiments of Euclidean space topology. For convenience, a compendium of point set topology results is given in the appendix. It would be advantageous if algebra were studied at least concomitantly. It is not supposed that the reader's mathematical awareness is frozen in time, and later chapters are more sophisticated in their appeal to general mathematical knowledge. The first chapters are, by comparison, more descriptive.

A brief word about some of the contents and the presentation: The cutting and pasting of an earlier edition has been relegated in large part to the problems. The large number of standard examples collected in Chapter 3 provides the reader with varied patterns for perceiving the associated space relationships. Mutilated cells are introduced in order to give the beginner an intuitive view of the cocycles. Simplicial approximations play a central role as a direct as well as a heuristic aid in mapping problems. The matrix representation for the associated homomorphism is a useful tool. Accordingly the author has stressed matrix manipulation from the start and has therefore preferred the classical (matrix) demonstration of the fundamental decomposition for the homology groups of the finite complex. Besides the conventional simplicial complex and triangulable space developments, there is a reasonably full treatment of supports and gratings for locally compact spaces after Leray. By keeping the space aspects continually in sight there are notable gains in directness of proofs and the later sheaf developments are natural generalizations of the gratings. Proofs of invariance and uniqueness are deferred to Chapter 11, by which time the reader has become familiar with what homology can do. For the specific grating proofs offered, the writer has essentially followed indications given by Fary. A merit of Fary's type of proof is that it introduces a category concept of independent interest. The grating approach is also used for the fixed point index (in preference to the writer's work on this subject). Equivariant maps are combined with the Smith index. The collection of examples here will be of interest even if the Spectral Sequence developments are preferred. Cup and cap products are presented from varied viewpoints, though the Steenrod reduced powers enter implicitly only through the Smith homomorphisms. Recent Russian extensions of Alexander type duality are covered. The functorial viewpoint is given substantial treatment. Notable aspects show up in various resolutions and in applications of adjointness. The chapter on sheaf theory presents both the sheaf space or *l'espace étalé* and the more consistently functorial definitions.

The writer has not tampered unduly with terminology. A few variants are the introduction of m-strings, replete complex for the customary ordered complexes, general fiber bundle and fiber bundle instead of fiber bundle and locally trivial fiber bundle, serration for possibly non-continuous sections, cut homomorphism for section homomorphism, and generally section for cross section. Complex is used in the sharper sense of triviality for $n < 0$. Concrete cell (and complex) was preferred to geometrical cell in consonance with support notions. Full grating replaces fine couverture. A bolder innovation is the use of the term *omology* to connote the siblings *homology* and *cohomology*.

A check on clarity and accuracy has been afforded by the classroom presentation of all the material. Some of the writer's students have helped with the text and with the galley proofs, notably Douglas Taylor and Melvin Thornton. Special thanks for reading parts of the text in various drafts are due Professors D. A. Buchsbaum, A. H. Copeland, Jr., P. E. Conner, J. Dugundji, I. Fary, M. E. Hamstrom, S. T. Hu, G. R. Livesay, B. O'Neill, J. Rotman, and A. H. Stone. The list omits many mathematicians whose comments, lectures, and correspondence have been helpful.

The author would appreciate being apprised of the gross errors that have escaped surveillance as well as of minor inadvertencies.

Grateful acknowledgement is made of support from the Graduate College of the University of Illinois, the Air Force Office of Scientific Research, and the National Science Foundation.

CONTENTS

NOTE TO THE READER

In each chapter the indexing is by section number before the decimal, and equation number after. Thus (3.12) pinpoints equation .12 in section 3. In references to other chapters, the chapter number is prefixed. For example (143.12) is read Equation .12 in Section 3 of Chapter 14. (Since, except for the last chapter there are at most nine sections in a chapter, this is a unique specification.) The first section of the Appendix lists the main conventions and reference to it is indicated by (**A**).

chapter 1

PRELIMINARY ALGEBRAIC BACKGROUND

In order to consider modern formulations of Algebraic Topology directly, we must first present a few special elementary algebraic notions and a technical vocabulary bearing on groups and on integer matrices.

1. GROUP. Let us denote the real numbers excepting 0 by $R^1 = \{x\}$. We shall build upon some elementary examples. The pair of real numbers in the order (x, y) is called the **ordered pair** (x, y). We indicate the collection of all ordered pairs by $R^1 \times R^1$. Let $z = \psi(x, y)$ be a real number given as a function of (x, y). The correspondence of (x, y) and z is written $\psi: R^1 \times R^1 \to R^1$. The familiar product xy represents a particular choice of the function ψ, namely $\psi(x, y) = xy$. With this function for any three real numbers, we have $\psi(\psi(x, y), z) = \psi(x, \psi(y, z))$, or $(xy)z = x(yz)$. There is a real number, namely 1, such that $\psi(1, x) = \psi(x, 1) = x$. Finally, for every real number x in R^1, there is a real number y such that $\psi(x, y) = \psi(y, x) = 1$, and it is customary to denote y by x^{-1}. Another consequence of the choice $\psi(x, y) = xy$ is $\psi(x, y) = \psi(y, x)$. Similar remarks could be made for the real numbers under the operation of addition, that is to say for the choice $\psi(x, y) = x + y$ and now R^1 is understood to include 0 which plays the role of 1. For instance, in place of $1x = \psi(1, x) = x$ we have $0 + x = \psi(0, x) = x$. We shall be interested in collections in addition to those of the real numbers where a function ψ exists with properties formally similar to those listed above [with the exception that $\psi(x, y)$ and $\psi(y, x)$ need not be the same]. We refer to such a function as a **product** and again drop the cumbersome notation $\psi(x, y)$ in favor of xy or $x + y$. We make these remarks precise.

Definition 1.1. A **group** or **abstract group** G is a collection of elements g admitting a **product** or **composition** defined on $G \times G$ to G and denoted by $g \cdot g'$, or simply gg' subject to:

(a) $((g_1 \cdot g_2) \cdot g_3) = (g_1 \cdot (g_2 \cdot g_3))$.

(b) There is an element termed the **neutral** element or **identity** 1 (or in later usage, e) such that $g \cdot 1 = 1 \cdot g = g$ for every g in G.

(c) For every g there is a unique element designated by g^{-1} satisfying $g^{-1} \cdot g = g \cdot g^{-1} = 1$. This element g^{-1} is called the **inverse** of g.

Special groups of immediate utility to us are described in the examples at the end of this section. The group G is **Abelian** if for all pairs (g_1, g_2), $g_1 \cdot g_2 = g_2 \cdot g_1$. In this case we often write $+$ as the group operation, 0 for the neutral element, and $-g$ for the inverse element to g. Thus $g_1 \cdot {g_2}^{-1}$ is here $g_1 + (-g_2) = g_1 - g_2$. We define $2g$ as $g + g$, and ng is similarly defined. The literature reflects a growing tendency to use $+$ as a non-commutative operation also. This section concentrates on the Abelian group as the case entering our early applications.

Definition 1.2. Suppose G is an Abelian group with composition $+$; then G' is a **subgroup** of G if **(a)** $G' \subset G$ and **(b)** G' is a group with the composition of G. Often **(b)** is expressed by saying the composition $+'$ in G' is **induced** by $+$, which means $+$ restricted to elements of G'. Thus if g_1' and g_2' are in G', their composition as elements of G is defined by $g_1' + g_2'$. Clearly then G' is Abelian.

Definition 1.3. If N is a subgroup of the Abelian group G, an **equivalence** $g_1 \sim g_2$ with g_i in G is defined by $g_1 - g_2 \in N$, which is often expressed $g_1 \equiv g_2$ modulo N, or mod N. The totality of equivalents to g (under N) is called the **coset,** or **equivalence class,** determined by g and consists of $\{g + n \mid n \in N\}$. It is often denoted by $[g]_N$ or, if N is understood, simply by $[g]$, so $g_1 \sim g_2$ has the meaning $[g_1] = [g_2]$. Any element in a coset is referred to as a **representative** of the coset. Define the composition operation $\dot{+}$ for the collection of cosets $\{[g]\}$ by

$$[g_1] \dot{+} [g_2] = [g_1 + g_2]. \tag{1.3a}$$

We must show that (1.3a) is really a consistent definition; that is to say, if different representative elements are chosen, the same coset sum is obtained. Let $g_1' \sim g_1$, $g_2' \sim g_2$. Then $g_1' = g_1 + n_1$, $g_2' = g_2 + n_2$, where n_1, $n_2 \in N$. By (1.3a), $[g_1'] \dot{+} [g_2'] = [g_1' + g_2'] = [g_1 + g_2 + n_1 + n_2] = [g_1 + g_2]$. With the composition $\dot{+}$, $\{[g]\}$ is a group called the **quotient,** or **factor** (or **difference**), **group** of G by N. We denote it by G/N, though $G - N$ might seem more natural. In practice we write $+$ instead of $\dot{+}$, since the context sufficiently indicates whether G or G/N is in question.

Definition 1.4. If G and J are Abelian groups, then a single valued function ψ on G to J, with $\psi(g_1 + g_2) = \psi(g_1) + \psi(g_2)$, is called a **homomorphism.** Thus a homomorphism may be defined as an **additive map** and is sometimes referred to as a **linear map,** since $\psi(ng_1 + mg_2) = n\psi(g_1) + m\psi(g_2)$, where n and m are integers. The homomorphism is an **isomorphism into** J, or a **monomorphism,** if ψ is 1–1 on G to $\psi(G)$. Then ψ^{-1} is a homomorphism on $\psi(G)$ to G. It is **onto,** or an **epimorphism,** if $\psi(G) = J$. If ψ is both an epimorphism and a monomorphism, ψ is an **isomorphism onto** J, or simply an **isomorphism.** In this case we often write $G \overset{\psi}{\approx} J$, or $G \approx J$. When G is considered a subgroup of J, the monomorphism determined by the inclusion map is called an **injection.**

Definition 1.5. If G and J are Abelian groups, and if ψ is a homomorphism of G into J, the set $ker\, \psi = \{g \mid \psi(g) = 0 \text{ in } J\}$, is easily verified to be a subgroup of G and is called the **kernel** of ψ. The **image** of ψ written $Im\, \psi$ consists of all the elements $\psi(g)$, $g \in G$, and can be verified to be a subgroup of J.

Theorem 1.6. *If the Abelian group G contains the subgroup N, the transformation ψ on G to G/N defined by $\psi(g) = [g]_N$ is a homomorphism, often referred to as the* **natural** *homomorphism.*

Lemma 1.6. *If N and M are subgroups of the groups G and H respectively, and if ψ is a homomorphism of G into H under which $\psi(N) \subset M$ then ψ induces a homomorphism $\psi'\colon G/N \to H/M$ defined by*

$$\psi'[g]_N = [\psi g]_M.$$

We place on record two isomorphism theorems which are cornerstones for Algebraic Topology. Since they are not needed until Chapter 4, the beginning reader need not tarry over their proofs or implications at this time. They are referred to as the **first** and as the **second Noether isomorphism theorems,** respectively.

Theorem 1.7. *If N and G' are subgroups of G,*

$$\frac{G'}{G' \cap N} \approx \frac{G' + N}{N}, \tag{1.7a}$$

where $G' + N = \{g \mid g = g' + n,\quad g' \in G',\ n \in N\}$ is a subgroup of G.

Theorem 1.8. *If the Abelian group G contains the subgroup N and N' is a subgroup of N then*

$$\frac{G}{N} \approx \frac{G/N'}{N/N'}.$$

Definition 1.9. The elements $\{g_a \mid a \in A\}$ are **generators** of the Abelian group G if every element g of G is of the form

$$g = \sum_{a \in \pi} n_a g_a$$

for a in some finite subset π of A and the n_a's are integers. The number of distinct elements in a finite group is its **order.**

Definition 1.10. A collection $\{g_a\}$ in the Abelian group G is **independent** if there are no relations of the form

$$n_1 g_1 + \cdots + n_N g_N = 0,$$

where at least one n_i is not 0. The maximal number of linearly independent elements in the Abelian group G is called the **rank** of G and is written $r(G)$ or $|G|$ (and may be a transfinite cardinal number). It can be shown that $r(G)$ is the same for all choices of independent elements.

Definition 1.11. An independent set of generators of the Abelian group G is called a **basis** or a **base.**

Definition 1.12. An Abelian group G admitting a basis is a **free Abelian group.**

An important result is

Theorem 1.13. *A subgroup of a free Abelian group is a free Abelian group.*

Definition 1.14. The **order** of an element g of an Abelian group is the least positive integer $\{m \mid mg = 0\}$ or ∞. An Abelian group with one generator g is either a **cyclic group of order** m or is **infinite cyclic** if it is free. The **torsion subgroup** consists of all elements of finite order in the group.

Lemma 1.15. *A homomorphism on the free Abelian group G to a group J is uniquely determined (by additivity) by its values on a basis. Conversely for any assignment of range values in J to a map of elements of the basis $\{g_a\}$, there corresponds a homomorphism.*

In both cases if $g = \sum_{\pi} n_a g_a$, g_a in the basis, the transformation of g is by

$$\psi(g) = \psi(\sum_{\pi} n_a g_a) = \sum_{\pi} n_a \psi(g_a).$$

EXAMPLE 1-1. J is the group of integers under ordinary addition and $2J$ is the subgroup of J with elements $\{2m \mid m \in J\}$. (A common alternative notation is Z for J). Two integers m, m' are equivalent, $m \sim m'$ if $m - m' = 2m''$ for some m'', or $m = m' \bmod 2$, where we write mod 2 for mod $2\mathrm{J}$. A coset of $\mathrm{J}/2\mathrm{J}$ consists of the collection $\{m_0 + 2m \mid m \in \mathrm{J}\}$.

Hence the cosets are

$$[0] = \{0 + 2m \mid m \in \mathrm{J}\} = 0, \pm 2, \pm 4, \pm 6, \ldots$$
$$[1] = \{1 + 2m \mid m \in \mathrm{J}\} = \pm 1, \pm 3, \pm 5, \ldots$$
$$[1] + [1] = [1 + 1] = [0].$$

The group J_2 consists of two elements, 0 and g_1, with $g_1 + g_1 = 0$. It is customary to write 1 for g_1, and then $1 + 1 = 0$; the correspondence $0 \leftrightarrow [0]$, $1 \leftrightarrow [1]$ yields $\mathrm{J}_2 \approx \mathrm{J}/2\mathrm{J}$.

Example 1-2. $p\mathrm{J}$ is the group of integer multiples, of p, that is, $\{pm \mid m \in \mathrm{J}\}$. Then $m \sim m' \Leftrightarrow m - m' = pm''$, or $m = m' \bmod p$, where mod p is written for mod $p\mathrm{J}$. Any coset of $\mathrm{J}/p\mathrm{J} = \{m_0 + pm \mid m \in \mathrm{J}\}$. Thus

$$[0] = 0, \pm p, \pm 2p, \ldots$$
$$[p - 1] = \ldots, \quad -1, \quad 2p - 1, \quad -p - 1, \quad 3p - 1, \ldots$$

The operation $+$ is defined by $[r] + [s] = [r + s]$. The group J_p has elements $(0, g_1, \ldots, g_{p-1})$, or more simply $(0, +, \ldots, p - 1)$. The operation $+$ is defined by $r + s = t \bmod p$, $0 \leq t \leq p - 1$. The correspondence $j \leftrightarrow [j]$ yields the isomorphism $\mathrm{J}_p \approx \mathrm{J}/p\mathrm{J}$.

Example 1-3. Write the elements of J_{12}, $0, 1, \ldots, 11$, with $r + s = t \bmod 12$, $0 \leq t \leq 11$. Thus, mod 12, $9 + 6 = 15 - 12 = 3$, $8 + 4 = 12 - 12 = 0$, $2 + 5 = 7$.

We exhibit an isomorphism ψ of J_3 into J_{12}, that is, a monomorphism. The fact that $\psi(1 + 2) = \psi(0) = 0$ bars defining ψ by $\psi(0) = 0$, $\psi(1) = 1$, $\psi(2) = 2$. Evidently, though, a satisfactory definition is $\psi(0) = 0$, $\psi(1) = 4$, $\psi(2) = 8$. We can refer to J_3 or $\psi(\mathrm{J}_3)$ as a subgroup of J_{12}. Then the equivalence relation is $r \sim s \Leftrightarrow r - s = 0 \bmod 4$. The cosets of $\mathrm{J}_{12}/\mathrm{J}_3$ are $[0] = (0, 4, 8)$; $[1] = (1, 5, 9)$; $[2] = (2, 6, 10)$; $[3] = (3, 7, 11)$; $[4] = [0]$. The group J_4 consists of elements 0, 1, 2, 3, with $m + n = (m + n) \bmod 4$. The correspondence $[i] \leftrightarrow i$; that is, $[0] \leftrightarrow 0$, $[1] \leftrightarrow 1$, etc., yields the isomorphism $\mathrm{J}_{12}/\mathrm{J}_3 \approx \mathrm{J}_4$,

Example 1-4. R^3 is the Abelian additive group of real number triples (r, s, t) with $(r, s, t) + (r', s', t') = (r + r', \; s + s', \; t + t')$. The neutral element is $(0, 0, 0)$. R' is the subgroup of elements of the form $(0, 0, t)$. Obviously $R' \approx R^1$. Then $(r, s, t) \sim (r', s', t')$, if $r - r' = 0$, $s - s' = 0$, t, t' arbitrary. The cosets of R^3/R^1 are

$$\{(r_0, s_0, t) \mid t \in R^1\} = [r_0, s_0, 0] = [r_0, s_0, t'] = \cdots$$

and depend only on (r_0, s_0). Hence there is a 1–1 correspondence with the pairs of real numbers (r_0, s_0), so $[r_0, s_0, t]$ corresponds to $(r_0, s_0) \in R^2$. In short, $R^3/R^1 \approx R^2$.

EXAMPLE 1-5. Let G consist of the triples (r, s, t) where $r \in \mathrm{J}_3$ and s and t belong to J. Define the sum $(r, s, t) + (r', s', t')$ as $(r + r' \bmod 3,\ \ s + s', t + t')$. Evidently $(0, 1, 0)$ and $(0, 0, 1)$ are elements of a basis and no basis element independent of these two can be found. Hence the rank of G is 2. However, to generate G, we need at least one more generator which we can take as $(1, 0, 0)$; that is, any $g \in G$ is of the form (m, n, k), and so is $m(1, 0, 0) + n(0, 1, 0) + k(0, 0, 1)$. G is not a free group.

In Examples 1-1 and 1-2 the correspondence ψ, defined by $\psi(m \mid m \in \mathrm{J}) = [m]$, where $[m]$ is in $\mathrm{J}/2\mathrm{J}$ or in $\mathrm{J}/p\mathrm{J}$ respectively, is a homomorphism. Similarly in Example 1-3, the correspondence $\psi(m \mid m \in \mathrm{J}_{12}) = n$, where $n = m \bmod 3$, $0 \leq n < 3$ is an epimorphism on J_{12} to J_3. Thus, $\psi(5) = 2$, $\psi(7) = 1$, etc. and *ker* ψ consists of $(0, 3, 6, 9)$.

Notation 1.16. The groups designated by J, J_p, Q, R, C are the additive groups of the integers, the integers mod p; the rational numbers, the real numbers, and the complex numbers respectively.

Until we reach Section 8, reference to a coefficient group is understood to refer to one of the groups cited in (1.16).

PROBLEMS

1-1. If a group G has m elements, show $ma = 0$ for any $a \in G$.

1-2. Let G have m elements. Suppose some $a \in G$ has order n. Show n is a factor of m.

1-3. Let $G = \{(g_1, g_2, g_3)\}$ be the triples with each $g_i \in \mathrm{J}_6$. Let $\{(h_1, h_2)\} = G'$ be the pairs with $h_i \in \mathrm{J}_3$. Define a nontrivial homomorphism ψ of G into G' and exhibit *ker* ψ. Exhibit $G/$*ker* ψ. Define a correspondence of G into G. which is not a homomorphism.

1-4. For the groups in Problem 1-3 define a nontrivial homomorphism θ of G' into G. What is *Im* θ? Give at least two θ's which are monomorphisms.

1-5. Let $G = \{(g_1, g_2, g_3)\}$ with $g_i \in \mathrm{J}$. Define a homomorphism ψ of $G \to G$ which is not an isomorphism and exhibit *ker* ψ, $G/$*ker* ψ, *Im* ψ, and $G/$*Im* ψ.

1-6. Show the polynomials in x form an additive group. Show that the positive real numbers constitute a group under multiplication, but that the negative reals do not. Show any basis for Q is nonfinite.

2. UNIMODULAR MATRICES. Much of our early formal work involves linear transformations. These developments gain clarity in the symbolism of matrices.

Definition 2.1. An m **by** n **matrix** or (m, n) matrix is a collection of elements arranged in n columns and m rows and is usually indicated by **A** or by

(a_i^j), where the upper index refers to column position and the lower to row position. For instance, a_2^3 is the element in the second column and the third row. This section concerns itself exclusively with integer matrices; that is to say a_i^j is an integer, but later a_i^j may be a real or complex number or an even more general entity. If $\mathbf{A} = (a_i^j)$ is an (m, n) matrix and $\mathbf{B} = (b_s^t)$ is an (n, r) matrix, the **product AB** is defined as the (m, r) matrix $\mathbf{C} = (c_u^v)$ where

(2.1a) $$c_u^v = \Sigma_j \, a_j^v \, b_u^j$$

Unless $r = m$, **BA** is not defined, and in any case **BA** need not be the same as **AB**. An (m, m) matrix is a **square matrix.** The **unit matrix I** and the 0 **matrix 0** are square matrices,

$$\mathbf{I} = \begin{pmatrix} 1 & & & & \mathbf{0} \\ & \cdot & & & \\ & & 1 & & \\ & & & \cdot & \\ \mathbf{0} & & & & 1 \end{pmatrix}, \qquad \mathbf{0} = (\mathbf{0}).$$

The **determinant** $\Delta(\mathbf{A})$ **of the square matrix** (a_i^j) is the determinant with entries a_i^j. A square matrix is **nonsingular** if $\Delta(\mathbf{A}) \neq 0$. The nonsingular square matrix **A** has an **inverse** denoted by $\mathbf{A}^{-1}$ where $\mathbf{A}\mathbf{A}^{-1} = \mathbf{A}^{-1}\mathbf{A} = \mathbf{I}$.

Definition 2.2. An integer matrix is **unimodular of order** n if it is an $n \times n$ matrix and its determinant is ± 1.

Lemma 2.3. *The unimodular matrices of order n constitute a generally non-Abelian group, with* **I** *the identity element under matrix multiplication, and those matrices whose determinant is* $+1$ *constitute a subgroup.*

Definition 2.4. Let **A** be an (m, n) matrix. Then **A′** is an **r-square submatrix** of **A** if after deletion of the rows and columns of **A**, in which no element of **A′** appears, there results an (r, r) square matrix.

Definition 2.5. If **A** is an (m, n) integer matrix, its **rank** is r if the determinant of at least one r-**square** matrix is not 0, while the determinants of all $r + 1$-**square** matrices are 0.

Definition 2.6. The (m, n) integer matrices **A** and **B** are **equivalent.** $\mathbf{A} \sim \mathbf{B}$, if $\mathbf{A} = \mathbf{MBN}$ where **M** and **N** are unimodular of order m and n respectively.

Definition 2.7. The **elementary operations** on a matrix consist of (a) interchange of rows (columns) i and j; (b) multiplication of row (column) i by

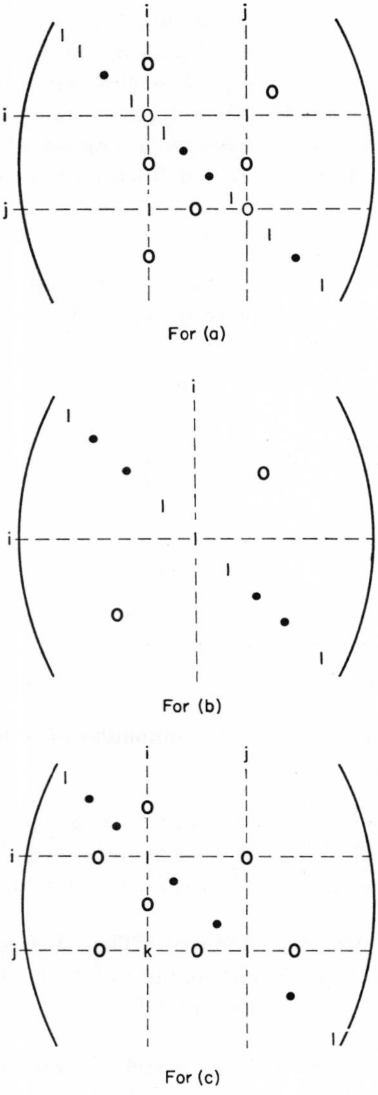

Figure 1-1

-1; (c) addition of k times row (column) i to row (column) j $(i \neq j)$. [Actually (b) can be obtained from (a) and (c)]. The relationship to (2.6) follows from the observation that the elementary row operations can be effected by multiplication on the left by unimodular matrices: Similar comments hold for column changes and matrix multiplication on the right. Thus **M** and **N** arise by stepwise combination of these three operations.

Definition 2.8. The elements $\{g^i \mid i = 1, \ldots, n\}$ transform into $\{h^j \mid j = 1, \ldots, m\}$ by the matrix **A**, $\mathbf{A} = (a_i^j)$, if $h^j = \Sigma_i \, a_i^j \, g^i$.

Lemma 2.9. *If* $\{g^i\}$ *is a base for the free group of rank* N (1.11), *then* $\{h^j\}$ *is a base also if and only if* $\{g^i\}$ *transforms into* $\{h^j\}$ *by a unimodular matrix.*

We can write $g^r = \Sigma \, b_i^r \, h^i$, $h^j = \Sigma \, a_i^j \, g^i$, where $\mathbf{B} = (b_r^i)$ and $\mathbf{A} = (a_i^j)$ are integer matrices. Hence $\mathbf{AB} = \mathbf{I}$ or $\Delta(a_i^j) \, \Delta(b_r^s) = 1$, which, since $\Delta(a_i^j)$ and $\Delta(b_r^s)$ are integers, cannot be satisfied unless $(\Delta(a_i^j))^2 = (\Delta(b_r^s))^2 = 1$.

Definition 2.10. The greatest common divisor of the determinants for the *i*-**square** matrices is designated by D_i. The ith invariant factor t_i is defined by $t_i = D_i/D_{i-1}$, with the convention $t_i = D_1$. (All matrices are assumed submatrices of a fixed matrix.)

Theorem 2.11. (*Frobenius*). *If* **B** *is an* (m, n) *integer matrix, then* **B** *is equivalent to* **B**′,

$$\mathbf{B}' = \begin{pmatrix} t_1 & & & & & & & & \\ & t_2 & & & & & & & \\ & & \cdot & & & & & & \\ & & & \cdot & & & & \mathbf{0} & \\ & & & & \cdot & & & & \\ & \mathbf{0} & & & & t_r & & & \\ & & & & & & 0 & & \\ & & & & & & & \cdot & \\ & & & & & & & & \cdot \\ & & & & & & & & & 0 \end{pmatrix} \tag{2.11a}$$

We observe that D_p is unaffected by an elementary operation. Suppose **B**′ is obtained from an application of an elementary operation of type (c). It is well known that if one column of a determinant Δ is the sum of two columns c_1 and c_2 then $\Delta = \Delta_1 + \Delta_2$ where Δ_1 results from omitting c_2 and Δ_2 from omitting c_1. It follows that D_p divides all p rowed determinants of **B**′ and hence D_p divides D_p'. If we adopt the position that **B** results from a type (c) operation on **B**′, then we conclude D_p' divides D_p. Accordingly $D_p = D_p'$.

Let α be the smallest absolute value of the various nonzero terms in **B**. By mediation of (2.7c), perhaps α can be decreased. Since α is a positive integer, a finite number of applications of (2.7c) yields a matrix with minimum absolute value, say β. Bring a term with this absolute value to the (1, 1) position by (2.7a). We can assume this is the only nonzero term in the first row (and in the first column), for if b is another nonzero term either b is divisible by β, in which case it can be reduced to 0 by (2.7c), or if not divisible by β, then for some k, $b + k\beta < \beta$, in contradiction with the definition of β. Evidently $\beta = D_1 = t_1$. Thus this first reduction yields a matrix $\mathbf{B}'$. Strip off the first row and first column from $\mathbf{B}'$ and obtain a matrix $\mathbf{C}$. This matrix is reduced in the same way again to a single nonzero term c in the (1, 1) position of $\mathbf{C}$ dividing every term of $\mathbf{C}$. The maximal divisor of all two-rowed minors of $\mathbf{B}'$ is therefore $t_1 c$, and since D_2 is unchanged by (2.7c) $D_2 = t_1 c$. Hence $t_2 = D_2/D_1 = c$. Repetition of this argument yields the representation $\mathbf{B}'$ of (2.11a). Since D_s is the G.C.D. of all s-rowed determinants of $\mathbf{A}$, and so of $\mathbf{B}'$, we know $t_1 \cdots t_{s-1} t_{s+1}$ is divisible by $D_s = t_1 \cdots t_{s-1} t_s$. It follows that t_{s+1}/t_s is an integer.

Theorem 2.12. *If* $\mathbf{A}$ *is an* (m, n) *integer matrix and* $\mathbf{B}$ *is an* (n, j) *integer matrix satisfying* $\mathbf{AB} = 0$, *then*

$$\text{(2.12a)} \qquad \begin{aligned} \mathbf{A}' &= \mathbf{MAN} \\ \mathbf{B}' &= \mathbf{N}^{-1}\mathbf{BJ} \end{aligned}$$

where $\mathbf{M}_i$ $\mathbf{N}$ *and* $\mathbf{J}$ *are unimodular,* $\mathbf{A}'\mathbf{B}' = 0$, *and* $\mathbf{A}'$ *has the canonical form* (2.11a), *and* $\mathbf{B}'$ *has the form*

$$\text{(2.12b)} \qquad \mathbf{B}' = \begin{pmatrix} t_1' & & & \mathbf{0} \\ & \cdot & & \\ & & t_r' & \\ \mathbf{0} & & & \\ & & & \mathbf{0} \end{pmatrix}$$

PROBLEMS

1-8. Establish (2.12).

1-9. Reduce

$$\begin{pmatrix} 1 & 0 & 1 & 0 & 2 \\ 0 & -5 & 0 & 10 & 0 \\ 4 & 0 & 34 & 15 & 8 \\ 0 & -10 & 0 & 0 & 50 \end{pmatrix} \text{ to } \begin{pmatrix} 1 & & & & \\ & 5 & & \mathbf{0} & \\ \mathbf{0} & & 5 & & \\ & & & 30 & 0 \end{pmatrix}.$$

chapter 2

CHAIN RELATIONSHIPS

1. SIMPLEXES AND CHAINS. A technique of combinatorial topology is the representation of spaces by blocks. It is the way that these units are juxtaposed that is the essential feature. The most natural blocks are probably the parallelopipeds or the generalized tetrahedra, and the latter are the usual elements chosen. For such choices the vertex assignments determine the juxtaposition.

Definition 1.1. An abstract n-**dimensional simplex** $\boldsymbol{\sigma}_n$ or n-simplex is a set of $n + 1$ marks or points, called **vertices** $\{v^i\}$. If $\{v^i \mid i \in \pi\}$ is a subset consisting of $m + 1$ vertices, the corresponding simplex is called a **face** of σ_n. The face opposite v^{i_0} consists of all vertices save v^{i_0} and is written $\sigma_{n-1}(i_0)$ or sometimes $\sigma_{n-1}^{i_0}$ or $\sigma^{i_0}(n-1)$.

Definition 1.2. An **ordered** p-dimensional simplex is an abstract simplex whose vertices v^i, $i = 0, \ldots, p$ are simply ordered. The vertices of a face have the induced order. For instance, $v^1 v^0$ is not a face of the ordered simplex $\sigma_2 = v^0 v^1 v^2$, but $\sigma_1(1) = v^0 v^2$ is a face. If $\sigma_n = v^0 \cdots v^n$, then $\sigma_{n-1}(i) = v^0 \cdots \widehat{i} \cdots v^n$, where $\widehat{i}$ indicates v^i has been erased. The face $v^0 \cdots v^s$ is the **forward** s **face**. The face $v^s \cdots v^r$ is the **back** $r - s$ **face**. The **join** of a simplex $\sigma_m = v^0 \cdots v^m$ and a simplex $\sigma_n = v^{m+1} \cdots v^{m+n+1}$ is the $m + n + 1$-simplex with representation $v^0 \cdots v^{m+n+1}$. It is written $\widehat{\sigma_m \sigma_n}$ or $\sigma_m\sigma_n$. Thus σ_m is the forward m-face and σ_n the back n-face of $\sigma_m \sigma_n$. The join of a single vertex σ_0 or v and σ_n, $v\sigma_n$, is a **cone** over σ_n with vertex v. A **replete** or **degenerate** simplex is obtained from an ordered simplex by identifying two or more vertices; for example, $v^0\ v^1\ v^2\ v^1$ is a replete 3-dimensional simplex and bears no relation to the replete simplex $v^0\ v^1\ v^1\ v^2$, unless otherwise stipulated.

Definition 1.3. Let the ordered simplex σ_n have the ordering $v^0 < \cdots < v^n$. The ordered simplexes whose vertex order is an even permutation of that of σ_n constitute an equivalence class. There are $(n + 1)!/2$ different equivalent orderings on this class. The simplexes with vertex ordering odd permutations of that of σ_n constitute another equivalence class. Arbitrarily attach the designation **positive orientation** to one equivalence class and negative orientation to the other class and write $(+\sigma_n)$ or $(-\sigma_n)$ respectively (or ${}^+\sigma_n$ and ${}^-\sigma_n$). For instance, $(+\sigma_n)$ is represented by any one of the ordered

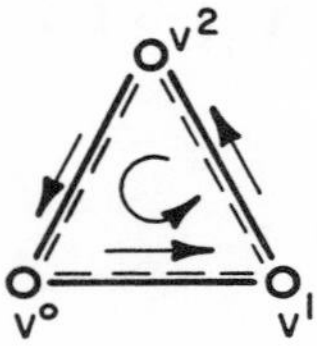

Figure 2-1

simplexes $v^0\, v^1\, v^2$, $v^1\, v^2\, v^0$, or $v^2\, v^0\, v^1$, while $-\sigma_2$ has the representatives $v^1\, v^0\, v^2$, $v^2\, v^1\, v^0$, or $v^0\, v^2\, v^1$. An alternative formulation introduces an orientation function $\alpha(\ )$ defined on ordered simplexes to the pair $1, -1$ and subject to the condition $\alpha(p_e\, \sigma) = \alpha(\sigma)$, $\alpha(p_0\, \sigma) = -\alpha(\sigma)$ where $p_e(p_0)$ indicates an even (odd) permutation of the order. Thus, an oriented simplex may be thought of as a pair (σ, α) not to be distinguished from $(p_e\, \sigma, \alpha p_e)$ where σ is now an ordered simplex (we are overworking the symbol in conformity with usual practice). If its vertices are numbered $v^0, v^1, \ldots$ the orientation assigned almost exclusively to σ_n and therefore termed **standard** is $\alpha(v^0. \cdots v^n) = 1$. Let σ_n be the ordered simplex $v^0 \cdots v^n$ and write $v^i\, \sigma_{n-1}(i)$ for $v^i\, v^0 \odot v^{i-1}\, v^{i+1} \cdots v^n$. The orientation on the face $\sigma_{n-1}(i)$ is induced by the orientation of σ_n if $\alpha(v^i\, \sigma_{n-i}(i)) = \alpha\, (\sigma_{n-i}(i)) = (-1)^i \alpha(\sigma_n)$. Thus if $\alpha(v^0\, v^1\, v^2) = 1$, then for the induced orientation $\alpha(v^0\, v^2) = \alpha(v^1\, v^0\, v^2) = -1$. Convenient visualization for the 2 simplex is afforded by a small indicatrix circle (Fig. 2-1) indicating the vertex ordering for the positively oriented simplex. The induced orientation on a side is that in the direction of the circle.

Definition 1.4. We distinguish among various r dimensional simplexes by a superscript. The ordered, replete, or oriented simplexes σ_q^a and σ_r^b are **incident** if σ_r^b is a face of σ_q^a, $r \leq q$; but if $r = q$, $\sigma_r^a = \sigma_r^b$. We write $\sigma_r^b < \sigma_q^a$. The incidence number denoted by $[\sigma_q^a, \sigma_r^b]$ or $\eta_b^a(q)$ takes on the values $0, \pm 1$ and is non 0 only if $\sigma_{r=q-1}^b < \sigma_q^a$. By definition, for the oriented simplex $[\sigma_n, \sigma_{n-1}(i)] = \alpha(\sigma_n)\alpha(v^i \sigma_{n-1}(i))$ so if the faces had the induced orientation (1.3), clearly

(1.4a) $$\eta_j(n) = [\sigma_n, \sigma_{n-1}(j)] = (-1)^j.$$

if $\sigma^k_{n-2} = v^0 \cdots \hat{j} \cdots \hat{k} \cdots v^n$ with the orientation induced by that of $\sigma_{n-1}(j)$, $\eta^j_k(n-1) = [\sigma_{n-1}(j), \sigma^k_{n-2}]$ and there is a two term sum

$$\Sigma\, \eta_i(n)\eta^i_k(n-1) = (-1)^{k-1}(-1)^{3j} + (-1)^{3k}(-1)^j \tag{1.4b}$$
$$= 0.$$

We restate (1.4b). Strike out v^j in $\sigma_{n-1}(i)$ and denote the resulting face by $\sigma_{n-2}(ij)$. Similarly on striking out v^i in $\sigma_{n-1}(j)$ there results a face $\sigma_{n-2}(ji)$. Up to orientation $\sigma_{n-2}(ji)$ and $\sigma_{n-2}(ij)$ are the same and denote the common face of $\sigma_{n-1}(i)$ and $\sigma_{n-1}(j)$. Assuming all orientations are induced by that of σ_n, (1.4b) asserts $\alpha(\sigma_{n-2}(ji)) = -\alpha(\sigma_{n-2}(ij))$.

That (1.4b) does not depend on the orientations chosen follows from the remark that if the orientation function is changed to α' the effect is to multiply the left-hand side of (1.4b) by $\alpha'(\sigma_n)\alpha'(\sigma^k_{n-2})$.

If σ_n is the ordered or replete simplex $v^0 \cdots v^n$, $\sigma_{n-1}(j)$ is an ordered face of σ_n, so it makes sense to lay down the requirement that (1.4a) remains valid for these types also. *Condition* (1.4b) *is the relation on which a vast scaffolding of algebraic topology rests.* We can free it from dependence on simplexes.

Definition 1.5. An **abstract cell** e_r is an entity bearing an integer **dimension** r or **degree** r or **grade** r. Paralleling the situation for simplexes, there is a relation of incidence for pairs of cells indicated by $<$ and an assignment of integer-valued incidence numbers $\eta^a_b(r)$ to pairs e^a_r, e^b_{r-1} where $\eta^a_b(r) \neq 0 \Rightarrow e^b_{r-1} < e^a_r$. It is furthermore required that the analogue of (1.4b) be satisfied, namely

$$\Sigma_b\, \eta^a_b(r)\eta^b_c(r-1) = 0, \tag{1.5a}$$

where it is assumed that for all but a finite number of b values either $\eta^a_b(r)$ or $\eta^b_c(r-1)$ is 0. If $e^b_{r-1} < e^a_r$, e^b_{r-1} is a face of e^a_r but this does not guarantee $\eta^a_b(r) \neq 0$ (Problem 2–1). In contrast with the simplex the 0-faces or vertices need not determine the cell uniquely.

Definition 1.6. A **cell complex** K is a collection of cells $\{e_r\}$ with the incidence relations described in (1.5). When the cells are simplexes we refer to a **simplicial complex.** A cell complex is **finite** if it has a finite number of cells. It is n-dimensional if there are cells of dimension n, but no higher. A subcollection L of cells of a complex K is called a **subcomplex** and is **algebraically closed** or simply **closed** if each cell in L has all its faces in L. (This is not necessarily the same as topological closedness for nonfinite complexes.) Unless comment to the contrary is made, a complex will be assumed closed. The **algebraic closure** of a cell, $Cl\, e_r$, is the subcomplex of K consisting of e_r and all its faces. The totality of cells including e_r, sharing the face e_r, is the **star** of e_r in K and is indicated by $St(e_r, K) = \bigcup_{e_r < e_m} e_m$. The closed star of e_r is $\overline{St(e_r, K)} = \bigcup_{e_r < e_m} Cl\, e_m$. The complex is **closure finite** or **star finite** according as $Cl\, e_r$ is a finite complex or $St(e_r, K)$ contains a finite number of cells only. It is **locally finite** if K is both closure and star finite. Evidently a simplicial complex is closure finite. The symbol $\dot{e}_r$ denotes $Cl\, e_r - e_r$ and is the **frontier** or **boundary subcomplex** of e_r.

PROBLEMS

2-1. Let e_2 be the square with vertices $v^0, \ldots, v^3$. The edges are the 1-cells and the vertices are the 0-cells. Define various orientations and determine the incidence numbers $\{\eta^i_j\}$. Verify (1.5a). Identify the edges $v^0 v^1$ and $v^3 v^2$. This yields a slit cylinder with this edge and two 1-cells consisting of the circles starting and ending at $v^0 = v^3$ and $v^1 = v^2$ respectively. Determine $\{\eta^i_j\}$. Finally identify v^0, v^1, v^2, v^3 and all the 1-cells to yield a sphere with one vertex. Define $\{\eta^i_j\}$.

2-2. Let the 2-cell e be a pentagon. Let **A** be a matrix with entries $\eta^i_j(2)$ with i the row indicator and j the column indicator. Let **B** be the similar matrix for $\eta^r_s(1)$. Show **AB** $= 0$. Reduce **A** and **B** to canonical forms. Show that the canonical form **B′** is a matrix with all invariant factors, 1. Why?

Remark. The term "star," like the term "map" depends on the nature of the arguments and the range of the values. Thus in (1.6) the arguments are complexes, the values of St are complexes. When, as in the appendix (**A**), the arguments are point sets (and covers), the values of St are point sets.

The n-**dimensional skeleton** K^n of the cell complex is the collection of all cells in K of dimension n or less. The n-dimensional **shell** $K^{[n]}$ consists of all the n-dimensional cells; that is, $K^{[n]}$ is the collection of all cells in K^n but not in K^{n-1}. K is **homogeneous of grade** n if every cell is the face of an n-dimensional cell.

A simplical complex is **ordered** if every simplex is ordered. This is understood to mean there is a given partial ordering of all the vertices of the complex under which the vertices attached to any simplex are simply ordered. It is **oriented** if every simplex has been assigned an orientation, or, equivalently, an orientation function α has been prescribed. It is **replete** if whenever $v^0, \ldots, v^n$ are the vertices of a simplex, every simplex replete or not, with some or all of these vertices is in the complex. Thus the replete simplicial complex is always an infinite complex. For instance, $v^0\, v^1$ and $v^1\, v^0$ are two simplexes in the ordered complex. The oriented complex would contain just one of these. The replete complex would contain any simplex such as $v^0\, v^1\, v^1\, v^1\, v^0\, v^1$.

The next definitions involve elementary point set ideas covered, for instance, in (A). In particular X_0 denotes the point set closure.

Definition 1.7. A **concrete** cell for a space X is the pair consisting of an abstract cell e_n and an associated subset $|e_n|$. For the n-simplex in $X = R^n$, $|\sigma_n|$ is an open set as described in (1.10). For instance (v^0, v^1) is the associated point set to the 1-simplex e_1 with vertices v^0, v^1. We note the point set closure of $|e_n|$, namely $\overline{|e_n|}$, by $\|e_n\|$. Particularly in the case of simplexes, we often refer to $|e_n|$ and to $\|e_n\|$ as the open and the closed cell respectively. For simplexes (or for polyhedral cells) we require that $\|e_n\|$ consist of the points in all the faces of e_n, that is,

$$\|e_n\| = |e_n| \cup \bigcup_{e_i < e_n} |e_i|. \tag{1.7a}$$

Thus in the closed Euclidean triangle if e_2 is the 2-simplex, then $\|e_2\|$ consists of the points in the open triangle, that is, $|e_2|$, plus those on the segments $|e_1^0 = (v^1\, v^2)| \cup |(e_1^1 = v^0\, v^2)| \cup |e_1^2 = (v^0\, v^1)|$ plus the vertices $|e_0^0 = v^0| \cup |e_0^1 = v^1| \cup |e_0^2 = v^2|$.

Remark. The $C\,W$ cells defined in (154.1) do not satisfy (1.7a) always.

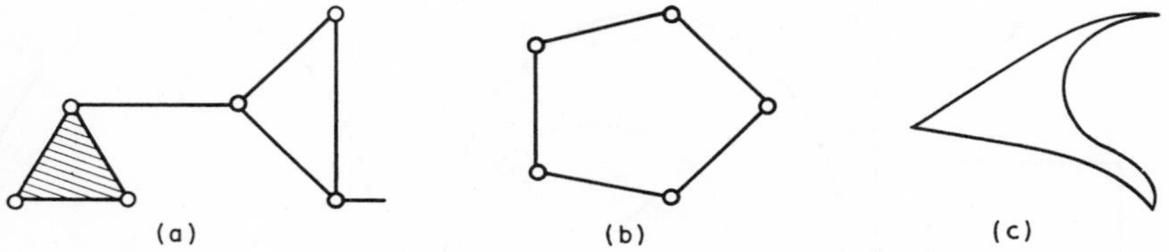

Figure 2-2

A **concrete complex** for a space X is: **(a)** a collection of concrete cells whose incidence relations are those of the underlying abstract cells and whose associated point sets are all contained in X; **(b)** if not empty, $\|{}_1e\| \cap \|{}_2e\| = \|{}_3e\|$; and **(c)** if e' denotes any cell not incident with e, then $|e|$ contains no limit points of $\bigcup\{e'\}$. Thus, $K = (0) \cup \left\{\frac{1}{n} \,\middle|\, n = 1, \ldots\right\}$ is a valid abstract 0-dimensional complex. However, if these vertices are taken as points on the real line, **(c)** is not satisfied for $e = (0)$, and so K is not a possible concrete complex. Write $|K_n|$ for $\bigcup |e_n|$ to indicate the space attached to the concrete complex K. As will appear below, $|K|$ need not be compact for nonfinite complexes.

While the simplexes and concrete cells for Euclidean spaces are normally given in terms of hyper planar boundaries, it is understood that homeomorphs are permitted so that the sides of a 2-simplex could be curved Fig. 2-2c. It is important that in a concrete complex two cells cannot share a proper part of a face. We shall say X is **triangulated** if there is a homeomorphism ψ on X onto a simplicial concrete complex K. We use the terminology **half space** in R^n, where the coordinates of R^n are $x_i, \ldots, x_n$, to describe the point set $\{x \mid x = (x_i, \ldots, x_n)\}$, subject either to $\Sigma\, a^i x_i \geq 0$ or to $\Sigma\, a^i x_i \leq 0$. The classical notion of a concrete cell is that of a **polyhedral cell,** namely the bounded common part of a collection of half spaces. Other cells enter when identification of edges or faces of a polyhedron are permitted. (Consult the examples following Section 31.) Other types come in with the dual cell (46.2) and still others in connection with the $C\,W$ complexes (154.1).

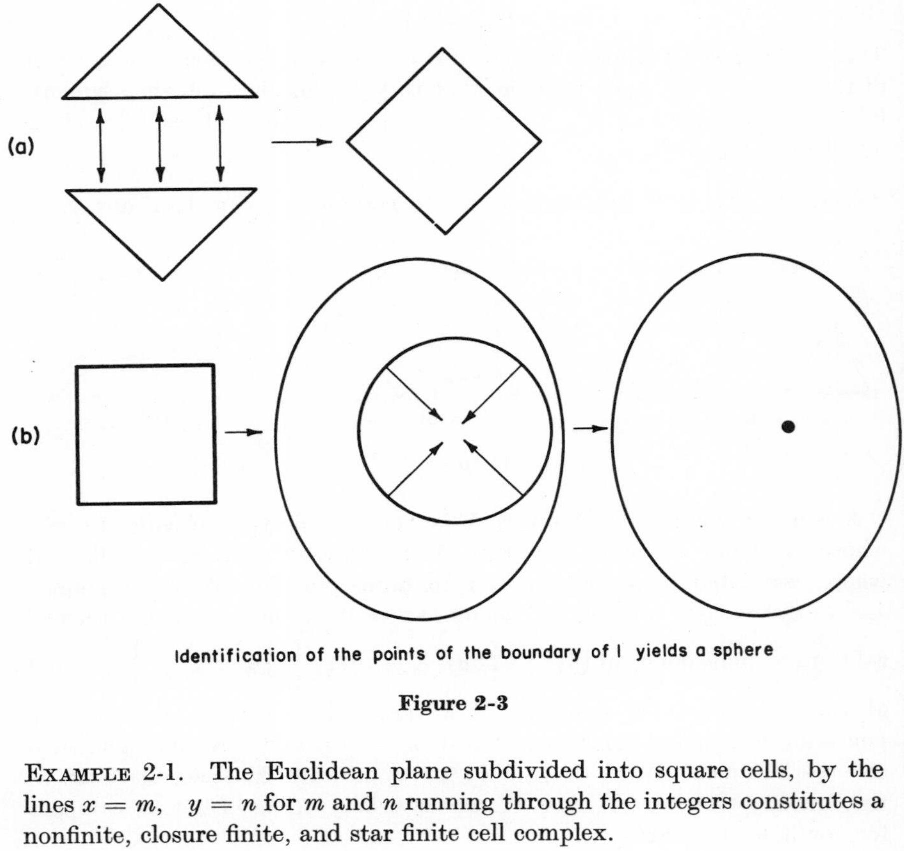

Identification of the points of the boundary of I yields a sphere

Figure 2-3

Example 2-1. The Euclidean plane subdivided into square cells, by the lines $x = m$, $y = n$ for m and n running through the integers constitutes a nonfinite, closure finite, and star finite cell complex.

Example 2-2. If $(-1, 1)$ is the open segment from -1 to 1 on the real axis, then since a complex is assumed algebraically closed it requires an infinite number of closed abutting segments to cover $(-1, 1)$; for instance

$$\bigcup \left[-\frac{n-1}{n}, -\frac{n-2}{n-1}\right] \cup \left[\frac{n-2}{n-1}, \frac{n-1}{n}\right] = (-1, 1).$$

Hence the triangulation of $(-1, 1)$ yields an infinite complex K. Evidently the same is true for any open set in Euclidean space. Here K is algebraically closed (1.6), but $|K|$ is topologically open on the real line.

EXAMPLE 2-3. In an infinite dimensional Euclidean space (that is, Hilbert space), the closed unit segments from the origin along the coordinate axes yield an infinite complex which is not star finite.

PROBLEM

2-3. Show that a polyhedral cell is the smallest convex set containing its vertices. Show that the smallest convex set containing a finite number of points is a polyhedral cell. When are all the original points corner points or vertices? (A convex set C is one containing the segment joining any pair of points in C. A corner point or extreme point is one not an inner point of a segment in C.)

Definition 1.8. In a simplicial complex K, an m-**string** is a finite, simply ordered collection of incident alternately m- and $m - 1$-simplexes, terminating with m-simplexes or $m - 1$-simplexes, which are said to be **joined** by the string, or **strung together.** A 1-string is called a **path** or **polygonal path.** The totality of vertices which can be strung to v^0 by paths together with and the simplexes in the stars of these vertices constitute a **component** of K determined by v^0. This is denoted by $K(v^0)$. If K consists of one component, K is **connected.** Thus the connectivity of K is determined by its 1-skeleton. (A connected 1-complex is called a **graph.**)

Remark. The prevailing terminology has been **chain** for our **string**, but then there is confusion with algebraic chains.

Lemma 1.9. *If K is star finite, every component is a countable complex.*

Consider the closed 1-simplexes in $\overline{St(v^0, K)}$, Σ_1. Let Σ_2 denote the closed 1-simplexes of $\overline{St(v^0 \mid K, v^0 \in \Sigma_1)}$. Similarly, Σ_n denotes the closed 1-simplexes of $\overline{St(v^b \mid K, v^b \in \Sigma_{n-1})}$. Any v^c that can be joined to v^0 by a path must be in some Σ_n, so

$$K(v^0) = \bigcup_{n=1}^{n \leq \infty} \Sigma_n.$$

The fact that Σ_1 is finite follows from the star finiteness of K. Hence Σ_n is finite also, whence $K(v^0)$ is at most denumerable.

PROBLEMS

2-4. Suppose L and M are n-dimensional subcomplexes of the concrete simplicial complex K. Denote the boundaries of the subcomplexes by $\dot{L}$ and $\dot{M}$. Define $\dot{L}$. How does $(L \cup M)^{\cdot}$ depend on $\dot{L}$ and $\dot{M}$?

2-5. Let K be a finite graph with an even number of 1-simplexes meeting at any vertex. Show K can be described by a pencil path never tracing any edge twice, i.e., K is **unicursal.** The assertion maintains if exactly two vertices are incident with an odd number of 1-simplexes. If the initial and final points coincide K is a unicursal cycle.

2-6. Königsberg Bridges. The seven bridges of Königsberg are to be crossed in a promenade once and only once for each. Show as Euler did, that this cannot be done.

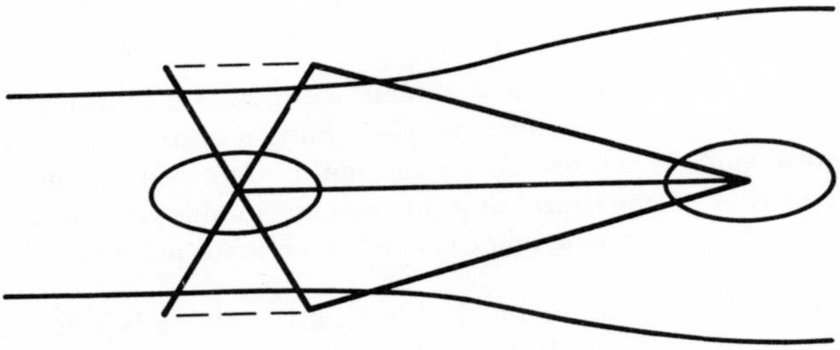

Figure 2-4

2-7. If each simplex in a graph K is oriented, then K is unicursal if the number of one segments directed toward a vertex is the number directed away.

2-8. If $K = \bigcup K_i$ where each K_i is a unicursal cycle (Problem 2-5) and K is a graph, then K is unicursal.

2-9. If K is a graph with some segments oriented, then the necessary and sufficient conditions that any two points can be joined by a path respecting orientations are that for each nonempty proper subset of vertices L there is a string ab such that $a \in L$ and $b \bar{\in} L$ and either ab is directed in this order or is undirected.

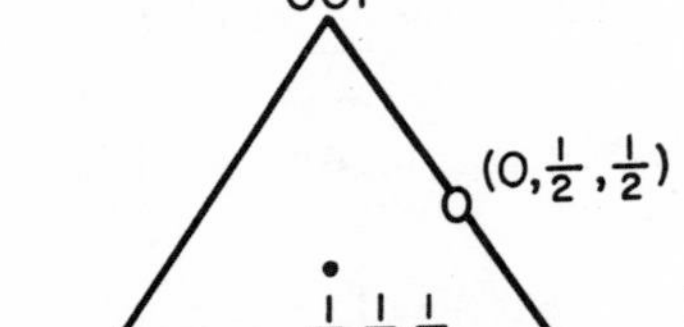

Figure 2-5

Definition 1.10. Let $v^0, \ldots, v^r$ be points in general position in a Euclidean r-dimensional space R^r (that is, not contained in any Euclidean subspace $R^{r'}$, $r' < r$). Let s be an arbitrary point in R^r. We assign $r + 1$ real numbers or coordinates to s, labeled $x_i = s(v^i)$, $i = 1, \ldots, r + 1$, subject to $\Sigma\, s(v^i) = 1$. These coordinates are called **barycentric coordinates.** For an interpretation, note that if a mass $s(v^i)$ is put on the ith vertex, v^i, the center of mass of the system is at s. Alternatively, if $\{x_i \mid i = 1, \ldots, r + 1\}$ is the Cartesian coordinate specification of R^{r+1} the barycentric coordinates are the Cartesian coordinates of points in the hyperplane $\Sigma\, x_i = 1$. v^i has the coordinates δ_i^j, $i = 0, 1, \ldots, r$. The open generalized tetrahedron $\{s \mid 0 < s(v^k) < 1,$ $k = 0, \ldots, r\}$ is the **open geometric**, or **Euclidean simplex** σ_r, or simply **simplex**, where the Euclidean imbedding is understood. The closed simplex is

$$\sigma_r = \{s \mid 0 \leq s(v^i) \leq 1, i = 0, \ldots, r\}.$$

PROBLEM

2-10. What are the barycentric coordinates of the points in the subtriangle with vertices v^2, $(\frac{1}{3}, \frac{1}{3}, \frac{1}{3})$ and $(0, \frac{1}{2}, \frac{1}{2})$?

The **barycenter** of σ_r is the point with coordinates $s(a_i) = (r + 1)^{-1}$. The introduction of barycenters as new vertices in the simplicial complex K yields a new simplicial complex ${}^1K$ called the (first) barycentric derived complex (of K) or the **barycentric** derived complex. Then ${}^nK$ is the nth barycentric derived complex of ${}^{n-1}K$.

Definition 1.11. Let orientation be prescribed by taking $+\sigma_n$ as the ordered simplex $v^0\, v^1, \ldots, v^n$. Write π_l for a set of $l + 1$ of the integers $0, \ldots, n$, and denote the face of σ_n, determined by $\{v^i \mid i \in \pi_l\}$ with the induced order of vertices, by σ^{π_l}. Denote the barycenter of σ^{π_l} and that of σ_n by (π_l) and (σ_n) respectively. We say the vertex $x = (\pi_l)$ lies on σ^{π_l} and write $\sigma(x)$ for σ^{π_l}. The vertices (π_0), $(\pi_1), \ldots, (\pi_n)$ constitute the vertices of a simplex if there is proper inclusion $\pi_i \subset \pi_{i+1}$, $i = 0, \ldots, n - 1$; and if so, the orientation $\alpha(\pi_0, \ldots, \pi_n)$ is positive or negative according to the evenness or oddness of the permutation of $(0, \ldots, n)$ given by

$$(\pi_0, \pi_1 - \pi_0, \ldots, \pi_n - \pi_{n-1}). \tag{1.11a}$$

The **leading simplex,** ${}^1\sigma_n$, in σ_n is given by $\pi_i = (0, \ldots, i)$, $i = 0, \ldots, n$. In the appended figure it is cross-hatched. Faces of $\pi_0, \ldots, \pi_n$ are given the induced orientation. This determines the orientation of simplexes in ${}^1K$. For instance when $n = 2$, with 2, 12, 012 constituting (π_0), (π_1), (π_2), the order according to (1.11a) is 2, 1, 0, an odd permutation of 0, 1, 2. Accordingly $((\pi_0), (\pi_1), (\pi_2))$ is negatively oriented.

The concrete simplicial complex $K = \{\sigma_n\}$ has the barycentric subdivision ${}^1K = \{{}^1\sigma_n\}$. With ${}^2K = {}^1({}^1K)$, etc., higher barycentric subdivisions are defined. The term **barycentric subdivision** or simply **subdivision** is used also when π_l is not a barycenter, but an arbitrarily chosen point in the open convex set determined by the vertices $(v_{i_m}), \ldots, (v_{i_n})$. Similar notions attach when convex cells replace the simplexes.

More generally for simplicial complexes, ${}^1K$ is a **subdivision** of K if each closed simplex of K is a union of closed simplexes of ${}^1K$. For instance, the three closed simplexes determined by adding the barycenter (012) to the vertices (0), (1), (2) constitute a subdivision but not a barycentric subdivision. If the simplexes are abstract, then the replacement of the original by the

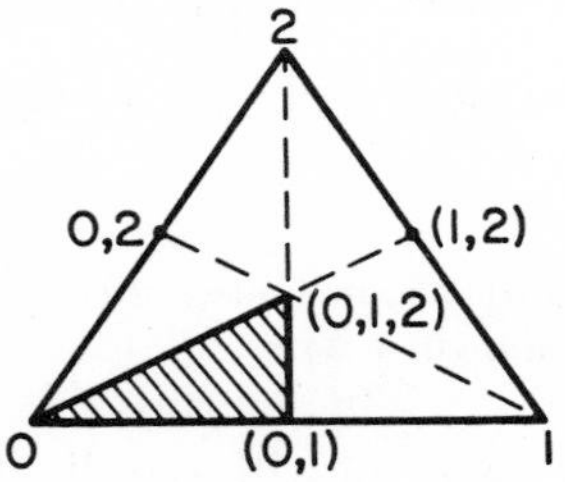

Figure 2-6

new vertices $\{(\pi_l)\}$ is again referred to as a **subdivision** of K. A polyhedral cell e_n can be subdivided by adding as new vertices the barycenters of each 1 cell in the 1-skeleton K^1 of e_n. This replaces each 1-simplex by two 1-simplexes to give ${}^1K^1$. Next add the barycenters of the 2 cells of the shell $K^{[2]}$ of e_n as new vertices. Each such vertex together with a 1-simplex of ${}^1K^1$ determines a 2-simplex. Thus each 2 cell in K^2 is replaced by a collection of 2-simplexes. Denote the result by ${}^1K^2$. We continue inductively. The subdivision ${}^1K$ of a polyhedral cell complex K is achieved by subdivision of

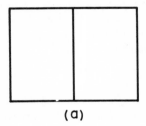

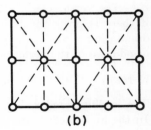

Figure 2-7

the separate cells. What is important to note is that ${}^1K$ is a simplicial complex. Figure 2-7 illustrates the process for K consisting of two closed rectangles.

Definition 1.12. Let K and L be simplicial complexes with their simplexes in 1-1 correspondence. If all incidence relations in the one are the same as the incidence relations in the other, for corresponding simplexes we say K

and L are **isomorphic.** If K is an abstract complex and L is a concrete complex isomorphic to K, then L is a **geometric realization** of K.

Lemma 1.13. *Every simplicial complex K with $N + 1$ vertices has a geometric realization as a concrete subcomplex of a concrete N-simplex and also as a subcomplex of the boundary of a concrete $N + 1$ simplex.*

Let K have the vertices $\{v^i \mid i = 0, \ldots, N\}$. Make correspond the linearly independent set of points $\{w^i \mid i = 0, \ldots, N\}$ in R^N. Define the closed concrete N simplex $e = e(K)$ in R^N by requiring the barycentric coordinates $s^i = s(w^i)$ to satisfy $0 \leq s^i$, $\Sigma\, s^i = 1$. The closed simplex $\bar{\sigma} = \{v^i \mid i \in \pi\}$ of K then corresponds to the closed face $e(\sigma)$ defined by the restriction $s^j = 0$, $j \bar{\in} \pi$. The open simplexes correspond when the condition $0 < s^i$, $i \in \pi$, is imposed. Evidently if σ'' is a common face of σ and of σ', then $e(\sigma'')$ is a common face of $e(\sigma)$ and of $e(\sigma')$. The collection of concrete simplexes $\{e(\sigma)\}$ is thus the geometric realization. The second assertion of the theorem is now trivial.

Remark. In (154) it will be shown that a realization can be given for a simplicial complex with an arbitrary number of vertices if it is star finite. Moreover any finite simplicial K^N can be realized in R^{2N+1}. We omit the easy proof since this fact is not used in this book.

The concrete finite simplicial complexes K and L are assumed disjunct subcomplexes composed of the faces of some concrete simplex σ_N and their concrete join is then a subcomplex of σ_N. Using the barycentric coordinates of σ_N, the associated point set of the join is $\{tk + (1 - t)l \mid k \in |K|, l \in |L|, 0 \leq t \leq 1\}$. Alternatively the concrete join of σ_q and σ_p for instance is obtained by imbedding them in disjunct hyperplanes of a Euclidean space; the expression just given for the associated point set is equally valid with Cartesian coordinates.

In the following problems joins are understood to be concrete joins and spheres are understood to be homeomorphs of Euclidean spheres. (Compare 155.1.)

PROBLEMS

2-11. Show that the diameter of the m-dimensional simplexes in ${}^nK$ is at most $\left(\dfrac{m}{m+1}\right)^n$, that of the largest m-dimensional simplex in K. Exhibit an infinite star finite complex with no upper bound to the diameter of its simplexes.

2-12. If the coordinate specification in R^n is $x = (x_0, \ldots, x_n)$, then "$n + 1$ points are in general position" is a statement equivalent to

$$\begin{vmatrix} 1 & x_0^0 & & \\ 1 & x_0^i & x_1^i & x_n^i \\ 1 & & & x_n^n \end{vmatrix} \neq 0.$$

2-13. Let abc be the vertices of the base triangle and $a'b'c'$ those of the roof triangle of a vertical prism. Give an explicit scheme for subdividing the prism into three, three-dimensional, closed simplexes. Generalize to a prism whose two bases are n-simplexes.

2-14. Show that the n-cube can be subdivided into $n!$ closed simplexes.

2-15. The join of simplexes σ_p and σ_q is a $p + q + 1$ dimensional simplex σ_{p+q} whose boundary consists of $(\dot{\sigma}_p \, \sigma_q) \cup (\sigma_p \, \dot{\sigma}_q)$.

2-16. If S^0 and S^m are spheres, $m = 1, 2$, show the join S^0S^m is a sphere. Generalize to $S^p \, S^q$. *Hint:* S^0 consists of two points.

2. CHAIN GROUPS. For fixed m, the cells $\{e_m^a \mid a \in A\}$ constitute the m shell $K^{[m]}$ (21.6). An **m-dimensional integer chain** is an expression:

(2.1a) $$c_m = \Sigma_{a\in\alpha} \, g_a \, e_m^a, \quad g_a \in \mathrm{J}, \quad e_m^a \in K^{[m]}.$$

The script range α may be replaced by a larger range β, or even by all of A, by the convention of writing $g_a = 0$ for $a \bar{\in} \alpha$. Thus c_m in (2.1a) is identified with $c_m = \Sigma_{a\in\beta} \, g_a \, e_m^a$, $g_a = 0$ if $a \in \beta - \alpha$. If $c'_m = \Sigma_{a\in\alpha'} \, g'_a \, e_m^a$, an addition is defined by

(2.1b) $$c_m + c'_m = \Sigma_{\alpha\cup\alpha'}(g_a + g'_a)e_m^a,$$

where $g_a = 0$ for $a \bar{\in} \alpha$ and $g'_a = 0$ for $a \bar{\in} \alpha'$. The chain

(2.1c) $$0_m = \Sigma_{a\in A} \, 0 \, e_m^a$$

is the 0 chain. The collection of m-dimensional integer chains constitutes an additive (Abelian) group designated by $C_m(K, J)$ or $C_m(K)$ under addition as defined in (2.1b) with the 0 chain as the neutral element. For fixed a, the chain $g_a \, e_m^a$ is an **elementary chain.**

It is plain that J can be replaced by an arbitrary Abelian group G, in which case we refer to the **m-dimensional chain group** over G. For instance, G may be J_p or Q. We then write $C_m(K, G)$. The chains, for example the elementary chains, refer to an algebraic situation. Thus, e_m^a as a cell is not the same thing as e_m^a as an elementary chain. (A guide to intuition is indeed afforded by viewing the chain $3e_m$ as a collection of three duplicates of e_m; this view is even more effective when $G = \mathrm{J}_2$, since then the chains do seem like collections of simplexes. This breaks down when $G = \mathrm{Q}$, for $\frac{1}{3}e_m$ has no comparable interpretation.) However we do require an association in the case of oriented complexes. Consider, for instance, the elementary simplicial chain $-g(v^0 \cdots v^n)$. If $+\sigma_n$ is taken as $v^0 \cdots v^n$ this is precisely $-g\sigma_n$. If, however, $+\sigma_n$ is $v^1\, v^0 \cdots v^n$ then we should write this as $g\sigma_n$. In brief, $-g\sigma_n$ and $g(-\sigma_n)$ are to correspond. This remark is already of use in (2.4).

Define a chain **basis** $\{c_m^b\}$ as a collection of chains such that any chain c_m in $C_m(K, G)$ is expressible uniquely as

(2.1d) $$c_m = \Sigma_{b\epsilon\pi}\, g_b\, c_m^b$$

If the number of elements, in A, namely $|A|$, is nonfinite, two types of chains are possible, depending on whether a is restricted to be in a finite set in (2.1a) or can run through an infinite set. Chains of the first type are called **finite chains**, and $C_m(K, G)$ is then the group of **finite chains**. For unrestricted a, the chains are **infinite chains**, and if A is nondenumerable, for instance the real numbers, the nonzero g_a's in (2.1a) need not be denumerable. The generators of the elementary chains constitute just one possible basis for the groups of finite chains. Until further notice we restrict consideration to finite complexes.

Let $\{E_m^i \mid i = 1, \ldots, N\}$ be a new base for $C_m(K)$. Then

(2.2a) $$E_m^i = \Sigma_j\, t_j^i\, e_m^j,$$

where t_j^i is an integer. We must be able to solve for e_m^j as a linear combination of $\{E_m^i\}$ with integer coefficients. This requires that $\mathbf{T} = (t_j^i)$ be a unimodular matrix. (The argument is really given in (12.6).) The insight afforded by matrix representations shows up in expressing the effect of this basis change on the chains. We observe first that the chain $c_m = \Sigma_i\, s_i\, e_m^i$ can be represented as the product of a row matrix by a column matrix though the elements are now no longer restricted to the integers or to the real or complex numbers. Let $\mathbf{s.}$ be the row matrix $(s_1, \ldots, s_N)$ and let $\mathbf{e}_m^{\boldsymbol{\cdot}}$ be the column matrix $\begin{pmatrix} e_m^1 \\ \cdot \\ \cdot \\ e_m^N \end{pmatrix}$. Then

(2.2b) $$c_m = \mathbf{s.}\, \mathbf{e}_m^{\boldsymbol{\cdot}}.$$

We express the fact that c_m is independent of the particular representations chosen:

$$\mathbf{s.e}_m = \mathbf{S.E}_m^{\boldsymbol{\cdot}} = \mathbf{s.T}^{-1}\mathbf{Te}_m^{\boldsymbol{\cdot}}$$

or

(2.2c) $$\mathbf{S.} = \mathbf{s.}\, \mathbf{T}^{-1} \qquad \mathbf{E}_m^{\boldsymbol{\cdot}} = \mathbf{Te}_m^{\boldsymbol{\cdot}}$$

Remark. The row matrix corresponds to a covariant vector and the column matrix to a contravariant one.

EXAMPLE 2-4. Let

$$E^1_m = e^1_m + 2e^2_m$$
$$E^2_m = e^1_m + 3e^2_m.$$

Then $\mathbf{T} = \begin{pmatrix} 1 & 2 \\ 1 & 3 \end{pmatrix}$ and $\mathbf{T}^{-1} = \begin{pmatrix} 3 & -2 \\ -1 & 1 \end{pmatrix}$. The chain $c = s_1\, e^1 + s_2\, e^2$ becomes $C = S_1\, E^1 + S_2\, E^2$, where $S_1 = 3s_1 - s_2$, $S_2 = -2s_1 + s_2$ according to (2.2c).

Definition 2.3. A **chain group homomorphism,** or equivalently a linear transformation on the chain groups for the complexes $L = \{e^i_m\}$ and $K = \{E^j_n\}$, is indicated by $\chi(m)$: $C_m(L, \text{J}) \to C_n(K, \text{J})$, where

(2.3a) $$\chi(m)\, e^i_m = \Sigma_j\, h^i_j(m) E^j_n.$$

$h^i_j(m)$, $i = 1, \ldots, M$; $j = 1, \ldots, N$, is an integer. Drop the dimension scripts m and n for the moment and designate the finite or infinite chains of $C_m(L, R)$ by $\{c\}$ and those of $C_n(K, R)$ by $\{d\}$. Then

(2.3b) $$\chi(c = \Sigma\, s_i\, e^i_m) = \Sigma_i\, s_i\, \chi(e^i_m)$$
$$= \Sigma_{i,j}\, s_i\, h^i_j(m) E^j_n.$$

We express (2.3b) in matrix symbolism. Let $\mathbf{H}$ be the M $\times$ N matrix $(h^k_j(m))$. Then (2.3a) becomes $\chi\, \mathbf{e}^{\cdot}_m = \mathbf{H}\, \mathbf{E}^{\cdot}_n$, and (2.3b) is written

(2.3c) $$\chi\text{: } \mathbf{s}.\, \mathbf{e}^{\cdot}_m = \mathbf{s}.\, \mathbf{H}\mathbf{E}^{\cdot}_n$$

EXAMPLE 2.5. Let

$$\chi(e^1_m) = 2E^1_n + 3E^2_n$$
$$\chi(e^2_m) = E^1_n - E^2_n.$$

Then $\mathbf{H} = \begin{pmatrix} 2 & 3 \\ 1 & -1 \end{pmatrix}$ and the chain $s_1\, e^1_m + s_2\, e^2_m$ becomes $S_1\, E^1_n + S_2\, E^2_n$, with $S_1 = 2s_1 + s_2$, $S_2 = 3s_1 - s_2$ by (2.3c).

The composition of several homomorphisms is straight-forward, but attention must be paid to the *order reversal* in passing from the homomorphisms to the matrices. (This is due to our writing homomorphisms on the left rather than on the right.) Let ${}_1C$ be the chain group over the basis $\{e\}$, ${}_2C$ that over $\{E\}$ and ${}_3C$ that over $\{F\}$. Let χ be the homomorphism on ${}_1C$ to ${}_2C$ and λ the homomorphism on ${}_2C$ to ${}_3C$. Specifically let λ and χ be given by the matrices $\mathbf{L}$ and $\mathbf{H}$ respectively. Thus

$$\lambda\mathbf{E}^{\cdot} = \mathbf{L}\mathbf{F}^{\cdot}$$
$$\chi\mathbf{e}^{\cdot} = \mathbf{H}\mathbf{E}^{\cdot}.$$

Then

(2.3d) $$\lambda\chi(c = \mathbf{s}.\, \mathbf{e}^{\cdot}) = \mathbf{s}.\, \mathbf{H}\mathbf{L}\mathbf{F}^{\cdot}$$

PROBLEM

2-17. Add the homomorphism μ on ${}_3C$ to ${}_4C$. What does (2.3d) become?

We are ready for the pivotal homomorphism relating chains over a simplex and chains over its faces.

Definition 2.4. Let $\sigma_m = v^0, \ldots, v^m$ be an ordered simplex. Then $C_m(\sigma_m, J)$ consists of $\{n\sigma_m \mid n \in J\}$. Let $K^{[m-1]}$ be the $m - 1$ shell of σ_m (1.6). Define the **boundary homomorphism** ∂_m, or ∂, on $C_m(\sigma_m, J)$ to $C_{m-1}(K^{[m-1]}, J)$ by

(2.4a) $$\partial_m n\sigma_m = \Sigma\, n\, (-1)^i v^0, \ldots, \hat{i}, \ldots, v^n = \Sigma\, n\, (-1)^i \sigma^i_{m-1}.$$

when σ^i_{m-1} is the face of σ_m opposite v^i (1.1). It is not necessary for (2.4a) that the vertices be distinct. Moreover one can verify at once that an even permutation of the vertices of (2.4a) yields

$$\partial n p_e \sigma_m = \Sigma\, n\, (-1)^i p_e\, \sigma^i_{m-1}.$$

Accordingly the boundary homomorphism (2.4a) is defined also for the oriented simplex σ_m, with σ^i_{m-1} given the induced orientation.

EXAMPLE 2-6. Let $+\sigma_2$ be the triangle $v^0\, v^1\, v^2$; then the boundary would be covered by walking around σ_2 along the paths $v^1\, v^2$, $v^2\, v^0$, and $v^0\, v^1$, which are respectively the faces opposite v^0, v^1, and v^2. If these are oriented canonically, that is, according to increasing script on the vertices, then $v^2\, v^0 = -v^0\, v^2$ and one obtains—in consonance with (2.4a) and (2.1)—$v^1\, v^2 - v^0\, v^2 + v^0\, v^1$ (cf. Fig. 2-1).

We present an alternative formulation of (2.4a), later found useful in the exposition of singular chains (83.1a). Thus let $t^i(m - 1)$ map a fixed simplex $\Delta_{m-1} = (u_0, \ldots, u_{m-1})$ onto σ^i_{m-1} by

(2.4b) $$t^j(m-1)\; u_i = v_i, \qquad i < j$$
$$= v_{i+1}, \qquad i \geq j$$

Then

(2.4c) $$\partial\sigma_m = \Sigma\, (-1)^i t^i(m-1)\sigma_{m-1}$$
$$\left(= \Sigma\, (-1)^i \frac{\partial\sigma_m}{\partial v^i} \quad \text{symbolically}\right).$$

More generally, with $\eta^i_j(m)$ the integer defined in (1.4), the boundary homomorphism is defined, when a cell e^i_m is involved, by

(2.4d) $$\partial_m\, e^i_m = \Sigma\, \eta^i_j(m)\, e^j_{m-1}.$$

In matrix form, for a finite cell complex K, (2.4d) yields

(2.4e) $$\partial_m \mathbf{e}^{\cdot}_m = \mathbf{A}(m)\, \mathbf{e}^{\cdot}_{m-1},$$

where $\mathbf{A}(m)$ is the **incidence matrix** $(\eta^i_j(m))$. Then (1.4), (1.4a), and (1.5a) amount to the requirement

(2.4f) $$\mathbf{A}(m-1)\mathbf{A}(m) = \mathbf{0}.$$

This states the all important relation

(2.4g) $$\partial_{m-1}\partial_m = 0,$$

that is to say a trivial homomorphism on $C_m(K, \mathrm{J})$ to $C_{m-2}(K, \mathrm{J})$. By linearity

(2.4h) $$\partial(c_m = \Sigma\, s_i\, e^i_m) = \Sigma\, s_i \eta^i_j(m)\, e^j_{m-1},$$

or equivalently,

$$\partial \mathbf{s}.\, \mathbf{e}^{\cdot}_m = \mathbf{s}.\, \mathbf{A}(m)\, \mathbf{e}^{\cdot}_{m-1}.$$

We consider the special case of (2.3) of greatest interest namely $m = n$.

Definition 2.5. **A chain homomorphism** χ is the collection of homomorphisms $\{\chi(m)\}$, on the individual m-dimensional chain groups, $C_m(L, \mathrm{J}) \to C_m(K, \mathrm{J})$, given by (2.3a) and (2.3b). It is a **chain map** or **chain mapping** or **allowable homomorphism** if, formally,

(2.5a) $$\partial\chi(m) = \chi(m-1)\,\partial.$$

That is to say, if $\mathbf{A}(m)$ and $\mathbf{B}(m)$ refer to the incidence matrices $(\eta^i_j(m))$ and $(\lambda^i_j(m))$ for $C_m(L, \mathrm{J})$ and for $C_m(K, \mathrm{J})$ respectively, then

(2.5b) $$\mathbf{s}.\, \mathbf{H}(m)\mathbf{B}(m)\mathbf{E}^{\cdot}_{m-1} = \mathbf{s}.\, \mathbf{A}(m)\mathbf{H}(m-1)\mathbf{E}^{\cdot}_{m-1}$$

If $\mathbf{s}.$ is taken successively as $(0, \ldots, 0, 1, 0, \ldots, 0)$ and coefficients of $\mathbf{E}^k_{m-1}$ are compared on both sides of (2.5b), there results in equivalent forms

(2.5c)

$$\Sigma_j\, h^i_j(m)\lambda^j_k(m) = \Sigma\, \eta^i_j(m) h^j_k(m-1), \qquad \mathbf{H}(m)\mathbf{B}(m) = \mathbf{A}(m)\mathbf{H}(m-1).$$

Notation: Henceforth we shall drop the dot on the $m \times 1$ and $1 \times n$ matrices. It lent clarity, but was never really needed. In fact, if $\mathbf{B}$ is an $m \times n$ matrix with $m > 1$, $n > 1$, then in the expression $\mathbf{a}\,\mathbf{B}\,\mathbf{c}$, the left multiplier can be a 1 rowed matrix, but not a matrix with 1 column while the right multiplier $\mathbf{c}$ can only be a matrix with 1 column and not one with 1 row. Thus $\mathbf{a}$ cannot be $\mathbf{a}^{\cdot}$ and $\mathbf{c}$ cannot be $\mathbf{c}.$.

Let K be a graph with some of the 1-simplexes oriented. The 1-string c is directed from the vertex a to the vertex b if its boundary $\partial c = b - a$.

That is if the chain sum of its oriented cells has this boundary. The 1-string c is undirected if it is made up of nonoriented simplexes. Assume for the problems that K is finite.

PROBLEMS

2-18. Let K be a graph. Let α and β be integer valued functions on 1-strings where $\alpha(c) \geq \beta(c) \geq 0$ for every directed 1-string c and where $\alpha(c) \geq 0$ for c undirected. Show there is an integer valued function γ on 1-strings satisfying $\alpha(c) \geq \gamma(c) \geq \beta(c) \geq 0$ for c directed iff for every proper subset of vertices, L,

$$\Sigma_{c \in A} \alpha(c) \geq \Sigma_{c \in B} \beta(c)$$

where $c \in A$ means c is either undirected or the boundary $\partial c = l^{\sim} - l$ where $l^{\sim} \in L^{\sim}$ and $l \in L$ and $c \in B$ if $\partial c = l - l^{\sim}$.

2-19. If K contains both oriented and nonoriented simplexes, then K is unicursal if (a) the star of every vertex contains an even number of one simplexes, (b) for every subset L of vertices $|I - O| \leq U$ where I and O are the numbers of directed 1-strings c with boundary $\partial c = l - l^{\sim}$ or with $\partial c = l^{\sim} - l$ respectively, and U is the number of undirected strings from L to L. *Hint:* For sufficiency apply Problem 2-7.

chapter 3

FUNDAMENTALS OF THE ABSOLUTE HOMOLOGY GROUPS AND BASIC EXAMPLES

1. THE FINITE COMPLEX. In this chapter we are concerned with the finite cell, or simplicial complex. We apply the canonical reductions of (12.12) to (22.4) the incidence matrices $\{\mathbf{A}(n)\}$.

Thus,

$$\mathbf{A}(n)' = \mathbf{M}\mathbf{A}(n)\mathbf{N},$$

(1.1a)

$$\mathbf{A}(n-1)' = \mathbf{N}^{-1}\mathbf{A}(n-1)\mathbf{J}.$$

Accordingly, with change of bases and $e(n)$ written for e_n

$$\mathbf{e}(n)' = \mathbf{M}\mathbf{e}(n),$$

(1.1b)

$$\mathbf{e}(n-1)' = \mathbf{N}^{-1}\mathbf{e}(n-1),$$

$$\mathbf{e}(n-2)' = \mathbf{J}^{-1}\mathbf{e}(n-2),$$

there results

$$\partial(\mathbf{e}(n)' = \mathbf{M}\mathbf{e}(n)) = \mathbf{M}\mathbf{A}(n)\mathbf{N}\mathbf{N}^{-1}\mathbf{e}(n-1),$$

or

$$\partial\mathbf{e}(n)' = \mathbf{A}(n)'\mathbf{e}(n-1)',$$

(1.1c)

$$\partial\mathbf{e}(n-1)' = \mathbf{A}(n-1)'\mathbf{e}(n-2)'.$$

We stress that $\mathbf{e}'$ is a matrix with entries chains and no longer cells. For instance, $\mathbf{e}(n)' = \begin{pmatrix} e^1(n)' \\ \cdot \\ \cdot \\ e^N(n)' \end{pmatrix}$, where $e^i(n)'$ is the chain $\Sigma\, m^i_r(n) e^r(n)$.

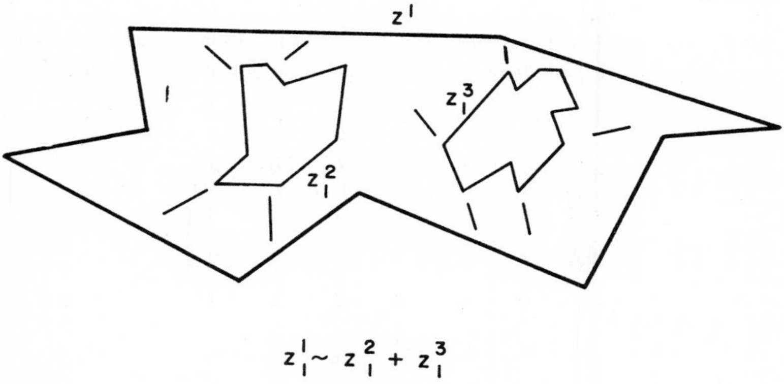

Figure 3-1

The elements (η^i_j) in $\mathbf{A}(n)'$ are the incidence numbers of the bases $\mathbf{e}(n)'$ and $\mathbf{e}(n-1)'$; that is, $\eta^i_j(n) = [e^i(n)', e^j(n-i)']$. Then

$$\partial\colon (c_m = \mathbf{s}\,\mathbf{e}_m) = \mathbf{s}\,\mathbf{A}(m)\mathbf{e}_{m-1}$$

whence

$$\partial\colon (c_m = \mathbf{s}'\,\mathbf{e}'_m) = \mathbf{s}'\mathbf{A}(m)'\mathbf{e}'_{m-1}, \tag{1.1d}$$

where, in view of (1.1a) and (1.1b),

$$\mathbf{s}' = \mathbf{s}\,\mathbf{M}^{-1}.$$

In the event that coefficients other than the integers are of interest, the necessary modifications can be made in the entries admitted. Thus, suppose that the coefficient group is J_p, p a prime; then all entries in any of the matrices above are to be reduced mod p. In particular, for J_2, the only entries are 0 or 1.

Remark. If matrices **M**, **N**, and **J** must be computed, perhaps the most straightforward though least inspired method is to make the reduction by the elementary operations so that at the ith step there is multiplication on the right or on the left by a matrix of type (12.11a, b, c), which we write $\mathbf{E}_i$.

Thus, if $\mathbf{A}' = \mathbf{E}_{j_r} \cdots \mathbf{E}_{j_2}\mathbf{E}_{j_1}\mathbf{A}\mathbf{E}_{i_1}\mathbf{E}_{i_2} \cdots \mathbf{E}_{i_j}$, then

$$\text{(1.1e)} \qquad \begin{aligned} \mathbf{M} &= \mathbf{E}_{j_r} \cdots \mathbf{E}_{j_1}, \\ \mathbf{N} &= \mathbf{E}_{i_1} \cdots \mathbf{E}_{i_j}, \quad \text{etc.} \end{aligned}$$

PROBLEMS

3-1. Verify the incidence matrices for the 2-dimensional sphere taken as the boundary of a tetrahedron are, with a suitable orientation for the simplexes

$$\mathbf{A}(2) \qquad \begin{array}{c} \\ e_2^0 \\ e_2^1 \\ e_2^2 \\ e_2^3 \end{array} \begin{array}{c} \begin{array}{cccccc} e_1^0 & e_1^1 & e_1^2 & e_1^3 & e_1^4 & e_1^5 \end{array} \\ \begin{pmatrix} 1 & 0 & -1 & 0 & 0 & -1 \\ 0 & -1 & 1 & 1 & 0 & 0 \\ -1 & 1 & 0 & 0 & -1 & 0 \\ 0 & 0 & 0 & -1 & 1 & 1 \end{pmatrix} \end{array}$$

$$\mathbf{A}(1) \qquad \begin{array}{c} \\ e_1^0 \\ e_1^1 \\ e_1^2 \\ e_1^3 \\ e_1^4 \\ e_1^5 \end{array} \begin{array}{c} \begin{array}{cccc} e_0^0 & e_0^1 & e_0^2 & e_0^3 \end{array} \\ \begin{pmatrix} 0 & -1 & 0 & 1 \\ -1 & 0 & 0 & 1 \\ 0 & 0 & -1 & 1 \\ -1 & 0 & 1 & 0 \\ -1 & 1 & 0 & 0 \\ 0 & -1 & 1 & 0 \end{pmatrix} \end{array}$$

3-2. Reduce to the standard form (12.12a). *Hint:* Make use of (1.1e). Find **M, N, J** and new bases.

2. THE ABSOLUTE GROUPS. Assume until further notice that the coefficient group is J. We introduce some subgroups and quotient groups of $C_n(K) = C_n(K, \text{J})$ determined by the boundary homomorphism

$$\text{(2.1a)} \qquad \partial_n\colon\ C_n(K) \rightarrow C_{n-1}(K)$$

Definition 2.2a. The group of **integral n-cycles** $Z_n(K) = \{z_n\}$ is the kernel of ∂ in (2.1a), *ker* ∂ (11.15). This is a subgroup of $C_n(K)$ and the elements of $Z_n(K)$ are the **cycles of dimension n.**

Definition 2.2b. The subgroup of $Z_n(K)$ consisting of *Im* ∂_{n+1}, that is, $\partial_{n+1} C_{n+1}(K)$, is denoted by $B_n(K)$ and is the group of **integral bounding cycles of dimension n.**

Definition 2.2c. If $z_n \in Z_n(K)$, but $z_n \bar{\in} B_n(K)$, then z_n is a **nonbounding cycle.**

Definition 2.2d. The cycle z_n is a **torsion cycle** if $z_n \bar{\in} B_n(K)$, but for some integer t, $t > 1$, $tz_n \in B_n(K)$. The smallest such integer, say $\bar{t}$, for assigned z_n is called a **torsion coefficient.**

Definition 2.3. Two n-dimensional integral cycles z_n^1 and z_n^2 are **homologous** if $z_n^1 - z_n^2 \in B_n(K)$. We express this by writing $z_n^1 \sim z_n^2$. In particular, the statement $z_n \sim 0$ means $z_n \in B_n(K)$. The homology relation $\sim$ is an equivalence relation and sections $Z_n(K)$ into cosets of homologous cycles. We give this a specific statement in defining the king group for the whole theory.

Definition 2.4. The n-dimensional **integral homology group** is the quotient group $H_n(K) = Z_n(K)/B_n(K)$. If η: $Z_n(K) \to H_n(K)$ assigns to z_n its coset with respect to $B_n(K)$, we denote ηz_n by $\mathbf{z}_n$ or for greater clarity by $\langle z_n \rangle_K$ or by $\langle z_n \rangle$.

New chain bases $\mathbf{e}(n)'$, $\mathbf{e}(n - 1)'$ (21.1b), consisting of classes important in applications, can be introduced. Let α_n be the number of n-dimensional simplexes, or cells, in the finite complex K; and write ρ_{n-1} for the rank of $\mathbf{A}(n)$.

Theorem 2.5. *The chain group $C_n(K, \text{J})$ is a free group. Its basis can be sorted into 5 types of basis chains distinguished by behavior with respect to ∂ and denoted by the presubscript $1, \ldots, 5$. Specifically ${}_1c_n^k \in B_n(K, \text{J})$, $\{{}_2c_n^k \mid k = 1, \ldots, \tau_n\}$ constitute the torsion cycles with corresponding torsion numbers $\{t_n^k \mid k = 1, \ldots, t_n\}$ where t_n^k divides t_n^{k+1}, $\{{}_3c_n^l \mid l = 1, \ldots, R_n\}$ are nonbounding cycles, all of whose integer multiples are also nonbounding, $\{{}_4c_n^m \mid m = 1, \ldots, \tau_{n-1}\}$ satisfy $\partial\, {}_4c_n^m = t_{n-1}^m\, {}_2c_{n-1}^m$, $\{{}_5c_n^i \mid i = 1, \ldots, \rho_n\}$ satisfy $\partial\, {}_5c_n^i = {}_1c_{n-1}^i$. The integer R_n is the* **Betti number** *and is*

$$R_n = \alpha_n - \rho_n - \rho_{n-1}. \tag{2.5a}$$

The assertions of the theorem are direct consequences of (12.10). The chain group generated by basic chains with back subscript i is designated by ${}_iC_n$ and can be identified in Fig. 3-2 as follows: The ${}_1C_n$ chains are the column heads in $\mathbf{A}'(n + 1)$ for which the diagonal term is 1. The torsion chains are those heading the columns with entry $t_n \neq 1$. Now turn to $\mathbf{A}(n)'$. Recall that the row heads in $\mathbf{A}(n)'$ are the column heads in $\mathbf{A}(n + 1)'$. The row heads corresponding to 1's on the main diagonal constitute the ${}_5C_n$ basis; those with $t_{n-1}^i \neq 1$ are the ${}_4C_n$ chains; and the chains remaining are the Betti, or nonbounding, cycles ${}_3C_n$. Their number is the Betti number R_n. The

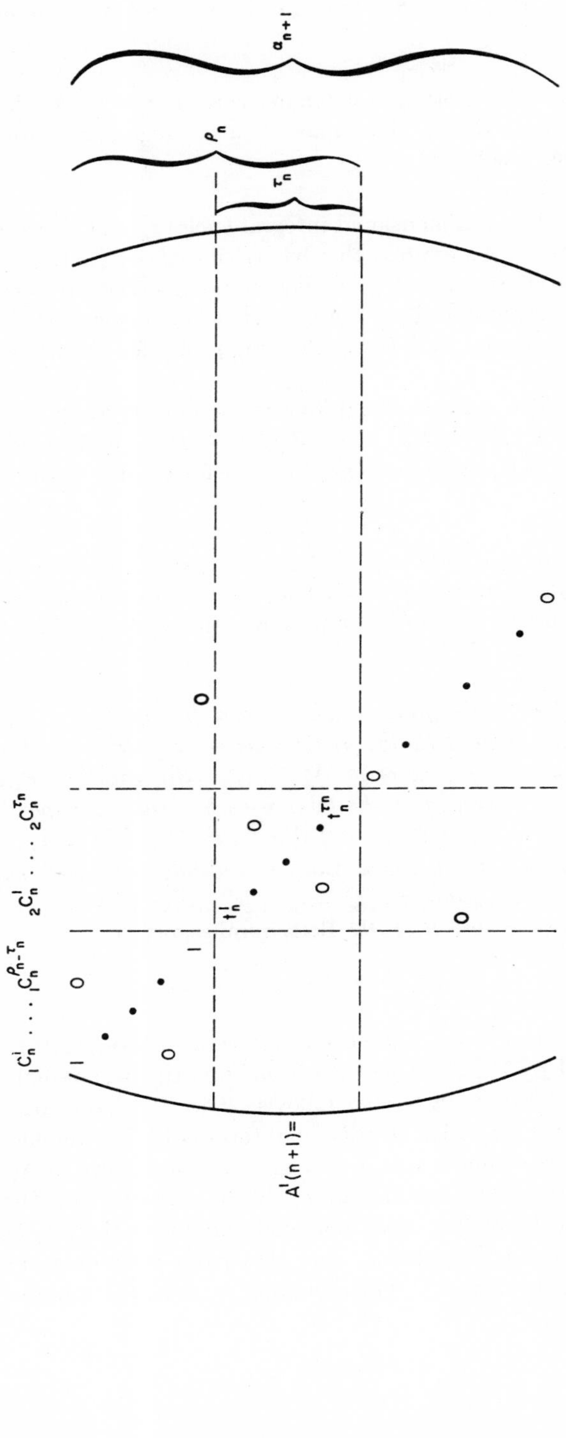

a_{n+1}
ρ_n
τ_n
$A^1(n+1)=$
${}_1C_n^1 \ldots {}_1C_n^{\rho_n-\tau_n}$
${}_2C_n^1 \ldots {}_2C_n^{\tau_n}$
t_n^1
$t_n^{\tau_n}$

Figure 3-2 (a)

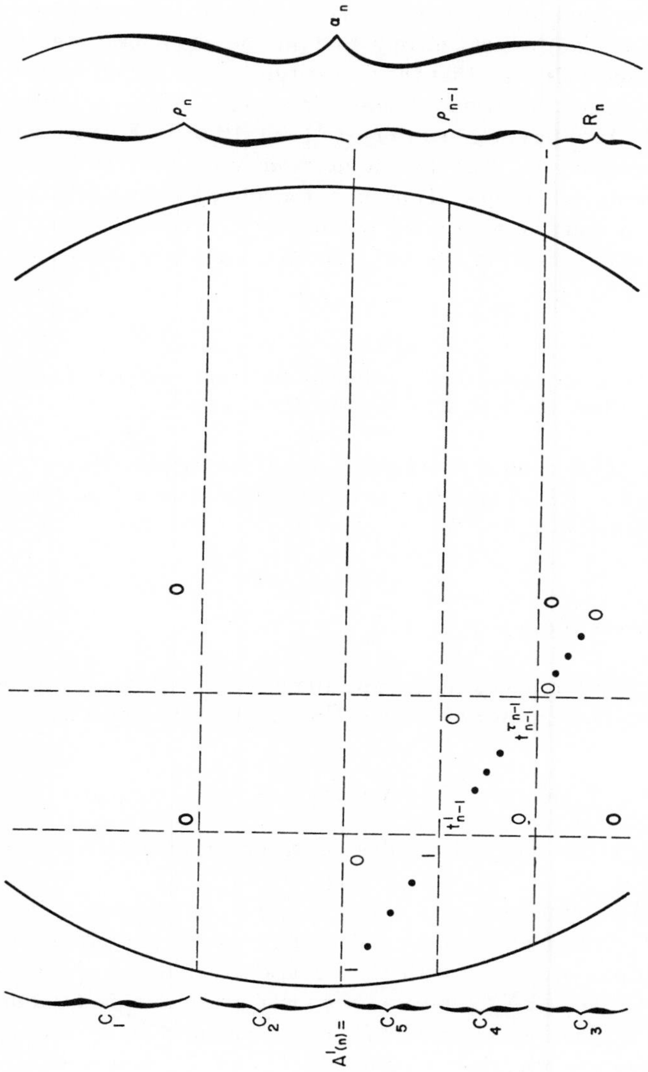

Figure 3-2(b)

group of n cycles $Z_n(K)$ is generated by the ${}_iC_n$, $i = 1, \ldots, 3$, chains, and $B_r(K)$ by ${}_1C_n$ chains.

Three observations ought be made to avoid possible misinterpretation. In the first place, (2.5) asserts merely that in the chain basis the cycles in $\{{}_2c_n^i\}$ are torsion cycles, not that they constitute a basis for all torsion cycles. Indeed, the latter assertion is false since ${}_1c_n + {}_2c_n^k$ is a torsion cycle. Similarly, $B_n(K, \text{J})$ has as generators $\{{}_1c_n^i\}$ and $\{t_n^k\, {}_2c_n^k\}$. Finally, the torsion coefficients entering in (2.5) do not necessarily include the various finite orders of cyclic subgroups. Thus if a torsion coefficient is a composite number say 6 and the associated torsion cycle is $c_n \in {}_2C_n(K, \text{J})$, then $2c_n$ and $3c_n$ are both torsion cycles, but 2 and 3 cannot both enter in $\{t_n^i\}$.

PROBLEM

3-3. Let K be a connected finite 1-dimensional complex such that $K - \sigma_1^i$ is not connected. Show $H_0(K, \text{J}) \approx \text{J}$ and $H_1(K, J) \approx 0$.

Lemma 2.6. *If K is an n-dimensional simplicial complex, then ${}_1C_n$ and ${}_2C_n$ are trivial and so are ${}_4C_0$ and ${}_5C_0$; so in particular there are no torsion coefficients in dimensions n, 0. Thus*

(2.6a) $$\rho_n = \tau_n = \tau_0 = 0.$$

R_0 is the number of components in K.

If J_p, p a prime, replaces the group J there are no p-divisible torsion coefficients and the new number of independent, nonbounding cycles in dimension m is

(2.6b) $$R_m(K, \text{J}_p) = R_m(p) = R_m + \tau_m(p) + \tau_{m-1}(p),$$

where $\tau_m(p)$ is the original number of m-dimensional torsion coefficients divisible by p.

Let L be a component of K. Let v_0 and v_1 be vertices in L. Let $\sigma_1^1, \sigma_1^2, \ldots, \sigma_1^m$ be the 1-simplexes in order, of the string joining v_0 and v_1 with the orientations consistent with the direction of passage along the string from v_0 to v_1. Then $\partial \sum_{i=1}^m \sigma_1^i = v_1 - v_0$, whence since v_i is a 0-dimensional cycle, $v_1 \sim v_0$. Thus, $\mathbf{v}_0$ is a basis of $H_0(L, \text{J})$; that is, $H_0(L, \text{J}) \approx \{n\, \mathbf{v}_0 \mid n \in \text{J}\}$.

If v_0 and v_1 are in distinct components L_0 and L_1, then $v_0 \not\sim v_1$. Indeed, assume the contrary; then $v_1 - v_0 = \partial \sum n_i \sigma_1^i$: that is, $i \in \pi_0$ if $\sigma_1^i \in L_0$ and $i \in \pi_1$ if $\sigma_1^i \in L_1$. Since a single vertex is nonbounding

$$\partial \textstyle\sum_{\pi_0} n_i \sigma_1^i = c_0 - v_0,$$

$$\partial \textstyle\sum_{\pi_1} n_i \sigma_1^i = v_1 - c_0'.$$

Since c_0 and c_0' consist of disjunct elements, $c_0 - c_0' \neq 0$, a contradiction. Hence R_0 gives the count of the components.

We verify (2.6b). On consulting Fig. 3-2 it is clear that when a t_m^i is replaced by 0, the chain heading the column of $\mathbf{A}(m+1)'$ containing t_m^i that is, the $(\rho_m - \tau_m + i)^{\text{th}}$ column is no longer a boundary cycle and so must be counted in ${}_3C_m$. When t_{m-1}^j is replaced by 0, the chain heading the row containing t_{m-1}^j enters ${}_3C_m$.

The ubiquity of simplexes makes it desirable to establish the next lemma.

Lemma 2.7. *The n-simplex σ_n has $H_0(\sigma_n, R) \approx R$, $H_p(\sigma_n, R) \approx 0$, $p \neq 0$.*

We resort to artifice for the proof and need consider only the case $p \neq 0$. Let $\sigma_n = A_0 \cdots A_n$. Then $A_i A_0 \cdots A_i \cdots A_n$, $0 < i < n$ is a degenerate $n+1$ dimensional simplex indicated by $A_i \sigma_n$, so $\partial A_i \sigma_n = \sigma_n + d_n + (-1)^{i+1} A_i A_0 \cdot\hat{\wedge}\cdot A_n$, where d_n consists of degenerate n dimensional simplexes and $(-1)^i A_i A_0 \cdot\hat{\wedge}\cdot A_n = \sigma_n$. Hence

$$\partial(A_i \sigma_n) = d_n. \tag{2.7a}$$

Suppose $z_p \in Z_p(\sigma_n, R) = \Sigma\, r_i\, \sigma_p^i$, where σ_p^i is the face of σ_n with vertices $A_{j_0} \cdots A_{j_p}$, $1 \leq p \leq n$. Then

$$\begin{aligned} A_0 z_p &= \Sigma\, r_i(A_0\, \sigma_p^i) \\ &= c_{p+1} + d_{p+1}, \end{aligned}$$

where c_{p+1} is a chain of nondegenerate simplexes and d_{p+1}, as before, is a chain of degenerate simplexes. Then

$$\begin{aligned} \partial A_0 z_p &= \partial(c_{p+1} + d_{p+1}) \\ &= z_p - A_0\, \partial z_p \end{aligned} \tag{2.7b}$$

Since c_{p+1} (and z_p) does not involve degenerate simplexes, none can enter in ∂c_{p+1}. Then (2.7a) implies

$$z_p = \partial c_{p+1}.$$

In short, every p dimensional cycle on σ_n is a bounding cycle if $p \neq 0$.

Definition 2.8. The **Euler-Poincaré characteristic** of the simplicial complex K is written $\chi(K)$ for

$$\chi(K) = \Sigma_i\, (-1)^i\, \alpha_i, \tag{2.8a}$$

where α_i is the number of simplexes of dimension i.

The following is a striking result.

Theorem 2.9. $\chi(K) = \Sigma_i\, (-1)^i\, R_i$

The demonstration is immediate. Thus, if there are simplexes of dimension $n+1$ but no higher (2.5a),

$$\begin{aligned}
\alpha_{n+1} &= R_{n+1} + \rho_n \\
\alpha_n &= R_n + \rho_n + \rho_{n-1} \\
&\cdot \\
&\cdot \\
&\cdot \\
&\cdot \\
\alpha_0 &= R_0 + \rho_0.
\end{aligned}$$

Substitution in (2.8a) yields (2.9).

PROBLEMS

3-4. Suppose K is a 1-complex with α_0, 0-dimensional and α_1, 1-simplexes. Suppose K is connected, i.e., $R_0 = 1$. Show one can remove $1 + \alpha_1 - \alpha_0$, 1-simplexes without destroying the connectivity of K. Draw a diagram to illustrate this.

3-5. Show (2.9) remains valid if simplexes are replaced by polyhedral cells. (21.7).

3-6. Prove there are only five regular polyhedra in R^3 by using the E.P. characteristic. *Hint:* Since every 1-simplex joins two 0-simplexes, $2\alpha_1/\alpha_0$ is the number of 1-simplexes meeting at every vertex. Similarly, every 1-simplex is common to exactly two 2-polyhedral cells, and each 2-polyhedral cell has exactly s 1-dimensional faces.

3-7. By the argument of the previous problem, determine the number of regular polyhedra in R^4 and in R^5. *Hint:* A connectedness requirement enters in R^{2n} and the number is infinite.

3. PRACTICAL CONSIDERATIONS. The computation of the homology groups or of the cycles of types 2 and 3 from the simplicial dissection is labor enough to make the most hardy blench. Thus the smallest numbers of 2-simplexes in the simplicial subdivision of a 2-sphere or of a torus are 4 and 14 respectively because of the crippling restriction that simplexes cannot share part of a face. If a dissection into cells is used, then to ensure that the same or isomorphic homology groups are obtained as with simplexes, we must supplement the restrictions of (21.5).

Definition 3.1. Let K be a finite simplicial complex. A **block cell** e^k_m is first of all constructed by banding together certain concrete simplexes $\{\sigma^r_m(k)\}$ and some of their faces where r runs through a range depending on e^k_m. We write $\sigma^t_n \subset e^k_m$ if σ^t_n is one of the simplexes just mentioned, and we assume each σ^t_n belongs to a unique e^j_m. Denote the complex made up of block cells by $\check{K}$. We lay down the further restrictions a block cell and a block complex must satisfy. For the closures we require

(3.1a) $$Cl\, e^r_m = \bigcup \{Cl\, \sigma^k_m \mid \sigma^k_m \subset e^r_m\}$$

and $$\| e^r_m \| = \bigcup \| \sigma^k_m \|.$$

The cells $\{e^r_m\}$ are to function as a smaller basis for defining Betti and torsion chains. Hence with the symbol a_i denoting either 1 or -1 we require there be a monomorphism $j_{\#}\colon C_m(\check{K}) \to C_m(K)$ defined by associating with each elementary chain e_m of $C_m(\check{K})$, a chain $\Sigma_{i\epsilon\pi}\, a_i\, \sigma^i_m \epsilon\, C_m(K)$ where the choice $a_i = \pm 1$ must be consistent with the further conditions (3.1b)–(3.1d) and $\sigma^i_m \subset e_m$ implies $a_i\, \sigma^i_m$ enters.

(3.1b) $$\partial j\, e^r_m = \Sigma_{i\epsilon\pi}\, \partial a_i\, \sigma^i_m(r) = j_{\#}\, \Sigma_s\, \eta_s\, e^s_{m-1}.$$

so $\check{\partial}$ can be defined by $\check{\partial} e^r_m = \Sigma_s\, \eta_s e^s_{m-1}$.

(3.1c) If $z_m = \Sigma\, a_i\, \sigma^i_m$ there is an m cycle $\gamma_m = \Sigma\, b_r\, e^r_m$ with $z_m - j_{\#}\, \gamma_m \sim 0$.

(3.1d) If $j_{\#}\, \check{c}_m = \partial c_{m+1} \epsilon\, C_{m+1}(K)$ there is a chain $\check{d}_{m+1} \epsilon\, C_{m+1}\, (\check{K})$ with $\check{c}_m = \partial \check{d}_{m+1}$.

Theorem 3.2. $H_m(\check{K}) \approx H_m(K)$.

Evidently (3.1c) and (3.1d) imply j_* is at once a monomorphism and an epimorphism. In the ensuing examples, the satisfaction of the conditions in (3.1) can be verified and will not be commented on.

Remark. The cells introduced here are merely computational devices and function as chains. Generality is gained if we replace e^j_m by the simplicial chain c^j_m, for instead of (3.1a) we could use

$$c^j_m = \Sigma\, b^j_k\, \sigma^k_m,$$

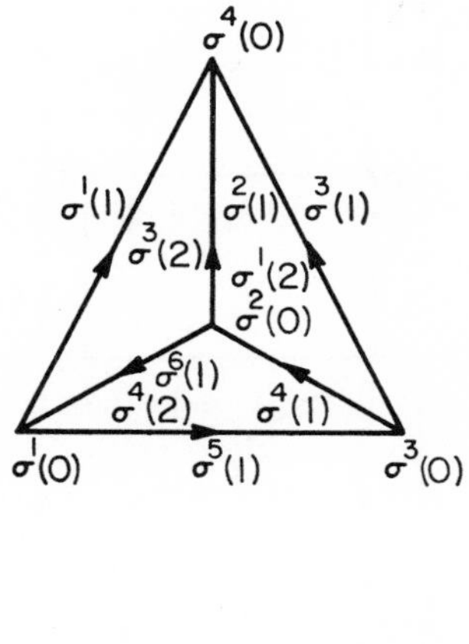

Figure 3-3

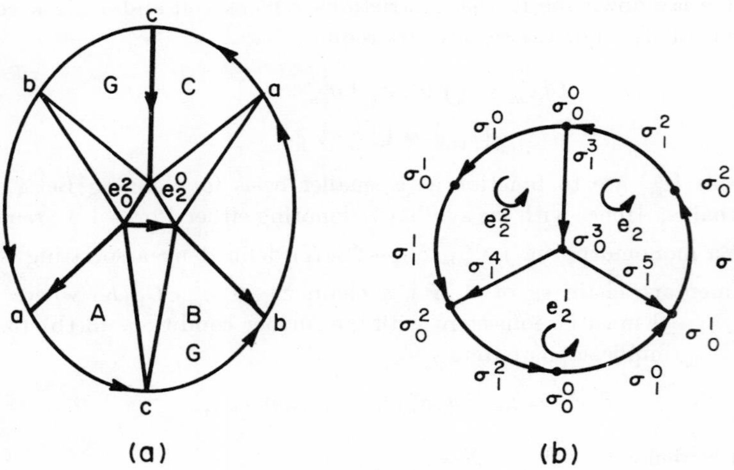

Figure 3-4

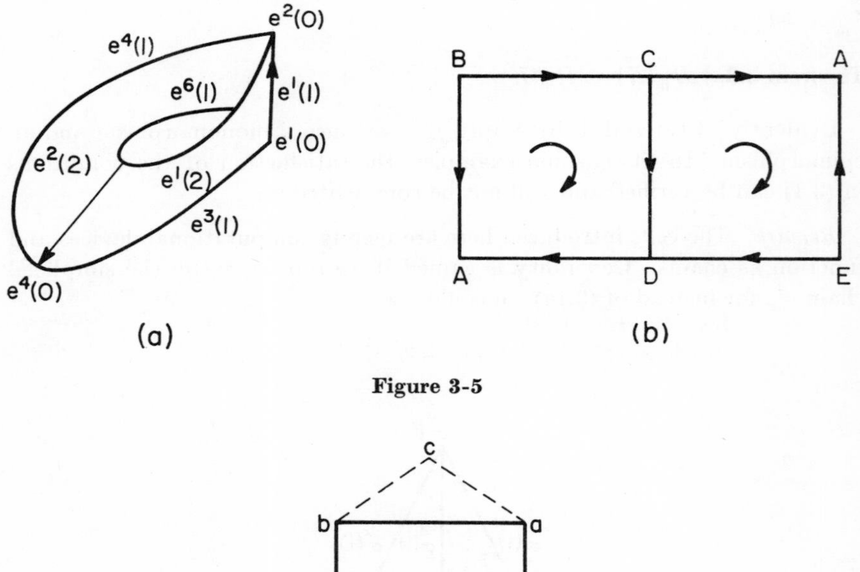

Figure 3-5

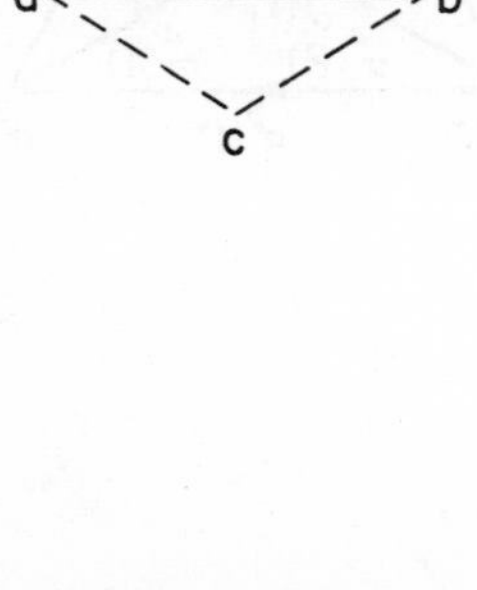

Figure 3-6

with the b_k^j not necessarily ± 1. However, the merit of the cells is their helpful geometric connotation.

In the examples and problems below we shall mean by homology characteristics the torsion coefficients and the Betti numbers.

EXAMPLE 3-1. *Tetrahedron*, $\sigma(3)$.

$$\mathbf{A}(3): \quad \begin{array}{c|cccc} & \sigma^1(2) & \sigma^2(2) & \sigma^3(2) & \sigma^4(2) \\ \sigma(3) & 1 & -1 & 1 & -1 \end{array}$$

$$\mathbf{A}(2): \quad \begin{array}{c} \\ \sigma^1(2) \\ \sigma^2(2) \\ \sigma^3(2) \\ \sigma^4(2) \end{array} \begin{array}{cccccc} \sigma^1(1) & \sigma^2(1) & \sigma^3(1) & \sigma^4(1) & \sigma^5(1) & \sigma^6(1) \\ 0 & 1 & -1 & 1 & 0 & 0 \\ 1 & 0 & -1 & 0 & -1 & 0 \\ 1 & -1 & 0 & 0 & 0 & 1 \\ & & & & & \end{array}$$

PROBLEM

3-8. Fill in the last row.

$$\mathbf{A}(1): \quad \begin{array}{c|cccc} & \sigma^1(0) & \sigma^2(0) & \sigma^3(0) & \sigma^4(0) \\ \sigma^1(1) & -1 & 0 & 0 & 1 \\ \sigma^2(1) & 0 & -1 & 0 & 1 \\ \sigma^3(1) & 0 & 0 & -1 & 1 \\ \sigma^4(1) & 0 & 1 & -1 & 0 \\ \sigma^5(1) & -1 & 0 & 1 & 0 \\ \sigma^6(1) & 1 & -1 & 0 & 0 \end{array}$$

The results have already been announced in (2.7) namely $R_0 = 1$, $R_1 = R_2 = R_3 = 0$, and there are no torsion cycles.

PROBLEM

3-9. Reduce $\mathbf{A}(i)$, $i = 1, 2, 3$, to canonical form and so verify these facts and show directly that $\sigma^1(1)$, $\sigma^6(1)$, $\sigma^5(1)$ can generate ${}_5C_{(1)}$ and $\sigma^1(1) + \sigma^6(1) - \sigma^2(1)$, $\sigma^5(1) + \sigma^4(1) + \sigma^6(1)$, $\sigma^4(1) - \sigma^2(1) + \sigma^3(1)$ constitute ${}_2C_1$.

EXAMPLE 3-2. *Projective Plane*. The projective plane is obtained by starting with the southern hemisphere and identifying points on the equator which are on opposite ends of a diameter. By projecting onto the horizontal plane, a disk is obtained with diametral points on the boundary identified. The simplified subdivision is indicated. (It is clearer to label the simplexes according to their vertex scheme in Fig. 3-4a, than to use the $\sigma^i(r)$ notation.) The incidence matrices for Fig. (3-4b) are:

$$\mathbf{A}(2):\quad \begin{array}{c} \\ e_2^0 \\ e_2^1 \\ e_2^2 \end{array} \begin{array}{c} \begin{array}{cccccc} \sigma_1^0 & \sigma_1^1 & \sigma_1^2 & \sigma_1^3 & \sigma_1^4 & \sigma_1^5 \end{array} \\ \begin{pmatrix} 0 & 1 & 1 & 1 & 0 & 1 \\ 1 & 0 & 1 & 0 & 1 & -1 \\ 1 & 1 & 0 & -1 & -1 & 0 \end{pmatrix} \end{array}$$

$$\mathbf{A}(1):\quad \begin{array}{c} \\ \sigma_1^0 \\ \sigma_1^1 \\ \sigma_1^2 \\ \sigma_1^3 \\ \sigma_1^4 \\ \sigma_1^5 \end{array} \begin{array}{c} \begin{array}{cccc} \sigma_0^0 & \sigma_0^1 & \sigma_0^2 & \sigma_0^3 \end{array} \\ \begin{pmatrix} -1 & 1 & 0 & 0 \\ 0 & -1 & 1 & 0 \\ 1 & 0 & -1 & 0 \\ -1 & 0 & 0 & 1 \\ 0 & 0 & 1 & -1 \\ 0 & 1 & 0 & -1 \end{pmatrix} \end{array}$$

Verify these; here $R_0 = 1$, $R_1 = R_2 = 0$. The chain sum of all the 2 simplexes has boundary $2(ac + cb + ba)$. Hence there is a torsion cycle, namely $ac + cb + ba$ and a torsion coefficient of 2. There is none if J_2 is used.

Example 3-3. *Mobius Band.* This is now a standard entertainment device. It is constructed by giving a rectangular strip of paper one twist about the long axis and then pasting together the two short sides. It can also be considered the subcomplex of the projective plane consisting of the simplexes aAB, ACb, ABC, BaC, Bba. A visualization of this band and a breakdown into cells is given in Figs. 3-5a and 3-5b. The incidence matrices are

$$\mathbf{A}(2):\quad \begin{array}{c|cccccc} & e^1(1) & e^2(1) & e^3(1) & e^4(1) & e^5(1) & e^6(1) \\ e^1(2) & -1 & -1 & 1 & 0 & -1 & 0 \\ e^2(2) & -1 & 1 & 0 & 1 & 0 & -1 \end{array}$$

$$\mathbf{A}(1):\quad \begin{array}{c} \\ e^1(1) \\ e^2(1) \\ e^3(1) \\ e^4(1) \\ e^5(1) \\ e^6(1) \end{array} \begin{array}{c} \begin{array}{cccc} e^1(0) & e^2(0) & e^3(0) & e^4(0) \end{array} \\ \begin{pmatrix} -1 & 1 & 0 & 0 \\ 0 & 0 & -1 & 1 \\ -1 & 0 & 0 & 1 \\ 0 & 1 & 0 & -1 \\ 0 & -1 & 1 & 0 \\ 1 & 0 & -1 & 0 \end{pmatrix} \end{array}$$

The reductions yield $R_0 = 1$, $R_1 = 1$, $R_2 = 0$. It may come as a surprise that though there is a twist there is no torsion.

PROBLEM

3-10. Verify these characteristics. Explicitly define the cells in terms of the simplexes of a simplicial subdivision of the torus and verify (3.1a), . . . , (3.1d).

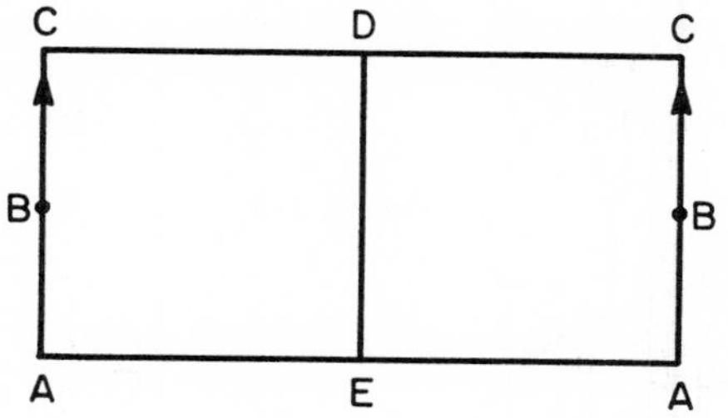

Figure 3-7

We can resurrect the projective plane from the Mobius band. Thus take a point exterior to the band and connect it by lines with all the points of the boundary (Fig. 3-6). The configuration so obtained is precisely that in Fig. 3-4.

PROBLEM

3-11. Show that removal of the central triangle ABC from the projective plane in Example 3-2 Fig. 3-4a leaves the Mobius band as the residual complex.

EXAMPLE 3-4. *Annulus,* or hollow finite cylinder.

PROBLEM

3-12. Show the homology characteristics are the same as for the Mobius band.

EXAMPLE 3-5. S^n *the n-Dimensional Sphere.* Take the equation for the metric sphere as

$$x_1^2 + \cdots + x_{n+1}^2 = 1.$$

Write x for the point on S^n with coordinates $x_1, \ldots, x_{n+1}$. This time we take closed concrete cells:

$$e^1(n) = \{x \mid x_{n+1} > 0\};$$
$$e^2(n) = \{x \mid x_{n+1} < 0\}.$$

Then

$$S^{n-1} = \{x \mid x_{n+1} = 0\}$$

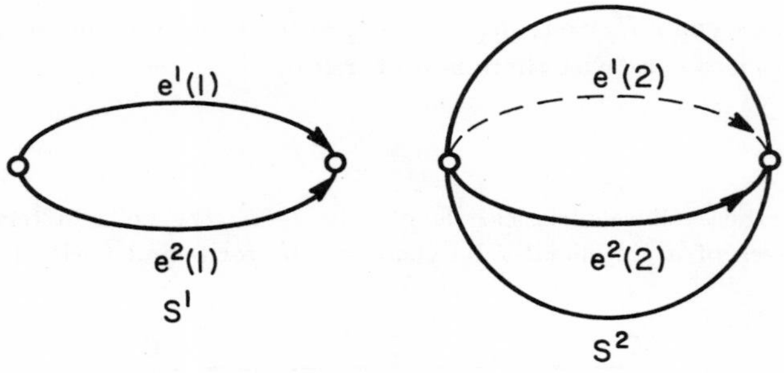

(a) (b)

Figure 3-8

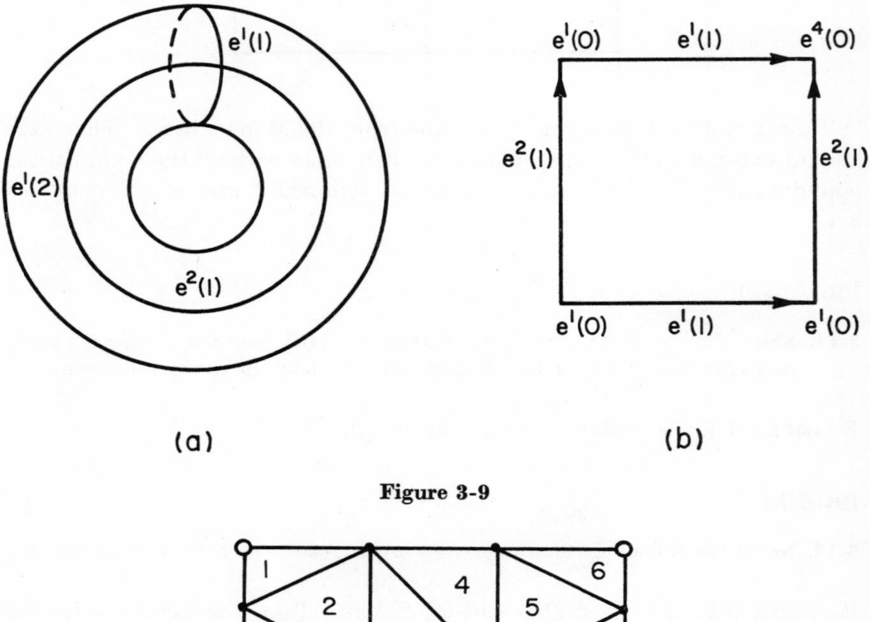

(a) (b)

Figure 3-9

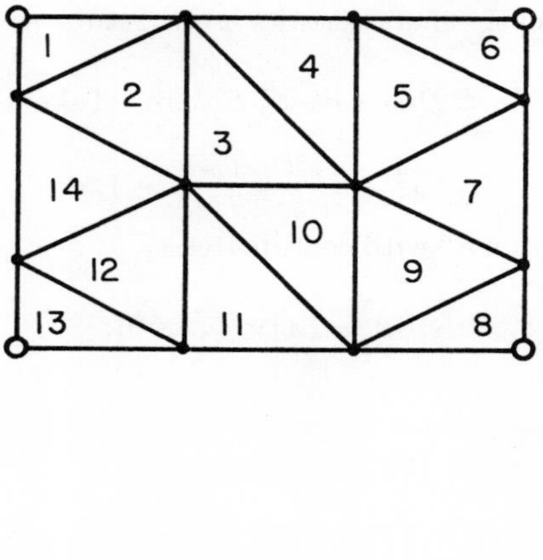

Figure 3-10

is common to both n cells. However, S^{n-1} consists of two $(n-1)$ cells sharing an S^{n-2}, etc. Thus, there are exactly two cells in each dimension. (Note, for instance, that the 2 cell has two vertices and two sides and that $e^1(1)$ and $e^2(1)$ are different cells with the same vertices, Fig. 3-8.)

$$\mathbf{A}(k): \quad \begin{array}{c|cc} & e^1(k-1) & e^2(k-1) \\ \hline e^1(k) & 1 & -1 \\ e^2(k) & 1 & -1 \end{array}$$

Hence, $R_0 = 1$, $R_1 = \cdots R_{n-1} = 0$, $R_n = 1$. There are no torsion coefficients.

PROBLEM

3-13. Reorient the cells $\{e^i(k)\}$ and show that the same results follow.

EXAMPLE 3-6. *Torus.* Figure 3-9 indicates the simple cell decomposition. Thus

$$\text{A}(2): \quad \begin{array}{c|cc} & e^1(1) & e^2(1) \\ \hline e(2) & 0 & 0 \end{array}$$

$$\text{A}(1): \quad \begin{array}{c|c} & e^1(1) \\ \hline e^1(1) & 0 \\ e^2(1) & 0 \end{array}$$

Hence, $R_0 = 1$, $R_1 = 2$, $R_2 = 1$. There is no torsion. The minimal triangulation requires fourteen 2-simplexes, Fig. 3-10. (Again (3.1a), . . . , (3.1d) ought to be verified.)

PROBLEMS

3-14. Analyze the double torus Fig. 3.11. Show that $e^1(1)$ is not in ${}_3C$ in the terminology of (2.5), that is, show $e^1(1)$ bounds. Show that $e^1(1)$ cannot be contracted to a point by sliding over the surface.

3-15. Denote the projective plane by a cell complex other than that in Example 3-2, and find the homology characteristics.

3-16. Snip off a small disk from a torus. Determine the homology characteristics of the resulting set (cf. Fig. 3-15).

3-17. Snip off m small disks from a torus $m > 1$. Determine the homology characteristics of the resulting set.

3-18. Determine the homology characteristics of the Klein bottle, Fig. 3-12.

We show now that any preassigned positive integer is a torsion coefficient for some two dimensional complex.

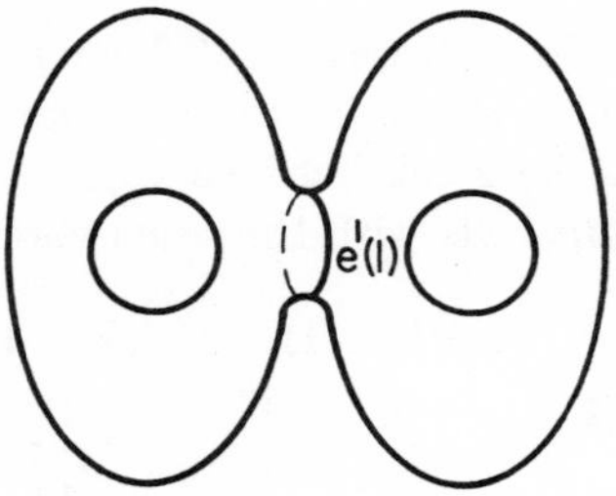

Figure 3-11

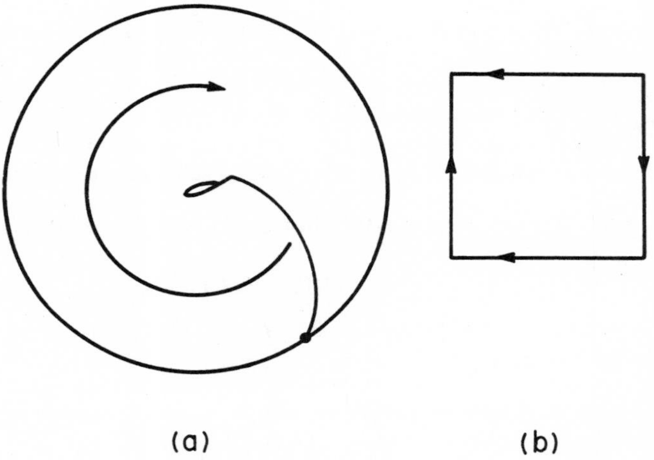

Figure 3-12

EXAMPLE 3-7. Let D be the two-dimensional disk divided into $2n$ equal sectors as in Fig. 3-13. Identify the boundary arc $x_i\, x_{i-1}$ with $x_1\, x_2$. The boundary becomes a collection of n identified, simple, closed curves so that D is a sort of n sheeted cone with the sheets all pressed together. In any case, denote the resultant complex by P_n. If c_2 is the chain sum of the cells of P_n and w is the boundary cycle, then $w = nz_1$ where z_1 is the cycle $x_1\, x_2$ and $c_2 = nz_1$. Thus there is a torsion coefficient $t = n$. Note P_2 is the usual projective plane, P^2.

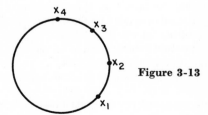

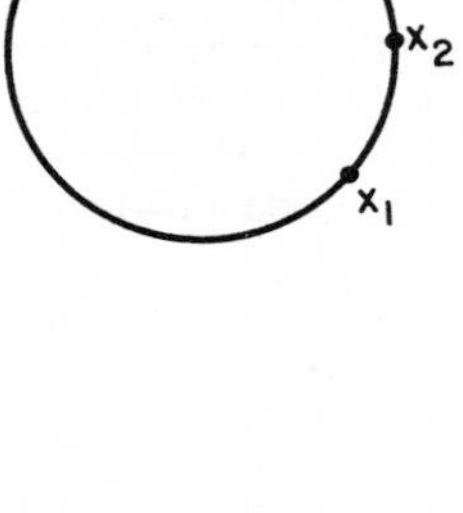

Figure 3-13

We consider a special property of the Mobius strip. With a broad enough paintbrush all of M can be painted without lifting the brush or crossing the boundary. It is natural, therefore, to say the Mobius band is **one-sided.** Alternatively, consider the two unit-normal vectors at a point p to be similar to flagpoles pointing in opposite directions at a point of M. Call one n_+ and the other n_-. Write (n_+, p) for the pair consisting of the positively directed unit normal and the point p. Similarly write (n_-, p). It is possible without flipping the normal around and without crossing the edge to transport (n_+, p) around M to end up with (n_-, p).

4. PSEUDO-MANIFOLDS. So far the orientation to be assigned a simplex in a simplicial complex has seemed arbitrary and nonsignificant. The example of the Mobius band draws attention to the curious property of one-sidedness. This property is not a property of the surface alone, but depends on the space in which it is imbedded. It is, however, related to the property of **orientability**, which is intrinsic to the complex, and by this token is independent of any enveloping space in which one may immerse the complex.

We shall be interested in a class of complexes whose uniformness of structure has made them a special object of study. (We suppress the prefatory "n-dimensional" below.)

Definition 4.1. A **simplicial pseudo-manifold** or **simple circuit** K^n is: **(a)** a homogeneous, n-dimensional complex (21.6), in which **(b)** each $n-1$ simplex is incident with exactly two n-dimensional simplexes; **(c)** there is an n string (21.8) joining any two n-simplexes.

Definition 4.2. The pseudo-manifold is **oriented coherently** if every $n-1$ face receives opposite induced orientations (21.3) from the two n simplexes with which it is incident. If a pseudo-manifold can be oriented coherently, it is called an **orientable** pseudo-manifold. If no coherent orientation exists it is a **nonorientable** pseudo-manifold.

EXAMPLE 3-8. The n-sphere and the torus are orientable pseudo-manifolds, while the projective plane is nonorientable.

PROBLEM

3-19. A 1-dimensional pseudo-manifold is orientable.

Lemma 4.3. **(a)** *If K is an orientable pseudo-manifold, then $R_n(K) = 1$ and the base cycle is $w_n = \Sigma\, \sigma_n^i$ where the sum is taken over all the coherently oriented n-simplexes.* **(b)** *If K is a nonorientable pseudo-manifold, $R_n(K) = 0$,* *and there is a single* $n - 1$*-dimensional torsion coefficient and its value is* 2. *In both cases,* $R_n(2) = 1$.

Suppose in fact

$$z_n = \Sigma\, a_i\, \sigma_n^i \tag{4.3c}$$

is a cycle. Suppose not all n-simplexes of K enter (4.3c). Take a string joining one of the simplexes entering (4.3c) to a simplex not included in (4.3c). We may consider the simplexes reordered so that $\sigma_n^1, \ldots, \sigma_n^{k+1}$ are the n-simplexes of a string with σ_n^{k+1} the first simplex absent from (4.3c). Then

$$\partial z_n = a_k\, \sigma_{n-1} + \cdots, \tag{4.3d}$$

where σ_{n-1} is the unique common face of σ_n^k and σ_n^{k+1} and the other terms on the right-hand side of (4.3d) do not involve σ_{n-1}. This contradicts the assumption that z_n is a cycle.

Since w_n is evidently a cycle, $a_1 w_n$ is a cycle also and so is $z_n' = -a_1 w_n + z_n$. However, z_n' lacks σ_n^1. By the argument just given, this is fatal unless indeed z_n' lacks all σ_n's, that is, $z_n' = 0$. Thus, z_n is an integral multiple of w_n.

To prove (4.3b) note that we have actually established that a necessary condition for z_n in (4.3c) to be a cycle is that all the simplexes of K enter and with the same coefficient up to sign. Hence by reorienting some of the simplexes, if necessary, we can arrange that $z_n = a\, \Sigma\, \sigma_n^i$. Observe that $\partial z_n = 2ac_{n-1}$, where c_{n-1} cannot be the 0 chain, for this would mean a coherent orientation of K. Since each σ_{n-1}^i entering c_{n-1} has a coefficient ± 1, it follows that the torsion coefficient of the torsion cycle c_{n-1} is 2 (that is, $2c_{n-1} = \partial w_n$). It may be of interest to finish up the proof by exhibiting the incidence matrices. We shall show:

$$\mathbf{A}(n)' = \begin{pmatrix} 1 & & & & & \\ & \cdot & & & & \\ & & 1 & & & \\ & & & \cdot & & \mathbf{0} \\ & & & & \cdot & \\ & \mathbf{0} & & & 1 & \\ & & & 0 & 0 & & 0 \end{pmatrix} \tag{4.3e}$$

$$\mathbf{A}(n)' = \begin{pmatrix} 1 & & & & & & \\ & \cdot & & & & & \\ & & 1 & & & & \mathbf{0} \\ & & & \cdot & & & \\ & & & & \cdot & & \\ & & & & & 1 & \\ & & \mathbf{0} & & & & 1 \\ & & & & 0 & 0 & 2 & & 0 \end{pmatrix} \tag{4.3f}$$

for the orientable and for the nonorientable cases respectively. Indeed, according to (4.1) each column of $\mathbf{A}(n)$ has just two entries, each of absolute value 1. Hence by interchanging rows or columns, if necessary, $\mathbf{A}(n)$ can be brought to the form

$$\mathbf{A}(n)'' = \begin{pmatrix} 1 & & & & & & \\ & \cdot & \mathbf{0} & & \mathrm{x} & & \\ & & 1 & & & & \\ & & & \cdot & & & \\ & \mathbf{0} & & & \cdot & & \\ & & & & 1 & & \\ -1\mathrm{x} & \cdots & \mathrm{x} & \mathrm{x} & \cdots & & \mathrm{x} \end{pmatrix}$$

By subtracting or adding each row to the last if called for the result is

$$\begin{pmatrix} 1 & & & & & \\ & \cdot & \mathbf{0} & & & \\ & & 1 & & \mathrm{x} & \\ & & & \cdot & & \\ & & & & \cdot & \\ & \mathbf{0} & & & 1 & \\ & & & & 0 \ \mathrm{x} & \cdots \ \mathrm{x} \end{pmatrix}$$

Suppose there are α_n rows. Any non-0 cross in the first $\alpha_n - 1$ rows can be wiped out by subtracting or adding one of the first α_n columns whence we arrive at (4.3e), except for doubt regarding the $\alpha_n\alpha_n$ term. In the orientable case we have exhibited a cycle w_n, so this term is 0. In the nonorientable case we have shown that there is at least one torsion coefficient, so this term is 2. From (4.3e) and (4.3f) it is plain that there is no $n - 1$ torsion for the orientable case and that the single $n - 1$-dimensional torsion coefficient is 2 for the nonorientable case. For $R_n(K, 2)$ or $R_n(2)$ we refer to (2.6b).

A generalization of the pseudo-manifold removes (4.1b).

Definition 4.4. An **n circuit** is a simplicial complex K^n satisfying: (**a**) the chain sum of all the n-simplexes is a cycle mod 2; (**b**) $R_n(K, 2) = 1$.

Thus, every pseudo-manifold is a circuit. However, a torus pinched along a simplex $[ab]$ is a 2-circuit, but not a pseudo-manifold, for there are four, 2-cells incident with ab.

PROBLEM

3-20. Show an n-cycle on an n-circuit is a multiple of some fixed n-cycle; that is, if $R_n \neq 0$, then $R_n = 1$. Show that the complex in Example 3-7 is a circuit.

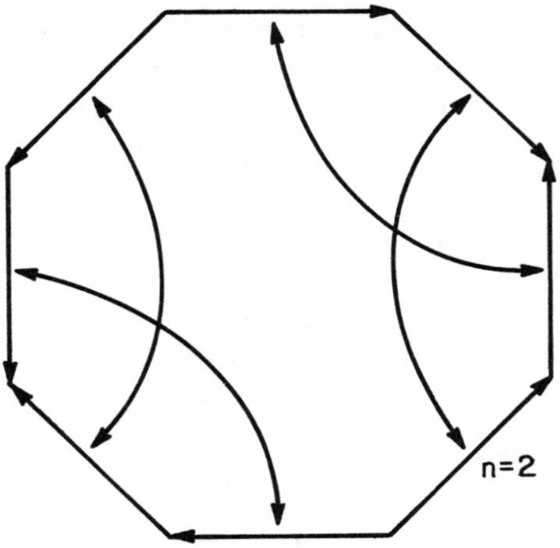

Figure 3-14

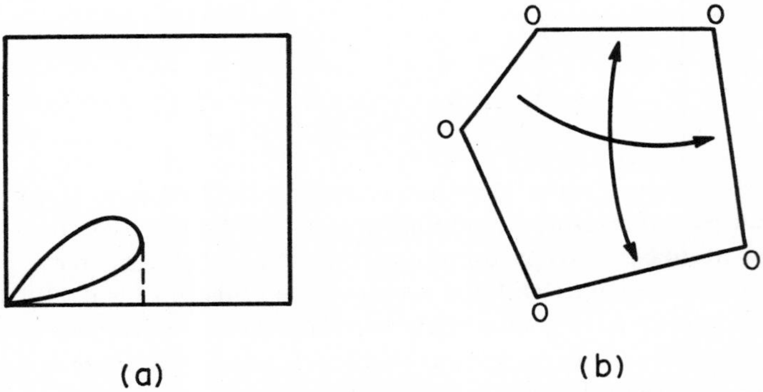

Figure 3-15

If p nonintersecting holes are bored through a solid sphere, the surface so obtained may be represented by a polygon with $4p$ sides identified in pairs, as follows:

PROBLEMS

3-21. Determine the homology characteristics of the double torus from this representation.

3-22. Reverse some arrows and get a nonorientable surface. For instance, consider $ABAB^{-1}CDC^{-1}D^{-1}$ as the boundary cycle. Determine the homology characteristics.

3-23. Show that the Klein bottle has the representation $ABA^{-1}B$. Show that the existence of a pair $\cdots A \cdots A \cdots$ in the fundamental cycle implies that the surface is nonorientable.

3-24. Snip off a disk from the double torus. What is the new polygonal representation?

In the following problems find the homology characteristics:

3-25. In S^2 identify the end points of one diameter. Identify 3 points. Replace 3 by r. Identify the end points of the horizontal diameter and identify the end points of a vertical diameter.

3-26. Snip off a disk from the torus and replace it by a Mobius band. (Thus identify the edges of the disk with the boundary of the triangle ABC in Example 3-2.)

EXAMPLE 3-9. *Projective n Space.* For the n-sphere S^n in the Euclidean $n + 1$-dimensional space with coordinates $x_1, \ldots, x_{n+1}$ we can choose the simplicial subdivision with vertices

(a) $$v_{2i} = \{\underbrace{0, 0, \ldots, +1}_{i}, 0, 0\}, \quad v_{2i-1} = \{\underbrace{0, 0, \ldots, -1}_{i}, 0, 0\}.$$

The concrete closed E^n_+ is the subset of S^n with $x_{n+1} \geq 0$. Its boundary is S^{n-1}. Then P^n, the *n-dimensional projective space,* is represented either by S^n with $x = (x_1, \ldots, x_{n+1})$ identified with $x = (-x_1, \ldots, -x_{n+1})$ or by E^n_+ with the boundary diametral points of S^{n-1} identified; that is, $x = (x_1, \ldots, x_n, 0)$, with $-x = (-x_1, \ldots, -x_n, 0)$. With either representation it is clear that P^n satisfies the defining conditions for a pseudo-manifold.

For S^n the simplexes are oriented according to the prescription that

(b) $$v_2\, v_4 \cdots v_{2(n+1)}$$

is positively oriented and each replacement of $2i$ by $2i - 1$ affects the orientation by the factor (-1). Thus, for $n = 7$, $v_1\, v_4\, v_6\, v_7\, v_{10}\, v_{12}\, v_{13}\, v_{16}$ has three replacements and so is negatively oriented.

The base cycle of S^n is z_n, the chain sum of the simplexes (4.3). The identification of diametral points to give P^n implies in particular that v_{2j} and v_{2j-1} are to be identified or, more generally, every simplex σ is identified with $(-1)^{n+1}\sigma$. In z_n consider the contribution of $(v_{i_1}, \ldots, v_{i_{n+1}}) + (v_{i_{1'}}, \ldots, v_{i_{n+1'}})$, where one of $i_j, i_{j'}$ is $2j$ and the other is $2j - 1$ for each j. This is of the form $\sigma + (-1)^{n+1}\sigma$. Hence, if n is odd, the contribution is 2σ, and if it is even, the contribution is 0. With the identification z_n becomes $z'_n = 0$, or $2 \Sigma\, \sigma^i_n$, according to whether n is even or odd. Since, there is no n cycle for n even we have, evidently, a nonorientable pseudo-manifold. For n odd $z'_n = \Sigma\, \sigma^i_n$ is a cycle, so P^{2n+1} is orientable.

Remark. The orientable n-pseudo-manifold is said to be oriented when choice of the generator of $H_n(K)$ is made.

PROBLEMS

3-27. Show $R_j(P^n, 2) = 1, \quad j = 1, \ldots, n$.

3-28. Show S^3 is the union of two solid noninterpenetrating tori (considered simplicial subcomplexes of a triangulated S^3).

3-29. A 2-dimensional pseudo-manifold K is dissected into several homogeneous subcomplexes $\{K_i, i = 1, \ldots, n\}$ by a series of nonintersecting cycle cuts $C_1^1, \ldots, C_1^m$. Show $\chi(K) = \Sigma\, \chi(K_i)$. Is it possible that $m > n + 1$ or $m < n + 1$? If K is orientable can any piece K_i be nonorientable?

3-30. Let $\{C_i \mid i = 1, \ldots, n\}$ be great circles on a sphere S^2 with no intersection common to three circles. How many pieces are there in this dissection of S^2? By identification of antipodal points pass to the similar problem for the projective plane and n nonconcurrent lines.

3-31. Identify the opposite faces of a Euclidean cube ($|x|, \ |y|, \ |z| \leq 1$) according to $(\pm 1, y, z)$, $(x, \pm 1, z)$, $(x, y, \pm 1)$. Show the result is a pseudo-manifold. Is it orientable?

3-32. Let the spherical shell $1 \leq r \leq 2$ have its two spherical boundary surfaces identified according to $(1, \theta, \phi) = (2, \theta + \pi, -\phi)$. Show the result is a pseudo-manifold. Is it orientable?

chapter 4

RELATIVE OMOLOGY MODULES

It will be convenient to introduce some further algebraic terminology.

1. FIELDS, RINGS, VECTOR SPACES, ALGEBRAS, AND CHAINS.

Definition 1.1. A collection of elements $\{r\}$ is a **ring** R under the operations $+$ and $\cdot$ if

(1.1a) R is an Abelian group under the operation $+$ with neutral element 0.

(1.1b) Under the multiplication $\cdot$, the associativity condition (11.1a) is satisfied. We drop the $\cdot$ and write rr' for $r \cdot r'$. The ring is **commutative** if $rr' = r'r$ for all r, r' in R.

(1.1c) The two-sided distributive law holds in the sense that for any triple of elements r, r', r'':

$$(r + r')r'' = rr'' + r'r,$$
$$r(r' + r'') = rr' + rr''.$$

The ring has a **unit** or **identity** written e or 1 if

(1.1d) $$er = r$$

(1.1e) $$re = r, \quad r \in R.$$

(It is a **left unit** if (1.1d) is satisfied and is a **right unit** if (1.1e) holds.) An **integral domain** is a commutative ring where $r_1 r_2 = 0$ only if r_1 or r_2 is 0.

Definition 1.2. A **field** F is an integral domain in which $F - (0)$ is an Abelian group with e the **identity** or **unit** under the operation $\cdot$.

Examples of rings are the integers, again denoted by J under the usual addition and multiplication, or the even integers 2J. The latter ring has no unit. Neither of these is a field (though both are integral domains). With multiplication added, the following groups become fields (though the notation is unchanged): R, Q, C, J_p, p a prime (for instance $2x = 1 \bmod 3$ has the solution $x = 2$, etc). Until further notice, reference to a **coefficient ring** R will refer to one of these rings or to J. In any case a *coefficient* ring is always commutative and has a unit.

Definition 1.3. A **vector space over a field** F, denoted by V for the moment, is an Abelian group, with a function or pairing, on $F \times V$ to V written rv, $r \in F$ (that is, in the terminology of analysis, r is a scalar and v is a vector). It is required that

(1.3a) $$(r_1 + r_2)(v_1 + v_2) = r_1 v_1 + r_2 v_2 + r_1 v_2 + r_2 v_1$$

(1.3b) $$r_1 (r_2 v) = (r_1 r_2)v,$$

(1.3c) $$1v = v.$$

Definition 1.4. If F is replaced by a commutative ring R with an identity, we use the term **module over R** (rather than vector space over R).

An important reason for introducing the module is that on the one hand any Abelian group can be considered a module over the ring of the integers, (that is, $ng = \underbrace{g + \cdots + g}_{n}$) and on the other, vector spaces are modules. (The reason for not using the terminology "vector space over R" is that unless the ring is a field, the cardinal number of elements in a basis may vary with the basis.) For application in later chapters we admit the case that R is not commutative, but does have a unit. A **left module** A over R is an Abelian group with the pairing $R \times A$ to A, that is to say the action of R is indicated by writing ra. The conditions are those in (1.3a), (1.3c). For a right module, the pairing is $A \times R$ to A, so the action of R is denoted by ar. The conditions (1.3a), . , (1.3c) are modified by switching the R terms to the right.

The homomorphism ψ of the module G to the module J, both over the same ring, is a map satisfying

(1.4a) $$\psi(r_1 g_1 + r_2 g_2) = r_1 \psi(g_1) + r_2 \psi(g_2)$$

The homomorphism ψ of the ring $R = \{r\}$ to the ring $S = \{s\}$ is a map satisfying

(1.4b) $$\psi(r_1 + r_2) = \psi(r_1) + \psi(r_2)$$

(1.4c) $$\psi(r_1 r_2) = \psi(r_1)\, \psi(r_2)$$

Remark. The terms defined so far are sometimes referred to as "abstract" —thus abstract group, abstract ring, · · · , etc. When the sets of elements are considered spaces, the compositions are understood to be continuous. For instance, the map defined by $r \times v \longrightarrow rv$ is required to be continuous on $R \times V$ to V. The groups, rings, etc., are then referred to as "topological groups," "topological rings," etc., and in this case homomorphisms are understood to be not only continuous but open maps as well. Quotient groups (or rings) can be formed only if N in (11.3) is a closed set.

EXAMPLE 4-1. Let R^2 be the ring of ordered pairs of real numbers $\{(r, s)\}$ with pointwise addition and multiplication; that is:

$$(r, s) + (u, v) = (r + u,\ s + v),$$

$$(r, s)(u, v) = (ru, sv).$$

Note that $(0, s)(u, 0) = (0, 0)$. Hence, R^2 has 0 divisors and is therefore neither an integral domain nor a field, notwithstanding the fact that R lies in both these last categories.

PROBLEMS

4-1. Exhibit the required substructures, i.e., kernel, image etc., for ring homomorphisms in Problems 1-3, 1-4, and 1-5.

4-2. Using R and R^2 as models, show that a homomorphic map of an integral domain into a ring need not be an integral domain. Show that a homomorphic map of a ring into an integral domain need not be an integral domain.

4-3. If R is a commutative ring, then

$$(a + b)^m = a^m + {}_mC_1\, a^{m-1}\, b + \cdots + {}_mC_r\, a^{m-r}\, b^r + \cdots.$$

4-4. If R is an integral domain and has a finite number of elements, then R is a field.

Definition 1.5. An **algebra** (more precisely an associative algebra) over the commutative ring R with unit 1 is (**a**) a *left* module over R possibly lacking a unit, (**b**) the multiplication satisfies $(r\ a)(r'\ a') = rr'aa'$ where r, r' are in R. Left may be replaced by right. A ring is an algebra over J.

2. DIRECT SUMS, PRODUCTS, AND GRADES. The notions below have an easy intuitive content. Suppose, for instance, that each module of a collection of not necessarily distinct modules is given a unique label, so $\{G(a) \mid a \in A\}$. For instance, the x and y axes in the Cartesian plane both refer to the real line and are distinguished by their labels; thus, R_x and R_y. We need the notion of the **Cartesian product**, denoted by $\Pi_A\, G(a) = \{g\}$, where g is a collection of elements $\{g(a)\}$, one for each $a \in A$; that is, $g = g(a \mid A)$. This explains treating g as a function on A. (Compare Appendix 5.1.) For example, if the label set A consists of 1, 2, 3 and $G(1) = G(2) = G(3) = \text{J}$, then $g = (7, -9, 14) \in \Pi\, G(a) = G(1) \times G(2) \times G(3)$. We say that $\Pi\, G(a)$ is a **direct product** (or a **strong direct sum**), provided it is a module for which the addition operation is defined as componentwise addition by:

$$(2.1a) \qquad (g = g(a \mid A)) + (g' = g'(a \mid A)) = (g(a) + g'(a) \mid A),$$
$$rg = rg(a \mid A).$$

We write $\Sigma\, G(a)$ or $\Pi_A\, G(a)$ for the direct product. The projection $p(a)$ is the homomorphism on $\Sigma\, G(a)$ to $G(a)$ defined by $p(a')g(a \mid A) = g(a')$ and (2.1a) can be expressed

$$g + g' = \{p(a)g + p(a)g' \mid A\}$$
$$rg = \{rp(a)g \mid A\}.$$

We have shown how to construct a direct product for an arbitrary family of modules $\{G(a)\}$. This is sometimes referred to as the **external** direct product. Of interest to us is the question as to when an assigned module G is a direct product of the family $\{G(a)\}$. In this case G is an **internal** direct product. Evidently this requires that G be isomorphic to $\Sigma\, G(a)$; that is, there is a family of projections $\{p(a) \mid A\}$ such that for arbitrary choice of $g(a)$ in $G(a)$, there is a unique $g \in G$ for which $g(a) = p(a)g$ for each a.

We shall be primarily interested in the case $G(a) \approx G$, $a \in A$. Then $\Sigma\, G(a)$ is the **module of infinite chains** with elements $g = \Sigma\, p(a)g = \Sigma\, g(a)$.

Example 4-2. $A = \{a \mid 0 \le a \le 1\}$ is the unit segment; $G(a) = R$ is the additive group of the reals $g = \{g(a \mid A)\}$; $G = \Sigma\, G(a)$ is the set of all arbitrary functions on A to R.

Definition 2.2. Let $i(b)\colon G(b) \longrightarrow G$ be an injection (11.4). If for arbitrary $g \in G$ and some finite subset π of A, $g = \Sigma_\pi\, i(b)g(b)$ uniquely, then G is the **direct sum** (sometimes called the **weak direct sum**) of $\{G(a)\}$. This is indicated by $G = \oplus\, G(a)$.

Sometimes $\oplus\, G(a)$ is interpreted as the submodule of the direct product consisting of elements $\{g(a) \mid g(a) = 0 \in G(a),\ a \bar{\in} \pi\}$. When $G(a) = G$, independently of a in A, $\oplus\, G(a)$ is the module of **finite chains**. The components $i(a)G(a)$ of the direct sum are termed **direct summands** or **direct factors**. Thus only the neutral element of G is common to distinct direct summands.

Example 4-3. Let G_n be a module given by the multiples of x^n, that is, $G_n = rx^n$, $r \in \text{R}$ or J. Then $\oplus\, G_n$ consists of polynomials; that is,

$g = \Sigma_\pi r_j x^j$. The composition operation is the usual polynomial addition. Similarly, $\Pi\ G_n$ is the module of formal (infinite) series.

A unification of concepts obtains if one notes

$$G(a) \xrightarrow{i(a)} G \xrightarrow{p(a)} G(a)$$

with (**a**) $p(a)i(a)g(a) = g(a)$ and (**b**) $p(b)i(a)g(a) = 0 \in G(b),\ a \neq b$.

Then the direct product occurs when $\{i(a)\}$ is determined by $\{p(a)\}$, and the direct sum occurs when $\{p(a)\}$ is determined by $\{i(a)\}$. (If A is a finite set, the direct sum and the direct product amount to the same.) For instance if $\{p(a)\}$ is assigned, then if $\{i(a)\}$ exists satisfying (**a**) and (**b**), G is a direct product.

PROBLEM

4-5. Show that $G = \oplus\ G(a)$ for A finite is equivalent to $(\Sigma\ i(a)p(a))g = g$.

EXAMPLE 4-4. $J_6 = J_2 \oplus J_3$. Indeed let J_6 be written $\{(j) \mid j = 0, \ldots, 5\}$. Then $(0) = 0 \oplus 0$, $(3) = 1 \oplus 0$, $(4) = 0 \oplus 1$, $(1) = 1 \oplus 1$, $(2) = 0 \oplus 2$, $(5) = 1 \oplus 2$.

EXAMPLE 4-5. Let $\{e_i\}$ be a set of orthogonal base vectors for a Euclidean space G or for an infinite dimensional Euclidean space (that is, a separable Hilbert space). Any vector of G can be expressed uniquely by $\Sigma\ r_i e_i$. Write $\{r_i e_i \mid r_i \in R\}$ as $G(i)$. In the finite dimensional case, G is a direct sum. In the infinite dimensional case, however, not every formal sum $\Sigma\ r_i e_i$ is admissible as an element of G because of convergence difficulties. Hence G is not a direct product. (Thus, if G refers to odd functions in $L_2(-1, 1)$ and if $e_i = \sin ix$, G is not the direct product given by the Fourier sine expansions.)

PROBLEMS

4-6. Show that $J_4 \neq J_2 \oplus J_2$.
4-7. Show that $J_{12} = J_3 \oplus J_4$.

Remark. If $\{G(a)\}$ is a family of topological modules, there is a natural topology to put on the direct products and sums, since both are contained in $\Pi\ G(a)$. For a direct product the topology is that of $\Pi\ G(a)$ interpreted now as a topological product. If A is *nonfinite*, the direct sums are taken in the discrete topology, and not in the expected relative topology of $\oplus\ G(a)$ as a subset of $\Pi\ G(a)$. A reason for this is that if $G(a) = G$ were compact, then $\oplus\, G(a)$ would not be a closed subset of $\Pi\, G(a)$. When A is finite and $G(a) = G$ is compact, the chain module $\oplus\, G(a)$ is compact and is also $\Sigma\, G(a)$.

Lemma 2.3. *If $\psi(a)$ is a homomorphism on $G(a)$ to G' and G is the direct sum of $\{G(a) \mid A\}$, then $\{\psi(a)\}$ induces a homomorphism on G to G' defined by* $\psi(\oplus_\pi g(a)) = \Sigma_\pi\, \psi(a) g_a$.

Definition 2.4. A **graded module** G is a module representable as a direct sum of a finite or denumerable number of modules i.e., $G = \oplus G(i)$, where the index i is referred to as the **degree** or **grade.** The elements of $G(i)$ all have the degree i and are said to be **homogeneous** of grade i. Some of the modules may be trivial. If the degree script is a subscript, G is a **lower-graded module.** If it is a superscript, G is an **upper-graded module.** Thus we have G^i or G_i.

EXAMPLE 4-6. If K is a complex, the i-chain group over G, that is, $C_i(K, G)$, is a direct product if the chains are infinite, and is a direct sum if the chains are finite and corresponds to the homogeneous module G_i of grade i in the graded module $\oplus\, G_i = C(K, G)$.

A homomorphism ψ of the graded module G into the graded module Q is of **degree** r if $\psi\colon G(m) \longrightarrow Q(m + r)$ where r is independent of m. Unless otherwise stated, $r = 0$, and one says simply "homomorphism" rather than "homomorphism of degree 0." However, for the boundary and the coboundary homomorphism introduced later, r takes on the values -1 and $+1$ respectively. Accordingly, ψ may be considered a collection $\{\psi(i)\}$, with $\psi(i)G(i) = \psi G(i)$. G' is an allowable **submodule** of the graded module G if G' is graded and $G(i)' = G(i) \cap G'$.

Theorem 2.5. *If J is a graded subgroup of the graded group G and J' is a graded subgroup of J then*

$$G/J \approx \oplus(G(i)/J(i)), \tag{2.5a}$$

and

$$(J(r) + J')/J' \approx J(r)/(J(r) \cap J'). \tag{2.5b}$$

Write $[g]$ for the coset of g in G/J. Note that $J(i) = G(i) \cap J$. By the first isomorphism theorem (11.7),

$$(G(i) + J)/J \overset{\psi(i)^{-1}}{\approx} G(i)/G(i) \cap J = G(i)/J(i). \tag{2.5c}$$

Indicate the elements of $G(i)/G(i) \cap J$ by the bracket notation $[\;]_i$. Hence, if $g(i) \in G(i)$,

$$[g(i)] \xrightarrow{\psi(i)^{-1}} [g(i)]_i.$$

Since G is a direct sum, the element g has the unique representation $\oplus\, g(i)(= \oplus\, i(j)g(j))$, so that $[g]$ has the decomposition $\oplus\, [g(i)]$ and so is the image of ψ. Thus, according to (2.3), $\{\psi(i)\}$ induces the homomorphism ψ on $\oplus\, G(i)/J(i)$ to G/J by

$$\psi(\oplus\, [g(i)]_i) = \oplus\, \psi_i\, [g(i)]_i = \oplus\, [g(i)].$$

Then kernel $\psi = 0$ since $\Sigma\, [g(i)] = 0$ implies $\Sigma\, g(i) \in J$, and, since $J(i) = G(i) \cap J$, this means $g(i) \in J$ or $[g(i)]_i = 0$ for each i. Thus, ψ is an isomorphism.

This argument establishes (2.5b) as a concomitant of (2.5c).

Theorem 2.6. *If ψ is a homomorphism of the graded module J into the graded module G, with $\psi J \subset G$ and $\psi J' \subset G'$ where G' and J' are submodules of G and J, then ψ induces a homomorphism Ψ of J/J' into G/G' with*

$$\Psi\colon J(i)/J(i)' \longrightarrow G(i)/G(i)'.$$

We define some upper-graded structures. The definition for the lower structures amounts to replacing superscripts by subscripts.

Definition 2.7. G is an upper-graded ring if as an additive group it is a direct sum of the subgroups $\{G^i\}$ and $G^iG^j \subset G^{i+j}$. If there is an identity its degree is 0. G is a **graded algebra** over the ring R if it is graded as a module.

In the next three definitions the ring or algebra is understood to be graded.

Definition 2.8. $'G$ is an **allowable subring** or **subalgebra** of the graded ring or algebra G if $'G^n = {}'G \cap G^n$. Furthermore $'G$ is an **ideal** of G if it is an allowable subring or subalgebra, and $'GG + G\,'G \subset {}'G$. (This is technically a two-sided ideal.) An ideal takes the place of the normal subgroup in forming quotient rings. Thus, since $(g_1 + {}'G)(g_2 + {}'G) = g_1 g_2 + {}'G$, let $g_1 \sim g_2$ if $g_1 - g_2 \in {}'G$. Define $G/'G$ as the collection of cosets $[g]$, with $[g_1] + [g_2] = [g_1 + g_2]$ and $[g_1][g_2] = [g_1 g_2]$.

Definition 2.9. If $'G$ is an ideal of G, then the quotient ring or algebra is graded and as a module

$$G/'G = \oplus\, G^r/'G^r \tag{2.5a}$$

Definition 2.10. **A homomorphism of degree** r of the graded ring G into the graded ring $'G$ is a ring homomorphism taking $G(i)$ into $'G(i + r)$. If the degree is not stated it is understood to be 0 (except for the boundary homomorphisms).

The next three theorems paraphrase the situation for groups.

Theorem 2.11. *If ^2G is an ideal of ^1G and ^1G is an ideal of G, then $^1G/^2G$ is an ideal of $G/^2G$ and there is a natural homomorphism yielding $G/^2G/^1G/^2G \approx G/^1G$,* (11.8).

Theorem 2.12. *If ^1G is an ideal of G and ^2G is a subring of ^1G, then $\oplus_p(^1G^p \cap {}^2G)$ is an ideal of ^2G and $(^1G + {}^2G)/^1G \approx {}^2G/(^1G \cap {}^2G)$* (11.7) *and* (2.5).

Theorem 2.13. *If ψ is a homomorphism on the ring G_1 to G_2 which carries the ideal J_1 of G_1 into the ideal J_2 of G_2, then $\psi'[g_1]_{J_1} = [\psi g_1)_{J_2}$ defines a homomorphism*

$$\psi' : G_1/J_1 \to G_2/J_2$$

PROBLEM

4-8. Demonstrate (2.11), (2.12), (2.13).

Here and throughout the book we shall use the notation of (32.4), namely $\mathbf{z}_m$ or $\langle z_m \rangle_K$ is an element of $H_m(K)$.

We add a little detail to the statements in (32.5).

Theorem 2.14. *$H_m(K)$, (32.4), is isomorphic to the direct sum $\boldsymbol{B}_m(K) \oplus \boldsymbol{T}_m(K)$. Here $\boldsymbol{B}_m(K)$ is the* ***Betti*** *group, a free group, while $\boldsymbol{T}_m(K)$, the* ***torsion*** *group, consists of all elements of finite order in $H_m(K)$. $\boldsymbol{B}_m(K)$ is generated by $\{\langle {}_3c^i_m \rangle\}$. $\boldsymbol{T}_m(K) = \oplus\, T^k_m$ where T^k_m is the cyclic group of order t^k_m and generator $\langle {}_2c^k_m \rangle$. For $i < j$, the ith torsion coefficient t^i_m divides t^j_m.*

Refer to (32.5). We have the direct sum decomposition $Z_m(K) = {}_3C_m \oplus {}_2C_m \oplus {}_1C_m$. Since $B_m(K) = {}_1C_m$, there is obtained the direct sum,

$$\frac{Z_m(K)}{B_m(K)} = \left(\frac{{}_3C_m \oplus {}_1C_m}{{}_1C_m}\right) \oplus \left(\frac{{}_2C_m \oplus {}_1C_m}{{}_1C_m}\right).$$

Writing $\boldsymbol{B}_m(K)$ for the quotient group in the first set of parentheses and $\boldsymbol{T}_m(K)$ for that in the second set of parentheses yields the assertion of the theorem. Observe that since $t^i_m\, {}_2c^j_m$ is in ${}_1C_m$, $t^j_m\, {}_2c^j_m \sim 0$.

Corollary 2.15. *$H_m(K, G)$ is generated by ${}_3\mathbf{c}^i_m$ so the typical element is $\Sigma\, g_i\, {}_3\mathbf{c}^i_m$ if G is a field.*

The old torsion cycles in ${}_2C_m$ are now bounding cycles, for if $\partial c_{m+1} = t\, {}_2c_m$, then since $(1/t) \in G$, $\partial c'_{m+1} = {}_2c_m$, where $c'_{m+1} = (1/t)c_{m+1}$.

Remark. Theorem 2.14 is covered directly also by a known theorem on the decomposition of finitely generated Abelian groups. Moreover finer discrimination can be achieved by replacing the invariant factors t^i_m by elementary divisors.

The following example is instructive.

EXAMPLE 4-7. Let K be the projective plane and let L be a 2-complex disjunct from K, with torsion coefficient 3 (Example 3-7). Let c^1_2 and c^2_2 be the chain sum of the 2-simplexes of K and of L respectively, with $\partial c^1_2 = 2c^1_1$, $\partial c^2_2 = 3c^2_1$. Consider the complex $M = K \cup L$. $T_1(M)$ is generated by a single basic torsion class $\langle c^3_1 = c^2_1 - c^1_1 \rangle$ with torsion coefficient 6. It may seem surprising since K and L are disjunct that there are not still the two torsion coefficients 2 and 3, but actually a trace is left since $2\mathbf{c}^3_1$ and $3\mathbf{c}^3_1$ belong to $\boldsymbol{T}_1(M)$.

PROBLEM

4-9. Let K be a 2-complex with cell incidence matrices $\mathbf{A}(2) = \begin{pmatrix} 2 & 0 \\ 0 & 3 \end{pmatrix}$, $\mathbf{A}(1) = \mathbf{0}$. Find the reduced matrices and the new basis chains and interpret.

3. CHAIN MODULES. The chains and the chain modules were described in (22) in terms of a basis. However, the groups or submodules generated by basis elements can evidently be considered the component modules or direct summands of direct products or direct sums. Accordingly, the definitions in (22) can be restated using the language of direct products and direct sums, and we permit a little harmless repetition.

Definition 3.1. Let K be a cell complex consisting of ordered simplexes or cells. Take the n cells of $K^{[n]}$ as an indexing range. Let G be a module. If K is star finite, the r-dimensional infinite chain module $C^s_r(K, G)$ is the direct product $\{\Sigma\, G(e^i_r) \mid e^i_r \in K^{[r]}, G(e^i_r) \approx G\}$; that is, e^i_r corresponds to a, $K^{[n]}$ to A, and $G(e^i_r)$ to $G(a)$ in the notation of (2). The module ${}_fC_r(K, G)$ of finite chains arises on replacing direct product by direct sum. Thus, $C_r(K, G) = \oplus\, G(e^i_r)$ can be viewed as the collection of independent functions $\{c_r\}$ on $\{e^i_r \mid K^{[r]}\}$ to G; so $c_r(e^i_r) = g(e^i_r)$, where $c_r(e^i_r) = 0$ for all but a finite set of elements of $K^{[r]}$. If K is closure finite only, the module ${}_fC_r(K, G)$ of finite chains finds use. We drop the f when it is understood that only finite chains enter. Oriented simplexes introduce the relations $-g(\sigma_r) = g(-\sigma_r)$. The index set $\{\sigma^i_r\}$ is then restricted to the positively oriented simplexes. Moreover in conformity with (22) we write for the typical element of these modules $c_r = \Sigma_\pi\, g_i\, \sigma^i_r$, instead of $\Sigma_\pi\, g(\sigma^i_r)$; that is, we write $g(\sigma^i_r)$ as $g_i\, \sigma^i_r$.

More generally we note in passing that we can write the direct product or direct sum

(3.1a) $$C_r(K, G) = \Sigma\, C_r^i(K, G),$$

or

(3.1b) $$_fC_r(K, G) = \oplus\, C_r^i(K, G),$$

where $\{C_r^i(K, G)\}$ represents direct summands. For finite complexes, (3.1b) repeats the change of basis developments of (31.1), and (32.5). First we may identify $C_r^i(K, J)$, $i = 1, \ldots, 5$, with the modules $_iC_r(K, J)$ in (32.5). In the event that each $C_r^i(K, G)$ has a unique generator c_r^i, we say that $C_r(K, G)$ has the r-**dimensional chain basis** $\{c_r^i\}$ since every chain is a unique finite sum of the basis chains though the group may not be free.

The definition of the homomorphism ∂ is given in (22.4). We recall that the simplicial case rests on

(3.2a) $$\partial g\sigma_r = \Sigma\, g\, (-1)^i\, \sigma_{r-1}(i).$$

For cell complexes the incidence numbers $\eta_j^i(r) = [e_r^i, e_{r-1}^j]$ (21.5) enter, and we restate (22.4h) in the form

$$\partial \oplus g_i e_r^i = \oplus\, g_i\, \eta_j^i(r)\, e_r^j.$$

This refers to finite chains, the natural situation for K closure finite.

If we turn to infinite chains, formally

(3.2b) $$\partial\, \Sigma_i\, g_i e_r^i = \Sigma_{i,j} g_i\, \eta_j^i(r)\, e_{r-1}^j.$$

If this is to have meaning for arbitrary choice of the coefficients $\{g_i\}$, the coefficient of e_{r-1}^j in (3.2b) must involve a finite sum only. The natural sufficient condition is that $\eta_j^i(r)$ differs from 0 when j is fixed for at most a finite set of i values, indicated by π_j, for then the coefficient of e_{r-1}^j is $\Sigma_{i\in\pi_j} g_i\, \eta_j^i(r)$. This restriction holds when K is star finite. Note also that $\partial\partial\, \Sigma\, g_i\, e_r^i$ yields the formal sums $\Sigma\, \eta_j^i(r)\eta_k^i(r-1) = 0$. Under the restriction just made the latter sum is a finite sum. Accordingly, infinite chains can be used when K is star finite. (It is true that for $G = J_p$, for instance, some weakening of the star finiteness restriction is possible since the condition $\eta_j^i(r) = 0 \bmod p$ can replace $\eta_j^i(r) = 0$, but this is of little interest.)

4. RELATIVE CHAIN MODULES. It is often desirable to distinguish between an aggregate which may be a group or a ring or a vector space, etc., viewed as an independent entity and viewed as part of a containing aggregate.

Definition 4.1. Let L be a subcomplex of K. Then $i\colon L \longrightarrow K$ is an **inclusion** correspondence, or mapping, of the cells, $\{e^r\}$ in L and the same cells considered now as members of K. This induces an **injection monomorphism,** or simply **injection,** $i_{\#}\colon C_r(L, G) \to C_r(K, G)$, though we sometimes write $C_r(L, G)$ in place of $Im\ i_{\#}$ or of $i_{\#} C_r(L, G)$. Write $e(L)$ and $e(K - L)$, for the moment, to indicate which subcomplexes claim these cells. We suppose L is a closed subcomplex of K. Then

$$i_{\#} \Sigma g_a e_r^a(L) = \Sigma g_a e_r^a(L) + \Sigma 0_b e_r^b(K - L),$$

where 0_b is the zero of $G(e_r^b)$. Write

$$C_r(K/L, G) = C_r(K, G)/i_{\#} C_r(L, G). \tag{4.1}$$

We refer to the chains in $C_r(K/L, G)$ as **relative chains.** It is sometimes useful to introduce the projection homomorphism on $C_r(K)$ to $C_r(K)$. This is defined first on the elementary chains by $p(L)e_r = 0$ if the corresponding cell $e_r \bar{\in} L$ and $p(L)e_r = e_r$ if the corresponding elementary cell $e_r \in L$. Then $p(L)p(L) = p(L)$. Furthermore $p(L)C_r(K) = i_{\#} C_r(L)$.

Lemma 4.2. *If L is closed, then the boundary operator ∂ induces a homomorphism $\partial_{K,L}$ on $C(K/L, G) \longrightarrow C(K/L, G)$ defined by $\partial_{K,L}[c_r] = [\partial c_r]$, where $[c_r] \in C_r(K/L, G)$ and $[\partial C_r) \in C_{r-1}(K/L, G)$, and a homomorphism ∂_L on $i_{\#}C(L, G) \longrightarrow i_{\#}C(L, G)$* (Example 4-6).

With L closed, $\partial i_{\#} C_r(L, G) \subset i_{\#} C_{r-1}(L, G)$. Accordingly, (11.6) applies.

Remark. While we might expect to write, in analogy to (4.1) with ${}^1C$ for $C(K - L)$, $C_r(L, G) = C_r(K, G)/i_{\#}\, {}^1C_r(K - L, G)$, the restriction of ∂ does not behave properly when $K - L$ is not closed in K. Thus, $\partial \mid i_{\#}\, {}^1C_r(K - L, G) \not\subset i_{\#}\, {}^1C_{r-1}(K - L, G)$; so ∂ would not induce a boundary homomorphism on the quotient group.

We now extend to relative chains the definitions in (32.2).

Definition 4.3. It is customary to write ∂ both for the boundary homomorphism and for all induced homomorphisms as well. Thus ∂ may represent $\partial_{K,L}$. Let A refer either to K or to the pair K/L. Then $C_r(A, G) \xrightarrow{\partial} C_{r-1}(A, G)$ and $\partial\partial(C_r(A, G))$ is the 0 chain of $C_{r-2}(A, G)$. Write $Z_r(A, G) = ker\ \partial$. Then $Z_r(K, G)$ is the module of **absolute** r-cycles, and $Z_r(K/L, G)$ is the module of **relative** r-cycles.

Write $B_r(A, G) = Im\ \partial$. Then $B_r(K, G) = \{c_r \mid c_r = \partial c_{r+1}(K, G)\}$ is the module of absolute bounding r cycles, and $B_r(K/L, G) = \partial C_{r+1}(K/L, G)$ is the module of r-dimensional, relative bounding cycles.

Lemma 4.4.

$$[c_r(K)] \in Z_r(K/L, G) \Leftrightarrow \partial c_r(K) \in i_{\#} C_{r-1}(L, G)$$

$$[c_r(K)] \in B_r(K/L, G) \Leftrightarrow c_r(K) = i_{\#}c_r(L) + \partial c_{r+1}(K)$$

where the coefficient module has been omitted in $c_r(K)$ and $c_r(L)$.

Definition 4.5. In either the absolute or the relative case, if z_r and z'_r are cycles and $z_r - z'_r$ is a bounding cycle, then z_r is **homologous** to z'_r, written $z_r \sim z'_r$. This is an equivalence relation.

Definition 4.6. The module $H_r(A, G) = Z_r(A, G)/B_r(A, G)$ is the r-dimensional homology module. Thus, $H_r(K, G)$ is the **absolute homology module** and $H_r(K/L, G)$ the **relative homology module.**

An elementary observation is that neither the fact that $L \subset K$ nor that $C_n(L, G)$ is included in $C_n(K, G)$ for all n gives any indication of the relationships of the homology groups.

EXAMPLE 4-8. Let K be a 2-simplex, L its boundary, and M one side of the boundary. Then $C_i(M, G) \subset C_i(L, G) \subset C_i(K, G)$, $i = 0, 1, 2$. While $H_1(M, G) = 0$, $H_1(L, G) \neq 0$, and $H_1(K, G) = 0$.

It is advantageous to take the antecedents of $C_r(K/L)$, $Z_r(K/L)$, and $B_r(K/L)$ in $C_r(K, G)$. We indicate them by replacing the argument K/L by K, L. Thus, with $\Delta^{-1} = \partial^{-1} i_\#(r-1)$ using the commutative appended diagram [or just (4.4)]: If $c_r(K) \xrightarrow{j_\#} [c_r(K)]$ then subgroups of $C_r(K, G)$ are

$$\begin{aligned} (4.7)\quad Z_r(K, L, G) &= j_\#^{-1} Z_r(K/L, G) = \Delta^{-1} C_{r-1}(L, G), \\ B_r(K, L, G) &= j_\#^{-1} B_r(K/L, G) = \partial C_{r+1}(K, G) + i_\#(r) C_r(L, G). \end{aligned}$$

$$\begin{array}{ccccc} & & \longrightarrow C_{r+1}(K) \longrightarrow & & \\ & & \downarrow \partial & & \\ C_r(L) & \xrightarrow{i_{\#(r)}} & C_r(K) \longrightarrow & & \\ \downarrow \partial & & \downarrow \partial & & \\ C_{r-1}(L) & \xrightarrow{i_{\#(r-1)}} & C_{r-1}(K) \longrightarrow & & \end{array}$$

Theorem 4.8. $H_r(K, L, G) \approx H_r(K/L, G)$.

Indeed by (4.4) and (4.5)

$$\begin{aligned} \frac{Z_r(K, L, G)}{B_r(K, L, G)} &= \frac{\Delta^{-1} C_{r-1}(L, G)}{\partial C_{r+1}(K, G) + i_\# C_r(L, G)} \\ &\approx \frac{\Delta^{-1} C_{r-1}(L, G)/i_\# C_r(L, G)}{\dfrac{\partial C_{r+1}(K, G) + i_\# C_r(L, G)}{i_\# C_r(L, G)}} \\ &= \frac{Z_r(K/L, G)}{B_r(K/L, G)}. \end{aligned}$$

Remark: In view of (4.8) we shall often write $C_r(K, L, G)$ for $C_r(K/L, G)$ (though this notation is somewhat inconsistent with (4.7)).

5. EXACT SEQUENCES

Definition 5.1. Let D, E, F be consecutive R modules in the sequence of R modules and indicated R homomorphisms:

$$B \xrightarrow{s} C \xrightarrow{t} D \xrightarrow{i} E \longrightarrow F \longrightarrow G \longrightarrow H \longrightarrow \tag{5.1a}$$

The sequence is **exact** at E if $Im\ i$ [or $i(D)$] coincides with $ker\ j$. The sequence is an **exact sequence** if it is exact at every module.

The exact sequence

$$0 \longrightarrow A \xrightarrow{i} B \xrightarrow{j} C \longrightarrow 0 \tag{5.1b}$$

is sometimes called a **short exact sequence.**

In (5.1a), if $C = 0$, i is a *monomorphism* while if $G = 0$, j is an *epimorphism.* In the exact sequences (5.1a) s is an epimorphism of B onto C if and only if i is a monomorphism of D into E. In particular, D and E can be trivial modules to give $A \to B \to 0$ and $0 \to A \to B$ respectively for the epimorphism and the monomorphism.

PROBLEMS

4-9. In (5.1b) show $C \approx B/ker\ j \approx B/Im\ i$.

4-10. In the diagram below the horizontal line is an exact sequence. Both triangles are commutative. Prove m exists so that (**a**) $0 \longrightarrow (v\ r\ A') \xrightarrow{m}$

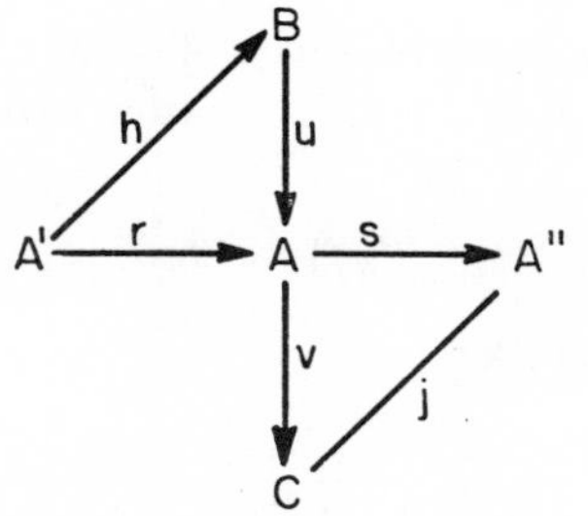

Figure 4-1

$(v\ u\ B) \xrightarrow{n} (s\ u\ B) \longrightarrow 0$ is exact at $(v\ r\ A')$ and at $(s\ u\ B)$ where $n = jv\ u\ B$. (**b**) Using m, n of part (**a**), show successively $ker\ n = v(uB \cap ker(jv)) = v(uB \cap rA') \approx (v\ r\ A')$, and therefore (**a**) is exact at $(v\ u\ B)$ also.

4-11. In the following diagram the horizontal line is exact and both triangles are commutative. Prove that s induces an isomorphism $\dot{s}$ on $(uB)/(rA')$ onto (jB).

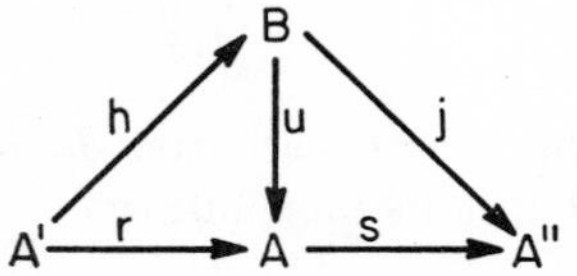

Figure 4-2

4-12. Let the rows below be exact sequences of modules

$$\begin{array}{ccccccccc} 0 & \longrightarrow & A' & \xrightarrow{i} & A & \xrightarrow{j} & A'' & \longrightarrow & 0 \\ & & \cup & & \cup & & \cup & & \\ 0 & \longrightarrow & B' & \xrightarrow{i'} & B & \xrightarrow{j'} & B'' & \longrightarrow & 0 \end{array}$$

where i' and j' are the restrictions of i and j to B' and to B. Show that these induce the exact sequence

$$0 \longrightarrow A'/B' \xrightarrow{i''} A/B \xrightarrow{j''} A''/B'' \longrightarrow 0.$$

Suppose that A is a submodule of the R-module B. Then

(5.2)
$$0 \longrightarrow A \xrightarrow{i_\#} B \xrightarrow{\eta_\#} B/A \longrightarrow 0$$

is exact, where $i_\#$ is an injection (4.1) and $\eta_\#$ is called the **natural homomorphism.**

Definition 5.3. Let $Hom_R(A, G)$ (or $Hom(A, G)$) be the R module of homomorphisms of the R-module A into the R-module G. Specifically, if $f \in Hom(A, G)$, $r \in R$, then $(rf)a = r(fa)$ and $(f_1 + f_2)a = f_1a + f_2a$.

Definition 5.4. The homomorphism $\psi: A \rightarrow B$ induces the homomorphism $'\psi: Hom(B, G) \rightarrow Hom(A, G)$ (note the order reversal of A and B) defined by

(5.4a)
$$('\psi f)a = f\psi a,$$

where $a \in A$ and $f \in Hom(B, G)$.

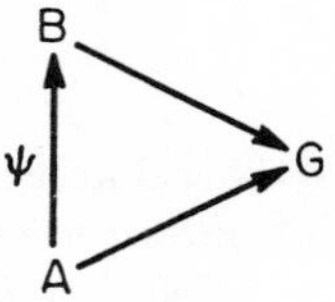

Figure 4-3

If the homomorphism θ is on G_1 to G_2, then θ the induced homomorphism on $Hom(A, G_1)$ to $Hom(A, G_2)$ is defined by $(\theta' f)a = \theta(fa)$ for $f \in Hom(A, G_1)$.

Suppose A, B and G are R modules. Then

Lemma 5.5. *The exactness of* (5.2) *implies the exactness of*

$$(5.5a) \qquad 0 \longrightarrow Hom(B/A, G) \xrightarrow{\eta^{\#}} Hom(B, G) \xrightarrow{i^{\#}} Hom(A, G),$$

where $i^{\#}$ *and* $\eta^{\#}$ *are induced by* $i_{\#}$ *and* $\eta_{\#}$, *and of*

$$(5.5b) \qquad 0 \longrightarrow Hom(G, A) \longrightarrow Hom(G, B) \longrightarrow Hom(G, B/A).$$

If A is a direct summand of B we can add $\rightarrow 0$ to (5.5a), for one can then extend a homomorphism on A to G to B to G so that $i^{\#}$ is onto. Specifically if $f_3 \in Hom(A, G)$; there is an antecedent $f_2 \in Hom(B, G)$ defined by $f_2 i_{\#} a = f_3(a)$ and $f_2(b) = 0$ for $b \bar{\in} i_{\#}A$.

This remark may be applied to the case that A and B are finite chain modules, say $A = C(L, \text{J})$, $B = C(K, \text{J})$, for then B is a direct sum.

PROBLEMS

4-13. If A, B, A_α, and B_α are Abelian groups, demonstrate

$$Hom(\oplus A_\alpha, B) \approx \Pi\, Hom(A_\alpha, B)$$
$$Hom(A, \Pi\, B_\beta) \approx \Pi\, Hom\,(A, B_\beta)$$

4-14. If F is a free Abelian group, establish $Hom(F, \text{J}) \approx \Pi\, Hom({}_i\text{J}, \text{J}) \approx \Pi\, {}_i\text{J}$.
4-15. Establish (5.5).

6. COCHAINS. Definition 6.1. $C^r(K, R) = Hom(C_r(K, \text{J}), R)$ (5.3) is the module of r-cochains over the module R, and its elements are denoted by f^r [or $f^r(K, R)$ if there is doubt]. $C(K, R) = \Sigma\, C^r(K, R)$ is an upper-graded module in $Hom(C(K, \text{J}), R)$. If R is a ring, it will appear later that $C^r(K, R)$ can be given a ring structure.

Definition 6.2. If R is a coefficient ring, let its unit (41.1) be written 1, and the generalized Kronecker delta $\delta_i^j = 1 \in R$ or 0 depending on whether $i = j$ or $i \neq j$. Let $\{\text{J}e_r^i\}$ be the elementary chains of $C_r(K, \text{J})$. The cochain $f_i^r \in C^r(K, R)$ such that $f_i^r(e_r^j) = \delta_i^j$, is an **elementary cochain** (associated with e_r^i).

A coboundary homomorphism δ is introduced in strict duality with ∂, according to the indication of (5.4a) by

$$(6.2a) \qquad (\delta f^r)\sigma_{r+1} = f^r\, \partial\sigma_{r+1} = \Sigma_i\, (-1)^i f^r\, \sigma_r(i),$$

$$(6.2b) \qquad \delta f_i^r = \Sigma\, \eta_i^j\, f_j^{r+1}.$$

As expected, there are two main categories of cochains, namely the **finite cochains** and the **infinite cochains,** if $K^{[r]}$ is not finite. The situation is the dual of that in (43.2), which amounts to saying that we interchange the upper and lower scripts. Less cryptically, if we understand m^a to be in some G and f_a^n to generate an elementary cochain, and if

(6.3a) $$f^n = \Sigma_A m^a f_a^n,$$

then, formally

$$\begin{aligned}\delta f^n &= \Sigma\, m^a\, \delta f_a^n \\ &= \Sigma_B (\Sigma_A m^a \eta_a^b) f_b^{n+1}.\end{aligned}$$

We suppose that f_a^n, m^a, and f_b^{n+1} are non-0 for $a \in A$ or $b \in B$, respectively. If $|A|$ (or $|B|$) is nonfinite, we have an infinite cochain; otherwise, a finite cochain. The coefficient of f_b^{n+1}, namely $\Sigma_A m^a \eta_a^b$, must be a finite sum. For the infinite cochain (6.3a) this requires that for each b, $\eta_a^b = 0$ except for a finite collection of a values. Accordingly, K is closure finite since for elementary cochains, as will appear later, η_a^j is the incidence number introduced in connection with ∂. For the finite cochain (6.3a), the requirement that δf^n be a finite cochain is met by the condition: for each a, $\eta_a^b \neq 0$ for a finite collection of b's only or equivalently, K is star finite. (As in the discussion of (43.1) some nonsignificant generalizations are possible for cyclic coefficient groups.)

The group of finite cochains is designated, when there is doubt, by the prefix f, for example, ${}_fC^r(K, R)$. The module of infinite cochains $C^r(K, R)$ has no basis if $K^{[r]}$ is nonfinite. However, ${}_fC^r(K, \text{J})$ has a basis.

Definition 6.4. $C^r(K - L, G) = Hom(C_r(K, L, \text{J}), G)$. We therefore identify A and B of (5.2) with $C^r(K, G)$ and $C^r(K - L, G)$. The argument $K - L$ is justified by the following lemma.

Lemma 6.5.

$$C^r(K - L, G) \approx \{f^r \mid f^r \in C^r(K, G), f^r \mid i_\# C_r(L, \text{J}) = 0\} = C^r(K, L, G).$$

For $f^r \in C^r(K - L, G)$ define $'f^r \in C^r(K, G)$ by $'f^r(c_r(K)) = f^r[c_r(K)]$ (4.4). So $'f^r\, i_\#(r) C_r(L) = f^r\,[i_\#(r) C_r(L)] = 0$. The correspondence $f^r \xrightarrow{\eta\#} {}'f^r$ is obviously a homomorphism. The kernel is the neutral element of $C^r(K - L, G)$, and $\eta^\#$ is clearly onto, for if $l^r \in C^r(K, G)$ annihilates $i_\# C_r(L, J)$, define f^r by $f^r[c_r(K)] = l^r\, c_r(K, \text{J})$. Hence $\eta^\#$ is an isomorphism.

Lemma 6.6. $C^r(K, G)/\eta^\# C^r(K - L, G) \approx C^r(L, G)$.

Note that $C_r(K, \text{J})$ is a direct sum of $C_r(L, \text{J})$ and $C_r(K - L, \text{J})$. Identify $C_r(L, \text{J})$ and $C_r(K, \text{J})$ with A and B in (5.2). It then follows that $\rightarrow 0$ can be added to the right hand side of (5.5a). Accordingly,

$$C^r(L, G) = Hom(C_r(L, \text{J}), G) \approx \frac{Hom(C_r(K), G)}{\eta^{\#}\, Hom\, C_r(K/L, G)} \approx \frac{C^r(K, G)}{\eta^{\#}\, C^r(K - L, G)} .$$

Definition 6.7. δ is a homomorphism on $C^r(K, G) \to C^{r+1}(K, G)$ defined in (6.1), so (6.7a) $(\delta f^r)(c_{r+1}(K, \text{J})) = f^r(\partial c_{r+1}(K, \text{J}))$. δ_L is a homomorphism on $C^r(L, G) \to C^{r+1}(L, G)$ given by $\delta_L(f^r(L, G)) = \delta_L[f^r(K, G)] = [f^{r+1}]$, where $[f^r(K)] \in C^r(K, G)/\eta^{\#}\, C^r(K - L, G)$. We drop the script L in general since the operand of δ sufficiently indicates the situation.

Definition 6.8. $Z^r(K, G)$ is the kernel of δ and is the group of **absolute** cocycles.

$Z^r(L, G)$ is the kernel of δ and is the group of **relative** cocycles.

$B^r(K, G)$ is the map of $C^{r-1}(K, G)$ by δ and is the group of absolute coboundaries.

$B^r(L, G)$ is the map of $C^{r-1}(L, G)$ by δ and is the group of relative coboundaries.

$H^r(K, G) = Z^r(K, G)/B^r(K, G)$ is the absolute cohomology group.

$H^r(L, G) = Z^r(L, G)/B^r(L, G)$ is the relative cohomology group.

Remark. The disquieting possibility that the end results obtained depend on the triangulation chosen will be refuted in Chapters 7 and 12.

Definition 6.9. With each homomorphism $\psi_{\#}$ on $C_p(K_1, L_1, \text{J})$ to $C_p(K_2, L_2, \text{J})$ there can be associated a dual homomorphism $\psi^{\#}$ on $C^p(K_2, L_2, R)$ to $C^p(K_1, L_1, R)$ defined by

(6.9a) $$(\psi^{\#} f_2^r)c_r(K_1, L_1, \text{J}) = f_2^r\, \psi_{\#}\, c_r(K_1, L_1, \text{J}) \qquad (5.4)$$

Terminology. In the interests of succinctness and easy interpretation we reluctantly abandon Hellenic roots and offer the Cockneyish "omology" to denote either homology or cohomology.

We give the matrix formulations for the finite absolute integral chains. Denote base chains in $C_m(K_1, \text{J})$ by $\{e_m^i\}$ and in $C_m(K_2, \text{J})$ by $\{E_m^j\}$. Similarly, let f_i^m and F_i^m refer to the associated elementary cochains of $C^m(K_1, \text{J})$ and $C^m(K_2, \text{J})$. Let $\mathbf{F}^m = (F_1^m \cdots F_N^m)$ and let $f^m = (f_1^m \cdots f_M^m)$. Write the general cochain over K_2 as $L^m = \Sigma_1^N x^i F_i^m$ and let $c_m = \Sigma_1^M y_j e_m^j$. Then by (6.9a)

$$\begin{aligned}\psi^{\#} L^m c_m &= L^m \psi_{\#} c_m \\ &= \Sigma x^i F_i^m \Sigma y_j h_r^j E_m^r \\ &= \Sigma x^i y_j h_r^j \delta_i^r \\ &= \Sigma x^i y_j h_i^j = \mathbf{yHx}\end{aligned}$$

with $\mathbf{y}$ and $\mathbf{x}$ the row and column matrices $(y_1, \ldots, y_M)$ and $\begin{pmatrix} x^1 \\ \vdots \\ x^N \end{pmatrix}$ respectively.

If $(\psi^{\#}\mathbf{F})\mathbf{x} = \psi^{\#} L^m = \Sigma z^r f_r^m = \mathbf{f}^m\mathbf{z}$, $\psi^{\#} L^m c_m = \mathbf{yz}$. Since $\mathbf{y}$ and $\mathbf{x}$ are arbitrary $\mathbf{z} = \mathbf{Hx}$ and

(6.9b) $$\psi^{\#}\mathbf{F}^m = \mathbf{f}^m \mathbf{H}(m).$$

Lemma 6.10. *Suppose the basis* $\{c_m^i\}$ *is changed to* $\{'c_m^j\}$ *by*

(6.10a) $$'\mathbf{c}_m = \mathbf{U}(m)\mathbf{c}_m,$$

where $\mathbf{U}(m)$ *is a unimodular matrix. Then the basis* $\{f_i^m\}$ *becomes* $\{'f_i^m\}$, *where*

(6.10b) $$'\mathbf{f}^m = \mathbf{f}^m \mathbf{U}(m)^{-1}.$$

Thus in (6.9b) replace $\mathbf{H}(m)$ by $\mathbf{U}(m)$ and note that then

(6.10c) $$\mathbf{f}^m = {}'\mathbf{f}^m \mathbf{U}(m),$$

whence (6.10b) is immediate.

Remark. This can be written out explicitly

$$\begin{aligned}'c_m^i &= \Sigma u_j^i(m) c_m^j \\ 'f_j^m &= \Sigma \bar{u}_j^i(m) f_i^m,\end{aligned}$$

where $\mathbf{U} = (u_j^i)$ and $\mathbf{U}^{-1} = (\bar{u}_j^i)$.

Remark. Let L_1 and L_2 be closed simplicial subcomplexes of K. Let $C^m(K, L_1, L_2) = C^m(K - L_1) \cap C^m(K - L_2)$. We can define in the obvious way a natural coboundary homomorphism δ on $C^m(K, L_1, L_2) \to C^{m+1}(K, L_1, L_2)$ and can, therefore, define $Z^m(K, L_1, L_2)$ and $H^m(K, L_1, L_2)$.

PROBLEM

4-16. Show δ defined in the preceding remark induces a coboundary homomorphism on cocycle groups such that if $f^{m-1} \in Z^{m-1}(L_1, L_1 \cap L_2)$ then $\delta f^{m-1} \in Z^m(K, L_1, L_2)$. *Hint:* Extend f^{m-1} to F^{m-1} on the pair K, L_2 by requiring $f^{m-1}(\sigma_{m-1}) = 0$ if σ_{m-1} is in L_2 or in $K - L_1$. Hence,

$$0 = \delta f^{m-1} \mid L_1 = \delta F^{m-1} \mid L_1 \quad \text{etc.}$$

Remark. The comparable situation for space vectors may be illuminating. Let $e^1, \ldots, e^n$ be a system of nonorthogonal base vectors through the origin of the Euclidean n space R^n. Let E_j be the hyperplane determined by $n - 1$ of the e^i's, omitting $i = j$. Then E_j is a dual to e^j. Let f_j be a vector orthogonal to E_j. Accordingly, f_j is associated with a dual notion (an $n - 1$ hyperplane) to that of that of e^i. Let $f_j \cdot e^r$ be the scalar product of f_j and e^r defined by $\|f_j\| \|e^r\| \cos(f_j, e^r)$, where $\|f_j\|$ is the length of f_j and $\|e^r\|$ is the length bf e^r. Then

$$\begin{aligned} f_j \cdot e^r &= 0 \qquad \text{if } r \neq j \\ &= \|f_j\| \|e^j\| \cos(f_j, e^j) \neq 0, \quad r = j. \end{aligned}$$

If $\|e^j\| = 1$, choice of $\|f_j\| = 1/(\cos(f_j e^j))$ yields $f_j \cdot e^j = 1$. The choice of an orthogonal vector frame obscures the situation, because then f_j and e^j are superposed. A linear transformation shows up the difference in transformation properties of the e's and the f's and illustrates the relation.

7. DUALS. The concept of duality enters whenever there is a relation of order or incidence. For a concrete complex there is a natural ordering of subcomplexes by inclusion as well as the incidence relation described by the term, face. The obvious dual ordering of subcomplexes of the dual complex would be by inclusion of their complements so the reversal of the incidence or face order relationship would replace closures by stars. Closure of a complex would thus imply openness in the dual complex and closure finiteness would become star finiteness. These notions are now made precise. Recall ${}^1K$ is the barycentric derived complex of K.

Let K be a concrete simplicial complex and let L be the closed subcomplex consisting of the boundary simplexes of K. Specifically σ_n is in L only if **(a)** σ_n is a proper face of only one simplex of K or **(b)** σ_n is a face of an element in L. Let $\sigma_0^i = v^i$ be a vertex of K. Then the dual cell E_i^0 is a concrete cell with associated point set that of the subcomplex $St(v^i, {}^1K) \cap ({}^1K - {}^1L)$ or $|St(v^i, {}^1K) \cap ({}^1K - {}^1L)|$ that is, simplexes entirely in ${}^1L$ are lopped off. If $\sigma_p^j \in K$ has the ordered vertices $\{v^i \mid i \in \pi\}$, the associated point set of the dual cell E_j^p consists of the union of the open simplexes in

(7.1c) $$\bigcap_{i \in \pi} \overline{St(v^i, {}^1K)} \cap ({}^1K - {}^1L).$$

Thus the cells dual to those in L are mutilated by having their faces on ${}^1L$ removed.

In view of (7.1c), E_i^q is defined as a face of E_j^p, or $E_i^q < E_j^p$, if and only if $\sigma_p^j < \sigma_q^i$, so in passing to duals the $<$ relation of two elements is reversed. The incidence number $\eta_j^i(p)$ is defined by

(7.1d) $$\begin{aligned} \eta_j^i(p+1) &= [E_j^p, E_i^{p+1}] \\ &= [\sigma_{p+1}^i, \sigma_p^j]. \end{aligned}$$

Definition 7.2. The **dual complex** K^* consists of all $\{E_i^p\}$ none of whose faces are in ${}^1L$. The **bordered dual** K^+ consists of all $\{E_i^p\}$ and thus includes the mutilated or half cells. The utility of K^+ counts in the fact that it gives rise to what we have termed the **Correspondence Principle.** The complexes K^* and K^+ are star finite and open.

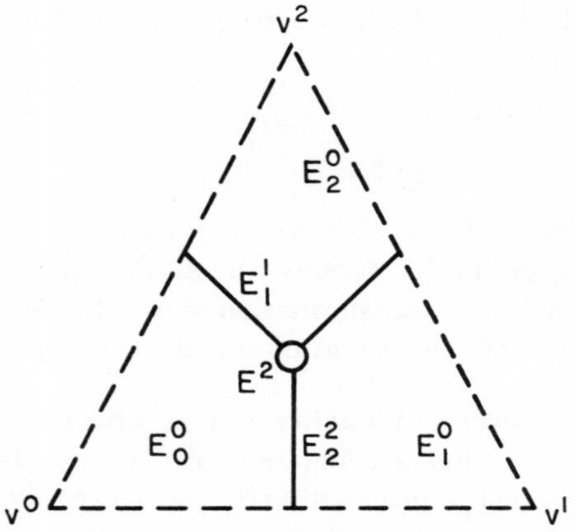

Figure 4-4

As an instance let $K = \sigma_2$ with vertices v^0, v^1, v^2. σ_1^i is the ordered 1-simplex opposite v^i. The diagram above represents K^+. Here L is the complex $\{\sigma_1^i \mid i = 0, 1, 2\}$, and the associated point set indicated by the dotted line is not part of the point set of K^+. The point set for K^+ is, therefore, that of the open simplex σ_2. The cells E_i^1 have only one vertex, each, namely E^2. On the other hand, K^* consists of E^2 alone.

Remark. The dual cells defined here may be quite different in type from simplexes. Thus they need not be convex nor connected, nor of the same dimension at all points. These possibilities are illustrated by the cell E^0, the cross-hatched area plus the segment $[0a]$ in the appended Fig. 4-5.

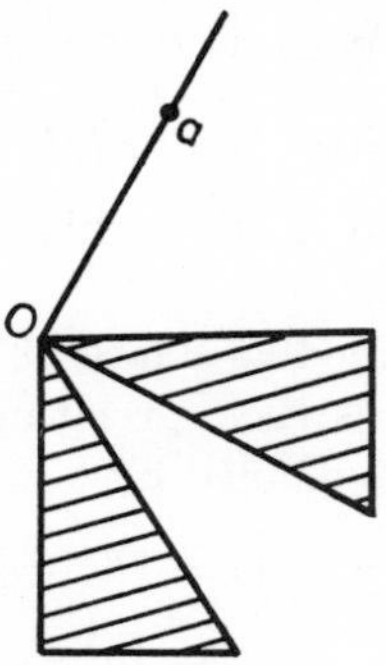

Figure 4-5

PROBLEMS

4-17. Show the cell defined by (7.1c) is nonvacuous only if the collection $\{v_i \mid i \in \pi\}$ constitutes the vertices of a simplex of K.

4-18. Let L denote the simplexes in $St(v, K)$. Let $\bar{\sigma}$ be a closed simplex in L with $v\bar{\sigma}$ the join of a vertex v and $\bar{\sigma}$. Show the identity of the point sets of $St(v\bar{\sigma}, K)$ and of $v\, St(\bar{\sigma}, L)$.

Remark. If K is homogeneous of dimension n then for oriented simplexes the Euclidean point set associated with E_i^p has dimension $n - p$. However when K is not homogeneous the cell E_i^p may consist of pieces of varying dimension $n_i - p$. The noteworthy feature is that p enters with a negative sign, so false connotations may be avoided by dropping the term "dimension" in favor of "degree" or "grade." Thus σ_p^i has lower-grade p or lower-degree p while E_i^p as well as f^p have upper-grade p or upper-degree p. When both E_i^p or f^p and σ_p^i are combined it is sometimes useful to drop the terms "upper" and "lower" and say σ_p has grade p while E^p or f^p has grade $-p$.

Instead of using simplexes, there are advantages in starting with general cells for K and, in particular, with cells which are polytopes or hypercubes. Barycentric subdivision, etc., proceeds just as before to yield smaller cubes, and K^* and K^+ are defined in an obvious way.

The n-cube P_n is a homeomorph of $\mathbf{P}_{j=1}^{j=n} I_j$, where I_i is the unit segment $0 \leq t_i \leq 1$. Denote by $P_{n-1}(i, +)$ the face given by

$$I_1, \ldots, I_{i-1}, I_{i+1}, \ldots, I_n$$

and by $P_{n-1}(i, -)$, that for which the ith coordinate is $t_i = 0$. For oriented cubes, consistent orientations of faces are obtained by the prescription: If P_n is positive, then all $P_{n-1}(i, +)$ are positive and $P_{n-1}(i, -)$ are negative, and by recurrence the orientations of the faces of $P_{n-1}(i, +)$ are determined. There is, of course, a gain in symmetry by using the n-cube P_n as the building cell e_n instead of σ_n. For instance,

$$\partial g P_n = \Sigma\, g P_{n-1}(i, +) - \Sigma\, g P_{n-1}(i, -).$$

chapter 5

MANIFOLDS AND FIXED CELLS

1. SIMPLICIAL MANIFOLDS. The dual cells and mutilated cells introduced in (47.1) may differ widely from those admitted in (33.1). For considerations involving the homology groups, it is desirable to give special attention to the latter cells. These have the same homology characteristics as the simplexes. *We understand in this section that all cells have a simplicial subdivision that K is a finite homogeneous n-complex and that* $L = \phi$ (47.1.)

Definition 1.1a. Denote by $\bar{e}^j_m$ the closed *cell* and by $\dot{e}^j_m$ or Lk e^j_m the collection of simplexes in $\bar{e}^j_m - e^j_m$.

1.1b. **A combinatorial dual cell** e^j_m (also a regular dual cell) is one for which $H_0(\bar{e}^j_m, R) = R$, $H_n(\bar{e}^j_m, R) = 0$, $H_0(\dot{e}^j_m, R) = R$, $H_n(\dot{e}^j_m, R) = 0$, $n \neq 0$, $m - 1$, $H_{m-1}(\dot{e}^j_m, R) = R$. Furthermore, $\dot{e}^j_m$ is to be a pseudo-manifold for $m > 1$. In short, $\bar{e}^j_m$ and $\dot{e}^j_m$ are like a ball or a disk and its boundary so far as the homology groups go (and e^j_m is generally a block cell.) If $e^j_m = E^{n-m}_j$ (47.1c) it is a combinatorial dual cell.

Definition 1.2. Suppose P is an orientable $n - 1$-dimensional pseudo-manifold, and let A_0 be a vertex not included in the vertices of P. Let $A_0\, P$ denote the subcomplex consisting of the join of A_0 to each of the simplexes of P. Let Q denote $St(A_0, A_0\, P)$ or equivalently the open part of $A_0\, P$. For instance if P is a circle, Q is a 2-dimensional cone or, what is equivalent, a disk sans boundary. Suppose that the simplexes of P are oriented coherently (34.2). Our purpose now is to prescribe a coherent orientation for the simplexes of Q. Let σ^i_{n-1} and σ^{i+1}_{n-1} share the common face σ^j_{n-2}. For clarity take an ordering of vertices such that

$$\sigma^i_{n-1} = A_1\, A_2\, A_3 \cdots A_n$$
$$\sigma^{i+1}_{n-1} = A_2\, A_{n+1}\, A_3 \cdots A_n$$
$$\sigma^j_{n-2} = A_2\, A_3 \cdots A_n.$$

Evidently $[\sigma^i_{n-1}, \sigma^j_{n-2}] = 1 = -[\sigma^{i+1}_{n-1}, \sigma^j_{n-2}]$ as required. The simplexes of Q are oriented by

$$\sigma^i_n = A_0\, A_1 \cdots A_n = A_0\, \sigma^i_{n-1}$$
$$\sigma^{i+1}_n \qquad\qquad = A_0\, \sigma^{i+1}_{n-1}$$
$$\sigma^j_{n-1} \qquad\qquad = A_0\, \sigma^j_{n-2}$$

and satisfy the coherence condition

$$[\sigma^i_n, \sigma^j_{n-1}] = -[\sigma^{i+1}_n, \sigma^j_{n-1}].$$

Observe that there are just two coherent orientations for P, namely, the one chosen and another in which each σ^i_{n-1} is replaced by $-\sigma^i_{n-1}$ and so on

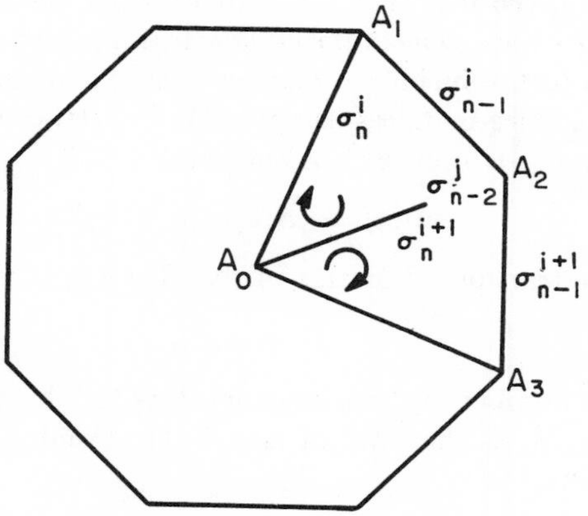

Figure 5–1

consistently. Accordingly, Q admits just two coherent orientations following the receipt above.

We apply the above to the case of the combinatorial m cell $e_{n-m} = E^m$ interpreting $\dot{E}^m$ as P and E^m as Q. Thus E^m can be given one of just two orientations, and the choice must be consistent with

$$[E^m_i, E^{m+1}_j] = [\sigma^j_{m+1}, \sigma^i_m].$$

(If this requirement is not conceded immediately, an induction argument can be used to establish formally that the requirement can be met.)

Definition 1.3. A **combinatorial cell complex** is a complex whose cells are combinatorial cells. An **n-dimensional simplicial manifold** M is an n-dimensional pseudo-manifold whose dual complex K^* is a combinatorial cell complex (and the cells are plainly block cells).

Remark. Actually the requirement that M be an n-dimensional pseudo-manifold is redundant, but it is included to allow immediate passage to the Poincaré Duality theorem. Explicit mention of the dual cell can be avoided. Thus M is an n-dimensional simplicial manifold (relative to L) if each of its simplexes (in $K - L$) has a star boundary whose homology groups are those of an $n - 1$ sphere.

Theorem 1.4. *Poincaré Duality Theorem. For an n-dimensional concrete simplicial manifold M, $R_m = R_{n-m}$, $t^i_{m-1} = t^i_{n-m}$.*

We write e^i_{n-m} for E^m_i. Since there is a 1 to 1 correspondence between the elements $\{\sigma^i_m\}$ and $\{E^m_i\}$, the number α_{n-m} of cells $\{e_{n-m}\}$ is α_m. Next,

$$[\sigma^i_m, \sigma^j_{m-1}] = [E^{m-1}_j, E^m_i] = [e^j_{n-m+1}, e^i_{n-m}]. \tag{1.4a}$$

We are accepting the fact that *the Betti numbers and torsion coefficients are the same whether we use combinatorial cells or simplexes* (33.2). This being so, if $\{\mathbf{A}(m)\}$ refers to the incidence matrices using simplexes and $\{{}_1\mathbf{A}(n - m)\}$ refers to the incidence matrices using combinatorial cells, the invariants just cited are the same. However (1.4a) implies

$$\mathbf{A}(m) = {}_1\mathbf{A}(n - m + 1)', \tag{1.4b}$$

where ${}_1\mathbf{A}'$ is the transposed matrix of ${}_1\mathbf{A}$. Then

$$\rho_m = \rho_{n-m-1} \tag{1.4c}$$

where ρ_n is the number of distinct generators for the cycles of types 1 or 2 or, more simply, ρ_m is the rank of $\mathbf{A}(m + 1)$. Combining (1.4c) with $\alpha_m = \alpha_{n-m}$ there results,

$$\begin{aligned} R_m &= \alpha_m - \rho_m - \rho_{m-1} \\ &= \alpha_{n-m} - \rho_{n-m-1} - \rho_{n-m} \\ &= R_{n-m}. \end{aligned}$$

Recall that the coefficients t_{m-1}, t_{n-m} are invariant factors of $\mathbf{A}(m)$ and of $\mathbf{A}(n - m + 1)$ respectively. Hence, $t^i_{m-1} = t^i_{n-m}$.

Remark. A more inclusive statement of Poincare duality is that

$$H_m(M, R) \approx H_{n-m}(M, R)$$

for R a field and $\boldsymbol{T}_m(M) \approx \boldsymbol{T}_{n-m-1}(M)$.

Definition 1.5. An **open n-dimensional simplicial manifold** M is a concrete combinatorial cell complex considered imbedded in a Euclidean space whose point set boundary $\dot{M}$ can be so triangulated that $M \cup \dot{M}$ is a concrete cell complex with $\dot{M}$ an $n - 1$-dimensional simplicial manifold. However, now M is an infinite complex.

PROBLEMS

5-1. Let S^1, S'^1, and S^2 refer to two circles and a 2-sphere. We suppose here that all three have a single point in common. Show that the homology groups are the same as those of the torus. (This shows what can happen when we do not require the complex to be a manifold or a pseudo-manifold.)

5-2. L consists of simplexes of dimension $n - 2$ or less. Show L does not separate S^n into two or more components.

5-3. From $H_1(S^1 \times S^1 \times S^1, \mathrm{J}) \approx \mathrm{J} \oplus \mathrm{J} \oplus \mathrm{J}$ deduce immediately $H_2(S^1 \times S^1 \times S^1, \mathrm{J})$. *Hint:* Use the remark following (1.4).

5-4. Let M be a connected 2-dimensional manifold. Let m be the maximum number of 1 cycles interpreted as cuts which can be made without disconnecting M. Prove that $m = 2 - \chi(M)$.

5-5. Remove a disk with boundary S^1 from S^2. Identify opposite points of S^1 with respect to the center of S^1. The resulting surface M_1 is said to have a **cross cap.** Show that M_1 is nonorientable and that $\chi(M_1) = 1$.

5-6. Remove r disks from S^2. Treat each circle boundary as in the previous problem and obtain M_r, a surface with r cross caps. Show that M_r is nonorientable and that $\chi(M_r) = 2 - r$.

5-7. Remove $2p$ disjunct disks from S^2 to get K, a complex with $2p$ triangulated circle boundaries. Assume that K is triangulated so that the circle boundaries are triangulated isomorphically in pairs. Identify each pair of circles to get a manifold M with p handles (called the sphere with p **handles**). Show that $\chi(K) = \chi(M)$.

We do not concern ourselves here with the point set definition of a manifold (cf. 97), except to show how the familiar examples of such manifolds arise. Thus the space obtained by identifying all faces of a cube is an S^3. In fact, they can all be identified with a single point.

5-8. If T^2 is a torus show that the identification of corresponding points of $T^2 \times 0$ and of $T^2 \times 1$ in $T^2 \times I$ yields the three-torus $T^3 = S^1 \times S^1 \times S^1$.

2. REALIZATIONS OF COCYCLES. The cocycles and cohomology modules seem at first less intuitive than the cycle and homology modules. Various models will be used throughout this work. The two guiding notions at this stage are that the cochains may be thought of (**i**) as module-valued functions on simplexes or cells, rather than as homomorphisms on chain modules, or (**ii**) as chains on the dual complex. The view in (**ii**) yields a picture of cochains as transverse to chains and this may be expressed (for whatever help is afforded) by saying the cochains and cocycles are *through* rather than *in* sets. In the following examples we shall use (**ii**) as a direct guide to the cocycles.

The procedure is based on determining an m-cycle over K^+ [cf. (47)],

(2.1a) $$z^m = \Sigma\, r^i\, E_i^m.$$

According to (47.1d),

(2.1b) $$\begin{aligned} \partial\sigma_{p+1}^i &= \Sigma\, \eta_j^i(p+1)\sigma_p^j \\ \partial E_j^p &= \Sigma\, \eta_j^i(p+1)E_i^{p+1}. \end{aligned}$$

Let f_j^p be the elementary cochain corresponding to σ_p^j so that $f_j^p(\sigma_p^m) = \delta_j^m$. Then

$$\begin{aligned} (\delta f_j^p)\sigma_{p+1}^r &= f_j^p\, \partial\sigma_{p+1}^r \\ &= f_j^p \Sigma_s\, \eta_s^r(p+1)\sigma_p^s \\ &= \Sigma_s\, \eta_s^r\, \delta_j^s = \eta_j^r. \end{aligned}$$

The cochain $f^m = \Sigma\, r^i f_i^m$ obtained by replacing E_i^m by f_i^m in (2.1a) is a cocycle and is non-cobounding when z^m is nonbounding because the verification of these facts for z^m is abstractly identical with that for f^m.

Definition 2.2. We refer to the notion of the correspondence between chain and cycle on K^+ and cochain and cocycle on K generated by the substitution of f_i^m for E_i^m as the **Correspondence Principle**. (Interpretation of n as a suitable $n - m$ dimension (1.4a) may be helpful.)

The following examples are intended to illustrate the principles and ideas. *We assume* J_2 *is the coefficient group.*

EXAMPLE 5-1. *The simplex* $K = \sigma_2 = (v^0\, v^1\, v^2)$.

Let f_i^r be the elementary cochain (2.1b). The 1 cycle $\sigma_1^0 + \sigma_1^1 + \sigma_1^2$ is a boundary, namely $\partial\sigma_2$. The blind hope that similarly $F^1 = f_0^1 + f_1^1 + f_2^1$ will be at least a cocycle is dashed immediately, since $(\delta F')(\sigma_2) = 1 \neq 0$. Thus, the mutilated cells E_i^1 (47.1) give $E_0^2 = \partial E_i^1$, $i = 0, 1, 2$. Hence, for instance, a 1 cycle on K^+ is $E_0^1 - E_1^1$, whence, replacing E_i^1 by f_i^1, there results $F^1 = f_0^1 - f_1^1$ which is indeed a cocycle. Here F^1 takes on the value 1 for σ_1^0 and for σ_1^2, and 0 for σ_1^1. Define g^0 by $g^0(v^2) = 1$, $g^0(v^0) = g^0(v^1) = 0$. Then $\delta g^0 = F^1$, so F^1 is a coboundary as expected.

EXAMPLE 5-2. *The* n *sphere* $S^n = |\partial\sigma^{n+1}|$.

The generating nonbounding cycle is $\Sigma\, \sigma_n^i$. The formal analogue would be f^n defined by $f^n(\sigma_n^i) = 1$. (This is, of course, a cocycle since there are no $n+1$-simplexes, but for n even f^n is easily seen to be a coboundary. Indeed, if g^{n-1} is defined by $g^{n-1}\sigma_{n-1}^i(j) = 1$, then

$$\begin{aligned} (\delta g^{n-1})\sigma_n^i &= \Sigma\,(-1)^j\, g^{n-1}\, \sigma_{n-1}^i(j) \\ &= \Sigma\,(-1)^j = 1 = f^n(\sigma_n^i). \end{aligned}$$

For n odd it is, however, true that f^n so defined is a nonbounding cocycle.)

To apply the correspondence principle (2.2) we seek a nonbounding n-cycle. Evidently E_i^n is a single vertex in K^+ and hence is a nonbounding cycle. Therefore f_i^n is a nonbounding cocycle. This is plain, but independent verification is given to illustrate a straightforward technique. All n cochains are cocycles, so only the possibility $f_i^n = \delta h^{n-1}$ need be eliminated. Thus h^{n-1} does not vanish for at least one face of σ_n^i. Let such a face be $\sigma_{n-1}^i(j)$. Since every $n - 1$ face is shared by just two n-simplexes, suppose that σ_n^m has $\sigma_{n-1}^i(j)$ as a face also. (Naturally we content ourselves with the case $n = 1$ and leave the slightly more tedious case $n = 2m + 1$, $m > 0$, as an exercise.) Here S^1 is the boundary of a simplex and consists of ab, bc, ca, while $f^1(ab) = 1$, $f^1(bc) = f^1(ca) = 0$. If $f^1 = \delta h^0$ then

$$h^{n-1}(b) - h^{n-1}(a) = 1$$

$$h^{n-1}(c) - h^{n-1}(b) = 0$$

$$h^{n-1}(a) - h^{n-1}(c) = 0$$

Plainly these three equations are inconsistent. If g is defined by $g(a) = 0$, $g(b) = 0$, $g(c) = 1$, another nonbounding cocycle is $f^1 + \delta g = F^1$, where

$$F^1(ab) = F^1(bc) = F^1(ca) = 1.$$

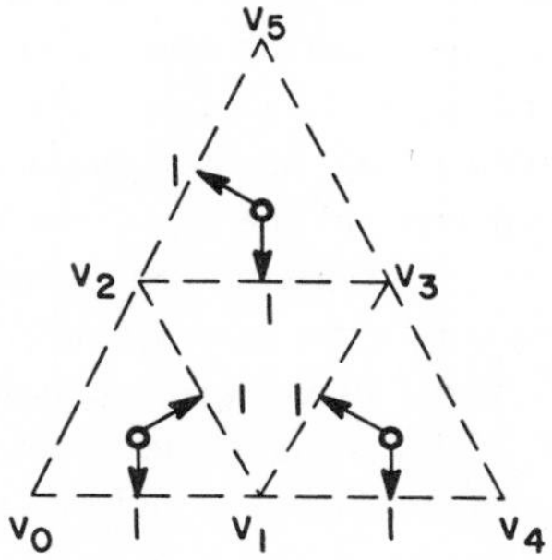

Figure 5-2

EXAMPLE 5-3. Although a nonbounding m-cycle is not affected by the adjunction of new m-simplexes this is not always true of cocycles. From K^+ it appears that a cocycle would be given by taking the chain sum of the differences of the pairs of oriented cells, indicated by heavy lines, in each dotted line triangle in Fig. 5-2. This is also easily verified for a cochain whose values on each of the dotted segment 1-simplexes are indicated by the number put next to that segment in Fig. 5-2. According to the prescription, f^1 takes the value 0 for the simplexes $(v_4\, v_3)$, $(v_3\, v_5)$, and $(v_0\, v_2)$, and takes the value 1 for the other simplexes, using counterclockwise orientation.

It is impossible that $f^1 = \delta g^0$. Indeed, it would be necessary that, mod 2

$$g^0(v_3) - g^0(v_2) = 1$$
$$g^0(v_2) - g^0(v_1) = 1$$
$$g^0(v_1) - g^0(v_3) = 1,$$

an inconsistent system of equations.

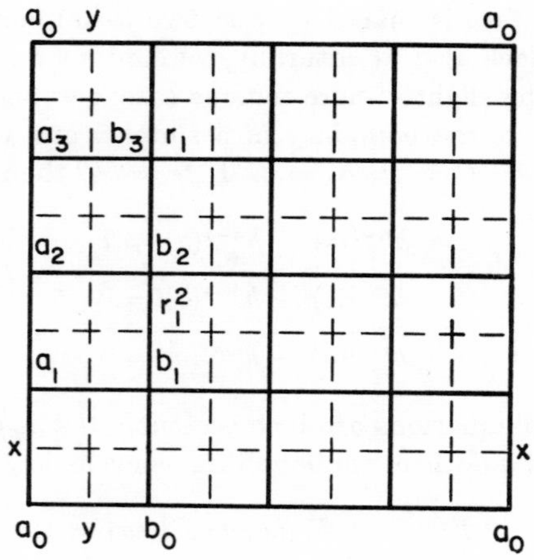

Figure 5-3

Example 5-4. The *torus* $T^2 = S^1 \times S^1$. Here we take squares as the base cells. Then T^2 can be represented by the square $a_0\, a_0\, a_0\, a_0$, with opposite edges identified pointwise as is clear from the observation that if these identified points are joined along the two seams, one resurrects the torus. In Fig. 5-3 the labelled squares are the base cells, and orientation is counterclockwise for each square. The chain sum of all squares yields a 2-cycle. The chain sum of the one-simplexes in any row z_1^1 or in any column z_1^2 yields a nonbounding 1 cycle. These cycles are not homologous, and their cosets are the generators of $H_1(T^2)$. Other cycles homologous to z_1^2 are obtained by shifting z_1^2 one or two segments to the right or replacing a segment by the chain sum of the three other sides of a square having the segment as a face.

Here K^+ consists of a collection of squares centered at the vertices of the original squares of K. We indicate this by the broken line - - - in Fig. 5-3. The horizontal line labeled $x - x$ in the diagram is a nonbounding cycle on K^+. Another independent one is $y - y$. Translating $y - y$ into terms of cochains we have f^1 defined as 1 on the 1-simplexes $a_0\, b_0$, $a_1\, b_1$, $a_2\, b_2$, $a_3\, b_3$ and defined as 0 on all others. That f^1 is not a coboundary, δg^0, can be established also by straightforward testing, for we should have to satisfy:

$$g^0(a_0) + 1 = g^0(b_0) = g^0(c_0) = g^0(a_0).$$

For the more conventional triangulation into "2-simplexes," cf. Fig. 5-4.

The cycle $z - z$ indicated by the double line is nonbounding on K^+. The corresponding cocycle is labeled $'F^1$ and takes on the value 1 on AB, CB, CD, AD and $A\alpha$ and the value 0 on all other 1-simplexes. To demonstrate that $'F^1$ is not cobounding without appealing to this property of $z - z$, note that $\delta g^0 = {'F^1}$ requires $g^0(\alpha) = g^0(\beta) = g^0(a) = g^0(A)$ as well as the contradictory $g^0(\alpha) - g^0(A) = 1$.

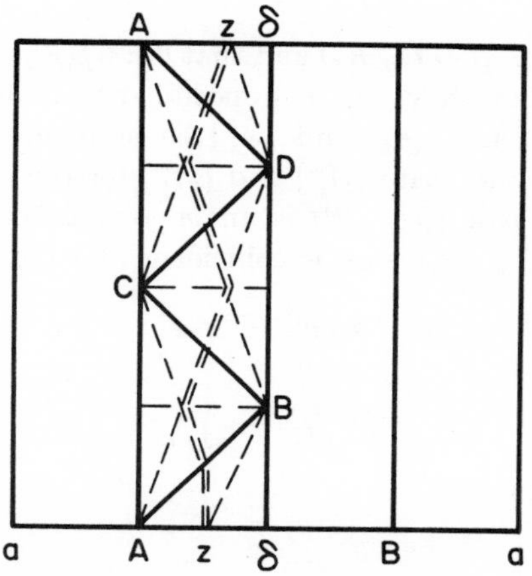

Figure 5-4

3. THE LEFSCHETZ NUMBER. Throughout this section our complexes are finite. The following facts connected with matrices will be applied immediately.

Definition 3.1. If $\mathbf{A}$ is a square $n \times n$ matrix with entries the integers or the real or complex numbers, then the **trace** of $\mathbf{A}$, written $\text{Tr}\mathbf{A}$, is the sum of the terms in the main diagonal; that is, $\text{Tr}\mathbf{A} = \Sigma\, a^i_i$. The **characteristic equation** of $\mathbf{A}$ is, in determinant form, $|\mathbf{A} - x\mathbf{I}| = \mathbf{0}$, where x is an indeterminate and $\mathbf{I}$ is the identity matrix. This is evidently

$$x^n - (\text{Tr}\mathbf{A})x^{n-1} + \cdots = 0.$$

Lemma 3.2. *If* $\mathbf{V}$ *is a nonsingular matrix then*

$$\text{Tr}\mathbf{V}\mathbf{A}\mathbf{V}^{-1} = \text{Tr}\mathbf{A}.$$

We prove a little more. Indeed, since $\mathbf{I} = \mathbf{V}\mathbf{I}\mathbf{V}^{-1}$,

$$\begin{aligned} |\mathbf{V}\mathbf{A}\mathbf{V}^{-1} - x\mathbf{I}| &\equiv |\mathbf{V}\mathbf{A}\mathbf{V}^{-1} - x\mathbf{V}\mathbf{I}\mathbf{V}^{-1}| \\ &= |\mathbf{V}(\mathbf{A} - x\mathbf{I})\mathbf{V}^{-1}| \\ &= |\mathbf{V}|\,|\mathbf{A} - x\mathbf{I}|\,|\mathbf{V}^{-1}| = |\mathbf{A} - x\mathbf{I}|, \end{aligned}$$

whence

$$x^n - \text{Tr}\mathbf{V}\mathbf{A}\mathbf{V}^{-1}\,x^{n-1} + \cdots \equiv x^n - \text{Tr}\mathbf{A}x^{n-1} + \cdots.$$

Comparison of coefficients of x yields the lemma.

Corollary 3.3. *If* $\mathbf{A}$, $\mathbf{B}$, *and* $\mathbf{V}$ *are* $n \times n$ *matrices with* $\mathbf{V}$ *nonsingular and* $\mathbf{VA} = \mathbf{BV}$, *then* $\mathrm{Tr}\mathbf{A} = \mathrm{Tr}\mathbf{B}$.

Definition 3.4. Denote by $C_{\#}(K, G)$ the graded chain group or module $\oplus\, C_m(K, G)$ and denote by $C^{\#}(K, G)$ the graded cochain group $\oplus\, C^m(K, G)$. The chain $c_m = \Sigma\, a_i\, e^i_m$ **contains** each e^i_m for which $a_i \neq 0$, and we write $c_m \supset e^i_m$. Similarly, $f^m = \Sigma\, b^j f^m_j \supset f^m_k$ if $b^k \neq 0$.

Suppose that $\psi_{\#}$: $C_{\#}(K_1) \to C_{\#}(K_2)$ and that $\theta_{\#}$: $C_{\#}(K_2) \to C_{\#}(K_1)$ are homomorphisms. Note that they act in opposite directions. Then $\theta_{\#}$ induces $\theta^{\#}\, C^{\#}(K_1) \to C^{\#}(K_2)$. Let $\{{}_1e^i_m\}$ and $\{{}_2e^j_m\}$ be base cells for $C_m(K_1)$ and for $C_m(K_2)$ respectively, and write $\{{}_1f^m_i\}$ and $\{{}_2f^m_j\}$ for the corresponding associated cochains. The pair $({}_1e^i_m, {}_2f^m_j)$ is an m-**coincidence** for the homomorphisms $(\psi_{\#}, \theta^{\#})$, or $({}_1e^i_m, {}_2e^j_m)$ is an m-**coincidence** for $(\psi_{\#}, \theta_{\#})$ if

(3.4a) $$\psi_{\#}\, {}_1e^i_m \supset {}_2e^j_m$$

and

(3.4b) $$\theta^{\#}\, {}_1f^m_i \supset {}_2f^m_j,$$

which is equivalent to

(3.4c) $$\theta_{\#}\, {}_2e^j_m \supset {}_1e^i_m.$$

We shall understand, as usual, that

(3.4d) $$\begin{aligned}\psi_{\#}\, {}_1\mathbf{e}_m &= \mathbf{H}(m)\, {}_2\mathbf{e}_m \\ \theta_{\#}\, {}_2\mathbf{e}_m &= \mathbf{K}(m)\, {}_1\mathbf{e}_m,\end{aligned}$$

and hence

$$\theta^{\#}\, {}_1\mathbf{f}^m = {}_2f^m\, \mathbf{K}(m).$$

If $K_2 = K_1 = K$ and $\theta_{\#}$ is the identity isomorphism,

$$\theta_{\#}\, e^i_m = e^i_m.$$

then a coincidence would be (e^i_m, f^m_i), or a coincidence is tantamount to the existence of a cell e^i_m, called a **fixed cell**, for which $\psi_{\#}\, e^i_m \supset e^i_m$.

For the rest of Section 3 we assume that $\dim K_1 = \dim K_2 = n$.

Lemma 3.5. **(a)** *The pair* $({}_1e^{(i)}_m, {}_2f^m_{(j)})$ *for the fixed values* $i = (i)$, $j = (j)$ *is an* m*-coincidence if and only if the term* $h^{(i)}_{(j)}(m)$ *in* $\mathbf{H}(m)$ *and the term* $k^{(j)}_{(i)}(m)$ *in* $\mathbf{K}(m)$ *are both different from* 0. **(b)** *A sufficient condition for the existence of some coincidence is*

$$\Sigma\, (-1)^m\, \mathrm{Tr}(\mathbf{H}(m)\mathbf{K}(m)) \neq 0.$$

Indeed, $\psi_{\#}\, {}_1\mathbf{e}_m = \mathbf{H}(m)\, {}_2\mathbf{e}_m$, whence

$$\psi_{\#}\, {}_1e^{(i)}_m = \Sigma_k\, h^{(i)}_k\, (m)\, {}_2e^k_m \supset {}_2e^{(j)}_m$$

if $h^{(i)}_{(j)}(m) \neq 0$. Similarly, $k^{(j)}_{(i)}(m) \neq 0$. This will certainly be true if $\Sigma_{i,j}\, h^i_j(m) k^j_i(m) = \mathrm{Tr}(\mathbf{H}(m)\mathbf{K}(m)) \neq 0$, whence **(3.5b)** follows immediately.

Lemma 3.6. Tr $\mathbf{K}(m)\mathbf{H}(m)$ *is unaffected by changes of bases.*

Let new bases be introduced by

$$\text{(3.6a)} \qquad \begin{aligned} {}_1'\mathbf{e}_m &= \mathbf{U}(m)\, {}_1\mathbf{e}_m \\ {}_2'\mathbf{e}_m &= \mathbf{V}(m)\, {}_2\mathbf{e}_m, \end{aligned}$$

where $\mathbf{U}(m)$ and $\mathbf{V}(m)$ are unimodular matrices (with integer entries). Then by (3.4d) and (3.6a)

$$\psi_{\#}\, \mathbf{U}(m)^{-1}\, {}_1'\mathbf{e}_m = \mathbf{H}(m)\mathbf{V}(m)^{-1}\, {}_2'\mathbf{e}_m.$$

Hence,

$$\psi_{\#}\, {}_1'\mathbf{e}_m = \mathbf{U}(m)\mathbf{H}(m)\mathbf{V}(m)^{-1}\, {}_2'\mathbf{e}_m = {}'\mathbf{H}(m)\, {}_2'\mathbf{e}_m.$$

Similarly from (46.9b) and (3.6a)

$$\theta^{\#}\, {}_1'f^m\, \mathbf{U}(m) = {}_2'f^m\, \mathbf{V}(m)\mathbf{K}(m)$$

or

$$\theta^{\#}\, {}_1'f^m = {}_2'f^m\, \mathbf{V}(m)\mathbf{K}(m)\mathbf{U}(m)^{-1} = {}_2'f^m\, {}'\mathbf{K}(m).$$

Accordingly,

$$\begin{aligned} \mathrm{Tr}\, {}'\mathbf{H}(m)\, {}'\mathbf{K}(m) &= \mathrm{Tr}\, (\mathbf{U}(m)\mathbf{H}(m)\mathbf{V}(m)^{-1}\, \mathbf{V}(m)\mathbf{K}(m)\mathbf{U}(m)^{-1}) \\ &= \mathrm{Tr}\, \mathbf{U}(m)\mathbf{H}(m)\mathbf{K}(m)\mathbf{U}(m)^{-1} \\ &= \mathrm{Tr}\, (\mathbf{H}(m)\mathbf{K}(m)). \end{aligned}$$

Definition 3.7. The **Lefschetz number** for the pair $(\psi_{\#}, \theta_{\#})$ is

$$L(\psi_{\#}, \theta_{\#}) = \Sigma\, (-1)^m\, \mathrm{Tr}(\mathbf{H}(m)\mathbf{K}(m)).$$

In view of (3.6), the Lefschetz number is impervious to change of base. We renew our acquaintance with (32.5). It is convenient to write a_m for a chain of type ${}_4C$ or ${}_5C$, b_m for the cycles in either ${}_1C$ or ${}_2C$, and d_m from now on will refer to the ${}_3C$ chains or Betti cycles. Thus,

$$\text{(3.7a)} \qquad \partial a^i_{m-1} = t^i_m\, b^i_m,$$

where t^i_m now is either 1 or a torsion number that is, $t^i_m \neq 0$. Consider the consequences of the allowability of the homomorphisms

$$\text{(3.7b)} \qquad 0 = \psi_{\#}\, {}_1d^i_m = \partial\psi_{\#}\, {}_1d^i_m$$

$$\text{(3.7c)} \qquad t^i_m\, \psi_{\#}\, {}_1b^i_m = \psi_{\#}\, \partial_1 a^i_{m+1} = \partial\psi_{\#}\, {}_1a^i_{m+1}.$$

From (3.7c) it is plain that $\psi_{\#}\, {}_1b_m$ is either of type ${}_1C$ or type ${}_2C$ (32.5) and is therefore composed uniquely of ${}_2b_m$ terms. From (3.7b) we can infer only that $\psi_{\#}\, {}_1d_m$ is a sum of ${}_2d_m$ and ${}_2b_m$ terms. Finally, $\psi_{\#}\, {}_1a_m$ apparently may involve ${}_2a_m$, ${}_2b_m$, or ${}_2d_m$ terms. Thus,

$$\text{(3.7d)} \qquad \mathbf{L}(m) = \begin{array}{c} \\ {}_ra \\ {}_rd \\ {}_rb \end{array} \begin{array}{c} \begin{array}{ccc} {}_sa & {}_sd & {}_sb \end{array} \\ \begin{pmatrix} \mathbf{L}_{11} & \mathbf{L}_{12} & \mathbf{L}_{13} \\ 0 & \mathbf{L}_{22} & \mathbf{L}_{23} \\ 0 & 0 & \mathbf{L}_{33} \end{pmatrix} \end{array},$$

where $\mathbf{L}(m)$ and $\mathbf{L}_{ij}$ stand for $\mathbf{H}(m)$ and $\mathbf{H}_{ij}(m)$, and in this case $(r, s) = (1, 2)$ or for $\mathbf{K}(m)$ and $\mathbf{K}_{ij}(m)$ in which case $(r, s) = (2, 1)$. It is understood that all chains are for dimension m; that is, ${}_ra$ is ${}_ra_m$, etc. In terms of the a, d, b bases, the form of $\mathbf{A}(m + 1)$ is given by

$$\text{(3.7e)} \qquad \mathbf{A}(m+1) \quad \begin{array}{c|c|c|c} & a_m & d_m & b_m \\ \hline a_{m+1} & \mathbf{0} & \mathbf{0} & \begin{matrix} t & & & \mathbf{0} \\ & t & & \\ & & \ddots & \\ & & & t \\ \mathbf{0} & & & t \end{matrix} \\ \hline d_{m+1} & \mathbf{0} & \mathbf{0} & \mathbf{0} \\ \hline b_{m+1} & \mathbf{0} & \mathbf{0} & \mathbf{0} \end{array}$$

Denote the upper right hand block in (3.7c) by $\mathbf{A}(m + 1)_{13}$. Then

$$\mathbf{H}(m + 1)_{11}\, {}_2\mathbf{A}(m + 1)_{13} = {}_1\mathbf{A}(m + 1)_{13}\, \mathbf{H}(m)_{33}.$$

Similarly,

$$\text{(3.7f)} \qquad \mathbf{K}(m + 1)_{11}\, {}_1\mathbf{A}(m + 1)_{13} = {}_2\mathbf{A}(m + 1)_{13}\, \mathbf{K}(m)_{33}.$$

Since there are no ${}_1C$ or ${}_2C$ cycles in dim n and no ${}_4C$ or ${}_5C$ chains in dim 0,

$$\text{(3.7g)} \qquad \begin{aligned} \mathbf{H}(0)_{11} &= \mathbf{0} = \mathbf{K}(0)_{11} \\ \mathbf{H}(n)_{33} &= \mathbf{0} = \mathbf{K}(n)_{33}. \end{aligned}$$

Theorem 3.8. $L(\psi_{\#}, \theta_{\#}) = \Sigma_0^n(-1)^m \operatorname{Tr} \mathbf{H}(m)_{22}\, \mathbf{K}(m)_{22} = L(\psi_* \theta_*)$.

$$\mathbf{H}(m)\mathbf{K}(m) = \begin{pmatrix} \mathbf{H}_{11}\,\mathbf{K}_{11} & \times & \\ \mathbf{0} & \mathbf{H}_{22}\,\mathbf{K}_{22} & \times \\ \mathbf{0} & \mathbf{0} & \mathbf{H}_{33}\,\mathbf{K}_{33} \end{pmatrix},$$

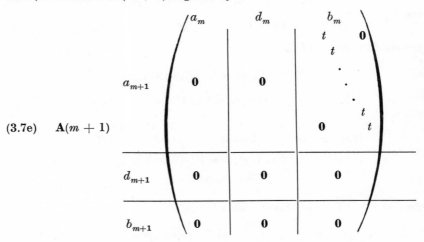

where $\mathbf{H}_{ij}$ stands for $\mathbf{H}(m)_{ij}$ and stands for $\mathbf{K}_{ij}$ for $\mathbf{K}(m)_{ij}$. Accordingly,

$$\text{Tr}\,\mathbf{H}(m)\mathbf{K}(m) = \text{Tr}\,(\mathbf{H}(m)_{11}\,\mathbf{K}(m)_{11}) + \text{Tr}\,(\mathbf{H}(m)_{22}\,\mathbf{K}(m)_{22}) + \\ + \text{Tr}\,(\mathbf{H}(m)_{33}\,\mathbf{K}(m)_{33}).$$

Observe that according to (3.7g)

$$\mathbf{H}(m+1)_{11}\,{}_2\mathbf{A}(m+1)_{13}\,\mathbf{K}(m)_{33} = {}_1\mathbf{A}(m+1)_{13}\,\mathbf{H}(m)_{33}\,\mathbf{K}(m)_{33} \\ = \mathbf{H}(m+1)_{11}\,\mathbf{K}(m+1)_{11}\,{}_1\mathbf{A}(m+1)_{13}.$$

Since ${}_1\mathbf{A}(m+1)_{13} \neq 0$,

$$(\mathbf{H}(m+1))_{11}\,\mathbf{K}(m+1)_{11} = {}_1\mathbf{A}(m+1)_{13}\,\mathbf{H}(m)_{33}\,\mathbf{K}(m)_{33}\,{}_1\mathbf{A}(m+1)_{13}$$

whence,

$$\text{Tr}\,\mathbf{H}(m+1)_{11}\,\mathbf{K}(m+1)_{11} = \text{Tr}\,\mathbf{H}(m)_{33}\,\mathbf{K}(m)_{33},$$

on bearing in mind (3.7g),

$$\Sigma_{m=0}^{m=n}\,(-1)^m\,\text{Tr}(\mathbf{H}(m)_{33}\,\mathbf{K}(m)_{33}) + \Sigma\,(-1)^m\,\text{Tr}\,\mathbf{H}(m)_{11}\,\mathbf{K}(m)_{11} = 0.$$

The conclusion we arrive at is that for the computation of $L(\psi_\#, \theta_\#)$ we need only consider the homomorphisms restricted to the nonbounding cycles (or cocycles) assumed the components of the vectors ${}_1\mathbf{d}$. Specifically it suffices to take $\psi_\#\,{}_1\mathbf{d}_m = \mathbf{H}(m)_{22}\,{}_2\mathbf{d}_m$ and $\theta_\#\,{}_2\mathbf{d}_m = \mathbf{K}(m)_{22}\,{}_1\mathbf{d}_m$. Moreover, we may consider $H_m(K_1, G)$ and $H_m(K_2, G)$, where G is either the real or complex field, and then the homomorphisms ψ_* and θ_* on $H_m(K_1, G)$ to $H_m(K_2, G)$ and the reverse are determined by simply replacing $\mathbf{d}_m$ by $\langle\mathbf{d}_m\rangle$. Thus

$$\psi_*\langle{}_1\mathbf{d}_m\rangle = \mathbf{H}(m)_{22}\langle{}_2\mathbf{d}_m\rangle$$
$$\theta_*\langle{}_2\mathbf{d}_m\rangle = \mathbf{K}(m)_{22}\langle{}_1\mathbf{d}_m\rangle$$

Definition 3.9. If $K_1 = K_2 = K$ and $\psi_\#$ is a homomorphism on $C_m(K_1)$ to $C_m(K)$, define the Lefschetz number $L(\psi_*)$ as $L(\psi_*, i_*)$, where i_* is the identity isomorphism. Thus, $L(\psi_*) \neq 0$ asserts the existence of a fixed simplex of some dimension:.

(3.9a) $$L(\psi_*) = \Sigma\,(-1)^m\,\text{Tr}\,\mathbf{H}(m)_{22}.$$

It would seem that the fixed simplex number is a drastic specialization of the coincidence number. Actually it can replace it. Indeed, let $\tau_\# = \theta_\#\,\psi_\#$; that is, $\tau_\#\colon\ C_m(K_1, G) \to C_m(K_1, G)$. Then

(3.9b) $$L(\tau_*) = L(\psi_*, \theta_*),$$

as is clear, for instance, also from the fact that the m-dimensional matrix for τ_* must be $\mathbf{K}(m)_{22}\,\mathbf{H}(m)_{22}$.

If τ_* is the identity isomorphism,

(3.9c) $$L(\tau_*) = \chi(K),$$

where $\chi(K)$ is the Euler-Poincare characteristic (32.7).

PROBLEM

5-9. Let K be connected and n-dimensional, and let $\psi_*: H_m(K, J) \to H_m(K, J)$, $0 \leq m \leq n$. Write $(\psi_*)^2$ for $\psi_*\psi_*$ and similarly for $(\psi_*)^N$. Suppose that $(\psi_*)^N H_m(K, J) = 0$, $m \neq 0$, $N > 1$, and $(\psi_*)^N H_0(K, J) = H_0(K, J) = J$. Prove that $L(\psi_*) \neq 0$.

Definition 3.10. We say that ψ is a **simplicial map** of K_1 into K_2 if $\psi({}_1\sigma_m) = {}_2\sigma_n$, $n \leq m$, with the map linear on each simplex. This implies, of course, that vertices go into vertices. If ψ is a simplicial map, it **induces** a homomorphism $\psi_\#$ on $C_m(K_1, G)$ to $C_m(K_2, G)$ by

(3.10a) $$\psi_\# \, r \, {}_1\sigma_m^i = r \, {}_2\sigma_m^j.$$

if $\psi_1\sigma_m^i = {}_2\sigma_m^j$, and

(3.10b) $$\psi_\# \, r\sigma_m^i = 0$$

if $\psi({}_1\sigma_m^i) = {}_2\sigma_n^j$, $n < m$. Once $\psi_\#$ is obtained, the homomorphism ψ_* on $H_m(K_1, G)$ to $H_m(K_2, G)$ is defined,

(3.10c) $$\psi_* \, \mathbf{z}_m(K_1, G) = \langle \psi_\# \, z_m(K_1, G) \rangle_2,$$

where the first coset is with respect to the bounding cycles $B_m(K_1, G)$ and the second with respect to $B_m(K_2, G)$. Thus coincidence can be interpreted in terms of maps ψ, θ of simplexes as well as homomorphisms of the elementary chains.

Example 5-5. Suppose $K_1 = K_2 = K$ is acyclic; that is $H_0(K, R) = \{rv_0 \mid r \in R\}$, $H_m(K, R) = 0$, where v_0 is any vertex of K thought of as a 0 cycle. For instance K may be a subdivided n-simplex or cube or convex polyhedron. Let ψ be a simplicial self map of K. Let v and w denote vertices as well as the associated 0-cycles. Then $\psi v = w$ induces $\psi_\# \, v = w$ and, since $v \sim w$, $\psi_* \, \mathbf{v} = \mathbf{v}$. Then $L(\psi) = 1$. Hence there is a fixed simplex; that is to say, every simplicial self map of a finite acyclic complex into itself has a fixed simplex.

Example 5-6. Let S^n be the triangulated n-sphere, and again suppose that ψ is a simplicial self map of S^n. Then

$$H_0(S^n, R) = \{rv_0 \mid r \in R\},$$
$$H_i(S^n, R) = 0, \qquad i \neq 0, n,$$
$$H_n(S^n, R) = \{r \, {}_3c_n \mid {}_3c_n = \Sigma \pm \sigma_n^i\}.$$

Accordingly,

$$\psi_* \, \mathbf{v}_0 = \mathbf{v}_0$$
$$\psi_* \, {}_3\mathbf{c}_n = a \, {}_3\mathbf{c}_n,$$

where a is an integer. Therefore, $L(\psi) = 1 + (-1)^n a$. Consider the special case $\psi_{\#}\Sigma\, \sigma_n^i = \Sigma\sigma_n^i$. Then $a = 1$ and $L(\psi_*) = 0, 2$ for n odd and for n even respectively. Thus for even dimensional spheres $n > 0$ there must be a fixed simplex, but the odd dimensional case is left open.

EXAMPLE 5-7. Suppose that K is the triangulated torus. Let z^1 and z^2 be the two generators of ${}_3C_1(K, G)$. Let T be the base 2 cycle $\Sigma\, \sigma_2^i$ of ${}_3C_2$. Suppose

$$\psi_{\#}\, z_1 = 2z_1 - z_2$$

$$\psi_{\#}\, z_2 = -3z_1 - 3z_2$$

$$\psi_{\#}\, T = T$$

Then $L(\psi_{\#}) = 1 + (-1)^1 (-1) + 1 = 3$. Hence there is a fixed simplex.

The treatment of fixed points and coincidences of spaces under general maps is based on the developments above of the fixed simplex and coincidences for linear simplex to simplex maps and is given in later chapters.

Definition 3.11. In the expression for $L(\psi_{\#})$ the summation sign can be avoided by introducing the trace of one large matrix $\mathbf{H}$ with blocks along the main diagonal given by $(-1)^m\, \mathbf{H}(m)$. This amounts to replacing the chain map $\psi_{\#} = \{\psi_{m\#}\}$ by $\psi_{\#}^- = \{(-1)^m\, \psi_{m\#} = \psi_{m\#}^-\}$. Accordingly $\partial\psi_{\#}^- = -\psi_{\#}^-\, \partial$. We call $\psi_{\#}^-$ an **alternating chain map**.

chapter 6

OMOLOGY EXACT SEQUENCES

1. DIFFERENTIABLE GROUPS, MODULES, RINGS, ALGEBRAS. With the simplicial modules as a concrete representation we proceed to the essentials of the developments concerned with the relative and absolute omology structures. In the case of cohomology theory, products enter naturally. Accordingly the algebraic structure to be considered is the ring or algebra (42.7). By introducing the convention that the product of any two elements is 0, it is possible to view the group (or module) as a ring without unit. We shall often use the term "ring," or "algebra," then, with the understanding of the trivial multiplication swindle when application is made to modules and in this case interpret the ideal as a closed submodule. (Rings may not have units. For instance neither the relative cohomology ring nor the compact grating (81.13) need have identities.)

Definition 1.1. A graded module G is **differentiable** if it admits a homomorphism d to itself; thus $d = \oplus d(n)$ where $dG = \oplus d(n)G(n)$. We write $dG(n)$ for $d(n)G(n)$ with (**a**) $dG^n \subset G^{n+1}$ and $dG_n \subset G_{n-1}$ according as G is upper or lower graded. Thus d corresponds either to δ or to ∂. We require also that (**b**), $d\,d$ annihilates G and for the ring, or algebra, that $dg^p\, g^q = (dg^p)g^q + (-1)^p\, g^p\, dg^q$. (A generalization useful later in the book is that an automorphism α: $G \to G$ exists with $d\,\alpha g + \alpha\, dg = 0$. Then $(-1)^r g^r$ in (1.1b) is replaced by αg^r. The graded differentiable structure is indicated by the letters DG.

Remark. d is not a ring homomorphism but merely a module homomorphism. Moreover for the homology case it is generally the lower graded module that is of interest while for the cohomology situation it is the upper graded ring, or algebra.

Definition 1.2. The differentiable ring G has an **allowable subring**, or **ideal**, J, if J is a subring or an ideal of G (42.8) and $dJ \subset J$.

Definition 1.3. If G and J are DG rings then ψ is an **allowable homomorphism** on G to J if (**a**) ψ is a homomorphism on the graded ring G to the graded ring J (42.10) and (**b**) $\psi\, dg = d\, \psi g$.

Remark. When other grades are introduced to give **bigrading**, the grade developed supra may be called the **total** grade, or **degree**.

It has become the practice to identify the complex with the chain modules. More generally

Definition 1.4. A DG module $K = \{K(n), d\}$ which satisfies the condition $K(0) = 0$, $n < 0$, is an **upper** (**lower**) complex or **cochain** (**chain**) complex. Thus

$$0 \longrightarrow K^0 \xrightarrow{d^0} K^1 \xrightarrow{d^1} K^2 \longrightarrow \cdots$$

or

$$\longrightarrow K_n \xrightarrow{d_n} K_{n-1} \xrightarrow{d_{n-1}} \cdots \longrightarrow 0$$

if $d^{i+1}\, d^i = 0$ or $d_i\, d_{i+1} = 0$. We have already observed d_i or d^i is written d. In brief, K_n corresponds to the older $C_n(K, R)$ or $C_n(K, L, R)$ and K^n to $C^n(K, R)$, etc. When the distinction between the upper and the lower complex is not relevant we use simply, **complex.** When the ring or algebra structure is to be stressed we may use **ring** or **algebraic complex** in place of upper complex.

If the graded rings are chain or ring complexes, an allowable homomorphism is often referred to as a **chain map** or a **cochain map** or more tersely as a **map**.

Remark. Although in general our interest is in allowable homomorphisms we shall have occasion to use two which are not. The operator d is of degree ± 1 and is merely a module homomorphism. The homomorphism D entering in the definition of homotopy later is another module homomorphism.

Definition 1.5. If G is a DR, i.e., **differentiable ring**, $Z(G)$ is the kernel of the module homomorphism $d\colon G \to G$, and the elements of $Z(G)$ are called **cycles** if G is lower graded and **cocycles** if it is upper graded. $Im\ d$, or $d\ G$, is denoted by $B(G)$, and its elements are called either **boundaries** or **bounding cocycles** or **bounding cycles** according as G is upper or lower graded. Throughout this chapter we will assume G is a differentiable ring. Thus $Z(G^n) = Z^n(G) = ker\ (G^n \xrightarrow{d} G^{n+1})$ and $B(G^n) = B^n(G) = Im(G^{n-1} \xrightarrow{d} G^n)$. We often omit the argument G and write say Z^n for $Z^n(G)$.

Lemma 1.6. *$Z(G)$ is a differentiable subring of G. $B(G)$ is a differentiable ideal of $Z(G)$.*

Definition 1.7. $H(G) = Z(G)/B(G)$. We continue with the previous notation (32.4). Thus either $\langle z\rangle_G$ or $\mathbf{z}$ or $\mathbf{z}_G$ denotes the coset of $H(G)$ determined by $z \in Z(G)$. We also write $z \xrightarrow{\lambda} \mathbf{z}_G$.

Lemma 1.8. *$H(G)$ is a graded ring $= \oplus(Z(G_n)/(B(G_n)) = \oplus H_n(G)$ where $H_n(G)$ is a module if G is lower graded. $H(G)$ is a graded ring $= \oplus Z^n/B^n = \oplus H^n$ where H^n is a module if G is upper graded.*

This follows at once from (42.12) since $Z_n = Z \cap G_n$ and $B_n = B \cap G_n = B \cap (G_n \cap Z)$.

Lemma 1.9. *If ψ is an allowable homomorphism on the differentiable rings $J \to G$, then ψ induces a homomorphism $\psi*$ of $H(J) \to H(G)$, where $\psi*$ is interpreted as ψ^* or as ψ_* according to the grading of the rings.*

$$z \in Z(J) \Rightarrow dz = 0_J = \psi\, dz \Rightarrow d\psi z = 0_G \Rightarrow \psi(z) \in Z(G)$$
$$b \in B(J) \Rightarrow b = dc \Rightarrow \psi b = \psi\, dc = d(\psi c) \Rightarrow \psi(b) \in B(G).$$

Thus ψ induces the homomorphism $H(J) \to H(G)$ by $\psi * \mathbf{z}_J = \mathbf{z}_G$.

This may also be expressed by the formula

(1.9a) $$\psi_* \, \mathbf{z}_J = \langle \psi z\rangle\, G,$$

so $\psi*$ is well defined.

Theorem 1.10. *If J is a differentiable ideal of G then*

(1.10a) *G/J is a differentiable ring with $d\#\ [g] = [dg]$.*
(1.10b) *The natural homomorphism $\eta\colon G \to G/J$ defined by $\eta(g) = [g]$ is allowable and induces a homomorphism $\eta*\colon H(G) \to H(G/J)$.*
(1.10c) *The injection $i\colon J \to G$ mapping $j \in J$ onto the same element, considered now as a member of G, is allowable and induces a homomorphism $i*$, $i*\colon H(J) \to H(G)$. (The homomorphisms ought, of course, be written η^*, i^* for upper graded groups and η_*, i_* for lower graded groups.)*

(1.10a) follows from (1.2). For (1.10b): Let $z \in Z(G)$; then $dz = 0$. Hence $d\#\eta z = [dz] = [0]$, so $\eta(z) \in Z(G/J)$. Since J is an ideal, $[g_1g_2] = [g_1][g_2]$ and so

$\eta(z_1z_2) = \eta(z_1)\eta(z_2)$. If $b \in B(G)$, then $[b] = [dw]$, so $\eta b = [b] = [dw] = d_{\#}[w]$, and so η: $B(G) \subset B(G/J)$. Accordingly η induces the homomorphism $\eta*$ of $H(G) \to H(G/J)$. Again η is a ring homomorphism of $B(G) \to B(G/J)$ since if $b_i = da_i$, $[b_1b_2] = d[a_1]d[a_2]$ and by (1.9) $\eta*$ takes $\mathbf{z}_1\mathbf{z}_2$ into $\eta*\,\mathbf{z}_1\ \eta*\,\mathbf{z}_2$ and hence is a ring homomorphism. For (1.10c): since $d(j \mid J) \subset J$, $d(i(j)$ restricted to $i(J)$ is $di(j) \subset i(J)$. Thus $di(j) = idj$; that is, i is an allowable homomorphism and so (1.10c) then follows from (1.9) with the ring aspects established as in the proof of (1.10b).

Lemma 1.11. *Let J be a d-ideal of G. Then d induces a module homomorphism $d*$; $H(G/J) \to H(J)$.*

For clarity we indicate explicitly what the cosets are with respect to. Let $[g]_J \in Z(G/J)$ be a representative of $\langle [g]_J \rangle_{G/J} \in H(G/J)$. Thus $d[g]_J = 0$ or $dg \in J$. Define $d*$ by

(1.11a) $$d*\langle [g]_J \rangle_{G/J} = \langle dg \rangle_J.$$

If $[g]_J \in B(G/J)$, then $[g]_J = [dg']_J$ and so for some j, $g = dg' + j$. Then $d*\langle [g] \rangle_{G/J} = \langle ddg' + dj \rangle_J = \langle dj \rangle_J = 0$. Observe that

$$d*(\langle [g_1] \rangle_{G/J} + \langle [g_2] \rangle_{G/J}) = d*\langle [g_1] + [g_2] \rangle_{G/J}.$$

Then (1.11a) is independent of the representative of $[g]_J$ chosen, for if $\langle [g_1] \rangle_{G/J} = \langle [g_2] \rangle_{G/J}$ then $[g_1 - g_2]_J \in B(G/J)$ and from what we have shown $0 = d*\langle [g_1 - g_2] \rangle = d*\langle [g_1] \rangle - d*\langle [g_2] \rangle$. Hence $d*$ is a homomorphism.

We now state one of the most important conclusions in the book.

Theorem 1.12. *Let G be a DG ring or module with J an allowable ideal, or submodule. Then for allowable i and j the exactness of*

(1.12a) $$0 \longrightarrow J \xrightarrow{\ i\ } G \xrightarrow{\ \eta\ } G/J \longrightarrow 0$$

implies the exactness of $\xrightarrow{d*} H(J) \xrightarrow{i*} H(G) \xrightarrow{\eta*} H(G/J) \xrightarrow{d*}$ *or, in an equivalent representation, of*

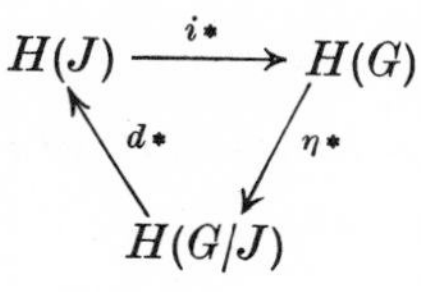

Specifically

(1.12b) $$ker\ \eta* = Im\ i*$$

(1.12c) $$ker\ d* = Im\ \eta*$$

(1.12d) $$ker\ i* = Im\ d*$$

Remark. When G is a nontrivial ring, $\eta*$ and $i*$ are ring homomorphisms on the associated H's, whereas $d*$ is invariably only a module homomorphism.

$$\langle g_0 \rangle \in ker\ \eta* = \{\langle g \rangle_G \mid \eta g \in B(G/J),\ g \in Z(G)\} \quad (1.11a)$$

Hence $\eta g_0 = d[g']$ or $g_0 = dg' + j'$. We shall be a little more precise in that we point out that j' is viewed here as an element of G which falls in the subgroup J and so should be written $i(j)$, i.e., $g_0 = dg' + i(j)$. Hence $0 = dg_0 = ddg' + di(j) = i(dj)$. Since i defines an monomorphism of J into G, it follows that $dj = 0$. Hence $j \in Z(J)$ and $i(j) \in Z(G)$. We have shown that $\langle g_0 \rangle_G = \langle i(j) \rangle_G = i*\langle j \rangle_J$ or $ker\ \eta* \subset Im\ i*$. We shall write as sufficiently expressive $\langle j \rangle_G$ in place of $\langle i(j) \rangle_G$. Observe that $\eta*(i*\langle j \rangle_J) = \langle \eta i j \rangle_{G/J} = 0$, whence $ker\ \eta* \supset Im\ i*$. We have established (1.12b).

Suppose that $\langle [g_1] \rangle \in ker\ d* = \{\langle [g] \rangle \mid dg \in B(J), [g] \in Z(G/J)\}$. Hence $dg_1 = di(j)$ for some $j \in J$. Let $g' = g_1 - i(j)$. Hence $dg' = 0$, so $g' \in Z(G)$. Moreover $[g'] = [g_1]$, and so $\langle g' \rangle_G$ is the antecedent of $\langle [g_1] \rangle_{G/J}$ for $\eta*\langle g' \rangle = \langle [g'] \rangle = \langle [g_1] \rangle$. Thus $ker\ d* \subset Im\ \eta*$. On the other hand, for $g \in Z(G)$, $d*(\eta*\langle g \rangle_G) = d*\langle [g] \rangle = \langle dg \rangle_J = 0$ since $dg = 0$. We have established (1.12c).

Suppose that $\langle j \rangle \in ker\ i* = \{\langle j \rangle \mid i(j) \in B(G)\}$. Hence $i(j) = dg$. Since $[dg] = 0$, $d*\langle [g] \rangle = \langle dg \rangle_J = \mathbf{j}$. Thus $\mathbf{j}$ in $ker\ i*$ has the antecedent $\langle [g] \rangle$ in $H(G/J)$. On the other hand with $[g] \in Z(G/J)$, $i*(d*\langle [g] \rangle) = i*\langle dg \rangle_J = \langle dg \rangle_G = 0$. Hence (1.12d) is established.

Since the homology rings involved are graded (1.12) can be stated in sequence form. If the rings are upper graded, $d*$ raises dimensions by 1. If they are lower graded, $d*$ lowers dimensions by 1. We drop the asterisk and *write d for* d^* or d_*. Then the following are exact sequences.:

$$(1.13a) \qquad \longrightarrow H_m(J) \xrightarrow{i_*} H_m(G) \xrightarrow{\eta_*} H_m(G/J) \xrightarrow{d} H_{m-1}(J) \longrightarrow$$

$$(1.13b) \qquad \longrightarrow H^0(J) \xrightarrow{i^*} H^0(G) \xrightarrow{\eta^*} H^0(G/J) \xrightarrow{d} H^1(J) \longrightarrow .$$

PROBLEM

6-1. Show that $ker\ i^* = Im\ d = Z^m(J) \cap B^m(G)/B^m(J)$ and $ker\ d = Im\ \eta_* = Z^m(G)/(B^m(G) + J)$.

In the application to lower complexes let L be a closed subcomplex of K. Then G, J, and G/J correspond to $C(K, R)$, $C(L, R)$, and $C(K, L; R)$ respectively. For the upper complex $G, J, G/J$ correspond to $C(K, R), C(K - L, R)$, and $C(L;\ R)$ respectively. The reasons for these associations are to be found in (46). We restate (1.13a) and (1.13b) in our earlier terminology.

Theorem 1.14. *The following are exact sequences*

(1.14a) $$\longrightarrow H_m(L, R) \xrightarrow{i_*} H_m(K, R) \xrightarrow{\eta_*} H_m(K, L; R) \xrightarrow{d} H_{m-1}(L, R) \longrightarrow \cdots$$

(1.14b) $$H^0(K - L, R) \xrightarrow{i^*} H^0(K, R) \xrightarrow{\eta^*} H^0(L, R) \xrightarrow{d} H^1(K - L, R) \longrightarrow \cdots$$

If G' is another module and J' is a submodule of G' and if ψ is an allowable homomorphism on G to G' which carries J to J', there is an induced allowable homomorphism ψ on G/J to G'/J' and hence induced homomorphism on the homology modules (1.9a). The homomorphisms $i*$, $\eta*$, $\psi*$, are **natural** in the sense that each square in the following diagram is **commutative**; that is to say the result of the operation on an element going down and then over to the right is the same as first going over and then going down. Alternatively this commutativity is called the **naturality condition.**

(1.15) $$\begin{array}{ccccc} H(J) & \xrightarrow[i_*]{} & H(G) & \xrightarrow[\eta_*]{} & H(G/J) \\ \downarrow{\scriptstyle \psi_*} & & \downarrow{\scriptstyle \psi_{1*}} & & \downarrow{\scriptstyle \psi_{2*}} \\ H(J') & \xrightarrow[i'_*]{} & H(G') & \xrightarrow[\eta'_*]{} & H(G'/J') \end{array}$$

If G is a DG ring, and J is an allowable ideal, $H(G) \approx H(J)$ follows as a consequence of $H(G/J) \approx 0$. It will be important to consider the case where J need not be an ideal.

Theorem 1.15. *Let K be an allowable subring of the DG ring G, thus $K \xrightarrow{i} G$. Suppose that for every $g \in G$ with dg in iK, there is an element k in K for which $g - ik \in B(G) = dG$. Then there is a ring isomorphism $H(K) \underset{\approx}{\xrightarrow{i^*}} H(G)$.*

We claim $ker\ i^* = 0$. Thus let $\mathbf{k} \in ker\ i^*$. Then $ik = dg$. By hypothesis, for some $k' \in K$, $g - ik' \in B(G)$ whence $ik = idk'$. Accordingly $\mathbf{k} = 0$. To establish $Im\ i^* = H(G)$ take $\mathbf{g}$ arbitrarily in $H(G)$. Then $dg = 0$, which is certainly in iK. Therefore for some $k \in K$, $g - ik \in B(G)$. Hence $idk = 0$ so $dk = 0$ and $\mathbf{g} = i^* \mathbf{k}$.

Example 6-1. Let S^2 be triangulated and take S^1 as a closed subcomplex of S^2. We omit the coefficient group, R, which is a field. (Hence all the homology modules entering below are vector spaces.) Our interest is in $H_2(S^2, S^1)$. Then (1.14a) becomes

$$\begin{array}{ccccccccc} \longrightarrow H_2(S^1) & \xrightarrow{i_*} & H_2(S^2) & \xrightarrow{\eta_*} & H_2(S^2, S^1) & \xrightarrow{\partial} & H_1(S^1) & \xrightarrow{i_*} & H_1(S^2). \\ \wr\wr & & \wr\wr & & & & \wr\wr & & \wr\wr \\ 0 & & R & & & & R & & 0 \end{array}$$

The known isomorphisms such as $H_2(S^2) \approx R$ are given in Example 3-5. Exactness of the sequence of the first three terms implies $\eta_* R \approx R$. Hence $H_2(S^2, S^1) \approx (\eta_* R) \oplus D$, where D is to be determined and the direct sum representation exists by (42.14) or by the observation that $H_2(S^2, S^1)$ is a finite dimensional vector space and may, therefore, be represented as the direct sum of any linear subspace $(\eta_* B)$ and its vector complement. Furthermore, according to Problem 4-9, $D \approx (\eta_* R \oplus D)/\eta_* R \approx H_1(S^1) \approx R$. Thus $H_2(S^2, S^1) \approx R \oplus R$. (Evidently the restriction of R to a field is irrelevant.) This result is intuitively evident upon reflection, for if all boundaries are taken mod S^1 then e^+ and e^- behave like independent nonbounding cycles.

PROBLEM

6-1. Exhibit a connected complex K with three independent nonbounding 2-cycles and with $H_1(K, \mathrm{J}) \approx \mathrm{J}$.

In connection with the next three problems we refer to some current phraseology. Suppose A and C are subcomplexes of the complex X or, for later use, are subspaces of the space X.

Definition 1.16. If $A \xrightarrow{i} C \xrightarrow{j} X$ where the maps are inclusions, we say that the m-cycle z_m on A **bounds on** C if $z \in Z_m(A)$ and $i_\# z \in B_m(C)$. The situation is illustrated in Fig. 6-1a. If $X, A \xrightarrow{k} X, C$ is an inclusion map, then the m-cycle on X mod A bounds on X mod C, or $z \sim 0$ mod C, if $z \in Z_m(X, A)$ and if $k_\# z \in B_m(X, C)$. (See Fig. 6-1b.) The coefficient group is understood to be arbitrary in both situations above. Figure 6-1c illustrates a cycle on A mod E which bounds on X mod D.

PROBLEMS

6-2. Let z_r be a cycle on L which bounds on K. Show that there is a cycle, $z_{r+1} \in Z_{r+1}(K, L)$ with $\partial z_{r+1} \sim z_r$.

6-3. Let $z_r \in Z_r(K, L)$ with $\partial z_r \in B_r(L)$. Show that there is a cycle $w_r \in Z_r(K)$ with $w_r - z_r \in B_r\ (K, L)$.

6-4. Formulate the situation in Fig. 6-2c in terms of homomorphisms of relative cycles and boundaries.

2. OTHER EXACT SEQUENCES. There is a simple algorithm underlying the derivation of a variety of special homology sequences. The *DG* modules, or rings, M and N are here considered complexes (1.4) subject to the allowable homomorphisms ψ. Thus

(2.1a) $$M \xrightarrow{\psi} N$$

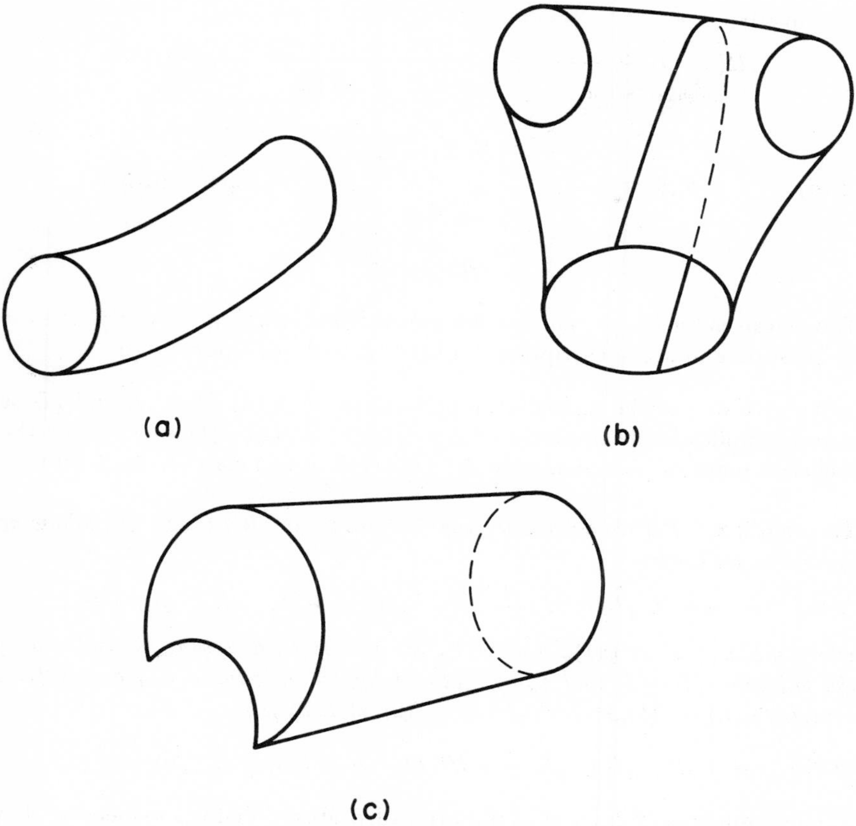

Figure 6-1

With i and η interpreted as an injection and the natural epimorphism, the following sequence is patently exact:

$$0 \longrightarrow ker\,\psi \xrightarrow{\ i\ } M \xrightarrow{\ \eta\ } M/ker\,\psi \longrightarrow 0. \tag{2.1b}$$

Observe now that ψ: $M \to \psi(M)$ induces the isomorphism $\dot{\psi}$: $M/ker\ \psi \to \psi(M)$ so that there is exactness in

$$0 \longrightarrow ker\ \psi \xrightarrow{\ i\ } M \xrightarrow{\ \dot{\psi}\eta\ } \psi(M) \longrightarrow 0 \tag{2.1c}$$

Identify $ker\ \psi$, M, $\psi(M)$ with J, G, and G/J in (1.13). Since ψ is allowable, the exactness of the homology and cohomology sequences follows at once.

Specifically

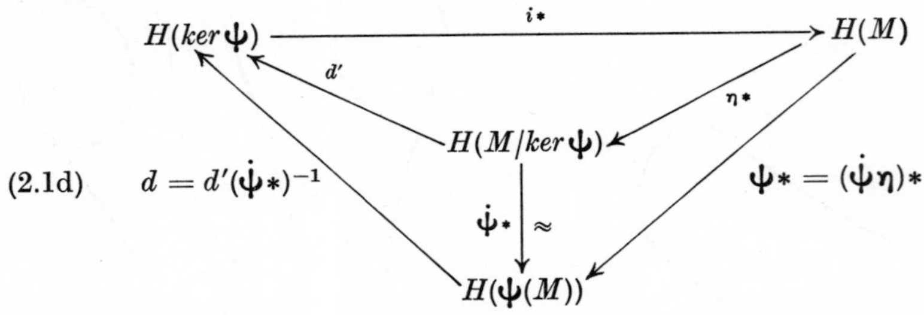

The asterisks on $i*$, $\psi*$, and $\eta*$ are superscripts when upper complexes are in question and are subscripts when lower complexes enter.

We give one of the immediate applications of (2.1d). Let ${}_1L$ and ${}_2L$ be closed simplicial subcomplexes of $L = {}_1L \cup {}_2L$. Let $\psi(1)$ and $\psi(2)$ be the inclusion maps of ${}_1L$ and ${}_2L$ into L. Let $i(1)$ and $i(2)$ map ${}_1L \cap {}_2L$ into ${}_jL$.

Theorem 2.2. *For an arbitrary coefficient group, or ring* (41.2), *the following sequences are exact:*

(2.2a) $$\longrightarrow H_r({}_1L) \oplus H_r({}_2L) \xrightarrow{\psi_*} H_r(L) \xrightarrow{d} H_{r-1}({}_1L \cap {}_2L) \xrightarrow{i_*}$$

where $\psi_*({}_1\mathbf{z} \oplus {}_2\mathbf{z}) = \psi(1)_*\,{}_1\mathbf{z} + \psi(2)_*\,{}_2\mathbf{z}$, ${}_i\mathbf{z} = \mathbf{z}({}_iL)$ *and* $\psi(j)_*$ *is induced by the injection* ${}_jL \to L$ *and* i_* *is induced by the injections* $i(1)$ *and* $i(2)$ *so* $i_*\mathbf{z}({}_1L \cap {}_2L) = i(1)_*\mathbf{z}({}_1L \cap {}_2L) \oplus - i(2)_*\mathbf{z}({}_1L \cap {}_2L)$;

(2.2b) $$\longrightarrow H^{r-1}({}_1L \cap {}_2L) \xrightarrow{\delta} H^r(L) \xrightarrow{\psi^*} H^r({}_1L) \oplus H^r({}_2L) \xrightarrow{i^*}$$

The sequences (2.2a) and (2.2b) are called **Mayer-Vietoris sequences**. Let ${}_1K$ be a duplicate of ${}_1L$ and ${}_2K$ of ${}_2L$ where K_1 and K_2 are disjunct; write $K = {}_1K \cup {}_2K$. Then $\mu(i)$: ${}_iK = {}_iL$, $i = 1, 2$ is the duplication map. For instance we designate the typical simplex of ${}_1L$ and of ${}_2L$ by $\sigma_r^i({}_1L)$ and $\sigma_r^j({}_2L)$, respectively, subject to the convention that if $\sigma_r^i({}_1L) \in {}_1L \cap {}_2L$ then the superscript i designates it in ${}_2L$; i.e., $\sigma_r^i({}_1L)$ is the same as $\sigma_r^i({}_2L)$. We denote this simplex by $\sigma_r^i({}_1L \cap {}_2L)$ also. The simplex in ${}_1K$ corresponding to $\sigma_r^i({}_1L)$ is written $\sigma_r^i({}_1K)$, etc. Of course $\sigma_r^i({}_1K)$ and $\sigma_r^i({}_2K)$ are invariably disjunct simplexes.

As in (1.4) interpret ${}_iP_r$ as $C_r({}_iK, R)$, $i = 1, 2$ and ${}_iN_r$ as $C_r({}_iL, R)$ with R the coefficient ring, or field. Then ${}_iN$ and ${}_iP$ are lower complexes and so are $M = {}_1N \oplus {}_2N$ and $N = {}_1N + {}_2N$. Thus $M_r = {}_1N_r \oplus {}_2N_r = C_r({}_1L, R) \oplus C({}_2L, R)$, $N_r = C_r({}_1L, R) + C_r({}_2L, R) = C_r(L, R)$.

We have

(2.2c) $$\mu(i)_\#\colon\ {}_iP \xrightarrow{\approx} {}_iN$$
$$\mu(i)_*\colon\ H_r({}_iK, R) \xrightarrow{\approx} H_r({}_iL, R)$$

since of course $H_r({}_iK)$ and $H_r({}_iP_r)$ are identical concepts. Define $\mu_\#$ by $\mu_\#\colon {}_1P \oplus {}_2P \rightarrow N$ where $\mu_\#\, {}_1P \oplus {}_2P = \mu(1)_\#\, {}_1P + \mu(2)_\#\, {}_2P$. Let $\psi_\# = \mu_\#(\mu(1)_\#^{-1} \oplus \mu(2)_\#^{-1})$ be on M to N corresponding to ψ in (2.1a). Thus

$$M = {}_1N \oplus {}_2N \xrightarrow{\mu(1)_\#^{-1} \oplus \mu(2)_\#^{-1}} {}_1P \oplus {}_2P \xrightarrow{\mu_\#} N.$$

In view of (2.2c)

(2.2d) $$\psi_\# M_r = N_r = C_r(L, R).$$

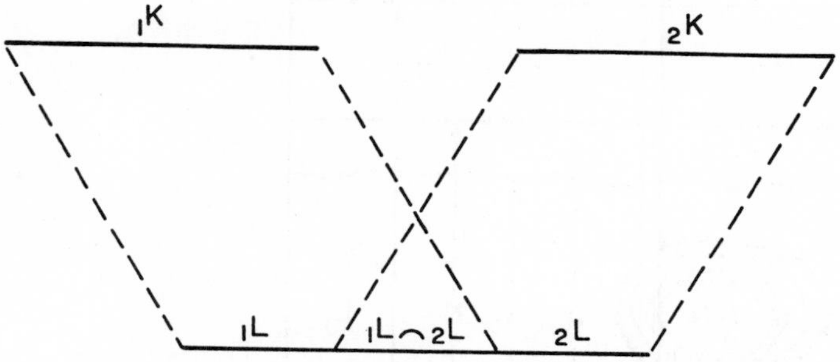

Figure 6-2

The only r chains of M that go to 0 under $\mu_\#$ are of the form

$$\Sigma\, g_i\, \sigma_r^i({}_1L \cap {}_2L) \oplus -g_i\, \sigma_r^i({}_1L \cap {}_2L).$$

Hence for grade r,

(2.2e) $$\begin{aligned} ker\ \psi_\# &\approx {}_1N_r \cap {}_2N_r \\ &= C_r({}_1L \cap {}_2L, R). \end{aligned}$$

Since a direct sum implies complete autonomy for each summand

(2.2f) $$\begin{aligned} H_r(M) &= H_r({}_1N) \oplus H_r({}_2N) \\ &= H_r({}_1L) \oplus H_r({}_2L). \end{aligned}$$

The substitution of (2.2d), (2.2e), and (2.2f) in (2.1d) yields (2.2a) and in particular d is the composition

$$H_r(L) \xleftarrow{\approx} H_r({}_1N \oplus {}_2N/{}_1N \cap {}_2N) \xrightarrow{\partial} H({}_1L \cap {}_2L),$$

(as indicated in (2.1a)).

PROBLEMS

6-5. Define $\psi^\#$ and $i^\#$ and establish (2.2b).

6-6. If A is a subcomplex of K_1 and K_2 show that

$$\longrightarrow H(A) \xrightarrow{\delta} H(K_1 - A) \oplus H(K_2 - A) \longrightarrow H(K_1 \cup K_2) \longrightarrow .$$

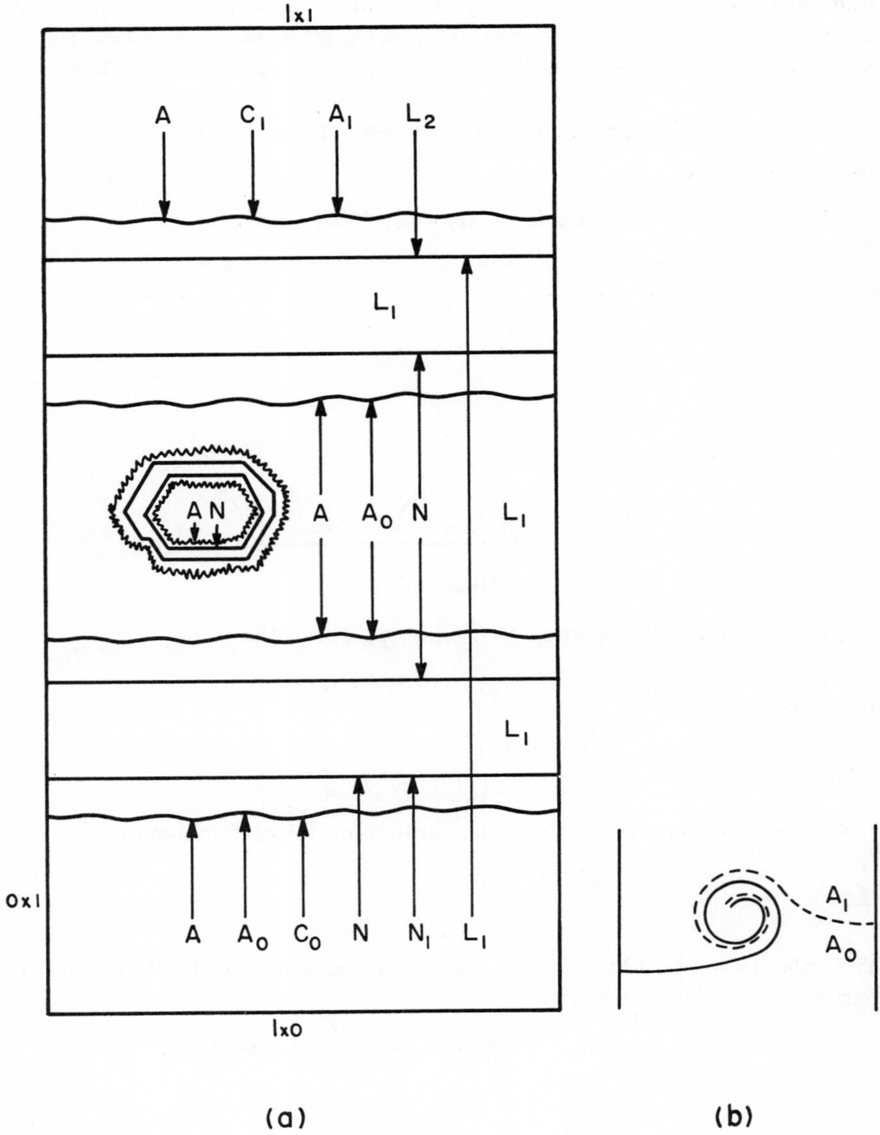

Figure 6-3

Remark. The usual axiomatic development of omology theory considers the dissection of a space into pairs, that is to say, the relative groups, as fundamental. Then exactness of (1.14a) or (1.14b) is a natural axiom. An alternative view would be to make basic, building up a space by accretion of subspaces. Such a viewpoint would supplant (1.14) by (2.2) as an axiom.

EXAMPLE 6-2. Let A be a closed subset of the square I^2. Suppose (a) $(I \times 0) \cup (I \times 1) \subset A$ and (b) no path (i.e., homeomorph of a segment $\{t \mid 0 \leq t \leq 1\}$) in $I^2 - A$ connects $0 \times I$ and $1 \times I$. We assert: $I \times 0 \cup I \times 1$ *is in a single component of* A. Suppose that the assertion is invalid. Let C_0 and C_1 be the components of A containing $I \times 0$ and $I \times 1$. Since a component of the compact set A, say C, is the intersection of all sets which are simultaneously open and closed in A, closed sets A_0 and A_1 exist such that $A = A_1 \cup A_0$ and $C_i \subset A_i$, $i = 0, 1$ and compactness ensures that the distance $d(A_0, A_1)$ is positive, say ρ. Triangulate I^2 with simplexes of diameter inferior to $\rho/4$ so that I^2 is now a complex. Let N be the star of A_0 with respect to this triangulation. Let N_1 be the component of N containing $I \times 0$. Let $\bar{N}_1$ be $Cl\, N_1$ in the triangulation of I^2. Thus $\bar{N}_1$ is connected. Let L_2, a subcomplex of $I^2 - N_1$, be the component containing $I \times 1$. Thus L_2 is a closed subcomplex of I^2.

Define L_1 as $Cl(I^2 - L_2)$. Then L_1, too, is connected. The only concern is with x a vertex not in $L_2 \cup \bar{N}$ but if some path joins L_2 and x it must meet $\bar{N}$. Evidently the point set boundary of L_1, namely $||L_1 \cap L_2||$, is disjunct from A. According to (2.2a)

$$\begin{array}{ccccccccc} \longrightarrow H_1(I^2) & \longrightarrow & H_0(L_1 \cap L_2) & \xrightarrow{i_*} & H_0(L_1) \oplus H_0(L_2) & \xrightarrow{\psi_*} & H_0(I^2) & \longrightarrow & 0. \\ \wr\wr & & & & \wr\wr \quad\quad \wr\wr & & \wr\wr & & \\ 0 & & & & R \quad \oplus \quad R & & R & & \end{array}$$

By exactness

$$(R \oplus R/i_*\, H_0(L_1 \cap L_2)) \approx H_0(I_2) \approx R.$$

Hence

$$i_*\, H_0(L_1 \cap L_2) \approx R,$$

where i_* is a monomorphism. Therefore $H_0(L_1 \cap L_2) \approx R$ or $L_1 \cap L_2$ contains a path (21.8), meeting $0 \times I$ and $1 \times I$ in contradiction with (b). The assertion is untrue if A is open cf. Fig. 6-3b.

PROBLEMS

6-7. Let all subcomplexes mentioned be closed and suppose that $A \subset C_1 \cap C_2 \subset K$. Let z_r be a cycle on A which bounds both in C_1 and in C_2 and suppose that $C_1 \cap C_2$ is a proper subcomplex of C_1 in which z_r does not bound. Show there is a nonbounding cycle z_{r+1} on $C_1 \cup C_2$. Consider the inclusion maps of A into C_i and into $C_1 \cap C_2$ and describe the induced homomorphisms applied to z_r.

6-8. Suppose that $K \supset L_1 \cup L_2$ and $F \subset L_1 \cap L_2$. If the groups in (2.2) are replaced by $H(K, M)$ or by $H(M, F)$ for $M = L_i$, $L_1 \cup L_2$, or $L_1 \cap L_2$ show that the resulting sequences are exact.

We proceed to still another important homology sequence. (We intend subsequent generalizations to spaces. Hence we use the notation A and X rather than the L, K associated with complexes.)

Definition 2.3. If $X \supset A \supset B$ represents closed complexes we refer to (X, A, B) as a **triple**. The maps below are all inclusions, and

$$B \xrightarrow{i} A \xrightarrow{j} X$$

$$A, B \xrightarrow{\theta} X, B$$

$$X, B \xrightarrow{\psi} X, A.$$

Theorem 2.4. *The homology sequence for the triple X, A, B, namely*

(2.4a) $$\longrightarrow H_n(A, B) \xrightarrow{\theta_*} H_n(X, B) \xrightarrow{\psi_*} H_n(X, A) \xrightarrow{\partial'} H_{n-1}(A, B) \longrightarrow$$

is exact where the homomorphism ∂' is defined in (2.4h) *below. The cohomology sequence is*

(2.4b) $$\longleftarrow H^n(A, B) \xleftarrow{\theta^*} H^n(X, B) \xleftarrow{\psi^*} H^n(X, A) \xleftarrow{\delta'} H^{n-1}(A, B) \longleftarrow$$

The coefficients in the groups above are from a group or ring (41.2).

We give the proof for the homology case alone. The basic homomorphism corresponding to (2.1a) namely

$$\{[c_r]_B\} = \frac{C_r(X)}{(ji)_\# C_r(B)} \xrightarrow{\psi_\#} C_r(X)/j_\# C_r(A) = \{[c_r]_A\},$$

is induced by ψ. Evidently *ker* $\psi_\#$ consists of those relative chains, $\{[c_r]_B\}$ where $c_r \in j_\# C_r(A)$; this is to say

(2.4c) $$\ker \psi_\# = j_\# C_r(A)/(ji)_\# C_r(B) \approx C_r(A)/i_\# C_r(B) \approx C_r(A, B).$$

Hence the correspondent of (2.1c) is

(2.4d) $$\begin{array}{ccccccccc} & & & & & & \dfrac{C_r(X, B)}{\theta_\# C_r(A, B)} & & \\ & & & & & \nearrow^{\eta_\#} & \downarrow \dot{\psi}_\# & & \\ 0 \longrightarrow & C_r(A, B) & \xrightarrow{\theta_\#} & C_r(X, B) & \xrightarrow[\psi_\#]{} & & C_r(X, A) & \longrightarrow 0. & \end{array}$$

The boundary homomorphism ∂_1 on $C_r(X, B)$ to $C_r(X, B)$ is defined by $\partial_1[c_r]_B = [\partial c_r]_B$. An element of $C_r(X, B)/\theta_\# C_r(A, B)$ is written $[[c_r]_B]_{A,B}$ where $c_r \in C_r(X)$. Since the subcomplexes A and B are closed, if $c_r \in j_\# C_r(A)$

then $\partial c_r \in j_\# C_{r-1}(A)$, and if $c_r \in (ji)_\# C_r(B)$, then $\partial c_r \in (ji)_\# C_{r-1}(B)$. Thus ∂_1 takes $C_r(A, B)$ into $C_r(A, B)$. Accordingly ∂_1 induces a homomorphism ∂_2 on

$$\frac{C_r(X, B)}{\theta_\# C_r(A, B)} \to \frac{C_{r-1}(X, B)}{\theta_\# C_{r-1}(A, B)}$$

defined by

$$\partial_2[[c_r]_B]_{A,B} = [[\partial c_r]_B]_{A,B}. \tag{2.4e}$$

Definition of the boundary homomorphism d in the homology group corresponding to $C_r(X, B)/\theta_\# C_r(A, B)$, to $H_{r-1}(A, B)$ is merely a matter of substituting $C_r(X, B)$ for G and $C_r(A, B)$ for J in (1.11). Perhaps it is worthwhile to do this. Thus the cycles of $C_r(X, B)/\theta_\# C_r(A, B)$ are the elements of *ker* ∂_2. Specifically, by reason of (2.4d), it is required that $\partial c_r \in j_\# C_r(A)$. The bounding cycles, or *Im* ∂_2, are denoted by $B(X, A, B)$. Write z when a cycle is understood. Then the direct application of (1.11) yields

$$d\langle[[z_r]_B]_{A\ B}\rangle_{X,A,B} = \langle[dz_r]_B\rangle_{A,B}. \tag{2.4f}$$

We consider ψ_*. Thus in view of (11.8),

$$\frac{C_r(X, B)}{\theta_\# C_r(A, B)} \approx \frac{C_r(X)/(ji)_\# C_r(B)}{j_\# C_r(A)/(ji)_\# C_r(B)} \approx C_r(X)/j_\# C_r(A).$$

Specifically

$$\dot\psi_\#[[c_r]_B]_{A,B} = [c_r]_A.$$

In particular $\dot\psi_\#$ is allowable, if $\partial z_r \in j_\# C_r(A)$. Then

$$0 = \partial_2\, \dot\psi_\#[[z_r]_B]_{A,B} = \partial_3[z_r]_A$$

where ∂_3 is the boundary homomorphism on $C_r(X, A)$. Then

$$\dot\psi_*\langle[[z_r]_B]_{A,B}\rangle_{X,A,B} = \langle[z_r]_A\rangle_{X,A} \tag{2.4g}$$

Therefore with $\partial' = d\dot\psi_*^{-1}$ we obtain

$$\partial'\langle[z_r]_A\rangle_{X,A} = d\langle[[z_r]_A]_{A,B}\rangle_{X,A,B} \tag{2.4h}$$

PROBLEMS

6-9. Establish (2.4b) and in particular define δ'.

6-10. If z_r is a cycle on X mod $A \cup B$ where ∂z_r is a bounding cycle on $A \cup B$ mod A show that there is an r cycle w_r on X mod A such that $z_r - w_r \in B_r(X, A \cup B)$.

6-11. In the terminology of (2.4), if $z_r \in Z_r(X, B)$ and $w_r \in Z_r(A, B)$ where $z_r - \theta_\# w_r \in B_r(X, B)$ show that $\psi_\# z_r \in B_r(X, A)$.

6-12. Show that

$$ker\ \partial = Im\ \psi_* = \{Z_m(X, A)/(\partial C(X) + C_m(B))\}$$
$$Im\ \partial = ker\ \theta_* = \{Z_m(A) \cap \partial C(X)/\partial C(X) + C_m(B)\}.$$

6-13. Show that on replacing lower by upper grades in Problem 6-12 $m + 1$ by $m - 1$ and ∂ by δ, the relations for $ker\ \delta$ and $Im\ \psi^*$ are obtained.

Remark. Chain and cochain groups over triads, . . . , or n-ads instead of pairs find use in Chapter 12. For L_1 and L_2 closed subcomplexes of K,

$$C^m(K, L_1, L_2) = C^m(K - L_1) \cap C^m(K - L_2),$$

where we omit the fixed coefficient group or ring (41.2). The coboundary homomorphism is defined in the obvious way, so the derived modules are immediate and

$$H^m(K, L_1, L_2) = Z^m(K, L_1, L_2)/B^m(K, L_1, L_2).$$

Pairs are considered triples with one of the entries the empty set. For instance the inclusion map i: $L_1, L_1 \cap L_2 \to K, L_2$ is interpreted below as i: $L_1, \phi, L_1 \cap L_2 \to K, \phi, L_2$. Let j be the inclusion map j: $K, \phi, L_2 \to K, L_1, L_2$). Then

$$\longrightarrow H^{m-1}(L_1, L_1 \cap L_2) \xrightarrow{\delta} H^m(K, L_1, L_2) \xrightarrow{j^*}$$
$$H^m(K, L_2) \xrightarrow{i^*} H^m(L_1, L_1 \cap L_2)$$

is exact.

PROBLEM

6-14. Prove the assertion of exactness of the above sequence.

3. CHAIN HOMOTOPY. Definition 3.1. If $_1A$ and $_2A$ are complexes, and $\boldsymbol{h}$ and $\boldsymbol{l}$ are allowable homomorphisms on $_1A$ to $_2A$, while D is a homomorphism, generally nonallowable, on $_1A$ to $_2A$ which changes degrees by 1, then $\boldsymbol{h}$ is **chain homotopic** to $\boldsymbol{l}$ and we write $\boldsymbol{h} \simeq \boldsymbol{l}$ if

$$\boldsymbol{l}a - \boldsymbol{h}a = D\,da + dDa$$

for all $a \in {_1A}$. Generally we shall say **homotopic** in place of **chain homotopic** for there is little danger of confusion with homotopy of maps of spaces. If $_1A = {_2A}$ and $\boldsymbol{l}$ is the identity isomorphism, then $\boldsymbol{h}$ is a **deformation** or **homotopy operator**.

Lemma 3.2. *If* $\boldsymbol{h} \simeq \boldsymbol{l}$, *then* $h_* = l_*$ *on* $H(_1A)$ *to* $H(_2A)$.

Let $z(a) \in Z(_1A)$ so $\langle z(a)\rangle_1 \in H(_1A)$. Bearing in mind that with $b \in B(_2A)$, $\langle db\rangle = 0$,

$$l_*\langle z(a)\rangle_1 - h_*\langle z(a)\rangle_1 = \langle \boldsymbol{l}z(a) - \boldsymbol{h}z(a)\rangle_2$$
$$= \langle dDz(a) + D\,dz(a)\rangle_2 = 0$$

Lemma 3.3. *Let C be a subcomplex of $A = {}_1A = {}_2A$. Let $\boldsymbol{l}$ and D restricted to C yield elements of C, If $\boldsymbol{h} \simeq \boldsymbol{l}$, then $\boldsymbol{h}$ takes C into C also, and the induced homomorphisms h'_* and l'_* are the same on $H(A/C)$ to $H(A/C)$.*

Since $a \in C$ implies $da \in C$, $\boldsymbol{l}a - D\,da - dDa$ is the sum of elements in C and hence is in C. Thus $\boldsymbol{h}(a \mid C) \in C$. Write $'d$ for the induced boundary operator on A/C. Thus $'d[a] = [da]$. Then since $\boldsymbol{l}$ and $\boldsymbol{h}$ take C into C, they induce homomorphisms $'\boldsymbol{l}$ and $'\boldsymbol{h}$ on A/C to A/C by $'\boldsymbol{l}[a] = [\boldsymbol{l}a]$, etc. Thus

$$'\boldsymbol{l}[z(a)] - '\boldsymbol{h}[z(a)] = [D\,dz(a) + dDz(a)]_C = 'd[Dz(a)]_C$$

since $dz(a) \in C$.

Theorem 3.4. *If C is a subcomplex of A and D takes C into C and the deformation $\boldsymbol{h}$ takes A into C, then the inclusion homomorphism $\boldsymbol{i}$: $C \to A$ induces an isomorphism $H(C) \to H(A)$.*

If $a_0 \in A$ with $da_0 \in C$, then $[a_0] \in Z(A/C)$. Then $a_0 = dDa_0 + D\,da_0 + \boldsymbol{h}a_0 = dDa_0 +$ elements in C. Hence $[dDa_0] = [a_0] \in B(A/C)$. Accordingly $H(A/C)$ is trivial whence the exactness of (1.13a) or (1.13b) guarantees that i_* is an isomorphism.

Definition 3.5. The alternate chain maps (53.11) give rise to a homotopy definition with D^- replacing D. Thus $\psi_1 - \psi_2 = D^-\,d - dD^-$. We indicate this by $\psi_1 \underset{\sim}{\simeq} \psi_2$.

If L, M are closed subcomplexes of K and $L \subset M \subset K$, then $C(L, \mathrm{Q})$ is a direct summand of $C(K, \mathrm{Q})$. Let p be the projection of $C(K, \mathrm{Q})$ onto $C(L, \mathrm{Q})$. More generally let G be a DG module with J a DG submodule. We introduce black face letters for the induced matrix representations.

Lemma 3.6. *Let $\psi_1 \underset{\sim}{\simeq} \psi_2$ for two alternate chain maps on J to G. Let $pG \subset J$ with $p^2 = p$. A sufficient condition that* $\mathrm{Tr}\,(p\boldsymbol{\psi}_1) = \mathrm{Tr}\,(p\boldsymbol{\psi}_2)$ *is that* $\mathrm{Tr}\,\mathbf{pd\,D^-} = \mathrm{Tr}\,\mathbf{dp\,D^-}$. *This implies no boundary simplex is fixed.*

Evidently

$$(\mathbf{p}\boldsymbol{\psi}_1) - (\mathbf{p}\boldsymbol{\psi}_2) = \mathbf{pdD^-} - \mathbf{pD^-\,d}.$$

Take the trace of both sides and observe that the trace of a product of matrices is independent of order of the matrices. This yields the first assertion immediately. The d matrix is of course the incidence matrix.

4. TENSOR PRODUCTS. We now define the tensor product. We restrict attention to the case that the modules involved are over an integral domain and in particular are Abelian groups but a more general formulation in terms of onesided modules over noncommutative rings will be given in Chapter 10.

Definition 4.1. Let A and B be modules over the integral domain R (41.1). Thus, the elements of A are of the form $\Sigma_\pi r_i a_i$ while those of B are $\Sigma_{\pi'} r_j b_j$, $a_i \in A$, $b_j \in B$. Let $F = A \times B$ be the free Abelian group consisting of formal finite sums of all ordered pairs a, b written $a \times b$. Thus,

$$F = \{\Sigma_\pi \Sigma_{\pi'} r_i a_1 \times r_j b_j\}. \tag{4.1a}$$

Let M be the smallest Abelian group generated by the elements

$$\begin{gathered}(a + a') \times b - a \times b - a' \times b,\\ a \times (b + b') - a \times b - a \times b',\\ ra \times b - a \times rb.\end{gathered} \tag{4.1b}$$

Equivalently M is the group hull or smallest Abelian group containing these elements. The coset of $a \times b$ is now denoted by $a \otimes b$ rather than our usual $[a \times b]_M$.

Lemma (4.2a) $(a + a') \otimes b = a \otimes b + a' \otimes b,$

(4.2b) $a \otimes (b + b') = a \otimes b + a \otimes b',$

(4.2c) $ra \otimes b = a \otimes rb$

and if A and B are Abelian groups, then $r \in J$.

Definition 4.3. The results (4.2a), . . , (4.2c) indicate F/M is an Abelian group. If $r(a \otimes b)$ is defined by

$$r(a \otimes b) = (ra) \otimes b = a \otimes (rb) \tag{4.3a}$$

then the **tensor product** over R is the R module F/M. Two special cases are noteworthy. If A and B are Abelian groups or equivalently if $R = J$, then $A \otimes B$ is an Abelian group. If R is a field so that A and B are vector spaces over the field R, then $A \otimes B$ is a vector space. Here especially one often uses *linear transformation* for *homomorphism*.

PROBLEM

6-12. Show associativity of the tensor product.

The **natural homomorphism** η on $A \times B$ to $A \otimes B$ defined by η: $a \times b = a \otimes b$ is bilinear or bihomomorphic, i.e.,

(4.3b)

$$\eta((r_1 a_1 + r_2 a_2) \times b) = r_1 a_1 \otimes b + a \otimes r_2 b_2 = r_1(a \otimes b_1) + r_2(a \otimes b_2).$$

(4.3c)

$$a \otimes (r_1 b_1 + r_2 b_2) = a \otimes r_1 b_1 + a \otimes r_2 b_2 = r_1(a \otimes b_1) + r_2(a \otimes b_2).$$

A useful algorithm for defining homomorphisms of tensor products derives from (4.3b) and (4.3c) and is given explicit statement in:

Lemma 4.4. *Let C be an Abelian group and let A and B be modules over R; then if h is a bihomomorphism on $A \times B$ to C satisfying* **(a)** *$h(ra \times b) = h(a \times rb)$, a homomorphism g exists yielding commutativity in the appended diagram*

(4.4b)

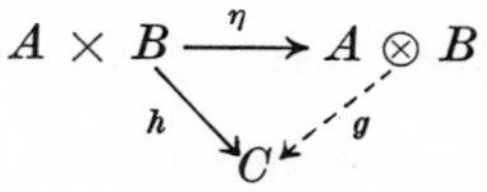

where g is defined by $g(a \otimes b) = h(a \times b)$. (If A, B, and C are vector spaces over the field R, then g is a linear transformation.) Moreover g is unique.

Corollary 4.5. *Let $\phi\colon A \to A'$ and $\psi\colon B \to B'$ denote homomorphisms of modules over the ring R. Then $\phi \otimes \psi$ defined on $A \otimes B$ to $A' \otimes B'$ by*

(4.5a) $$(\phi \otimes \psi)(a \otimes b) = (\phi a) \otimes (\psi b) \in A' \otimes B'$$

is a homomorphism. If the modules are over a field, then $\phi \otimes \psi$ is a linear transformation.

Indeed, in

(4.5b)

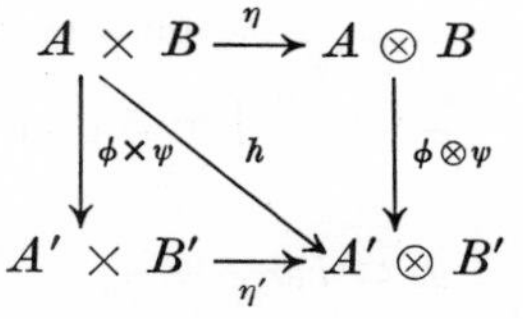

$a \times b \to \phi(a) \times \psi(b) \to \phi(a) \otimes \psi(b)$, defines a bihomomorphism on $A \times B$ to $A' \otimes B'$ whence (4.4) applies and cognizance is to be taken of (4.3a).

PROBLEM

6-13. Let $A \xrightarrow{\phi_1} A' \xrightarrow{\phi_2} A''$ and $B \xrightarrow{\psi_1} B' \xrightarrow{\psi_2} B''$ be R modules over R with ϕ_i, ψ_i homomorphisms. Then show that $(\phi_2 \otimes \psi_2)(\phi_1 \otimes \psi_1) = (\phi_2\phi_1) \otimes (\psi_2\psi_1)$ is a homomorphism on $A \otimes B$ to $A'' \otimes B''$.

Caution must be used in concluding that monomorphisms of A and B result in monomorphisms of $A \otimes B$, though this is valid for isomorphisms.

Example 6-3. If $A = 2\mathrm{J}$, $B = B' = \mathrm{J}_2$, $A' = \mathrm{J}$ [*cf.* the notation in (4.6) below], then with $\phi(2n) = n$, ϕ defines an isomorphism of $2\mathrm{J} \to \mathrm{J}$. Thus, with ψ the identity isomorphism, $\phi \otimes \psi$ yields with $b = 1$ or 0 in J_2

$$\phi \otimes \psi\colon 2n \otimes 1, 0 = n \otimes 1, 0$$

$$2\mathrm{J} \otimes \mathrm{J}_2 \approx \mathrm{J} \otimes \mathrm{J}_2.$$

EXAMPLE 6-4. If in Example 6-3 we define ϕ as the monomorphism $\phi(2n) = 2n$ then $\phi \otimes \psi$ does not define a monomorphism and, indeed, is trivial. Thus,

$$(\phi \otimes \psi)(2n \otimes 1) = (2n \otimes 1) = (n \otimes 2) = (n \otimes 0) = 0.$$

(At first blush it might appear that a similar conclusion ought to follow in Example 6-3, but the difference is, or course, that there if n is odd:

$$(\phi \otimes \psi)(2n \otimes 1) = n \otimes 1 \neq 0.)$$

The breakdown illustrated requires there be elements of finite order in A or B.

Theorem 4.6. *Let ϕ and ψ be epimorphisms of A on $A/1 \approx A'$ and B on $B/K \approx B'$. Then if L is the group generated by $\{a \otimes b \mid a \in I \text{ or } b \in K\}$, $\phi \otimes \psi$ defines an epimorphism*

$$A \otimes B \to \frac{A \otimes B}{C} \approx \frac{A}{I} \otimes \frac{B}{K}.$$

If ϕ and ψ are isomorphisms, then $\phi \otimes \psi$ is an isomorphism.

We use $[a \otimes b]$, $[a]$, $[b]$ for the elements of $(A \otimes B)/L$, A/I, and B/K respectively. Let $\Sigma\, i_r \otimes b_s + \Sigma\, a_u \otimes k_v$ be a typical element λ of L. Then

$$(\phi \otimes \psi)\lambda = \Sigma\, 0 \otimes [b_s] + \Sigma\, [a_u] \otimes 0 = 0.$$

Therefore,

$$L \subset ker(\phi \otimes \psi). \tag{4.6a}$$

We need this result to be able to define a homomorphism,

$$\theta\colon \frac{A \otimes B}{L} \to \frac{A}{I} \otimes \frac{B}{K}$$

by

$$\theta[a \otimes b] = [a] \otimes [b].$$

Next we turn to (4.4) and identify $(A/I) \times (B/K)$, $(A/I) \otimes (B/K)$, $[A \otimes B]$ with $A \times B$, $A \otimes B$ and C in (4.4b). Moreover h is the bilinear map $h([a] \times [b]) = [a \otimes b]$. This defines h uniquely since if $a - a' = i \in I$, then $h([i] \times [b]) = [a \otimes b - a' \otimes b] = [i \otimes b] = 0$. Therefore a homomorphism $g\colon \frac{A}{I} \otimes \frac{B}{K} \to A \otimes B$ is specified by

$$g([a] \otimes [b]) = h([a] \times [b]) = [a \otimes b] \quad (4.4)$$

and so both $g\theta$ and θg are identity isomorphisms. Hence, $(A \otimes B)/L \approx A/I \otimes B/K$ and $L = ker(\phi \otimes \psi)$.

PROBLEM

6-14. Let A_α and B_β be vector spaces over the common field R with A and B the direct sums $A = \Sigma \oplus A_\alpha$, $B = \Sigma \oplus B_\beta$. Show that $A \otimes B$ is a vector space and that $A \otimes B \approx \oplus_{\alpha,\beta} A_\alpha \otimes B_\beta$.

Lemma 4.7. *If A_0 is a one-dimensional vector space generated by a_0, there is an isomorphism p defined by $p(ra_0) \otimes b = rb$.*

Since a one-dimensional vector space can be regarded as the field itself, the assertion is the expected one. We give the easy proof in some detail to bring out the application of (4.4). Consider the mapping h: $A_0 \times B \to B$ defined by $h((ra_0) \times b) = rb$. Since $\{(ra_0) \times b\}$ constitute the generators of a free group (4.1), h is linear on $A_0 \times B$ to B. Then h maps the elements of M (cf. (4.1)) into 0, and is onto. Moreover h induces p. That p is onto is beyond doubt. We assert $ker\, p = 0$. Suppose, in fact, that

$$p\, \Sigma\, r_i\, a_0 \otimes b_i = \Sigma\, r_i\, b_i = 0.$$

Then,

$$\begin{array}{c} a_0 \otimes \Sigma\, r_i\, b_i = 0 \\ \| \\ \Sigma\, a_0 \otimes r_i\, b_i = \Sigma\, r_i\, a_0 \otimes b_i. \end{array}$$

Example 6-4 shows that the monomorphisms $A_1 \xrightarrow{i} A$ and $C_1 \xrightarrow{j} C$ do not invariably yield a monomorphism $A_1 \otimes C_1 \xrightarrow{i \otimes j} A \otimes C$. This reflects the fact that for non-0 elements of $ker(i \otimes j)$ the relations which in $A \otimes C$ guarantee 0 must involve elements not in $A_1 \otimes C_1$. We establish that for a specific element of $ker\,(i \otimes j)$ only a finite number of relationships of $A \otimes C$, which have been lost in the restriction to $A_1 \otimes C_1$, need be supplied to get 0.

Lemma 4.8. *Suppose A and C are modules and $\Sigma\, a_i \otimes c_i = 0$ in $A \otimes C$. Then there exist finitely generated submodules, $A_1 \supset \{a_i\}$ and $C_1 \supset \{c_i\}$ such that*

$$\Sigma\, a_i \otimes c_i = 0 \quad in \quad A_1 \otimes C_1.$$

By (4.3), $\Sigma_\pi\, a_i \otimes c_i = 0$ implies

$$\Sigma_\pi\, a_i \times c_i \in M. \tag{4.8a}$$

Denote the elements of M by $\{m_j\}$. Then, $\Sigma\, a_i \times c_i = \Sigma_{\pi'}\, m_j$ where the righthand side is a finite sum of elements of M. Each m_j involves, at most, three elements of A and three elements of C. Let A_1 be the module generated by the A elements entering (4.8a) through $\{m_j\}$ and $\{a_i\}$. Similarly, let C_1 be the module generated by the $\{m_j\}$ terms of (4.8a) and $\{c_i\}$. Accordingly, $\Sigma\, a_i \otimes c_i = 0$ in $A_1 \otimes C_1$.

The power of (4.8) lies in the fact that in arguments involving vanishing of a specific element of $A \otimes C$ we may assume that A and C are finitely generated.

Lemma 4.9. *If $\{a_m \mid 1 \leq m \leq p\}$ and $\{b_n \mid 1 \leq n \leq q\}$ are bases for the vector spaces A and B over the field R, then:*

(4.9a) *$\{a_m \otimes b_n\}$ constitutes a basis for the vector space $A \otimes B$;*
(4.9b) *$a \neq 0$, $b \neq 0$, then $a \otimes b \neq 0$.*

Problem 6–14 applies directly to (4.9a). For (4.9b) consider the one dimensional vector spaces including a and b respectively. Since direct sums only are involved, we can apply (4.9a).

Remark. Results somewhat similar to those of (4.7) and (4.9) constitute (113.8).

The following result is related to ideas we shall need in (103.4) and in subsequent sections.

Lemma 4.10. *If $0 \longrightarrow A \xrightarrow{i} B \xrightarrow{j} C \longrightarrow 0$ is an exact sequence of modules over the ring R, and if E is a module over R also, then with 1 the identity isomorphism on E to E,*

(4.10a) $$A \otimes E \xrightarrow{i\otimes 1} B \otimes E \xrightarrow{j\otimes 1} C \otimes E \longrightarrow 0$$

is an exact sequence of modules over R. If A is a direct summand of B, there is exactness in

(4.10b) $$0 \longrightarrow A \otimes E \xrightarrow{i\otimes 1} B \otimes E \xrightarrow{j\otimes 1} C \otimes E \longrightarrow 0.$$

In particular, this is true when A, B, C, and E are vector spaces over the field R.

The exactness of (4.10a) involves straightforward verification using (4.6). Example 6-4 precludes a blanket conclusion of exactness at $A \otimes E$ in (4.10a). If B is the direct sum of A and some module D, then according to (32.2) there is a projection p on B to A and a projection q on B to D with

$$p \otimes 1\colon B \otimes E \approx A \otimes E,$$

$$q \otimes 1\colon B \otimes E \approx D \otimes E.$$

Since pi is the identity and qi annihilates A (32.2),

$$(p \otimes 1)(i \otimes 1) = (pi) \otimes 1$$

is the identity isomorphism of $A \otimes E$ and $(q \otimes 1)(i \otimes 1) = 0$. Apply $p + q = 1$ to infer $ker(i \otimes 1) = 0$.

Since vector spaces are direct sums over a basis (4.10b) applies to them.

Remark. The full exactness assured when A is a direct summand of B appears not only in (4.10b), but has already been noted in (45.5a) and in (45.5b). Actually (4.10b) may be realized under wider conditions, for the crux of the situation is that the elements of finite order alone are responsible for breakdown of exactness at $A \otimes E$. Definition (103.4) bears on this situation.

If K is the simplicial chain complex $\oplus (K_n = C_n(K, J))$ and G is an Abelian group then both K and G are modules over J. *We shall henceforth consider $C_n(K, G)$ to be defined by $K_n \otimes G$.* A derivation d' is defined by $d'(K_n \otimes G) = (dK_n) \otimes G$, so $B_n(K \otimes G) = d'K_n \otimes G$, $Z_n(K \otimes G) = \ker d'_n$. Since, for simplicial chains $Z_n(K, J)$ is a summand of $C_n(K, J)$, $0 \to B_n(K) \otimes G \to Z_n(K) \otimes G \to H_n(K) \otimes G \to 0$, is exact (4.10b), whence

$$\frac{Z_n(K)}{B_n(K)} \otimes G = H_n(K) \otimes G \approx \frac{Z_n(K) \otimes G}{B_n(K) \otimes G}. \tag{4.11}$$

We remark that $H_p(K, J) \otimes G$ is not necessarily isomorphic to $H_p(K \otimes G)$. For instance if $\partial\, {}_4c_{p+1} = t\, {}_2c$, $|t| \neq 1$, then with $G = J_t$, ${}_4c_{p+1} \otimes J_t \in Z(K \otimes J_t)$, yet ${}_4c_{p+1} \otimes J_t \bar{\in} (Z(K)) \otimes J_t$. On the other hand if $G = tJ$, ${}_2c \bar{\in} B(K, J)$ and hence ${}_2c \otimes tJ \bar{\in} B(K, J) \otimes tJ$, yet ${}_2c \otimes tJ \in B(K \otimes tJ)$. The general situation can now be described. Write $G(t) = \{g \mid g = tg', g' \in G\}$, $G[t] = \{g \mid tg = 0\}$.

Lemma 4.12. *For the finite simplicial complex K and the abstract group G,*

(4.12a)

$$H_m(K, G) \approx H_m(K \otimes G) \approx \mathbf{P}_i\, (G(t^i_m)\, {}_2c^i_m) \oplus \mathbf{P}_i(G\, {}_3c^i_m) \oplus \mathbf{P}_k G[t^k_{m-1}]\, {}_4c^k_m.$$

PROBLEM

6-15. Using the paragraph preceding the lemma as a guide, demonstrate (4.12) after first showing

$$Z_m(K \otimes G) = \mathbf{P}_r(G\, {}_1c^r_m) \oplus \mathbf{P}_i(G\, {}_2c^i_m) \oplus \mathbf{P}_j(G\, {}_3c^j_m) \oplus \mathbf{P}_k(G[t^k_{m-1}]\, {}_4c^k_m);$$
$$B_m(K \otimes G) = \mathbf{P}(G\, {}_1c^r_m) \oplus \mathbf{P}(G(t^i_m)\, {}_2c^i_m).$$

Definition 4.13. Let $K = \{K_n, d\}$ and $L = \{L_m, d'\}$ be lower module complexes over the same ring R. Then $K \otimes L = \{K_p \otimes L_q, d\}$ is a double-graded complex

$$K \otimes L = \oplus\, (K_{pq} = K_p \otimes L_q)$$

with boundary operator $\bar{d}$ defined by

$$\bar{d}(e_p \otimes E_q) = d\, e_p \otimes E_q + (-1)^p\, e_p \otimes d'\, E_q.$$

A single-graded augmented complex denoted by $(K \otimes L)$ is defined by

$$(K \otimes L)_n = \Sigma_{p+q=n} K_p \otimes L_q$$

augmented by the ideal element ε_{-1}, so $(K \otimes L)_{-1} \approx R\varepsilon_{-1}$. The upper complex case is covered by using superscripts.

Let $K = \{e^i_p\}$ and $L = \{E^i_q\}$ be lower complexes over the integers. The homomorphism $\psi_{\#}$: $K \to L$ is defined by

$$\psi_{\#}\, e^i_p = \Sigma_j\, a^i_j(p) E^j_p. \tag{4.14a}$$

This extends to a homomorphism on $K \otimes G \to L \otimes G$ for G a group, thus

$$\psi_{\#}(e^i_p \otimes g) = \Sigma\, (a^i_j(p) E^j_p \otimes g)$$

where $e^i_p \otimes g$ corresponds to ge^i_p in our previous notation.

The associated $\psi^{\#}$ is defined by

$$(\psi^{\#}\, F^p(L))\, e_p(K) = F^p(L)(\psi_{\#}\, e_p(K))$$

when $F^p(L)$ is in $Hom(L, G)$. We have

$$\psi^{\#}\, F^p_j = \Sigma\, a^i_j(p) f^p_i. \tag{4.14b}$$

We define a bigraded **mixed** complex $K^* \otimes L = \oplus\, K^m \otimes L_n$ with boundary operator $d = d_1 + d_2$ where d_1 is the operator δ_1 on K^m and $d_2(k^m \otimes l_n) = (-1)^m\, k^m \otimes \partial l_n$, so $d^2 = 0$. It will be convenient sometimes to consider the upper-grade m as equivalent to a lower-grade $-m$. The bigraded complex yields a single-graded complex or total complex according to

$$(K^* \otimes L)_r = \Sigma_{n-m=r} K^m \otimes L_n. \tag{4.14c}$$

The boundary operator d decreases the total grade by 1 and so the total complex is a lower complex.

We fix the symbol for a familiar constant

$$i(m) = (-1)^{\frac{m(m-1)}{2}} \tag{4.14d}$$

We define the **graph** $\Gamma(\psi_{\#})$ of $\psi_{\#}$ as a 0 dimensional chain of $K^* \otimes L$

$$\begin{aligned}\Gamma(\psi_{\#}) &= \Sigma_{i,m}\, i(m) f^m_i \otimes \psi_{\#}\, e^i_m \\ &= \Sigma_{i,j,m}\, i(m) a^i_j(m) f^m_i \otimes E^j_m.\end{aligned} \tag{4.14e}$$

Lemma 4.15. *If $\psi_{\#}$ is a chain map, $\Gamma(\psi_{\#})$ is a 0 cycle.*

This is a straightforward consequence of (22.5) when $d = d_1 + d_2$ is applied to $\Gamma(\psi_{\#})$.

chapter 7

SIMPLICIAL METHODS AND INVERSE AND DIRECT LIMITS

There are several courses open to us in studying the omology theory of spaces. In the simplest case, a space may happily be made up of concrete simplexes. If not, we may still be able to approximate the space by a simplicial complex or triangulations of successively finer mesh. Maps between spaces are then approximated by piecewise linear or simplicial maps. This approach is in the classical tradition, and the approximations lend themselves naturally to applications to problems, say in Analysis. Moreover other omology formulations borrow from this material. For these reasons we turn now to some invariance properties of the omology characteristics of a concrete complex.

By what the French refer to as an abuse of language, we say two simplicial complexes are isomorphic if their simplexes can be put in 1 to 1 correspondence, so that all incidences correspond, and it is then clear the complexes are homeomorphic. The reverse implication is that two homeomorphic complexes can be so subdivided as to become isomorphic. The reverence in which this implication has been held can be judged by the fact that it is referred to as a *Hauptvermutung*, but surprisingly enough, a counterexample has been found recently, so that the long-cherished hope that the topological theory of complexes could be founded on the notion of isomorphic subdivisions must be abandoned.

1. SUBDIVISION. If we subdivide a complex—(21.10), (21.11)—do we get the same or isomorphic homology groups? The answer is "yes." A back prime indicates the first barycentric subdivision below.

Definition 1.1. The homomorphism Sd (for subdivision homomorphism) on $C_n(K) \to C_n('K)$ is defined by Sd $gv_i = gv_i \in C_0('K)$ and by induction

$$\text{(1.1a)} \qquad \text{Sd}\, g\sigma_n = g\Sigma \pm {}'\sigma_n^i = (\sigma_n)\text{Sd}\, \partial g\sigma_n$$

where the sum is taken over all the ordered nondegenerate n simplexes in the subdivision of σ_n. An alternative algorithm to determine whether the sign $+$ or $-$ is affixed to ${}'\sigma_n^i$ is that of (21.1a).

EXAMPLE 7-1. $\text{Sd}\, g\sigma_2 = g((012)(0)(01) + (012)(01)(1) + \cdots$
$- (012)(02)(2) - (012)(0)(02)).$

Sd will generally be used instead of the iterate, also. Thus

$$(\text{Sd})^m\colon \quad C_n(K) \to C_n({}^mK)$$

That is to say Sd is used for the composition

$$C(K) \xrightarrow{\text{Sd}} C('K) \xrightarrow{\text{Sd}} C({}^2K) \longrightarrow$$

Moreover the map associated with Sd is sometimes written *Sd* and is the identity map.

Definition 1.2. Define a correspondence p: $'K \to K$ by choosing for each vertex $'v_i$ any one of the vertices, v_n, in $\sigma('v_i)$, (22.2). If the complexes are concrete, the correspondence is extended to a linear mapping on each closed simplex.

It may be verified at once that one only of the simplexes into which σ is subdivided is mapped into σ. The other simplexes of the subdivision map into lower dimensional faces of σ. (Cf. Figs. 2-5 and 2-6). We define

$$p_\# \, g\, {}'\sigma_m^i = g\sigma_m^i, \qquad \text{if } p\, {}'\sigma_m^i = \sigma_m^i$$

$$p_\# \, {}'\sigma_m^j = 0, \qquad \text{if } p\, {}'\sigma_m^i = \sigma_r, \qquad r \neq m.$$

Unless otherwise indicated we choose a *standard* p defined by $p\pi_l = v_r$, r the end member of the word π_l. In Fig. 2-6 the cross-hatched, or **leading**, triangle maps onto σ and all other triangles map into lower dimensional faces (11.10a).

The degree 0 enters in a special fashion since all 0-chains are perforce cycles. It is therefore desirable to restrict the 0-chains that can be cycles.

Definition 1.3. Introduce an ideal element σ_{-1} as the boundary for every elementary 0-chain; thus $\partial g\, \sigma_0^i = g\sigma_{-1}$, whence $\partial\, \Sigma\, g_i\, \sigma_0^i = (\Sigma\, g_i)\sigma_{-1}$. The sum $\Sigma\, g_i$ is referred to as the **index**, In, of the chain $\Sigma\, g_i\, \sigma_0^i$. Thus a 0-chain is now a cycle only if In $(\Sigma\, g_i\, \sigma_0^i) = 0$.

With the introduction of C_{-1} we refer to the **augmented chain groups**, or **modules**, $\tilde{C}_0(K)$. Similarly we have the **augmented cycle** and **augmented**

homology groups $\tilde{Z}_0(K)$, $\tilde{H}_0(K)$, $\tilde{H}(K)$. Let f^{-1} be the ideal cocycle satisfying $f^{-1}\sigma_{-1} = 1$. The cocycle f^0 defined by $f^0\sigma_0^i = 1$, is now the coboundary δf^{-1}. Hence for connected complexes $\tilde{H}^0(K) = 0$. Henceforth we assume $\psi_\# \sigma_{-1}(K_1) = \sigma_{-1}(K_2)$. This has the consequence that an allowable homomorphism $\psi_\#$ on $\tilde{C}(K_1)$ to $\tilde{C}(K_2)$ preserves the index of a 0 chain. Thus

$$\partial\psi_\# \Sigma g_i\, \sigma_0^i = \Sigma h_r\, \sigma_{-1} = (\Sigma h_r)\sigma_{-1} = \Sigma\psi_\#\, g_i\, \sigma_{-1} = \Sigma g_i\, \sigma_{-1}$$

i.e., $\Sigma g_i = \Sigma h_r$. (Hence the zero homomorphism $\psi_\#$ is *not* allowable on $\tilde{C}(K_1)$ to $\tilde{C}(K_2)$.)

Definition 1.4. For each ${}_1\sigma \in K_1$ let $Q({}_1\sigma)$ be a subcomplex of K_2 with the monotoneity property ${}_1\sigma(i) < {}_1\sigma$ implies $Q\,{}_1\sigma(i) \subset Q\,{}_1\sigma$. Then Q on the simplexes of K_1 to the subcomplexes of K_2 is called a **carrier function**. If L_1 and L_2 are subcomplexes of K_1 and K_2 and ${}_1\sigma \in L_1$ implies $Q({}_1\sigma) \in L_2$, then Q is a carrier function on K_1, L_1 to K_2, L_2. Let $\psi_\#$ be an allowable homomorphism on $C(K_1, L_1)$ to $C(K_2, L_2)$. If for every chain c involving faces of a single simplex ${}_1\sigma$, $\psi_\#(c)$ is a chain involving simplexes in $Q({}_1\sigma)$ alone, then Q is a carrier of $\psi_\#$ and we write $\psi_\#\, {}_1\sigma \subset Q({}_2\sigma)$. (This definition admits ∂ or D as a possible homomorphism $\psi_\#$.) If ψ: $K_1, L_1 \to K_2, L_2$ and $\psi({}_1\sigma) \subset Q({}_1\sigma)$, we again say Q **carries the map** ψ and carries also the induced homomorphism $\psi_\#$. If $Q({}_1\sigma)$ is acyclic, ($H\,Q({}_1\sigma) \approx G$ or, equivalently, $\tilde{H}\,Q({}_1\sigma) = 0$) for all ${}_1\sigma \in K_1$, we say Q is **acyclic**.

Lemma 1.5. *Let K_1 and K_2 be simplicial complexes and let Q be a carrier function. Suppose that $\psi_\#$ and $\theta_\#$ are allowable homomorphisms on $\tilde{C}(K_1)$ to $\tilde{C}(K_2)$. If Q carries both $\psi_\#$ and $\theta_\#$ and Q is acyclic, then $\psi_\# \approx \theta_\#$.*

Define $D\sigma_{-1} = 0 \in C_0(K_2)$. Since indexes of 0 chains are preserved for every $v_i \in K_1$, $1 = \text{In}\, v^i = \text{In}\, \psi_\#\, v^i = \text{In}\, \theta_\#\, v^i$ for every vertex. Hence $\psi_\#\, v^i - \theta_\#\, v^i \in Z(Q(v^i))$, and since $Q(v^i)$ is acyclic, $\psi_\#\, v^i - \theta_\#\, v^i = \partial\, c_1(Q(v^i))$ for some chain c_1 over $Q(v^i)$. Write $D(v^i)$ for $c_1(Qv^i)$. Note that $D(v^i) \subset Q(v^i)$ and $\partial Dv^i + D\partial v^i = \psi_\#\, v^i - \theta_\#\, v^i$. The argument is continued by induction. Thus suppose that D is defined for all chains over the r skeleton K_1^r with

(1.5a) $$D\partial c_r + DDc_r = \theta_\#\, c_r - \psi_\#\, c_r$$

and that Dc_r is a chain on $Q(c_r)$. If K_1^r is a proper subcomplex of K_1 let σ_{r+1} be arbitrary in K_1^{r+1}. Define

(1.5b) $$W = \theta_\#\, g\sigma_{r+1} - \psi_\#\, g\sigma_{r+1} - D\partial g\sigma_{r+1}.$$

Since $Q(\sigma_{r+1}(i)) \subset Q(\sigma_{r+1})$, (1.4), it follows that each term on the righthand side of (1.5b), and hence the chain W, is carried by $Q(\sigma_{r+1})$. By the induction hypothesis

$$\partial D\partial g\sigma_{r+1} = \theta_\#\partial g\sigma_{r+1} - \psi_\#\partial g\sigma_{r+1} - D\;\partial 2\;{}_g\sigma_{r+1}$$

it follows that $\partial W = 0$ so $W \in Z_{r+1}\, Q(\sigma_{r+1})$. Hence by acyclicity there is a chain which we denote by $Dg\sigma_{r+1}$ satisfying

$$W = \partial Dg\sigma_{r+1}.$$

Accordingly, substitution for W in (1.5b) establishes the required property of D for K_1^{r+1}.

Corollary 1.6. *If ψ and θ map each simplex of K_1 (linearly for concrete complexes) into a pair of faces of a common simplex of K_2, then $\psi_\# \simeq \theta_\#$.*

Indeed for each ${}_1\sigma \in K_1$ let $Q({}_1\sigma)$ be the closed simplex containing both $\psi({}_1\sigma)$ and $\theta({}_1\sigma)$. Then (1.5) applies. Simplicial maps of the type in (1.6) are called **contiguous**, or **modifications**.

Theorem 1.7. Sd *is an isomorphism of $H_*(K) \to H_*('K)$ and p_* of*

$$H_*('K) \to H_*(K).$$

We verify at once that Sd and $p_\#$ are allowable homomorphisms on $\tilde{C}_*(K) \to \tilde{C}_*\,'K$ and on $\tilde{C}_*('K) \to \tilde{C}_*(K)$ respectively. Let $i_\#$ and $j_\#$ be the identity isomorphisms of $\tilde{C}_*(K) \to \tilde{C}_*(K)$ and of $\tilde{C}_*('K) \to \tilde{C}_*('K)$. Suppose that $\mathrm{Sd}\, g\sigma_r = g \,\Sigma\, '\sigma_r^i$. Then the homomorphism $p_\#$ satisfies $p_\#\, \mathrm{Sd}\, g\sigma_r = g\sigma_r$ or

(1.7a) $$p_\#\, \mathrm{Sd} = i_\#.$$

Let $'\sigma_r^i \in {}'K$. Let $'\sigma_r^i$ have the vertex scheme $\{(\pi_l) \mid l = 0, \ldots, r;\ (\pi_r) = (0, \ldots, r)\}$. Then $'\sigma_r^i$ arises from the subdivision of σ_r with vertex scheme $v_0, \ldots, v_r$. Since $p_\#\, g\, '\sigma_r^i$ is either 0 or $g\sigma_r^i$, it follows that both $j_\#\, g\, '\sigma_r^i$ and $\mathrm{Sd}\, p_\#\, g\, '\sigma_r^i$ are on $Sd\ \sigma_r$ which is an acyclic subcomplex of K. Indeed note first that the simplexes in $Sd\ \sigma_r$ are all part of one complex, $Cl\ St((\sigma_r), {}^1L)$, where ${}^1L$ is the barycentric subdivision of σ_r and (σ_r) indicates the barycenter of σ_r. Suppose that $z_r = \Sigma r_i\, {}^1\sigma_r^i$, ${}^1\sigma_r^i \in \mathrm{Sd}\ \sigma_r$, is a cycle on $Sd\ \sigma_r$. Then, borrowing the idea used in (33.2), write $(\sigma_r)z_p = \Sigma r_i\, (\sigma_r)\, {}^1\sigma_p^i = c_{p+1} + d_{p+1}$ where all the degenerate simplexes enter the chain d_{p+1}. Then $\partial((\sigma_r)z_p) = c_{p+1} + d_{p+1} = z_p$. We now throw out all degenerate simplexes and arrive at

$$\partial c_{p+1} = z_p.$$

Thus every p-dimensional cycle on $Sd\ \sigma_r$ is bounding. Hence by (1.5)

(1.7b) $$\mathrm{Sd}\, p_\# \simeq j_\#.$$

In consequence of (1.7a) and (1.7b) we have $\mathrm{Sd}_*\, p_* = j_*$, $p_*\, \mathrm{Sd}_* = i_*$ where i_* and j_* represent the identity isomorphisms. The assertions of (1.7) follow, for according to the first Sd_* is onto and p_* is a monomorphism while according to the second p_* is onto and Sd_* is a monomorphism.

An alternate proof based on (63) is given in (84.2).

PROBLEMS

7-1. If Q is an acyclic carrier on K_1, L_1 to K_2, L_2, show that there is an allowable homomorphism $\psi_\#$ carried by Q. *Hint:* Use an induction argument assuming $\psi_\#$ known on the $m-1$ skeleton. $\psi_\#$ can be defined on σ_m since $\psi_\# \partial\sigma_m$ is an $m-1$-cycle on $Q(\sigma_m)$ and acyclicity of $Q(\sigma_m)$ yields an m chain c_m which can be used for $\psi_\#\sigma_m$.

7-2. If the acyclic carrier Q in the preceding problem carries a chain homotopy D, and if the simplexes in $Q(\sigma_m)$ are of dimension $\leq m$, then the allowable homomorphism $\psi_\#$ is unique; that is, $D\sigma_m = 0$.

2. PAIRING AND KRONECKER INDEX.

Definition 2.1. Let R_1, R_2, and R be three Abelian groups and suppose that ψ is a homomorphism on $R_1 \otimes R_2$ to R which is linear (or bihomomorphic) in each factor separately. Such a homomorphism **pairs** R_1 and R_2 to R or is a **product** on R_1 and R_2 with values in R, and we write $\psi(r_1 \otimes r_2)$ as $r_1 \times r_2$ or simply $r_1 r_2$ so that $r_1 \times (r_2 + r_2') = r_1 \times r_2 + r_1 \times r_2'$ and $(r_1 + r_1') \times r_2 = r_1 \times r_2 + r_1' \times r_2$. The product or pairing is **commutative** if $r_1 r_2 = r_2 r_1$. It is **orthogonal** if $r_1 r_2 = 0$ for all r_2 in R_2 implies $r_1 = 0$ and $r_1 r_2 = 0$ for all r_1 in R_1 implies $r_2 = 0$. Unless otherwise stated *pairing shall be understood in the sense of commutative, orthogonal pairing.*

Remark. A common pairing is in the case $R_1 = R_2 = R$ is a ring or field. When R_1 is a group and R_2 is its character group (129.2), then the pairing is naturally commutative since R_1 can, on its part, be considered the character group of R_2 and hence $r_1(r_2) = r_2(r_1)$. However for proper perspective even beyond the cases of interest to us, to ensure formal commutativity it is not necessary that the products in both directions have *a priori* definitions, since if $r_2 r_1$ had no natural definition we could ascribe to it the value $r_1 r_2$.

If the cells of K are say $\{e_p^i\}$, then the chain group over R_1 is $C_p(K, J) \otimes R_1$, and has the elementary chains $\{e_p^i \otimes R_1\}$ or $\{r_1 e_p^i\}$. Then $C^p(K, R_2) = Hom(C_p(K, J), R_2)$ and the elementary cochains are $\{r_2 f_i^p\}$.

Symbolically nothing is more natural than to write

$$f(rc) = rfc, \qquad r \in R \tag{2.2a}$$

for f a cochain and c a chain, but of course the left side is not defined unless r is an integer. The extension of the interpretation of (2.2a) is an accomplishment of the Kronecker index.

Definition 2.2. Let R_1 and R_2 be Abelian groups paired to R. Let $\{ge_p^i\}$ be the elementary chains on the cell complex K, L and suppose f_i^p is the cochain associated with e_p^i (46.2). The **Kronecker index** In, of the cochain f^p and the chain c_p, where $f^p = \Sigma\ {}_2g^i f_i^p$ and $c_p = \Sigma\ {}_1g_j\, e_p^j$, is a member of R.

(2.2b) $$\begin{aligned}\text{In}\,(f^p, c_p) &= \Sigma\ {}_2g^i\ {}_1g_j\ \delta_i^j i(-p) = i(-p)\ \Sigma\ {}_2g^j\ {}_1g_j \\ &= (-1)^p\ \text{In}\,(c_p, f^p)\end{aligned}$$

Thus the Kronecker index is a pairing

$$\text{In: } Hom(C_p(K), R_2) \otimes (C_p(K) \otimes R_1) \to R.$$

It is understood that either finite cochains or finite chains occur so that the sum in (2.2b) is over a finite set.

The restriction to absolute chains or cochains is not essential. Thus we may require that $\{r_1\, e_p^j\}$ constitute the basis for the chains $C_p(K, L;\ R_1) = C_p(K, L, \text{J}) \otimes R_1$ where L is a closed subcomplex of K and then require that $r_2 f_i^p$ be the elementary cochains for $C^p(K - L, R_2)$, with $f_i^p\, e_p^j = \delta_i^j$.

Remark. Another view of the Kronecker index is that of the analogue of a scalar product or contraction of a contravariant vector c and a covariant vector f.

Remark. Suppose that ${}_1f^0$ is the unit cochain; that is, $f^0(e_0^i) = 1$ for all i. Then with finite chains

$$\text{In}(f^0, \Sigma g_i\, e_0^i) = \Sigma g_i,$$

which has been used as the definition of the index of a zero chain (1.3).

Lemma 2.3. In $(df^p, c_{p+1}) = (-1)^p$ In (f^p, dc_{p+1}), *where* $f^p \in C^p(K - L, R_2)$, $c_{p+1} \in C_{p+1}(K, L, R_1)$.

It is sufficient to prove this for the elements of a base. Denote the typical elementary chains of $C_p(K, L, R_1)$ by $[r_1\, e_p^i] \in C_p(K, L, R_1) = C_p(K, R_1)/C_p(L, R_1)$—(43.2a)—and the cochains by $r_2 f_i^p$. Then since L is closed $d[c_p^i] = [dc_p^i]$, and

$$dr_2 f_j^p = \Sigma\ \eta_j^i(p+1) r_2 f_i^{p+1}$$

$$dr_1[e_{p+1}^m] = [r_1\, de_{p+1}^m] = \Sigma\ \eta_i^m(p+1)[e_p^i].$$

Since f^p vanishes on chains in L it is significant on the classes $[c_p^i]$ only.

$$\begin{aligned}\text{In}\,(r_2\, df_j^p,\ [r_1\, e_{p+1}^m]) &= i(-(p+1))\,\Sigma\ \eta_j^i(p+1)\ \delta_i^m r_2\, r_1 \\ &= i(-(p+1))\,\Sigma\ \eta_j^m(p+1) r_2\, r_1\end{aligned}$$

$$\text{In}\,(f_j^p,\ [de_{p+1}^m]) = i(-p)\,\Sigma\ \eta_i^m(p+1)\ \delta_j^i = i(-p)\,\Sigma\ \eta_j^m\ r_2\, r_1$$

Since $\dfrac{i\,(-\,(p+1))}{i(-p)} = (-1)^p$, the lemma follows.

We assume tacitly throughout this section that $f^p \in C^p(K - L, R_2)$ and $c_p \in C_p(K, L, R_1)$.

Lemma 2.4. *If* f^p *is a cocycle and* z_p *is a cycle such that either* $f^p \sim 0$ *or* $z_p \sim 0$, *then* $\mathrm{In}\,(f^p, z_p) = 0$.

Indeed

$$\mathrm{In}\,(df^{p-1}, z_p) = (-1)^p\,\mathrm{In}\,(f^{p-1}, 0) = 0.$$

Lemma 2.5. *If* $f^p \in Z^p$ *and* $z_q \in Z_q$ *then* $\mathrm{In}\,(f^p, z_p) = \mathrm{In}\,(\mathbf{f}^p, \mathbf{z}_p)$.

Thus with $'f^p - f^p = \delta f^{p-1}$ and $_1z_p - z_p = \partial c_{p+1}$ (2.4) yields $\mathrm{In}\,(f^p, z_p) = \mathrm{In}\,(f^p, {}_1z_p) = \mathrm{In}\,('f^p, {}_1z_p)$.

Theorem 2.6. *The Kronecker index induces a pairing on the groups* $H_p(K, L, R_1)$ *and* $H^p(K - L, R_2)$ *to* R.

This is the consequence of (2.4) and of (2.5).

Suppose that $R_1 = R_2 = R$ is a field but maintain the notation R_1 to indicate possible generalizations. For convenience write g for an element of R_1 and h for an element of R_2.

Lemma 2.7. *If* $\mathrm{In}\,(f^p, z_p) = 0$ *for every* $z_p \in Z_p(K, L;\ R_1)$, *then*

$$f^p \in B^p(K - L, R_2).$$

If $\mathrm{In}\,(f^p, z_p) = 0$ *for every* $f^p \in Z^p(K - L, R_2)$, *then* $z_p \in B_p(K, L, R_1)$.

Write $g[c_p^i]$ for an elementary chain and

$$f^p = \Sigma\, h^j f_j^p \in C^p(K - L, R_2).$$

Suppose that

$$z_p = \Sigma\, g_i[c_p^i] \in Z_p(K, L, R_1).$$

Then $0 = \partial z_p = \Sigma g_i\, \eta_r^i(p)[c_{p-1}^r]$, and so

$$\Sigma g_i\, \eta_r^i(p) = 0 \tag{2.7a}$$

for every r. By hypothesis

$$\Sigma g_i\, h^i = 0. \tag{2.7b}$$

Define $f^{p-1} = \Sigma \lambda^s f_s^{p-1}$ by $\Sigma \lambda^s \eta_s^i = h^i$. A sufficient condition for existence of a solution $\{\lambda^s\}$ of this system is: if $\{g_i\}$ satisfies $\Sigma g_i\, h^i = 0$, then $\Sigma g_i\, \eta_s^i = 0$. However this is precisely the statement in (2.7a) and (2.7b).

We assert $f^p = \delta f^{p-1}$. Indeed with f_i^p referring to elementary cochains,

$$\begin{aligned}(\delta f^{p-1})[c_p^i] &= f^{p-1}\,\partial[c_p^i] \\ &= \Sigma f^{p-1}\,\eta_r^i(p)[c_{p-1}^r] \\ &= \Sigma\lambda^s\,\eta_r^i(p) f_s^{p-1}[c_{p-1}^r] \\ &= \Sigma\lambda^s\,\eta_r^i(p)\,\delta_s^r \\ &= \Sigma\lambda^s\,\eta_s^i(p) = h^i\end{aligned}$$

Lemma 2.8. *If R_1 and R_2 are orthogonally paired and if* In $(f^p, z_p) = 0$ *for every $z_p \in B_p$ then $f^p \in Z^p$.*

Thus

$$\text{(2.8a)} \qquad \text{In}\,(f^p, dc_{p+1}) = 0 = \text{In}\,(df^p, c_{p+1}).$$

Suppose that $df^p = f^{p+1} = \Sigma_j h^j f_j^{p+1}$. Then fix i and let g_i be any element of R.

$$\text{In}\,(f^{p+1}, g_i\, e_{p+1}^i) = \Sigma_j h^j g_i\, \delta_j^i = h^i g_i = 0$$

implies $h^i = 0$ since R_1 and R_2 are orthogonally paired. Hence $f^{p+1} = 0$. Accordingly (2.8a) demands $df^p = 0$.

3. NERVES. Certain abstract complexes arise in the description of the mutual intersections of the sets in a cover of a space.

Definition 3.1. Let $\alpha = \{a_j \mid j \in J\}$ be a cover of a space X. To each element a_i associate an abstract element, referred to as a **vertex** (a_i). If $\bigcap_\pi a_i \neq \varnothing$ associate the abstract simplex with vertices $\{(a_i) \mid i \in \pi\}$. The complex thus obtained is referred to as the **nerve** of α and is designated by the small corresponding Latin letter. Thus the nerve of α is a, that of β is b, etc. A natural open cover for a concrete complex is $\alpha = \{a_i = St(v^i, K) \mid v^i$ a vertex of $K\}$ and is referred to as the **star cover**.

If X_0 is a subset of X, we can define an algebraically closed subcomplex ${}_0a$ of a by the requirement that a simplex $\{(a_i) \mid i \in \pi\} \in {}_0a$ if $\bigcap_\pi a_i \cap X_0 \neq \varnothing$. Further developments will be found in (82).

If $\beta = \{b_i\}$ refines α (**A7**), that is, $\alpha < \beta$, a projection $p_a{}^b$ on b to a is defined by $p_a{}^b(b_i) = (a_j)$ where $a_j \supset b_i$. In general, for α and β fixed there may be several distinct projections. Evidently projections are transitive in the sense that if $\alpha < \beta < \gamma$ then $p_a{}^b p_b{}^g$ is a projection $p_a{}^g$. This is sometimes referred to as a **matching** condition.

Lemma 3.2. *If α is the star cover of K then a is isomorphic to K.*

In view of (3.2) we can identify (a_i) with the vertex v^i of K.

Remark. The nerve a reflects the finite intersection relations of α. (There would be advantage to defining infinite dimensional simplexes when more than a finite number of elements a_i have a common intersection.) For our purposes the covers will invariably be open covers or closed covers.

4. INVARIANCE. If K_1 and K_2 are different triangulations of a space then K_2 **refines** K_1, written $K_1 < K_2$, if the star cover α_2 of K_2 refines the star cover α_1 of K. Let K_1 have the vertices $\{v_i\}$ and K_2, $\{w_j\}$. A **projection** $p_1{}^2$: $K_2 \to K_1$, $K_2 > K_1$ is defined by $p_1{}^2\, w_i = v_j$ only if

$$St(w_i, K_2) \subset St(v_j, K_1). \tag{4.1a}$$

Theorem 4.2. *The homology groups of a finite complex are independent of mode of triangulation.*

Denote the nth barycentric subdivision of K by ${}^nK$. Let K_1 and K_2 be two triangulations. If neither refines the other a Lebesgue number argument (**A**) shows some subdivision $K_3 = {}^nK_1$ refines both. Since

$$\begin{array}{ccc} H(K_3) & \approx & H(K_1) \\ \wr\wr & & \\ H(K_2) & & \end{array}$$

would imply $H(K_1) \approx H(K_2)$, we may assume that $K_2 > K_1$. If $K_2 = {}^nK_1$ then Sd_*, the identity, establishes the desired result. In the general case for some n and m we have $K_1 < K_2 < {}^nK_1 < {}^mK_2$. Then let q, ${}^np$, ${}^m_nq$ be the projections on $K_2 \to K_1$, ${}^nK_1 \to K_2$, and ${}^mK_2$ to ${}^nK_1$ respectively. By the transitive property for projections, $q\,{}^np$ is a projection on ${}^nK_1$ to K_1, so (1.7) applies. Thus $(q\,{}^np)_*$ is an isomorphism. Similarly $({}^np\,{}^m_nq)_*$ is an isomorphism. Hence ${}^np_*$ is an isomorphism. Thus

$$H({}^nK_1) \approx H(K_2)$$

and therefore since Sd_* is an isomorphism (1.7),

$$H(K_1) \approx H(K_2).$$

Arguments involving concrete simplexes and their mapping or boundary properties will not be affected by a homeomorphism.

Definition 4.3. We say a pair of spaces X, A with $A \subset X$ is a **triangulable pair** (22.17) if some homeomorphism h of X on $|K|$ maps A onto $|L| \subset |K|$, where K is a concrete finite simplicial complex. Thus K admits an affine geometry on each simplex. $|K|$ retains this property and has besides a Euclidean metric. No differentiable homeomorphism h need exist but for our purposes the triangulable space X can replace K (similarly for pairs) and if ψ: $X, A \to X', A'$ the transition to the underlying complexes needs only the interpretation $h'\psi h^{-1}$.

Definition 4.4. If X is triangulable then $H(X)$ is defined as $H(K)$ for an arbitrary triangulation of X.

Remark. We are asking for faith on the part of the reader. It is only with the invariance theorem (111.11) or as an inference from (112.2) that we can justify identifying $H(X)$ and $H(K)$.

5. SIMPLICIAL APPROXIMATION. **Definition 5.1.** Let K_1 and K_2 be concrete simplicial complexes with $\sigma(z)$ the simplex containing z. Let ϕ map $K_1 = \{x\}$ into $K_2 = \{y\}$ in such a way that vertices go into vertices and ϕ is linear on each simplex so that simplexes map onto simplexes. Such a map is **simplicial** on K_1 to K_2. For instance, if $\{v^i \mid i = 0, \ldots, n\}$ constitute the vertices of $\sigma(x)$, x can be represented as $\Sigma\, \lambda_i\, v^i$ where $\{\lambda_i \mid i = 0, \ldots, n\}$ are the barycentric coordinates of x. Then $\phi(x) \in \sigma(\phi(x))$ has the representation $\Sigma\lambda_i\, \phi(v^i)$. If $\phi(v^i) = \phi(v^j)$, $j \in \pi_i$, $\Sigma_{\pi_i}\, \lambda_j$ is the barycentric coordinate relative to $\phi(v^i)$. The simplicial map Ψ is a **simplicial approximation** to the map ψ of $|K_1|$ to $|K_2|$, if $\Psi(x) \in \overline{\sigma(\psi(x))}$. Though Ψ is on K_1 to K_2 we shall often identify it with the induced map on $|K_1|$ to $|K_2|$.

PROBLEM

7-3. Show that Ψ is a simplicial approximation to ψ on $|K_1|$ to $|K_2| \Leftrightarrow \psi St(v, K_1) \subset St(\Psi v, K_2)$ for every vertex $v \in K_1$.

Lemma 5.2. *If K_1 and K_2 are finite simplicial complexes and ψ: $|K_1| \to |K_2|$, then for some subdivision ${}^mK_1$ there is a simplicial approximation Ψ defined on ${}^mK_1$ to K_2 and $\Psi \simeq \psi$.*

Denote the vertices of K_2 by $\{y^i\}$. Let $\alpha = \{\psi^{-1}(St(y^i, K_2) = a_i)\}$ be a cover of $|K_1|$. For m sufficiently large $\beta = \{b_i = St(v^i, {}^mK_1), v^i$ a vertex of ${}^mK_1\}$ refines α. This occurs when the diameters of the sets b_i are inferior to the Lebesque number $d(\alpha)$, (A). Define ψ on the vertices of ${}^mK_1$ to K_2 by $\Psi(v^i) = y^j$ if $\psi(b_i) \subset a_j$. Extend the mapping linearly over each simplex of ${}^mK_1$ as described in (5.1).

A homotopy can be defined moving $\Psi(x)$ to $\psi(x)$ along the unique segment path $[\Psi(x), \psi(x)]$ since this segment lies entirely in $\overline{\sigma(\psi(x))}$, $h(x, t) = (1 - t)\psi(x) + t\Psi(x)$.

Restrictions to finite concrete simplicial complexes in mapping problems are usually made to ensure compactness. Let Ψ_1, Ψ_2 be simplicial approximations to ψ on the same subdivision K to L. Since $\Psi_1(x) \cup \Psi_2(x) \in \sigma\psi(x)$, Ψ_1 and Ψ_2 are contiguous (1.6) and so $\Psi_{1*} = \Psi_{2*}$.

Lemma 5.3. *If ψ is a map of the triangulable space X to the triangulable space Y, any two simplicial approximations Ψ_1 and Ψ_2 induce the same homomorphism on $H(X)$ to $H(Y)$.*

Let Ψ_1: $K_1 \to L_1$ and Ψ_2: $K_2 \to L_2$ be simplicial approximations to ψ on the indicated triangulations. Let L_3 refine both L_1 and L_2 and let K_3 be a common refinement of K_1 and K_2 for which a simplicial approximation on K_3 to L_3 exists. The vertices of K_1, K_2, and K_3 are $\{v^i\}$, $\{w^j\}$ and $\{u^k\}$, and those of L_1, L_2, L_3 are $\{r^i\}$, $\{s^j\}$, $\{t^k\}$. The projection $p_n{}^m$ is on K_m to K_n, while $P_n{}^m$ is on L_m to L_n, $m > n$, $m, n = 1, 2, 3$. $p_n{}^m{}_*$, $P_n{}^m{}_*$ are isomorphisms (61.7), a fact important for us below.

We remark that $\Psi_1 p_1{}^3$, $\Psi_2 p_2{}^3$, $P_i{}^3$, Ψ_3 are simplicial maps. Thus

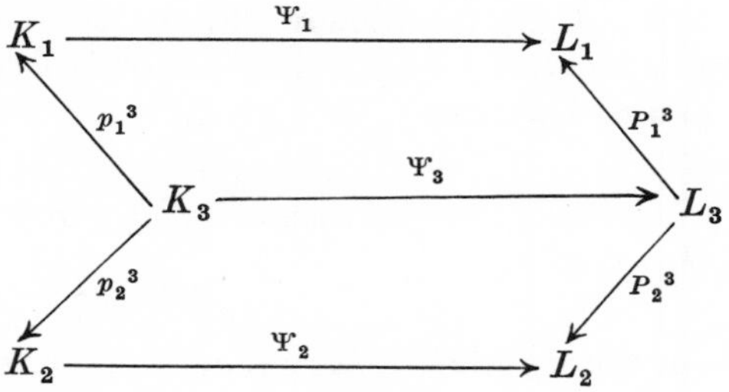

Moreover

$$St(u^i, K_3) \subset St(p_1{}^3\, u^i = v^j, K_1). \tag{5.3a}$$

Since Ψ is a simplicial approximation to ψ,

$$\psi\, St(v^j, K_1) \subset St(\Psi_1\, v^j, L_1)$$

whence by (5.3a)

$$\psi\, St(u^i, K_3) \subset St(\Psi_1\, p_1{}^3\, u^i, L_1).$$

Hence $\Psi_1\, p_1{}^3$ is a simplicial approximation to ψ on K_3 to L_1. Similarly $\Psi_2\, p_2{}^3$ is a simplicial approximation to ψ on K_3 to L_2. Also

$$\psi\, St(u^i, K_3) \subset St(\Psi_3\, u^i, L_3) \subset St(P_1{}^3\, \Psi_3\, u^i, L_1).$$

Hence $P_1{}^3\,\Psi_3$ and $P_2{}^3\,\Psi_3$ are simplicial approximations to ψ on K_3 to L_1 and to L_2 respectively. Then by the remark above,

$$\Psi_{1*}\, p_{1*}^{3} = (\Psi_1\, p_1{}^3)_* = (P_1{}^3\, \Psi_3)_* = P_{1*}^{3}\, \Psi_{3*}.$$

Similarly $\Psi_{2*}\, p_{2*}^{3} \approx P_{2*}^{3}\, \Psi_{3*}$. Thus, using (4.3), $\Psi_{2*} \approx \Psi_{3*} \approx \Psi_{1*}$.

Lemma 5.4. *Let ψ, λ be maps on $|K_1|$ to $|K_2|$. Then $\varepsilon > 0$ exists such that for all λ satisfying $d(\psi, \lambda) < \varepsilon$, $\psi_* = \lambda_*$ when K_1 and K_2 are concrete finite simplicial complexes.*

$|K_1|$ is a compact subset of some Euclidean space. Let the finite open cover $\{St(v^i, K_2)\}$ be shrunk to $\{U_i\}$, (A, 13.2), thus $U_i \subset \bar{U}_i \subset St(v^i, K_2)$. Let L consist of the isolated vertices of K_2 so for these $St(v^i, K_2) = v^i$, and let

$$\delta = inf_{v^i \epsilon L}\, d(v^i, K_2 - v^i).$$

Since K_2 is a finite complex, δ is positive. For a suitable subdivision of K_1, again denoted by K_1, with vertex scheme $\{w_j^i\}$, the cover $St(w_j^i, K_1)$ refines $\{\psi^{-1} U_i\}$. For $v^i \bar{\epsilon} L$,

$$d(\bar{U}_i, K_2 - St\,(v^i, K_2)) = \eta_i > 0.$$

Denote by η the smallest of $\{\eta_i\}$ and choose a positive number ρ smaller than either η or δ. If $d(\psi, \lambda) = \inf_{x \epsilon K_1} (\psi(x), \lambda(x)) < \rho$, then when $\psi\, St(v_j, K_1) \subset U_i$, $\lambda\, St(v_j, K_1) \subset St(V_i, K_2)$. Accordingly, Ψ, the simplicial map defined by the vertex correspondence $v_j \to V_i$, is simultaneously a simplicial approximation both to ψ and to λ whence $f_* = \psi_* = \lambda_*$.

Theorem 5.5. *If $f \simeq g$ on $|K_1|$ to $|K_2|$ where K_i is a finite concrete simplicial complex, $i = 1, 2$, then $f_* = g_*$.*

Let h_t define the homotopy, that is, $h_0 = f$, $h_1 = g$. For each t, let $\rho_t > 0$ satisfy (5.4) for h_t, playing the role of ψ in that lemma. By continuity, for some positive ρ_{t_0}, $d(h_{t_0}, h_t) < \rho_{t_0}$ for $|t - t_0| < \delta_{t_0}$. The intervals $(I_{t_0} = \{t |\, t - t_0| < \delta_{t_0}\})$, with t_0 taking on all values in the set $0 \leq t_0 \leq 1$, cover I. Hence for t_0 restricted to some ordered finite set $\{t_i\}$, $\{I_{t_i}\}$ is a cover of I. Thus $h_{t*} = h_{t_i *}$ for $t \epsilon I_{t_i}$, and hence since adjacent intervals overlap and I is connected; h_{t*} is independent of t for $t \epsilon I$.

PROBLEM

7-4. Prove $\tilde{H}_* (\overline{St(v, K)}, G) = 0$ for v a vertex of the finite simplicial complex K.

6. IMBEDDING. Shrinking a space onto an imbedded subspace has important consequences. If through each point of the enveloping space there is a unique path leading to the imbedded space, a natural shrinking or deformation moves points along these paths, assuming it is possible to do this in some uniform manner to ensure continuity. In the case of complexes, for instance, imbedding in a shrinkable neighborhood allows replacing cycles mod a subcomplex L by those mod the neighborhood of L.

Definition 6.1. Let L be a subcomplex of the concrete complex K. Then with $\{v^i\}$ the vertices of L, the **normal neighborhood (regular neighborhood)**

of L in K is denoted by $N(L)$ and is defined by

$$N(L) = \bigcup_{v^i \in L} |\mathrm{St}(v^i, K)|.$$

Then with ${}^mK$, ${}^mL$ the mth barycentric subdivisions, define $N^m(L)$ as the normal neighborhood of ${}^mL$ in ${}^mK$; that is, $N({}^mL) \subset {}^mK$. $\|N(L)\|$ denotes the closed neighborhood.

Definition 6.2. The **hull** of L in K—written $\hat{L}$—is the minimal closed complex in K, containing vertices of L alone. If the hull of L coincides with L then L is **total**.

Lemma 6.3. *If L is total in K, $|L|$ is a strong deformation retract of $N(L)$.*

For an arbitrary point $x \in N(L)$, $\sigma(x)$ has vertices $\{v^i\}$ of which $\{v^i \mid i \in \pi\}$ alone are in L so that x has the barycentric coordinates $\{\lambda_i\}$ with respect to $\{v^i\}$. The *normal* projection of x is defined by

$$rx = \{\lambda_i / \Sigma_\pi \lambda_k \mid i \in \pi\} \cup \{\lambda_j = 0 \mid j \bar{\in} \pi\}.$$

Then

(6.3a) $$h(x, t) = trx + (1 - t)x$$

defines a strong deformation retraction on $N(L)$ to $|L|$.

Lemma 6.4. *If $L \subset K$, then the barycentric subdivision $'L$ is total in $'K$.*

The vertex (π_l) of $'L$ enters only when the simplex $\sigma^{\pi_l} \in L$ (21.1). Suppose that $(\pi_0), \ldots, (\pi_l)$ constitute the vertices in $'L$ of a simplex $'\sigma$ in $'K$; then $'\sigma$ must be part of a subdivision of σ^{π_l} and hence $'\sigma \in {}'L$.

Theorem 6.5. *$|L|$ is a strong deformation retract of $\|N^m(L)\|$ for $m \geq 2$.*

This asserts more than (6.3) in that the point set closure (21.7) of the normal neighborhood enters. Suppose that L is total then $\sigma_n \in N(L)$ implies σ_n is the join $\sigma_{m-1}\,\sigma_{n-m}$ with $\sigma_{m-1} \in L$ and $\sigma_{n-m} \in K - L$. Suppose that $'\sigma \in N('L)$. Let $\sigma \in K$ be the unique simplex containing $'\sigma$. Let (π_l) be a vertex of $'\sigma$ in $'L$. Then the face σ^{π_l} of σ is in L and $\sigma \in N(L)$ by (6.1). No two vertices of K can be vertices of a simplex in $'K$ so $\|'\sigma\| \subset |\sigma| \cup |L|$, whence $N('L) \subset N(L)$. Suppose now that $x \in \|N('L)\|$. If the maximal value of the barycentric coordinates of a point $x \in \|N(L)\|$ is taken on for a vertex in L, then $x \in \|N('L)\|$ and conversely. If the maximal value is assumed for two vertices, one in L and one not in L, then x is in the boundary of $N('L)$. Since all coordinates with respect to L vertices increase with t under the deformation (6.3a) it follows that $x \in \|N('L)\|$ guarantees that the entire deformation path is in $\|N('L)\|$.

Even if L is not total, $'L$ is, so it has been shown that $\|{}^2L\|$ is a strong deformation retract of $\|N^2(L)\|$ and more generally that $\|L\|$ is a strong deformation retract of $\|N^m(L)\|$, $m \geq 2$.

Remark. The ideas extend to the case that $|L|$ is now any closed subset of $|K|$. Thus now

$$N(L) = \bigcup_{\|\sigma^i\| \cap |L| \neq \phi} |\sigma^i|$$

and is open since $|\sigma^i|$ is open.

$$N^m(L) = \bigcup_{\|\sigma^i\| \cap |L| \neq \phi} \{|\sigma^i| \mid \sigma^i \in {}^mK\}.$$

7. INVERSE AND DIRECT SYSTEMS. **Definition 7.1.** Let A be a directed set $\{A, <\}$. Let $\{S_a \mid A\}$ be a collection of topological spaces. Suppose $p_a{}^b$, $a < b$ is a map of $S_b \to S_a$ such that **(a)** $p_a{}^a$ is the identity map and **(b)** $p_a{}^c = p_a{}^b \cdot p_b{}^c$ for $a < b < c$. (Note the order "from" "to" on $p_a{}^b$ is backward, i.e., $p \swarrow$). Then $\{S_a, p_a{}^b\}$ is an **inverse system of spaces** and the **inverse limit** $\underleftarrow{\text{L}}\, S_a = S^-$ or $S^-(A)$ is the subset of $\Pi_A S_a$ consisting of functions $\{s(a \mid A)\}$ satisfying the **matching condition** $s(a) = p_a{}^b\, s(b)$ for any $a < b$. Denote by $\Gamma_a{}^b$ the *graph* $\{(s(a), s(b)) \mid p_a{}^b\, s(b) = s(a)\}$ in $S_a \times S_b$. Thus an equivalent definition of S^- is $\bigcap \Gamma_a{}^b \times \Pi_{c \neq a,b} S_c$. The topology of S^- is that induced by $\Pi_A S_a$. $s\,(a)$ is the a-**coordinate** of $s \in S^-$. S^- may be empty.

Example 7-2. A topological product $\Pi_A S_a$ may be looked upon as an inverse limit. With π a finite subset of A, and the inclusion ordering on $\{\pi\}$, let $T_\pi = \Pi_\pi S_a$ be the collection of functions t_π on $\{\pi\}$ with coordinate values $t_\pi(a) \in S_a$. Define $r_{\pi'}{}^\pi\, t_\pi$ as the restriction of t_π to the domain π' where $\pi' < \pi$. For instance if A is the ordered set of integers and $\pi = 3, 5, 7, 8$, $\pi' = 3, 8$. Then $r_{\pi'}{}^\pi\, t_\pi = t_{\pi'}$ is a function on 3, 8 with values those of t_π on 3 and on 8. Then $\underleftarrow{\text{L}}\{T_\pi, r_{\pi'}{}^\pi\} = \Pi_A S_a$.

Example 7-3. If the subsets $\{S_a\}$ of a topological space S are simply ordered by inverse inclusion so $a < b$ with $S_b \subset S_a$, and if $p_a{}^b$ is the inclusion map S_b to S_a then, $\bigcap S_a$ is homeomorphic to $\underleftarrow{\text{L}}\{S_a, p_a{}^b\}$.

Lemma 7.2. *If G_a is an Abelian topological group and $p_a{}^b$ is a homomorphism, then $\Sigma^- = \{G_a, p_a{}^b\}$ is an inverse system of groups. $\underleftarrow{\text{L}}\, G_a$ is a group G^- with elements g under the composition law $g + g' = \{g(a) + g'(a)\}$ where $g = \{g(a)\}$ and $g' = \{g'(a)\}$ are in G^-.*

Consistency follows from $p_a{}^b(g(b) + g'(b)) = g(a) + g'(a)$ (7.16).

Remark. If the cardinal $|A|$ is at least $\aleph_1$, $p_a{}^b$ may be an epimorphism whenever $a < b$ and yet $\underleftarrow{\mathsf{L}}\, \{S_a, p_a{}^b\} = \varnothing$ or in the case of Abelian groups, $\underleftarrow{\mathsf{L}}\, \{G_a, p_a{}^b\} = 0$.

PROBLEM

7-5. Let $\Sigma^- = \{S_a, p_a{}^b\}$ be an inverse system of compact spaces ordered by inverse inclusion. Let $Y_a = \{s(a) \mid s \in S^-\} \subset S_a$ that is to say Y_a, consists of the ath coordinates of points in S^-. Let U_a be an open set in S_a containing Y_a. Show for some b, $a < b$, $p_a{}^b S_b \subset U_a$.

Definition 7.3. Let A be a directed set, G_a a discrete Abelian group, and $p_a{}^b$ a homomorphism on $G_a \to G_b$, $a < b$, satisfying (**a**) $p^a{}_a$ is the identity isomorphism and (**b**) $p^b{}_c\, p^a{}_b = p^a{}_c$ for $a < b < c$. (Here the "from" "to" order on p is forward, i.e., $p \searrow$). Then $\{G;\ p^a{}_b\}$ is a **direct system**. Let $g_b \sim g_c$ if for some d following b and c, $p^b{}_d\, g(b) = p^c{}_d\, g(c)$. Then the elements of the **direct limit**, written $\underrightarrow{\mathsf{L}}\, G_a = G^+$, consist of the equivalence classes $[g(b)]$. Every element $g(a)$ determines an element $[g(a)]$ so we can define $p_a\ G_a \to G^+$ by $p_a\, g(a) = [g(a)]$. The group operation on G^+ is defined by $[g(b)] + [g(c)] = [p^b{}_d\, g(b) + p^c{}_d\, g(c)]$ where d follows b and c. The direct limit is untopologized. The elements of $G^-(A)$ and those of $G^+(A)$ are, of course, of different natures. In particular, $g_1(a)$ may be distinct from $g_2(a)$ and yet both may be representatives of the same element of $G^+(A)$ since we may have $[g_1(a)] = [g_2(a)]$. Moreover there may be no b-coordinate for $g \in G^+(A)$, i.e., no representative from G_b for $g = [g(a)]$. On the other hand if $g \in G^-(A)$, then $g(a)$ exists and is uniquely specified for every $a \in A$. In fact for an arbitrary distinct pair $g_1(a)$, $g_2(a)$ not only is it impossible that these correspond to the same $g \in G^-(A)$ but also it may very well happen that no g has either of these as a possible coordinate. [Indeed $G^-(A)$ and $G^+(A)$ are related as a group and its character group (126.2) in many cases or, in an extension to vector spaces, as a linear space and its conjugate space.]

Definition 7.4. Let $\Sigma_1^+ = \{G_a, p^a{}_b, A\}$ and $\Sigma_2^+ = \{G_x, p^x{}_y, X\}$ be direct systems. Let $\psi^a{}_x$ be a homomorphism, not necessarily unique, of $G_a \to G_x$. Then $\Psi = \{\psi^a{}_x\}$ is a *homomorphism of* Σ_1^+ *into* Σ_2^+ if: (**a**) for every a and for some x, $\psi^a{}_x \in \Psi$. (**b**) With $\psi^b{}_x$ and $x < y$, $a < b$, Ψ includes $p^x{}_y\, \psi^b{}_x\, p^a{}_b$. (**c**) If ${}^1\psi^a{}_x$ and ${}^2\psi^a{}_x$ are in Ψ, then for every $g(a) \in G_a$ there is a y in X, such that $p^x{}_y\, {}^1\psi^a{}_x\, g(a) = p^x{}_y\, {}^2\psi^a{}_x\, g(a)$. Evidently (**a**) and (**b**) imply that with $\psi^b{}_x \in \Psi$ there is a homomorphism $\psi^a{}_y$ for all $a < b$ and $x < y$, that is to say for a coinitial set of A and a cofinal set of X.

Definition 7.5. Since the coordinates of $g \in G^-(A)$ are unique, the natural definition of a homomorphism $\Phi = \{\phi_x{}^a\}$ *on* $\Sigma_1^- = \{G_a, p_a{}^b, A\}$ to $\Sigma_2^- = \{G_x, p_x{}^y, X\}$ is that (**a**) for each x there is a unique antecedent a, indicated when necessary by a_x, with $\phi_x^a \in \Phi$, and if $x < y$ then $a_x < a_y$; and (**b**) for $x < y$, the following diagram is commutative

$$\begin{array}{ccc} G_x & \xleftarrow{\;p_x^y\;} & G_y \\ \uparrow{\scriptstyle \phi_x^a} & & \uparrow{\scriptstyle \phi_y^b} \\ G_{a_x} & \xleftarrow{\;p_a^b\;} & G_{b_y} \end{array}$$

Lemma 7.6. (7.6a). *Ψ induces a homomorphism ψ of $G^+(A)$ into $G^+(X)$.*
(7.6b). *If A' is cofinal in A and ψ consists of the injections $\psi^{a'}{}_a = p^{a'}{}_{a}$, then ψ induces an isomorphism of $G^+(A')$ onto $G^+(A)$.*

(Any homomorphism ψ of $G^+(A) \to G^+(X)$ can be considered as induced by some Ψ on Σ_1^+ to Σ_2^+ by defining $\psi^a{}_x g(a) = g(x)$ only if $[g(x)]$ corresponds to $[g(a)]$ under ψ, etc.) We need only show that if $g(a)$ and $g(b)$ are in the same equivalence class in $G^+(A)$ then $\psi^a{}_x g(a)$ and $\psi^b{}_z g(b)$ are equivalent, for then cosets of $G^+(X)$ correspond to cosets of $G^+(A)$. We have $p^a{}_e g(a) = p^b{}_c g(b) = g(c)$. Choose $w > x$, $w > z$. Then $p^x{}_w \psi^a{}_x$ and $p^z{}_w \psi^c{}_z p^a{}_c$ are two elements of Ψ playing the roles of ${}^1\psi^a{}_w$ and ${}^2\psi^a{}_w$ in (7.4c). There results $p^x{}_u \psi^a{}_x g(a) = p^z{}_u \psi^c{}_z g(c)$, $w < u$, so $\psi^a{}_x g(a)$ is equivalent to $\psi^c{}_z g(c)$ and similar reasoning shows these are equivalent to $\psi^b{}_y g(b)$.

For (7.6b) observe that each equivalence class constituting $G^+(A)$ has a representative in some $G_{a'}$ and in particular this is true for the 0 class also. Thus the homomorphism is onto. With $\psi^{a'}{}_{a'}$ the identity isomorphism, the kernel is 0.

Lemma 7.7. *Φ as defined in* (7.5) *induces a homomorphism ϕ: $G^-(A)$ into $G^-(X)$.*

Let $g = \{g(a)\} \in G^-(A)$. Let $h(x) = \phi_x^{a_x} g(a_x)$. To show that g maps onto an element h of $G^-(X)$ we need only verify that $p_y^x\, h(x) = h(y)$. However from (7.5a), since $y < x$ implies $a_y < a_x$,

$$\begin{aligned} h(y) &= \phi_y^{a_y} g(a_y) = \phi_y^{a_y} p_{a_y}{}^{a_x} g(a_x) \\ &= p_y^x\, \phi_x^{a_x} g(ax) = p_y^x\, h(x). \end{aligned}$$

Lemma 7.8. *If every S_a is a Hausdorff space then* (**a**) *$S^-(A)$ is closed in $\Pi_A S_a$;* (**b**) *if S_a is compact for each $a \in A$, then $S^- \neq \phi$.*

Since p_a^b is continuous and S_a and S_b ar e T_2, Γ_a^b is closed in $S_a \times S_b$ and $\Gamma_a^b \times \Pi_{c=a,b} S_c = S_a^b$ is closed in $\Pi_A S_a$. Then (7.6a) follows from $S^-(A) = \bigcap S_a^b$ (7.1).

Any collection $\{S_{a_i}{}^{b_i} \mid i = 1, \ldots, N\}$ has the *F.I.P.* In fact for $b_0 > \{b_i, a_i \mid i = 1, \ldots, N\}$ and $s(b_0)$ an arbitrary point in S_{b_0}, any point $s = \{s(a) \mid s(a_i) = p_{a_i}{}^{b_o} s(b_o), s(b_i) = p_{b_i}{}^{b_o} s(b_o)\} \subset \Pi_A S_a$ is in each set of the collection in view of (7.1b). Since $\Pi_A S_a$ is compact, (7.8b) follows.

Definition 7.9. If $\Sigma^-(A) = \{S_a, p_a{}^b, A\}$ ($\Sigma^+(A) = \{S_a, p^a{}_b, A\}$) is an inverse (direct) system, and if $(X, <) \subset (A, <)$ and if $p_x{}^y\, p^x{}_y$, $x \in X$, $y \in X$ are projections in $\Sigma^{\mp}(A)(\Sigma^+(A))$ then $\Sigma^-(X)(\Sigma^+(X))$ is a subsystem of $\Sigma^-(A)(\Sigma^+(A))$.

Lemma 7.10. *If $\Sigma^-(X)$ is a subsystem of $\Sigma^-(A)$ and p is the projection of $\Pi_A S_a$ onto $\Pi_X S_x$ then:*
(7.10a) *p induces the projection p' $S^-(A)$ onto $S^-(X)$;*
(7.10b) *if G_a is a topological group then $G^-(A)$ and $G^-(X)$ are homomorphic;*
(7.10c) *If X is cofinal in A then p' is a homeomorphism of $S^-(A)$ in $S^-(X)$ and the homomorphism in* (7.10b) *is an isomorphism.*

The assertions (7.10a) and (7.10b) are immediate. Since there are fewer matching requirements for elements of $S^-(X)$ than for elements of $S^-(A)$, p' need not be onto.

To prove the first half of (7.10c) we remark that if $s(A) \in S^-(A)$ then for $a \in X$, $s(a) = p_a{}^x s(x)$ for some $x \in X$. Thus the values of $\{s(a) \mid a \bar{\in} X\}$ are uniquely determined by $\{s(a) \mid X\}$ so p' is $1-1$ on $S^-(A)$ onto $S^-(X)$. Since the projection of $\Pi_A S_a$ onto $\Pi_X S_x$ is continuous and open the induced projection p' is also continuous and open on $S^-(A)$ onto $S^-(X)$ and so p' is a homeomorphism. $ker\, p' = \{g(A) \mid g(X) = 0\}$. Since X is cofinal in A and $g(X) = 0$ means $g(a \mid X) = 0$, therefore $g(a \mid A) = 0$ or $g(A) = 0$. Also p' is onto.

Theorem 7.11. *Let G'_a be a closed subgroup of G_a. Let $\Sigma^- = \{G_a, p_a{}^b, A\}$ be an inverse system, and let $p_a{}^b\, G'_b \subset G'_a$ so that $\{G'_a, p_a{}^b, A\}$ is an inverse system also. Then $p_a{}^b$ induces a homomorphism $\pi_a{}^b \colon G_b/G'_b \to G_a/G'_a$ with $\pi_a{}^c = \pi_a{}^b\, \pi_b{}^c$,*

(**a**) $\underleftarrow{\mathsf{L}}\, \{G_a/G'_a, \pi_a{}^b, A\} \supset G^-(A)/G'^-(A)$.

(**b**) *If G'_a is compact for all a then the inclusion in* (**a**) *is replaced by an isomorphism.*

Let $[g_a]$ be the generic element of G_a/G'_a where $g_a \in G_a$. Define $\pi_a{}^b\,[g_b]$ as $[p_a{}^b\, g_b]$. Then $\pi_a{}^c = \pi_a{}^b\, \pi_b{}^c$ follows at once from the corresponding relation for $\{p_a{}^b\}$. Then $\{g_a\} \in G^-(A)$ guarantees that $\{[g_a]\} \in \underleftarrow{\mathsf{L}}\, \{G_a/G'_a\, \pi_a{}^b\} = Q^-(A)$. Let Φ be the homomorphism defined by $\{\phi_a\,(g_a) = [g_a]\}$. Then $\{\phi_a\}$ induces a topological homomorphism $\Phi\colon\ G^-(A) \to Q^-(A)$ according to (7.7). $Ker\, \Phi = \{g_a \mid G'_a\} = G'^-$. Since $\Pi_A G'_a = \bigcap_A (G'_a \times \Pi_{b \neq a} G_b)$ is closed in

$\Pi_A G_a$, (7.8) ensures that G'^- is closed in G^- so the quotient group is topological. Thus (7.10a) is valid.

For the second conclusion we have only to show each element in $Q^-(A)$ has a correspondent in $G^-(A)$. The coset $\{\dot{g}_a \mid \dot{g}_a - g_a \in G'_a\} = C_a$ is a translation of G_a and is compact. Suppose $\{[g_a]\} \in Q^-(A)$. Then $\{C_a, p_a{}^b\}$ is an inverse system of compact spaces. Accordingly (7.8b) asserts the existence of $g = \{g_a \in \Phi^{-1}[g_a]\} \in G^-(A)$.

Corollary 7.12. *If* $\Phi = \{\phi^a_b\}$ *determines a homomorphism of* $\Sigma_1^- = \{G_a, p_a{}^b, A\}$ *into*

$$\Sigma_2^- = \{H_a, q_a{}^b, A\},\ ker\ \Phi = \underleftarrow{\mathsf{L}}\ \{ker\ \phi^a_a, p_a{}^b\}$$

and $Im\ \Phi = \underleftarrow{\mathsf{L}}\ \{Im\ \phi^a_a, q_a{}^b\}$. *When* G_a *is compact, the last inclusion is an equality.*

If $g \in ker\ \Phi$, then as an element of G^-, $g = \{g(a) \mid g(a) = p_a{}^b\, g(b)\}$ where $g(a) \in ker\ \phi^a_a$. However $\phi^a_a\, p_a{}^b\, g(b) = q_a{}^b\, \phi^b_b\, g(b) = 0$. Hence $g \in \underrightarrow{\mathsf{L}}\ ker\ \phi^a_a$. The reverse implication is obvious. In short $ker\ \Phi = \underleftarrow{\mathsf{L}}\ ker\ \phi^a_a$. Note

$$G(a)/ker\ \phi^a_a \xrightarrow{\approx} \phi^a_a\, G(a) = Im\ \phi^a_a.$$

Then (7.11a) and (7.11b) apply.

Definition 7.13. Let E be a vector space over some field, and let A be a vector subspace. Let $x \sim y$ mean $x - y \in A$. The equivalence class of x is called a **variety**. For example, in the Euclidean 3 space with A the horizontal plane, any plane, parallel to A, is a variety.

PROBLEM

7-6. If E is a finite dimensional vector space and $\{L_a \mid a \in A\}$ is a collection of varieties such that $\bigcap_\pi L_a \neq \phi$, show that $\bigcap_A L_a \neq \phi$.

The property announced in the problem above enters proof involving linear spaces in the same way that the families of closed *F.I.P.* sets enter for compact spaces.

PROBLEMS

7-7. Show that (7.8b) is valid with S_a a finite vector space over a fixed field.
7-8. Show that (7.11b) is valid with G_a, G'_a finite dimensional vector spaces over a fixed field.

Theorem 7.14. *Let*

$$(7.14a) \qquad \longrightarrow G_m(a) \xrightarrow{h_{m-1}(a)} G_{m-1}(a) \xrightarrow{h_{m-2}(a)} \cdots \longrightarrow G_0(a)$$

be an exact lower sequence of compact groups or of finite dimensional vector spaces for fixed $a \in A$ *and* $m = 0, \ldots .$ *Suppose for fixed* m *the column* $\{G_m(b), p_a{}^b;(m)\} = \Sigma_m^-$ *is an inverse system and that* $\Sigma_m^- \xrightarrow{h_m = \{h_m(a)\}} \Sigma_{m-1}^-$ *constitutes a homomorphism* (7.5). *Then the inverse limits* $\{G_m^-\}$ *form an exact sequence*

$$\longrightarrow G_m^- \xrightarrow{h_m} G_{m-1}^- \longrightarrow .$$

Let ${}_0G_m(a) = ker\, h_m(a)$ and let ${}_1G_m(a) = Im\, h_{m-1}(a)$. The relations $ker\, h_m = \mathsf{L}\, {}_0G_m(a) = Im\, h_{m-1} = \varprojlim {}_1G_m(a)$ are valid by (7.12).

Example 7-4. A standard example demonstrating that some restrictions are necessary is $G_0(a) = 0$, $G_1(a) = \mathrm{J}$, $G_2(a) = \mathrm{J}$, $G_3(a) = \mathrm{J}_2$, $G_4(a) = 0$, then

$$\begin{array}{ccccccccc} & & \downarrow & & \downarrow & & & & \\ 0 & \longrightarrow & \mathrm{J} & \xrightarrow{h_2} & \mathrm{J} & \xrightarrow{h_1} & \mathrm{J}_2 & \longrightarrow & 0 \\ & & \downarrow{\scriptstyle p} & & \downarrow{\scriptstyle p} & & \downarrow{\scriptstyle 1} & & \\ 0 & \longrightarrow & \mathrm{J} & \xrightarrow{h_2} & \mathrm{J} & \xrightarrow{h_1} & \mathrm{J}_2 & \longrightarrow & 0 \\ & & \downarrow & & \downarrow & & \downarrow & & \end{array}$$

with h_2 and h_1 defined by $h_2(m) = 2m$, $h_1(m) = m \bmod 2$, $p_{a+1}{}^a\, m = 3m = p(m)$, and 1 is the identity. Then $\varprojlim\{\mathrm{J} = G(a), p_{a+1}{}^a\} = \{n(a) \mid n(a) \in G(a) \times \mathrm{J}, n(a) \times 3n(a+1)\}$. Hence $n(a)$ must be 0 for all a. Accordingly the limit sequence is

$$0 \to 0 \to 0 \to \mathrm{J}_2 \to 0$$

which is not exact.

Theorem 7.15. *Let*

$$(7.15a) \qquad \longrightarrow G^m(a) \xrightarrow{h^m(a)} G^{m+1}(a) \longrightarrow$$

be an exact sequence. Let the column $\Sigma_m^+ = \{G^m(a), p^a{}_b(m)\}$ *be a direct system, and suppose that* $h_m = \{h_m(a)\}$ *defines a homomorphism of* $\Sigma_m^+ \to \Sigma_{m+1}^+$. *Then the direct limits* $\{G^m\}$ *constitute an exact sequence* $\ldots \longrightarrow G^m \xrightarrow{h^m} G^{m+1} \longrightarrow \ldots$

We make tacit use of the equivalence relation (7.3) and of (7.4b) and (7.4c). If $g^m = [g^m(a)] \in Im\, h^{m-1}$, there is a $g^{m-1} = [g^{m-1}(b)]$ such that for some c following both a and b,

$$(7.15b) \qquad h^{m-1}(c)\, p^b{}_c(m-1)\, g^{m-1}(b) = p^a{}_c\, g^m(a).$$

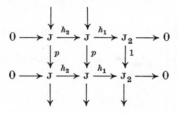

If $g^m = [g^m(a)] \in ker\ h^m$, $h^m g^m = [h^m(a)g^m(a)] = 0$, and so for some $b > a$,

$$p^a{}_b(m)h^m(a)g^m(a) = h^m(b)p^a{}_b(m)\, g^m(a) = 0 \tag{7.15c}$$

We claim $Im\ h^{m-1} \subset ker\ h^m$ for if $[g^m(a)] \in Im\ h^{m-1}$. Then using (7.15b),

$$h^m[g^m(a)] = [h^m(c)h^{m-1}(c)p^b{}_c\, g^{m-1}(b)] = 0.$$

Likewise $ker\ h^m \subset Im\ h^{m-1}$, for if $h^m[g^m(a)] = 0$, then for $[g^m(b)] = [g^m(a)]$ in view of (7.15c)

$$h^m(b)(g^m(b)) = 0,$$

whence by exactness of (7.15), some $g^{m-1}(b)$ is an antecedent of $g^m(b)$ under $h^m(b)$.

Corollary 7.16. *Let $\{G(a), p^a{}_b\}$ be a direct system of DG modules*

$$\underset{\rightarrow}{\mathsf{L}}\, H^m(a) \approx \frac{\underset{\rightarrow}{\mathsf{L}}\, \{Z^m(a), p^a{}_b{}^\#\}}{\underset{\rightarrow}{\mathsf{L}}\, \{B^m(a), p^a{}_b{}^\#\}}$$

Note $0 \rightarrow B^m(a) \rightarrow Z^m(a) \rightarrow H^m(a) \rightarrow 0$ and apply (7.15).

Lemma 7.17. *Let $\{K(a), p^a{}_b\}$ be a direct system of D.G. modules over a fixed ring R. Then for the cohomology modules.*

$$\underset{\rightarrow}{\mathsf{L}}\{HK(a)\} \approx H(\underset{\rightarrow}{\mathsf{L}}K(a)).$$

Denote $\underset{\rightarrow}{\mathsf{L}}\, K(a)$ by K and $\underset{\rightarrow}{\mathsf{L}}\{H(K(a)), p^a{}_b\}$ by $\check{H}$. Define $p(a)^*\colon H(K(a)) \rightarrow H(K)$ by $p(a)^* \langle z(a)\rangle = \langle [z(a)]\rangle$. Since $p(b)^*\, p^a{}_b{}^*\, \mathbf{z}(a) = \langle p^a{}_b{}^\#\, z(a)\rangle = \langle [z(b)]\rangle$, $\{p(a)^*\}$ constitutes a homomorphism $p^*\colon \check{H} \rightarrow H(K)$.

We assert $Im\ p^* = H(K)$. Let z be a cocycle representative of $\mathbf{z} \in H(K)$. Then z is in K and hence $z = [k(a)]$ where $k(a) \in K(a)$. Thus $0 = dz = d[k(a)] = [d_a\, k(a)]$, wherefore, for some $b > a$, $p^a{}_b{}^\#\, k(a)$ is annihilated by d_b and in consequence is an element $z(b)$ of $Z(b)$. Accordingly, $p(b)^*\, \mathbf{z}(b) = \langle [z(b)]\rangle = \mathbf{z}$.

On the other hand, suppose $p^*\, \mathbf{h} = 0$ for an $\mathbf{h}$ in $\check{H}$. Since $\mathbf{h} = [\mathbf{z}(a)]$, for some $a \in A$,

$$p(a)^*\, \mathbf{z}(a) = 0 \quad \text{or} \quad [z(a)] \in B(K)$$

and hence for some b, $p^a{}_b\, z(a) = d\, w(b)$. Then

$$\mathbf{h} = [p^a{}_b{}^*\, \mathbf{z}(a)] = [d\mathbf{w}(b)] = 0,$$

that is to say $ker\ p^* = 0$.

Definition 7.18. With proper interpretation (7.3) essentially indicates a generalization where $p^a{}_a$ is not the identity isomorphism but is any element

$p(a)$ in the automorphism group $P(a)$ of the possibly non-Abelian group $G(a)$ with group operation designated by $\circ$. Thus the matching conditions are to be

(7.18a) $$p^b{}_c\, p^a{}_b = p(c)\, p^a{}_c, \qquad a < b < c,$$

for some $p(c) \in P(c)$. For any $p(c)$ in $P(c)$, there is a $p(d) \in P(d)$ such that

(7.18b) $$p^c{}_d\, h(c) = h(d) p^c{}_d, \qquad c < d.$$

Then $g(a_1)$ is equivalent to $g(a_2)$ if for some b following a_1 and a_2

(7.18c) $$p^{a_1}{}_b\, g(a_1) = p(b)\, p^{a_2}{}_b\, g(a_2).$$

The equivalence class determined by $g(a)$ is again indicated by $[g(a)]$, and we defined the product of the equivalence classes as usual by

(7.18d) $$[g(a)] \circ [g(b)] = [p^a{}_c\, g(a) \circ p^b{}_c\, g(b)].$$

PROBLEMS

7-9. Show that (7.18c) defines an equivalence relation and that $G = \{[g(a)]\}$ is a group.

7-10. Let $\{G_{ab}\}$ be an inverse system over $A \times B$ where A and B are directed sets. Show $\underset{\overleftarrow{A\times B}}{\mathsf{L}}\, G_{ab} \approx \underset{\overleftarrow{A}}{\mathsf{L}}\,\underset{\overleftarrow{B}}{\mathsf{L}}\, G_{ab} \approx \underset{\overleftarrow{B}}{\mathsf{L}}\,\underset{\overleftarrow{A}}{\mathsf{L}}\, G_{ab}$.

8. COINCIDENCES AND FIXED POINTS. We are now in a position to extend the theory developed in (53) to general maps of finite concrete complexes as promised in Example 5-7. Suppose that ψ is a simplicial map on $'K = \{'\sigma\}$ to $L = \{e\}$ and suppose that θ is a simplicial map on $'L = \{'e\}$ to $K = \{\sigma\}$ where the primes indicate some order of barycentric subdivision. Thus

$$'K \xrightarrow{\psi} L \xrightarrow{Sd} {'L} \xrightarrow{\theta} K \xrightarrow{Sd} {'K}$$

If $\psi\, '\sigma_r^i = e_r^k$ write $\psi_\#\, '\sigma_r^i = \Sigma_s\, 'e_r^{ks}$ where the chain on the right-hand side is over all the simplexes in the barycentric subdivision of e_r^k. Similarly if $\theta\, 'e_r^t = \sigma_r^u$, then

$$\theta_\#\, 'e_r^t = \Sigma_v\, '\sigma_r^{uv}$$

where $\|\bigcup_v\, '\sigma_r^{uv}\| = \|\sigma_r^u\|$. If $\psi\, '\sigma_r^i = e_m^k$, $m \neq r$ or $\theta\, 'e_r^t = \sigma_m^u$, $m \neq r$, then $\psi_\#$ and $\theta_\#$ take such elementary chains into 0. A *coincidence* for $\psi_\#$, $\theta_\#$ is a pair $'\sigma_r^i$, $'e_r^t$ defined as in (53.4).

Lemma 8.1. *Let f map $|K|$ into $|L|$ and let g map $|L|$ into $|K|$. Let ψ_1 and ψ_2 be simplicial approximations to f and let θ_1 and θ_2 be simplicial approximations to g. Then $L(\psi_1, \theta_1) = L(\psi_2, \theta_2)$, (53.8), and $L(\psi_1) = L(\psi_2)$ (53.9).*

This is an immediate consequence of (4.2), (5.3), (5.4), (53.8), and (53.9).

Definition 8.2. In view of (6.1) and (5.2), if the facts of f and g are as in (8.1), we can define the coincidence number $L(f, g)$ as $L(\psi, \theta)$ for any pair of simplicial approximations to f and g. Similarly $L(f)$ can be defined as $L(\psi)$ for ψ a simplicial approximation to f. A **coincidence** is a pair $\bar{x}$, $\bar{y}$ with $f(\bar{x}) = \bar{y}$, $g(\bar{y}) = \bar{x}$.

Theorem 8.3. *If f and g are as in* (8.1), *and if $L(f, g) \neq 0$, there is a coincidence. Similarly $L(f) \neq 0$ implies that there is a fixed point.*

Since K and L are finite complexes, they may be considered in a Euclidean space with metric d. If there is no coincidence, then by the compactness of $|K|$, $d(x, gfx) > \delta$ for fixed δ and all $x \in |K|$. We may assume the diameter of the simplexes inferior to $\delta/16$, since this can be achieved, if necessary, by barycentric subdivision. Introduce simplicial approximations to f and g such that

$$\inf_{x \in |K|} d(f(x), \psi(x)) < \delta/16, \quad \inf_{y \in |L|} d(g(y), \quad \theta(y)) < \delta/16.$$

Thus ψ: $'K \to L$ and θ: $'L \to K$ where the prime denotes some order of barycentric subdivision. Let $\psi\,'\delta_r = e_r \in L$. Suppose that $\|e_r\| = \|\bigcup\,'e_r^i\|$. Let $\theta\,'e_r^i = \sigma_r^j$. Let $\|\sigma_r^j\| = \|\bigcup_k\,'\sigma_r^{jk}\|$. Then by the triangle inequality points in $\|'\sigma_r\|$ and in $\|\sigma_r^j\|$ are distant at least $\epsilon/16$ and hence $\|'\sigma_r\| \cap \|'\sigma_r^{jk}\| = \varnothing$. Hence $'\sigma_r$ is not a fixed simplex for $\theta\,\psi$ and hence there is no coincidence pair $('\sigma_r, 'e_r)$. (If $\psi\,'\sigma_r = e_s$ or $\theta\,'e_1^i = \sigma_s^j$ with $s \neq r$, then $\psi_\#\,'\sigma_r = 0$ or $\theta_\#\,'e_r^i = 0$.) Our conclusion is that $L(\psi, \theta) = 0$, a contradiction with (8.1) and (8.2).

Theorem 8.4. *For some neighborhood $U(f)$ of f and $V(g)$ of g, $L(f', g') = L(f, g)$ where $f' \in U(f)$, $g' \in V(g)$. Moreover $L(f, g)$ is unaffected by homotopies of f and g.*

We need only refer to (5.3) for the first assertion, and to (5.4) for the second, (**A**, 17).

Example 7-5. Let K_1 and K_2 be triangulated circles in Fig. 7-1. Points on the circles can be specified by giving the angle coordinate θ. Let $f(\theta) = 2\theta$. Thus ${}_1\sigma_1^1$ maps onto ${}_2\sigma_1^1$ and ${}_1\sigma_1^2$ maps onto ${}_2\sigma_1^2$, etc. Take this simplicial map as ψ. The induced homomorphism $\psi_\#$ takes the nonbounding cycle $\Sigma_{i=1}^{i=8}\,{}_1\sigma_1^i$ into $2\,\Sigma_{j=1}^{j=4}\,{}_2\sigma_1^j$. If we identify K_1 and K_2 as regards homology, we get $\mathbf{H}(1)_{22} = (2)$ (53.8), and so $L(f_*) = L(\psi_*) = -1 \neq 0$. Hence there is a fixed point.

The earlier examples in (53.) can now be sharpened too.

EXAMPLE 7-6. If f is a self-map of an acyclic concrete complex K, there must be a fixed point, i.e., $f(x) = x$ for some point x in K.

Remark. In general the absence of fixed points does not guarantee $L(f) = 0$ if a compact metric space replaces the finite concrete complex, unless local connectivity conditions are satisfied.

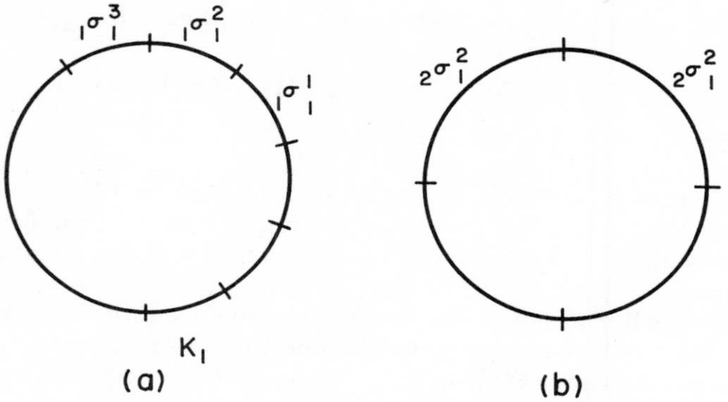

Figure 7-1

Lemma 8.5. *Let K be a concrete finite complex. Suppose $\chi(K) \neq 0$. If ψ is a homeomorphism of X, then for some x, $(\psi)^m(x) = x$ for $m \leq M =$* sup $(\Sigma R_{2i+1}, \Sigma R_{2j})$ *where R_k is the k dimensional Betti number.*

Let $\psi(r)_*$ be the induced automorphism of the vector space $H_r(X, Q)$. If the theorem were false, then $L(\psi(r)_*^s) = 0$ for $s = 1, \ldots, M$. We write $\boldsymbol{\psi}(r)$ for the matrix representation of $\psi(r)_*$. Accordingly for each s from 1 to M,

$$\Sigma\,(-1)^r\,Tr(\boldsymbol{\psi}(r)^s) = 0. \tag{8.5a}$$

If the characteristic roots of $\boldsymbol{\psi}(r)$ are $\lambda_1(r), \ldots, \lambda_{R_r}(r)$ the characteristic roots of $\boldsymbol{\psi}(r)^s$ are their s^{th} powers. Accordingly (8.5a) is equivalent to

$$-\Sigma_{i,r}\,\lambda_i(2r+1)^s + \Sigma_{j,r}\,\lambda_j(2r)^s = 0. \tag{8.5b}$$

The numbers of terms in each summation are respectively ΣR_{2r+1} and ΣR_{2r} respectively and one of these, say the second sum, is M. Since assigning the powers, from 1 to M, to M complex numbers determines them up to order it is impossible that the first sum could have less than M terms, that is $\Sigma R_{2r+1} = \Sigma R_{2r}$ or more strikingly

$$\chi(K) = \Sigma\,(-1)^k\,R_k = 0,$$

in contradiction with the hypothesis.

EXAMPLE 7-7. A self-map f of the n sphere S^n, sufficiently near the identity map (8.4) must have fixed points if n is even.

Independently of n if $f(S^n)$ does not include S^n, there is a fixed point. Indeed for n even, $L(f) = L(i)$ (8.4), where i is the identity map, i.e., $a = 1$ in Example 5-6. If n is odd, since $f(S^n)$ is not all of S^n, for a sufficiently fine subdivision the simplexes in $S^n - f(S^n)$ are not maps of any simplexes, and hence starting with the simplicial approximation h attached to this subdivision, a must be 0 in Example 5-6. Accordingly $\mathbf{H}(n)_{22} = (\mathbf{0})$ (53.8) and

$$L(f) = L(\psi_*) = 1 + (-1)^n \quad 0 = 1 \neq 0.$$

PROBLEMS

7-11. Show that all self-maps of P, the projective plane, have a fixed point.

7-12. Show that a self-map of a torus arbitrarily near the identity need not leave any point fixed. Give a class of examples of such fixed point free maps.

7-13. Show a self-map of the double torus near the identity has a fixed point.
Consider the maps in the last two problems to be given by taking the flow of a thin layer of fluid spread over the torus or double torus and interpret the results.

7-14. Exhibit a self-map f of the torus such that all sufficiently near maps must have fixed points.

Let S^n be interpreted now as the Euclidean unit sphere $\{x \mid \|x\| = 1\}$ centered at 0. At each $x \in S^n$ let v_x be a unit tangent vector. The direction of v_x is specified by angle parameters and if these depend continuously on x, then $\{v_x\}$ constitutes a continuous tangent vector field.

Theorem 8.6. *If n is even, there is no continuous vector field on S^n.*

Indeed consider $f(x)$ the point of intersection with S^n of the ray through θ and the end point of v_x. Then the segment joining x and $f(x)$ subtends the angle $\pi/4$ at the origin and hence $\|tx + (1 - t)f(x)\| > \frac{1}{2}$. Then

$$h(x, t) = \frac{tx + (1 - t)f(x)}{\|tx + (1 - t)f(x)\|}$$

defines a homotopy with the identity, on $S^n \times \mathrm{I}$ to I. Accordingly $L(f) = 1 + 1 = 2$. Then $f(x) = x$ for some point in contradiction with the assumption that $\|v_x\| = 1$.

Theorem 8.7. *If f maps S^n into S^n, n even, then either there is a fixed point or some point is mapped into its antipode.*

Suppose there is no fixed point. Then the vector s_x from x to $f(x)$ in the containing R^{n+1} is nonnull. We assert that for some $\bar{x}$, $\bar{x}$ and $f(\bar{x})$ are antipodal points. If not for every x, the projection of s_x on the tangent hyperplane at x is a nonnull vector, v_x. Then $v_x = u_x/\|u_x\|$ defines a continuous tangent vector field on S^n contrary to (8.6).

chapter 8

GRATINGS

Thus far we have hardly mentioned any topological aspects. These enter primarily in two ways: first, a topological space X takes the place of a complex K and maps are now understood to be continuous; second, the coefficient group, or ring, may be topological, and this is reflected in a topology for the homology groups. In this connection we note that the concept of the coefficient group is further refined in this chapter and in Chapter 17 groups and rings of a local character enter.

1. SUPPORTS. Let X be a point set. Its points may be related by some algebraic structure properties; for instance X may be a group or by the possession of topological features, as, for example, if X is a sphere. A differential graded module of chains or cochains can be built up neglecting the structure of X and using merely the discrete points as abstract elements. One would expect the homology modules thus obtained to be trivial in higher dimension since no relationships of the points are involved. In dimension 0, since no separation criteria are imposed, the whole point set X presumably acts like a component and one might expect the 0-dimensional homology modules to be essentially the coefficient group or ring.

To get nontrivial modules one expects, therefore, to replace these formal differential graded chain or cochain rings by their quotient by an ideal defined in terms of the algebraic or the topological relations in order to put separation into effective atoms or points. In this section it is the topological relations that are of interest, and this ideal is based on the topological property named support in the sequel.

This viewpoint is well suited for applications of topology and for integration of the ideas with those of other mathematical disciplines from Analysis through Differential Geometry.

Definition 1.1. We associate a point set of the space X called its **support** with each element g of an algebraic complex, $G = \{\bigoplus G^n, d\}$ (61.4) and denote it by $\|g\|$, if the following postulates are satisfied:

(1.1a) $$\|0\| = \varnothing.$$

(1.1b) $$\|g\| = \bigcup \|g^r\| \quad \text{if} \quad g = \bigoplus g^r.$$

(1.1c)

$$\|g - g'\| \subset \|g\| \cup \|g'\|, \quad (c')\ \|rg + sg\| \subset \|g\| \cup \|g'\| \quad \text{if} \quad r, s \in R.$$

(1.1d) $$\|dg\| \subset \|g\|.$$

(1.1e) $$\|gg'\| \subset \|g\| \cap \|g'\|.$$

(1.1f) If $$x \bar{\in} \|g\| \quad \text{then} \quad U(x) \cap \|g\| = \varnothing$$

for some neighborhood $U(x)$. This insures supports are closed.

The graded ring is **torsion free** when

(1.1g) $$\|rg\| = \|g\| \quad \text{for} \quad r \neq 0.$$

Definition 1.2. An algebraic complex over the ring R with supports whose union covers X is called an R-**grating** on X. If $R = J$ we say simply, grating. The algebraic complex itself is sometimes referred to as an **abstract** grating. A **lower grating** refers to a lower complex with supports. The coefficient ring, R, *will be understood to be an integral domain with unit.* Roman letters are used for gratings, thus A, G.

The reader may turn to (3.1), (4.1), and (6.1) for examples of significant gratings.

Lemma 1.3. *Let* G_0 *be an ideal* (61.2) *of the abstract* R *grating* G. *Let* $\|\mathrm{G}_0\| = \bigcup_{g \in \mathrm{G}_0} \|g\|$. *Define* $\|[g]\| = \overline{\|g\| - \|\mathrm{G}_0\|}$, *where* $\|g\| - \|\mathrm{G}_0\|$ *is interpreted as* $\|g\| \cap \|\mathrm{G}_0\|^{\sim}$, *for* $[g] \in \mathrm{G}/\mathrm{G}_0$. *Then this is an assignment of supports under which* G/G_0 *is an* R *grating over* $\overline{\|\mathrm{G}_0\|^{\sim}}$.

Evidently G/G_0 is a ring complex. $\|[g]\|$ is closed in X and is uniquely specified, for suppose $[g_1] = [g_2]$. Then $g_1 - g_2 \in \mathrm{G}_0$ whence $\|g_1 - g_2\| \subset \|\mathrm{G}_0\|$ and so

$$\|[g_1]\| = \overline{\|g_1 - g_2 + g_2\| - \|\mathrm{G}_0\|} \subset \overline{\|g_1 - g_2\| \cup \|g_2\| - \|\mathrm{G}_0\|}$$

Thus $\|[g_1]\| \subset \|[g_2]\|$, and a similar argument gives $\|[g_1]\| \supset \|[g_2]\|$. The verification of the postulates in (1.1) is direct. (We make no use of this result, and for special quotient gratings of interest to us the supports are defined in (1.8) below.)

Definition 1.4. Let A be a grating on X. Denote by A_Y the collection $\{a \mid \|a\| \cap Y = \varnothing$, or by (1.1f), $\|a\| \cap V(y \mid Y) = \varnothing\}$. However, write ${}_0A$ for A_X, i.e., for the elements whose support is the null set. The grating A is **separated** or **reduced** if ${}_0A = 0$, that is to say, if the element 0 is the unique element with vacuous support. A nonseparated R grating may be referred to as a **pregrating** (a terminology supported by a glimpse behind the veil at Chapter 17.)

Lemma 1.5. A_Y *is an* R *grating and is an ideal of* A.

Lemma 1.6. *The* R *grating* $A/{}_0A$ *is a separated grating over* X *with supports defined by* $\|[a]\| = \|a\|$ *for* $[a] \in A/{}_0A$.

$$[a] = [a'] \Rightarrow \|a\| = \|a'\|$$

We shall refer to $A/{}_0A$ as the **reduced** R grating for A.

Definition 1.7. ψ is a **grating homomorphism** on the R grating A over X into the R grating B over X if **(a)** ψ is an allowed homomorphism of the algebras (61.13) of which the primary property is commutativity with d and also that **(b)** $\|\psi(a)\| \subset \|a\|$. (Except for d and D the degree of the homomorphism is generally understood to be 0.) When the module properties alone are in question the homomorphism ψ is often referred to as a **chain** or **cochain mapping**.

Lemma 1.8. *If* Y *is a subset of* X, $A/A_Y = \{[a] = [a]_Y\}$ *is an* R *grating over* Y *with supports defined by* $\|[a]\| = \|a\| \cap Y$ *and* $d[a] = [da]$.

Definition 1.9. The R grating A/A_Y is called the **cut or section**, of A by Y and is generally denoted by YA. Moreover the homomorphism $A \to YA$ is denoted by the same letter Y rather than the expected $Y^{\#}$ and satisfies (1.7). It is referred to as a **cut** (or **section**) **homomorphism**. Thus $Ya = [a]$ and $dYa = Y\,da$. A case of frequent occurrence is that of single point x taken for Y. The induced homomorphism on the homology rings (61.7), $H(A) \to H(YA)$ is denoted by Y^* or again by Y. The dual use of Y as a point set and as a cut homomorphism occasions no confusion in practice.

Remark. The definition of support given in (1.3) is of course valid for any ideal while that of (1.8) is special for A_Y. (If the ideal A_Y is used in (1.3), the support obtained may be larger than that assigned in (1.8) and may include points in $Y^{\sim}$, if for instance every element of A_Y is in A_Z also, where $Z \supset Y$.) An alternative definition valid for any ideal is: If $a^i \in A^i$ then $\|[a^i]\| = \bigcap\{\|b^i\| \mid b^i - a^i \in G_0$ an ideal$\}$ plus (1.1b). It is of interest that though (11.8) is valid for R gratings (11.7) need not be.

Remark. The homomorphism Y corresponds to η in (61.10b) and in the upper complex case the correspondence is with $j^{\#}$ (cf. 45.5). Accordingly $Y\mathrm{A}$ in these cases is $C^*(L, G) \approx C^*(K, G)/C^*(K - L, G)$, with Y interpreted as L while for the case of lower complexes Y is the homomorphism $C_*(K, G) \to C_*(K, G)/C_*(L, G)$, and the set Y is now to be interpreted as $K - L$. Hence $Y\mathrm{A}$ amounts to $C_*(K/L, G)$.

For convenience in later reference we set down two elementary observations.

Lemma 1.10. (a) *If* $\|a + b\| = \varnothing$ *then* $\|a\| = \|b\|$.
(b) *If* $Ya = Yb$ *then* $Yca = Ycb$.

From (1.1c)

$$\|a\| = \|a + b - b\| \subset \|a + b\| \cup \|b\| = \|b\|.$$

Similarly $\|b\| \subset \|a\|$. Of course if the grating is separated then $\varnothing = \|a + b\|$ implies $a = -b$ immediately.

For (1.10b) we observe that from $\|a - b\| \cap Y = \varnothing$ follows

$$Y \cap \|c(a - b)\| \subset \|c\| \cap \|a - b\| \cap Y = \varnothing.$$

PROBLEM

8-1. $\|Ya + Yb\| = \varnothing \Rightarrow \|Ya\| = \|Yb\|$.

The aptness of the notation $Y\mathrm{A}$ for the cut homomorphism is brought out by the following easy lemma.

Lemma 1.11. *If* $Y_2 \subset Y_1$, $Y_2(Y_1\mathrm{A}) = Y_2\mathrm{A}$.

PROBLEM

8-2. Demonstrate that $Yac = YaYc$. Demonstrate (1.11) by using (11.7).

We summarize the application of Chapter 6. Thus we define $Z(\mathrm{A}) = ker(\mathrm{A} \xrightarrow{d} \mathrm{A})$, $B(\mathrm{A}) = Im\, d$ and $H(\mathrm{A}) = Z(\mathrm{A})/B(\mathrm{A})$ as in (61.5) and in (61.6), with $H(\mathrm{A}) = \oplus\, (H^n(\mathrm{A}) = \langle Z(\mathrm{A}) \cap \mathrm{A}^n \rangle)$. Not only A^n but also $H^n(\mathrm{A})$ is a module over the coefficient ring R and $H^p(\mathrm{A})\, H^q(\mathrm{A}) \subset H^{p+q}(\mathrm{A})$. The homomorphism $\psi\colon \mathrm{A} \to \mathrm{A}'$ (1.7) induces a ring homomorphism $\psi^*\colon H(\mathrm{A}) \to H(\mathrm{A}')$ by $\psi^* \mathbf{z} = \langle \psi z \rangle$.

PROBLEMS

8-3. Let A' be a subgrating of A. If $a \in \mathrm{A}$ with $da \in \mathrm{A}'$ let there exist a $b \in \mathrm{A}$ with $a + db \in \mathrm{A}'$. Show this implies $H(\mathrm{A}') \approx H(\mathrm{A})$.

8-4. If Y is closed or open in the locally compact space X, then the cut homomorphism satisfies $Y\mathbf{z} = 0$, $\mathbf{z} \in H(\mathrm{A})$, is equivalent to $\|z\| \cap Y = \varnothing$ for some cocycle z in the coset $\mathbf{z}$. Show $Y\mathbf{zw} = Y\mathbf{z}Y\mathbf{w}$.

Besides the homomorphism in (1.8) other homomorphisms may enter for pairs of spaces X and Y. However in contradistinction with these earlier defined homomorphisms certain restrictions on the maps or the gratings must now be assumed.

Definition 1.12. Let ψ be a *closed map* of Y into X (i.e., a map taking closed sets into closed sets). If besides the antecedent of each point is a compact set ψ is **proper** and in this case it is immediate that the inverse of a compact set is again compact. Define an R grating over X, $'\mathrm{A}(X) = \psi_+ {}^{\cdot}\mathrm{A}(Y)$, called the **image of** ${}^{\cdot}\mathrm{A}(Y)$, by agreeing ψ_+ is the identity isomorphism on the abstract R gratings. Thus

(1.12a) $$0 \longrightarrow {}^{\cdot}\mathrm{A}(Y) \xrightarrow{\psi_+} {}'\mathrm{A}(X).$$

The supports are defined by $\|\psi_+ a(Y)\| = \psi\ \|a(Y)\|$.

We write $\psi^{\#}\, a$ for a to indicate that new supports in Y are being assigned to elements in a grating A over X,

(1.12b) $$\|\psi^{\#}(a)\| = \psi^{-1}\ \|a\|.$$

Then $\psi^{\#}\,\mathrm{A}$ is the separated grating $\mathrm{A}/\{a \mid \|\psi^{\#}(a)\| = \varnothing\}$. We refer to it as the **induced grating** under ψ. In general $\psi^{\#}$ is not an allowable homomorphism.

If $\psi(Y) = X$ then A and $\psi^{\#}\,\mathrm{A}$ are abstractly isomorphic as rings. If ψ is the *inclusion map*, then $\psi^{\#}\,\mathrm{A} = Y\mathrm{A}$; there is another homomorphism of use *here*, namely the *restriction homomorphism* written ${r^X}_Y$. Write $\mathrm{A} = \mathrm{A}(X)$ for an R grating for which the notion $a = a(X)$ *is trivial over an open set* $U(x)$ has meaning. Require that $x_0 \in \|a(X)\|$ means $a(X)$ is trivial on no $U(x_0)$. Then $\mathrm{A}(X \mid Y) = {r^X}_Y\, \mathrm{A}(X)$ amounts to changing the support to

(1.12c) $$\|{r^X}_Y\, a(X)\| = \{y \mid a(X) \text{ nontrivial on any } U(y) \cap Y\}$$

Since $a(X)$ may be nontrivial on $U(y_0)$ and trivial on $U(y_0) \cap Y$ it may well happen that for $y_0 \in Y$, $y_0 \in \|a(X)\|$ yet $y_0 \bar{\in} \|{r^X}_Y\, a(X)\|$. Let ${}_0\mathrm{A}(X \mid Y) = \{a(X) \mid a(X)$ is trivial over some $U(y_0) \cap Y$ for every $y_0 \in Y\}$. This is not *ker* ${r^X}_Y$ of course.

Suppose $\mathrm{A}(X)$ is separated. Then $\mathrm{A}(X \mid Y)$ is not separated unless ${}_0\mathrm{A}(X \mid Y) = 0$. Write $\mathrm{A}(Y)$ for the separated grating. For comparison with the cut homomorphism Y, (1.9), *ker* $Y = \mathrm{A}_Y \subset {}_0\mathrm{A}(X \mid Y)$.

If Y is closed the diagram below, which sums up the relations of Y and $r^X{}_Y$, has exact rows and columns and the two squares are commutative

$$
\begin{array}{ccccccccc}
 & & 0 & & 0 & & & & \\
 & & \downarrow & & \downarrow & & & & \\
0 & \longrightarrow & A_Y & \xrightarrow{\;i\;} & A & \xrightarrow{\;Y\;} & Y\,A & \longrightarrow & 0 \\
 & & \downarrow{\scriptstyle r^X{}_Y} & & \downarrow{\scriptstyle \approx} & & \downarrow & & \\
0 & \longrightarrow & {}_0A(X \mid Y) & \longrightarrow & A(X) & \longrightarrow & A/{}_0A(X \mid Y) \approx A(Y) & \longrightarrow & 0 \\
 & & & & \downarrow & & \downarrow & & \\
 & & & & 0 & & 0 & &
\end{array}
\qquad (1.12d)
$$

Lemma 1.13. *Let j be an allowable homomorphism of the R gratings $A \to B$. If A and B are on the same space or more generally if* **(a)** $j \mid {}_0A \subset {}_0B$ *then j induces an allowable homomorphism on the separated R gratings, namely* $\mathrm{j}\colon A/{}_0A \to B/{}_0B$. *If j is onto, then* j *is onto.*

If A and B are on the same space, then **(a)** is automatically satisfied for $\|ja\| \subset \|a\| = \varnothing$. In all cases where **(a)** is valid, j is defined by $\mathrm{j}[a] = [ja]$, where $[a]$ is the coset of A relative to ${}_0A$ and similarly $[b]$ is relative to ${}_0B$. Hence

$$\mathrm{j}\, d[a] = [dja] = [jda] = d\, \mathrm{j}[a].$$

If $[b] \in B/{}_0B$ then for some $a \in A$, $ja = b$ and so $\mathrm{j}[a] = [ja] = [b]$.

There is a special interest in certain subgratings singled out by restrictions on the subsets which can be supports.

Definition 1.14. A **family of supports**, F, is a collection of closed subsets of X satisfying

(a) If $Y \in F$ every closed subset of Y is in F,

(b) finite unions of sets in F are in F.

(c) Y in F implies that the closure of some neighborhood of Y is in F also.

A grating or subgrating whose supports lie in F is called an F *grating* and is sometimes indicated by ${}_FA$ (also ${}_FH(\ \ )$). We single out the F families used in this book.

(d) All closed sets. In this case the script F is usually dropped.

(e) Compact sets. A superscript dot announces this case. For instance ${}^{\cdot}A$ is a **compact grating**; that is, all supports are compact sets. ${}^{\cdot}H$ is derived from ${}^{\cdot}A$.

(f) Closed paracompact sets. This is termed a **paracompactifying family** and may be distinguished by the letter P instead of F; thus, ${}_PA$ or H_P.

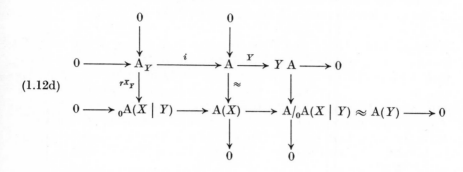

The notation in the next definition finds application only later though logic dictates its presentation now. For comparing cohomology rings under a map of spaces, it is clear that if families of support enter, conditions are needed to ensure that sets in a family map into sets in a family.

Definition 1.15. Let F and G be support families over X and over Y respectively. We shall use the following notation: If X_0 is a subset of X, then $F \mid X_0 = \{A \in F, A \subset X_0\}$ denotes a family of supports both in X_0 and in X. $F \cap X_0 = \{X_0 \cap A \mid A \in F\}$ is a family of supports in X_0. Suppose ψ maps X to Y. $\psi^{-1} G \subset F$ shall mean $\psi^{-1} Y_1 \in F$ for every $Y_1 \in G$. Let U be open in Y; then $F(U) = \{A \mid A$ *closed in* $\psi^{-1}(U)$ and $y \in U$ imply for some $V(y) \subset U$, $\psi^{-1} V(y) \cap A \in F\}$. This is a support family on $\psi^{-1}(U)$ and includes $F \mid \psi^{-1}(U)$. Note that if $V \subset U$, then $F(U) \cap \psi^{-1}(V) \subset F(V)$.

If every A in F has $\overline{\psi(A)} \in G$, then F and G are **adapted**. If, besides $\psi(A \mid A \in F) = \overline{\psi(A)}$, then F and G are **well adapted**. If F and G are well adapted and if $\psi^{-1}(G) \subset F$, then they are **very well adapted**.

For instance, if F and G are all closed sets, they are adapted. If F and G are compact support families, they are well adapted. If X, Y are locally compact and paracompact, and if F and G consist of all the closed sets, then if ψ is proper (1.12), F and G are well adapted.

We suppose throughout this chapter that X is locally compact. An important objective is to show that the R gratings over X in some class yield isomorphic omology modules, or algebras. Conceivably a different class of gratings would yield different omology algebras. The significant observation is that if the various R gratings chosen satisfy certain reasonable conditions, the omology algebras are the same up to an isomorphism. The reasonable conditions referred to involve the nature of the support family and local and global properties.

We can view a coefficient ring R as an R grating whose elements are all of 0 degree for which $dr = 0$ and with supports given by $\|r\| = X$ for $r \neq 0$ and $\|0\| = \varnothing$. Suppose there is an allowable isomorphism $i: R \to \mathrm{A}^0$ defined by $i(r) \in A^0$, $di(r) = 0$ and $\|i(r)\| = X$ for $r \neq 0$. Then $i(R)$ can be considered a subalgebra of $x\mathrm{A}$ for $i(R) \cap \mathrm{A}_x = 0$ in view of the definition of $\|i(r)\|$. Hence

$$i(R) \approx i(R)/i(R) \cap \mathrm{A}_x \approx (i(R) + \mathrm{A}_x)/\mathrm{A}_x \subset \mathrm{A}/\mathrm{A}_x = x\mathrm{A}.$$

Thus i induces the homomorphism

$$i^*: H(R) \to H(x\mathrm{A}).$$

Since d_R is trivial, $R = Z(R)$, $B(R) = 0$, and so $R = H(R)$. Accordingly there is a homomorphism of R into $H(x\mathrm{A})$. For the case of the simplicial groups over the one point simplex, this homomorphism is an isomorphism. More generally,

Definition 1.16. The R grating A is **R-simple** or satisfies the **Poincaré axiom** if for each $x \in X$, $H(x\mathrm{A}) \approx H^o(x\mathrm{A}) \approx R$ so in particular $H^p(x\mathrm{A}) = 0$ for $p > 0$.

The condition of R simplicity is a local restriction. Some global condition relating to the fragmentation of X into small pieces is needed to connect the omology algebras of the space with their behaviour in the pieces.

Definition 1.17. With X locally compact, a finite, irreducible, open cover $\beta = \{b_i \mid i = 1, \ldots, N\}$ is a **fine cover** or is **open at infinity** if $\bar{b}_i$ is compact, $i < N$, and $b_N^\sim$ is compact.

This definition reflects the fact that if X is compactified by adding the ideal point ∞, an open cover of a compact space $X \cup \infty$ is obtained, with ∞ disjunct from b_i, $i < N$.

EXAMPLE 8-1. X is the real line, $\beta = b_1, b_2$ where

$$b_1 = \{x \mid 0 < x < 2\} \qquad b_2 = \{x \mid x < \tfrac{1}{2}\} \cup \{x \mid x > 1\}$$

is a fine cover.

Definition 1.18. (**a**) If F is a compact family, the compact R grating A is a **fine grating** if for every fine cover $\beta = \{b_i, i \leq N\}$ there are module endomorphisms e_i: $\mathrm{A} \to \mathrm{A}$ for which $\Sigma_{i=1}^{i=N} e_i = e$, the identity endomorphism and $\|e_i\, a\| \subset \bar{b}_i \cap \|a\|$.

From these relations and (1.3e) follows $\bigcup \|e_i\, a\| = \|a\|$ (1.18b). (**b**) If F is a paracompactifying support family for A, then A is P-**fine** if for every locally finite open cover $\beta = \{b_i\}$, endomorphisms e_i exist, satisfying $\Sigma\, x\, e_i\, a = xa$, $x \in X$ and $\|e_i\, a\| \subset \bar{b}_i \cap \|a\|$. Because of the local finiteness of the cover, the sum in (1.18b) is really over the finite range $\{i \mid x \in b_i\}$. (We may refer to this as a parafine grating realizing it need not be waxlike, and that the cover need not be denumerable.) It is important to note that the endomorphisms referred to in (1.18a) and (1.18b) do not have to commute with d; nor must they be ring homomorphisms.

Lemma 1.19. *Suppose* A *is an* R *simple, separated grating over* X, X *and let* Y *be an arbitrary subset of* X. *Then* $\mathrm{A}/\mathrm{A}_Y = Y\mathrm{A}$ *is* (**a**) R *simple,* (**b**) *separated,* (**c**) *if* A *is fine, then if* Y *is closed in* X, A/A_Y *is fine also.*

Assertion (a) is an immediate consequence of (1.10) and Problem 8-2. We give a detailed proof though. Denote the elements of A/A_Y by $[a]_Y$ and those of $(\mathrm{A}/\mathrm{A}_Y)/(\mathrm{A}/\mathrm{A}_Y)_x$ by $[[a]_Y]_x$. Then $[[a]_Y]_x$ stands for the collection

$$\{[b]_Y \mid \|[b]_Y - [a]_Y\| \cap x = \varnothing,\ x \in Y\} =$$
$$= \{[b]_Y \mid \|b - a\| \cap x = \varnothing,\ x \in Y.\}$$

Similarly $[a]_x \in x\mathrm{A}$ stands for the coset $\{b \mid \|b - a\| \cap x = \varnothing,\ x \in Y\}$. Hence the correspondence $[[a]_Y]_x$ and $[a]_x$ is $1 - 1$, and so $x\mathrm{A} \approx xY\mathrm{A}$.

For **(b)**: $\|[a]_Y\| = \|a\| \cap Y = \varnothing$ implies, according to (1.10) that $a \in \mathrm{A}_Y$, and hence $[a]_Y = 0$. Since $\mathrm{A}/\mathrm{A}_Y = \mathrm{A}/_0\mathrm{A}/\mathrm{A}_Y/_0\mathrm{A}$, **(b)** is true even if A is not separated.

For **(c)**: Let $\beta = \{b_i \mid b_i \subset \bar{b}_i \subset Y,\ i = 1, \ldots, N - 1\}$, b_N be a fine cover of Y. Let b_i' be open on X with $b_i' \cap Y = b_i$. Since $\bar{b}_i$ is compact for $i \leq N - 1$, there is a finite open cover of $\bar{b}_i$ by sets open on X with compact closures. Let the union of these covering sets for $\bar{b}_i$ be called c_i. Write $d_i = b_i \cap c_i$ for $i \leq N - 1$. Replace b_N by $b_N \cup (X - Y) = d_N$. Suppose for the moment that Y is arbitrary. Nevertheless $d_N^{\sim} = (b_N^{\sim}) \cap Y = Y - b_N$, a compact set. Hence d_N is open and therefore the cover $\Delta = \{d_i\}$ is a fine cover (1.17). Since A is fine, there are endomorphisms e_i with $\|e_i\, a\| \subset \bar{c}_i$. Hence $Y \cap \|e_i\, a\| \subset \bar{d}_i \cap Y = \bar{b}_i$, $i \leq N - 1$. Accordingly, with e_i' defined by $e_i'[a]_Y = [e_i\, a]_Y$ we have $\|e_i'[a]_Y\| \subset \bar{b}_i$. Closure of Y is needed now for the inference $\|[a]_Y\|$ is closed. Manifestly

$$(\Sigma\, e_i)a = a,\ [\Sigma\, e_i\, a]_Y = (\Sigma\, e_i')[a]_Y = [a]_Y.$$

We now consider a condition equivalent to fineness. Some R gratings admit a two-sided multiplicative identity $u_0 \in \mathrm{A}$. However the existence of an identity is not a necessary property of a grating and indeed is absent for compact R gratings on noncompact spaces. Moreover it is sufficient in most arguments to have merely local identities. These enter our developments as concrete realizations of the endomorphisms $\{e_i\}$ in (1.18). [Evidently where the multiplication of the grating is trivial as in the lower gratings, for instance, there can be no talk of units and (1.20) and (1.22) below do not apply.]

Definition 1.20. The element $u \in \mathrm{A}$ is a **local identity** or **unit** relative to the closed set Y and the open set $V \supset Y$ if $\|u\| \subset \bar{V}$ and $\|au - a\| \cup \|ua - a\| \subset Y^{\sim}$. The notation u_Y is used or simply u alone in place of the more descriptive u_Y, V or Y, V^u. The reason for requiring two-sidedness of the local identity is to ensure certain uniqueness and cycle properties in connection with cuts.

Lemma 1.21. (i) *If* ${}_iu$, $i = 1, 2$ *are local identities in the* R *grating* A *relative to* Y_i *and* V_i *then* $Y_1 \cap Y_2 \cap \|{}_1u - {}_2u\| = \varnothing$.

If the R *grating* A *is torsion free*, (1.2g), *then* (ii) Yu_Y *is a cycle in* $Y\mathrm{A}^0$, *and* (iii) $\mathbf{u}_Y$ *is a multiplicative identity of* $H(Y\mathrm{A})$. *For gratings* (R, *the ring of integers*) (**iv**) *neither* mxu_Y *nor* $mx\mathbf{u}_Y$ *is* 0 *for any nonzero integer* m *when* $x \in Y$. *Furthermore* (**v**) $xu_Y = mxa$, $x \in Y$, *implies* $m = \pm 1$. (*In* (**iv**) *and in* (**v**) R *can be taken as a principal ideal ring* (102.6).)

For (**i**) note that $Y_1 \cap Y_2$ A is a ring admitting two identities ${}_1u$ and ${}_2u$. However the identity in a ring is unique. (Alternatively

$$Y_1 \cap Y_2 \cap \|{}_1u - {}_2u\| \subset Y_1 \cap Y_2 \cap (\|{}_1u - {}_2u\,{}_1u\| \cup \|u_2 - {}_1u\,{}_2u\|) = \varnothing \quad (1.19).)$$

For (**ii**) write u for Yu_Y. Then $u = \Sigma\, u^i$ where $u^i \in YA^i$. Therefore $ua^p = \Sigma\, u^i a^p = a^p$ and hence $u^0\, a^p = a^p$ for $a^p \in YA^p$. Thus u^0 also is an identity on the ring YA. Therefore $u = u^0$, i.e., $u^0 \in YA^0$. Next $u^2 = u$ whence, by (**ii**),

(1.21a) $$du\, u + (-1)^0\, u\, du = du.$$

Since $\|du\| \subset \|u\|$, (1.21a) asserts $du = 0$. For (**iii**), since $B(YA^0) = 0$, u is a representative of the nontrivial coset $\mathbf{u} \in H(YA)$. Under the natural ring homomorphism $Z(YA) \xrightarrow{\eta'} H(YA)$, $ua = a = au$ becomes $\mathbf{ua} = \mathbf{a} = \mathbf{au}$. For (**iv**) since the coefficient ring is J if $mx\mathbf{u} = 0$ then $mxu \in B(A^0) = 0$ or $mxu = 0$ contradicting the assumption that A is torsion free. If $x\mathbf{u} = xm\mathbf{a}$ then, since $H(xYA) \approx \{Jx\mathbf{u}\}$, $x\mathbf{a} = xn\mathbf{u}$. Hence $x\mathbf{u} = mnx\mathbf{u}$ or $mn = 1$ whence $m = \pm 1$. If $xu = xma$ then $x\mathbf{u} = xm\mathbf{a}$ whence $m = \pm 1$. This shows (**v**).

Definition 1.22. An R grating A, is **full** if it is compact, reduced, R simple, and torsion free and if for each compact set C and fine cover $\beta = \{b_i\}$ (1.17), there are local identities u_C^i with $\|u_C^i\| \subset \overline{b_i}$ such that $\Sigma\, u_C^i$ is an identity on C. We refer to $\{u_C^i\}$ as a **partition** of the (local) identity U relative to C and β and note that u_C^i is an identity relative to any compact set Q in $C_\cap \bigcap_{j \neq i} b_j^\sim$ and open set b_i. When the support family is paracompactifying then a full, or for emphasis, P-**full** grating arises by replacing compact by closed paracompact.

Lemma 1.23. *If* A *is a full* R *grating and* Y *is closed then* YA *is full.*

The demonstration is like that for (1.19c)

The next lemma is in the spirit of (1.19) and (1.22) and fulfills the intuitive expectation that local isomorphism implies global isomorphism for nice gratings and thereby indicates how in practice one can demonstrate isomorphisms.

Lemma 1.24. *Let* A *and* B *be separated compact R gratings over X and suppose that* A *is fine. Let ψ be an allowable homomorphism on* A $\to$ B *which, induces an isomorphism on xA $\to$ xB. Then ψ is an isomorphism.*

For $a \in$ A, $x \in \|a\|$ implies $x \in \|\psi(a)\|$ according to the last hypotheses. Hence $\|\psi(a)\| \supset \|a\|$. This together with (1.7a) yields

(1.24a) $$\|\psi(a)\| = \|a\|$$

Therefore if $\psi(a) = 0$, $a = 0$. Hence *ker* $\psi = 0$.

To show ψ is onto, choose b at will in B. The hypotheses affirm that for each $x_0 \in \|b\|$, some element of A, denoted by $a(x_0)$ or a_0 satisfies

(1.24b) $$\bar{\psi}(x_0\, a_0) = x_0\, \psi(a_0) = x_0\, b.$$

Since $[\psi(a_0) - b]_{x_0} = 0$,

$$x_0 \cap \|\psi(a_0) - b\| = \|[\psi(a_0) - b]_{x_0}\| = \varnothing.$$

Hence for some open set $U(x_0)$ with compact closure $\bar{U}(x_0)$,

$$\bar{U}(x_0) \cap \|\psi(a_0) - b\| = \varnothing$$

or $x\psi(a_0) - xb = 0$, $x \in \bar{U}(x_0)$. There is a finite open cover of the compact set $\|b\|$, $\{U_i = U(x_i \mid \|b\|),\ i = 1, \ldots, n-1\}$. Then

(1.24c) $$xb = x\psi(a_i), \quad x \in \bar{U}_i, \quad a_i = a(x_i).$$

Let $U_n = X - \|b\|$ so that $\mu = \{U_i \mid i = 1, \ldots, n\}$ is a fine cover of X. Set $a_n = 0$. Then (1.24c) is valid for $i = 1, \ldots, n$. Since allowable endomorphisms decrease supports (1.7a), $x_0\psi(a) = x_0\psi(a')$ implies $x_0\psi(e_j\, a) = x_0\psi(e_j\, a')$; that is to say, $x_0\, \psi(e_j\, a)$ is independent of the choice of a satisfying (1.24b). Define the endomorphism $E_j(x)$: xB $\to$ xB by $E_j(x)(xb) = x\psi(e_j\, a)$, where $a = a(x)$ satisfies (1.24b) (cf. (1.18a)). It is important that

(1.24d) $$\begin{aligned} \Sigma_j\, E_j(x)xb &= x\psi\, \Sigma\, e_j\, a \\ &= x\psi(a) = xb. \end{aligned}$$

From $\|\psi(e_j\, a)\| = \|e_j\, a\| \subset \bar{U}_j$ and from (1.24c) results

$$E_j(x)xb = 0 = x\psi(e_j\, a_j), \quad x \bar{\in} \bar{U}_j.$$

Hence

(1.24e) $$E_j(x)(xb) = x\psi(e_j\, a_j)$$

for all x. For $a = \Sigma\, e_j\, a_j$ the combination of (1.24d) and (1.24e) compels $xb = x\psi(a)$. Hence for all x

$$x \cap \|b - \psi(a)\| = \varnothing; \quad \text{i.e.,} \quad \|b - \psi(a)\| = \varnothing.$$

Since B is separated, $b = \psi(a)$.

Definition 1.25. A simple notion that pervades various fields of Algebraic Topology is that of a **section.** It may enter whenever there is a triple A, X, p where X is a topological space, A is either a space or a topologized algebraic structure, and p maps A onto X. For Y a subset of X, a section s over Y is a map on Y to A with ps the identity on Y to Y. To each $a \in \mathrm{A}$, assign a section s_a according to the specification $s_a(x) = [a]_x \in x\mathrm{A}$. Here $ps_a(x) = x$; $Y = X$. Supports are defined by

$$\|a\| = \{x \mid s_a(x) \neq 0 \in x\mathrm{A}\}. \tag{1.25}$$

The collection of sections over X constitutes a grating S which may be viewed as the completion of A for it always includes an isomorph of A. We return to these ideas in (175.1).

Lemma 1.26. *If* A *is an* R *simple fine grating or a full grating and* Y *is closed in* X, $^{\bullet}(^{\bullet}\mathrm{A}/^{\bullet}\mathrm{A}_{X-Y}) \approx {}^{\bullet}\mathrm{A}_Y$.

Consider the homomorphisms

$$^{\bullet}\mathrm{A}_Y \xrightarrow{i} {}^{\bullet}\mathrm{A} \xrightarrow{\eta} {}^{\bullet}\mathrm{A}/^{\bullet}\mathrm{A}_{X-Y}$$

where i is the inclusion homomorphism and $\eta(a \mid {}^{\bullet}\mathrm{A}) = [a]$ the coset with respect to $^{\bullet}\mathrm{A}_{X-Y}$. However $\|a\| \cap (X - Y)$ may not be compact. Let $\psi = \eta i$. Write b for the typical element of $^{\bullet}\mathrm{A}_Y$. Then, $\|\psi(b)\| \subset X - Y$ (1.8).

We claim $ker\ \psi = 0$. Thus $\psi(b) = 0$, if $ib \in {}^{\bullet}\mathrm{A}_{X-Y}$ or $\|\psi(b)\| \cap (X - Y) = \varnothing$. Since $\|b\| \cap Y = \varnothing$ and $\|\psi(b)\| \subset \|b\|$ this implies $\|b\| = \varnothing$ or $b = 0$.

We claim ηi is onto. Suppose $h \in {}^{\bullet}(^{\bullet}\mathrm{A}/^{\bullet}\mathrm{A}_{X-Y})$. Hence $h = \eta g$ with $g \in {}^{\bullet}\mathrm{A}$, and

$$\|g\| \cap X - Y = \|h\|. \tag{1.26a}$$

Cover $\|h\|$ by a finite number of open sets, U_i, with $\bar{U}_i$ compact and in $X - Y$. Thus $\|h\| \subset U = \bigcup U_i \subset X - Y$.

U, $X - \|h\|$ constitutes a fine cover of X, since $\bar{U}$ is compact. By the fineness hypothesis on A, $g = {}_1g + {}_2g$ with $\|{}_1g\| \subset \bar{U}$. $\|{}_2g\| \subset X - \|h\|$ where ${}_ig = e_i\, g$. Since $\|{}_1g\| \cup \|{}_2g\| = \|g\|$, $\|{}_1g\| \subset X - Y$ and $\|{}_2g\| \subset Y$, for if $x \in X - Y \cap \|{}_2g\|$ then $x \in (X - Y) \cap \|g\| = \|h\|$, an impossibility. Similar conclusions follow for the full grating. Therefore,

$$g - {}_1g = {}_2g \in \mathrm{A}_{X-Y}.$$

Thus ${}_1g \in \mathrm{A}_Y$ and $\eta i\ {}_1g = \eta g = h$.

Definition 1.27. We define $H(X)$ as $H(\mathrm{A})$ for full or P full R gratings. In particular, to emphasize that a compact R grating is under consideration we shall write $^{\bullet}H(X)$ for $H(^{\bullet}\mathrm{A})$. The justification for this depends on the uniqueness theorem (111.9). Where nonfull gratings enter, we shall indicate this by the notation, for instance by $H_S(X)$ or $H(SX)$, for the singular theory (4.1).

Theorem 1.28. *For Y a closed subspace of X, the sequence*

(1.28a) $$\longrightarrow {}^{\bullet}H^*(X - Y) \xrightarrow{i^*} {}^{\bullet}H^*(X) \xrightarrow{\eta^*} {}^{\bullet}H^*(Y) \longrightarrow$$

is exact.

Let ${}^{\bullet}\mathrm{A}$ be a full R grating over X. Then ${}^{\bullet}\mathrm{A}/{}^{\bullet}\mathrm{A}_Y$ and ${}^{\bullet}({}^{\bullet}\mathrm{A}/{}^{\bullet}\mathrm{A}_{X-Y})$ are full gratings over Y and over $X - Y$, respectively, by (1.19c) and (1.26). Adopting (1.27), we have, therefore, $H({}^{\bullet}\mathrm{A}) = {}^{\bullet}H(X)$, $H({}^{\bullet}\mathrm{A}/{}^{\bullet}\mathrm{A}_{X-Y}) = {}^{\bullet}H(X - Y)$, and $H({}^{\bullet}\mathrm{A}/{}^{\bullet}\mathrm{A}_Y) = {}^{\bullet}H(Y)$. Let J, G in (61.10) be identified with ${}^{\bullet}\mathrm{A}_Y$ and ${}^{\bullet}\mathrm{A}$. Thus

(1.28b) $$0 \longrightarrow {}^{\bullet}\mathrm{A}_Y \xrightarrow{i} {}^{\bullet}\mathrm{A} \xrightarrow{\eta} {}^{\bullet}\mathrm{A}/{}^{\bullet}\mathrm{A}_Y \longrightarrow 0.$$

Then (61.13b) translates into (1.28a) when account is taken of (1.26).

PROBLEM

8-5. Show that $i^*\,{}^{\bullet}H^*(X - Y)$ consists of cosets containing elements with supports in $X - Y$. Show therefore (by arguing from supports) that the product induced in the cohomology rings is such that if $\mathbf{f} \in {}^{\bullet}H^*(Y)$ and if $\mathbf{g} \in {}^{\bullet}H^*(X - Y)$ then $\mathbf{fg} = 0$.

Lemma 1.29. *If* A *and* E *are R gratings over X, then* $\mathrm{A} \otimes \mathrm{E}$ *is an R grating when supports are given by*

$$\|\Sigma\, a \otimes e\| = \{x \mid \Sigma\, xa \otimes xe \neq 0\}.$$

This grating need not be reduced even if both A *and* E *are reduced. The reduced grating* $(\mathrm{A} \otimes \mathrm{E})/_0(\mathrm{A} \otimes \mathrm{E})$ *is denoted by* $\mathrm{A} \circ \mathrm{E}$ *where X is locally compact or paracompact.*

The ideas we need are in (64.13) but we state explicitly what we shall use, since there are minor changes. Thus we start with the interpretation of A and E as Abelian groups and grade by

$$(\mathrm{A} \otimes \mathrm{E})^n = \oplus_{p+q=n}\, \mathrm{A}^p \otimes \mathrm{E}^q.$$

We obtain an algebraic structure by requiring of the generators

$$r(a \otimes e) = (ra \otimes e) = (a \otimes re)$$

$$(a \otimes e)(a' \otimes e') = (-1)^{\dim a'}\, aa' \otimes ee'$$

$$d(a^n \otimes e) = da \otimes e + (-1)^n\, a \otimes de.$$

These relations are extended by linearity. Since R is commutative no ambiguity follows from the action of rs, r, and s in R. Remark further that we may assume that A is a grating and that E is an R grating in which case $r(a \otimes e) = (a \otimes re)$, $r \in \mathrm{E}$.

We depart from our customary cut homomorphism notation (1.9) to gain clarity and write ϕ and ψ for the cut homomorphisms defined on $\mathrm{A} \xrightarrow{\phi} \mathrm{A}/\mathrm{A}_x = x\mathrm{A}$ and $\mathrm{E} \xrightarrow{\psi} \mathrm{E}/\mathrm{E}_x = x\mathrm{E}$ by $\phi a = xa = [a]_x$, $\psi e = xe = [e]_x$.

According to (64.6), $ker(\phi \otimes \psi)$ is generated by $\{a \otimes e \mid a \in \mathrm{A}_x \text{ or } e \in \mathrm{E}_x\}$; that is to say, if $0 \neq h$ and $x \bar{\in} \|h\|$ then $h = \Sigma\, a_i \otimes e_i$ where either $xa_i = 0$ or $xe_i = 0$. Hence for some V_x^i, either $\|a_i\|$ or $\|e_i\|$ is disjunct from V_x^i. Accordingly, with $V = \bigcap V_x^i$, one of $\|a_i\|$ or $\|e_i\|$ does not meet V for each i. Hence the set of points not in $\|h\|$ is open so $\|h\|$ is closed. The remaining conditions on supports are evidently met.

Since $\|a\| \cap \|e\| = \varnothing$ implies $\|a \otimes e\| = \varnothing$, $\mathrm{A} \otimes \mathrm{E}$ need not be reduced. However, the grating $x\mathrm{A} \otimes x\mathrm{E}$ is reduced. Indeed $\|\Sigma\, xa_i \otimes xe_i\| = \varnothing$ means $\Sigma\, xa_i \otimes xe_i = 0$. In short, $xA \otimes xE$ is equivalent to $xA \circ xE$.

The general definition of $a \circ e$ is, of course, that of the coset of $a \otimes e$ with respect to ${}_0(\mathrm{A} \otimes \mathrm{E})$. Since $x \bar{\in} \|a\| \cap \|e\|$ demands $xa \otimes xe = 0$, $\|a \otimes e\| \subset \|a\| \cap \|e\|$. Accordingly

$$\|a \circ e\| \subset \|a\| \cap \|e\|. \tag{1.29a}$$

An indication of the care required in using $\circ$ products is given in the following natural appearing result.

Lemma 1.30. *If R is any ring with a unit and* A *is a full grating over the locally compact space X then* $\mathrm{A} \circ R \approx \mathrm{A} \otimes R$.

It is understood that R is interpreted as a grating in the sense of (1.15). In particular $\|r\| = X$ for $r \neq 0$. It is sufficient to show that if $\|h\| = \varnothing$ where $h \in \mathrm{A} \otimes R$ then $h = 0$. For any x, $xh = 0$. Since $x(\mathrm{A} \otimes R) \approx x\mathrm{A} \otimes R \approx \mathrm{A}/\mathrm{A}_x \otimes R$, $h \in \mathrm{A}_x \otimes R$. Hence

$$h = \Sigma_\pi\, a_i \otimes r_i \tag{1.30a}$$

where $a_i \in \mathrm{A}_x$. It might appear that since $xh = 0$ for all x therefore $xa_i = 0$ for all x and so each $a_i = 0$. This argument is invalid since the representation (1.30a) changes in general with x that is to say to gain $h \in \mathrm{A}_x \otimes R$ we cannot in general use (1.30a) with the same a_i's.

Let $W(x)$ be the closure of the open set $V(x)$. From $h \in \mathrm{A}_x \otimes R$ follows $h \in \mathrm{A}_{W(x)} \otimes R$ for some $W(x)$. Write X_0 for $\bigcup_\pi \|a_i\|$ (1.30a) then for $\{x_j \mid j \leq N-1\}$, $\bigcup V(x_j) \supset X_0$. Write b_j for $V(x_j)$. For some open set b_N, $X_0 \subset b_N^{\sim} \subset \bigcup_{i \leq N-1} b_i$. Hence $\{b_i \mid i \leq N\}$ is a fine cover of X. Let u be a local identity relative to X_0 and let $\{u_j\}$ be a partition relative to $\{b_i\}$. Note $h \in \mathrm{A}_j \otimes R$, $j \leq N$, where $\mathrm{A}_j = \{a \mid \|a\| \cap b_j = \varnothing\}$. Moreover $\|u_j\, a\| \subset \bar{b}_j \cap \|a\|$ implies $u_j\, \mathrm{A}_j = 0$. Let $(u_j \otimes 1)(a \otimes r) = u_j\, a \otimes r$. Then with 1 the identity of R where $\|1\| = X$, $\|u_j \otimes 1\|$ is compact and so

$$(u_j \otimes 1)h \subset (u_j \otimes 1)(\mathrm{A}_j \otimes R) = 0$$

Since $\Sigma\, u_j$ is u, $h = \Sigma(u_j \otimes 1)h = 0$.

In the next sections we take up various specific gratings and the induced omology rings. It will appear that underlying each is a notion of a cell or simplex. These may enter by direct block decomposition of the space, or through the nerves of covers. It is true that the singular and Alexander gratings, for instance (3.2) and (6.1), can be defined without mention of blocks or covers. Nevertheless alternative formulations of these gratings can be given in which the complex notion and the cover notions are central, the first through the medium of maps of simplicial complexes. This is natural. The omology modules of a space depend on the connectivity structure of a space; the structure can be probed by covers by various types of sets. For omology theory such covers are restricted to those admitting at most a denumerable collection of elements covering any one point. This is

Figure 8-1

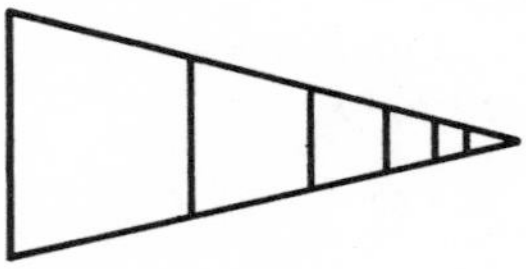

merely a reflection of the fact that the dimensions of the cells used for omology theory are perforce finite. Evidently a good deal of structure can slip through because of this restriction, but satisfactory definitions of omology groups of nonfinite dimension have not yet been given.

Let X be the plane ladder consisting of a pair of rays from the origin and a denumerable collection of rungs approaching the origin. Suppose covers by sets of diameter $\geq r_0$ only are used. Evidently only a finite number of the infinite collection of nonbounding cycles of X can be revealed by such cover probes. This suggests that to build up a satisfactory omology theory using covers of a type designated by A one should require that the chosen family of such covers be cofinal in the collection of all covers of type A. Except when the spaces studied are compact the finite open or closed covers will not satisfy the criterion of cofinality suggested. The locally compact space seems in point and illustrates the possibility of alternatives, since, for instance, the fine cover in this case (1.17) has been taken finite. One can use a one point compactification and thus remain within the confines of compact spaces or one can consider the omology groups to be some sort of limit (77) of omology groups over all the compact subsets. For these subsets finite covers are, of course, available. To round out the discussion it will be noted that a notion of fineness of a grating seems to require at least locally finite covers to assure adequacy of simplicial nerves. Therefore the paracompact spaces are a sort of limit of generality in this direction. In order to investigate more general spaces grating methods as developed above must be replaced by other procedures (cf. 177.8, for instance). When problems connected with maps and various topological indices are in question, the locally compact spaces and compact gratings are natural and for this reason are the ones emphasized in the greater part of this book.

2. COVERS. The covers used in this book are generally open covers, but occasionally closed covers also are employed. For normal spaces, the omology rings are indifferent as to whether open or closed covers are used. Further aspects of structure may be revealed by using other probe sets (for instance, those characterized by a connectivity property), but the covers just mentioned seem natural for problems involving maps.

Definition 2.1. The sets X, X_0 with $X_0 \subset X$ constitute a **pair**. The sets X, X_1, X_0 with $X_0 \subset X_1 \subset X$ constitute a **triple**. The sets X, X_1, X_0 with $X_0 \cup X_1 = X$ constitute a **triad**.

Definition 2.2. ψ maps the pair X, X_0 into the pair Y, Y_0 if $\psi(X) \subset Y$ and $\psi(X_0) \subset Y_0$. We write ψ_0 for $\psi \mid X_0$. The maps of the triples and triads are similarly defined and we write also (ψ, ψ_0, ψ_1) with $\psi_i = \psi \mid X_i$.

If $X_0 \subset X$, then X_0 may be viewed either as a space in its own right or as a subspace of X. In the first case modifications and maps carry no restriction while in the second consistency with operators on X may be required.

Definition 2.3. If $X_0 \subset X$, then the map which assigns to each X_0 the same point considered now a member of X is termed the inclusion map. The notation i, j: i_0, j_0, etc., is used generally for an inclusion map.

Definition 2.4. Let X, X_0 be a pair. With every open cover of X there are open subcovers $'\alpha$ covering X_0. We tacitly assume the covers referred to below, are open covers. The collection $\{\alpha, '\alpha\}$ is ordered by $\alpha, '\alpha < \beta, '\beta \Leftrightarrow \alpha < \beta, '\alpha < '\beta$. $\alpha, '\alpha$ is called a **covering pair** for the pair X, X_0.

Lemma 2.5. *If $X \supset X_0$ with a covering pair $(\alpha, '\alpha)$, the nerve a contains the nerve $'a$ of $'\alpha$ as a subcomplex.*

Since $'\alpha$ need not consist of all elements of α which meet X but only enough to cover it, we expect

Lemma 2.6. *The collection $\{\alpha, \alpha \cap X_0\}$ is cofinal in the family of all cover pairs $\{\alpha, '\alpha\} \Leftrightarrow X_0$ is closed.*

We may as well assume that each element of $'\alpha$ meets X_0. For each $x_0 \in X_0$ let $U(x_0)$ be an open set of X contained in some element of $'\alpha$. The cover $\{U(x_0 \mid X_0)\} \cup (\alpha \cap (X - X_0))$ is taken as β. Then $\beta \cap X_0 = \{U(x_0 \mid X_0)\}$. On the other hand if X_0 is not closed there is a point x_1 in $\bar{X}_0 - X_0$. Then the cover $\alpha = (X, X - x_1)$, $'\alpha = X - x_1$ cannot be refined by a cover of type $\beta, \beta \cap X_0$ since any $b_i \in \beta$ which contains x_1 must intersect X_0 yet is not contained in X_0.

Definition 2.7. If $X \supset X_0$, if $\Sigma = \{\alpha, '\alpha\}$ is cofinal, and if $\alpha, '\alpha < \beta, '\beta$ implies $a_i \in \alpha$ is contained in a unique b_j of β, then Σ is a **spectrum**. An example of a spectrum is a family $\{\alpha, '\alpha\}$ where α is a covering such that any open subset of an element a_i of α is itself an element of α.

For the cover α of X let $C(x; a_i)$ be the characteristic function (**A**) of $a_i \in \alpha$ and $x \in X$ and $'C(x; 'a_i)$ that of $'a_i \in '\alpha$, $x \in X_0$. Let $b(\bar{x}) = \{x \mid C(x, a_i) = C(\bar{x}, a_i)$ for all $a_i \in \alpha$, $x \in X\}$ and let $'b(\bar{x}) = \{x \mid 'C(x, 'a_i) = 'C(\bar{x}_1, 'a_i)$ for all $'a_i \in '\alpha$, $x, \bar{x} \in X_0$. Then $\{b(\bar{x}), 'b(\bar{x})\} = \beta, '\beta$ is a covering pair. [To insure $b(\bar{x}), 'b(\bar{x})$ are open, star finiteness of α is sufficient.] Alternatively, the maximal nonzero intersections constitute the $\beta, '\beta$ covering pair.

3. SIMPLICIAL GRATINGS.

We cite some specific gratings of use throughout this book.

Definition 3.1. If σ_r is a Euclidean simplex (21.10), then $\|\sigma_r\|$ is the closed convex hull of its vertices. If K is a simplicial complex, then the chain groups or modules with ordered or oriented simplexes constitute the abstract grating with trivial multiplication, and supports are defined by

$$\|\Sigma_\pi\, g_i\, \sigma_r^{\,i}\| = \bigcup \{\|\sigma_r^{\,i}\| \mid g_i \neq 0\}.$$

Definition 3.2. The replete chains have entered implicitly in earlier chapters. Suppose the vertex scheme of a simplex σ is $v^0 \ldots v^n$. A basis for the replete chains on σ_n, denoted by $_+C(\sigma_n)$, is defined by introducing as basis elements $\{c\}$ the ordered sets of vertices $\{v^{i_j} \mid j = 0, \ldots, m\}$ where v^{i_j} is one of the vertices of σ_n, and *repetitions are permitted*. Accordingly it is possible that $n < m$. These basis elements for the chain modules may be referred to as **elementary replete chains.** Then the elementary replete chain c_m is on σ_n, written $c_m \subset \sigma_n$, if the vertices of c_m are a subset of those of σ_n. Further, the chain $\Sigma\, g_i\, c^i_m$ is on σ_n if each c^i_m, with $g_i \neq 0$, is on σ_n. Let $v^0, \ldots, v^n$ be the distinct vertices entering the replete simplex e_m. Then $\|e_m\| = \|\sigma_n = v^0 \cdots v^n\|$. This yields the replete simplicial grating.

Introduce the relation $c_m = 0$ if a vertex is repeated and also $c_m + c'_m = 0$ if c_m and c'_m differ only by a permutation of two adjacent vertices, say v^j and v^{j+1}. These relations generate a submodule R. The oriented chain module $C(K)$ is $_+C(K)/R$.

Definition 3.3. We extend the notion of a join (21.2) to chains and understand by the join of v and a chain $c_n = \Sigma\, g_i\, e^i_n$ the $n + 1$ dimensional chain $c_{n+1} = v\, c_n = \Sigma\, g_i(v\, e^i_n)$. The chains may be replete, ordered, or oriented.

4. SINGULAR GRATINGS. Definition 4.1. Let σ_r be an ordered simplex and let u_r map $\|\sigma_r\|$ into X. The pair (σ_r, u_r) is equivalent to the pair $('\sigma_r, 'u_r)$ if there is a barycentric order preserving map T of $\|\sigma_r\|$ onto $\|'\sigma_r\|$ such that the relation

$$'u_r\, T = u_r \tag{4.1a}$$

is valid. A **singular simplex** is the equivalence class of the pairs (σ_r, u_r) and is denoted by u_r just as for the map alone. An alternative definition is that u_r is the map of the fixed **standard simplex** Δ_r whose vertices $\{v^i \mid 0 \leq i \leq r\}$ are the points $(\delta^i_1, \ldots, \delta^i_r)$ with respect to a Euclidean frame, where δ^j_i is the Kronecker symbol. The **leading vertex** of u_r is $u_r \mid v^0$. Let $t^j(r)$ be the linear map on $\Delta_r = v^0 \cdots v^r$ onto the jth face of Δ_{r+1} defined by

$$\begin{aligned} t^j(r)v^i &= v^i \qquad i < j \\ &= v^{i+1}, \qquad i \geq j. \end{aligned} \tag{4.1b}$$

If $\sigma_{r-1}(i)$ is the ith face of σ_r, the ith face of the singular simplex u_r is $(\sigma_{r-1}(i), u_r \mid \|\sigma_{r-1}(i)\|)$ and is denoted by $u_{r-1}(i)$. The boundary operator yields the equivalent representations

$$\begin{aligned} \partial u_r &= \Sigma\,(-1)^i\, u_{r-1}(i) \\ &= \Sigma\,(-1)^i\,(\Delta_r, u_r\, t^i_r) \qquad \text{[compare (22.4c)].} \end{aligned} \tag{4.1c}$$

Supports are defined by $\|u_r\| = u_r\,\|\sigma_r\|$. This set is independent of the representative chosen for u_r and is compact. The collection $\{u_r\}$ is referred to as the singular complex. It is evidently closure finite. Hence we use finite chain groups and the discrete topology. These are defined with $\{u_r\}$ as basis. The trivial multiplication is introduced making all products of chains the zero chain. We have now a grating $\mathrm{C}(SX, R)$ or $_S\mathrm{C}(X, R)$ which is referred to as the **singular chain grating** of X.

Since the support of a singular simplex cannot be empty, the ideal composed of elements with empty support consists of the 0 element of the grating, so our definition of $C(SX, G)$ is direct. Analogous considerations are still valid when certain equivalence relations are introduced; for instance, if σ_r is required to be oriented and T merely orientation preserving or even when no equivalence relation T is introduced.

Remark. It may be shown that the homology groups for these various ways of defining singular elements are isomorphic. With oriented simplexes certain paradoxical situations occur connected with degenerate simplexes and chains. If all equivalence relations are dropped, there is gain in manipulative simplicity at the cost of increase of the size of the chain groups.

For completeness we consider also singular cubes. Corresponding to Δ_n, the Euclidean n-cube, I^n, specified by coordinates $\{t_i \mid 0 \leq t_i \leq 1, i = 1, \ldots, n\}$ is the **standard** fixed cube. The map w_n, w_n: $I^n \to X$ is the **singular n-cube.** The ith face is $(\lambda_i^\varepsilon w_n)$ defined by

$$(\lambda_i^\varepsilon w_n)(t_1, \ldots, t_n) = w_n(t_1, \ldots, t_{i-1}, 0, t_{i+1}, \ldots, t_n)$$

or $w_n(t_1, \ldots, t_{i-1}, 1, t_{i+1}, \ldots, t_n)$ according as $\varepsilon = 0$ for the back face and $\varepsilon = 1$ for the forward face.

$$\partial u = \Sigma\, (-1)^i\, (\lambda_i^1 - \lambda_i^0)\, w_n.$$

Then $Q(X) = \oplus\, Q_n(X)$ is the chain module. A singular cube is **degenerate** when w_n does not depend on one of the parameters $t_1, \ldots, t_n$. Let the chain module involving degenerate singular cubes be denoted by $D(X)$. Then

$$\mathrm{A}(X) = Q(X)/D(X)$$

is the **singular cubic chain grating** when supports are defined by $\|w_n\| = w_n(I^n)$.

We shall need to subdivide singular simplexes.

Definition 4.2. We restrict ourselves for the moment to Δ_n. Then Sd is allowable (71.7). Moreover, $\mathrm{Sd} \simeq 1$, the identity isomorphism. This we proceed to show by defining D (63). First $D\,\Delta_0 = 0$ and $\mathrm{Sd} \mid \Delta_0$ is the identity. The vertices of Δ_n are denoted by $\{(i) \mid i = 0, \ldots, n\}$ and the barycenter of Δ_m by (Δ_m). Then, with $\frown$ denoting the join,

$$\text{(4.2a)}\quad D\Delta_1 = (\Delta_1)\frown\Delta_1 - (\Delta_1)(0)(\Delta_1) - (\Delta_1)(\Delta_1)(1) = (\Delta_1)\,\Delta_1 - (\Delta_1)\mathrm{Sd}\,\Delta_1$$

The induction definition admits that D has been defined for Δ_i, $i \leq p - 1$ and satisfies (63.1)

$$\text{(4.2b)}\qquad \partial D\,\Delta_i = \Delta_i - \mathrm{Sd}\,\Delta_i - D\,\partial\Delta_i.$$

Define

$$\text{(4.2c)}\qquad D\,\Delta_p = (\Delta_p)\frown\Delta_p - (\Delta_p)\frown\mathrm{Sd}\,\Delta_p - (\Delta_p)\frown D\,\partial\Delta_p.$$

Then

$$\partial D\,\Delta_p = \Delta_p - \mathrm{Sd}\,\Delta_p - D\,\partial\Delta_p - (\Delta_p)\,\partial(\Delta_p - \mathrm{Sd}\,\Delta_p - D\partial\Delta_p).$$

Apply (4.2b) to the terms in $\partial\Delta_p$. Then

$$\partial D\,\Delta_p = \Delta_p - \mathrm{Sd}\,\Delta_p - D\,\partial\Delta_p$$

whence, since (4.2b) is true for $i = 0$ or $i = 1$, it is valid for $i = p$ as well. This furnishes an alternative proof of (71.7), granting the allowability of Sd.

If Sd is iterated, let $D^m = \Sigma_{m=0}^{m-1} D \operatorname{Sd}^j$. Then (4.2b) yields

(4.2d) $$\partial D^m \Delta_p = \Delta_p - \operatorname{Sd}^m \Delta_p - D^m \partial \Delta_p.$$

On replacing Δ_p by u_p, the formal developments just concluded are seen to be valid for the singular chains under obvious definition of Sd. Specifically the barycentric subdivision of u_n, namely Sd u_n is the singular chain defined in analogy with (71.1a), by

(4.2e) $$\operatorname{Sd} u_n = (Sd\, \Delta_n, u_n) = \Sigma \pm ({}^1\Delta_n{}^i, u_n) = \Sigma \pm {}^1u_n{}^i,$$

where $({}^1\Delta_n^i, u_n)$ stands for the equivalence class (4.1) of $({}^1\Delta_n^i, u_n \mid {}^1\Delta_n^i)$ since ${}^1\Delta_n^i$ is not a standard simplex. With singular chains replacing simplexes, (4.2c) is

(4.2f) $$\partial D^m c_p = c_p - \operatorname{Sd}^m c_p - D^m \partial c_p$$

where $c_p = \Sigma\, g_j\, u_p{}^j$.

PROBLEM

8-6. Let K be a finite complex and suppose L is a closed subset. Show any singular chain on $N({}^1L)$ is deformable onto a subdivision of L. Cf. Remark in (76).

Let $\alpha = \{a_i\}$ be an open cover, possibly noncountable, of X. Denote by $\boldsymbol{A}$ the complex consisting of singular simplexes $\{u\}$ with $\|u\|$ in some set a_i of α. We say $\boldsymbol{A}$ has mesh α and that the simplexes of $\boldsymbol{A}$ are of **diameter** $< \alpha$ and write $\alpha < \|u_p\|$.

Lemma 4.3.

(4.3a)
$$\begin{array}{ccc} H(\boldsymbol{A}, R) & \longrightarrow & H(SX, R) \\ \nwarrow & & \swarrow \\ & H(SX/\boldsymbol{A}, R) & \end{array}$$
is exact.

(4.3b) $$H_*(SX, G) \approx H_*(\boldsymbol{A}, G).$$

Our first assertion follows by (61.12) from the exactness of

$$0 \to C(\boldsymbol{A}) \to C(SX) \to C(SX)/C(\boldsymbol{A}) \to 0.$$

Let $b_i = u_p{}^{-1}(a_i \cap \|u_p\|)$, $a_i \in \alpha$. The diameter of the simplexes in the mth subdivision of Δ_p goes to 0 with $m \to 0$. Hence, for some m each simplex in $Sd^m\, \Delta_p$ lies entirely within some b_i by a Lebesgue number argument (**A**11.17) since only a finite number of b_i's need be considered. Let m_j be this m value for the singular simplex $u_p = u_p^j$. Let $m \geq \sup m_j$ over all u_p^j's entering c_p.

Suppose throughout that the coefficient ring is R and that

(4.3c) $$c_p \in Z_p(SX/\boldsymbol{A}), \qquad p \geq 1.$$

Then, for some m, $\mathrm{Sd}^m c_p \in {}_SC_p(A)$. According to (4.3c) $\partial c_p \in {}_SC_{p-1}(A)$ whence $D^j \partial c_p \in {}_SC_p(A)$ by analogue with (4.2c) and so $\partial(D^m c_p) = c_p \bmod {}_SC(A)$, i.e., $c_p \in B_p(SX/A)$. Accordingly $Z_p(SX/A) = B_p(SX/A)$ or

$$H_p(SX/A) = 0, \qquad p \geq 1. \tag{4.3d}$$

However, for $p = 0$, $u_0 \Delta_0$ is a point, so $c_0 \in C_0(A)$ whence (4.3d) is valid for $p \geq 0$. All this being so, (4.3b) follows from (4.3a).

If the cover α is not open, but $\alpha' = \{\_a_i\}$ is a cover also where $\_a_i$ is the **interior** of a_i, then α is an **effectively open cover** and A and A' are the associated complexes of mesh α and α' respectively. An important application of the following corollary is made in (92.1c).

Corollary 4.4. *If α is an effectively open cover of X, then*

$$H_*(SX, G) \approx H(A, G)(\approx H(A', G)).$$

The argument for (4.3b) goes through in detail.

5. THE SINGULAR COCHAIN GRATING. Definition 5.1. We paraphrase (46.1) for the definition of the singular R grating on X. This is ${}_SC(X, G) = Hom(C(SX, \text{J}), R)$. Its elements are cochains determined by their values on the singular simplexes, by linearity. Thus

$$f^p(u_p)(= f^p(u_pT)(4.1)) \in R$$

$$df^p(u_{p+1}) = \Sigma^{p+1}(-1)^i f^p(u_p(i))$$

where again

$$u_p(i) = u_{p+1} \mid \sigma_q{}^i.$$

Write Δ_{p+q} as $\Delta_p \cdot {}_q\Delta$ where Δ_p is the forward p face and ${}_q\Delta$ is the back q face (21.2). Then u_{p+q} can be written $u_p \cdot {}_qu$ or $u_p \cdot u_q$ where $u_p = u_{p+q} \mid \Delta_p$ and $u_q = u_{p+q} \mid {}_q\Delta$.

PROBLEM

8-7. Express $u_p \cdot {}_qu$ in terms of the t_r^i maps.

A product on ${}_SC^p(X, R) \otimes {}_SC^q(X, R)$ to ${}_SC^{p+q}(X, R)$ is defined by $(f^p g^q)\, u_{p+q} = f^p(u_p)\, g^q(u_q)$.

Supports are defined by the requirement that $x \bar{\in} \| f^p\|$ if for some neighborhood $V(x)$, $f^p(u_p \mid \|u_p\| \subset V(x)) = 0$ where $\|u_p\|$ is defined in (4.1).

We define

$$C^p(SX, R) = {}_SC^p(X, R)/{}_SC^p(X, R)_0$$

where ${}_SC^p(X, R)_0 = \{f^p \mid \|f^p\| = \varnothing\}$ is sometimes *shortened to* $C({}_0SX)$.

It is highly significant that both the singular chain grating and the singular grating exist for general spaces, so that restrictions to locally compact or paracompact spaces are here matters of convenience and not of necessity.

Lemma 5.2. $H^p(SX/A, R) \approx 0$.

Write $[c_p]$ for the typical element of $C_p(SX/A, \text{J})$. Let $z^p \in Z^p(SX/A, R)$, $p \geq 1$. Then $0 = \delta z^p[c_{p+1}] = z^p[\partial c_{p+1}]$, so

$$z^p \mid B_p(SX/A, \text{J}) = 0. \tag{5.2a}$$

By (4.3d), (5.2a) is tantamount to

$$z^p \mid Z_p(SX/A, \text{J}) = 0. \tag{5.2b}$$

We need the fact that $C_m(SX/A, \text{J})$ is a free group. Hence taking $\psi = d$ in (62.1c)

$$C_m(SX/A, \text{J}) \approx Z_m(SX/A, \text{J}) \oplus B_{m-1}(SX/A, \text{J}). \tag{5.2c}$$

Accordingly there is a cochain, f^{p-1}, defined on $B_{p-1}(SX/A, \text{J})$ to R such that

$$z^p[c_p] = f^{p-1}([c_{p-1}] = \partial\,[c_p]). \tag{5.2d}$$

Since we are dealing with free groups a different decomposition than that in (5.2c) is valid also,

$$C_{p-1}(SX/A, \text{J}) \rightleftharpoons B_{p-1}(SX/A, \text{J}) \oplus Q.$$

Hence f^{p-1} can be extended to F^{p-1} on $C_{p-1}(SX/A, \text{J})$ by demanding $F^{p-1} \mid Q = 0$. Accordingly taking (5.2d) into account

$$z^p = \delta\, F^{p-1}. \tag{5.2e}$$

For $p = 0$, since every 0 chain is in $C_0(A, \text{J})$

$$Z_0(SX/A, \text{J}) \subset C_0(SX/A, \text{J}) = \frac{C_0(SX, \text{J})}{C_0(A, \text{J})} = 0. \tag{5.2f}$$

The lemma follows from (5.2e) for $p \geq 1$ and from (5.2f) for $p = 0$.

The next result finds employment in (92.1c).

Corollary 5.3. *If α is an effectively open cover, then $H^*(SX, R) \approx H^*(A, R)$.*

Except for a single reference to (4.4) instead of (4.3), the demonstration of (5.2) is valid for α merely effectively open. Then exactness of the cohomology sequence of the pair SX, A implies (5.3).

Theorem 5.4. $H^p(SX/{}_0SX, R) \approx H^p(SX, R), \qquad p \geq 0.$

The exactness of

$$\begin{array}{ccc} H^*({}_0SX, R) & \longrightarrow & H^*(SX, R) \\ & \nwarrow \quad \swarrow & \\ & H^*(SX/{}_0SX, R) & \end{array}$$

is immediate and hence it is sufficient to prove $H({}_0SX, R) \approx 0$. Let $z^p \in Z^p({}_0SX, R)$, $p \geq 1$. Since $\|z^p\| = \varnothing$, for each $x \in X$ and some neighborhood $V(x)$, $z^p(u_p) = 0$ whenever $\|u_p\| \subset V(x)$. The collection $\{V(x) = a_x\}$ constitutes an open cover of X which we denote by $\alpha' = \{a_x\}$ with associated complex A. Thus $z^p \in Z^p(SX/A, R)$. In view of (5.2), $z^p = \delta w^{p-1}$, where $w^{p-1} \in C^{p-1}(SX/A, R)$, or $w^{p-1} u_{p-1} = 0$ for $\|u_{p-1}\| > \alpha$ (4.3). Hence $w^{p-1} \in C^{p-1}({}_0SX, R)$. Accordingly $Z^p({}_0SX, R) \approx B^p({}_0SX, R)$ or

(5.4a) $$H^p({}_0SX, R) \approx 0, \qquad p \geq 1.$$

For $p = 0$ note that $f^0 \in C^0(SX, R)$ implies $f^0 u_0 = 0$ for all u_0. Plainly $C^0({}_0SX, R) = 0$. Hence (5.4a) is valid for $p \geq 0$.

Remark. (5.4) does not have a counterpart in the Alexander grating (6.1).

Theorem 5.5. *The singular homology or cohomology grating in R^n is acyclic.*

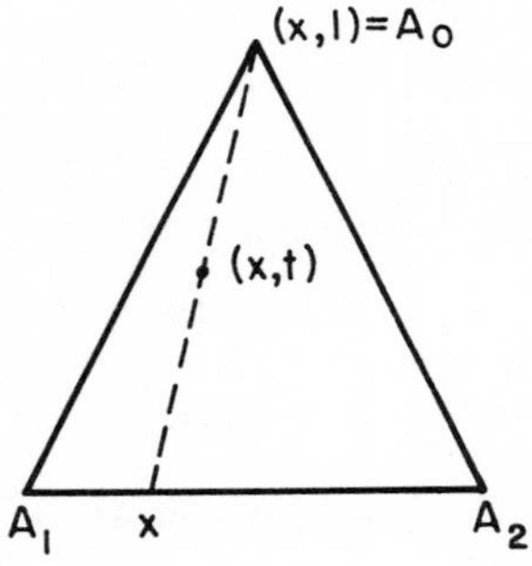

Figure 8-2

Let u_p be the singular simplex with representative ($\sigma_p = v^1 \ldots v^{p+1}$, u_p) (4.1). Let σ_{p+1} be the join of a new vertex v^0 and σ_p so that σ_{p+1} has the points $\{(x, t) \mid x \in \sigma_p, t \in I, (x, 1) = v^0\}$. Then σ_{p+1} is the cone over σ_p (21.2). Let y_0 be the singular simplex with $y_0(v^0) = y_0$. Define $D\, u_p = u_{p+1}$ by

(5.5a) $$u_{p+1} = (D\, u_p)\colon (x, t \mid x \in \sigma_p, t \in I) = (1 - t)u_p(x) + ty_0.$$

Then, for $p > 0$, on summing from $i = 1$

$$D\, \partial u_p = \Sigma\, (-1)^{i-1}\, Du_{p-1}{}^i = \Sigma\, (-1)^{i-1}\, u_p^{\,i}\,.$$

We write the ith face of u_{p+1} as $u_p{}^i$ so $(D\,u_p)^i = u_p{}^i$. Then $(D\,u_p)^0 = u_p{}^0$ corresponds to $u_{p+1} \mid \sigma_p = u_p$.

$$\begin{aligned} \partial D\,u_p &= \Sigma\,(-1)^i (D\,u_p)^i \\ &= (D\,u_p)^0 + \Sigma\,(-1)^i (D\,u_p)^i \\ &= u_p - D\,\partial u_p. \end{aligned} \tag{5.5b}$$

For $p = 0$, since $\partial u_0 = 0$, $D\,\partial u_0 = 0$ whence by (5.4a),

$$\begin{aligned} D\,\partial u_0 + \partial D u_0 &= D u_0 \Big|_{t=0}^{t=1} \\ &= u_0 - y_0. \end{aligned} \tag{5.5c}$$

Hence, referring to (63.1) the import of (5.5b) and (5.5c) is that there is a deformation

$$h\colon u_p = 0 \qquad p > 0,$$
$$h\colon u_0 = y_0.$$

We apply (63.2).

To derive the corresponding result for cohomology groups we need merely define the endomorphism $\bar{D}$ by

$$(\bar{D}\,f^p)(u_{p-1}) = f^p(D\,u_{p-1}).$$

Definition 5.6. An arc is the homeomorph of the unit interval $0 \le t \le 1$. The images x_0 and x_1 of 0 and 1 are called the **end points** of the arc and the arc **joins** x_0 and x_1. The space X is **arcwise connected** if every pair of points, x_0 and x_1, are end points of some arc; X is locally (arcwise) connected or $0 - lc$ or lc^0 if any open set $U(\bar{x})$ contains an open set $V(\bar{x})$ such that if x and y are in $V(\bar{x})$ they are end points of an arc in $U(\bar{x})$; X is q-**locally connected** if every singular q cycle on $V(\bar{x})$ bounds on $U(\bar{x})$. We then write (U, V) and say U dominates V. It is lc^p if it is $q - lc$ for $q \le p$. It is lc^∞ if it is $q - lc$ for $q < \infty$.

Theorem 5.7. *If X is lc^∞, its singular R grating is full.*

First we demonstrate R simplicity. If $f^p \in Z^p(x_0\,\mathrm{A})$ then for some $U(x_0)$ a neighborhood of x_0, $(\delta f^p)(u_{p+1}) = 0$ if $\|u_{p+1}\| \subset U(x_0)$. *For* $p = 0$, $Z_0(x_0\,\mathrm{A}) = \{f^0 \mid f^0(x_1) = f(x_2) = \text{constant in } V(x_0)\}$.

For $p > 0$, if c_p and c_p' are two singular chains on $V(x_0)$ with $\partial(c_p - c_p') = 0$, then for some c_{p+1} on $U(x_0)$, $c_p - c_p' = \partial c_{p+1}$. Hence, if $f^p \in Z^p(x_0\,\mathrm{A})$, $p > 0$,

$$f^p\,c_p - f^p\,c_p' = f^p\,\partial c_{p+1} = (\delta f^p)(c_{p+1}) = 0.$$

Accordingly f^p depends only on ∂c_p over $V(x_0)$; i.e., $f^p\,c_p = g^{p-1}(\partial c_p)$, where so far g is defined on bounding cycles alone, in $V(x_0)$. Let $W(x_0)$ be dominated by $V(x_0)$. Any cycle on $W(x_0)$ is bounding over $V(x_0)$ so g^{p-1} is defined on the cycles over $W(x_0)$. Since the singular chains form a free group $Z_{p-1}(W(x_0))$ is a direct summand, so $c_{p-1}(W(x_0)) = Z_{p-1}(W(x_0)) \oplus D(W(x_0))$, $D(W(x_0)) \approx B_{p-2}W(x_0)$. We extend g^{p-1} to $'g^{p-1}$ on $Z_{p-1}(Wx_0)$ to $C_{p-1}(W(x_0))$ by setting $'g^{p-1} \mid D(W(x_0)) = 0$. Let $c_p \in C_p(W(x_0))$. Then $f^p(c_p) = {'g^{p-1}}\, \partial c_p = (\delta' g^{p-1})c_p$. Accordingly $f^p = \delta' g^{p-1}$ on $W(x_0) \subset V(x_0)$ and hence $[f^p] = 0$.

Let $\alpha = \{a_i \mid i = 1, \ldots, N\}$ be a fine cover of X and let C be any compact subset of X. Let W be an open set with compact closure with

$$C \cup \textstyle\bigcup_{i=1}^{i=N-1} \bar{a}_i \subset W.$$

Write b_i for $W \cap a_i$, $i = 1, \ldots, N$. There is a partition of the identity relative to the cover $\beta = \{b_i\}$ of $\bar{W}$. That is, there exist maps F^i on $\bar{W}$ to R with $0 \leq F^i \leq 1$ with $F^i(x \mid x \bar{\in} \bar{b}_i) = 0$ and $\Sigma F^i(x \mid \bar{W}) = 1$. Evidently F^N can be extended to $\bar{W}^\sim$ so that $\{x \mid F^N(x) \neq 0\}$ is compact. Let u_0 be the singular simplex $u_p \mid v^0$ where v^0 is the first vertex of Δ_p, (4.1). (Such a u_0 is sometimes called the **leading vertex** of u_p.) Define u_i^0 by $u_i^0(u_0) = F^i(u_0(v^0))$. Then $\{u_i^0\}$ constitute the local identities u_C^i required in (1.22).

6. ALEXANDER GRATING. The most representative grating is perhaps the one next described.

Definition 6.1. The cochains f^p constituting $\mathrm{C}^p(X, R)$ are now defined as maps of ordered $p + 1$ triples $x_1, \ldots, x_{p+1}$ in X into a ring R. The points $\{x_i \mid i = 1, \ldots, p + 1\}$ need not be distinct. The $p + 1$ triple may be considered a replete simplex u_p on X. Indeed with K the replete complex of such simplexes, f^p can be viewed as a member of *Hom* $(C_p(K, \mathrm{J}), R)$ in consonance with (46.1). Addition and multiplication are defined by

$$(f^p + g^p)(x_0, \ldots, x_p) = f^p(x_0, \ldots, x_p) + g^p(x_0, \ldots, x_p).$$

(6.1a) $$(f^p g^q)(x_0, \ldots, x_{p+q}) = f^p(x_0, \ldots, x_p)g^q(x_p, \ldots, x_{p+q}).$$

Since R is a ring, the right-hand side is meaningful and $\mathrm{C}(X, R) = \oplus\, \mathrm{C}^p(X, R)$ is a graded algebra with generally noncommutative multiplication.

We define supports by the condition $x \bar{\in} \|f^p\|$ only if for some open neighborhood $V(x)$ and all $p + 1$ tuples in $V(x)$,

(6.1b) $$f^p(x_0, \ldots, x_p \mid x_i \in V(x)) = 0.$$

The coboundary operator d is defined as expected from the replete simplex analogy, by

(6.1c) $$(df^p)(x_0, \ldots, x_{p+1}) = \Sigma(-1)^i f^p(x_0, \ldots, \hat{i}, \ldots, x_{p+1})$$

The defining relations (6.1a) show that $\{f^p \mid \|f^p\| = \varnothing\}$ is an ideal which we denote by ${}_0\mathrm{C}(X, R)$. Then

$$\mathrm{A} = \mathrm{A}(X, R) = \mathrm{C}(X, R)/{}_0\mathrm{C}(X, R)$$

is the *Alexander-Wallace-Spanier* R grating or more succinctly Alexander R grating (where $\mathrm{C}(X, R)$ or C is the Alexander R pregrating, or unreduced grating) and Alexander R **·grating** when the supports are compact.

We check that (1.1d) is verified by the induced operator $d[f^p] = [df^p]$ where $[f^p] \in \mathrm{A}(X, R)$, $f^p \in \mathrm{C}(X, R)$. Indeed from $x \bar{\in} \|[f^p]\| (= \|f^p\|)$ follows

$$\varnothing = \|f^p\| \cap x \supset \|df^p\| \cap x = \|[df^p]\| \cap x.$$

A product space interpretation is convenient. Thus let X^{p+1} be the product space

$$X^{p+1} = X \times \cdots \times X.$$

The **diagonal** Δ^{p+1}, or simply Δ, consists of the points $\{(x_0, \ldots, x_p) \mid x_0 = x_1 = \cdots = x_p\}$. A **vicinity**, V^{p+1} (of Δ^{p+1}) is an open set in X^{p+1} containing Δ^{p+1}. If $\alpha = \{a_i\}$ is a cover of X, then $\bigcup_{a_i \in \alpha}(a_i \times \cdots \times a_i)$ constitutes a vicinity. A cochain f^p in $\mathrm{C}^p(X, R)$ is a function on X^{p+1} to R and ${}_0\mathrm{C}(X, R) = \{f^p \mid f^p \mid V^p = 0$ for some vicinity, possibly dependent on $f^p\}$. If R is the topologized ring of real numbers or complex numbers, and if the maps $\{f^p\}$ are continuous on X^p to R, the grating A is referred to as the **continuous** Alexander grating.

Lemma 6.2.

(6.2a) $$H(\mathrm{C}) = H(\mathrm{C}, R) \approx R$$

(6.2b) A *is* R *simple.*

We use the idea of the cone construction as in the proof in (5.5). Let y_0 be an arbitrary fixed point in X acting as the vertex of a cone

Define D by

$$(Df^p)(x_1, \ldots, x_p) = f^p(y_0, x_1, \ldots, x_p), \qquad p > 0.$$

Therefore, for $p > 0$,

$$\begin{aligned}(dDf^p)(x_1, \ldots, x_{p+1}) &= \Sigma(-1)^{i+1}\,(Df^p)(x_1, \ldots, \hat{\imath}, \ldots, x_{p+1})\\ &= \Sigma_1(-1)^{j+1} f^p(y_0, x_1, \ldots, \hat{\jmath}, \ldots, x_{p+1}).\\ (D\,df^p)(x_1, \ldots, x_{p+1}) &= (df^p)(y_0, x_1, \ldots, x_{p+1})\\ &= \Sigma_0(-1)^j f^p(y_0, x_1, \ldots, \hat{\jmath}, \ldots, x_{p+1}).\end{aligned} \tag{6.2c}$$

Accordingly

(6.2d) $dDf^p + D\,df^p = f^p - 0 \qquad \text{for } p > 0.$

For $p = 0$, define $Df^0 = 0$, whence from (6.2c)

(6.2e) $(dDf^0 + D\,df^0)(x_1) = f^0(x_1) - f^0(y_0)$.

From (6.2d) and (6.2e) the homotopy **h** (63.2) satisfies

(6.2f) $\mathbf{h}(f^p) = 0, \qquad p > 0,$

$\mathbf{h}(f^0) = f^0(y_0),$

Evidently **h** decreases supports and is allowable. Hence

(6.2g) $h^*\colon H^p(\mathrm{C}, R) \to 0, \qquad p > 0.$

Suppose $f^0(y_0) = r_0 \in R$. Then (6.2f) asserts $\mathbf{h}f^0$ takes on the value r_0 for every point of X. This means the 0-dimensional cochains are constant functions and therefore are automatically cocycles. Since there are no -1-dimensional cochains, $B^0(\mathrm{C}, R) = 0$ so $h^*\mathbf{f}^0 \in h^*\, H^0(\mathrm{C}, R)$. For each r, define f^0 by $f^0(y_0) = r$. Therefore

(6.2h) $h^*\, H^0(\mathrm{C}, R) \xrightarrow{\approx} R.$

By (63.2), (6.2g) and (6.2h) are tantamount to (6.2a).

Plainly $\mathbf{h}\mathrm{C}_{y_0} \subset \mathrm{C}_{y_0}$ since **h** decreases supports. Hence **h** induces a homomorphism h on $y_0\,\mathrm{C} = \mathrm{C}/\mathrm{C}_{y_0} \approx \mathrm{A}/\mathrm{A}_{y_0} = y_0\,\mathrm{A}$ to $y_0\,\mathrm{A}$, given by

$$h[f^p] = [\mathbf{h}f^p] = 0, \qquad p > 0$$

$$h[f^p] = [\mathbf{h}f^0].$$

By reason of (6.2f) $[\mathbf{h}f^0]$ and hf^0 are in 1–1 correspondence and hence $h^*H(y_0\,\mathrm{C}, R) \approx R$. In (63.3), interpret A as C, C as C_{y_0}, l as the identity whence $H(y_0\,\mathrm{A}, R) = H(y_0\,\mathrm{C}, R) \approx R$.

Theorem 6.3. **(a)** *The Alexander R ˙grating is full, and* **(b)** *the continuous Alexander R ·grating is full also as well as P-full.*

For (6.3a): The fine cover $\alpha = \{a_i \mid \bar{a}_i \text{ compact}, 1 \le N - 1, a_{\tilde{N}} \text{ compact}\}$ admits a fine subcover $\beta = \{b_i \mid b_i \subset \bar{b}_i \subset a_i\}$ (**A** 13.2). Denote by $\bar{\beta}$, $\{\bar{b}_i \mid b_i \in \beta\}$. We obtain a partition of X by

$$c_1 = \bar{b}_1,\ c_i = \bar{b}_i - (\textstyle\bigcup_{j=1}^{j=i-1} \bar{b}_j).$$

Thus, each point of X is in a unique c_i. Define u_i as the characteristic function of c_i; i.e., u_i is a local identity. Hence, $\|u_i\| = \bar{c}_i$ [and so $u_i = u_{d_i,q_i}$ where $d_i \subset c_i$ in the notation of (1.20)],

(6.3c) $(u_i f^p)(x_0, \ldots, x_p) = u_i(x_0) f^p(x_0, \ldots, x_p).$

Hence

$$\|u_i f^p\| \subset \|u_i\| \cap \|f^p\| \subset \bar{c}_i \subset \bar{b}_i \subset a_i.$$

Moreover

$$\begin{aligned}((\Sigma u_i)f^p)(x_0, \ldots, x_p) &= (\Sigma u_i(x_0))f^p(x_0, \ldots, x_p)\\ &= f^p(x_0, \ldots, x_p)\end{aligned}$$

since x_0 is in some c_i. This disposes of (6.3a).

For (6.3b): Continuous local identities u_i can be exhibited by taking the partitions of unity (**A**, 15.1b) for a fine cover just as in the last part of the proof of (5.7). Finally if β is a locally finite cover, it is a point finite cover, and so by (**A**, 15.1a) there is a partition of the identity relative to β whence with the prescription (6.3c) again, P-fullness is established.

Let C(X) and C(Y) be Alexander R pregratings on X and on Y respectively. If ψ: $X \to Y$ defines a possibly noncontinuous transformation, then $\psi^{\#}$ is allowable on $\mathrm{C}^p(Y)$ to $\mathrm{C}^p(X)$. Indeed

$$\begin{aligned}(d\psi^{\#} f^p)(x_0, \ldots, x_{p+1}) &= \Sigma(-1)^i f^p(\psi(x_0), \ldots, \hat{i}, \ldots, \psi(x_{p+1}))\\ &= (df^p)(\psi(x_0, \ldots, \psi(x_{p+1}))\\ &= \psi^{\#}\, df^p(x_0, \ldots, x_{p+1}).\end{aligned}$$

The continuity requirement on ψ enters if one wishes $\psi^{\#}$ to induce a homomorphism on the separated gratings. Thus for continuous ψ, $\psi^{\#}$: ${}_0\mathrm{C}^p(Y) \to {}_0\mathrm{C}^p(X)$. Indeed $f \in {}_0\mathrm{C}^p(Y)$ is assurance that for some vicinity, v^{p+1}, of the diagonal in $Y, f \mid V^{p+1} = 0$. The continuity of ψ carries over to the induced map, also written ψ, on $X^{p+1} \to Y^{p+1}$. Hence $W^{p+1}(X) = \psi^{-1} V^{p+1}$ is a vicinity of the diagonal on X^{p+1} and

$$\psi^{\#} f \mid V^{p+1} = f \mid V^{p+1} = 0.$$

Accordingly $\psi^{\#}$ induces a homomorphism on

$$\mathrm{A}^p(Y) = \mathrm{C}^p(Y)/{}_0\mathrm{C}^p(Y) \to \mathrm{C}^p(X)/{}_0\mathrm{C}^p(X) = \mathrm{A}^p(X).$$

Let X, A be a pair with i the inclusion map i: $A \to X$. Then $\mathrm{C}^p(X, A)$ consists of functions $\{f^p\}$ with $\|f^p\| \cap A = \varnothing$. Since supports are to be closed, if $a \bar{\in} A$, $f^p(a_0, \ldots, a_p) = 0$ for $a_0, \ldots, a_p \in U(a)$. Hence $f^p \mid V^{p+1}(A) = 0$. This can also be expressed by $f^p \in i^{\#-1}\, {}_0\mathrm{C}(A)$. The separated grating is then $\mathrm{C}^p(X, A)/{}_0\mathrm{C}(X) = \mathrm{A}^p(X, A)$. If ψ maps $X, A \to Y$, B then $\psi^{\#}$ $\mathrm{A}(X, A) \to \mathrm{A}(Y, B)$ is allowable. If compact gratings are being discussed, then ψ is understood to be proper. More generally, when F families of supports are assumed, ψ is to be adapted with respect to them.

Remark. The inherent simplicity of the Alexander grating is one thing, the matter of exhibiting a nonbounding cocycle even in the simplest cases is something else again. For instance, on S^1 such a cocycle, f^1, is defined by representing the circle as the reals mod 1. Then $f^1(x_0, x_1) = 1$ if $x_0 < 0 < x_1 < x_0 + \frac{1}{2}$, $= -1$ if $x_0 \geq 0 > x_1 > x_0 - \frac{1}{2}$, $= 0$ otherwise. (If mod 1 is dropped a nonbounding cocycle in $Z^1(R^1, \mathrm{J})$ ensues with closed support $\bigcup \pm m$.)

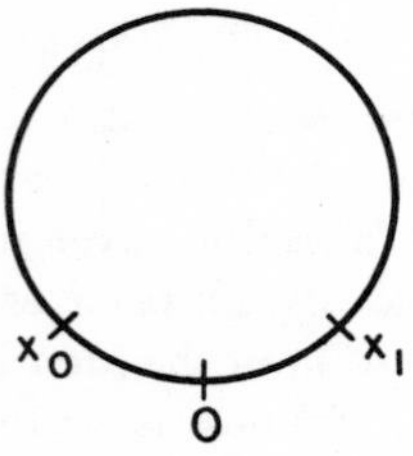

Figure 8-3

A nonbounding cocycle on S^n can be represented by using a convex cell generalization of the definition of f^1. The following problems continue these remarks.

PROBLEMS

8-7. Show $\|f^1\|$ is the point $x = 0$. Interpret the construction. Show f^1 is nonbounding.

8-8. Define a nonbounding cocycle on S^n, explicitly.

7. ČECH OMOLOGY. The omology rings or modules can be formulated in terms of covers and inverse and direct limits. Let X, A be a pair of spaces (2.1) and suppose $\{(\alpha, \alpha')\}$ constitutes a cofinal family of open covers (2.4). Let a be the nerve of α and a' the nerve of α' so a' is a closed sub complex of a. If $(\alpha, \alpha') < (\beta, \beta')$, there is a generally nonunique projection $p^{b,b'}_{a,a'}$ of (b, b') into (a, a'). Suppose A is closed in X. Then by (2.6) the cover pair is determined by α and we shall write $p_a{}^b$ bearing in mind $p_a{}^b \mid b' \subset a'$. The homomorphisms on the chain modules are defined by linearity. Thus if $p_a{}^b\sigma_m(a) = \sigma_n(b)$ then

$$p_a{}^b{}_\# \, \sigma_m(a) = \sigma_m(b), \qquad m = n,$$
$$= 0 \qquad m \neq n.$$

Lemma 7.1. *If $p_a{}^b$ and $p_a'{}^b$ are two projections, then $p_a{}^b{}_\# \simeq p_a'{}^b{}_\#$ whence $p_a{}^b{}_* = p'{}_a{}^b{}_*$. Similarly $p^{a*}_b = p'^{a*}_b$.*

With suitable reordering, if necessary

$$p_a{}^b((b_1), \ldots, (b_n)) = (a_1), \ldots, (a_n),$$
$$p_a'^b((b_1), \ldots, (b_n)) = (a_{1'}), \ldots, (a_{n'}),$$

where i and i' may not be the same. Since

$$\bigcap a_i \supset \bigcap b_i \subset \bigcap a_{i'},$$

$$\bigcap a_i \cap \bigcap a_{i'} \neq \varnothing.$$

Hence $(a_1), \ldots, (a_n)$ and $(a_{1'}), \ldots, (a_{n'})$ are faces of a common simplex. The lemma then follows from (71.6) under the obvious modification for pairs of complexes.

Definition 7.2. Denote by $H_m(a, a', G)$ the obvious homology groups. The system $\Sigma^- = \{H_m(a, a', G), p_a{}^b{}_*\}$ is an inverse system. We define the **Čech groups,** $H(X, A, G)$, by

$$\text{(7.2a)}\qquad \begin{aligned} H_m(X, A, G) &= \underleftarrow{\mathsf{L}}\, \Sigma^-, \\ H^m(X, A, G) &= \underrightarrow{\mathsf{L}}\, \{H^m(a, a', G), p^a{}_b{}^*\}. \end{aligned}$$

Let $z_m(a) \in Z_m(a, a', G)$. Since $p_a{}^b{}_\#$ is determined only up to homotopy, it is natural to use equality and matching in the sense of homology. Thus a Čech cycle, z, is

$$\text{(7.2b)}\qquad z = \{z_m(a, a', G) \mid z_m(a, a', G) \sim p_a{}^b{}_\#\, z_m(b, b', G)\}$$

and the *Čech group of cycles* is defined by

$$Z_m(X, A, G) = \underleftarrow{\mathsf{L}}\, \{Z_m(a, a', G), p_a{}^b{}_\#\}.$$

Similarly the bounding cycles are given by

$$B_m(X, A, G) = \underleftarrow{\mathsf{L}}\, \{B_m(b, b', G), p_a{}^b{}_\#\}.$$

In general the module $Z_m(X, A, G)/B_m(X, A, G)$ may not be the same as $H_m(X, A, G)$, but in the important case that X is compact, the modules are identical according to (77.12).

EXAMPLE 8-2. In the plane suppose A is the union of B, C, and D.

$$B = \{(x, y) \mid y = \sin 1/x, \qquad 0 < x \leq \tfrac{2}{3}\pi\}$$

$$C = \{(0, y) \mid |y| \leq 1\}$$

$$D = \{(x, y) \mid (x - \tfrac{1}{3}\pi)^2 + (y - 1)^2 = (\tfrac{2}{3}\pi)^2, \qquad y \leq 1\}.$$

Then A carries a nonbounding Čech cycle but no nonbounding singular cycle, i.e., $H_1(SA, \mathrm{J}) = 0 \neq H_1(A, \mathrm{J})$.

We sketch the explanation. Since the map of a segment is locally connected, no concrete 1 simplex can contain a point in C as well as a point in B. Hence, no finite union of concrete simplexes can do this. Thus, any finite chain is carried by a finite number of disjunct arcs and these cannot close up and so cannot carry a nonbounding cycle.

For the Čech groups let C be a small circle interior to A. Let $\beta = \{b_j\}$ be a finite open cover of C with nerve b containing a nonbounding cycle. Let θ be the center of C and let $z \in C$. The ray θz extended to ω cuts A in one or

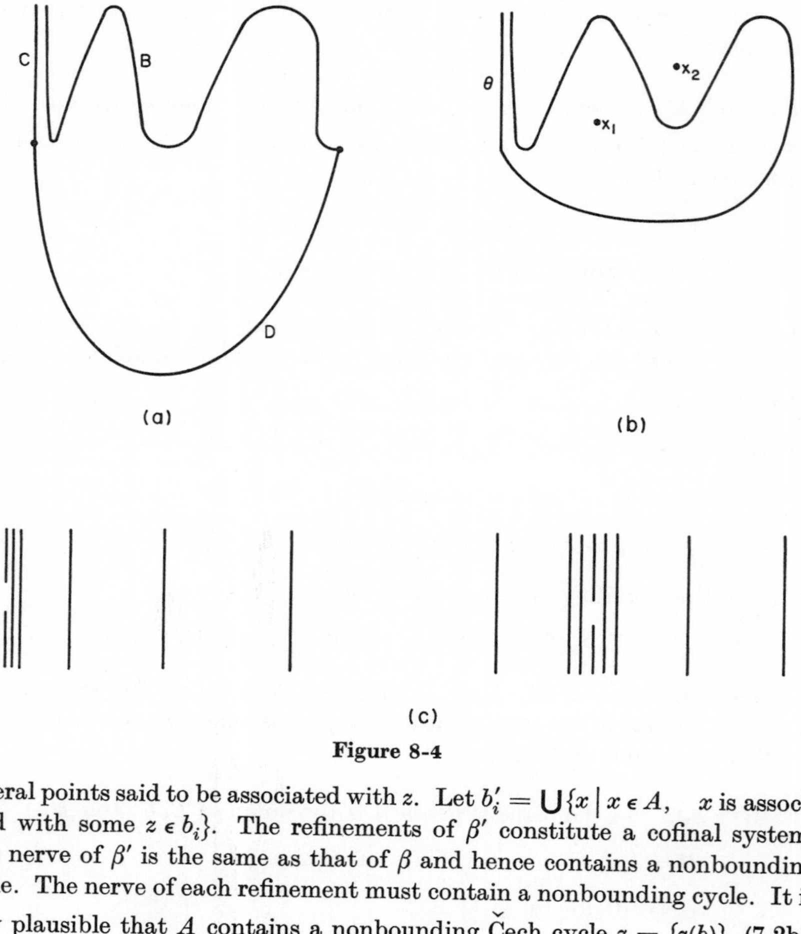

Figure 8-4

several points said to be associated with z. Let $b_i' = \bigcup\{x \mid x \in A, \quad x \text{ is associated with some } z \in b_i\}$. The refinements of β' constitute a cofinal system. The nerve of β' is the same as that of β and hence contains a nonbounding cycle. The nerve of each refinement must contain a nonbounding cycle. It is now plausible that A contains a nonbounding Čech cycle $z = \{z(b)\}$, (7.2b).

In the next two striking examples a single point is removed from a closed set.

EXAMPLE 8-3. From A of Example 8-2, remove the point $x, y = 0, 0 = \theta$ so $A' = A - \theta$. Then $B = R^2 - A$ constitutes the interior points of $R^2 - A'$. Evidently B consists of two components K_1 and K_2. Let x_1 and x_2 be points of K_1 and K_2. There is no continuum (i.e., a compact, connected set) in $R^2 - A'$ with x_1 and x_2 as end points. Hence $x_1 - x_2$ is nonbounding if a compact support is required, and so ${}_S\tilde{H}_0(R^2 - A', J) \neq 0$.

EXAMPLE 8-4. Let A consist of the segments, $(x, y) = \left(\frac{1}{n}, |y| \leq 1\right)$, $n = 1, 2, \ldots,$ and $(0, 0 < |y| \leq 1)$, that is to say $\theta = (0, 0) \bar{\in} A$. Let $B = R^2 - A$. In contradistinction to the situation in Example 8-2 every pair of points in the interior of B can be connected by a simple arc entirely in B yet $\tilde{H}_0(SB, J) \neq 0$. To see this, note that A is homeomorphic to the subset A_e for which $x = \frac{1}{2n}$ or 0 or to A_0 for which $x = \frac{1}{2n+1}$ or 0. Let Q^- denote the reflection of Q in the y axis. Since A_0 is homeomorphic to A_0^- it follows that A is homeomorphic to $A_e \cup A_0^-$ and hence to $A \cup A^-$, and that $B' = R^2 - A \cup A^-$ is homeomorphic to B. The significant point is that θ cannot be connected to other points in B' by an arc in B'.

PROBLEM

8-9. Show for the Alexander grating cohomology that $\tilde{H}^0(B, J) \neq 0$ both in Example 8-3 and in Example 8-4.

EXAMPLE 8-5. Let $\omega = \{w_i\}$ be a locally finite compact cover of X by sets which are the compact closures of open sets. Let $X_\pi = \bigcap_\pi w_i$, $|\pi| = p + 1$. Write σ^π for the associated simplex of the nerve so σ^π has vertices $\{(w_i) \mid i \in \pi\}$. Let $A^p = \{a^p\}$ consist of the p-cochains on w where $\|a^p\| = \bigcup X_\pi$ and the union is over all X_π such that $a^p(\sigma^\pi) \neq 0$. To see the supports are closed, let $x \bar{\in} \|a^p\|$. By the local finiteness, for some open set $V(x)$ at most a finite number of the sets meet $V(x)$. The union of this finite collection of X_π's is compact and so for some open set $U(x)$, $U(x) \cap \|a^p\| = \varnothing$. The grating A is R simple. Indeed because of the local finiteness, xA amounts to a cochain ring over a finite dimensional simplex.

We round off consideration of the Čech developments with the Čech lemma (Compare (91.2) and (91.3)). Our use of this lemma or those in (91) comes later in (128). For its proof we need some facts about covers which we list in the form of problems.

PROBLEMS

8-10. If A and B are disjunct subsets of a disk D^n in R^n, then disjunct open sets U and V exist in D^n with $A \subset U$ and $B \subset V$.

8-11. Let A be a subset of the fully normal space X. Let μ be a denumerable star finite open cover of A. Show there is a swelling (**A**) to an open cover of a neighborhood of A.

8-12. Let A be a subset of the fully normal space X. Let $\{u_i \mid i = 1, \ldots, n\}$ be open in A. Show there are sets v_i open in X with $v_i \supset u_i$ and such that if (a) $\cap u_i = \varnothing$, then $\cap v_i = \varnothing$ or if (b) the open set V contains $\cap u_i \neq \varnothing$, then $\cap v_i \subset V$. Show that if $\{u_i\}$ is a denumerable star finite cover of A, then (c) there is a swelling to a cover $\{v_i\}$ of a neighborhood of A, satisfying (a) and (b). If μ and ν are denumerable star finite covers of A and of a neighborhood of A, respectively, (d) there are refinements μ' and ν' with $v' = A \cap u'$ for each $v' \in \nu'$ and some $u' \in \mu'$ and the nerves of ν' and of μ' are isomorphic.

Lemma 7.3. Čech. *Let X be paracompact. Let $\{{}_i\nu\}$ constitute a cofinal collection of denumerable star finite covers of A over all the open neighborhoods of A. If ${}_iv$ is the nerve of ${}_i\nu$ then for the Čech groups*

$$H_*(A, R) = \underleftarrow{\mathsf{L}}\, \{H_*({}_iv, R), {p_i^j}_*\}$$

$$H^*(A, R) = \underrightarrow{\mathsf{L}}\, \{H^*({}_iv, R), {p^i_j}^*\}.$$

Let ${}_j\mu$ be a denumerable star finite open cover of A. Then $H_*(A, R)$, can be defined as $\underleftarrow{\mathsf{L}}\, H_*({}_ju, R)$. For each μ and ν, according to Problem (8-12d) there are refining open covers μ' and ν' whose nerves are abstractly isomorphic. Then

$$\underleftarrow{\mathsf{L}}\, H_*({}_iv, R) = \underleftarrow{\mathsf{L}}\, H_*({}_iu, R) = H_*(A, R).$$

Let Υ be a collection of open covers $\mu = \{u_a \mid A\}$ of X. Let X' be an extension of X, say a completion or a compactification, such that every $\mu \in \Upsilon$ becomes an open cover $\mu' = \{u_a' \mid A\} \in \Upsilon'$ of X' where the nerves u and u' are isomorphic. Then the Čech groups of X with respect to Υ are isomorphic to those of X' with Υ. In particular Υ' may be cofinal though Υ is not. We cite two instances of this where Υ determines some type of compactification of X.

Theorem 7.4. (**a**) *If X is completely regular and Υ is the collection of all finite open covers, $H(X) \approx H(\beta X)$ where βX is the Čech-Stone compactification.*

(**b**) *If X is locally compact and Υ is the collection of all fine covers* (1.17), *$H(X) \approx H(X \cup \infty, \infty)$ where $X \cup \infty$ is the one point compactification with the ideal point ∞.*

The Alexander ·grating yields the omology groups in (7.4b), in particular $\cdot H^1(R^1, \mathrm{J}) \approx \mathrm{J}$. It can be shown that (7.4a) implies $H^1(R^1, \mathrm{J})$ is isomorphic with the additive group of real valued continuous functions mod bounded functions.

chapter 9

FUNDAMENTAL OMOLOGY RELATIONS AND APPLICATIONS

We preface the developments of this section by an important observation, to wit: In view of the isomorphism to be established in (111.8), in the following theorems' hypotheses, the Alexander ${}^{\bullet}$grating can be replaced by any full grating. Grating references will *imply* local compactness. (Since only compact supports enter Section 1, H is written for ${}^{\bullet}H$.)

1. CONTINUITY THEOREM. Notation 1.1. Let $\Sigma^- = \{X_n, A_n, p_m{}^n, m, n \in M\}$ be an inverse system of compact pairs with inverse limit $X, A = \{(x, a) = [(x_m, a_m)]\} = \varprojlim \Sigma^-$ which must, of course, be compact. Then the projection p_m takes (x, a) into (x_m, a_m) and

(1.1a) $$\underbrace{X, A \xrightarrow{p_n} X_n, A_n \xrightarrow{p_m{}^n} X_m, A_m}_{p_m}, \qquad m < n.$$

The induced homomorphisms are indicated by

(1.1b) $$\underbrace{H^*(X_m, A_m) \xrightarrow{p^m{}_n{}^*} H^*(X_n, A_n) \xrightarrow{p_n{}^*} H^*(X, A)}_{p_m{}^*}$$

where the coefficient group is arbitrary.

Theorem 1.2. Continuity Theorem. *For the system in* (1.1) *and the Alexander grating*

(1.2a) $$\underset{\rightarrow}{\mathsf{L}}\,\{H^*(X_m, A_m;\ p^n{}_m{}^*\} \xrightarrow[\approx]{p^*} H^*(X, A),$$

where

(1.2b) $$p^*[\mathbf{f}_m] = p_n^*\,\mathbf{f}_n. \qquad [\mathbf{f}_n] = [\mathbf{f}_m]$$

for any n, *with* $[f_m^*]$ *the element of the direct limit determined by* $f_m^* \in H^*(X_m, A_m)$.

Figure 9-1

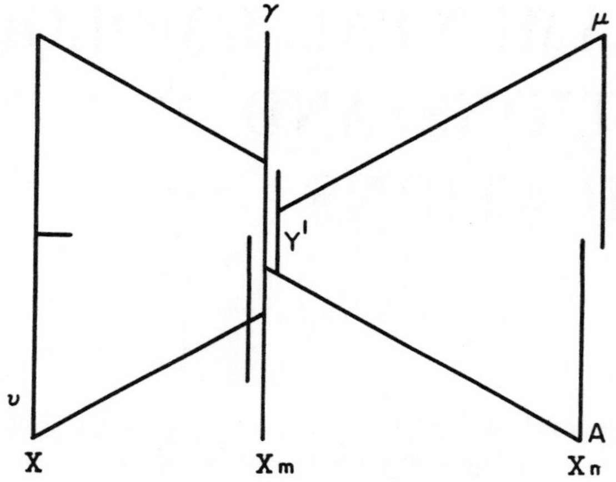

scheme for proof of Theorem 1.2

Compare the demonstration of (1.5).

We give the proof for the single space alone, i.e., $A_m = \varnothing$. Minor obvious modifications in the restrictions on the covers yield the result for pairs. References to covers here are to finite open covers. Grades are dropped and f is written for f^p. If ν is a cover and u_i is an open set, then the locution, 'u_i *is in some element* v_j *of* ν, is expressed by $u_j \subset \nu$. Let $\nu = \{v_j\}$ be a cover of X. Let γ and ω be X_m covers with $\gamma \overset{*}{>} \omega$, $p_m^{-1}\omega > \nu$. Let γ' be the subcollection of γ, consisting of sets meeting $p_m X$. Then $\bigcup_{\gamma'} g_j = G_m$ is an open subset of X_m. For some n, $m < n$, $p_m{}^n X_n \subset G_m$, since X is an inverse limit of compact spaces. Let $\mu = \{u_j \mid u_j = (p_m{}^n)^{-1} g_j\}$ be a cover of X_n. Then

(1.2c) $$\nu \overset{*}{<} p_m^{-1}\,\gamma',\ (p_m{}^n)^{-1}\omega \overset{*}{<} \mu.$$

Choose a point, x_j, in $p_n^{-1}\,u_j$. Define ψ: $X_n \to X$ by

(1.2d) $$\psi(u_j) = x_j.$$

In general ψ is neither unique nor continuous. In any event

(1.2e) $$\psi(u_j) \subset St\,(p_n^{-1}\,u_j;\ p_n^{-1}\,\mu) \subset \nu.$$

We show $ker\, p^* = 0$. Let $[\mathbf{f}_m] \in ker\, p^*$. Let f_m be a representative of $\mathbf{f}_m$. Thus

(1.2f) $$0 = p_m^* \mathbf{f}_m = \langle p_m^\# f_m \rangle.$$

Since f_m is a cocycle, for some vicinity, V_m^{p+2} of X_m^{p+2},

(1.2g) $$df_m \mid V_m^{p+2} = 0.$$

According to (1.2f), $p_m^\# f_m$ is a coboundary on X. Thus for a vicinity of X^{p+1},

$$(p_m^\# f_m - dg) \mid V^{p+1} = 0,$$

for $g \in C^{p-1}(X)$. Assume $\nu^{p+1} = \bigcup_{v_i \in \nu}(v_i \times \cdots \times v_i = v_i^{p+1}) \subset V^{p+1}$. Note ν^{p+1} and μ^{p+1} are vicinities, not covers.

Since $\psi\, u_j^{p+1} \subset v_i^{p+1}$, ψ: $\mu^{p+1} \rightarrow \nu^{p+1}$ according to (1.2d), whence

(1.2h) $$(d\psi^\# g - \psi^\# p_m^\# f_m) \mid \mu^{p+1} = 0.$$

We can assume that $\omega^{p+2} \subset V_m^{p+2}$ (1.2g). By (1.2c)

(1.2g) $$p_m{}^n (u_j) \cup p_m{}^n p_n \psi (u_j) \subset \omega.$$

This is equivalent to $\rho_1 u_j \cup \rho_2 u_j \subset w_i$, where $\rho_1 = p_m{}^n$ and $\rho_2 = p_m{}^n p_n \psi$. Then ρ_1 and ρ_2 map a simplex $\sigma = x_0 \ldots x_p$ in u_j into simplexes with vertices in w_i. The join of these latter two simplexes constitutes a simplex which can be taken as the carrier of $\rho_1(\sigma)$ and of $\rho_2(\sigma)$ and is an acyclic subcomplex of w. This implies, by (71.5) and (1.2h).

$$\mathbf{f}_n = p^m{}_n{}^* \mathbf{f}_m = \psi^* p_n^* p^m{}_n{}^* \mathbf{f}_m$$
$$= \psi^* p_m^* \mathbf{f}_m = 0.$$

In consequence $[\mathbf{f}_n]$ is 0.

To show p^* is onto, suppose $\mathbf{f} \in H^p(X)$ with representative f. Then, for some vicinity $V^{p+2}\, df \mid V^{p+2} = 0$. Pick ν to satisfy $\nu^{p+2} \subset V^{p+2}$ and μ as in (1.2c). We see that $\psi(\mu^{p+2}) \subset \nu^{p+2}$, whence $d\psi f \mid \mu^{p+2} = 0$. This being so,

$$p^*[\langle \psi^\# f \rangle] = p_n^* \langle \psi^\# f \rangle = \langle p_n^\# \psi^\# f \rangle = \langle (\psi\, p_n)^\# f \rangle.$$

Suppose $b_j = p_n^{-1}(u_j \mid \mu) \subset \nu$. By (1.2c) and (1.2e),

$$\psi(p_n b_j) \subset St(p_n^{-1}(p_n b_j); p_n^{-1} \mu)$$
$$= St(u_j; p_n{}^{-1} \mu) \subset \nu.$$

Accordingly $\rho_1 b_j \cup \rho_2 b_j \subset \nu$, where ρ_1 is the identity map and $\rho_2 = \psi p_n$. Then, by the reasoning used in (1.2g), namely that ρ_1 and ρ_2 map a simplex in the complex on μ^{p+1} (1.1) into two simplexes which are faces of their join on ν^{p+1}, we get from (71.5), $\mathbf{f} = \langle (\psi p_n)^\# f \rangle = \langle p_n{}^\# \psi^\# f \rangle$ or, some element $\langle \psi^\# f \rangle$ in $H^*(X_m)$ maps into $\mathbf{f}$.

Theorem 1.3. Continuity. *For the system in* (1.1) *and the Cech homology groups*

(1.3a) $$\underleftarrow{\mathsf{L}}\ \{H_*(X_m, A_m);\ p_m{}^n{}_*\} \approx H_*(X, A).$$

Corollary 1.4. *Let C be a closed subset of the compact space X. Suppose $z \in Z_m(X, C)$ and is nonbounding. There exists a minimal closed set E containing C, such that $z \sim 0$ mod E,* (61.16).

Let E_α be a closed subset containing C for which $j(\alpha)_* z = 0$ where $j(\alpha)$ is the inclusion map of C in E_α. Suppose $\{E_\alpha \mid \alpha \in A\}$ is a maximal collection of such subsets, which is simply ordered by inverse inclusion. Write $j(\alpha)$ also and $p(\alpha)$ for the inclusion map $X, C \to X, E_\alpha$ and for the projection $X, E \to X, E_\alpha$ where $E = \bigcap E_\alpha$. The following square is commutative,

$$\begin{array}{ccc} H_m(X, C) & \xrightarrow{j_*} & H_m(X, E) \\ \downarrow{\scriptstyle i_*} & & \downarrow{\scriptstyle p(\alpha)_*} \\ H_m(X, C) & \xrightarrow{j(\alpha)_*} & H_m(X, E_\alpha). \end{array}$$

According to (1.3), $j_* \mathbf{z}$ is the element $p(\alpha)_*\, j_* \mathbf{z}$ of $\underleftarrow{\mathsf{L}}\ H_m(X, E_\alpha) = H_m(X, E)$ and is trivial since $0 = j(\alpha)_* i_* \mathbf{z} = p(\alpha)_*\, j_* \mathbf{z}$.

The demonstration of (1.2) makes clear that the essential role of the coverings is to define vicinities of the diagonal. We have not exploited the grating technique which goes directly to the vicinities by way of the support notion. We call attention to the succinctness of such techniques in the demonstration of the following analogue of (1.2).

Theorem 1.5. *In the notation of* (1.1) *$\{X_m\}$ consists of all closed neighborhoods of X in W. Understand by A the compact Alexander grating over W and by $H(X)$ and $H(X_m)$ the modules $H(X\mathrm{A})$ and $H(X_m\mathrm{A})$ respectively. Then*

(1.5a) $$\underrightarrow{\mathsf{L}}\ H^*(X_m) \underset{\approx}{\xrightarrow{p^*}} H^*(X).$$

The result (1.5a) is still valid when W is paracompact and locally compact, and $\{X_m\}$ consists of all closed neighborhoods of X and the cohomology theory is over any R grating with merely closed supports.

We show first that p^* is onto. Accordingly let $f \in \mathrm{A}$ with $Xf \in Z(X\mathrm{A})$ and $\langle Xf \rangle$ an assigned element of $H(X\mathrm{A})$. Then $d(Xf) = X\, df = 0$ whence $X \cap \|df\| = \varnothing$. We now recognize the compactness of $\|df\|$. Let $y \in \|df\|$. Then open sets with compact closure exist, namely $N(y)$ and $U(y)$ for which $N(y) \subset \overline{N(y)} \subset U(y)$ with $U(y) \cap X = \varnothing$. By compactness a finite number of sets N_i taken from $\bigcup_{y \in \|df\|} N(y)$ cover $\|df\|$. Hence $\bigcup N_i = N \subset \bar{N} = \bigcup \bar{N}_i \subset \bigcup U_i$ with $\bigcup U_i \cap X = \varnothing$. Let $V = \bar{N}^{\sim}$. Then V is an open set containing X and $\bar{V} \cap \|df\| = \varnothing$. This means $\bar{V}$ is an X_m for some m and furthermore $\bar{V}f \in Z(\bar{V}\mathrm{A})$. In view of (81.11), $\langle Vf \rangle = \langle Xf \rangle$.

Second, we show $ker\ p^* = 0$. Suppose then $f \in Z(X_m\ \mathrm{A})$ where $Xf = 0$. Hence for some $g \in A$, $X(f - dg) = 0$. This implies $X \cap \|f - dg\| = \varnothing$ and hence for some open set V, $X \subset V \subset \bar{V}$, $\bar{V} \cap \|f - dg\| = \varnothing$. Since $\bar{V}$ is an X_n, we have shown that for $X_r = X_n \cap X_m$, $X_r f = X_r \langle dg \rangle = 0$.

PROBLEMS

9-1. Translate the support notions in the proof of (1.5) into vicinity notions as in (1.2). For instance, note that if $f \in H(X_m\ \mathrm{A})$, then f determines $[f]$ and Xf is $p_m{}^*f$, etc. Prove (1.2) by paralleling the demonstration of (1.5).

9-2. Demonstrate (1.5) when A is the Alexander grating, $\{X_m\}$ now consists of all the closed neighborhoods of the closed subset X in W and W is paracompact and locally compact.

Remark. The continuity theorems are equivalent to the form of the Čech lemma, (87.3) where finite covers are used and A is closed.

EXAMPLE 9-1. Consider Example 8-2. Let $X(m)$ be

$$\left\{(x, y) \mid 0 \leq x \leq \frac{1}{m}, |y| \leq 1\right\} \cup B \cup C \cup D$$

ordered by inverse inclusion, with $p_m{}^n$ the inclusion map. Then $H^1(X_m, R) \approx R$. Evidently $X = B \cup C \cup D = \varprojlim(X_m, p_m{}^n)$. Hence for the Alexander grating $H^1(X, R) \approx R$ according to (1.2).

PROBLEM

9-3. Suppose X, A, B are compact. Establish the Čech homology analogues of (62.2) and (62.5) when the coefficients are in a field, say R. Establish the cohomology analogues of (62.2) and (62.5) for cohomology based on a full grating. *Hint:* The inverse limits of the exact homology sequences for nerves of finite covers yield exact sequences here.

Remark. In some of our later theorems we assume the results in Problem 9-3.

PROBLEMS

9-4. Let X be compact. Show $H_r(X \times I, X \times 0 \cup X \times 1) \approx H_{r+1}(X)$.

9-5. The spaces referred to are assumed compact, the homology theory is that of Čech, the coefficients are from R and the results of Problem 9-3 are admitted.

Let $A \xrightarrow{i(\alpha)} X(\alpha)$ be an inclusion map. Suppose $z_r \in Z_r(A, B, R)$, where $i(\alpha)_{\#} z_r \in B_r(X(\alpha), A; R)$. Let $X = \bigcap_A X(\alpha)$. Show there exists an element $w_{r+1} \in H_{r+1}(X, A, R)$ with $\partial w_{r+1} = z_r$.

2. EXCISION. Theorem 2.1. Excision. *Let X, A be a pair of arbitrary spaces and write $Y = X - U$, $B = A - U$. Furthermore, let j be the inclusion map j: $Y, B \to X, A$ whence j^*: $H^*(X, A) \to H^*(Y, B)$. Then j^* is an isomorphism in the following cases*

(2.1a) *U is an open set subject to $\bar{U} \subset A_-$ the interior of A, and the Alexander or the singular grating is used, or*

(2.1b) *X, A is a compact pair and $U = A_-$ provided the Alexander grating is used. This is strong excision.*

(2.1c) *U is arbitrary subject to $\bar{U} \subset A_-$ and the singular grating is used.*

Write lower case and capitals to distinguish elements of the gratings over Y, B and over X, A respectively. We assert first $j^{\#}$ is onto. Thus let $f^p \in \mathrm{C}^p(Y, B)$. Define $F^p \in \mathrm{C}^p(X, A)$ by $F^p\, x^{p+1} = 0$ or $f^p\, x^{p+1}$ according as x^{p+1} is, or is not, in $Y^{p+1} \cup B^{p+1}$. Then $f^p = j^{\#}\, F^p$.

We next assert $j^{\#}\, Z^p(X, A) = Z^p(Y, B)$. Since $j^{\#}$ is allowable $j^{\#}\, Z^p(X, A) \subset Z^p(Y, B)$. If $f^p \in Z^p(Y, B)$, $\|df^p\| = \varnothing$, $\|f^p\| \cap B = \varnothing$. [We can equally well express this as $df^p \in {}_0\mathrm{C}(Y, B)$.] We have seen that for some $F^p \in \mathrm{C}^p(X, A)$, $f^p = j^{\#}\, F^p$. Then $\varnothing = \|dj^{\#}\, F^p\| = \|j^{\#}\, dF^p\|$. To show this implies $\|dF^p\| = \varnothing$ it is sufficient to prove the more general proposition that $\|j^{\#}\, G^p\| = \varnothing$ carries the consequence $\|G^p\| = \varnothing$. Thus $V^{p+1}(Y)$ exists for which $j^{\#}\, G^p \mid V^{p+1} = 0$. Let $y^{p+1} = y_0 \times \cdots \times v_p \in V^{p+1}$ so, since j is the inclusion map,

$$0 = j^{\#}\, G^p(y_0, \ldots, y_p) = G^p(jy_0, \ldots, jy_p)$$
$$= G^p(y_0, \ldots, y_p).$$

In brief, $G^p \mid V^{p+1} = 0$. Moreover $\|G^p\| \cap A = \varnothing$, or, equivalently, for some vicinity W^{p+1} of A^{p+1}, $G^p\, W^{p+1} = 0$. Since $(X - \bar{U})^{p+1}$ and $(A_-)^{p+1}$ are open subsets of X^{p+1}, $N = (V^{p+1} \cap (X - \bar{U})^{p+1}) \cup (W^{p+1} \cap (A_-)^{p+1})$ is a vicinity for X^{p+1} and $G \mid N = 0$. Hence $\|G\| = \varnothing$.

Write $j^{\#}$ for the homomorphism induced on the separated gratings $\mathrm{A}(X, A) \to \mathrm{A}(Y, B)$. We claim $\ker j^* = 0$. Suppose $f = dg \in B^p(Y, B)$ and suppose $F \in Z^p(X, B)$ with $j^{\#}\, F = f$. Since $j^{\#}$ is an epimorphism $g = j^{\#}\, G$ where $G \in \mathrm{A}^{p-1}(X, A)$, $g \in \mathrm{A}^{p-1}(Y, B)$. Hence f is the image of an element dG in $\mathrm{B}^p(X, A)$ since $f = dj^{\#}\, G = j^{\#}\ (dG)$. Thus $j^{\#}\ (F - dG) = 0$ whence $\|j^{\#}(F - dG)\| = \varnothing$ or $\|F - dG\| = \varnothing$. Therefore

$$j^*\, \mathbf{f} = 0 \Rightarrow \mathbf{f} = 0.$$

We sum up the situation in the commutative diagram

$$\begin{array}{ccccc} & & Z^p(X, A) & \xrightarrow{j^{\#}\text{onto}} & Z^p(Y, B) \\ & & \Big\downarrow{\scriptstyle \eta\ \text{onto}} & & \Big\downarrow{\scriptstyle \eta_1\ \text{onto}} \\ 0 & \longrightarrow & H^p(X, A) & \xrightarrow{j^*} & H^p(Y, B) \end{array}$$

To see that j^* is onto, note that if **f** is in $H^p(Y, B)$ any element in the non-empty collection $\eta j^{\#-1} \eta_1^{-1}$ **f** is an antecedent of **f** under j^*.

Assertion (2.1a) for the singular grating is subsumed under (2.1c).

For (2.1b): Let $\{a_m \mid m \in M\}$ be the collection of all open subsets of A with $\bar{a}_m \subset A_-$. Index $\{a_m\}$ by inclusion; thus $m \subset n \Leftrightarrow a_m \subset a_n$. Let $X_m, A_m = X - a_m, A - a_m$ and introduce the inclusion maps

$$p_n{}^m\colon (X_m, A_m) \to (X_n, A_n),$$

$$q_m(X_m, A_m) \to (X, A).$$

By (2.1a), $q_m{}^*$ is an isomorphism for all m. Moreover $q_m = q_n p_n{}^m$ induces $q_m^* = p^n{}_m{}^* q_n^*$ whence $p^n{}_m{}^*$ is an isomorphism. Note that $\underleftarrow{\mathsf{L}}\ ((X_m, A_m); p_n{}^m) = (\bigcap(X_m), \bigcap A_m) = X - A_-, A - A_-$. Let p_m be the inclusion map of $(X - A_-, A - A_-) \to X_m, A_m$. Then basing our justification on (1.1) we claim

$$\underrightarrow{\mathsf{L}}\ {}^\bullet H^*(X_m, A_m) \xrightarrow{\approx} {}^\bullet H^*(X - A_-, A - A_-).$$

Since $p^m{}_n{}^*$ is an isomorphism, so is $p_m{}^*$. Then $p_m{}^* q_m^*$ is the composition of isomorphisms and hence is the isomorphism sought,

$$(p_m q_m)^*\colon {}^\bullet H^*(X, A) \xrightarrow{\approx} {}^\bullet H^*(X - A_-, A - A_-).$$

Under the hypotheses in (2.1c) $\gamma = (Y, A)$ is an effectively open cover of X (84.3), i.e., $(Y_- = X - \bar{U}, A_-)$ is a cover. We turn to (84.4). The complex of mesh γ will be denoted by Γ (and corresponds to A in (84.3)). We use Γ also for the lower complex (61.4). In this sense

(2.1d) $$\Gamma = C(Y) + S(A)$$

where $C(Y)$ is the group of chains in Y and $S(A)$ or $C(A)$ is the group of chains in A. If X is replaced by A in (84.4), the result is

$$H(SA) \approx H(SA \cap \Gamma).$$

This together with $H(SX) \approx H(\Gamma)$ is fed into the hopper of the 5 lemma (101.2) and we extract

(2.1e) $$H(SX/SA) \approx H(\Gamma/\Gamma \cap SA).$$

We make repeated use of the Noether isomorphism theorem (11.7) to get

$$\text{(2.1f)} \qquad \Gamma/\Gamma \cap S(A) \approx \frac{\Gamma + S(A)}{S(A)} \approx \frac{C(Y) + S(A)}{S(A)} \approx \frac{C(Y)}{S(A) \cap C(Y)}.$$

The chains in $S(A) \cap C(Y)$ are in Y and in A and hence constitute $C(A - U)$; i.e., the groups in (2.1f) are isomorphic to $C(Y)/C(A - U)$ and using this fact in (2.1e) there results

$$H(SX/SA) \approx H((S - U)/(A - U)) \approx H(Y, B).$$

The argument goes through for cohomology if (85.3) is used instead of (84.4).

3. EXTENSION. Lemma 3.1. *If j is an inclusion map of $X, A \to Y, B$ where X, A, B are closed subsets of Y, then*

$$j^{\#} \mid B^p(Y, B) = B^p(X, A).$$

Let $f \in C^p(X, A)$. Define $F^p \in C^p(Y, B)$ by

$$\text{(3.1a)} \qquad F \mid jX^{p+1} = fX^{p+1} \quad \text{and}$$

$$\text{(3.1b)} \qquad F \mid (Y^{p+1} - jX^{p+1}) = 0;$$

Then

$$(j^{\#} F)(x_0, \ldots, x_p \mid X) = F(jx_0, \ldots, jx_p)$$
$$= f(x_0, \ldots, x_p)$$

so

$$\text{(3.1c)} \qquad j^{\#} F = f,$$

whence $j^{\#}$ is onto. In particular, if $f \in {}_0\mathrm{C}^p(X, A)$ then $f \mid V^{p+1}(X) = 0$. Define the vicinity W^{p+1} of $\Delta^{p+1}(Y)$ by $(Y^{p+1} - (jA)^{p+1}) \cup jV^{p+1}$.

Note $F \mid W^{p+1} = 0$, by (3.1b), (3.1a), and (3.1c). Therefore

$$\text{(3.1d)} \qquad j^{\#} \mid {}_0\mathrm{C}^p(Y, B) = {}_0\mathrm{C}^p(X, A).$$

Hence $j^{\#}$ induces $\mathrm{J}^{\#}$, an epimorphism

$$\mathrm{J}^{\#}\colon \frac{\mathrm{C}^p(Y, B)}{{}_0\mathrm{C}^p(Y, B)} = \mathrm{A}_p(Y, B) \to \frac{\mathrm{C}^p(X, A)}{{}_0\mathrm{C}^p(X, A)} = \mathrm{A}^p(X, A),$$

We shall use the coset notation [ ] for the elements of A^p. Our immediate aim is to show that $\mathrm{J}^{\#}$ is allowable. Thus $y \cap \|F\| = \varnothing$ implies that for some neighborhood W of y, $F(W^{p+1}) = 0$. Hence $j^{\#} F(j^{-1} W^{p+1}) = 0$. We need consider only the case $y \in jX$. Therefore $y \bar{\in} \| j^{\#} F\|$ or $\| j^{\#} [F]\| \subset \|[F]\|$. We have left only the formal verification that $dj^{\#} [F] = j^{\#} d[F]$.

If $f \in B^p(X, A)$, then $f = dg + h$ where $g \in \mathrm{C}^{p-1}(X, A)$, $\|h\| \subset A$. By (3.1c) and (3.1d) some G is an antecedent of g under $j^{\#}$ and some H of h. Since

$h \in {}_0C(X, A)$, $H \in {}_0C(Y, B)$ or $\|H\| \subset B$. Hence $dg = dj^{\#} G = j^{\#} dG$ or $J^{\#}[(dG + H)] = [f]$.

For the next three results *assume that X is paracompact* (and not necessarily locally compact) and that A and B are closed subsets of X.

Lemma 3.2. *Let μ be an open cover of X. Then for some open cover ν, $\mu \overset{*}{<} \nu$ and open set U, $U \supset A$, there is a correspondence $\psi: X \to X$, generally non-continuous,*

(3.2a) *ψ is the identity on* $(X - \bar{U}) \cup A$,

(3.2b) $\psi \mid \bar{U} \cap B \subset A \cap B$,

(3.2c) $\psi \mid (\bar{U} - A) \subset A$,

(3.2d) *If $v \in \nu$, $\psi(v) \subset St(v, \nu)$.*

Since X is paracompact, $\nu = \{\bar{v}_i \mid i \in I\}$ exists with $\mu < \nu^*$, (A), requiring

$$\left.\begin{matrix} v_j \cap A \neq \varnothing \\ v_j \cap B \neq \varnothing \end{matrix}\right\} \Rightarrow v_j \cap A \cap B \neq \varnothing$$

Since a T_2 paracompact space is normal, there is an open set U satisfying

(3.2e) $$A \subset U \subset \bar{U} \subset U\{v_j \mid \nu_A\},$$

where $\nu_A = \{v_j \mid v_j \cap A \neq \varnothing\}$. Let λ be a correspondence assigning to each v_j a point of X with the stipulations:

(3.2f) $$\lambda(v_j \mid \nu_A) \in v_j \cap A,$$

(3.2g) $$\lambda v_j \in A \cap B \quad \text{if} \quad v_j \cap B \neq \varnothing.$$

Define ψ by

(3.2h) $$\psi(x \mid (X - \bar{U}) \cup A) = x.$$

If $x \in \bar{U} - A$, then, for some v_j, designated by $v(x)$, $x \in v(x) \in \nu_A$. Let

(3.2i) $$\psi(x) = \lambda v(x) \subset A, \quad (3.2f).$$

Note $\bar{U} \cap B \cap A \subset (X - U) \cup A$ to which (3.2h) applies while (3.2i) applies to $\bar{U} \cap B \cap (X - A) = (\bar{U} - A) \cap B$. Thus (3.2a, b, c) are established.

If $x \in v_j \cap (X - \bar{U}) \cup A$, by (3.2h) $\psi(x) \in v_j \subset St(v_j, \nu)$. If $x \in v_j \cap \bar{U} - A$, (3.2i) asserts $\psi(x) \in v(x)$ with $v(x) \cap v_j \neq \varnothing$ so again $\psi(x) \in St(v_j, \nu)$.

Definition 3.3. If $i\colon Y, B \to X, A$ is an inclusion map then $\mathbf{z_p} \in H_p(Y, B)$ **extends** to (X, A) if $i_* \mathbf{z_p} \neq 0$. Similarly $\mathbf{f^p} \in H^p(Y, B)$, extends to X, A if for some $\mathbf{F^p} \in H^p(X, A)$, $i^* \mathbf{F^p} = \mathbf{f^p}$.

The diagram below is helpful for (3.3) and (3.4).

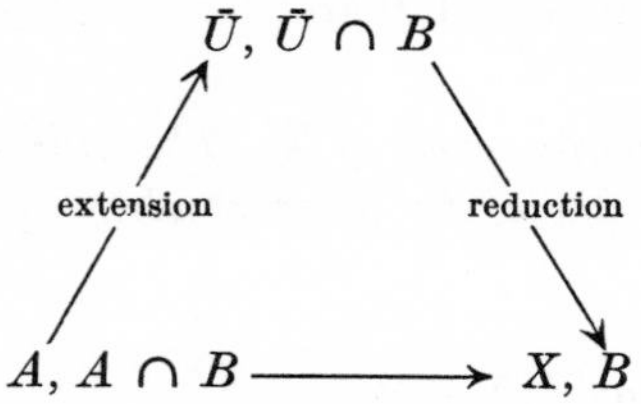

Theorem 3.4. Extension. *Let* $\mathbf{f} \in H^p(A, A \cap B)$. *Then for some open set,* U, *with* $A \subset U$, $\mathbf{f}$ *extends to* $\mathbf{F} \in H^p(\bar{U}, \bar{U} \cap B)$.

Let f represent $\mathbf{f}$. That is to say, for some open cover ν of X,

$$\delta f \mid \nu^{p+2} \cap A^{p+2} = 0,$$
$$f \mid \nu^{p+1} \cap (A \cap B)^{p+1} = 0.$$

Let U and ψ be defined as in (3.2) and let i be the inclusion map:

$$\bar{U}, \bar{U} \cap B \underset{i}{\overset{\psi}{\rightleftarrows}} A, A \cap B$$

Hence ψi is the identity whence $i^* \psi^* \mathbf{f} = \mathbf{f}$. Then $\mathbf{F} = \psi^* \mathbf{f}$ is the extension sought, for $i^* \mathbf{F} = i^* \psi^* \mathbf{f} = \mathbf{f}$.

4. REDUCTION. Theorem 4.1. Reduction theorem: *Let j be the inclusion map*

(4.1a) $$j\colon A, A \cap B \to X, B$$

and suppose $\mathbf{f} \in H^p(X, B)$ *is in ker* j^*. *Then for some open set,* U, *containing* A,

(4.1b) $$i^* f = 0$$

where i is the inclusion map

(4.1c) $$i\colon \bar{U}, \bar{U} \cap B \to X, B$$

Identify j in (4.1a) with j in (3.1) for X, A, Y, and B replaced by A, $A \cap B$, X, and B. Then $j^* \mathbf{f} = 0$ implies $j^\# f \in B^p(A, A \cap B)$ and hence for some F in $B^p(X, B)$, $j^\# F = j^\# f$. Thus with $z = f - F$, $\mathbf{z} = \mathbf{f}$, and $z \mid A^{p+1} = 0$. Since $\|f\| \cup \|F\| \cap B = \varnothing$ we can find an open cover μ of X for which $z \mid B^{p+1} \cap \mu^{p+1} = 0$ and $\delta z \mid \mu^{p+2} = 0$.

Again introduce ψ, U, ν as in (3.3). Then, since ψ takes X, B into X, B, $\psi^\# z \in Z^p(X, B)$. If p is the identity map, then p and ψ take $St(v_j, \nu)$ into the same $u_i \in \mu$ (3.3d). The simplexes $\sigma = x_0 \ldots x_r = p(x_0) \ldots p(x_r)$ and $\psi(x_0) \ldots \psi(x_r)$ where $x_0, \ldots, x_p \subset v_j$, have as join a simplex τ in $St(v_j, \nu) \subset u_i \in \mu$. Therefore Q, with $Q(\sigma) = \tau$, is an acyclic carrier of $p_{\#}$ and $\psi_{\#}$ whence $p_* = \psi_*$ and $p^* = \psi^*$ (71.5). Accordingly

$$\mathbf{z} = p^* \, \mathbf{z} = \psi^* \, \mathbf{z}. \tag{4.1d}$$

Let $\psi^{\#} z = w$. Then

$$w \mid \bar{U}^{p+1} \subset z \mid \psi \bar{U}^{p+1} \subset z \mid A^{p+1} = 0 \qquad \text{(3.3a, 3.3b)}. \tag{4.1e}$$

In the notation of (3.4c), (3.4d) indicates $i^* \, \mathbf{f} = i^* \, \psi^* \, \mathbf{z}$ while (4.1e), $i^* \, w$ is the 0 coset in $H^p(\bar{U}, \bar{U} \cap B)$.

Theorem 4.2. *The reduction theorem* (4.1) *is valid for X, a locally compact space when B is compact.*

PROBLEM

9-6. Show that (4.2) and (3.4) remain valid for locally compact X if merely the boundary of B is compact and B is a closed subset.

We present for comparison a *purely* grating approach to a special case.

Theorem 4.3. *Let X be locally compact and* (a) *let Y be a compact subset or* (b) *let X be locally compact and paracompact with Y a closed subset. Let $j\colon Y \to X$ be the inclusion map. If $f \in \ker j_*$, then for some open set U containing Y, $i^*f = 0$ where i is inclusion on $\bar{U}$ to X. The supports are compact for* (a) *and merely closed for* (b).

The grating homomorphism replacing $j^{\#}$ is the cut homomorphism Y. Thus our hypotheses state $Yf = 0$ or $Y(f - dg) = 0$ for some $g \in A$. That is $Y \cap \|f - dg\| = \varnothing$. In both the cases covered in the hypotheses there is an open set U with $Y \subset U \subset \bar{U}$ where $\bar{U} \cap \|f - dg\| = \varnothing$. Indeed when X is locally compact and paracompact this is simply a consequence of the normality of a paracompact space. Hence $\bar{U}(f - dg) = 0$ which is tantamount to the conclusion sought.

5. HOMOTOPY. The homotopy theorem about to be presented is somewhat more general than that usually stated. It is understood that $^{\bullet}H^*(X, A)$ is defined by a full R grating.

Lemma 5.1. *Let X, A be locally compact and suppose T is compact and connected. Let a_t and b_t be inclusion maps with composition, $e_t = b_t a_t$ on $X, A \to X \times T$, $A \times T$ given by $e_t\colon x = x \times t$ where $X, A \xrightarrow[a_t]{} X \times t$,*

$A \times t \xrightarrow[b_t]{} X \times T,\ A \times T$. *Then* e_t^* *is independent of* t *on* $^{\bullet}H^*(X \times T, A \times T) \rightarrow {}^{\bullet}H^*(X, A)$.

We give the proof for the case $A = \varnothing$ but the demonstration of the more general case proceeds the same way in all particulars. Besides we start with the case X is compact. Let p be the projection of $X \times T$ onto X, then $p\colon x \times t = x = p\, e_t\, x$. Hence

(5.1a) $$e_t^*\, p^* = 1^*,$$

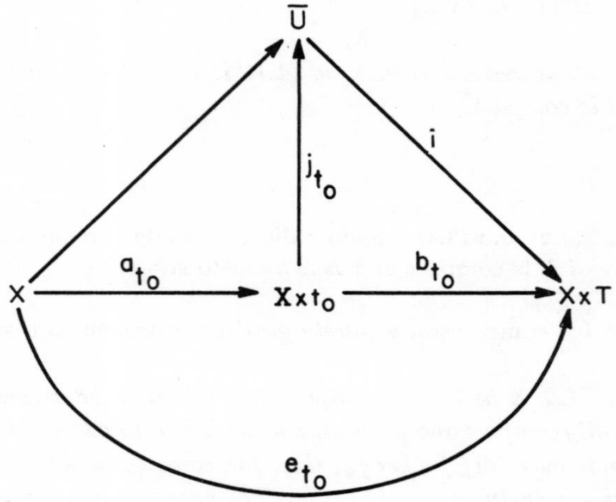

the identity isomorphism on $^{\bullet}H^*(X) \rightarrow {}^{\bullet}H^*(X)$. Moreover a_t^* is an isomorphism also. Let $\mathbf{f} \in {}^{\bullet}H^*(X \times T)$ and suppose for some $t_0 \in T$, $b_{t_0}^* f = 0$. We invoke the Reduction Theorem (4.1) with the identification b_{t_0}, $X \times t_0$, $X \times T$, $\varnothing$ with j, A, X, and B respectively. Hence there is an open set U in $X \times T$ containing $X \times t_0$ with the inclusion map $i\colon \bar{U} \rightarrow X \times T$ such that the cut homomorphism $\bar{U}$ (81.10) on the grating yields $\bar{U}^*\, \mathbf{f} = 0$ (4.1b). By the compactness of X, $X \times t_0$ can be covered by a finite number of product neighborhoods lying in U, whence follows at once that for some $V(t_0)$, $X \times V(t_0) \subset U$. Let j_t be the inclusion map $j_t\colon X \times t \rightarrow \bar{U}$, $t \in V(t_0)$. For every $t \in V(t_0)$

$$^{\bullet}H(X \times T) \xrightarrow{\bar{U}^*} {}^{\bullet}H(\bar{U}) \xrightarrow{j_t^*} {}^{\bullet}H(X \times t) \underset{\approx}{\xrightarrow{a_t^*}} {}^{\bullet}H(X).$$

Accordingly, with $e_t^* = a_t^*\, j_t^*\, \bar{U}^*$,

(5.1b) $$\begin{aligned} e_t^*\, \mathbf{f} &= a_t^*\, j_t^*\, \bar{U}^*\, \mathbf{f} \\ &= 0,\ t \in V(t_0). \end{aligned}$$

Let $\mathbf{f} \in {}^{\bullet}H^*(X \times T)$ and let $\mathbf{g} = e_{t_1}^* \mathbf{f} \in {}^{\bullet}H^*(X)$ for $t_1 \in T$. Then, by (5.1a), $e_{t_1}^*(\mathbf{f} - p^* \mathbf{g}) = 0$, and so, in view of (5.1b), $e_t^*(\mathbf{f} - p^* \mathbf{g}) = 0$, $t \in V(t_1)$ or

(5.1c) $$e_t^* \mathbf{f} = \mathbf{g},\ t \in V(t_1).$$

Let C be a maximal set for which (5.1c) is true. Then C is an open set, as a union of open sets, $\{V(t)\}$. If for some t_2, $e_{t_2}^* \mathbf{f} = \mathbf{g}_2 \neq \mathbf{g}$ then this relation is valid for an open set C_2, etc. The mutual disjointness of the open sets, $\{C_i\}$, stands in conflict with the connectedness of T. Hence $C = T$.

Suppose now that X is merely locally compact. The crux of our argument was the existence of $V(t_0)$ for (5.1b). In the present case compactify X to ${}^{\bullet}X = X \cup \infty$. The reduction theorem in the form (4.2) applied to ${}^{\bullet}X \times t_0$ yields ${}^{\bullet}U$, a neighborhood of ${}^{\bullet}X \times t_0$. Let $q\colon {}^{\bullet}X \times t = t$. Since ${}^{\bullet}X - {}^{\bullet}U$ is compact, $q({}^{\bullet}X - {}^{\bullet}U)$ is a compact subset of T. Accordingly $V(t_0) = T - q({}^{\bullet}X - {}^{\bullet}U)$ is an open set satisfying (5.1b).

Definition 5.2. Let T be compact and connected. The maps ψ_1 and ψ_2 on Y, B to X, A are T-**homotopic**, written $\psi_1 \underset{T}{\simeq} \psi_2$ if there is a map $h\colon\ Y \times T,$ $B \times T \to X,\ A$ with $h(y, t_1) = \psi_1(y)$ and $h(y, t_2) = \psi_2(y)$ for all $y \in Y$.

Theorem 5.3. *Let $\psi_1 \underset{T}{\simeq} \psi_2$ on the locally compact spaces on X, B to X, A. Suppose the associated map h is proper for each $t \in T$ then $\psi_1^* = \psi_2^*\colon\ {}^{\bullet}H^*(X, A) \to {}^{\bullet}H^*(Y, B)$.*

With the symbols e_t and h defined in (5.1) and (5.2) we have $\psi_1 = he_{t_1}$, $\psi_2 = he_{t_2}$. Then $\psi_1^* = e_{t_1}^* h^* = e_{t_2}^* h^* = \psi_2^*$, by (5.1).

Corollary 5.4. *If a compact set can be shrunk to a point on itself it is acyclic.*

This corollary can provide the justification for the use of some of the general cells defined earlier, other than simplexes, in computing omology modules. (Compactness cannot be dropped, cf. (87.4) for R^1.)

Corollary 5.5. *If A is a deformation retract of X then ${}^{\bullet}H^*(X, R) \approx {}^{\bullet}H^*(A, R)$ if the retraction function is proper.*

Let i be the inclusion map and r the retraction; then $A \xrightarrow{i} X \xrightarrow{r} A$ yields ri is the identity map while $ir \simeq j$ where j is the identity map on X. Hence $r^*\, i^*$ and $i^*\, r^*$ are identity isomorphisms, so r^* is an isomorphism.

PROBLEM

9-7. If X is compact show $H^*(X \times I, R)\ ) \approx H^*(X, R)$.

Theorem 5.6. *If h is a deformation on $X \times I$ to X, where X is an arbitrary space then $h_*(\ ,1)$ is an isomorphism of ${}_SH_*(X) \to {}_SH_*(X)$. If Y is a deformation retract of X then ${}_SH_*(X) \approx {}_SH_*(Y)$.*

We define a deformation on $C(SX, \text{J})$ to $C(SX, \text{J})$. Thus let $h\colon X \times I \to X$ be a deformation, that is to say $h(x, 0) = x$. Denote the points of a Euclidean space of sufficiently high dimension by $\{s\}$ and understand every σ is in this space. If (σ, u) is a singular simplex let $u'(\bar{\sigma} \times I)$ be defined by $u'(s, t) = h(u(s), t)$, $s \in \bar{\sigma}$. Thus (a) $u'(s, o) = u(s)$. Moreover (b) if σ' is any face of σ, then $(\sigma', u \mid \bar{\sigma}') < (\sigma, u)$ implies $(u' \mid \bar{\sigma}' \times I)(s, t) = u(s, t)$ for $s \in \sigma'$. For convenience write $u'(0)$ and $u'(1)$ for the singular simplexes $(\sigma \times 0, u' \mid \bar{\sigma} \times 0)$ and for $(\sigma \times 1, u' \mid \bar{\sigma} \times 1)$. Let $\psi_\# u'(0) = u'(1)$. Then by relation (b), $\psi_\#$ replaces all elementary chains on faces attached to $u(0)$ by chains on faces attached to $u'(1)$ which implies $\partial\psi_\# u'(0) = \partial u'(1) = \psi_\# \partial u'(0)$, that is to say $\psi_\#$ is allowable. We write $A_0, \ldots, A_m$ for the vertices *of* $\sigma \times 0$ and $A_0^1, \ldots, A_m^1$ for those of its replica $\sigma \times 1$. Then $\sigma \times I$ can be triangulated with $m + 1$ dimensional simplexes $\{\sigma_{m+1}^i = A_0^1 \ldots A_i^1 A_i \ldots A_m \mid i = 0, \ldots, m + 1\}$. Define $E(\sigma)$ by $E(\sigma) = \Sigma(-1)^i \sigma_{m+1}^i$. A mechanical computation checks that $E\,\partial\sigma + \partial E\sigma = \sigma \times 0 - \sigma \times 1$.

Replace σ by $(\sigma, u' \mid \bar{\sigma})$ and σ_{m+1}^i by $(\sigma_{m+1}^i, u' \mid \bar{\sigma}_{m+1}^i)$ the singular simplex denoted in our usual notation by $u_{m+1}'^i$. Hence with $D(\sigma, u)$ or Du replacing $E(\sigma)$ there results $Du_m = \Sigma(-1)^i u_{m+1}'^i$ and

$$D\,\partial u + \partial Du = u - \psi_\# u.$$

This extends by linearity to the general singular chain and we infer ψ_* is an isomorphism (63). The proof of the last statement of the theorem then follows as in (5.5).

Theorem 5.7. *If $f \simeq g$ on $X \to Y$ then $f_* = g_*$ for the singular homology groups.*

The proof in (5.6) maintains with obvious modifications.

PROBLEMS

9-8. Demonstrate (5.7).

9-9. Let ψ be a real valued continuous function on $R \times I$ where $\psi(x, t) = \psi(x + 2\pi, t) = -\psi(x + \pi, t)$ for all $x \in R$, $t \in I$. Let $Z = \{(x, t) \mid \psi(x, t) = 0\}$. Show Z contains a connected set from $R \times 0$ to $R \times 1$.

9-10. Let $S(2)$ be a circle of radius 2 and with center at the origin. Let $h\colon S(2) \times I \to R^2 - 0$. Show that if $h(S(2) \times 1)$ lies inside $\{x \mid \|x\| \le \frac{1}{2}\}$, then for some t the curve $h(S(2) \times t)$ intersects the circle $\{x \mid \|x\| = 1\}$ in 2 antipodal points.

EXAMPLE 9-2. A delayed version of the excision theorem is sometimes practical. Consider the inclusion map $S^n, E^n_- \xrightarrow{\psi} E^n_+, S^{n-1}$ where S^n is the sphere $\Sigma_{i=1}^{n+1} x_i^2 = 1$, E^n_+ is that part of S^n with $x_{n+1} \geq 0$ and E^n_- that part with $x_{n+1} \leq 0$. Then ψ is not an excision map. However let μ be the inclusion map of E^n_+, S^{n-1} into D^n, A^n where D^n is the part of S^n above $x_{n+1} \geq -\epsilon$ and $A^n = E^n_- \cap D^n$. Evidently E^n_+ is a strong deformation retract of D^n and under the same retraction S^{n-1} is a strong deformation retract of A^n. An excision map e exists on $S^n, E^n_- \to D^n, A^n$. Hence $\psi = e\mu$.

6. MANIFOLDS. Definition 6.1. The space $M = \{y\}$ is a **class** r, or C^r **manifold,** if it meets the conditions stated below. (**a**) It is connected; (**b**) there is an open covering $\mu = \{U_i\}$ and homeomorphisms ψ_i^{-1}: $U_i \to R^n$, the Euclidean n space, or more particularly $\psi_i^{-1}(y) = x_i^1(y), \ldots, x_i^n(y)$ where $x_i^j(y)$ is termed the jth coordinate of y and U_i a **coordinate neighborhood**; and (**c**) if $y \in U_i \cap U_j$ and $\psi_i^{-1} U_i \cap U_j = V_{ij} \subset R^n$ then $(\psi_j^{-1} \psi_i)(\psi_i^{-1}(U_i \cap U_j)) \in C^n(V_{ji})$, that is to say on translating $\psi_j^{-1} \psi_i$ into coordinate transformations, the functional relationship between $x_i^1, \ldots, x_i^n$ and $x_j^1, \ldots, x_j^n$, $x_j^n(x_i^1, \ldots, x_i^n)$, admits continuous derivatives through those of order r for $(x_i^1, \ldots, x_i^n)$ restricted to $\psi_i^{-1}(U_i \cap U_j)$. Similarly $(\psi_i^{-1} \psi_j)\ \psi_j^{-1}(U_i \cap U_j) \in C^r(V_{ji})$.

Remark. It is known that a class r manifold $r \geq 1$, can be triangulated. Hence the facts in (61) are available.

Definition 6.2. A homeomorphism which is the identity outside some compact set is termed an **almost constant homeomorphism.** The almost constant homeomorphisms of a locally compact space, X, obviously constitute a group $G(X)$ with the neutral element the identity homeomorphism. The stability subgroup at x_0 is $G_0(X) = \{g \mid gx_0 = x_0\}$.

The following theorem allows wide generalization of the restrictions on X.

Theorem 6.3. (6.3a) *An arcwise connected n dimensional manifold X is homeomorphic to the homogeneous space* (of left cosets), $G(X)/G_0(X)$; (6.3b) $G_0(X)$ *has a local section in* $G(X)$ (81.25).

Let the metric of X be denoted by ρ. We metrize $G(X)$ by

(6.3c) $$d(g, g') = \sup \rho(g(x), g'(x)), (A).$$

Let x_0 be an arbitrary point of X, fixed throughout the discussion. We refer to the neighborhoods in (6.1) as admissible. Let $U(x_0)$ be an admissible neighborhood. There is a map γ of $U(x_0)$ to $G(U)$; that is to say $\gamma(x) = g_x \in G(U) \subset G(X)$ subject to $g_x(x_0) = x$ where

(6.3d) $$d(g_x, e) \leq \rho(x_0, x).$$

Indeed we may as well assume $U(x_0)$ is an isometric image of an open disk $D_n \subset R_n$ and the existence of γ with the properties in question is immediate for $G(D_n)$. For x_1, x_2 in $U(x_0)$, denote $g_{x_2}g_{x_1}^{-1}$ by $g_{x_1x_2}$ an element in $G(U) \subset G(X)$ which takes x_1 into x_2. If x_1 and x_2 are arbitrary, let $l(x_1, x_2)$ be a path joining them. A finite number of admissible neighborhoods cover $l(x_1, x_2)$ and composition of transformations $g_{y_iy_{i+1}}$ for y_i, y_{i+1} in an admissible neighborhood, yields $g_{y_iy_{i+1}} \in G(X)$.

Define ψ on $G(X)$ to X by $\psi(g) = g(x_0)$. From what has already been established, it is plain ψ is onto. We assert ψ is an open map. Indeed let $N_\varepsilon = \{g \mid d(g, e) < \delta\}$. Suppose $y = g(x_0) \in \psi N_\varepsilon$, then

$$\rho(x_0, y) \leq d(x_0, g(x_0)) < \delta.$$

Let $\delta' < \delta - \rho(x_0, y)$, with $\{x \mid \rho(x, y) < \delta'\} = V(y)$, an admissible neighborhood of y. If $x \in \gamma^{(y)}$, then just as in (6.3d) there is a g_x with $g_x(y) = x$ and $d(g'_x, e) < \rho(x, y) < \delta'$, or $g_x \in N_\varepsilon$. Therefore $V(y) \subset \psi N_\delta$.

Since $G_0 = \{g \mid gx_0 = x_0\}$, $\psi(gg_0) = gg_0(x_0) = g(x_0)$ if $g_0 \in G_0$. Hence ψ induces ψ a 1–1 correspondence of G/G_0 onto X. Therefore from

$$\underbrace{G \xrightarrow[p]{} G/G_0 \xrightarrow{\psi'} X}_{\psi}$$

we deduce at once ψ' is continuous since ψ is (*A*). Moreover ψ' is open since ψ and γ are. In short, ψ' is a homeomorphism.

Let $U(x_0)$ be admissible. Let $s = \gamma\psi'$ be the map of $\psi'^{-1}U(x_0)$ to G. That s is a section (81.25) over $\psi'^{-1}U(x_0)$ follows from

$$ps[h] = p\gamma h(x_0) = [g_{h(x_0)}] = [h].$$

PROBLEM

9-11. Verify that (6.3c) is not necessary for the proof that ψ is open.

7. GEOMETRIC APPLICATIONS. Throughout the next two sections (7) and (8), the coefficients are understood to be in a field [except in (7.3)], R^n is as usual the n-dimensional Euclidean space, and the term *carrier of a cycle* is understood in the sense of (87.3).

Theorem 7.1. *Let M be compact and let z_n be a nonbounding Cech cycle in M. Suppose C^0 and C^1 are disjunct compact sets in $M \times I$ and suppose C^1 does not meet $M^0 = M \times 0$ while C^0 does not meet $M^1 = M \times 1$. Then there is an n cycle w_n on $M \times I$, whose carrier does not meet $M^0 \cup M^1 \cup C^0 \cup C^1$ and $w_n \sim z_n(0)$ where $z_n(0)$ on M^0 corresponds to z_n on M.*

Since $M \times I$ is compact, $M^0 \cup C^0$ and $M^1 \cup C^1$ can be covered by a finite collection of open sets in $M \times I$ whose union is N^0 and N^1 respectively, with

$N^0 \cap N^1 = 0$. Let $X^1 = \overline{N^1}$. Write $X^0 = \overline{M \times I - X^1}$ and $Q = X^0 \cap X^1$. Thus Q is the frontier of X^1 and is disjunct from both $M^0 \cup C^0$ and $M^1 \cup C^1$. Consider

$$\begin{array}{ccccccccc} & & H_n(M^0) & & & & & & \\ & & \downarrow l & & & & & & \\ (7.1a) \quad \longrightarrow & H_n(Q) \xrightarrow{i} & H_n(X^0) & \xrightarrow{j} & H_n(X^0, Q) & \xrightarrow{\partial} & H_{n-1}(Q) \longrightarrow \\ & & \downarrow r & I & \downarrow e & & \\ & & H_n(M \times I) & \xrightarrow{s} & H_n(M \times I, X^1). & & \end{array}$$

Here i, r, s, and l are induced by the obvious inclusion maps and e is induced by an excision map for $X^1 - X^1_- = Q$, $M \times I - X^1_- = X^0$, (X_-, the interior of X). In short e is an excision isomorphism. Since all the homomorphisms in the square I are induced by either inclusions or excisions, commutativity obtains. Let $z_n(0)$ be a representative of $\mathbf{z}_n(0) \in H_n(M^0)$. Since $z_n(0) \sim z_n(1)$ over $M \times I$, $z_n(0) \sim 0 \bmod M^1$ and hence $z_n(0) \sim 0 \bmod X^1$. We have

(7.1b) $$srl\mathbf{z}_n(0) = 0,$$

whence

(7.1c) $$e^{-1}\, srl\, \mathbf{z}_n(0) = 0,$$

or

(7.1d) $$jl\, \mathbf{z}_n(0) = 0.$$

The upper horizontal sequence is exact so the kernel of j includes the image of i. Since $l\, \mathbf{z}_n(0)$ is in the kernel of j, there must exist an element $\mathbf{w}_n \in H_n(Q)$ such that $i\, \mathbf{w}_n = l\, \mathbf{z}_n(0)$ or $i\, w_n \sim l\, z_n(0)$.

PROBLEM

9-12. Establish (7.1) by a Mayer Vietoris sequence argument.

Lemma 7.2. *Let K^0 and K^1 be compact spaces with union K and common part Q. Suppose L is a compact subset of K^0. Let z_n be an n cycle of L with $z_n \sim 0$ on K. Then there is a cycle w_n in Q homologous to z_n over K^0.*

The Mayer Vietoris sequence is

$$\begin{array}{ccccccc} & & & H_n(L) & & & \\ & & & \downarrow l & & & \\ \longleftarrow H_{n-1}(Q) & \xleftarrow{\partial} & H_n(K) & \xleftarrow{\phi} & H_n(K^0) \oplus H_n(K') & \xleftarrow{\psi} & H_n(Q) \longleftarrow \end{array}$$

We have $\phi l\, \mathbf{z}_n = 0$ according to the hypothesis. Thus $l\, \mathbf{z}_n$ is in the kernel of ϕ whence, by exactness, some $w_n \in N_n(Q)$ satisfies $\psi \mathbf{w}_n = l\, \mathbf{z}_n$.

Theorem 7.3. *Suppose M is a closed orientable n-dimensional manifold, with $M \times I$ in R^{n+1}, and with fundamental cycle z_n. C is a continuum in $M \times I$ meeting both M^0 and M^1. Suppose N is a closed n-dimensional orientable manifold with base cycle w_n, where $w_n \sim z_n(0)$ over $M \times I$, and $\|N\|$ is a carrier of w_n. Then $\|N\|$ meets C.*

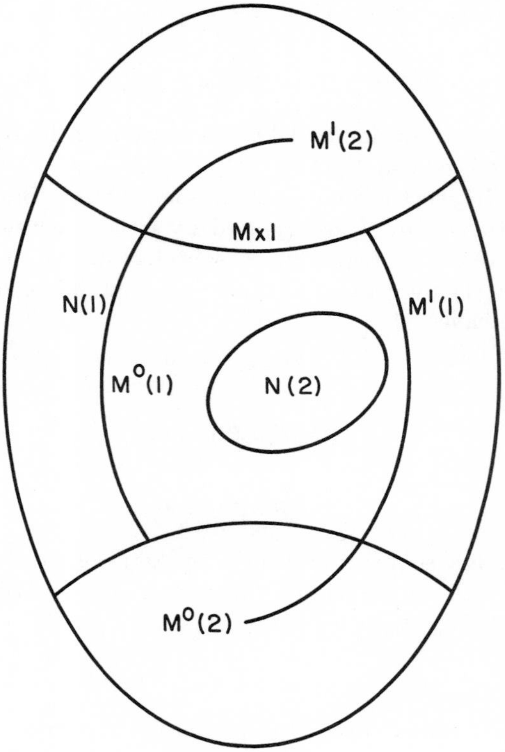

Figure 9-2

Compactify R^{n+1} by adding the point ∞ to get S^{n+1}. Let the coefficient group be J (though any in (41) would serve). Suppose that N separates S^{n+1} into the domains $N(1)$ and $N(2)$, M^j separates S^{n+1} into the domains $M^j(1)$, and $M^j(2), j = 0, 1$. Suppose $N(1)$ contains M^0 and M^1. By suitable labeling we can be sure that $M^0(1) \supset M^1$ and $M^1(1) \supset M^0$. Then

$$\overline{M^0(1)} \cap \overline{M^1(1)} \supset M \times I.$$

Indeed, if some point (m, τ) of $M \times I$ were not in $M^0(1)$, the line

$$\{(m, t) \mid \tau \leq t \leq t_1\}$$

would cut M^0.

Consider the sets $K^0 = L = X^0 = M \times I - N(2)$, $K^1 = \overline{N(2)}$, $X^1 = \overline{M^0(2) \cup M^1(2)}$. The compact sets $X^0, X^1, X = X^0 \cup X^1$ constitute our triad. Note $w_n - z_n(0) \sim 0$ over $K = K^0 \cup K^1$. Evidently also $w_n - z_n(1) \sim 0$ over K. Recourse to (7.2) establishes there are cycles $c^0 = l_0 w_n$ and $c^1 = l_1 w_n$ on N where l_0 and l_1 are integers such that (**a**) $c^0 \sim w_n - z_n(0)$ and (**b**) $c^1 \sim w_n - z_n(1)$, both over K^0. Since neither $z_n(0)$ nor $z_n(1)$ bounds on $M \times I$, $m_i = 1 - l_i \neq 0$, and $c_n = m_0 z_n(1) - m_1 z_n(0)$ is a cycle on $X^0 \cap X^1 = M^0 \cup M^1$ whose homology class in $H_n(X^0 \cap X^1)$, denoted by $\mathbf{c}_n$, is not 0. On the other hand c_n is evidently a bounding cycle on both X^0 and X^1. Thus $\mathbf{c}_n$ is in the kernel of the Mayer Vietoris map ψ into $H_n(X^0) \oplus H_n(X^1)$ and therefore is the image (under ∂) of $H_{n+1}(X)$. Since X is a proper subset of S^{n+1}, $H_{n+1}(X) = 0$ and so $\mathbf{c}_n = 0$. In short M^0 and M^1 cannot both be in domain $N(1)$ [or in $N(2)$]. Also M^0 (or M^1) cannot meet both $N(1)$ and $N(2)$ for then so does $M^0(2)$ whence

$$0 \neq M^0(2) \cap N \subset \widetilde{M \times I} \cap N = 0, \quad \widetilde{M \times I} = S^{n+1} - M \times I.$$

Suppose $\|N\| \cap C = \phi$; then, since the common boundary of $N(1)$ and $N(2)$ is N it would follow that C is contained entirely in one or the other of $N(1)$ or $N(2)$. This would stand at variance with our requirement that C meet both M^0 and M^1.

PROBLEM

9-13. Let S_1 and S_2 be two n spheres intersecting in a nondegenerate $n - 1$ sphere. Show that every point of the subset Σ (of $S_1 \cup S_2$) consisting of points not interior to either S_1 or S_2 admits a neighborhood on Σ homeomorphic to R^n and hence that Σ is an n manifold.

Lemma 7.4. *Under the hypotheses of* (7.1) *there is an n-manifold which separates $C^0 \cup M^0$ from $C^1 \cup M^1$.*

In the argument for (7.1) the finite collection of open sets constituting N^0 and N^1 can be taken as open spheres, the closures of any pair of which are either disjunct or share interior points. Hence

$$Q = \bigcup_{i=1}^{i=N} Q_i,$$

where each Q_i is an n dimensional manifold. Since $i\colon H_n(Q) \to H_n(M \times I)$ is nontrivial $i\colon H_n(Q_j) \to H_n(M \times I)$ is nontrivial for some j, say $j = 1$, so Q_1 carries a cycle w_n homologous to $z_n(0)$. We identify Q_1 with N in (7.3) to gain the conclusion sought.

Theorem 7.5. *Let M be a closed orientable n-manifold with $M \times I$ in R^{n+1}, and let z_n be its fundamental cycle. Let Y be a closed subset of $M \times I$ that* *separates $M \times 0$ and $M \times 1$. Then some closed connected subset of Y separates also and has a nontrivial n dimensional homology group.*

Let the distance of Y from $M \times 0 \cup M \times 1$ be d. Cover Y by a finite number of closed spheres of radius $d/2^i$ at most, subject to the condition that any two closed spheres are either disjunct or share inner points. The union of these spheres is denoted by Y_i and $Y_i \supset Y_{i+1}$. Since the boundary of Y_i, namely $\dot{Y}_i$, must separate, some of the individual components of $\dot{Y}_1$ must separate as well by the argument of (7.4). Denote the components of Y_1 containing a separating component of $\dot{Y}_1$ by $\{Y_1(r_1)\}$ or simply by (r_1) where $r_1 = 1, \ldots, N$ depending on d and refer to these as *admissible components.* The admissible components of $Y_1(r_1)$ are denoted by $(r_1 r_2)$, etc., where r_2 depends on r_1. A specified admissible component $(r_1 r_2 \cdots r_{n-1})$ may contain no admissible component for the next stage, that is to say there may be no $(r_1 \cdots r_n)$. However, at the nth stage there are always admissible components. Hence by the Zermelo axiom there is a sequence of admissible sets $\{(r_1 \cdots r_n)\}$ whose intersection Z is a connected subset of Y. To verify that Z separates, let C be an arbitrary continuum joining $M \times 0$ and $M \times 1$. Since $(r_1 \ldots r_n)$ separates, $C \cap (r_1 \cdots r_n)$ contains a point, say x_n. The compactness of $M \times I$ guarantees $\{x_n\}$ has a limit point, $\bar{x}$, which must be in both C and Z.

To show $H_n(Z, R) \neq 0$ when R is a field, compactify R^{n+1} with the point ∞ to get N^{n+1}. Since Z separates $M \times I$ it separates N^{n+1}. Let A_1 and A_2 be two separated sets such that $A_1 \cup A_2 = S^{n+1} - Z$. Then ${}_SR_0 \geq 2$ where ${}_SR_0$ is the singular homology Betti number in dimension 0. We anticipate the Alexander duality relation (127.3), namely $R_n(Z) = {}_SR_0(S^n - Z) - 1$ when R_n is the Betti number for the Cech group. Hence $R_n \neq 0$

PROBLEM

9-14. Demonstrate $H_n(Z, R) \neq 0$ by use of the continuity theorem (91.3) in conjunction with (7.4) where attention is paid to the homology homomorphisms on $\{r_1, \ldots, r_n\}$.

Remark. A direct Zorn's lemma argument can be used for the separation part of (7.5).

Definition 7.6. A point to set transformation $f\colon\ Y \to X$ is **continuous** if $f(y)$ is closed and f^{-1} is both open and closed.

Definition 7.7. In S^n or in R^n (**a**) the set A is **linked** by the disjunct set L if there is a cycle $z_{n-1}(L)$ which is nonbounding on any compact subset of $R^n - A$ in the sense of Cech in (61.16).

(**b**) If $Y \subset R^n$, the continuous transformation f: on Y to R^n **links** A if $A \cap f(Y) = \phi$ and if for all compact sets C such that $f(Y) \subset C \subset R^n - A$, $f_* H_{n-1}(Y) \to H_{n-1}(C)$ is nontrivial.

By way of motivation for some interesting applications suppose X and S are two concentric circles in the plane. Suppose, initially, that X encloses S

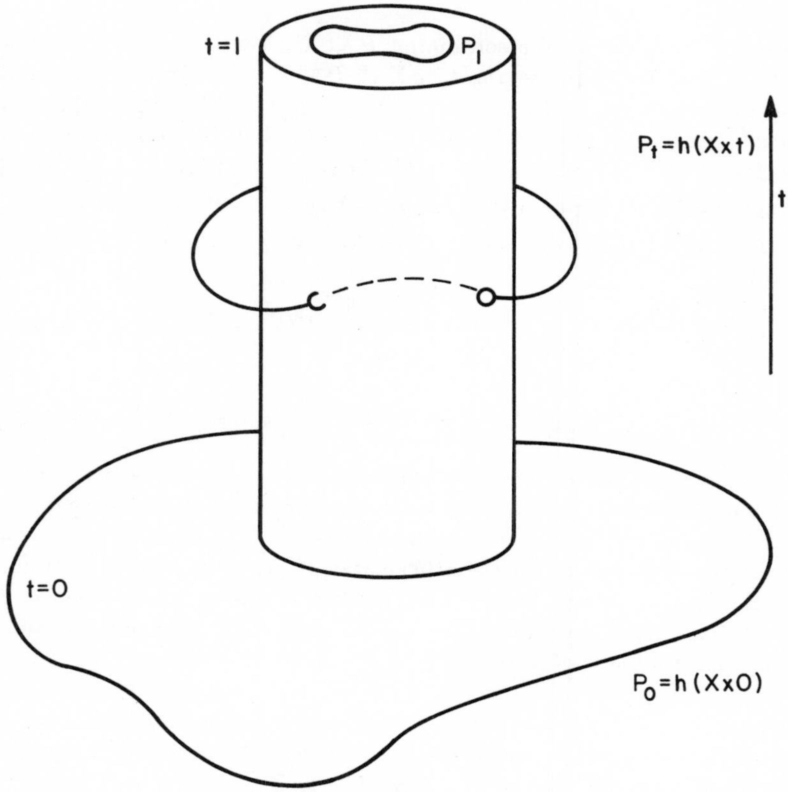

Figure 9-3

and that h is a deformation (63.1) eventuating in X being taken inside S so that at the end X is not outside any point of S. (A banal generalization allows h: $X \times 0$ to be P_0, a curve containing S in its interior rather than restricted by h: $X \times 0 = X = P_0$.) The terminology *inside* S and *outside* S is given precision in the framework of homology by the notion of linking (7.7). With this guiding picturalization in mind, we present a mild advance on the above ideas (7.5).

Let $S = \{y\}$ be a compact connected subset of $R^n = \{x\}$. Write I_ε for $\{t \mid -\varepsilon \leq t \leq 1 + \varepsilon, \varepsilon > 0\}$. The cylinder $\Sigma' = S \times I_\varepsilon$ is thought of as in R^{n+1}, and contains $\Sigma = S \times I$. S_0 and S_1 denote $S \times 0$ and $S \times 1$.

Lemma 7.8. *Let X be a compact subset of R^n and let h denote a homotopy on $X \times I$ to R^{n+1}. If $P_t = h(X \times t) \times t$ and $P = \bigcup_t P_t$, we require P_0 link S_0 whereas P_1 does not link any point of S_1. Then $P \cap \Sigma$ separates $(S \times (-\delta))$ and $(S \times (1 + \delta))$.*

Write $E \times I_\delta$ for a cube containing $P \cup \Sigma'$. Let $Q = \{(y, t) \mid P_t$ links y in $R^n \times t\} \subset \Sigma$. Suppose $(y_0, t_0) \in \Sigma \cap P^{\sim}$, $t_0 \in I$. Since P is compact for neighborhoods Δ_{t_0}, $U(y_0) \subset R^n$, $(U(y_0) \times \Delta_{t_0}) \cap (\bigcup_{t \in \Delta} P_t) = \varnothing$. Denote $(U(y_0) \cap S) \times \Delta_{t_0}$ by $V_0 \subset \Sigma$. Accordingly P_{t_0} and P_t are homotopic over $E - U(y_0)$, with homotopy function $h^1 = h$ restricted to $X \times \Delta_{t_0}$. Let $U(y_0)$ be a spherical neighborhood $\supset y$. Let $E - U(y_0) \xrightarrow{i} E - y_0$ and $E - U(y_0) \xrightarrow{j} E - y$, be inclusion maps. Therefore i_* and j_* are isomorphisms. Consider

$$\begin{array}{ccccccc} H_{n-1}(X) & \xrightarrow{h(t_0)_*} & H_{n-1}(P_{t_0}) & \longrightarrow & H_n(E - U(y_0)) & \xrightarrow[\approx]{i_*} & H_{n-1}(E - y_0) \\ & \searrow^{h(t)_*} & \downarrow \approx & \mathrm{I} & \downarrow \approx & & \\ & & H_{n-1}(P_t) & \longrightarrow & H_n(E_* - U(y_0)) & \xrightarrow[\approx]{j_*} & H_{n-1}(E - y) \end{array}$$

where I is commutative. The composition along the upper row is a nontrivial homomorphism if the similar composition is nontrivial at the lower level. In brief, if $(y_0, t_0) \in Q$, then some neighborhood N of (y_0, t_0) belongs to Q also. This implies Q is open. On the other hand, if (y_0, t_0) is neither in Q nor on $P \cap \Sigma$, then y_0 is not linked, and neither is any y in N. Hence $T = \Sigma - P \cap \Sigma - Q$ is open also. The assertion of the lemma follows from the observation that $Q \supset S \times 0$ and $T \supset S \times 1$.

Theorem 7.9. *Let S be a closed orientable n dimensional manifold in R_n and suppose X and h satisfy the conditions of* (7.8). *Suppose f is a continuous point to set mapping on S to S. Then, for some positive t, $y \in P_t$ and $P_t \cap f(y) \neq \varnothing$.*

By (7.8) and (7.5) some compact connected subset A of $P \cap \Sigma$ separates $S \times (-\delta)$ and $S \times (1 + \delta)$. Let $f \times I$ map $S \times I_\delta$ to $S \times I_\delta$ by

(7.9a) $$f(x, t) = (f(x), t).$$

Let C be a component of $f(A)$. Then $C = \bigcap C_i$ where C_i is both open and closed in $f(A)$. Hence, by (7.6), $f^{-1}(C_i)$ is open and closed in A and therefore $f^{-1}(C_i) = A = f^{-1}(C)$. According to (7.9a), $\tau = \{t \mid (y, t) \in C\} = \{t \mid (y, t) \in A\}$.

Let t_0 and t_1 be the extreme t values in τ. We may assume $0 < t_0, t_1 < 1$. Suppose $C \cap A = \varnothing$. Then some arc joins $S \times (-\delta)$ and $(y_0, t_0) \in C$. Similarly some arc joins $S \times (1 + \delta)$ and $(y_1, t_1) \in C$. Thus there is a continuum, disjunct from A, joining $S \times (-\delta)$ and $S \times (1 + \delta)$. This contradicts the definition of A. Hence $A \cap C \neq 0$, or, for some t,

$$f(P_t) \cap P_t \neq \varnothing$$

Corollary 7.10. *Let S and X be concentric n-dimensional spheres of radius 1 and 2 respectively. Let $h(\ ,\ )$ be a deformation taking X inside S. Then for some t, the deformed sphere intersects S in 2 antipodal points or, indeed, in 2 points whose distance apart, ρ, is prescribed (≤ 1 of course).*

Let $f(x \mid S) = \{y \mid d(x, y) = \rho\}$. Then f is a continuous point to set map and (7.9) applies.

8. DEGREE. Definition 8.1. Let X, A, B be a triple of closed spaces, $X \supset A \supset B$. Let ψ: $X, A, B \to E^n, S^{n-1}, x_0$ and write ψ_1 for $\psi \mid X, A$ and ψ_2 for $\psi \mid A, B$. Let $\mathbf{f}$ and $\mathbf{g}$ be generators of $H^{n-1}(S^{n-1}, x_0)$ and of $H^n(E^n, S^{n-1})$ respectively with $\delta\mathbf{f} = \mathbf{g}$. The **degree** of ψ_1 is defined as the element $\psi_1^* \mathbf{g}$ (which is the same as $\delta\psi_2^* \mathbf{f}$). When X, A, B is E^n, S^{n-1}, x_0 the degree of ψ is defined as the **integer** m where $\psi_1^* \mathbf{g} = m\mathbf{g}$.

The facts about sphere maps enter through the exact sequences

$$\text{(8.1a)}\quad \begin{array}{ccccccc} H^{n-1}({}_1S^{n-1}, x_1) & \xrightarrow[\approx]{\delta} & H^n({}_1E^n_-, {}_1S^{n-1}) & \xrightarrow{\approx} & H^n({}_1S^n, {}_1E^n_+) & \xrightarrow{\approx} & H^n({}_1S^{n-1}, x_1) \\ \uparrow{\scriptstyle\psi} & & \uparrow{\scriptstyle\psi} & & & & {\scriptstyle\psi^1}\uparrow \\ H^{n-1}({}_2S^{n-1}, x_2) & \longrightarrow & H^n({}_2E^n_-, {}_2S^{n-1}) & \longrightarrow & H^n({}_2S^n, {}_2E^n_+) & \longrightarrow & H^n({}_2S^n, x_2) \end{array}$$

where the upper hemisphere of S^n is labeled E^n_+ and the lower hemisphere is called E^n_-.

PROBLEM

9-15. There exist maps, ψ: ${}_1S^n\ x_1 \to {}_2S^n\ x_2$ of arbitrary degree for $n \geq 1$. *Hint:* For $n = 1$ this is clear from $\psi(z) = z^k$ for $|z| = 1$. Proceed by induction using (8.1a) since if ψ exists on ${}_1S^{n-1} \to {}_2S^{n-1}$ of degree k, then extend ψ to ${}_1S^n \to {}_2S^n$ by making the two great circles through the north and south poles correspond if the first cuts ${}_1S^{n-1}$ in x and the second cuts ${}_2S^{n-1}$ in $\psi(x)$.

chapter 10

HOMOLOGICAL ALGEBRA

1. TWO BASIC LEMMAS. The following is a well-known, useful group theoretic result to which we must refer.

Lemma 1.1. *Suppose* ϕ *and* ψ *are homomorphisms of the groups* G *and* H, *viz.,* $G \xrightarrow{\phi} H \xrightarrow{\psi} G$ *and suppose* $\psi\phi$ *is the identity on* G, *and that* $Im\ \phi$ *is a normal subgroup of* H, *then* H *is a direct sum*

$$H \approx Im\ \phi \oplus ker\ \psi. \tag{1.1a}$$

Furthermore, ψ *is an epimorphism and* ϕ *is a monomorphism. The conclusion* (1.1a) *maintains if* G *and* H *are* R *modules.*

For an arbitrary element h write $h = lk$ where $l = \phi\psi h$, $k = (\phi\psi h)^{-1} h$. Note

$$\psi k = \psi h^{-1}\, \psi h = e^2, \tag{1.1b}$$

where e^1 is the identity of H and e^2 the identity of G. Thus $k \in ker\ \psi$. On the other hand, $l = \phi(\psi h) \subset Im\ \phi$ and we assert this factorization is unique. Indeed, suppose $\bar{h} \in Im\ \phi \cap ker\ \psi$. Then, for some $\bar{g} \in G$, $\phi\bar{g} = \bar{h}$ whence $e^2 = \psi\phi\bar{g} = \bar{g}$. Therefore (1.1b) implies $\bar{h} = e^1$. Further note that since $Im\ \phi$ is a normal subgroup of H,

$$kl = lk. \tag{1.1c}$$

Indeed, let $\bar{h} = klk^{-1}l^{-1}$. Then $\psi(\bar{h}) = e^2$ (1.1c). On the other hand, since $Im\ \phi$ is a normal subgroup of H, $l' = hlh^{-1} \in Im\ \phi$, so $\bar{h} = l^{-1} l' \in Im\ \phi$. Thus $\bar{h} \in Im\ \phi \cap ker\ \psi = e^1$, the assertion of (1.1c). From (1.1c) it follows that if $h_i = l_i k_i$, $i = 1, 2$, then (1.1a) is valid for

$$h_1 h_2 = l_1 k_1 l_2 k_2 = l_1 l_2 k_1 k_2.$$

Finally, $\phi g = \phi g^1$ implies $g = \psi\phi g = \psi\phi g^1 = g^1$ so ϕ is a monomorphism. Since $\psi H \supset \psi\phi G = G$, ψ is an epimorphism.

Lemma 1.2. 5-Lemma. *Let the following diagram, involving modules over a common ring R, have commutative squares and exact rows*

$$\begin{array}{ccccccccc}
A_1 & \xrightarrow{\phi_1} & A_2 & \xrightarrow{\phi_2} & A_3 & \xrightarrow{\phi_3} & A_4 & \xrightarrow{\phi_4} & A_5 \\
\downarrow & & \downarrow & & \downarrow & & \downarrow & & \downarrow \\
\alpha_1 & \text{I} & \approx \alpha_2 & \text{II} & \alpha_3 & \text{III} & \approx \alpha_4 & \text{IV} & \alpha_5 \\
\downarrow & & \downarrow & & \downarrow & & \downarrow & & \downarrow \\
B_1 & \rightarrow \phi_1' \rightarrow & B_2 & \rightarrow \phi_2' \rightarrow & B_3 & \rightarrow \phi_3' \rightarrow & B_4 & \rightarrow \phi_4' \rightarrow & B_5
\end{array}$$

Suppose also that α_1 is onto, that α_2 and α_4 are isomorphisms, and that α_5 is a monomorphism. Then α_3 is an isomorphism.

We shall understand that $a_i \in A_i$ and $b_j \in B_j$. Let $a_3 \in ker\, \alpha_3$ so $0 = \phi_3' \alpha_3 a_3 = \alpha_4 \phi_3 a_3$. Since α_4 denotes an isomorphism, $\phi_3 a_3 = 0$, so some a_2 is an antecedent of a_3 under ϕ_2. Therefore $\phi_2' \alpha_2 a_2 = \alpha_3 \phi_2 a_2 = 0$, and we conclude that for some b_1, $\phi_1' b_1 = \alpha_2 a_2$. Let a_1 satisfy $\alpha_1 a_1 = b_1$. We assert $\phi_1 a_1 = a_2$. Indeed $\alpha_2 \phi_1 a_1 = \phi_1' b_1 = \alpha_2 a_2$. Since α_2 is an isomorphism $\alpha_2(\phi_1 a_1 - a_2) = 0$ implies our assertion. Hence $a_3 = \phi_2 a_2 = \phi_1 \phi_2 a_1 = 0$. We sketch the proof that α_3 is onto. Pick b_3 arbitrarily, then $\phi_3' b_3$ corresponds to $\alpha_4 a_4$ and $\phi_4' \phi_3' a_3 = 0$, so since α_5 is a monomorphism, $\phi_4 a_4 = 0$, whence for some a_3, $\phi_3 a_3 = a_4$, so by commutativity of III $\alpha_3 a_3 - b_3 \in Im\ \phi_2' = Im \phi_2' \alpha_2 = Im\ \alpha_3 \phi_2 \subset Im\ \alpha_3$. Hence $b_3 \in Im\ \alpha_3$.

Corollary 1.3. *Suppose ϕ: $K, L \rightarrow K_1, L_1$ where these are compact spaces, or simplicial complexes, and suppose* (61.13c) *holds for the homology sequence. If $H_*(K) \overset{\phi_*}{\approx} H_*(K_1)$ and $H_*(L) \overset{\phi_*}{\approx} H_*(L_1)$ then $\phi_*: H_*(K, L) \approx H_*(K_1, L_1)$.*

Apply the 5 lemma to (61.13f).

Definition 1.4. Let

(1.4a) $$0 \longrightarrow A' \overset{i}{\longrightarrow} A \overset{j}{\longrightarrow} A'' \longrightarrow 0$$

be an exact sequence of Abelian groups or of R modules. The sequence **splits** if $Im\ i$ is a direct summand. This is tantamount to saying there are homomorphisms i' and j' called left and right splittings respectively, such that $i'i$ is the identity on A' and jj' is the identity on A'' (cf. 1.1). Thus $A \approx i(A) \oplus j'(A'')$.

2. PROJECTIVE AND INJECTIVE MODULES. Unless otherwise stated, we shall understand below that the ring R is an integral domain;

Theorem 2.1. *If F, A', and A are R modules and F is free, and if f and g are the R homomorphisms indicated in the diagram, then there exists a homomorphism h satisfying $f = gh$; that is to say, f can be factored.*

(2.1a)
$$\begin{array}{ccccc} & & F & & \\ & \overset{h}{\swarrow} & \downarrow f & & \\ A' & \xrightarrow[g]{} & A & \longrightarrow & 0 \quad \text{exact} \end{array}$$

Let $\{e_i\}$ be a basis for F. By exactness fe_i has an inverse ${}_ia'$ in A'. Define $he_i = {}_ia'$ and extend the definition of h overall F by linearity, $h\Sigma r^i e_i = \Sigma r^i {}_ia'$. Note h may be modified by adding an arbitrary element of $ker\ g$ to he_i.

Definition 2.2. An R module P satisfying the theorem above with P replacing F and arbitrary A', A, f, and g is called **projective** or **a projective.**

The dual is obtained by reversing all arrows in the first diagram. Thus if for arbitrary A, A', s, and r, t exists satisfying $s = tr$, then J is **injective** or **an injective** [(cf. (2.1b)].

(2.1b)
$$\begin{array}{ccccc} & & J & & \\ & & s\uparrow & \overset{t}{\nwarrow} & \\ 0 & \longrightarrow & A & \xrightarrow{r} & A' \quad \text{exact} \end{array}$$

The most convenient formulation for application is given by the following easy lemma.

Lemma 2.3. *An R module P is projective if* (44.5a) *is exact on the right, viz., if from the exactness of*

(2.3a)
$$0 \to A' \to A \to A'' \to 0$$

follows the exactness of

(2.3b)
$$0 \to Hom(P, A') \to Hom(P, A) \to Hom(P, A'') \to 0.$$

An R module J is injective if (44.5b) *is exact on the right; that is to say, if from the exactness of* (2.3a) *follows the exactness of*

(2.3c)
$$0 \to Hom(A'', J) \to Hom(A, J) \to Hom(A', J) \to 0.$$

The extent of the generalization achieved is given by the following lemma.

Lemma 2.4. *A module, P, is projective iff P is a direct summand of a free module, F.*

Lemma 2.5. *An injective module is a direct summand of any containing module.*

Sufficiency follows immediately from (2.1) since summands behave autonomously. For the necessity demonstration represent P as F/B where B is the submodule generated by the relations. Then by (2.1), with f the identity, $i = gh$ and (1.1a) applies (even though here we deal with modules).

The last assertion is clear from the diagram and (42.2)

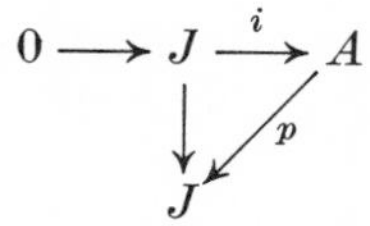

EXAMPLE 10-1. We exhibit a projective module which is not free. Let b be a generator with $3b = 0$. The module over the ring J_6 (not an integral domain) is denoted by $J_6(b)$. This has just three elements. On the other hand, a free module would needs have at least 6 elements. Hence $J_6(b)$ is projective, but not free.

PROBLEMS

10-1. Show that if $\oplus P_i$ is projective, then each P_i is projective and conversely.
10-2. Show that if ΠI_i is injective, each I_i is injective and conversely.
10-3. Let A be an injective Abelian group. Show that for any integer $m \neq 0$, and for any $a \in A$ there is a $b \in A$ such that $a = mb$. (The converse is also true, but harder to show.)

Definition 2.6. The module A over the integral domain R is a **divisible module** if for every $a \in A$ and $r \in R$ there is a b in A for which $a = rb$. If $R = J$, the group case, the diagram (2.1b) holds and so there is duality between free and divisible groups. If every ideal in an integral domain is a principal ideal, that is to say of the form Rr for some fixed r, then the integral domain is a **principal ideal domain**. Thus J and Q are included.

Remark. Many statements valid for J or for Q remain valid when a principal ideal domain R enters. Thus every projective module over a principal ideal domain is a free module, and similarly injective modules are the same as divisible modules. (This last observation is the extension of Problem 10-3 to modules.)

Lemma 2.7. *If R is a principal ideal domain, any module A can be imbedded in an injective module.*

First let $F(A)$ be the free module generated by the nonzero elements of A and let $F(A) \xrightarrow{j} A$ be the epimorphism which attaches to each element in

$F(A)$ its correspondent in A. Then $ker\, j$ constitutes the module of relations and $A \approx F(A)/ker\, j$. Let $\check{R}$ be the field of quotients of R. Evidently

$$0 \longrightarrow ker\, j \xrightarrow{i'} \check{R} \otimes F(A)$$

where i' is defined by $a \to 1 \otimes a$ and is the composition of the monomorphism $ker\, j \xrightarrow{i} F(A)$ and $F(A) \xrightarrow{l} \check{R} \otimes F(A)$. We now need the fact that for principal ideal domains a divisible module is injective. If C is a submodule of the divisible module B, then a glance at the cosets, shows B/C is divisible. Hence

(2.7a) $$A \approx \frac{F(A)}{i\; ker\, j} \subset \frac{\check{R} \otimes F(A)}{li\; ker\, j} = I(A) \quad \text{an injective module.}$$

An application of (2.7a) is made in (177.4). (Actually $I(A)$ as defined in (2.7a) is an injective module even when R is not a principal ideal domain, but is a Dedekind ring, that is to say, for every ideal I of R there exist elements $r_1, \ldots, r_n \in R$ and $i_1, \ldots, i_n$ in I so that $\Sigma\, r_j\, i_j = 1$.)

For R modules the exactness of

(2.8a) $$0 \longrightarrow M \xrightarrow{i} P \xrightarrow{j} A \longrightarrow 0$$

yields exactness of

(2.8b) $$M \otimes B \xrightarrow{i \otimes 1} P \otimes B \xrightarrow{j \otimes 1} A \otimes B \longrightarrow 0$$

merely, except when special conditions are imposed. These involve, generally, absence of torsion in certain of the terms, at least when R is an integral domain to obviate zero divisors. Thus generally $ker(i \otimes 1)$ is not 0. We show below that under fairly general conditions $ker(i \otimes 1)$ depends on A and B alone, and reflects contributions of terms having torsion.

PROBLEM

10-4. Show using (64.10) that if either A or B is a free group $ker(i \otimes 1) = 0$ in (2.8b).

EXAMPLE 10-2. $0 \longrightarrow J \xrightarrow{i} Q$ is exact with J and Q the integers and the rationals as always. Let T consist of elements of finite order. Then $i \otimes 1 : J \otimes T \to Q \otimes T$, but $J \otimes T \approx T$ while $Q \otimes T = 0$, so $0 \not\to J \otimes T \to Q \otimes T$. Incidentally Q is torsion free but not free.

Definition 2.9. We write $\mathrm{Tor}_1^R(A, B)$ or simply $Tor(A, B)$ or $A * B$ for $ker(i \otimes 1)$ in (2.8b).

Definition 2.10. The importance of the Tor justifies an alternative definition for the case that A and B are Abelian groups. Let G be the Abelian group with generators $\{(a, b; t)\}$ where $a \in A$, $b \in B$, and t is a positive integer satisfying $ta = tb = 0$. We call t a **torsion coefficient** for (a, b). The group relations are

$$(2.10a)\quad (a_1 + a_2, b_1 + b_2; t) = (a_1, b_1; t) + (a_1, b_2; t) + (a_2, b_1; t) + (a_2, b_2; t) \quad \text{if } ta_i = tb_i = 0, \quad i = 1, 2;$$

$$(2.10b)\quad (a, b; t_1 t_2) = (t_i\, a, b; t_j), \quad \text{if } t_1 t_2\, a = t_j b = 0, \quad i \neq j,$$
$$= (a, t_i\, b; t_j), \quad \text{if } t_j\, a = t_1 t_2 b = 0, \quad i \neq j.$$

Then G is denoted by $Tor(A, B)$ and is isomorphic to the so designated group in (2.9). Since, if a or b is the neutral element, $(a, b; t) = 0$, it follows that $Tor(A, 0) = 0 = Tor(0, B)$. If $ta = 0$ implies $t = 0$—that is to say, if A is torsion free—$Tor(A, B) = 0$.

Remark. While $a \otimes c$ has meaning, $a * c = Tor(a, c)$ does not.

Lemma 2.11. *A and C are groups with A cyclic of order n. Then* $Tor(A, C) \approx C_n$ *the subgroup of C consisting of elements whose orders divide n.*

From $0 \longrightarrow J \xrightarrow{n} J \longrightarrow A \longrightarrow 0$, with n the homomorphism $e \longrightarrow ne$, there results $A \approx J/nJ = J_n$. Since J is free, there is exactness in

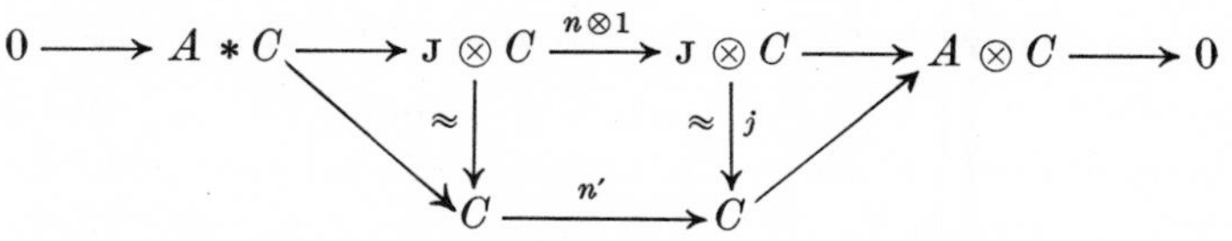

Since $jm \otimes c = mc$, $ker(n \otimes 1) = \{m \otimes c \mid nmc = 0\}$. Hence replacing mc by c', $ker\; n' = \{c' \mid nc' = 0\} \approx A * C$. (Modules can replace the groups in this lemma.)

Corollary 2.12. *If A and C are cyclic groups of order p and q respectively, then* $Tor(A, C)$ *is cyclic of order GCD p and q; i.e.,* (p, q).

Corollary 2.13. *If* $n = pq$, *then* J_n *is the direct sum of* J_p *and* J_q *if p and q are relatively prime.*

Theorem 2.14. *If* $0 \longrightarrow M \xrightarrow{i} P \xrightarrow{j} A \longrightarrow 0$ *is exact where P is projective, then* $ker\; i \otimes 1$ *defined in* (2.8b); *i.e.,* $Tor_1(A, B)$, *is unchanged up to isomorphism by replacement of M, P by another pair* M_1, P_1 *a projective.*

If the equivalence of (2.9) and (2.10) is taken on faith, there is nothing to prove, for in (2.10) no dependence on M or P occurs.

PROBLEM

10-5. Demonstrate (2.14). *Hint:* Consider the horseshoe

$$\begin{array}{ccccccccc} 0 & \longrightarrow & M & \xrightarrow{i} & P & \xrightarrow{j} & A & \longrightarrow & 0 \\ & & \Big\downarrow{\scriptstyle w} & & \Big\downarrow{\scriptstyle q} & & \Big\downarrow{\scriptstyle \text{identity}} & & \\ 0 & \longrightarrow & M_1 & \xrightarrow{i_1} & P_1 & \longrightarrow & A & \longrightarrow & 0 \end{array}$$

and determine nonunique homomorphisms q and w to make the squares commutative. Then tensor everything by B.

To obtain dual concepts we are guided in a general way by the suggestion that if a definition involves a homomorphism of groups or modules, etc., then the dualization will reverse the direction of the homomorphism and will replace subgroup by quotient group, and conversely. We apply these rules immediately.

Definition 2.15. If A and B are modules over R and $A \xrightarrow{\psi} B$ denotes a homomorphism, then **cokernel** ψ or $cok\ \psi = B/Im\ \psi$ and **coimage** $\psi = A/ker\ \psi \approx Im\ \psi$.

Suppose $A = B$ is an upper chain complex and let ψ be the boundary homomorphism d. Introduce the symbols, $Z'(A) = cok\ d = A/dA = A/B(A)$ and $B'(A) = coimage\ d = A/ker\ d = A/ZA \approx BA$. If $A^n \xrightarrow{d} A^{n+1}$, then $B'^n(A) = A^n/Z^n(A) \xrightarrow{\dot{d}} B^{n+1}(A)$ where $\dot{d}$ is induced by d. We exhibit a factorization of d which relates the various entities introduced. Actually a similar breakdown can be defined for an arbitrary homomorphism (and is used in defining exact categories later).

(2.15a)
$$\begin{array}{ccccccccccc} A & \longrightarrow & Z'(A) & \underset{\text{onto}}{\xrightarrow{\eta}} & B'(A) & \underset{\approx}{\xrightarrow{\dot{d}}} & B(A) & \underset{\approx\text{into}}{\xrightarrow{j}} & Z(A) & \longrightarrow & A \\ & & \wr\wr & & \wr\wr & & & & & & \\ & & A/B(A) & & A/Z(A) & & & & & & \end{array}$$
$$d' : Z'(A) \longrightarrow Z(A)$$

The following sequence is exact

(2.15b) $$0 \longrightarrow B(A) \xrightarrow{j} Z(A) \xrightarrow{\lambda} Z'(A) \xrightarrow{\eta} B'(A) \longrightarrow 0.$$

For instance $Z(A) \xrightarrow{\lambda} A/B(A)$ has kernel $B(A)$.

Since $\eta Z'(A) = B'(A)$ and $\dot{d}$ and j are at least monomorphisms

(2.15c) $$d'\ Z'(A) \approx B(A)$$

and

(2.15d) $$cok\ d' = Z(A)/B(A) = H(A) = ker\ \eta = ker\ d'.$$

Thus

$$0 \longrightarrow H^n(A) \longrightarrow Z'^n(A) \xrightarrow{d} Z^{n+1}(A) \longrightarrow H^{n+1}(A) \longrightarrow 0 \tag{2.15e}$$

$$H^n(A) \approx \ker d', \qquad H^{n+1}(A) \approx Z^{n+1}(A)/Im\, d'$$

is exact for reasons indicated by the appended isomorphisms.

Reference 2.16. We set down for purposes of reference two pairs of basic exact sequences,

$$0 \longrightarrow B^n(A) \xrightarrow{i} Z^n(A) \xrightarrow{\eta} H^n(A) \longrightarrow 0 \tag{2.16a}$$

$$0 \longrightarrow Z^n(A) \longrightarrow A^n \longrightarrow B^{n+1}(A) \longrightarrow 0 \tag{2.16b}$$

$$0 \longrightarrow B_n(A) \xrightarrow{i} Z_n(A) \xrightarrow{\eta} H_n(A) \longrightarrow 0 \tag{2.16c}$$

$$0 \longrightarrow Z_n(A) \longrightarrow A_n \longrightarrow B_{n-1}(A) \longrightarrow 0 \tag{2.16d}$$

3. RESOLUTIONS. Definition 3.1. If $K = \{K_n, d\}$ is a lower complex and G is a module over R, and if there is a homomorphism e on K_0 to G so that $edK_1 = 0$ where

$$\longrightarrow K_n \xrightarrow{d} K_{n-1} \longrightarrow \cdots \longrightarrow K_1 \xrightarrow{d} K_0 \xrightarrow{e} G \longrightarrow 0, \tag{3.1a}$$

then e is the **augmentation** and K is **over** G. If G is interpreted as the trivial complex $\{G_n, d\}$ with $G_n = 0$, $n > 0$, $d = 0$, then $e = \{e_n\}$ can be considered on K to G. If K_n is projective for each n, K is a **projective complex.** The complex is **acyclic** if $H(K) \underset{e_*}{\overset{\approx}{\longrightarrow}} H(G) = G$. Note this implies (3.1a) is exact. If K is both projective and acyclic, then (3.1a) is a **projective resolution** of G.

For upper complexes

$$0 \longrightarrow G \xrightarrow{e} K^0 \xrightarrow{d} K^1 \longrightarrow \cdots, \tag{3.1b}$$

and e can be interpreted on G to K. The complex is **acyclic** if $G \overset{e^*}{\approx} H(K)$ and is an **injective resolution** if K^i is an injective and K is acyclic.

Definition 3.2. Let G and G' be modules over R and let $f: G \to G'$ be a module homomorphism. Let K and K' be lower (or upper) complexes with augmentations e and e'. Then f can be **lifted** to an allowable homomorphism $F: K \to K'$ if $e' F = fe$ and F is **over** f ($Fe' = e'f$). (Lifted homomorphisms will be understood to be allowable.)

Theorem 3.3. *If K is projective over G, K' is acyclic over G', and if $f\colon G \to G'$, then f can be lifted to F and if ${}_1F$ and ${}_2F$ are both over f, then ${}_1F \simeq {}_2F$, If K and K' are projective resolutions, over G, they are homotopically equivalent.*

Since K_0 is projective, F_0 exists to satisfy $e'\,F_0 = fe$ where

$$\begin{array}{ccccc} K_0 & \xrightarrow{e} & G & & \\ {\scriptstyle F_0}\swarrow & \searrow & \vdots{\scriptstyle f} & & \\ K'_0 & \xrightarrow{e'} & G' & \longrightarrow & 0 \end{array}$$

Since K_1 is projective, and $e'\,F_0\,d$ and $e'\,d' = 0$, the diagram

$$\begin{array}{ccccc} & & K_1 & & \\ & & \downarrow{\scriptstyle F_0\,d} & & \\ K'_1 & \xrightarrow{d'} & K'_0 & \xrightarrow{e'} & G' \end{array}$$

is equivalent to a diagram with K'_0, G' replaced by *ker* e' and by 0 respectively. Hence there is an F_1 satisfying $d'\,F_1 = F_0\,d$. More generally, with $F_n\colon K_n \to K'_n$ and $d'\,F_n = F_{n-1}\,d$, where $n < p$, there results from $d'^2\,K'_p = 0$ in the diagram below

$$\begin{array}{ccccc} & & K_p & \xrightarrow{d} & K_{p-1} \\ & & \downarrow{\scriptstyle F_{p-1}\,d} & & \\ K'_p & \xrightarrow[d']{} & K'_{p-1'} & \xrightarrow[d']{} & K'_{p-2'} \end{array}$$

that there is an $F_p\colon K_p \to K'_p$ satisfying $d'\,F_p = F_{p-1}\,d$.

We now establish the last part of the theorem. If ${}_1F$ and ${}_2F$ are over f, then in

$$\begin{array}{ccccc} & & K_0 & & \\ & & \downarrow{\scriptstyle (F'_0 - F_0)} & & \\ K'_1 & \longrightarrow & K'_0 & \xrightarrow[e']{} & G \end{array}$$

$e'({}_1F_0 - {}_2F_0) = fe - fe = 0$, and so, since K_0 is projective, $D_0\colon K_0 \to K'_1$ exists with $d'\,D_0 = {}_1F_0 - {}_2F_0$. Proceed inductively. Suppose $D_n\colon K_n \to K'_{n+1}$ is defined for $0 < n < r$ with $d'D_n + D_{n-1}\,d = {}_1F'_n - {}_2F_n$. Then, in the diagram

$$\begin{array}{ccccc} & & K_r & & \\ & & \downarrow{\scriptstyle {}_1F_r - {}_2F_r - D_{r-1}\,d} & & \\ K'_{r+1} & \xrightarrow[d']{} & K'_r & \xrightarrow[d']{} & K'_{r-1} \end{array}$$

$d'({}_1F_r - {}_2F_r - D_{r-1}\,d) = 0$, so there is a homomorphism D_r satisfying

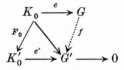

$d'D_r = {}_1F_r - {}_2F_r - D_{r-1}\ d$. In short, ${}_1F_r = {}_2F_r + d'D_r + D_{r-1}\ d$ or ${}_1F \simeq {}_2F$.

The last conclusion follows on setting $G = G'$ and taking f as the identity isomorphism.

Theorem 3.4. *Every module G has a projective resolution with free modules. If K and K' are projective resolutions of G and G' and f is a homomorphism of $G \to G'$, there is an F over f.*

Let $G = F/M$ where F is a free module and M a module of relations. In particular, F may be the module obtained by taking each g in G as a basis element of F so that F consists of all finite sums $\Sigma_\pi r^i g_i$, $r^i \in R$, $g_i \in G$. Hence

$$0 \longrightarrow M \longrightarrow F \xrightarrow{e} G \longrightarrow 0.$$

Write M_0, F_0 for M, F. Then M_0 may be considered in place of G, so there results

$$0 \longrightarrow M_1 \xrightarrow{i_1} F_1 \xrightarrow{j_1} M_0 \longrightarrow 0$$

$$0 \longrightarrow M_r \xrightarrow{i_n} F_r \xrightarrow{j_r} M_{r-1} \longrightarrow 0\ .$$

Define d_r as the monomorphism $i_{r-1}j_r\colon F_r \to F_{r-1}$. Hence we have $\{K_r, d_r\} = \{F_r, d_r\}$, i.e., a free resolution

$$\to F_1 \to F_0 \to G \to 0.$$

For the injective resolution the argument is similar to that in (3.3) and (3.4), so the following theorem follows by duality from (3.3) and (3.4).

Theorem 3.5. *Every module G admits an injective resolution. If K and K' are injective resolutions of G and G', then $f\colon G \to G'$ can be lifted.*

PROBLEM

10-6. Demonstrate (3.5) in detail.

Definition 3.6. If (a) $0 \to A' \to A \to A'' \to 0$ is exact, and if K', K, K'' are projective (injective) resolutions of the corresponding A's, then if (b) $0 \to K' \to K \to K'' \to 0$ is exact, we say (b) is a **projective (injective) resolution of** (a).

Theorem 3.7. *If K' and K'' are projective (injective) resolutions of A' and A'', a projective (injective) resolution, K, satisfying* (3.6b) *can be constructed.*

An induction argument is used. Thus suppose K_i has been defined for $i = 0, \ldots, n - 1$, that is to say there is exactness in the rows and columns of

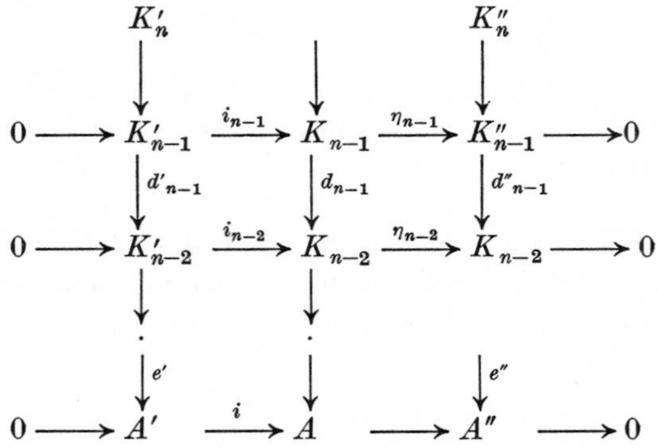

Let $K_n = K'_n \oplus K''_n$. Then K_n is plainly projective by Problem 10-1. Define i_n and η_n as the injection and projection $k'_n \xrightarrow{i_n} k'_n \oplus 0$ and $k'_n \oplus k''_n \xrightarrow{\eta_n} k''_n$ respectively. Since K''_n is projective, there is a homomorphism $\psi''_n\colon K''_n \longrightarrow K_{n-1}$ satisfying $\eta_{n-1}\psi''_n = d''_n$. Since K''_{n-1} is projective (or by the induction starting with $n - 1 = 0$) we have

$$K_{n-1} = K'_{n-1} \oplus K''_{n-1}.$$

We can make ψ''_n unique by requiring $\psi''_n(k''_n) = 0 \oplus d''_n(k''_n)$. Thus define

$$\psi'_n\, k'_n = i_{n-1}\, d'_n\, k'_n = d'_n\, k'_n \oplus 0.$$

Let d_n be defined on K_n to K_{n-1} as $\psi'_n \oplus \psi''_n$; i.e., $d_n(k'_n \oplus k''_n) = d'_n\, k'_n \oplus d''_n\, k''_n$. In this induction argument it is consistent to assume as well that for $i \leq n$, $d_i(k'_i \oplus k''_i) = d'_i\, k'_i \oplus d''_i\, k''_i$. Hence $d_{n-1}\, d_n = 0$. Moreover e is defined as $ie' \oplus \psi''_0$.

PROBLEM

10-7. Define the non unique ψ''_n above by $\psi''_n\, k''_n = \lambda_n(k''_n) + d''_n(k''_n)$ where λ_n is a homomorphism on K''_n to K'_{n-1}. Show that with $d_n = \psi'_n \oplus \psi''_n$, the condition $d_{n-1}\, d_n = 0$ for all n requires $d'_{n-2}\, \lambda_{n-1} + \lambda_{n-2}\, d''_{n-1} = 0$, so that our text choice $\lambda_i = 0$ above is consistent with this condition. Also $e'' = \psi''_0\eta$ and $ie'\, \lambda_1 + \psi''_0\, d''_1 = 0$.

4. KUNNETH THEOREM. Our purpose in this section will be to establish a far reaching result known as the Kunneth Theorem, connecting the omology groups of two chain complexes and those of their tensor product. One immediate consequence is the Universal Coefficient Theorem which gives full information about the effect on the omology groups of varying the coefficient group. Throughout this section A and C are generally understood to be complexes with derivations d_A and d_C respectively, and μ is an involution on A; i.e., $\mu^2 a = a$ with $\mu d_A = -d_A \mu$.

Lemma 4.1. *$A \otimes C$ is a lower complex with d defined by*

(4.1a) $$d\colon a \otimes c = (d_A a) \otimes c + (\mu a) \otimes d_C c.$$

The verification that $d^2 = 0$ is immediate.

Definition 4.2. If $\mathbf{h} \in H_*(A)$ and $\mathbf{g} \in H_*(C)$, then α, defined by $\alpha(\mathbf{h} \otimes \mathbf{g}) = \langle \mathbf{h} \otimes \mathbf{g} \rangle$, induces a homomorphism

$$H_*(A) \otimes H_*(C) \xrightarrow{\alpha} H_*(A \otimes C).$$

References below to α are invariably to this homomorphism. According to (4.1), $h \otimes g \in Z_*(A \otimes C)$. To see that the choice of representatives is immaterial, we point out that if $h = d_A k$, then

$$d_A k \otimes g = d(h \otimes g).$$

In the sequel we make constant tacit use of the fact that subgroups of free groups are free.

Lemma 4.3. *If $d_A = 0$ and A is free, then*

(4.3a) $$\alpha\colon A \otimes H_*(C) \to H_*(A \otimes C)$$

is an isomorphism.

It is immediate that $Z(A) = A$ and $B(A) = 0$. Accordingly $H_*(A) \approx A$. It follows from (2.16d), (64.10b), or Problem 10-4, and the fact that A is free, that

(4.3b) $$0 \longrightarrow A \otimes Z(C) \xrightarrow{1 \otimes i_C} A \otimes C \xrightarrow{1 \otimes d_C} A \otimes B(C) \longrightarrow 0$$

is exact.

Similarly, from (2.16c) we infer the exactness of

(4.3c) $$0 \to A \otimes B(C) \to A \otimes Z(C) \to A \otimes H(C) \to 0.$$

(4.3d) $$d(\mu A \otimes C) \approx A \otimes d_C C,$$

whence

(4.3e) $$\begin{aligned} Z(A \otimes C) &= ker\, d(\mu \otimes 1) = Im\,(1 \otimes i_C) \\ &= A \otimes Z(C). \end{aligned}$$

Therefore,

$$
\begin{aligned}
A \otimes H(C) &\approx A \otimes Z(C)/A \otimes B(C) && (4.3c),\\
&\approx Z(A \otimes C)/B(A \otimes C) && (4.3d), (4.3e),\\
&\approx H_*(A \otimes C).
\end{aligned} \tag{4.3f}
$$

One verifies at once that the isomorphism in (4.3f) is indeed α.

Corollary 4.4. *If A is free, then*

$$H_*(A') \otimes H_*(C) \overset{\alpha}{\approx} H_*(A' \otimes C)$$

where A' can be $B(A)$ or $Z(A)$.

Since $A' = B(A)$ or $Z(A)$ has $d_{A'} = 0$, (4.4) results from (4.3).

Lemma 4.5. *If A, A', C, and C' are lower complexes, and if ψ and λ are homomorphisms on $A \xrightarrow{\psi} A'$, $C \xrightarrow{\lambda} C'$, then*

$$
\begin{array}{ccc}
H_*(A) \otimes H_*(C) & \xrightarrow{\psi_* \otimes \lambda_*} & H_*(A') \otimes H_*(C') \\
\downarrow{\scriptstyle \alpha} & & \downarrow{\scriptstyle \alpha'} \\
H_*(A \otimes C) & \xrightarrow{(\psi \otimes \lambda)_*} & H_*(A' \otimes C')
\end{array} \tag{4.5a}
$$

is commutative.

Let $\mathbf{z} \in H(A)$, $\mathbf{w} \in H(C)$. Then

$$
\begin{aligned}
\alpha'(\psi_* \otimes \lambda_*)(\mathbf{z} \otimes \mathbf{w}) &= \alpha'((\psi_* \mathbf{z}) \otimes (\lambda_* \mathbf{w}))\\
&= \langle \psi z \otimes \lambda w \rangle\\
&= (\psi \otimes \lambda)_* \langle z \otimes w \rangle\\
&= (\psi \otimes \lambda)_* \alpha(\mathbf{z} \otimes \mathbf{w}).
\end{aligned}
$$

since $(\psi \otimes \lambda)_* \langle z \otimes w \rangle_{A \otimes C} = \langle \psi z \otimes \lambda w \rangle_{A' \otimes C'}$.

Lemma 4.6. *If $Z(A)$ and $Z(C)$ are direct summands of A and C, then $(H_*(A) \otimes H_*(C))$ is a direct summand of $H_*(A \otimes C)$.*

We have the direct sum decomposition

$$A_r = Z_r(A) \oplus D_r. \tag{4.6a}$$

Let $p(z \oplus b) = z$ and $\eta(z) = \mathbf{z} \in H_*(A)$. Write $\psi = \eta p\colon A \to H_*(A)$. Interpret $H(A)$ as a chain complex with boundary operator ∂, wherefore

$$\psi_* = (\eta p)_*\colon H(A) \to H(HA) \approx H(A), \tag{4.6b}$$

is plainly the identity isomorphism. Similarly to (4.6b) define λ_* on $H(C) \to H(H(C)$. We turn to (4.5), taking cognizance of the fact that *both* $\psi_* \otimes \lambda_*$ *and* α' *are identity isomorphisms.* Indeed the righthand vertical homomorphism in (4.5a) with $A', C' = H(A), H(C)$ is

$$H(A) \otimes H(C) \xrightarrow{\alpha'} H(HA \otimes H(C)) = H(A) \otimes H(C).$$

That is $(\psi \otimes \lambda)_* \alpha$ is the identity isomorphism and this implies among other things the assertion of the lemma, (1.1).

A little more precision can be introduced. Thus from (4.6a) it is plain that $\psi_*: H_p(A) \approx H_p(A)$ and

$$\alpha: H_p(A) \otimes H_q(C) \to H_{p+q}(A \otimes C),$$

whence the image by α below is a direct summand,

(4.6b) $$\alpha\, \Sigma_{p+q=n} H_p(A) \otimes H_q(C) \to H_n(A \otimes C).$$

It will be convenient for us to rewrite (4.3b) with A and C interchanged,

(4.7a) $$0 \longrightarrow Z(A) \otimes C \xrightarrow{i\otimes 1} A \otimes C \xrightarrow{d_A\otimes 1} B(A) \otimes C \longrightarrow 0.$$

Lemma 4.7. *Let* $\Delta = ((i \times 1)^{-1}\, d)_*$. *Then*

(4.7b) $$H(A \otimes C) \xrightarrow{(d_A\otimes 1)_*} H(B(A) \otimes C) \xrightarrow{\quad\Delta\quad} H(Z(A) \otimes C)$$

is an exact sequence.

Identify the terms in (4.7a) with J, G, G/J in that order in (61.10). In (61.11) if $g \in H(G/J)$, $d_*\, g$ is defined as $\mathbf{j} = d\mathbf{g}$.

Note

$$\frac{A \oplus C}{(i \otimes 1)Z(A) \otimes C} \approx B(A) \otimes C.$$

Write $[a \otimes z]$ and $b \otimes z$ according as we refer to $Z(A \otimes C)/(i \otimes 1)\, Z(A) \otimes C$ or to $Z(B(A) \otimes C)$. Hence $[a \otimes z]$ corresponds to $[g]$ if $d(a \times z) \subset (i \otimes 1)(Z(A) \otimes C)$. If $b = d_A\, a$ then $a \otimes z \xrightarrow{d} b \otimes z$. It must be borne in mind that, in contrast with $d_A \otimes 1$, d is on $A \otimes C$ to $A \otimes C$. Hence $b \otimes z$ is here considered in $A \otimes C$ rather than in $B(A) \otimes C$. Utilizing the injection $j: B(A) \to Z(A)$ (2.14c), we have as elements of $A \otimes C$, $d(a \otimes z) = (i \otimes 1)(jb \otimes z)$. Accordingly with $(i \otimes 1)^{-1}\, d = d'$, and $\Delta = ((i \otimes 1)^{-1} d)_*$,

$$\begin{aligned} \Delta(\langle b \otimes z\rangle = \langle [a \otimes z]\rangle) &= (\langle i \times 1)^{-1}\, d(a \otimes z)\rangle \\ &= \langle jb \otimes z\rangle. \end{aligned}$$

The authority for the exactness of (4.7b) is, therefore, (61.12).

Lemma 4.8.

$$0 \to H(A)*H(C) \xrightarrow{t} H(BA) \otimes H(C) \xrightarrow{j_* \otimes 1} H(Z(A)) \otimes H(C) \xrightarrow{i_* \otimes 1} HA \otimes HC$$

(4.8a) $\alpha_1 \downarrow \approx \quad S_1 \quad \approx \downarrow \alpha_2 \quad S_2 \quad \downarrow \alpha$

$$\xrightarrow{(d\otimes 1)_*} H(B(A) \otimes C) \xrightarrow{\Delta} H(Z(A) \otimes C) \xrightarrow{(i\otimes 1)_*} H(A \otimes C)$$

has (**a**) *the commutative squares* S_1 *and* S_2 *and* (**b**) *exact rows and*

$$HA*HC = ker(j_* \otimes 1).$$

Here t is the inclusion homomorphism. The fact that α_1 and α_2 are isomorphisms is covered by (4.4). Let $\mathbf{b}$ and $\mathbf{z}$ be elements of $H(B(A)) \approx B(A)$ and of $H(C)$ respectively. Then $j_\# b \in Z(A)$, and since $Z(A) \approx H(Z(A))$, $\alpha_2(j_* \otimes 1)(\mathbf{b} \otimes \mathbf{z})$ yields the coset $\langle jb \otimes z \rangle$ where j is the i of (2.16b) and b and z are the obvious representatives. For the alternate route, $\alpha_1(\mathbf{b} \otimes \mathbf{z}) = \langle b \otimes z \rangle$ whence by the discussion of Δ in (4.7)

$$\Delta\alpha_1(\mathbf{b} \otimes \mathbf{z}) = \langle jb \otimes z \rangle = \alpha_2(j_* \otimes 1)(\mathbf{b} \otimes \mathbf{z}).$$

The commutativity in square S_2 follows from (4.5) on identifying $Z(A)$, A with A, A'. The upper sequence is exact in view of the definition of $*$ (2.9).

We now combine our findings and state our main conclusion.

Theorem 4.9. Kunneth. *If* A *and* C *are chain complexes and* A *is free while* $Z(C)$ *is a direct summand of* C, *then there exists a homomorphism* β *such that*

(4.9a) $$0 \longrightarrow H_*(A) \otimes H_*(C) \xrightarrow{\alpha} H_*(A \otimes C) \xrightarrow{\beta} H_*(A) * H_*(C) \longrightarrow 0$$

is exact and

(4.9b) $$H_*(A \otimes C) \approx H_*(A) \otimes H_*(C) \oplus H_*(A)*H_*(C).$$

(4.9c) $$H_n(A \otimes C) \approx \textstyle\sum_{n+s=n} H_r(A) \otimes H_s(C) + \sum_{p+q=n-1} Tor\,(H_p(A), H_q(C)).$$

We start with

$$\begin{aligned}(j_* \otimes 1)\alpha_1^{-1}(d \otimes 1) &= \alpha_2^{-1}\Delta(d \otimes 1)_* \\ &= \alpha_2^{-1}\,0 = 0,\end{aligned}$$

where the first line reflects the commutativity of S_1 and the second the exactness of the bottom sequence in (4.8a). Hence by exactness,

(4.9d) $$Im\,\alpha_1^{-1}(d \otimes 1)_* \subset Im\,t$$

and so t^{-1} defines a unique correspondent in $H(A)_* H(C)$ for each element in $Im\,\alpha_1^{-1}\,(d \otimes 1)_*$. We can therefore define β by

(4.9e) $$\beta = t^{-1}\,\alpha_1^{-1}(d \otimes 1)_*.$$

Let us check exactness at $H(A \otimes C)$. If $z \in ker\, \beta$ then, since α_1 and t are isomorphisms on the groups entering, $(d \otimes 1)_* z = 0$. It is clear then that $ker\, \beta = ker(d \otimes 1)_*$. By exactness $ker(d \otimes 1)_* = Im(i \otimes 1)_*$ whence by commutativity in S_2 there results

$$\alpha(i_* \otimes 1)\, H(Z(A) \otimes H(C)) = ker\, \beta.$$

Since α is a monomorphism (4.6) we conclude

$$\alpha(H_*(A) \otimes H_*(C)) = ker\, \beta.$$

We have left only to verify β is onto. By exactness and commutativity of S_1, if $\mathbf{h} \in H(A) * H(C)$, $\alpha_1 t\mathbf{h} \in ker\, \Delta = Im(d \otimes 1)_*$. Hence for some $\mathbf{f} \in H(A \otimes C)$, $\alpha_1 t\mathbf{h} = (d \otimes 1)_* \mathbf{f}$ so $\beta\mathbf{f} = \mathbf{h}$. Relation (4.9b) is a consequence of (4.9a) and (4.6).

The grading is such that

$$(H(A) \otimes H(C))_n = \Sigma_{r+s=n} H_r(A) \otimes H_s(C),$$

$$(Tor(H(A), H(C))_n = \Sigma_{p+q=n-1} Tor(H_p(A), H_q(C)),$$

$$(H(A \otimes C))_n = H_n(A \otimes C).$$

Since the terms entering (4.9a) and (4.9b) are graded modules and therefore direct sums, these relations are valid for the terms of grade n. In particular this yields (4.9c).

That Tor contains the torsion contribution in the Kunneth formula is clear from (2.11) and (2.12) with $H(A)$, $H(C)$ substituted for A and C. Hence if $R_p\,(X)$ is the Betti number attached to $H_p\,(X)$, then

$$R_p\,(X_1 \times X_2) = \Sigma_{r+s=p} R_r\,(X_1) R_s(X_2).$$

A special case of the Kunneth Theorem illuminates the nature of the influence of the coefficient group.

Theorem 4.10. Universal Coefficient Theorem. *Let A be a free lower complex and let G be an R module. Then*

(4.10) $$H_p(A \otimes G) \approx H_p(A) \otimes G + Tor(H_{p-1}(A), G).$$

We may assume G is a chain complex with $d = 0$. This entails $H(G) \approx H_0(G) \approx G$. Then $Z(G)$ is a direct summand of $H(G)$ and the hypotheses of (4.9) are satisfied. Thus (4.10) paraphrases (4.9c). In particular if A refers to the graded chain modules over the integers $C(K, J)$ we get

$$H_p(K, G) \approx H_p(K) \otimes G + Tor\,(H_{p-1}\,(K), G).$$

This formula is the invariant form, independent of bases and generators, of (64.12a). If G is a field the Tor term drops out of course.

Remark. The hypothesis that a chain complex is free operates solely in showing direct summands enter so that tensoring yields (64.10b) [rather than only (64.10a)] when $Z(C)$ is assumed a direct summand. Accordingly free can be replaced by projective. This is true throughout Section 4. Other fairly obvious generalizations are in order. Instead of demanding a group be free, one can require (**a**) it be finitely generated and (**b**) torsion free. These conditions are easily seen to imply the group is free. Moreover the condition (**a**) can be dropped, for any Abelian group is a direct limit of finitely generated groups using the direct system of all finitely generated subgroups of a group ordered by size.

It is important to formulate (4.9) and (4.10) for concrete complexes and for spaces. This requires some facts about topological products which are taken up in detail in Chapter 12.

Theorem 4.11. *Let X and Y be* (**a**) *concrete complexes with cubical cells or* (**b**) *arbitrary topological spaces. Then* (4.9) *and* (4.10) *are valid with $H(A)$, $H(C)$, and $H(A \otimes C)$ replaced by $H(X)$, $H(Y)$, and $H(X \times Y)$ provided that for case* (**b**) *the homology is singular homology.*

The more elementary (4.11a) is covered by (122.5). The extension to concrete simplicial complexes is immediate on the assumption that the cubical and simplicial subdivisions yield isomorphic groups. The more general situation is explicitly covered by (122.11c).

Example 10-3. For n-dimensional projective space P^n

$$\begin{aligned} H_r(P^n) &\approx \mathrm{J}_2, && r \text{ odd and } 0 < r < n \\ &\approx \mathrm{J}, && r = 0 \text{ or } r = n \text{ for } n \text{ odd} \\ &\approx 0, && r \text{ even or } r = n \text{ even.} \end{aligned}$$

From (4.10) there results

$$H_r(P^n, \mathrm{J}_2) \approx \mathrm{J}_2 \qquad \text{for all } r < n.$$

PROBLEMS

10-8. Let K and L be finite n dimensional complexes and let Π^m be the product complex $K \times \cdots \times K$ with m factors. Let R_r, P_r, T_r, S_r be the Betti numbers of K, Π^m, $K \times L$, and L respectively. Show

(**a**) $$P_r = \Sigma_{j_i + \cdots j_n = r} R_{j_i} \cdots R_{j_m}, \qquad r \leq mn,$$

(**b**) $$T_{r+1} = R_0 S_{r+1} + \Sigma_{i=0}^{i=r} R_{r-i+1} S_i$$

Prove (by an induction argument) that the Betti numbers of K are determined by those of Π^m (m fixed) and that the Betti numbers of L are determined by those of K and of $K \times L$.

10-9. Show that $H_2(P^2 \times S^1, J)$ has a single element of order 2 and that $H_1(P^2 \times S^1) = J$.

10-10. What are the homology groups of $S^2 \times S^1$, $S^2 \times S^2$, $S^1 \times P^2$, $P^2 \times P^2$?

5. DUALS. The facts about cochains can be obtained by dualizing the results above. We shall illustrate this by indicating how the duals of the tensor product and the *Tor* enter.

Definition 5.1. If A, B, and $C = B/A$ are groups, with B free, satisfying (44.2) then, in the notation of (44.5b) $Ext(C, G) \approx Hom(A, G)/$(homomorphisms on A to G which are extensible to B to G). Accordingly $Ext(C, G)$ is the group of extensions of C by G. Thus

(5.1a) $0 \longrightarrow Hom(C, G) \xrightarrow{j^{\#}} Hom(B, G) \xrightarrow{i^{\#}} Hom(A, G) \longrightarrow Ext(C, G)$

is exact. Further information on $Ext(C, G)$ is to be found in (7.11) and (7.9).

Lemma 5.2.

(5.2a) *If C is free then $Ext(C, G) = 0$*

(5.2b) *If C is cyclic of order p, a prime, then, $Ext\ (C, G) \approx G/pG$.*

(5.2c) *If C and G are direct sums, $\oplus C_\alpha$ and $\oplus G_\beta$, then $Ext(C, G) \approx \oplus Ext(C_\alpha, G_\beta)$*

Definition 5.3. Let A be a lower complex and let B be an upper complex. Let μ be an involution of A with $d_A\mu + \mu\, d_A = 0$. Grading is defined by $(Hom(A, B))^n = \Sigma_{p+q=n} Hom(A_p, B^q)$. Then $Hom(A, B)$ is an upper complex with d defined by

(5.3a) $$(dh)(a) = h(d_A\, a) + d_B(h\mu a).$$

Evidently $d^2 = 0$.

Lemma 5.4.

(5.4a) *If $h \in Z^*(Hom(A, B))$ and if $w \in Z_*(A)$ then $h(w) \in Z^*(B)$. If, besides the hypotheses of* (5.4a), *we require*

(5.4b) *$h \in B^*(Hom(A, B))$ or $w \in B_*(A)$ then $h(w) \in B^*(B)$.*

Since

(5.4c) $d_B\, h(w) = dh(\mu w) - hd_A\, (\mu w)$

has both terms zero on the right hand side of (5.4c), conclusion (5.4a) is immediate from (5.3a).

For (5.4b): suppose $w \in B_*(A)$; then $w = d_A v$ and $hd_A v = d_B h\mu v - (dh) v = d_B (h\mu v)$, since $dh = 0$ by (5.4a).

If $h \in B(Hom\, A, B)$ then $h = dk$ and $(dk)(w) = k\, d_A w + d_B(k\mu w) = d_B(k\mu w)$, since $d_A w = 0$ by hypothesis.

It is now plausible that in strict duality with the enunciation and proof of (4.9) we can establish in order that with α: $H^* Hom(A, C) \to Hom(H_*(A), H^*(C))$, if A is free and d_A is trivial, then α is an isomorphism. If A is free and $Z(C)$ is a direct summand of C, then $H^* Hom(A, C) \approx H^* Hom(A, H(C))$, etc. We arrive at:

Theorem 5.5. *If C is an upper complex and A is a free lower complex, then*

$$0 \longrightarrow Ext(H_{m-1}(A), H^n(C)) \xrightarrow{\beta^*} H^{m+n} Hom(A, C) \xrightarrow{\alpha^*} Hom\, H_m(A), H^n(C) \longrightarrow 0$$

If $Z(C)$ is a direct summand of C, then

$$H^* Hom(A, C) \approx Ext(H(A), H(C)) \oplus Hom\, H(A), H(C).$$

Remark. Theorem 5.5 asserts merely the module homomorphisms and may be invalid for ring homomorphisms.

Definition 5.6. An upper or lower complex $\{K(n)\} = K^*$ is of **finite type** if $K(n)$ is finitely generated for each n. If K_* is a lower complex over the integers $K^* = \{K^p = Hom(K_p, \mathrm{J})\}$ is the associated upper complex. We write as usual $H^*(K)$ for $H^*(K^*)$.

For finite complexes (or more generally for complexes of finite type) the relation (4.11) essentially carries over to the cohomology case. (Recall that R is an integral domain.)

Lemma 5.7. *Let K_* be a lower complex of finite type over the integers. Then $K^p \otimes R \approx C^p(K, R)$.*

Denote the cochains in $C^p(K, R) = Hom(C_p(K), R) = Hom(K_p, R)$ by F and those in K^p by f. Let $\{e^i \mid i = 1, \ldots, N\}$ be the base p cells of K. Then $\{\mathrm{J}e^i\}$ constitute the elementary chains of K_p. Then (46.2) the generating elementary cochains are $\{f_i^p\}$ for K^p and $\{F_i^p\}$ for $C^p(K, R)$. Define ψ and θ by

$$\psi\colon (f_i^p \otimes r) = rF_i^p,$$

$$\theta\colon F_i^p = \oplus_j F_i^p(e^j).$$

Thus

$$K^p \otimes R \xrightarrow{\psi} C^p(K, R) \xrightarrow{\theta} \oplus R^j, \quad R^j = R.$$

Then

$$\theta\psi(f_i^p \otimes r) = \oplus\, rF_i^p(e^j)$$

Evidently θ and $\theta\psi$ are isomorphisms and therefore so is ψ. Moreover ψ evidently commutes with δ.

Theorem 5.8. *Let K be an upper complex of finite type over the integers. Then*

$$H^m(K, R) \approx (H^m(K) \otimes R) \oplus (H^{m+1}(K) * R).$$

In view of (5.7), $H^m(K, R) \approx H^m(K \otimes R)$. Once a tensor product of free complexes is presented, the machinery used to demonstrate the Kunneth theorem can be set into operation to grind out (5.8). The facts that we now have upper complexes and that d raises grades by 1 are obviously details (that can be taken care of by replacing p by $(-p)$, for instance).

Let $R \otimes R \to R$ be a group isomorphism. We generalize (5.7).

Theorem 5.9. *Let K and L be lower complexes of finite type over the integers. Then the Kunneth formula holds in the form*

$$H^p(K \otimes L, R) \approx \Sigma_{n+s=p} H^r(K, R) \otimes H^s(L, R)$$
$$\oplus\, \Sigma_{n+s=p+1} H^r(K, R) * H^s(L, R).$$

If K is a lower complex $K_p = C_p(K, \mathrm{J})$ is free and since it is finitely generated, so is $K^p = Hom(K_p, R)$. The steps starting with (4.1) running through (4.9) are valid independently of whether upper or lower graded complexes enter when these complexes are free. Accordingly the Kunneth type of result is valid in the form

$$H^p(K \otimes L) = \Sigma_{n+s=p}\ H^r(K) \otimes H^s(L)$$
$$\oplus\, \Sigma_{n+s=p+1}\ H^t(K) * H^s(L)$$

As a special consequence of (5.5) we can state the Universal Coefficient Theorem in the form

Theorem 5.10. *If A is a free lower complex, in particular if A is the chain complex over J, then*

(5.10a) $$H^n(A \otimes G) \approx Hom(H_n(A), G) \oplus Ext(H_{n-1}(A), G)$$

Similarly from (5.9).

Corollary 5.11. *If X is a finitely generated chain complex over the integers, and G is a coefficient group, then*

$$0 \to H^n(X) \otimes G \to H^n(X, G) \to Tor(H^{n+1}(X), G) \to 0$$

A result similar to (5.9) holds if G is finitely generated while K may be an infinite chain complex. This infinite complex may be the singular complex, for instance. If neither K nor G is finitely generated, as say for the singular homology theory over Q, the result in (5.11) may be invalid as the following example shows.

EXAMPLE 10-4. Suppose $\tilde{H}_m(X) = 0$, $m < n$ and suppose $H_n(X) = \mathrm{Q}$. According to (5.10),

$$H^n(X \otimes \mathrm{J}) = H^n(X) \approx Hom(H_n(X), \mathrm{J}) = Hom(\mathrm{Q}, \mathrm{J}) = 0.$$

Again $H^n(X, \mathrm{Q}) \approx Hom(\mathrm{Q}, \mathrm{Q}) \approx \mathrm{Q}$. Since Q is a field, $Tor(H^{n+1}(X), \mathrm{Q}) = 0$. If (5.11) were valid, we should have exactness in $0 \longrightarrow 0 \xrightarrow{\alpha} \mathrm{Q} \longrightarrow 0 \longrightarrow 0$ an absurdity.

Theorem 5.12.

(a) *Suppose* $\mathrm{A}(1)$ *and* $\mathrm{A}(2)$ *are full gratings over the disjunct compact spaces* X_1 *and* X_2 *respectively. Then* $\mathrm{A}(1) \otimes \mathrm{A}(2)$ *is a full grating over* $X_1 \times X_2$ *with supports defined by* $\Sigma \|a_i(1) \otimes a_j(2)\| = \bigcup \|a_i(1)\| \times \|a_j(2)\|$.

(b) *The result is valid with* X_1 *and* X_2 *merely locally compact or paracompact.*

(c) *If the gratings are finitely generated modules there is a module isomorphism*

$$H(X_1 \times X_2) \approx H(X_1) \otimes H(X_2) \oplus Tor(H(X_1), H(X_2)).$$

If the coefficients are from a field R the isomorphism is a ring isomorphism (and there is no Tor term).

If $0 \neq h = \Sigma\, a_i(1) \times a_j(2)$, then

(5.12d) $$\|h\| = \bigcup \|a_i(1)\| \times \|a_j(2)\|.$$

Since $\mathrm{A}(1)$ and $\mathrm{A}(2)$ are full, neither $\|a_i(1)\|$ nor $\|a_j(2)\|$ is empty. Hence $\mathrm{A}(1) \otimes \mathrm{A}(2)$ is separated. One remarks parenthetically that if p and q project $X_1 \times X_2$ onto X_1 and onto X_2 respectively, then $p^{\#}\,\mathrm{A}(1) \circ q^{\#}\,\mathrm{A}(2)$ amounts to our usage for $\mathrm{A}(1) \otimes \mathrm{A}(2)$ and $\|a(1)\| \times X_2 \cap X_1 \times \|a(1)\| = \|a(1)\| \times \|a(2)\|$

The generic point of $X_1 \times X_2$ is written $(x_1 \times x_2)$ and we understand the cut homomorphism

$$(x_1 \times x_2)(\mathrm{A}(1) \otimes \mathrm{A}(2)) = (x_1\,\mathrm{A}(1) \otimes x_2\,\mathrm{A}(2)).$$

Since $x_1\,\mathrm{A}(1)$ and $x_2\,\mathrm{A}(2)$ are torsion free (63.1), if

$$h = \Sigma_{i,j}\, x_i\, a_i\,(1) \otimes x_2\, a_j\,(2) \neq 0,$$

then, for m a nonzero integer,

(5.12e) $$\|mh\| = \bigcup \|mx_i\, a_i\,(1)\| \times \|x_j\, a_j\,(2)\| = \|h\| \neq \varnothing$$

Accordingly x_1 A(1) $\otimes$ x_2 A(2) is torsion free.

It follows from the Kunneth theorem in the form (5.9) that for the one point cut

$$H(x_1\,\mathrm{A}(1) \otimes x_2\,\mathrm{A}(2)) \approx H(x_1\,\mathrm{A}(1)) \otimes H(x_2\,\mathrm{A}(2))$$

(5.12f) $$R \approx R \otimes R$$

where R is the coefficient ring.

Let $\beta = \{b_i\}$ be a finite open cover of the compact space $X_1 \times X_2$. This is refined by a finite open cover $\alpha = \{a_{rs} \mid a_{rs} = c_r \times d_s\}$ where $\gamma = \{c_r\}$ and $\delta = \{d_s\}$ are finite open covers of X_1 and of X_2 respectively. Let $u_r \mid \|u_r\| \subset c_r$ be a resolution of the identity relative to γ and let $\{V_s \mid \|v_s\| \subset d_s\}$ be a similar partition relative to δ (81.22). Then

(5.12g) $$\{u_r \times v_s \mid \|u_r \times v_x\| = \|u_r\| \times \|v_s\| \subset a_{rs}\}$$

is a resolution relative to α. Let π_i be the collection of pairs

$$\{rs \mid a_{rs} \subset b_i,\, a_{rs} \bar{\epsilon}\, b_j,\, j < i\}.$$

Then $\pi_i \cap \pi_k = \varnothing$, $i \neq k$. Let

(5.12h) $$\{w_i\} = \Sigma_{r,s\,\epsilon\,\pi_i}\, u_r \times v_s$$

Accordingly $\{w^i\}$ is a resolution of the identity relative to β.

Ad(**b**): If X_1 and X_2 are merely locally compact or paracompact, the first part of the argument leading to (5.12d) and (5.12e) is unchanged. The fullness demonstration goes through with the cover now a fine cover and with $\{w_i\}$ in (5.12h) the partition relative to an assigned compact set C.

Ad(**c**): (**a**) + (**b**) + (5.9) $\Rightarrow$ (**c**)

PROBLEM

10-11. Carry out the proof of (5.12b) in detail.

Theorem 5.13. *If* A *and* E *are full gratings over the locally compact space* X, *then* A $\circ$ E *is full. The result remains valid if* A *is full and* E *contains a unit and is torsion free.*

We absorb the information in (81.29).

If $\beta = \{b_i\}$ is a fine cover and C is compact, let v be an identity of E over C and let $\{u^i\}$ be a resolution of the identity in A associated with β and C.

Then $u \circ v$ is an identity in $\mathrm{A} \circ \mathrm{E}$ with a partition $\{u^i \circ v\}$ associated with β and C. Indeed since $(\Sigma\, u^i \circ v)\, a \circ e = (\Sigma\, u^i\, a) \circ ve$,

$$\|\Sigma\, u^i\, a \circ ve - a \circ e\| \subset \|\, \Sigma\, u^i\, a \circ ve - a \circ ve\| \cup \|\, a \circ ve - a \circ e.$$
$$\subset C^{\sim} \cap \|ve\| \cup \|a\| \cap C^{\sim}$$
$$\subset C^{\sim}.$$

Since A and E are torsion free (81.22) so is $\mathrm{A} \otimes \mathrm{E}$. Indeed suppose for $0 \neq h \in \mathrm{A} \otimes \mathrm{E}$, $mh = 0$ yet $m \neq 0$. Then, by (64.8), for some finitely generated subgratings $\mathrm{A}_1 \subset \mathrm{A}$ and $\mathrm{E}_1 \subset \mathrm{E}$, $h \in \mathrm{A}_1 \otimes \mathrm{E}_1$, $mh = 0$. Since A and E are torsion free so are A_1 and E_1 whence A_1 and E_1 are free with bases $\{a_i\}$ and $\{e_i\}$. Accordingly with $h = \Sigma_\pi\, r_i\, a_i \otimes e_j$, $m\, \Sigma\, r_i\, a_i \otimes e_j = \Sigma\, r_i\, ma_i \otimes e_i$ whence $ma_i = 0$ for every i in contradiction with the fact that A_i is torsion free. Therefore $\mathrm{A} \circ \mathrm{E}$ is torsion free and so is $xA \circ x\mathrm{E}$. Both $H(x\mathrm{A})$ and $H(x\mathrm{E})$ are given by xuR and xvR respectively so that by (5.9), for instance, since $Tor(H(xA), H(xE)) = 0$, $H(x\mathrm{A} \circ x\mathrm{E}) \approx H(x\mathrm{A}) \otimes H(xE) \approx R \otimes R \approx R$.

Corollary 5.14. *If K and L are finite concrete complexes*

$$H^p(\,|K| \times |L|, R) \approx \Sigma_{r+s=p} H^r(\,|K|, R) \otimes H^s(\,|L|, R)$$
$$\oplus\, \Sigma_{r+s=p+1}(H^r\,|K|, R) * H^s(|L|, R)$$

This is covered by (5.12e).

6. CATEGORIES. After having established an assertion for a special situation, one may seek extensive Universes of Discourse for which the assertion remains true. This section characterizes some such Universes. Roman numerals indicate the postulates.

Definition 6.1. A **category** $\mathfrak{A}$ is a collection of objects A and for each ordered pair of objects, a set designated by $G(A, A') = \{\alpha\}$, of **morphisms** or **maps** from A to A'. The collection of objects though a class need not constitute a set though this is the case for the categories of interest to us. It is required further that for each $\alpha_1 \in G(A, A')$ and $\alpha_2 \in G(A', A'')$ an element denoted by $\alpha_2\, \alpha_1$ in $G(A, A'')$ is determined. This is referred to as the composition of α_1 and α_2. We assume the compositions satisfy

(I) $(\alpha_2\, \alpha_1)\alpha = \alpha_2(\alpha_1\, \alpha)$ (associativity), α, α_1, $\alpha_2 \in G(A, A^1)$, $G(A^1, A^2)$ and $G(A^2, A^3)$ respectively.

(II) For each $A \in \mathfrak{A}$ there is a unique **identity** $e_A \in G(A, A)$ such that

$$e_A\, \beta = \beta$$
$$\gamma e_A = \gamma$$

for every $\beta \in G(B, A)$ and $\gamma \in G(A, B)$.

Remark. Precautionary measures are assumed taken to avoid antinomies of the 'set of all sets' type.

Definition 6.2. The morphism $\alpha \in G(A, B)$ is an **equivalence** if there is a map $\alpha' \colon B \to A$ such that

(6.2a)
$$\alpha' \alpha = e_A$$
$$\alpha \alpha' = e_B.$$

Accordingly we write $\alpha' = \alpha^{-1}$ and note that α^{-1} also is an equivalence.

EXAMPLE 10-5. Objects are sets. Morphisms are correspondences of sets. This category is often designated by $\mathfrak{S}$.

EXAMPLE 10-6. Objects are special pairs (X, x_0) where the single point x_0 is the base point. Morphisms on X, x_0 to Y, y_0 must take x_0 to y_0. This is the category of **based sets**.

EXAMPLE 10-7. Objects are topological spaces; morphisms are the (continuous) maps. Equivalence is then homeomorphism.

EXAMPLE 10-8. Let X be a fixed set. Objects are the subsets of X. If $X \supset A \supset B$, then $G(A, B)$ consists of a single morphism. If A does not contain B, $G(A, B)$ is empty.

EXAMPLE 10-9. Let X be a fixed set. A topology on X assigns the collection of open subsets. These open subsets constitute the objects of a category $\mathfrak{T}$. The morphisms are defined as in Example 10-8, namely $G(A, B)$ consists of a single morphism if $A \supset B$. If $A \not\supset B$, then $G(A, B)$ is empty.

EXAMPLE 10-10. Objects are pairs of topological spaces (X, X_0) with $X_0 \subset X$. Morphisms α satisfy $\alpha(X, X_0) \subset (Y, Y_0)$ where $\alpha X_0 \subset Y_0 \subset Y$. Again equivalences are homeomorphisms. (n-tuples of spaces are equally easily handled.) If the second element of the pair X_0 is a point, we get the category of **based spaces**.

EXAMPLE 10-11. Objects are modules over a fixed ring R. Morphisms are R homomorphisms. Equivalence is isomorphism.

EXAMPLE 10-12. Objects are Abelian groups. Morphisms are homomorphisms. Equivalence is isomorphism. This is the special case of Example 10-11 with R the ring of integers.

EXAMPLE 10-13. Objects are compact Abelian groups. Morphisms are open homomorphisms. Equivalence is open isomorphism.

EXAMPLE 10-14. Objects are spaces and morphisms are inclusion maps. Equivalence is identity.

EXAMPLE 10-15. Objects are continuous functions on $0 \leq t \leq 1$. Morphisms are the identity map and derivation. Here, $G(A, A')$ may be empty.

EXAMPLE 10-16. Objects are simplicial complexes. Morphisms are simplicial maps.

EXAMPLE 10-17. (a) Objects are upper complexes. Morphisms are chain maps. (b) Objects are lower complexes. Morphisms are chain maps.

EXAMPLE 10-18a. Objects are finite dimensional linear spaces. Morphisms are linear transformations.

EXAMPLE 10-18b. Objects are Banach spaces. Morphisms are linear (continuous, distributive) maps. (Another category has the same objects, but morphisms are now the completely continuous linear operators. These map bounded sets into conditionally compact sets. In general there are no identities.)

Particularly when the categories are concerned with algebraic objects, an additive property is imposed on the morphism. This applies to Examples 10-10, 10-11, 10-12, 10-17, 10-18.

Definition 6.3. $\mathfrak{A}$ has a **zero object** 0 if for any A, $G(0, A)$ consists of a single element and so does $G(A, 0)$. All zero objects are easily seen to be equivalent.

We have an **additive** category if there is a zero object and if $G(A, A')$ is an Abelian group and if furthermore composition is a bihomomorphism. Thus

(III) $\quad G(A', A'') \otimes G(A, A') \to G(A, A'')$, i.e., $\alpha' \otimes \alpha \to (\alpha' \alpha)$,

is a homomorphism on $G(A, A')$ keeping α' fixed, or on $G(A', A'')$ keeping α fixed. It is clear that the zero element $\theta = \theta(A, A')$ of $G(A, A')$ satisfies

(IV) $$G(0, 0) = \theta = G(0, A') = G(A, 0).$$

(The empty set in $\mathfrak{S}$, Example 10-5, is not a zero object. While $G(\phi, A) = \theta$, $G(A, \phi)$ is vacuous. For the based sets every pair (x, x) is a zero object.)

Thus an additive category satisfies **I**, **II**, **III**, **IV**.

Definition 6.4. (If U and V are sets and ψ is on U to V, ψ is a set monomorphism if $\psi(x) = \psi(x')$ implies $x = x'$; ψ is a set epimorphism if ψ is onto.)

For a general category we say $A \xrightarrow{\varphi} B$ is a **monomorphism** if for every object X the map $\Psi^{\cdot}.$: $G(X, A) \to G(X, B)$ defined by $(\Psi^{\cdot}.\ \mu)(x) = \psi\mu(x)$, is a set monomorphism, where $x \in X$ and $\mu \in G(X, A)$. We have an **epimorphism** if for every object Y the map $G(B, Y) \xrightarrow{\Psi^{\cdot}} G(A, Y)$ defined by $\lambda \in G(B, Y)$, $a \in A$, $(\Psi^{\cdot}\ \lambda)a = \lambda(\psi a)$ is a set monomorphism. If $\Psi^{\cdot}$ is both a monomorphism and an epimorphism, it is a **bijection** (so that a bijection is a sort of underprivileged isomorphism). This does not imply $\Psi^{\cdot}$ is an equivalence or isomorphism, though the converse is valid. In an additive category since $G(A, B)$ is an Abelian group, in the definitions just given "set" can be dropped from set monomorphism.

EXAMPLE 10-19. Objects are topological Abelian groups; maps are continuous homomorphisms. This is an additive category. Suppose A and B refer to the multiplicative group of the reals omitting 0, under the discrete and under the usual topologies respectively. Let $\Psi^{\cdot}$ be the map $\Psi^{\cdot}a = a$. Then $\Psi^{\cdot}$ is a bijection, but not an isomorphism, since $\Psi^{\cdot -1}$ doesn't exist.

We should like to have exact sequences and can proceed in two ways. Either we can place further restrictions on a category which will guarantee the existence of certain objects and maps simulating kernels, images, cokernels and coimages, or we can single out special classes of maps for which these concepts have meaning. We choose the first plan.

Definition 6.5. A and B are in an additive category and $\alpha \in G(A, B)$. By reason of **III** there may be an object, $k(\alpha)$, and a map $\kappa \in G(k(\alpha), A)$ for which

$$0 \longrightarrow G(C, k(\alpha)) \xrightarrow{\kappa} G(C, A) \xrightarrow{\alpha} G(C, B) \tag{6.5a}$$

is exact for all $C \in \mathfrak{A}$. If $\gamma \in G(C, A)$ where $\alpha\gamma = 0$, then, since κ is an injection, γ has a unique antecedent, $\tau \in G(C, k(\alpha))$. If $k'(\alpha)$, κ' constituted another pair, γ would have the unique antecedent τ' under κ'. Then $\kappa G(C, k(\alpha)) = \kappa'\, G(C, k'(\alpha))$ leads directly to the equivalence of $k(\alpha)$ and $k'(\alpha)$. This follows immediately if for instance $k(\alpha)$ and $k'(\alpha)$ are substituted for C. We refer to $(k(\alpha), \kappa)$ as a **kernel pair**. Similarly, a **cokernel pair** $(c(\alpha), \gamma)$ consists of an object $c(\alpha)$ and a map $\gamma \in G(B, c(\alpha))$ which, for all $D \in \mathfrak{A}$ yields an exact sequence

$$0 \longrightarrow G(c(\alpha), D) \xrightarrow{\gamma} G(B, D) \xrightarrow{\alpha} G(A, D)$$

Again $(c(\alpha), \gamma)$ is unique up to an equivalence on $c(\alpha)$.

V Both the kernel and cokernel pair exist for all maps in $\mathfrak{A}$.

Consider now $k(\alpha) \xrightarrow{\kappa} A$. Then $(c(\kappa), \lambda)$ is the cokernel pair for κ while

$(k(\gamma), \rho)$ is the kernel pair for $B \xrightarrow{\gamma} c(\alpha)$. It then follows that the factorization $\alpha = \rho \, \epsilon \, \lambda$ indicated below is valid,

$$(6.5b) \qquad k(\alpha) \xrightarrow{\kappa} \underbrace{A \xrightarrow{\lambda} c(\kappa) \xrightarrow{\epsilon} k(\gamma) \xrightarrow{\rho} B}_{\alpha} \xrightarrow{\gamma} c(\alpha).$$

In accordance with the usual practice we shall refer to just the object, say $k(\alpha)$ or $c(\alpha)$ when we really mean the pair $(k(\alpha), \kappa)$ or $(c(\alpha), \gamma)$ and we shall drop the 'pair' in the designations kernel pair or cokernel pair. The **image** and **coimage** abbreviations *Im* α and *Coim* α will denote $(k(\gamma), \rho)$ and $(c(\kappa), \lambda)$. Thus **V** implies that the image and coimage exist.

VI   *Coim* α is isomorphic or equivalent to *Im* α, that is to say for some $\varepsilon' \, \epsilon \, G(k(\gamma), c(\kappa))$

$$\varepsilon' \, \varepsilon = e_{c(\kappa)}, \quad \varepsilon \, \varepsilon' = e_{\kappa(\gamma)}.$$

Definition 6.6.   Suppose $\mathfrak{A}$ satisfies **I**, ... , **VI**. The sequence

$$A \xrightarrow{\alpha} A_1 \xrightarrow{\alpha_1} A_2,$$

is **exact** at A_1 if

$$ker \, \alpha_1 = Im \, \alpha$$

It then follows that the statement: A is equivalent to B is the same as the statement: $0 \to A \to B \to 0$ is exact.

Remark that a necessary and sufficient condition for exactness of $0 \longrightarrow A \xrightarrow{\alpha} A_1 \longrightarrow A_2$ for instance, is that

$$0 \to G(C, A) \to G(C, A_1) \to G(C, A_2)$$

be an exact sequence of groups for all C. (The groups, $G(A_i, C)$, are used for the epimorphism criterion.)

VII   For every pair A_1, A_2 in $\mathfrak{A}$ there is an object A in $\mathfrak{A}$ in the relation of a direct sum to A_1, A_2 (6.1). Specifically there are (injection) maps $i_1 \, \epsilon \, G(A_1, A)$, $i_2 \, \epsilon \, G(A_2, A)$ and (projection) maps $p_1 \, \epsilon \, G(A, A_1)$, $p_2 \, \epsilon$ $G(A, A_2)$ satisfying $p_1 i_1$ is the identity on A_1, $p_2 i_2$ is the identity on A_2, $p_2 i_1 = 0$, $p_1 i_2 = 0$, and $i_1 p_1 + i_2 p_2$ is the identity on A.

The direct sum and the direct product need not be equivalent in non-additive categories. We give an example.

EXAMPLE 10-20.   For the category of sets, the direct sum is the disjunct union $X \cup Y$; the direct product is the Cartesian product $X \times Y$. For instance with $X = [0, 1]$ and $Y = [0, \frac{1}{2}]$, $X \oplus X$ is represented in the plane by two disjunct segments while $X \times Y$ is a closed rectangle. For the category of based sets if $A = X$, $x_0 = ([0, 1], x_0)$ and $B = Y$, $y_0 = ([0, \frac{1}{2}], y_0)$ for $x_0 \, \epsilon \, [0, 1]$, $y_0 \, \epsilon \, [0, \frac{1}{2}]$ then $A \oplus B$ can be represented in the plane as the cross with x_0 and y_0 identified with (x_0, y_0) and X and Y non-collinear, $A \times B$ can be represented as the based rectangle or based set $([0, 1] \times [0, \frac{1}{2}], x_0 \times y_0)$.

Definition 6.7. If a category satisfies axioms **I**, . . . , **VII** it is an **exact** or an **Abelian category**.

Remark. In an exact category bijection and isomorphism are the same.

Remark. The nomenclature is not altogether standard. Some authors omit one or more of V, VI and VII and so make a distinction between an exact and an Abelian category.

Reference to our definitions of inverse and direct limits indicates that if these are to exist, the category must satisfy another condition:
VIIIa For every collection of objects $\{A_i, I\}$ the infinite direct sum exists.
VIIIb For every collection of objects $\{A_i, I\}$ the infinite product exists.

Definition 6.8. The definition of infinite direct sums or products is: Let

$$A_\lambda \xrightarrow{i_\lambda} A \xrightarrow{p_\lambda} A_\lambda$$

satisfy $p_\lambda\, i_\lambda$ is the identity, $p_\lambda\, i_\mu = 0$. If for every family of mappings α_λ on A_λ to B, $\lambda \in \Lambda$, there is a unique map $\alpha\colon A \to B$ with $\alpha i_\lambda = \alpha_\lambda$, then A has the **direct sum representation** $\oplus A_\lambda$. If for every family of maps β_λ on B to A_λ there is a unique map $\beta\colon B \to A$ with $p_\lambda \beta = \beta_\lambda$, then A has the **direct product representation** $A = \Sigma A_\lambda$. Thus p_λ is unnecessary for the direct sum definition, and i_λ for the direct product definition.

A strengthened form of (VIIIa) is important (171.9). Let $\mathfrak{A}$ satisfy (VIII a). Let $\{A_i \mid A_i \subset A\}$ be ordered by inclusion. Then the infinite direct sum of $\{A_i\}$ exists (VIII a) and its image in $\mathfrak{A}$ is called *sup* A_i. For each j let λ_j be a morphism on $A_j \to C$ subject to $\lambda_k = \lambda_j \mid A_k$ if $A_k \subset A_j$. Then the **Grothendieck Axiom** is

(VIIIc): There exists a unique morphism λ: *sup* $A_i \to C$ with $\lambda_j = \lambda \mid A_j$.

IX The category is **graded** if $G_n(A, A')$ is an Abelian subgroup of $G(A, A')$, where it is assumed that $G_m(A, A')$ and $G_n(A, A')$ are disjunct groups for $n \neq m$ and $G(A, A') = \oplus_\pi G_n(A, A')$. Such maps are said to be of degree n. In our applications the maps are generally of degree 0 except for d which may be of degree ± 1 or d_r of degree r. The composition requirement now is

$$G_n(A', A'') \otimes G_m(A, A') \to G_{n+m}(A, A'').$$

The identity map e_A is of degree 0.

Definition 6.9. The dual category, written $\mathfrak{A}^*$, has the same objects as $\mathfrak{A}$, but it will be convenient to designate them now as A^*. In particular 0^* is the null object. The collections of maps correspond according to

$$G^n(A^*, A'^*) \leftrightarrow G_n(A', A).$$

That is to say, to each map ψ of lower degree n from A' to A there corresponds a unique map ψ^* of degree $-n$, or of upper degree n, on A^* to A'^*. If $\psi(A') = A$, then $\psi^*(A^*) = A'^*$. Composition yields $(\psi_2 \psi_1)^* = \psi_1{}^* \psi_2{}^*$.

It is easy to see that $\mathfrak{A}^*$ is a category, since it is a mirror image of $\mathfrak{A}$. Indeed, given any valid diagram, its dual is the obviously valid diagram obtained by mechanically reversing arrows, starring the unstarred, and unstarring the starred, together with replacing maps of degree $-m$ by maps of degree m. In particular, the dual of an exact sequence is exact, the dual of a monomorphism is an epimorphism, and conversely.

Definition 6.10. $\mathfrak{A}'$ is a **subcategory** of $\mathfrak{A}$ if every object of $\mathfrak{A}'$ is an object of A and if for A', B' in $\mathfrak{A}'$ the morphisms $G(A', B'; \mathfrak{A}')$ are included in $G(A', B'; \mathfrak{A})$. Composition of morphisms in $\mathfrak{A}'$ is that induced by their composition in $\mathfrak{A}$. The subcategory $\mathfrak{A}'$ is **full** in $\mathfrak{A}$ if $G(A', B'; \mathfrak{A}') = G(A', B'; \mathfrak{A})$.

Definition 6.11. The **product** category $\mathfrak{A} \times \mathfrak{B}$ of two categories has as objects $A \times B$, $A \in \mathfrak{A}$, $B \in \mathfrak{B}$. For the morphisms $G(A \times B, A' \times B') = G(A, B) \times G(A', B')$ where $A, A' \in \mathfrak{A}$ and $B, B' \in \mathfrak{B}$. Composition is $(f', g')(f, g) = (f'f, g'g)$. *Here $A \times B$ merely denotes the pair A, B.*

Definition 6.12. Let Σ^+ be a direct system $= \{A_i, p^i{}_j \mid A_i \in \mathfrak{A}, i \in I\}$ (with I a fixed directed set and $\mathfrak{A}$ fixed, these constitute a category with morphisms defined as in (71.3)). A direct limit consists of an object A^+ written also $\underrightarrow{\mathsf{L}}\, \Sigma^+$ or $\underrightarrow{\mathsf{L}}\, A_i$ and a collection of morphisms p_i: $A_i \to A^+$ subject to

(6.12a) $$p_i = p_j p^i{}_j$$

(6.12b) For every $B \in \mathfrak{A}$ and morphisms λ_i: $A_i \to B$ satisfying $\lambda_i = \lambda_j p^i{}_j$ there is a unique morphism λ: $A^+ \to B$, $\lambda_i = \lambda p_i$. (Since p_i satisfying (6.12a) exists in (71.3), our earlier definition of direct limit is in agreement with that just given.)

The inverse limit is defined dually.

The significant transformations occurring in Algebraic Topology very often are functors and as such partake of various properties and procedures. Though the functorial character of certain maps may not appear in their original definition it is sometimes possible to introduce such categories that the maps in question become functors. Furthermore where transformations of functors are concerned, natural transformations and natural equivalence are desirable (the Kunneth Theorem isomorphism (104.9b) is not a natural equivalence).

7. FUNCTORS. Definition 7.1. Let $\mathfrak{A}$ and $\mathfrak{A}_1$ be exact categories with objects $\{A\}$ and $\{A_1\}$ and morphisms α (or α_1) on A to B (on A_1 to B_1). A **covariant additive functor** T on $\mathfrak{A}$ to $\mathfrak{A}_1$ is constituted by a pair of functions $({}^1T, {}^2T)$ with

(7.1a) $${}^1T\colon A \to {}^1T(A) \in \mathfrak{A}_1.$$

(7.1b) $${}^2T\colon G(A, B) \to G({}^1T(A), {}^1T(B)) \subset \mathfrak{A}_1$$

where $\alpha \in G(A, B)$ maps into ${}^2T\alpha \in G({}^1TA, {}^1TB)$. Since ${}^1T$ acts only on the objects and ${}^2T$ acts only on the morphisms, there is no confusion in writing T generally for either ${}^1T$ or ${}^2T$ and $T\alpha$ for ${}^2T\alpha$. We require that T preserve composition, that is to say,

(7.1c) $$T(\psi_2\,\psi_1) = T(\psi_2)\,T(\psi_1),$$

where $\psi_1 \in G(A, B)$, $\psi_2 \in G(B, C)$, and $T(\psi_2\,\psi_1) \in G(TA, TC)$. We require further that if e_A is the identity of $G(A, A)$ (7.1c) and $TA = A_1$, then

(7.1d) $$Te_A = e_{A_1}$$

and (the 'additive' property)

(7.1e) $$T(\alpha + \beta) = T\alpha + T(\beta).$$

Thus ${}^2T$ is a homomorphism.

A **contravariant additive functor** replaces (7.1b), (7.1c), and (7.1d) by

(7.1f) $$T\colon G(A, B) \to G(TB, TA)$$

(7.1g) $$T(\psi_2\,\psi_1) = T(\psi_1)\,T(\psi_2),$$

This is equivalent to the statement that T is covariant on the dual category to $\mathfrak{A}$.

The qualification "natural" is used in the following technical sense in the sequel. Let T and S be two functors on the category $\mathfrak{A}$ to the category $\mathfrak{C}$. Let ψ assign to each object A in $\mathfrak{A}$ a map $\psi_A \in G(T(A), S(A))$. Then ψ is a **natural transformation** of T to S if there is commutativity in

(7.1h) $$\begin{array}{ccc} {}^1T(A) & \xrightarrow{\psi_A} & {}^1S(A) \\ \downarrow {\scriptstyle {}^2T(\lambda)} & & \downarrow {\scriptstyle {}^2S(\lambda)} \\ {}^1T(B) & \xrightarrow{\psi_B} & {}^1S(B) \end{array}$$

for every $\lambda \in G(A, B)$. If ψ_A is an equivalence no matter what A is chosen, ψ is a **natural equivalence**.

PROBLEMS

10-12. If $\mathfrak{A}$ is a category for which $\underrightarrow{\mathsf{L}}$ exists (6.12), show $\underrightarrow{\mathsf{L}}$ is covariant on the direct systems Σ^+ to $\mathfrak{A}$.

10-13. Let $\mathfrak{A}$ be an exact category satisfying VIII a. Let Σ^+ be a direct system $\{A_i, p^i{}_j \mid A_i \in \mathfrak{A}\}$. Then $\underrightarrow{\mathsf{L}}\, \Sigma^+$ exists (6.12) and $\underrightarrow{\mathsf{L}}$ is a functor which is right exact on the category of direct systems in $\mathfrak{A}$ to $\mathfrak{A}$. *Hint:* $\underrightarrow{\mathsf{L}}$ can be defined as the (infinite) direct sum of A_i (VIII a) modulo relations just as in (77.3).

10-14. If in Problem 10-14 $\mathfrak{A}$ is an exact category satisfying (VIII c), $\underrightarrow{\mathsf{L}}$ is an exact functor. If $\lambda_{kl}\colon A_k \to A_l$ and $\lambda_k\colon A_k \to \underrightarrow{\mathsf{L}}\,\{A_i, p^i{}_j\}$, then $ker\ \lambda_k = \sup_{k \le l} ker\ \lambda_{kl}$.

The following example of a typical occurrence of product categories, is useful in Chapter 15.

EXAMPLE 10-21. Let $\mathfrak{A}$ be the category of spaces Example 10-7 and let M (for maps) be the functor on the product category $\mathfrak{A} \times \mathfrak{A}$ to $\mathfrak{A}$ defined by M$(X \times Y)$ is the function space Y^X in the co-open topology. The category $\mathfrak{A}$ may be replaced by that of based spaces and then the functor M is defined by

$$M((X, x_0) \times (Y, y_0)) = (Y^X, y_0^{x_0})$$

again in the co-open topology. We refer to M as the **map functor**.

EXAMPLE 10-22. Let $\mathfrak{S}$ be a category whose objects are sets. Let $\mathfrak{B}$ be any other category. The category $\mathfrak{B}^{\mathfrak{A}}$ has as objects all additive functors (more generally all functors) on $\mathfrak{A}$ to $\mathfrak{B}$. The morphisms are the natural transformations between functors. The exponential notation suggests the valid relation, when the objects of $\mathfrak{A}$ and of $\mathfrak{B}$ are sets,

$$(\mathfrak{C}^{\mathfrak{B}})^{\mathfrak{A}} = \mathfrak{C}^{\mathfrak{B} \times \mathfrak{A}}$$

in the sense of equivalence. A particular useful illustration yields

$$Hom(A, Hom(B, C)) = Hom(B \times A, C)$$

where again $A \times B$ merely indicates the pair A, B.

Let i_B be the identity morphism of $G(B, B)$. Let F_B be the functor on $\mathfrak{A}$ to $\mathfrak{B}$ which takes $\mathfrak{A}$ into B and furthermore F_B takes every morphism of $\mathfrak{A}$ into i_B. Since F_B and $F_{B'}$ are objects of $\mathfrak{B}^{\mathfrak{A}}$, if $\beta \in G(B, B')$, then a morphism ϕ_β is determined in $G(F_B, F_{B'})$. Accordingly we can consider $\mathfrak{B}$ a subcategory of $\mathfrak{B}^{\mathfrak{A}}$ if we identify B with F_B and every $\beta \in G(B, B')$ with the morphism, that is to say constant natural transformation, determined by β on F_B to $F_{B'}$.

An important category but one we do not exploit will now be described.

EXAMPLE 10-23. D is a category whose objects are ordered sets of integers where for each $m \geq 0\,[m]$ denotes the ordered set $(0, \ldots, m)$. The morphisms are functions preserving order. Thus $\alpha \in G([m], [n])$ means $\alpha(i) \leq \alpha(j)$, $0 \leq i \leq j \leq m$. Accordingly the identity correspondence is a morphism. If S denotes the category of sets the objects of S^D are called **css complexes** and are denoted by k. The css morphisms are the natural transformations from k to k'. The elements of the set $k(n)$ are referred to as n-simplexes.

Definition 7.2. The covariant functor T is **right exact** if the exactness of

(7.2a) $$A' \to A \to A'' \to 0$$

forces the exactness of

(7.2b) $$T(A') \to TA \to TA'' \to 0.$$

The **left exactness** of T is similarly defined. Finally T is **exact** if it is both left and right exact.

In most of our applications the category is graded. The exactness of (7.2a) implies exactness of

(7.2c) $$0 \xrightarrow{i} A'^n \xrightarrow{i} A^n \xrightarrow{\eta} A''^n \longrightarrow 0$$

if i, j, are of degree 0, but there is no relation of A^n to, say, A^{n+1}. The cohomology rings or modules, and also the homology rings or modules, achieve such a relation by reason of the d homomorphism. We can use the term **connected** for this relation and extend it to functors generally. This motivates the following definition.

Definition 7.3. A sequence $\{T^n\}$ of covariant functors on an exact category to an additive category is a **cohomology functor** if first the exactness of (7.2c) implies that a homomorphism α exists such that

(a) $$\longrightarrow T^n(A) \longrightarrow T^n(A'') \xrightarrow{\alpha} T^{n+1}(A') \longrightarrow T^{n+1}(A)$$

is of order 2 or is a complex; i.e., the composition of two consecutive homomorphisms is the trivial homomorphism. The second condition on a cohomology functor is that if

(b) $$\begin{array}{ccccccccc} 0 & \longrightarrow & A' & \xrightarrow{i} & A & \xrightarrow{\eta} & A'' & \longrightarrow & 0 \\ & & \downarrow{\scriptstyle j} & & \downarrow{\scriptstyle k} & & \downarrow{\scriptstyle l} & & \\ 0 & \longrightarrow & B' & \longrightarrow & B & \longrightarrow & B'' & \longrightarrow & 0 \end{array}$$

is commutative, and if the rows are exact, then

(c)
$$\begin{array}{ccccccc} \longrightarrow T^n(A'') & \xrightarrow{\alpha} & T^{n+1}(A') & \longrightarrow & T^{n+1}(A) & \longrightarrow \\ \downarrow{\scriptstyle (Tl)} & & \downarrow{\scriptstyle (Tj)} & & \downarrow{\scriptstyle (Tk)} & \\ \longrightarrow T^n(B'') & \xrightarrow{\alpha'} & T^{n+1}(B') & \longrightarrow & T^{n+1}(B) & \longrightarrow \end{array}$$

is commutative. If T is contravariant α is on $T^n(A')$ to $T^{n+1}(A'')$.

Definition 7.4. A most important functor is that taking complexes into omology modules. Naturally we denote this functor by H. It is covariant and fits the description in (7.3) if we write $T^n = H_{-n}$. The situation for the homology functor is plain from the following diagram

$$\begin{array}{ccc} K & \xrightarrow{\alpha_\#} & L \in \mathfrak{A} \\ {\scriptstyle {}^1T=H}\downarrow & & \downarrow \\ H(K) & \xrightarrow{\alpha_* = {}^2T\alpha_\#} & H(L) \in \mathfrak{A}_1, \end{array}$$

where K and L are in the category $\mathfrak{A}$ of lower complexes, and $H(K)$ and $H(L)$ are in the category $\mathfrak{A}_1$ of homology modules.

Two other familiar examples of functors are $A \otimes B$ and $Hom(A, B)$. The tensor product is a covariant additive functor in each variable separately while *Hom* is contravariant in the first, but covariant in the second under the following interpretation for the action on maps: If $\alpha \in G(A_1, A)$ and $\beta = G(B, B_1)$, then

(7.4a)
$$\alpha\colon A_1 \to A$$
$$\beta\colon B \to B_1.$$

(7.4b)
$$Hom(\alpha, \beta)\colon Hom(A, B) \to Hom(A_1, B_1)$$

is defined by

(7.4c)
$$(Hom(\alpha, \beta))\psi = \beta\psi\alpha \in Hom(A_1, B_1)$$

where $\psi \in Hom(A, B)$. The appropriate diagram is

(7.4d)
$$\begin{array}{ccc} A,\ B & \xrightarrow{T} & Hom(A, B) \\ {\scriptstyle \alpha}\uparrow\ \ \downarrow{\scriptstyle \beta} & & \downarrow{\scriptstyle Hom(\alpha,\beta)} \\ A_1,\ B_1 & \xrightarrow{T} & Hom(A_1, B_1) \end{array}$$

(Strictly speaking as illustrative of (7.1) we should make the restriction $A_1 = A$, α the identity or $B = B_1$, β the identity.)

An important nontrivial example of a covariant functor is the functor S on the category in Example 10-5, into that in Example 10-17. Here $X \to SX$ and $\psi\colon X \to Y$ yield $S\psi$, the chain map on $SX \to SY$.

EXAMPLE 10-24. Two functors defined on different categories cannot be the same, though the same mathematical symbols may be used. For instance with G a fixed Abelian group $Hom(K, G)$ is a contravariant functor when K is taken in the category of lower complexes over the integers with values in the category of upper complexes over G. An alternative possibility is to view K as an Abelian group. Then even if K_p is finitely generated, K is the infinite product ΣK_p. Thus if K is an object in the category of Abelian groups, then $Hom(K, G) = \Sigma\, Hom(K_p, G)$.

Suppose R is not commutative (but has a unit). If A is a right module over R and B is a left module over R we can form two tensor products namely $\otimes_J$ and $\otimes_R$. For $\otimes_J$ we make use only of the Abelian group structure of A and of B and form $\otimes$ now denoted as $\otimes_J$ as in (64.1). Then $A \otimes_R B$ is the Abelian group $A \otimes_J B$ modulo the relations $ar \otimes_J b - a \otimes_J rb$. Evidently $A \otimes_R R \approx A$ and $R \otimes_R B \approx B$ under the correspondences $a \otimes r \to ar$ and $r \otimes b \to rb$ respectively.

Suppose both A and B are left R modules or are both right R modules. Then $Hom(A, B)$ or $Hom_R(A, B)$ is the Abelian group of R homomorphisms. Thus $\psi \in Hom(A, B)$ if $\psi(ra) = r\psi(a) \in B$ or if $\psi(ar) = \psi(a)r \in B$ according as we are in the left or in the right module case. Evidently R is a left and a right module over itself. Hence $Hom(R, B) \approx B$ according to the correspondence $\psi_b(r) = rb$ in the left case and br in the right case.

In this book we generally content ourselves with stating our conclusions for commutative rings and two sided modules. This is not as special as it seems. All our results retain their validity for more general rings where homomorphisms are R homomorphisms, $\otimes_R$ replaces $\otimes$, Hom_R replaces Hom and the one sided modules are used. Indeed, except for obvious minor changes, *the proofs go over.*

We mention a functor of a different type. Let $\mathscr{I} = \{i\}$ be a directed set. Let $\mathfrak{A}$ be an Abelian category, and let $p^i_j \in G(A_i, A_j)\ j < i$ where the matching conditions (77.3) are satisfied. Then $\Sigma^+ = \{A_i, p^i_j\}$ is a direct system and the totality of such systems, together with their homomorphisms *ad* defined in (77.4) constitutes a category $\mathfrak{A}_1$. If $\mathfrak{A}$ satisfies **VIIIa**, the direct limit $\underrightarrow{\mathsf{L}}\, \Sigma^+$ can be defined and can be verified to be a covariant additive functor on $\mathfrak{A}_1$ to $\mathfrak{A}$ which is exact on the right, at least. Similarly, if the dual of **VIIIb** (i.e., the existence of infinite products) is valid for $\mathfrak{A}$, then the inverse limit functor can be introduced.

The treatment of $A \otimes C$ and $Hom(H, C)$ suggests these are functors in each of two variables keeping the other fixed. We make this precise.

Definition 7.5. Let $\mathfrak{A}_1$, $\mathfrak{A}_2$, $\mathfrak{A}_3$ be Abelian categories of modules, possibly over different rings. Let $\alpha_1 \in G(A_1, A_1')$ and $\alpha_2 \in G(A_2', A_2)$ (note the order A_2', A_2). We define a functor, $T(A_1, A_2)$, which is covariant in the first and contravariant in the second variable, and additive in both variables, by the prescription of the module $T(A_1, A_2)$ in $\mathfrak{A}_3$ and the maps

$$\begin{aligned} T(\alpha_1, A_2)&: T(A_1, A_2) \to T(A_1', A_2), \\ T(A_1, \alpha_2)&: T(A_1, A_2) \to T(A_1, A_2'). \end{aligned} \tag{7.5a}$$

Then $T(\beta_1 \alpha_1, A_1)$ and $T(A_1, \beta_2 \alpha)$ are $T(\beta_1, A_2)\, T(\alpha_1, A_2)$ and $T(A_1, \alpha_2)$ $T(A_1, \beta_2)$ respectively. Finally, as a consistency condition we require commutativity in

$$\begin{array}{ccc} T(A_1, A_2) & \xrightarrow{T(\alpha_1, A_2)} & T(A_1', A_2) \\ \Big\downarrow {\scriptstyle T(A_1,\alpha_2)} & & \Big\downarrow \\ T(A_1, A_2') & \xrightarrow{T(\alpha_1, A'_2)} & T(A_1', A_2'). \end{array} \tag{7.5b}$$

In a similar way functors which are covariant in both variables or contravariant in the first and covariant in the second can be defined. In particular, the last functor just defined is exemplified by $Hom(A_1, A_2)$.

PROBLEM

10-15. Define a functor of m variables, $m > 2$, which is covariant in r variables and contravariant in $m - r$ variables.

Definition 7.6. Let T be a *covariant* additive functor which is *exact on the right* and acts on $\mathfrak{A}$ to $\mathfrak{A}_1$ where $\mathfrak{A}$ is the category of *R modules* and $\mathfrak{A}_1$ that of *groups*. The morphisms for these categories are the homomorphisms. Let $A \in \mathfrak{A}$ and let $K_* = K_*(A) = \{K_n, d\}$ be a projective resolution of A. The terms of $K_*(A)$ are direct sums of chain modules, $\oplus K_n(A)$, so T determines a mapping $\dot{T}$ of $K_*(A)$ to $\mathfrak{A}_1$ yielding $\dot{T}K_*$. We often write $K(A)$ for $K_*(A)$.

$$\dot{T}K_*(A) = \oplus \dot{T}K_n \tag{7.6a}$$

so $(\dot{T}K(A))_n = (TK_n)$. If α is a homomorphism on $K_*(A)$ to $K_*(C)$, then, of course,

$$\dot{T}(\alpha)\colon \dot{T}K(A) \to \dot{T}K(C).$$

A differential d' is determined by the requirement (7.1b)

$$d'\, \dot{T}K(A) = \dot{T}dK(A) \tag{7.6b}$$

Hence $(\dot{T}K, d')$ is a lower complex.

Lemma 7.7. *If $\alpha \simeq \beta$ on $K(A)$ to $K(B)$, then $\dot{T}(\alpha) \simeq \dot{T}(\beta)$.*

For $k(A) \in K(A)$, $\alpha k(A) - \beta k(A) = dDk(A) + Ddk(A)$ (63.1). Taking account of the additivity of T and of (7.6b)

$$\begin{aligned}(\dot{T}(\alpha) - \dot{T}(\beta))\dot{T}K(A) &= (\dot{T}dD + \dot{T}Dd)\dot{T}K(A)\\ &= (d'(\dot{T}D) + (\dot{T}D)d')\dot{T}K(A)\\ &= (d'\,D' + D'\,d')\dot{T}K(A)\end{aligned}$$

where $D' = \dot{T}D$.

Definition 7.8. Let

$$Z_n(\dot{T}K) = ker(TK_n \xrightarrow{d'} (d'\,T)K_{n-1} = T(dK_n)),\ B_n(\dot{T}K) = T(dK_{n+1}).$$

Then

(7.8a) $$H_n(\dot{T}K_*) = Z_n(\dot{T}K_*)/T(dK_{n+1}).$$

The nth **derived functor** is written $\mathrm{T}_n = ({}^1\mathrm{T}_n, {}^2\mathrm{T}_n)$ where

(7.8b) $${}^1\mathrm{T}_n(A) = H_n(\dot{T}K_*).$$

To define ${}^2\mathrm{T}_n(\alpha)$ for $\alpha \in G(A, B)$, note that according to (3.3), α can be lifted to $\alpha' \in G(K_*(A), K_*(B))$. Then $\dot{T}\alpha'$: $\dot{T}K_*(A) \rightarrow \dot{T}K_*(B)$ is a lifting of $T\alpha$. We are aware of the fact that neither of the resolutions $K(A)$ or $K(B)$ is unique, nor is the lifting $\dot{T}\alpha'$ unique. However (3.3) and (7.5) assert that the nonuniqueness is up to homotopy only. Hence we infer that ${}^1\mathrm{T}_n(A) \rightarrow {}^1\mathrm{T}_n(B)$ as well as the homomorphism

(7.8c) $$(\dot{T}\alpha')_*: H\dot{T}K_*(A) \rightarrow H\dot{T}K_*(B)$$

is unique. We write ${}^2\mathrm{T}_n(\alpha)$, or $\mathrm{T}_n(\alpha)$ for $(\dot{T}\alpha')_n$. We use T *both for* T *and for* $\dot{T}$ from now on.

In the same way if T is covariant and exact on the left, then an injective resolution $K^*(A)$ is used (again it is immediate that $TK^*(A)$ is an upper complex) and the nth derived functor $\mathrm{T}^n = ({}^1\mathrm{T}^n, {}^2\mathrm{T}^n)$ is defined by

(7.8d) $$\begin{aligned}{}^1\mathrm{T}^n(A) &= H^n\ TK^*(A)\\ {}^2\mathrm{T}^n(\alpha) &= (T(\alpha')) \colon H^n\ TK^*(A) \rightarrow H^n\ TK^*(C)\end{aligned}$$

where α' is the lifting of $\alpha \in G(A, C)$ to $G(K(A), K(C))$.

To complete the discussion, T contravariant and exact on the right yields

(7.8e) $$\begin{aligned}{}^1\mathrm{T}^n(A) &= H^n\ TK_*\\ {}^2\mathrm{T}^n(\alpha) &= T(\alpha') \colon H^n(TK_*(C)) \rightarrow H^n\ TK_*(A)\end{aligned}$$

while T contravariant and exact on the left gives

(7.8f) $$\begin{aligned}{}^1\mathrm{T}_n(A) &= H_n(TK^*)\\ {}^2\mathrm{T}_n(\alpha) &= (T\alpha') \colon H_n(TK^*(C)) \rightarrow H_n\ TK^*(A)\end{aligned}$$

Remark. We can generalize the developments above by using functors of several variables and passing to their resolutions However, this requires multiple grading; for instance, $Hom(K_n, K^m)$ has two grades. This occasions no difficulty, but we prefer to defer such matters until we have essential need for them (Chapter 16).

It is important to observe that nothing in the tablets on Mount Zion barred using injective resolutions for right exact functors and projective resolutions for left exact functors. Only if we do so (7.9a) below will no longer be valid. We sum up the general situation above by the observation that the connecting homomorphisms when the functor is covariant point in the same direction as the homomorphisms between the terms in a resolution. Hence if the resolution is projective the derived functor is expressed in terms of homology (7.8b) while if the resolution is injective the derived functor is given by cohomology (7.8d). The connecting homomorphisms for contravariant functors points upstream. That is to say in the opposite direction to the homomorphisms of the resolutions. Accordingly cohomology is associated with the projective resolution (7.8c) and homology with the injective resolution (7.8f).

Generalization to other exact categories requires, if projective resolutions are always to be possible, that for every object A there be an epimorphism of a projective P onto A. If injective resolutions are to invariably exist, each object is to be isomorphic to a substruct of an injective object. (This is illustrated by the observations $G = K_0/d_1 K_1$ (3.1a) and $0 \to G \to K^0$ (3.1b) respectively.)

Theorem 7.9. *If T is a right (left) exact, covariant, additive functor, then up to natural equivalence,*

(7.9a) $$\mathrm{T}_0(A) = T(A), \quad (\mathrm{T}^0(A) = T(A)).$$

(7.9b) *If* $0 \longrightarrow A' \longrightarrow A \longrightarrow A'' \longrightarrow 0$ *is exact, then so is*

$$\longrightarrow \mathrm{T}_n(A') \longrightarrow T_n(A) \longrightarrow T_n(A'') \xrightarrow{d'} \mathrm{T}_{n-1}(A') \longrightarrow,$$

$$\longrightarrow T^n(A') \longrightarrow \mathrm{T}^n(A) \longrightarrow \mathrm{T}^n(A'') \xrightarrow{d'} \mathrm{T}^{n+1}(A') \longrightarrow.$$

From the exactness of

$$K_1 \xrightarrow{d} K_0 \xrightarrow{j} A \longrightarrow 0$$

there follows exactness of

$$T(K_1) \xrightarrow{d'} T(K_0) \xrightarrow{j'} T(A) \longrightarrow 0.$$

Then $dK_0 = 0$ implies $H_0(TK) = T(K_0)/\underset{\underset{d'(TK_1)}{\|}}{ker\, j'} \approx T(A)$ and (7.8) applies.

In the same way with the left exact functor we get $T^0(A) = TA$. If $0 \longrightarrow A^1 \xrightarrow{i} A \longrightarrow A'' \longrightarrow 0$ is exact then projective resolutions exist for which

$$0 \longrightarrow A' \xrightarrow{i} A \longrightarrow A'' \longrightarrow 0$$

is exact (3.4). Since K''_m is projective, K'_m is a direct summand of K.

Let i_1, i_2, p_1, p_2 be defined to make K_m a direct sum of K'_m and K''_m (6.4**VI**). Write ${}^1i_j, {}^1p_j, j = 1, 2$ for $T(i_j), T(p_j)$. Then $T(K_m)$ is a direct sum because by (7.1c) $T(i_j\, p_k) = T(i_j)\, T(p_k)$ so, for instance, ${}^1i_1\, {}^ip_2 = 0$, etc. That is to say, ${}^1i_1$ is an injection, and so

$$0 \rightarrow TK' \rightarrow TK \rightarrow TK'' \rightarrow 0$$

is exact. Then (61.12) yields the assertion of the theorem for the right exact case. The left exact case is treated analogously.

We apply the considerations in (7.8) to two important functors.

Definition 7.10. Let A and C be modules. Let $T(A) = A \otimes C$ for fixed C. Write

(7.10a) $$\mathrm{Tor}_n(A, C) = H_n(K_*(A) \otimes C) = T_n(A).$$

Let $T(A) = Hom(A, C)$. Write

(7.10b) $$\mathrm{Ext}^n(A, C) = H^n(Hom(K_*(A), C) = T^n(A).$$

Alternative definitions can be given, but we shall not establish their equivalence at this time. Thus with $T(A) = C \otimes A$ and $Hom(A, C)$ respectively, we have

(7.10c) $$\mathrm{Tor}_n(A, C) = H_n(A \otimes K_*(C))$$

(7.10d) $$\mathrm{Ext}^n(A, C) = H^n\, Hom(A, K^*(C)).$$

Lemma 7.11. *For groups,* $\mathrm{Tor}_n(A, C) = 0 = \mathrm{Ext}^n(A, C)$, $n > 2$ *and*

$$\mathrm{Tor}_1(A, C) = Tor(A, C),\ \mathrm{Ext}^1(A, C) = Ext(A, C).$$

In this case projective is the same as free. Since every subgroup of a free group is free, dK_1 is free and so $K_0 = dK_1 \oplus B$. Let $L_0 = dK_1$ and define d as an injection of L_0. Then $0 \longrightarrow L_0 \xrightarrow{d} K_0 \longrightarrow A \longrightarrow 0$. Thus there is a projective resolution with $K_n = 0$, $n > 2$. Similar remarks hold for injective resolutions using the fact that quotients of an injective module are then injective.

Let T be an exact covariant functor on the category of upper complexes to that of DG modules. Then Td satisfies $(Td)TA^p = TdA^p$, i.e.,

$$\begin{array}{ccc} A^p & \xrightarrow[T]{} & TA^p \\ {\scriptstyle d}\downarrow & & \downarrow{\scriptstyle Td} \\ A^{p+1} & \xrightarrow[T]{} & TA^{p+1} \end{array}$$

Theorem 7.12. $TH^n = H^nT$.

We start from the exact sequence

$$0 \longrightarrow Z^n(A) \xrightarrow{i} A^n \xrightarrow{d} B^{n+1}(A) \longrightarrow 0$$

and infer

(7.12a) $$0 \longrightarrow TZ^n \xrightarrow{Ti} TA^n \xrightarrow{Td} TB^{n+1} \longrightarrow 0$$

is exact. Similarly

(7.12b) $$0 \to TB^n \to TZ^n \to TH^n \to 0.$$

is exact. Let $Z(TA) = ker(TA^{n-1} \xrightarrow{Td} TA^n)$. Then from (8.1a), $Z^n(TA) = (Ti)\,TZ^n \approx TZ^n$. Let $B^{n+1}\,TA = Im(TA^n \xrightarrow{Td} TA^{n+1}) = TB^{n+1}$. From (7.12b) comes $\dfrac{TZ^n}{TB^n} \approx TH^n$. Accordingly

(7.12c) $$TH^n = H^nT.$$

PROBLEMS

10-16. If T is a torsion group and R is the group of the reals or is Q show

$$Tor(T, R/\text{J}) \approx T.$$

10-17. If the group G is torsion free, then $Ext(G, \text{J})$ is divisible.

10-18. If T is the torsion subgroup of G, then $0 \to T \to G \to G/T \to 0$ is exact and therefore $0 = Hom(T, \text{J}) \to Ext(G/T, \text{J}) \to Ext(G, \text{J}) \to Ext(T, \text{J}) \to 0$ is exact.

10-19. If T has finite order, show $Hom(T, R/\text{J}) \approx Ext(T, \text{J})$. *Hint:* Start with exactness of $0 \to \text{J} \to R \to R/\text{J} \to 0$ and note in the induced *Ext* sequence that $Ext(T, R) = 0$.

In line with an earlier remark in this section our developments can be interpreted as applying to one sided modules. We make this specific for easy reference later.

Definition 7.13. If A and C are right and left R modules respectively then the derived functors

(7.13a) $$Tor_n^R(A, C) = H_n(A \otimes_R K_*(C)) = H_n(K_*(A) \otimes_R C)$$

where the projective resolution $K_*(C)$ consists of left R modules and $K_*(A)$ of right R modules. If A and C are both left (right) R modules

$$\text{(7.13b)} \qquad Ext_R^n(A, C) = H^n(Hom_R(A, K^*(C))$$
$$= H^n(Hom_R(K_*(A), C)$$

where the injective resolution $K^*(C)$ and the projective resolution $K_*(A)$ consist of left (right) R modules.

Remark. We sum up the contribution of category arguments as in Sections 6 and 7. There is first of all the merit of generality. Of greater interest to us is the duality considered in (6.10). The dual category to $\mathfrak{C}$, namely $\mathfrak{C}^*$ is a trick for dualizing axioms, definitions and theorems since the objects are those of $\mathfrak{C}$ and only the directions of the maps are reversed. In particular $\mathfrak{C} = (\mathfrak{C}^*)^*$. Write T for theorem and $T(\mathfrak{C})$ for the theorem applied to the category $\mathfrak{C}$. If a theorem is true for all categories, then T^* is a theorem defined by $T^*(\mathfrak{C}) = T(\mathfrak{C}^*)$. T^* is then the dual of T. If T is true for categories with properties P, alone, then T^* holds for categories with properties P^*. Thus if $\mathfrak{C}$ satisfies P but not P^*, then T^* is not valid in C. (In this connection among the categories satisfying both P and P^*, it may well happen that the interesting categories for T differ from the interesting ones for T^*.) Our final comment is on the functorial aspects. If our categories admit certain constructions, we are constrained to consideration of functors which do not disturb such constructions.

8. ADJOINT FUNCTORS. A unifying viewpoint is summed up in the following description.

Definition 8.1. Let T be a functor on $\mathfrak{U}^* \times \mathfrak{B}$ to $\mathfrak{S}$, the category of sets. The **Universal Mapping Problem** for T at the object A, $A \in \mathfrak{U}$, is that of finding a solution pair $B = B(A)$, $t = t(A)$ where $B(A) \in \mathfrak{B}$ and $t(A) \in T(A, B)$ such that for each $C \in \mathfrak{B}$ there is a 1–1 correspondence ψ on $G(B, C) \to T(A, C)$ defined by $\psi(\gamma) = T(e_A, \gamma)t$. The scheme illustrates the situation with $A \times B$ written for the pair A, B

$$\begin{array}{ccccc} B & \longrightarrow & A \times B & \xrightarrow{T} & T(A, B) \\ \downarrow{\scriptstyle \gamma} & & \downarrow{\scriptstyle e_A \times \gamma} & & \downarrow{\scriptstyle T(e_A, \gamma)} \\ C & \longrightarrow & A \times C & \xrightarrow{T} & T(A, C) \end{array}$$

There need be no solution pair at a prescribed object A. On the other hand if B', t' is another solution pair at A, it is easily established that there is an equivalence

$$\bar{\gamma} \in G(B, B') \quad \text{with} \quad t' = \psi(\bar{\gamma}).$$

Remark. The existence of a kernel pair (106.4a), (106.8b) can be formulated as a universal mapping problem. Similarly the existence of a direct sum can be so formulated.

We shall use a dot here and later to indicate composition. We call attention to a functor determined by the morphisms, $G(A, B)$.

Definition 8.2. Assume the morphisms on C to D constitute a set $G(C, D)$, C and D in $\mathfrak{A}$. Let $\alpha \in G(A', A)$ and let $\beta \in G(B, B')$. Define

$$G(\alpha, \beta)\colon G(A, B) \to G(A', B')$$

to be a morphism of sets given by

$$G(\alpha, \beta)\psi = \beta \cdot \psi \cdot \alpha, \quad \psi \in G(A, B)$$

(Compare 7.4c). Thus G can be considered a functor on $\mathfrak{A} \times \mathfrak{A}$ to $\mathfrak{S}$ the category of sets, Example 10-5 and will be indicated by $hom(-, -)$. When the category $\mathfrak{A}$ is additive $\mathfrak{S}$ can be replaced by $\mathfrak{G}$ the category of groups and this is further reason for using *hom*. For this section we shall use the abbreviated notation (A, B) to stand for $hom(A, B)$.

Definition 8.3. Let S and T be covariant functors on $\mathfrak{A}$ to $\mathfrak{B}$ and on $\mathfrak{B}$ to $\mathfrak{A}$ respectively. Suppose there exists a natural equivalence ϕ between the *hom* functors defined in (8.2). Specifically suppose for each $A, B \in \mathfrak{A} \times \mathfrak{B}$

$$\varphi_{A,B} = \varphi\colon hom(S(A), B; \mathfrak{B}) \to hom(A, T(B); \mathfrak{A})$$

is a natural equivalence. We term S and T **adjoint** functors with S the **left** φ **adjoint** of T and T the **right** φ **adjoint** of S.

In particular with $\varphi = \varphi_{T(B),B}$

$$(STB, B;\ \mathfrak{B}) \xrightarrow{\varphi} (T(B), T(B);\ \mathfrak{A}). \tag{8.3a}$$

Let $I(\mathfrak{B})$ be the identity functor namely the identity in $\mathfrak{B}^{\mathfrak{B}}$. Define the transformation E on $ST(\mathfrak{B})$ to $I(\mathfrak{B})$ by

$$E(B) = \varphi^{-1}e_{T(B)}. \tag{8.3b}$$

Similarly from $(S(A), S(A)) \xrightarrow{\varphi} (A, TS(A))$ we infer there is a transformation E' on $I(\mathfrak{A})$ to $TS(\mathfrak{A})$ defined by

$$E'(A) = \varphi e_{S(A)} \tag{8.3c}$$

Example 10-25. Let $\mathfrak{A}$ be the category of sets and $\mathfrak{B}$ Abelian groups. Let S on a set be the free Abelian group generated by the set. Let T on a group be the set of elements. Then S is a left adjoint of T.

Theorem 8.4. *E and E' are natural transformations.*

We give the proof for E' alone. Let $\lambda : A \to A'$. Then in the usual notation for functors $S\lambda$: $S(A) \to S(A')$.

$$\begin{array}{ccc}
(S(A), S(A)) & \xrightarrow{\varphi} & (A, TS(A)) \\
\Big\downarrow{\scriptstyle (S(A), S\lambda)} & & \Big\downarrow{\scriptstyle (A, TS\lambda)} \\
(S(A), S(A')) & \xrightarrow{\varphi} & (A, TS(A')) \\
\Big\uparrow{\scriptstyle (S\lambda, S(A'))} & & \Big\uparrow{\scriptstyle (\lambda, TS(A'))} \\
(S(A'), S(A')) & \xrightarrow{\varphi} & (A', TS(A'))
\end{array}$$

Both squares are commutative. To see this merely identify either square with that in (7.1h) vertex for vertex and transformation for transformation. Since φ corresponds to ψ in (8.4), the commutativity is really "by definition" of the natural transformation φ. Hence

$$\begin{aligned}
TS\lambda \cdot E'(A) &= (A, TS\lambda)\varphi e_{S(A)} = \varphi(S(A), S\lambda)e_{S(A)} \\
&= \varphi(S\lambda \cdot e_{S(A)}) = \varphi(e_{S(A')} \cdot S\lambda) \\
&= \varphi(S\lambda, SA')e_{S(A')} = (\lambda, TSA')\varphi e_{SA'} \\
&= E'(A') \cdot \lambda
\end{aligned} \tag{8.4a}$$

This asserts commutativity in

$$\begin{array}{ccc}
I(A)A = A & \xrightarrow{E'(A)} & TS(A) \\
\Big\downarrow{\scriptstyle \lambda} & & \Big\downarrow{\scriptstyle TS\lambda} \\
I(A')A' = A' & \xrightarrow{E'(A')} & TS(A')
\end{array}$$

and therefore E' is a natural transformation.

Theorem 8.5. *Let S be a left φ adjoint of T and let the natural transformation E' be as in* (8.3c). *Then for every $\theta \in (S(A), B)$, $\varphi\theta = T\theta \cdot E'(A)$.*

Since φ is natural

$$\varphi\theta = \varphi(S(A), \theta)e_{S(A)} = \varphi(A, T\theta)e_{S(A)} = T\theta \cdot E(A)$$

Remark. This theorem shows that φ is determined by E'.

Theorem 8.6. *Let S_i be the left φ_i adjoint of T_i $i = 1, 2$. Let ψ: $S_2 \to S_1$ be a natural transformation. Then there is a unique natural transformation ζ on T_1 to T_2 such that*

$$\begin{array}{ccc}
(S_1(\mathfrak{A}), \mathfrak{B}) & \xrightarrow{\varphi_1} & (\mathfrak{A}, T_1(\mathfrak{B})) \\
\Big\downarrow{\scriptstyle (\psi(\mathfrak{A}), \mathfrak{B})} & & \Big\downarrow{\scriptstyle (\mathfrak{A}, \zeta(\mathfrak{B}))} \\
(S_2(\mathfrak{A}), \mathfrak{B}) & \xrightarrow{\varphi_2} & (\mathfrak{A}, T_2(\mathfrak{B}))
\end{array} \tag{8.6a}$$

is commutative. Similarly if ζ is assigned, a unique ψ exists. If either of ψ and ζ is a natural equivalence so is the other.

Suppose ζ satisfies our conditions. Then for arbitrary $\alpha \in (A, T(B))$ commutativity in (8.7a) yields

$$\zeta(B) \cdot \alpha = (A, \zeta(B))\alpha = \varphi_2[(\psi A, B)\varphi_1^{-1}\alpha] = \varphi_2[\varphi_1^{-1}\, \alpha \cdot \psi A]$$

Therefore if $A = T(B)$ and $\alpha = i_{T(B)}$

(8.6b) $$\zeta(B) \cdot i_{T(B)} = \zeta(B) = \varphi_2[\varphi_{-1}^{1} e_{T(B)} \cdot \psi T(A)]$$

In short ζ is uniquely specified. It remains to show ζ is a natural transformation. This requires a little work but is straightforward.

Corollary 8.7. *If S_i is a left φ_i adjoint of T, $i = 1, 2$ then S_1 and S_2 are the same up to a unique natural equivalence.*

This follows at once from (8.6).

9. EILENBERG STEENROD AXIOMS. A gross characterization of our developments is that starting with spaces or complexes or gratings certain graded groups or modules or algebras were attached which we called omology algebras. We may put the question: when is such a correspondence to bear the name omology? We restrict ourselves to the group case and consider a typical situation. Suppose then that $\mathfrak{C}$ is the category whose objects are certain pairs X, A of topological spaces and require that $G(X, A;\ Y, B)$ consist of (continuous) maps $X, A \to Y, B$. Let $H^*(X, A)$ be a graded Abelian group for each object X, A. If $\psi \in G(X, A;\ Y, B)$ let ψ^* be some uniquely determined homomorphism on $H^*(Y, B) \to H^*(X, A)$. Let d be a uniquely defined homomorphism of degree 1 on $H^*(A)$ to $H^*(X, A)$. Then the graded functor H^* (which incidentally is a certain contravariant functor on $\mathfrak{C}$ to the category of Abelian groups) together with d and the homomorphisms $\{\psi^*\}$ are the building stones for a cohomology theory in the sense of Eilenberg-Steenrod. The following axioms are satisfied.

(**a**) If ψ is the identity map on $X, A \to X, A$, then ψ^* is the identity isomorphism on $H^*(X, A) \to H^*(X, A)$.

(**b**) Transitivity. If $X, A \xrightarrow{\psi} Y, B \xrightarrow{\theta} W, C$, then $(\theta\psi)^* = \psi^*\theta^*$.

(**c**) Allowability: $\psi^*\, d = d\psi^*$.

(**d**) Exactness of the cohomology sequence for the pair X, A.

(**e**) Homotopy: If ψ_1 is homotopic to ψ_2, then $\psi_1^* = \psi_2^*$.

(**f**) Excision.

(**g**) Dimension. $H^0(x, R) \approx R$, $H^n(x, R) = 0$, $n > 1$.

These axioms are satisfied as we have seen when X is locally compact and A is closed and H is derived from a full grating or from the grating of singular cochains. Similar axioms can be given to characterize cohomology *rings*. Latterly various expanded cohomology systems have been defined by dropping the Dimension (or Poincare) Axiom (g).

chapter 11

UNIQUENESS PROOFS AND FIXED POINT INDICES

1. UNIQUENESS OF OMOLOGY ALGEBRAS. A central question is, of course, whether the omology algebras derived from variously defined gratings are the same up to isomorphism. Homomorphism assertions can be made for gratings which are fine or full. An extension to the case of closed supports will be treated also.

For concrete complexes (cf. (2.4)) a classical proof for the module homomorphism alone shows first that the singular omology modules are isomorphic to the simplicial modules. Invariance of the singular modules follows almost at once from their definition. Still another proof makes use of the cofinal family of open covers consisting of stars of barycentric subdivisions. Since the omology modules on each nerve are isomorphic to those for the original complex, passage to inverse or direct limits yields identification with the Čech or Alexander modules.

In the next sections we develop a proof of the equivalence of the omology algebras taken over various compact gratings on a fixed locally compact space. The demonstration leans heavily on the multiplicative properties of the gratings. Accordingly following the convention (61.5) the term *cycle* is to be understood as referring to upper-graded gratings and so to connote the co-situation. In particular the results imply the possibility, in some cases, of partitioning a space into a finite number of "simple" chunks analogous to a simplicial decomposition of a complex with comparable practical advantage paralleling that established in (74.3), that is to say a finite basis of elements in the grating may be sufficient to determine omology properties. Invariance theorems for the homology situation also can be obtained once results on the duality of homology and cohomology groups are established.

This is an added reason for the detailed development of the important special homology cases (74.7).

The proof introduces an interesting category concept and is therefore preferred to what must be owned are more powerful and more direct algebraic demonstrations. Of these latter there will be a sufficiency in later chapters.

Definition 1.1. Let ${}_j\mathrm{A}$, $j = 1, 2$ be full gratings (81.22) over X. If there is an allowable isomorphism i of ${}_1\mathrm{A}$ into ${}_2\mathrm{A}$ then ${}_2\mathrm{A}$ is an **extension** of ${}_1\mathrm{A}$. In particular $\|ia\| = \|a\|$, so ${}_1\mathrm{A}$ is a **full subgrating** of ${}_2\mathrm{A}$.

Lemma 1.2. *Let* $\mathbf{a} \in {}^{\bullet}H^p(\mathrm{A})$ *where* A *is a full grating. Then there is a finite closed cover of* X, $\{Y_j \mid j = 1, \ldots, N\}$ *such that* $Y_j^*\mathbf{a} = 0$ *for* $\mathbf{a} \in {}^{\bullet}H^p(\mathrm{A}), p > 0$ *and* $Y_j^*\mathbf{a} = r\mathbf{u}_j$ *where* $\mathbf{u}$ *is the unit* (81.21iii) *of* ${}^{\bullet}H(Y_j\,\mathrm{A})$, *when* $p = 0$.

Let a be a representative in $Z(\mathrm{A})$ of $\mathbf{a}$ and suppose $a \in \mathrm{A}^p$, $p > 0$. If $a = db$, $Y = X$ and there is nothing to prove. Suppose then that $a \in \mathrm{A}^p$ but a is not a bounding cycle. Since A is R simple, ${}^{\bullet}H^p(x\mathrm{A}) = 0$ and so $xa = xdc$ or $x \cap \|a - dc\| = \varnothing$ (87.10). By local compactness there is an open neighborhood $V(x)$ with $\bar{V}_x \cap \|a - dc\| = \varnothing$. Since $C = \|a\|$ is compact, its open cover $\{V_x \mid x \in \|a\|\}$ admits a finite subcover, $\{V_i \mid V_i = V_{x_i}, i = 1, \ldots, N - 1\}$ satisfying $\bar{V}_i \cap \|a - dc_i\| = \varnothing$. Let $U = \bigcup V_i$. Again by the compactness of $\|a\|$, there is a finite open subcover $\{W_j\}$ of $\|a\|$ with $W_j \subset \bar{W}_j \subset V_j$. Then $W = \bigcup W_j \subset \bar{W} \subset U$. Define V_N as $\tilde{W}$. The sets $\{\bar{V}_i \mid i = 1, \ldots, N - 1\}$ can be chosen as the Y_i's of the lemma; i.e., $\bar{V}_i\, a = \bar{V}_i\, dc_i\; i = 1, \ldots, N - 1$, $\bar{V}_N\, a = 0$, so $\bar{V}_i^*\langle a\rangle = 0$.

If $a \in \mathrm{A}^{\circ}$, $\mathrm{H}^{\circ}(xA) \approx R$ implies there is a local identity $u_{C=x}$ such that $x \cap \|a - ru_x\| = \varnothing$ for some $r \in R$. Again this yields

$$\bar{V}_x \cap \|a - ru_x\| = \varnothing$$

and the argument continues as above to give $\bar{V}_i\, a = \bar{V}_i\, ru_{x_i}$.

Definition 1.3. For fixed a let the smallest integer N for all competing decompositions satisfying (1.2) be denoted by *kat* **a**, the **category of** X **relative to the omology class a.** The terminology is consonant with the usual definition of category as the minimal number of acyclic sets which can constitute a cover.

The sets of the closed cover $\{Y_i \mid i = 1, \ldots, \mathit{kat}\,\mathbf{a}\}$ satisfying (1.2) may always be assumed of the form $Y_i = \bar{V}_i$ where V_i is open. Specifically $Y(a - dc) = 0$ implies $Y \cap \|a - dc\| = \varnothing$. Since $\|a - dc\|$ is compact Y is contained in some open set V, $\bar{V} \cap \|a - dc\| = \varnothing$ that is to say $\bar{V}(a - dc) = 0$. An open cover $\{V_i \mid i = 1, \ldots, \mathit{kat}\,\mathbf{a}\}$ for which $\{\bar{V}_i\}$ satisfies (1.3) is a **kat a cover**. Evidently *kat* $\mathbf{a} = 1$ is a paraphrase of $\mathbf{a} = 0$.

Lemma 1.4. *If* A *is a full grating and* **a** *is a nontrivial element of* $^{\bullet}H(\mathrm{A})$ *then for* X_0 *closed in* X, *kat* X_0 **a** $\leq$ *kat* **a** *and there is a binary open cover* W_1, W_2 *of* X *such that kat* $\bar{W}_i^*$ **a** $<$ *kat* **a**.

Let a be a representative in $Z(\mathrm{A})$ of **a**. The first assertion follows from the observation that $Y_i(a - dc_i) = 0$ is implied by $Y_i \cap \|a - dc_i\| = \varnothing$ whence of course $X_0 \cap Y_i \cap \|a - dc_i\| = \varnothing$.

Let $\{V_i\}$ be a *kat* **a** cover of X. Choose $W_1 = V_1$. From $\bar{W}_1 a = \bar{W}_1 dc$, follows that *kat* $\bar{W}_1$ **a** $=$ *kat* $\langle dc_1 \rangle = 1$. Since **a** $\neq 0$, *kat* **a** > 1. Let $W_2 = \bigcup_{j=2}^{kat\,\mathbf{a}} V_i$. From $\bar{V}_i \bar{W}_2 a = \bar{V}_i a = \bar{V}_i dc_1$, $i = 2, \ldots, N$, there follows

$$kat\ \mathbf{a} - 1 \geq kat\ \bar{W}_2^*\ \mathbf{a}.$$

Evidently $W_1 \cup W_2 \supset X$. We refer to the cover W_1, W_2 in (1.4) as a **reducing cover** for **a**.

Since our arguments deal generally with cocycle representations of omology classes the next lemma is stated directly in terms of such representatives.

Lemma 1.5. *Let* B *be a full subgrating of* A. *Let* $a \in \mathrm{A}^p$, $p > 0$ *with* $da \in \mathrm{B}$. (*If* B *is an ideal of* A *then this condition amounts to* $a \in Z(\mathrm{A/B})$.) *Let* $\{W_j \mid j = 1, 2\}$ *be a cover of* $\|a\|$. *Suppose there exist* a_1, a_2, c *in* A *and* b_1, b_2, b *in* B *satisfying*

$$\bar{W}_i(a + da_i) = \bar{W}_i\, b_i, \tag{1.5a}$$

$$\bar{W}_1 \cap \bar{W}_2(a_1 - a_2 + dc) = \bar{W}_1 \cap \bar{W}_2\, b. \tag{1.5b}$$

Then, for some $\rho \in \mathrm{A}$, $a + d\rho \in \mathrm{B}$.

If $a \in \mathrm{A}^0$ *then*

$$\bar{W}_i\, a = \bar{W}_i\, b_i \tag{1.5c}$$

and the conclusion is $a \in \mathrm{B}$.

Let C be a compact subset of X containing the supports of a, a_i, b_i and b, $i = 1, 2$. Denote a partition of the identity in B relative to C and to W_1, W_2 by $v^1 + v^2 = v$. Let i be the injection $\mathrm{B} \to \mathrm{A}$. We assert iv is a local identity over C. Indeed let u in A be a local identity over C. By the uniqueness of the unit or identity, $xiu = ixu = xv$. It follows that

$$\bar{V}_x \cap \|(iv - u)\| = \varnothing.$$

for some open set V_x. Using the compactness of C we derive

$$\bar{V}_i \cap \|iv - u\| = \varnothing,$$

for $\{V_i\}$ a cover of C. Hence $\|iv - u\| = \varnothing$ on all of C. Thus $Civ = Cu$. There is no loss in generality, therefore, in identifying iv with u and we write u_1, u_2 instead of iv_1, iv_2 to indicate the partition of the identity in A.

The idea of the proof is simply that since $\|u_i\, a\| \subset \bar{W}_i$, $\|\bar{W}_i\, u_i\, a\| = \|u_i\, a\|$, the equations $\bar{W}_i\, u_i\, a = 0$, $i = 1, 2$ imply $u_i\, a = 0$, or since $(u_1 + u_2)a = a$, $a = 0$.

Define ρ by $\rho = u_1\, a_1 + u_2\, a_2 + u_1\, dc$. Hence for $a \in A^p$, $p > 0$,

(1.5d) $$a + d\rho = a + u_1\, da_1 + u_2\, da_2 + du_1(a_1 + dc) + du_2\, a_2.$$

Since $a = u_1\, a + u_2\, a$ there results

(1.5e) $$a + u_1\, da_1 + u_2\, da_2 = u_1(a + da_1) + u_2(a + da_2).$$

In view of (1.5a) and (81.11b),

$$\bar{W}_i \cap \|u_i\,(a + da_i - b_i)\| = \varnothing.$$

However for any $a \in A$, $\|u_i\, a\| \subset \bar{W}_i$, hence $\|u_i(a + da_i - b_i)\| = \varnothing$. Thus, referring to (1.5e),

(1.5f) $$a + u_1\, da_1 + u_2\, da_2 = u_1\, b_1 + u_2\, b_2 \in B.$$

Since $u_1 + u_2$ is the identity on C, $\|d(u_1 + u_2)\| \cap C = \varnothing$, whence, using $\|du_i\| \subset \|u_i\| \subset \bar{W}_i$,

(1.5g) $$\|du_1\| \cap C = \|du_2\| \cap C \subset \bar{W}_1 \cap \bar{W}_2 \cap C.$$

Accordingly

$$\begin{aligned} du_1(a_1 + dc) + du_2\, a_2 &= du_1(a_1 - a_2 + dc) + (d(u_1 + u_2))a_2 \\ &= du_1(a_1 - a_2 + dc), \end{aligned}$$

has its support contained in $\bar{W}_1 \cap \bar{W}_2 \cap C$. From (1.5b) and (81.11b)

$$\bar{W}_1 \cap \bar{W}_2\, du_1(a_1 - a_2 + dc) = \bar{W}_1 \cap \bar{W}_2\, du_1\, b.$$

Then (1.5a) and (81.11) imply

$$W_1 \cap W_2 \cap \|du_1(a_1 - a_2 + dc - b)\| = \|du_1(a_1 - a_2 + dc - b)\|.$$

In short

(1.5h) $$du_1(a_1 - a_2 + dc) = du_1\, b.$$

Since $u_1\, b \in B$ it follows that $d(u_i\, b) \in B$ whence

(1.5i) $$du_1\, b = d(u_1\, b) - u_1\, db \in B.$$

The combination of (1.5d), (1.5f), (1.5h), and (1.5i) yields the assertion of the lemma for $p > 0$.

For the case $a \in A^0$, using $u_j = i\; v_j$, $a - u_1\, b_1 - u_2\, b_2 = u_1(a - b_1) + u_2(a - b_2)$. Then since $u_i(a - b_i) \subset \bar{W}_i$ there follows from the hypotheses (1.5c) that $\|u^1(a - b_1)\| = \varnothing = \|u^2(a - b_2)\|$. Hence $a = u_1\, b_1 + u_2\, b_2 \in B$.

PROBLEMS

11-1. Show *kat* **a** is the same whether calculated for open covers or for closed covers.

11-2. Show (a) $kat(r\mathbf{a} + s\mathbf{a}') \leq kat\, \mathbf{a}\, kat\, \mathbf{a}'$; (b) $kat(\mathbf{aa}') \leq \inf(kat\, \mathbf{a}, kat\, \mathbf{a}')$; (c) $kat\ Y\mathbf{a} \leq kat\ \mathbf{a}$ if Y is closed, and (d) if $kat\ \mathbf{a} = N$, then $(\mathbf{a})^N = \langle (a)^N \rangle = 0$. *Hint:* If V_i is in a *kat* **a** cover, then $V_i \cap \|a\| = \varnothing$ so $\|(a)^N\| \subset \bigcap V_i^{\sim}$.

Lemma 1.6. *Let* B *be a full subgrating of the full grating* A. *If* $a \in$ A *and* $da \in$ B, *in particular if* $da = 0$, *then for some* $b \in$ B, $a - b \in d$A.

We have not supposed B is an ideal of A. If it were, the lemma would amount to: $a \in Z(\mathrm{A}/\mathrm{B})$ implies $a \in B(\mathrm{A}/\mathrm{B})$.

For $p > 0$, the assertion is that whenever $a \in \mathrm{A}^p$ and $da \in \mathrm{B}^{p+1}$ then for some $c \in \mathrm{A}^{p-1}$, $a + dc \in$ B and, for $p = 0$, $a \in \mathrm{A}^0$. Consider the pairs F, E where F $= Y$B, E $= Y$A, Y closed in X, i.e., the Y cut of A or of B. We refer to these pairs as **cut pairs** (relative to A, B). From $ub = b$ for all $b \in$ B follows $u(Yb) = Yub = Yb$. We write *Kat* when referring to $^{\bullet}H(\mathrm{F})$ and *kat* for $^{\bullet}H(\mathrm{E})$ elements.

As a preliminary using cut pairs F, E throughout, we dispose of the case $e \in Z(\mathrm{E})$, $kat\ \mathbf{e} = 1$, for then $\mathbf{e} = 0$.

Suppose next that the assertion of the lemma is valid for $c \in \mathrm{E}^r$, $dc \in \mathrm{F}^{r+1}$; provided $r < n$, and for the case $r = n$, provided c is a cocycle, and $kat\ c < m$. Hence let $e \in Z^n(\mathrm{E})$ with $kat\ e = m$. It is, of course, conceivable no such e exists, in which case the lemma's assertion for $kat\ e < m + 1$ is conceded. An analogous remark applies to the other induction arguments used later. If, lamentably, e does exist, we choose a reducing cover, W_1, W_2. We refer to W_i as W for the moment. Thus $kat\ \bar{W}e < m$. Evidently $d\,\bar{W}e = \bar{W}\,de = 0$. Hence by the induction hypothesis $\bar{W}e + \bar{W}\,dc \in \bar{W}\mathrm{F}$. This is tantamount to

$$\bar{W}_i(e + dc_i) = \bar{W}_i f_i, \quad f_i \in \mathrm{F}, \qquad i = 1, 2. \tag{1.6a}$$

Hence

$$\bar{W}_i \cap \bar{W}_2\, d(c_1 - c_2) = \bar{W}_1 \cap \bar{W}_2(f_1 - f_2) \in \bar{W}_1 \cap \bar{W}_2\,\mathrm{F}.$$

Since the degree of $c_1 - c_2$ is $n - 1$ the induction hypothesis applies to this element and so for some $e' \in$ E

$$\bar{W}_1 \cap \bar{W}_2(c_1 - c_2 + de') = \bar{W}_1 \cap \bar{W}_2 f, \quad f \in \mathrm{F}. \tag{1.6b}$$

(Of course if $\bar{W}_1 \cap \bar{W}_2$ is empty this relation is *a fortiori* valid.) Then (1.6a) and (1.6b) are of the form (1.5a) and (1.5b) whence for some $\rho \in$ E, $e + d\rho \in$ F. Thus we have extended the range of the lemma to $e \in Z^n$ E with $kat\ \mathbf{e} = m$.

We next lay down the induction hypotheses that the assertion of the lemma is valid for $e \in \mathrm{E}^r$, $de \in \mathrm{F}^{r+1}$ $r \leq n$, where for $r = n$, $Kat\ d\mathbf{e} < m$

where de is now considered in $^{\bullet}H(\mathrm{F})$ both here and below. Accordingly let $e \in E^p$ with $Kat\, de = m$. Hence for a reducing cover $\{W_i\}$, $Kat\, W_i\, de < m$, calculated for F. The induction hypotheses are therefore satisfied for $W_i\, e$ when E, F are replaced by $\bar{W}_i\,\mathrm{E}$, $\bar{W}_i\,\mathrm{F}$. Accordingly we are assured that $\bar{W}_i(e + dc_i) = \bar{W}_i f_i$ for some pairs $\{(c_i, f_i)\}$. The argument now parallels that following (1.6a). Thus

$$\bar{W}_1 \cap \bar{W}_2\, d(c_1 - c_2) = \bar{W}_1 \cap \bar{W}_2(f_1 - f_2).$$

The induction hypotheses cover this situation, for $c_1 - c_2$ has degree $n - 1$. Accordingly $\bar{W}_1 \cap \bar{W}_2(c_1 - c_2 + dc) = \bar{W}_1 \cap \bar{W}_2 f$, $f \in \mathrm{F}$. We conclude from (1.5) that

$$e + d\rho \in \mathrm{E}.$$

The extension is valid for $n = 0$ since then $\bar{W}_i\, e = \bar{W}_i f$ implies that $e \in \mathrm{F}$.

Lemma 1.7. *Let* A *be a full* R *grating and let* E *be a separated* R *grating which contains local identities for each compact set. Let* $R = \mathrm{J}$ *or a field. For every* $a \in \mathrm{A}$ *let* $u(a)$ *be any local identity over* $\|a\|$ *in* E. *Then* $\psi\colon \mathrm{A} \to \mathrm{A} \circ \mathrm{E}$ *defined by* $a \to a \circ u(a)$ *is an injection and* A *is a full subgrating of the full grating* $\mathrm{A} \circ \mathrm{E}$.

To show ψ is unaffected by change of $u(a)$, let $w(a)$ be another local identity over $\|a\|$. Then $xa \circ xu(a) - xa \circ xw(a) = x(a \circ u(a) - a \circ w(a)) = 0$, for all x, bearing in mind both sides are 0 for $x \bar{\in} \|a\|$. Since $\mathrm{A} \circ \mathrm{E}$ is separated this means $a \circ u(a) = a \circ w(a)$.

That $ker\, \psi = 0$ follows from the observation that if $a \circ u(a) = 0$ then $xa \circ xu(a) = 0$. Let $x \in \|a\|$. Consider the gratings $x\mathrm{A}$, $x\mathrm{E}$, and $x(\mathrm{A} \circ \mathrm{E})$. Then $x\mathrm{E}$ has the unit xu. If $R = \mathrm{J}$, $m \times u = xe$, $e \in \mathrm{E}$, implies $m = \pm 1$. Hence xu can be chosen one of the basis elements of $x\mathrm{E}$; the same conclusion follows if R is a field, so $x\mathrm{A} \otimes Rxu$ is a direct summand of $x\mathrm{A} \otimes x\mathrm{E}$ or

$$0 \to x\mathrm{A} \otimes Rxu \to x\mathrm{A} \otimes x\mathrm{E}.$$

Hence $xa \circ xu(a) = 0$ implies $xa = 0$ whence $\|a\| = \varnothing$ or $ker\, \psi = 0$. That ψ is allowable follows at once from $du = 0$. Finally $\mathrm{A} \circ \mathrm{E}$ is full by (105.13).

Theorem 1.8. *If* A *and* E *are full gratings, then*

$$^{\bullet}H^*(\mathrm{A}) \approx {}^{\bullet}H^*(\mathrm{E})$$

is an isomorphism of algebras.

By (1.7), A and E are full subgratings of $\mathrm{A} \circ \mathrm{E}$. By (1.6) and (61.17), $H^*(\mathrm{A}) \approx H^*(\mathrm{A} \circ \mathrm{E})$. Similarly $H^*(\mathrm{E}) \approx H^*(\mathrm{A} \circ \mathrm{E})$.

Remark. The result holds for R gratings. We need only replace A and E, the full gratings, by $\mathrm{A} \otimes R$ and $\mathrm{E} \otimes R$ considering R a grating (81.12).

Instead of *kat* **a** it would perhaps be more natural to use height $a = \inf\{m \mid (\mathbf{a})^m = 0\} \leq kat\ \mathbf{a}$ assuming the inequality can hold (cf. Problem 11-2d).

Definition 1.9. In view of (1.8) we define the **full cohomology algebra** with coefficients in R, $\cdot H^*(X, R)$ as $\cdot H^*(\mathrm{A})$ for any full R grating. $\cdot H^*(\mathrm{A})$ is essentially *the cohomology algebra obtained by compactifying X by adding a point* ∞ (87.4b). Since the singular cochain grating need not be full $H^*(SX, R)$ need not be isomorphic to $\cdot H^*(\mathrm{A})$ for any full grating A. Hence the qualifying, full, has been appended.

PROBLEM

11-3. If A is a full subgrating of the full grating E, and if ψ_1 and ψ_2 are injections of A into E, show $\psi_1^* = \psi_2^*$: $\cdot H^*(\mathrm{A}) \to \cdot H^*(\mathrm{E})$.

We indicate briefly how these ideas can be extended to cover merely closed supports, i.e., supports in P here.

The most general locally compact paracompact space $X = \bigcup X_\rho$ where X_ρ is denumerable at infinity, that is to say, is the union of a denumerable number of compact sets, and is both open and closed in X. The range of ρ is arbitrary. Since $H(X)$ will be a sum of $H(X_\rho)$ terms, therefore until the end of this section our spaces are understood to be locally compact, paracompact and denumerable at infinity. For such spaces a special denumerable open cover $\nu = \{v_i \mid \bar{v}_i \text{ compact, } \bar{v}_i \text{ meets at most } \bar{v}_{i-1}, \bar{v}_{i+1}\}$ exists (A) and in references below ν is assumed to be this cover. We motivate our procedure. On each $\bar{v}_i$, (1.2) to (1.8) hold. As will appear, we will be faced with the situation that we have a denumerable collection $\{b_i \mid \|b_i\| \subset \bar{v}_i\}$ in B and we should like to attach a single element to this collection.

Definition 1.10. An **admissible sequence** $\{a_i \mid a_i \in \mathrm{A}^m\}$ is a denumerable collection such that $\|a_i\|$ meets $\bar{v}_j$ for only a finite subset, π_j, of i values. In particular for $x \in \bar{v}_j$, $\Sigma\, xa_i = \Sigma_{\pi_j}\, xa_i \in x\mathrm{A}$. If no a in A satisfies $xa = \Sigma\, xa_i$ for all x, we define an ideal element $\check{a}$ by the property $x\check{a} = \Sigma\, xa_i$, and refer to $\check{a}$ as the **generalized sum** of the admissible sequence and write also $\check{a} \sim \Sigma\, a_i$. Define $\|\check{a}\|$ as $\{x \mid \Sigma\, xa_i \neq 0\}$. Strictly speaking $\check{a}$ is an equivalence class since $\check{a}$ and $\check{b}$ are identified if $\Sigma\, xa_i = \Sigma\, xb_i$ for all x. Furthermore

$$\check{a} - \check{c} \sim \Sigma_i\, a_i + \Sigma_i\, c_j$$

$$\check{a}\check{c} \sim \Sigma\, a_i\, \Sigma\, c_j$$

$$d\check{a} \sim \Sigma\, da_i$$

and $\|d\check{a}\| \subset \|\check{a}\|$ since $\|da_i\| \subset \|a_i\|$. Then $\check{\mathrm{A}} = \{\check{a}\}$ constitutes a grating called the **completion** of A. If every generalized sum $\check{a}$ is in A, then A is a **complete grating.**

PROBLEM

11-4. If $\{a_i\}$ is admissible and C is any compact set, $\|a_i\| \cap C \neq \varnothing$ for at most a finite number of i values.

Definition 1.11. A **complete full** R grating is a separated grating with *closed* supports which is P-full (81.22) and is R-simple.

Lemma 1.12. *If* A *is a complete full* R *grating, and if the separated grating,* E *has an identity* u*, then with* $R = \text{J}$ *or a field,* $\psi\colon \text{A} \to \text{A} \circ \text{E}$*, defined by* $a \to a \circ u$*, is an injection.*

The proof is like that of (1.7). Except for emphasis R is omitted below.

Let $\{X_\alpha\}$ designate the compact subsets of X ordered by inclusion. A cofinal denumerable collection is $Y_m = \bigcup_{j \leq m} \bar{v}_j$. By reason of (1.11) the cut homomorphism Y_t acts on $Y_s \text{A}$ to give $Y_t \text{A}$ when $s < t$. Designate this homomorphism by $p_s{}^t$. Then ${}^n\Sigma^- = \{Y_s \text{A}^n, p_s{}^t\}$.

Lemma 1.13. *Let* A *be an arbitrary grating over* X*. Define* B^m *as* $\underleftarrow{\text{L}}\,{}^m\Sigma^-$*. Then* $\text{B} = \oplus \text{B}^m$ *is a grating with closed supports and* $\text{B} = \check{\text{B}}$, (1.10).

The elements of B^m designate matched sequences and we indicate the correspondence by $\doteq$. Thus

$$b \doteq \{a_r \mid a_r \in Y_r \text{A}^m\} \in \text{B}^m. \text{ Define } \|b\| \text{ as } \bigcup \|a_r\|.$$

It is immediate that B is then a grating. Moreover $b = \{Y_r b \mid Y_r b \in Y_r \text{A}^m\}$.

We need only show $\check{\text{B}} \subset \text{B}$. Thus let $\check{b} = \Sigma\, b_i$ where $b_i \in \text{B}^m$. Then $b_i = \{Y_r b_i \mid Y_r b_i \in Y_r \text{A}^m\}$. Suppose $\|b_i\| \cap Y_r = \varnothing$ except when $i \in \pi_r$. Define $c_r = Y_r \Sigma_{\pi_r} b_i$. Evidently $\pi_s \subset \pi_r$ if $s < r$. Hence

$$Y_s c_r = Y_s Y_r \Sigma_{\pi_r} b_i = Y_s \Sigma_{\pi_r} b_i = Y_s \Sigma_{\pi_s} b_i = c_s.$$

Accordingly $\{c_r \mid c_r \in Y_r \text{A}^m\}$ determines an element b in B which can be identified with $\check{b}$ since $xb = x\Sigma\, b_i$ for every x. In particular if A is fine or full then B has a unit.

Lemma 1.14. *There is an injection* $i\colon \text{A} \to \dot{\text{A}}$*. If* B *is a subgrating of* A*, then* $i\text{B}$ *is a subgrating of* $\check{\text{B}}$*. If* A *is fine, so is* $\check{\text{A}}$.

We need only check the last statement. Let $\beta = \{b_i \mid i = 1, \ldots, N\}$ be a fine cover of X and let $\{e_i \mid i = 1, \ldots, N\}$ be the associated endomorphisms. We identify ia and a. Since only a finite number of sets $\|a\|$ meet b_i, if $\check{a} \sim \Sigma\, a_r$, $\|e_i\,\check{a}\| = \|\Sigma_{r\in\pi}\, e_i\, a_r\| \subset \bar{b}_i \cap \|\check{a}\|$. Also $\Sigma_i\, xe_i\check{a} \sim \Sigma_{i=1}^{i=N}\, xe_i\, \Sigma_{\pi_i(x)}\, a_r$ where $\pi_i(x)$ depends on x. Since $\bigcup_{i=1}^{i=N} \pi_i(x)$ is a finite set, $\Sigma\, xe_i\, \check{a} = x\check{a}$.

Theorem 1.15. *If* B *is a complete full subgrating of the complete full grating A, then H*(B) $\approx$ *H*(A).

Suppose $da \in$ B. Replace X by $\bar{v}_i$ and A by $\bar{v}_i$ A. Since $\bar{v}_i$ is compact $\bar{v}_i\,\mathrm{A} = \bar{v}_i\,{}^{\bullet}\mathrm{A}$ (where ${}^{\bullet}$A is the subgrating with compact supports). Then $\bar{v}_i\, da \in \bar{v}_i\,\mathrm{B}$ is equivalent to $\bar{v}_i\, da \in \bar{v}_i\,{}^{\bullet}\mathrm{B}$ where, if $a = \Sigma\, a_r$ and $\|a_r\| \cap \bar{v}_i \neq \varnothing$ for $r \in \pi$, then $a = \Sigma_\pi\, a_r$. Therefore by (1.6),

$$\bar{v}_i\, a + \bar{v}_i\, d\rho_i = \bar{v}_i\, b_i, \quad \bar{v}_i\, \rho_i \in \bar{v}_i\,\mathrm{A}, \quad \bar{v}_i\, b_i \in \bar{v}_i\,\mathrm{B}.$$

We find it more convenient to use fineness instead of fullness to bring the demonstration to a conclusion. However the interpretation of the denumerable collections of endomorphisms $\{e_i\}$ and $\{f_j\}$ below, as partial identities is transparent. For the fine cover $(v_i, \bigcup_{j\neq i}^{j=\infty} v_j = w_i)$ let e_i, f_i be the associated endomorphisms; i.e., $e_i + f_i$ is the dentity and $\|e_i\, a\| \subset \bar{v}_i \cap \|a\|$, $\|f_i\, a\| = \bar{w}_i \cap \|a\|$. Let $\dot{e}_i = e_i\, \Pi_{j=1}^{j=i-1} f_j$. Thus $\|e_i\, a\| \subset \bar{v}_i \cap \|a\|$ and $\Sigma\, x\dot{e}_i\, a = xa$. Hence

$$x\dot{e}_i\, a = x\dot{e}_i\, d\rho_i = x\dot{e}_i\, b_i.$$

Since $\|e_i\, \rho_i\| \cup \|b_i\| \subset \bar{v}_i$, we can define elements of A and of $\check{B}$ by

$$\rho = \Sigma\, \dot{e}_i\, \rho_i, \; b = \Sigma\, \dot{e}_i\, b_i$$

$$xa + x\, d\rho = xb.$$

In short $a + d\rho = b$. The lemma follows by (61.17).

Theorem 1.16. *If* A *and* B *are complete full gratings over a locally compact, paracompact space, then H*(A) $\approx$ *H*(B) *and hence the algebra $H(X)$ can be defined as H*(A).

The injections A $\rightarrow$ A $\circ$ B $\leftarrow$ B guaranteed by (1.11) operate as in (1.8).

We do not neglect lower gratings. In the infinite complex case compactness amounts to a finiteness requirement. Hence we should expect that closed supports are available for the upper or lower gratings provided the dual lower or upper gratings have compact supports.

Definition 1.17. Let $\cdot A$ be the Alexander R grating with compact supports where R is an integral domain. Define the lower grating (Čech grating of infinite chains) by

$$C_* = Hom(\cdot A, R) \tag{1.17a}$$

with the boundary homomorphism ∂ defined by $(\partial c)a = c\,da$ and $x \bar{\epsilon} \|c\|$ if for some $U(x)$, $ca = 0$ whenever $\|a\| \subset U(x)$.

Theorem 1.18. *C_* is a complete full R (lower) grating.*

We show first that $\|c\| \cap \|a\| = \phi$ entails $ca = 0$. By the compactness of $\|a\|$ and the definition of $\|c\|$, there is a finite cover $\{V_i \mid i = 1, \ldots, N, \bar{V}_i \text{ compact}\}$ of $\|c\|$ for which $ca' = 0$ when $\|a'\| \subset \bar{V}_i$. Choose $V_{N+1} \subset X - \|a\|$. Since $\cdot A$ is fine endomorphisms e_i of $\cdot A$ exist with $e_{N+1}a = 0$ and $ce_ia = 0$ so $ca = \Sigma\, ce_ia = 0$. In particular $\|c\| = \phi$ implies $c = 0$.

Accordingly if $\{c_i\}$ is admissible, $c_ia \neq 0$ for a finite set $i \in \Pi(a)$ at most. Define $\check{c}$ by $\check{c}a = \Sigma_{i\in\Pi(a)}\, c_ia$ whence $\check{c}$ is a member of the right hand side of (1.17a) and so is in C_*.

Let $\{U_i\}$ be a locally finite cover of X. By (86.3b) $\cdot A$ is P fine so the usual endomorphisms $\{e_i\}$ exist. Define e_jc by $(e_jc)a = ce_ja$ whence $\|e_jc\| \subset \bar{U}_j \cap \|c\|$ so C_* is P fine.

The Alexander cohomology ring can be obtained by taking direct limits of the cohomology rings for the nerves attached to a cofinal collection of covers whose elements are open or are compact. A natural question is: For what class of spaces does the nerve of some one cover suffice to determine the cohomology module? An answer is given in (2.3), and the proof presents certain independently interesting features whose development is correlated with that of spectral sequences. The modest Corollary (2.4) is the long overdue assurance that the cohomology modules of the space of a concrete simplicial star finite complex are those of the abstract complex.

2. SIMPLE COVERS **Definition 2.1.** In sections 2 and 3, $\omega = \{w_i\}$ is a covering of X by compact sets. As usual the nerve is written w and a simplex σ of w with vertices $\{(w_i) \mid i \in \pi\}$ is determined when $\bigcap_\pi w_i \neq \varnothing$. The **nucleus** of σ is defined by

$$|\sigma| = \bigcap_{i\in\pi} w_i. \tag{2.1a}$$

The support of σ is given by

$$\|\sigma\| = \bigcup_{i\in\pi} w_i. \tag{2.1b}$$

Write C for the lower graded R grating of the chains $\{c\}$ over w. The elementary chains are denoted by $\{r\sigma_p^i\}$. Let E refer to the grating of cochains over w with $\|f\| = \bigcup\{|\sigma| \mid f(\sigma) \neq 0\}$. We say C and E are **determined** by the cover ω and that they are **dual gratings.**

If E is the dual of C denote the generators of the elementary chains by $\{e_i^p\}$. Then the supports are defined by the condition that $\|e_i^p \otimes \sigma_q^j\| = \varnothing$ if σ_p^i, the dual of e_i^p in C, is not a face of σ_q^j. Thus in particular $q - p \geq 0$ is necessary for nontrivial supports. If σ_p^i is a face of σ_q^j then

$$\|e_i^p \otimes \sigma_q^j\| = \|e_i^p\| \cap \|\sigma_q^j\| = \|e_i^p\|. \tag{2.1b}$$

The locally finite compact cover, ω, is **simple** if $\bigcap w_i$ is either empty or acyclic with respect to full grating cohomology.

Definition 2.2. If A is an arbitrary grating over X, the tensor product $A \otimes C$ refers to $\{\Sigma\, a_i^p \otimes \sigma_q^j\}$ where the grade of $a^p \otimes \sigma_q$ is $q - p$.
The boundary operator is

$$d(a^p \otimes \sigma) = d_A\, a^p \otimes \sigma + (-1)^p\, a^p \otimes d_C \sigma \tag{2.2a}$$

where d_C reduces grades by 1. Supports are determined as usual by the condition that $xa^p \otimes x\sigma_q \neq 0$. The reduced grating is $A \circ C$.

Theorem 2.3. *Let ω be a simple cover of the locally compact space X. Then ${}^{\bullet}H(w, R) = {}^{\bullet}H(X, R)$ where w is the nerve of ω and the cochains on w are finite while those on X have compact support.*

Let E be the upper grating defined by ω in (2.1) and let A be the compact Alexander grating on X. Then by the Kunneth theorem the compact grating $A \circ E$ is R simple. A finite sub complex w_C is determined by the union of the finite collection of sets of ω that meet an arbitrarily assigned compact set C. Define $e^o \in E$ by $e^o(w_i) = 1$ for $(w_i) \in w_C$ and $e^o(w_i) = 0$ for $w_i \bar{\in} w_C$. Let $\{u^i\}$ be a partition of the identity in A, associated with the compact set C and the fine cover $\beta = \{b_i\}$. Then $\{u^i \circ e^o\}$ is a partition of the identity in $A \circ E$ associated with β and C. Hence $A \circ E$ is a full grating and so ${}^{\bullet}H(A \circ E) \approx {}^{\bullet}H(A)$. Let i be the inclusion homomorphism on $E \rightarrow A \circ E$ defined by

$$i\colon e \rightarrow u \circ e \tag{2.3a}$$

where u is a unit over $\|e\|$. The subscripts A and E go with d_A and d_E below.

The plan of our proof is the following. First we show that ${}^{\bullet}H_A(A \circ E) \approx {}^{\bullet}H_A^\circ(iE)$. This result enables us to show that if $z \in Z(A \circ E)$ then z is of the form $u \circ z_E$ where $z_E \in Z(E)$. Next if $b \in B(A \circ E)$, b is of the form $u \circ b_E$ with $b_E \in B(E)$. It then follows that the assertion of the theorem is an easy consequence under the correspondence $\langle u \circ z_E\rangle \leftrightarrow \langle z_E\rangle_E$.

The elementary cochains $\{e_i^r\}$ constitute a basis for E. The conditions of

(104.3) are met if we identify A and Re_i^r with C and A. Accordingly using $Re_i^r \approx R$ and (81.30),

$$H(\|\sigma_r^i\| (\mathrm{A} \circ Re_i^r)) \approx H(\|\sigma_r^i\| (\mathrm{A} \circ \mathrm{E}))$$

(2.3b) $$H_{\mathrm{A}}^o(\|\sigma_r^i\| (\mathrm{A} \circ Re_i^r)) \approx H_{\mathrm{A}}^o(\|\sigma_r^i\| \mathrm{A}) \otimes Re_i^r$$
$$\approx \|\sigma_r^i\| R\langle u\rangle_{\mathrm{A}} \otimes e_i^r \approx \|\sigma_r^i\| R\langle u\rangle_{\mathrm{A}}.$$

Only the module isomorphism is guaranteed by (104.3) in general but here, since $u^2 = u$, it is easy to see these are algebra isomorphisms. Since $\|e_i^r\| \subset \|\sigma_r^i\|$ *we can drop* $\|\sigma_r^i\|$. Thus (2.3b) with the factor $\|\sigma_r^i\|$ jettisoned establishes that $H_{\mathrm{A}}(\mathrm{A} \circ \mathrm{E}) \approx H_{\mathrm{A}}^o(i\mathrm{E})$. (The use of (104.3) can be avoided by showing directly that $\|\sigma_r^i\| \mathrm{A} \circ Re_i^r \approx \|\sigma_r^i\| \mathrm{A}$.)

Any homogeneous A cocycle of A ∘ E is of the form $\Sigma\, a_i^p \circ e_i^q$ where each term $a_i^p \circ e_i^q$ is a cocycle since $\{e_i^q\}$ constitute a basis. For $p > 0$ we have shown $\langle a_i^p \circ e_i^q\rangle = 0$ and for $p = 0$, $\langle a_i^o \circ e_i^q\rangle$ corresponds to $\langle u\rangle \circ re_i^q$ so $H_{\mathrm{A}}(\mathrm{A} \circ \mathrm{E}) \approx H_{\mathrm{A}}^o(i\mathrm{E})$. (This does not necessarily imply the abstract grating isomorphism $H_{\mathrm{A}}(\mathrm{A} \otimes \mathrm{E}) \approx H_{\mathrm{A}}^o(i\mathrm{E})$).

It will be observed that some circumlocution connected with the use of d_{A} and the consequent $H_{\mathrm{A}}(\ )$, is dissolved by the introduction of the following definition: For $h \in \mathrm{A} \circ \mathrm{E}$, the **filter degree** of h is the smallest p such that $h \in \Sigma_{i=0}^p \mathrm{A}^i \circ \mathrm{E}$. Thus if $h = a^1 \circ e^8 + a^5 \circ e^3$ then the filter degree is 5.

The following reasoning is instructive and is a specialization of a line of argument used in Chapter 16 where the notion of filter degree is extended to more general gratings than those of product type A ∘ E. Suppose first that the filter degree of h is 0 so $h \in \mathrm{A}^0 \circ \mathrm{E}$. Then $dh = d_{\mathrm{A}}\, h + d_{\mathrm{E}}\, h$ where $d_{\mathrm{A}}\, h \in \mathrm{A}^1 \circ \mathrm{E}$. Thus the filter degree of $d_{\mathrm{A}}\, h$ is 1 while that of $d_{\mathrm{E}}\, h$ is 0. In consequence if h is a cycle, i.e., $dh = 0$, then $d_{\mathrm{A}}\, h = 0$. Therefore by (2.3a), $h = u \circ e$. Then $dh = 0$ implies $u \circ de = 0$ and since i is a monomorphism, this requires $de = 0$. In short $h \in Z(\mathrm{A}^0 \circ \mathrm{E})$ implies $h = u \circ e$ for $e \in Z(\mathrm{E})$.

We proceed by induction. Thus suppose it is established that if z has filter degree inferior to p then $z \sim u \circ z_{\mathrm{E}}$ where $z_{\mathrm{E}} \in Z(\mathrm{E})$. Take z of filter degree p. Write $z = z_1 + z_2$ where z_1 is of filter degree at most $p - 1$ and $z_2 \in \mathrm{A}^p \circ \mathrm{E}$. Then $d_{\mathrm{A}}\, z_2 \in A^{p+1} \circ \mathrm{E}$, while $d_{\mathrm{E}}\, z_2 \in \mathrm{A}^p \circ \mathrm{E}$. Hence z a cocycle requires $d_{\mathrm{A}}\, z^2 = 0$ whence, since $p \geq 1$, $\langle z_2\rangle = 0$, or

(2.3c) $$z_2 = d_{\mathrm{A}}\, g = dg + (-1)^{p-1}\, d_{\mathrm{E}}\, g$$

where the filter degree of $d_{\mathrm{E}}\, g$ is $p - 1$. Hence

(2.3d) $$z = (h_1 + (-1)^{p-1}\, d_{\mathrm{E}}\, g) + dg.$$

The term $h_1 + (-1)^{p-1}\, d_{\mathrm{E}}\, g$ is covered by the induction hypotheses so $z \sim u \circ e$. Moreover $0 = dz \sim u \circ de$ whence by (2.3a), $e \in Z(\mathrm{E})$. Accordingly i is an epimorphism on $Z(\mathrm{E})$ to $Z(\mathrm{A} \circ \mathrm{E})$.

Suppose $\langle u \circ e \rangle = 0$. Then $u \circ e = dh = d_A h + d_E h$, where h is of filter degree p. Write $h = h_1 + h_2$ where h_1 has filter degree inferior to p_A and $h_2 \in A^p \circ {}_1E$. Since the filter degree of $u \circ e$ is plainly 0 and that of $d_A h_2$ is $p + 1$,

(2.3e) $$d_A h_2 = 0.$$

Then by (2.3b), if $p = 0$, $h = h_2 = u \circ \dot{e}$ so $u \circ e = u \circ d\dot{e}$ and, since i is a monomorphism,

(2.3f) $$e = d\dot{e}.$$

For $p > 0$, (2.3e) and (2.3b) yield

$$h_2 = d_A g = dg + (-1)^{p-1} d_E g$$

with $p - 1$ for the filter degree of g and of $d_E g$. Thus

$$u \circ e = d(h_1 + (-1)^{p-1} d_E g).$$

However $h_1 + (-1)^{p-1} d_E g$ is of filter degree $p - 1$. Hence by recurrence one establishes that $u \circ e = dt$ where t is of filter degree 0 and so falls under the first case treated. Thus (2.3f) holds for all p.

Corollary 2.4. *Let K be a star finite concrete simplicial complex. Then $H(K) \approx {}^{\bullet}H(|K|)$ for the finite cochain modules and algebras or $H(K) \approx H(|K|)$ for the infinite cochains.*

Let ω be the cover by closed stars of vertices in K. Then (2.4) follows from (73.1) and (2.3) for the case of finite cochains. The infinite cochain case comes under (1.15).

PROBLEM

11-5. Show in detail how to apply (1.15) to get results on infinite cochains in (2.4).

Corollary 2.5. *If K is a concrete simplicial complex, then there is a ring isomorphism of algebras*

$${}^{\bullet}H(|K|) \approx {}^{\bullet}H(SK).$$

Evidently $|K|$ is locally connected in all dimensions so (85.1) and (2.4) apply.

Our developments in the next section will seem more natural after a description of some permissible changes in supports for cochain gratings of the type described in (2.1). We assume always that X *is compact* and that E *is a cochain grating determined by* ω. Moreover covers are to be finite.

Definition 2.6. E is **normal** if there is a finite open cover $\nu = \{v_i\}$ such that for any closed set $Y \subset v_i$, YE is acyclic. This generalizes R simplicity.

Definition 2.7. If $\omega' = \{w_i'\}$ is a swelling of ω, (**A**), and the nerve $w = w'$ then the cochain grating E$'$ is said to be a swelling of the grating E determined by ω.

Lemma 2.8. *Let $\nu = \{v_i\}$ be an open swelling of ω. Then there is a swelling ω' of ω with $w_i' \subset v_i$ for all i, for which* E$'$ *is normal.*

Lemma 2.9. *If E is normal and is determined by ω, then for some swelling ω' the cut $(\bigcap_\pi \omega_i')$E is acyclic for all π.*

Theorem 2.10. *If* E$'$ *is determined by ω' and* E *by ω so that $(\bigcap_\pi w_i')$E is acyclic for any π, then $H(\mathrm{E} \circ \mathrm{E}') \approx H(\mathrm{E}')$.*

Corollary 2.11. *If* E$'$ *is a swelling of* E, *then $^{\bullet}H(\mathrm{E}) \approx {}^{\bullet}H(\mathrm{E}')$.*

PROBLEM

11-5. Demonstrate (2.10) and (2.11).

In a sense the definition of swelling is too restricted as the following easy lemma shows.

Lemma 2.12. *Let* A *and* A$'$ *be separated gratings on the same space X where the elements of* A$'$ *are those of* A *but with smaller supports. Let* E *be a full grating on X. If*

$$\Sigma_\pi e_i \circ a_i = d\,\Sigma_\rho e_j \circ b_j \tag{2.12a}$$

in $\mathrm{E} \circ \mathrm{A}$ *where a_i and b_i are in* A *then*

$$\Sigma_\pi e_i \circ a_i' = d\,\Sigma_\rho e_j \circ b_j' \tag{2.12b}$$

in $\mathrm{E} \circ \mathrm{A}'$ *where a_i', b_j' are the correspondents of a_i, b_j.*

Some of the terms in (2.12a) may of course be 0.

We return to the question of existence of fixed points. The significance of this problem may be even more readily conceded if it is recognized as closely linked to the existence of zeros of an equation in a linear space or even on an Abelian group. Thus the solution of $\psi(x) = x$ is the same as $\theta(x) = 0$ where $\theta(x) = \psi(x) - x$. Our interest now is in the distribution of fixed points. For a suitable class of spaces we shall develop a fixed point index for ψ relative to an open set X_0. This is an integer whose nonvanishing guarantees the existence of a fixed point in X_0. When $X_0 = X$, this index will coincide with the Lefschetz number.

There are various ways of introducing such an index. On the logical side the preferred formulation would be in terms of axioms prescribing sufficient properties to determine the index uniquely. We choose a constructive definition in terms of gratings. This has advantages for applications. The march of ideas is direct and intuitive, but there are a number of details to adjust and this makes for lengthy exposition. One other point needs to be made. Our spaces will be compact. In the case of linear spaces extension to noncompact cases is possible. One can use the index provided the maps introduce compactness, for instance the maps may be required to be completely continuous. However the extension of the notion of degree has been more effective.

We shall tacitly assume X is connected except when this requirement is waived explicitly. Moreover we shall assume throughout this section that R is either J or Q. We may write $\mathrm{E}(\omega)$ to bring out that E is determined by ω.

3. FIXED POINT INDEX **Lemma 3.1.** *If* A *is a full R grating and* E *is a torsion free R simple grating with an identity* $^\circ e$ *and if* ψ *is a proper map of X into X then* $\mathrm{A} \circ \psi(\mathrm{E})$ *is full.*

Observe $\mathrm{B} = \psi(\mathrm{E})$ is R simple, torsion free and admits an identity. The Kunneth theorem shows $H(x(\mathrm{A} \circ \mathrm{B})) \approx R$. The partition of the identity associated with the compact set X_0 and the fine cover $\beta = \{b_i\}$ is given by $\{u^i \circ {}^\circ e\}$, where $\{u^i\}$ is the partition for $X_0 \subset X$.

Lemma 3.2. *Let* ω *be a finite simple cover of (the compact space)* X. *Let* A *and* C *be the dual gratings determined by* ω, (2.1). *Then* $H_*(\mathrm{C}) \approx H_*(\mathrm{A} \circ \mathrm{C})$.

The homomorphism $\mathrm{C} \xrightarrow{i} \mathrm{A} \circ \mathrm{C}$ is defined by $c \xrightarrow{i} u \circ c$, where u is the identity or at least the identity over $\|c\|$. An argument like that in (111.7) shows i is a monomorphism. The boundary operator is $d = d_{\mathrm{A}} + d_{\mathrm{C}}$ with

$$d(a^p \circ c) = d_{\mathrm{A}}\, a^p \circ c + (-1)^p\, a^p \circ d_{\mathrm{C}}\, c$$

where d_C decreases the grade. Thus $\{K_q^p = \mathrm{A}^p \circ \mathrm{C}_q\}$ is a mixed complex. The total grade of K_q^p is $q - p$ (2.2) so d is of degree -1. Note too, $\langle a^p \circ C_q \rangle_{\mathrm{A}}$ is an element of $H_{\mathrm{A}}^p(\mathrm{A} \circ \mathrm{C})$ and in particular $\langle u \circ c \rangle_{\mathrm{A}} \in H_{\mathrm{A}}^\circ(\mathrm{A} \circ \mathrm{C})$. Since the proof of (2.3) at no stage depends on the degree of d or of d_{E} that proof carries over bodily with C replacing E so that σ_r^i is written in place of e_i^r and d_C instead of d_E.

We now make an important observation that we avail ourselves of in (3.7) for instance. Let E be the upper grating determined by the simple cover ω of X and let E_1 be a subgrating whose supports cover X. Suppose Σf_i° summed over all of the basis elements of 0 grade in E_1 is a unit of E_1. Let C_1 be the lower grating generated by the dual basis $\{\sigma_r^i\}$ to that of E_1. Thus C_1 is a subgrating of C. We refer to E_1 and C_1 as **admissible subgratings** determined by ω. *Evidently both* (3.1) *and* (3.2) *retain their validity when* E_1 *and* C_1 *replace* E *and* C.

Definition 3.3. The space X is omology **smooth** or simply **smooth** or **convexoid** if it is compact and admits a family, Q, referred to as a **smooth family**, consisting of compact sets which together with their finite intersections are acyclic (or void) and such that for every $x \in X$ and open set $V \supset x$, there is an open set N and a finite union U_π of sets of Q satisfying $x \subset N \subset U_\pi \subset V$. An application of (2.3) establishes that a smooth space is locally connected in the strong sense that U_π above can be assumed a closed acyclic set.

Remark. More general smooth spaces can be defined by dropping the compactness restriction. Furthermore, we may express the main idea of (3.3) as the requirement that every open cover admit a refining simple cover F or more generally the refining cover need merely be a closed cover satisfying the restrictions that its elements and their intersections if not null are to be acyclic and that the last condition in (3.3) is to be met.

We suppose in the next sections that X *is compact and smooth with smooth family* Q *and that* Y *is a closed subset.* Suppose ψ is a proper self map of X. Denote by F the fixed point set $\{x \mid \psi(x) = x\}$. We shall use E and C for the cochain and chain gratings on the nerve w of a finite cover $\omega = \{b_i \mid b_i \in Q\}$ and u_Y for a partial identity on Y. Let $\Gamma(\psi) = \Sigma\, i(p)(\psi^{\#} f_i^p) \circ \sigma_p^i$ be the graph of the chain map $\psi_{\#}$ or $\psi^{\#}$ (81.12b). This is a zero cycle (64.15). Every simple cover in this section has its sets in some smooth family.

Lemma 3.4. *There is a simple finite cover* $\omega = \{b_i\}$ *satisfying*

(3.4a) $$Y \cap \bigcup \psi^{-1}(b_i) \cap b_i = \varnothing \Leftrightarrow F \cap Y = \varnothing .$$

The direct assertion is obvious. For the sufficiency aspect let $\alpha = \{a_i\}$ be a smooth family and write

(3.4b) $$b_\pi = \bigcup_{i \in \pi} a_i .$$

For each $x \in X$ choose $b_\pi(x) \in \{b_\pi\}$ to satisfy $x \subset N \subset b_\pi(x)$ for some open set N and also

(3.4c) $$b_\pi(x) \cap Y = \varnothing, \quad x \in Y^\sim, \qquad \psi^{-1}(b_\pi(x)) \cap b_\pi(x) = \varnothing, \quad x \in Y.$$

Compactness guarantees the existence of a finite subcover of X, $\{b_{\pi(j)} \mid j = 1, \ldots, M\}$. Denote any set a_i of (3.46) entering the collection $\{b_{\pi(j)}\}$ by b_i Then, according to (3.4c), either $b_i \cap Y = \varnothing$ or $\psi^{-1}(b_i) \cap b_i = \varnothing$ which ensures (3.4a).

Suppose $\{b_i\}$ and $\{'b_i\}$ are collections of sets with $\bigcap_\pi {'b_i} \neq \varnothing$ and $b_i \cap {'b_i} = \varnothing$. Then surely $\bigcap_\pi {'b_i} \cap b_j = \varnothing$, $j \in \pi$ whence $(\bigcap_\pi {'b_i}) \cap \bigcap_\pi b_j = \varnothing$. Since f_i^p and σ_r^i are elementary, the supports in E and C are defined by

$$\|f_i^p\| = \bigcap_\pi b_j \neq \varnothing$$

$$\|\sigma_p^i\| = \bigcup_\pi b_j$$

for suitable π. Hence writing $'b_j$ for $\|u_Y\| \cap \psi^{-1}(b_j)$, it appears that

(3.4d) $$\|du_Y\| \cap \bigcup \psi^{-1} \|f_i^p\| \cap \|\sigma_p^i\| = \varnothing$$

follows from

(3.4e) $$\|du_Y\| \cap \bigcup \psi^{-1}(b_i) \cap b_i = \varnothing.$$

Lemma 3.5. *When the partial identity u_Y satisfies*

(3.5a) $$\|du_Y\| \cap F = \varnothing$$

then, for a suitable finite simple cover $\omega = \{b_i\}$,

(3.5b) $$P(\psi, Y, u_Y, \omega) = u_Y \circ \Sigma\, i(p)\psi^{\#}(\ {}_i^p) \circ \sigma_p^i$$

is a 0 degree cycle of $\mathrm{A} \circ \psi^{\#}$ $\mathrm{E} \circ \mathrm{C}$ which under the correspondence $\mathrm{C} \leftrightarrow \mathrm{A} \circ \psi^{\#}$ $\mathrm{E} \circ \mathrm{C}$, (3.2), determines the 0 cycle $\Lambda(\psi, Y, u_Y, \omega)c_0$, where $\Lambda \in R$ and $\langle c_0 \rangle$ is the generator of $H_0(\mathrm{C})$.

Thus according to (3.4a) and (3.4d)

$$\|dP\| = \|du_Y\| \cap \bigcup \psi^{-1} \|f_i^p\| \cap \|\sigma_p^i\| = \varnothing$$

with $\|du_Y\|$ replacing Y. Since $\Sigma\, i(p)\, \psi^{\#} f_i^p \circ c_p^i$ is a zero cycle, (64.15), $dP = du_Y \circ \Gamma(\psi^{\#})$. Then (3.2) establishes the last assertion

(3.5c) $$P(\psi, Y, u_Y, \omega) \to \Lambda(\psi, Y, u_Y, \omega)c_0.$$

Definition 3.6. Define the Lefschetz number $L(\psi, \omega)$ as the coefficient Λ in (3.5) for $P(\psi, X, \omega)$ i.e.,

$$L(\psi, \omega)c_0 \leftarrow \Sigma\, i(p)\psi^{\#}(f_i^p) \circ \sigma_p^i.$$

Lemma 3.7. *If ${}_1\omega$ and ${}_2\omega$ are simple covers then*

$${}_1\Lambda = \Lambda(\psi, Y, {}_1\omega) = \Lambda(\psi, Y, {}_2\omega) = {}_2\Lambda.$$

Suppose first that ${}_1\omega$ and ${}_2\omega$ are covers in the *same* smooth family (3.3). Let E_i be the grating of finite cochains on w_i with elements $\{{}_i f_j^p, i = 1, 2\}$.

A basis for $E_1 \circ E_2$ is then $\{{}_1f_i^p \circ {}_2f_j^q\}$ with supports determined by

$$\|{}_1f_i^p \circ {}_2f_j^q\| = \|{}_1f_i^p\| \cap \|{}_2f_j^q\|.$$

Reversing the usual order we determine the chains as the duals of the cochains and obtain the chain grating ${}_{12}C$ with a basis $\{c_{p,q}^{i,j}\}$ where

$$({}_1f_i^p \circ {}_2f_j^q)(c_{m,n}^{r,s}) = \delta_i^r\, \delta_j^s\, \delta_m^p\, \delta_n^q,$$

and supports are

(3.7a) $$\|c_{p,q}^{i,j}\| = \|{}_1c_p^i\| \cap \|{}_2c_q^j\|$$

where $\{{}_rc_p^i\}$ constitutes the dual basis to $\{{}_rf_i^p,\ r = 1, 2\}$. Construct a chain grating ${}_3C = \{e_{p,q}^{i,j}\}$ where

(3.7b) $$c_{p,q}^{i,j} \leftrightarrow e_{p,q}^{i,j}$$

whence d on ${}_3C \to {}_3C$ is defined. Assign the supports

(3.7c) $$\|e_{p,q}^{i,j}\| = \|{}_1c_p^i\|.$$

Since supports are not increased (3.7c), there is defined an allowable homomorphism, h, on the chain grating ${}_3C$ to ${}_{12}C$. From

$$\|du_Y\| \cap \psi^{-1}\, \|{}_1f_i^0\| \cap \|{}_1c_0^i\| = \varnothing$$

it follows that

$$\|du_Y\| \cap \psi^{-1}\, \|{}_1f_i^0 \circ {}_2f_j^0\| \cap \|{}_1c_0^i\| = \varnothing.$$

Therefore

(3.7d) $$u_Y \circ \Sigma\, i(p + q)\psi^{\#}({}_1f_i^p \circ {}_2f_j^q) \circ e_{p,q}^{i,j}$$

is a cycle of $A \circ \psi^{\#}({}_{12}E) \circ {}_3C$ and hence, (cf. (3.1) and (3.2)), corresponds to a cycle, ${}_3P$, of ${}_3C$ which we write

(3.7e) $${}_3P \to {}_3\Lambda\, e_{0,0}^{i,j}$$

for an arbitrary choice of ij (since $e_{0,0}^{i,j} \sim e_{0,0}^{r,s}$ because X is connected). Clearly

$${}_{12}P = u_Y \circ \Sigma\, i(p + q)\psi^{\#}(f_i^p \circ f_j^q) \circ c_{p,q}^{i,j}$$

corresponds to ${}_{12}\Lambda(\psi, Y, {}_1\omega, {}_2\omega)c_{0,0}^{i,j}$. Algebraically ${}_{12}C$ and ${}_3C$ differ only in the substitution of e for c whence

$${}_{12}P \sim u_Y \circ {}_3\Lambda\, c_{0,0}^{i,j}.$$

However

$${}_{12}P \sim u_Y \circ {}_{12}\Lambda\, c_{0,0}^{i,j}$$

so

(3.7f) $${}_{12}\Lambda = {}_3\Lambda.$$

Define the homomorphism on ${}_3\mathrm{C}$ to ${}_1\mathrm{C}$ by

$$(3.7\text{g}) \qquad t\colon e^{i,j}_{p,q} = {}_1c^i_p \quad \text{for } q = 0$$
$$= 0 \qquad \text{for } q \neq 0.$$

To establish that t is allowable remark first that supports are not increased. Next note only elementary chains with $q = 0$ or 1 need be considered since even after the intervention of the ∂ operator, chains with $q > 1$ are annihilated by t. Thus

$$\partial t e^{i,j}_{p,0} = \partial\, {}_1c^i_p = \Sigma\, {}_1\eta^i_r(p)\, {}_1c^r_{p-1}.$$

The definition of $e^{i,j}_{p,q}$ implies that

$$(3.7\text{h}) \qquad \partial e^{i,j}_{p,q} = \Sigma\, {}_1\eta^i_r(p)\, e^{r,j}_{p-1,q} + (-1)^p\, {}_2\eta^j_s(q) e^{i,s}_{p,q-1}$$

or

$$\partial e^{i,j}_{p,0} = \Sigma\, {}_1\eta^i_r(p) e^{r,j}_{p-1,0}$$

so

$$t\, \partial e^{i,j}_{p,0} = \Sigma\, {}_1\eta^i_r(p)\, {}_1c^r_{p-1} = \partial t e^{i,j}_{p,0}.$$

The existence of the identity cocycle

$$(3.7\text{i}) \qquad u = \Sigma_r\, {}_2f^0_r$$

implies $du = 0 = \Sigma_{i,r}\, {}_2\eta^i_r\,(1)\, {}_2f^1_i$ or $\Sigma_r\, {}_2\eta^i_r(1) = 0$. Note $\partial t e^{i,j}_{p,1} = 0$. Therefore from (3.7h)

$$t\, \partial e^{i,j}_{p,1} = (-1)^p\, \Sigma_r\, {}_2\eta^j_r(1) c^i_p$$
$$= 0.$$

Accordingly from (3.7e).

$$t\, {}_3P \sim t\, {}_3\Lambda e^{i,j}_{0,0} = {}_3\Lambda\, {}_1c^i_0.$$

Write v for $\psi^{\#}\, u$ (3.7i). Therefore, since $\psi^{\#}({}_1f^p_i \circ {}_2f^0_j) = \psi^{\#}\, {}_1f^p_i \circ \psi^{\#}\, {}_2f^0_j$, there results

$$\Sigma_j\, \psi^{\#}({}_1f^p_i \circ {}_2f^0_j) = \psi^{\#}\, {}_1f^p_i \circ v$$

Happily t ignores the possible contributions of ${}_2f^q_j$ for $q > 0$ so

$$t\, {}_3P = u_Y \circ \Sigma_{i,j}\, i(p) \psi^{\#}\, {}_1f^p_i \circ \psi^{\#}\, {}_2f^0_j \circ {}_1c^i_p$$
$$= u_Y \circ \Sigma_i\, i(p) \psi^{\#}\, {}_1f^p_i \circ v \circ {}_1c^i_p.$$

The homomorphism defined by

$$a \circ \psi^{\#}\, {}_1f^p_i \to a \circ \psi^{\#}\, {}_1f^p_i \circ v, \qquad a \in \mathrm{A},$$

induces a monomorphism of the full grating $\mathrm{A} \circ \psi^{\#}(\mathrm{E}_i)$ into the full grating $\mathrm{A} \circ \psi^{\#}(\mathrm{E}_1 \circ \mathrm{E}_2)$ (3.1). Hence in view of (3.2)

$$(3.7\text{j}) \qquad t\, {}_3P \sim {}_1\Lambda\, {}_1c^i_0.$$

In short by (3.7f) and the interchangeability of ω_1 and ω_2

(3.7k) $$_{12}\Lambda = {}_1\Lambda.$$

Suppose now that $_1$E and $_1$C refer to admissible *sub*gratings determined by ω_1 (cf. Remark after (3.2)). The argument just concluded is unaffected. Again $_1\Lambda = {}_2\Lambda$ $(= {}_{12}\Lambda)$. This states the important conclusion that if the index i in the summation (3.5b) is restricted to elements f_i^h (or σ_p^i) in the admissible subgrating then Λ is *unchanged*. Our lemma is therefore valid when ω_1 and ω_2 are in the same family.

Write ω for $_2\omega$. Suppose $_1\omega$ and ω belong to *different* smooth families. By (3.7j) $_1\omega$ can be supposed to refine ω. Let p be the projection of $_1\omega$ into ω. Thus $p\,{}_1b_k = b_r$ if $_1b_k \subset b_r$. We may suppose ω expanded to ω^+ by the addition of replicas of its sets so that in reordering, if necessary, we can attain $p\,{}_1b_k = b_k$. That is to say the same set of ω may enter $\{b_k\}$ with several different indices. Denote nerves by $_1w$ and by w^+ respectively. The simplex $_1\sigma$ with vertices $\{({}_1b_k) \mid k \in \pi\}$ corresponds under p to a simplex σ' with vertices $\{(b_k) \mid k \in \pi\}$. Hence $_1w$ has as isomorph w' a subcomplex of w^+.

The simplicial lower gratings $_1$C and C$'$ on $_1w$ and on w' are therefore isomorphic as abstract gratings. The difference is in the supports (2.1) attached to $_1\sigma$ and to its correspondent σ' using $_1\omega$ and ω'. Let $_1$E be the upper grating determined by $_1\omega$, and let A be the Alexander grating. Then $\mathrm{A} \circ \psi^{\#}\,{}_1\mathrm{E}$ is a full grating (3.1). Hence according to (2.12) if the cycle

(3.7l) $$u_Y \circ \Sigma\, \psi^{\#}\,{}_1f \circ {}_1\sigma \sim \Lambda\, {}_1\sigma_0$$

then

(3.7m) $$u_Y \circ \Sigma\, \psi^{\#}\,{}_1f \circ \sigma' \sim \Lambda \sigma_0'.$$

Note Λ is the same in the two homologies.

Let E$'$ be the dual grating to C$'$. Then E$'$ and $_1$E are abstractly isomorphic and differ only in their supports. Let v and v' be the units of $\mathrm{A} \circ \psi\,{}_1\mathrm{E}$ and of $\mathrm{A} \circ \psi\mathrm{E}'$ respectively. Let j and j' take $c' \in \mathrm{C}'$ into $v \circ c'$ and into $v' \circ c'$ just as in (2.3a). Let P be the homomorphism on $\mathrm{A} \circ \psi^{\#}\mathrm{E}'$ to $\mathrm{A} \circ \psi^{\#}\,{}_1\mathrm{E}$ induced by p. The diagram below is commutative.

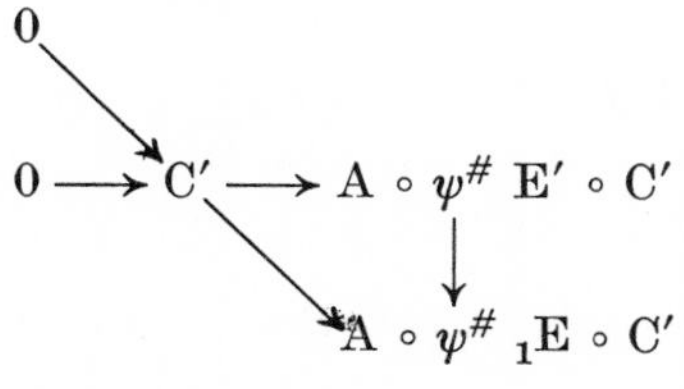

In particular $(P \otimes 1)j\,c' = j'\,c'$. Therefore

$$u_Y \circ \Sigma\, \psi^{\#}{}_1f \circ \sigma' \sim \Lambda c' \sim u_Y \circ \Sigma\, \psi^{\#} f' \circ \sigma'.$$

The gratings E and C determined by ω can be viewed as admissible subgratings determined by ω^+. Similarly E′ and C′ are admissible subgratings determined by ω^+. We have already shown in the course of the proof of (3.7) that Λ is the same computed for gratings determined by ω^+ and for their admissible subgratings. Accordingly (3.7) is valid when ${}_1\omega$ and ${}_2\omega$ belong to *arbitrary* smooth families.

Theorem 3.8. *Let γ and Γ be the graphs induced by the identity map and by ψ on the nerve of a simple cover ω. Then the Kronecker index $In(\Gamma, \gamma) = \Lambda(\psi, X, \omega) = L(\psi, \omega)$.*

Fix a simple cover, ω, whose sets are in the smooth family Q and construct E. Let $\{{}_1c_p^i\}$ be a new basis for the chains over E and let $\{{}_1f_i^p\}$ be the dual basis for the cochains determined as usual by ${}_1f_i^p\, {}_1c_p^j = \delta_i^j\, i(-p)$. Then

(3.8a)
$$ {}_1c_p^j = \Sigma\, a_r^j(p) c_p^r, \qquad {}_1f_i^p = \Sigma\, b_i^r(p) f_r^p. $$

where $\mathbf{A}(p) = (a_i^j(p))$ is a unimodular matrix and $\mathbf{B}(p) = (b_i^j(p))$ is $i(-p)$ $\mathbf{A}(p)^{-1}$. Since $\psi^{\#}$ is *linear*,

(3.8b)
$$ \Gamma(\psi, \omega) = u \circ \Sigma\, i(p)\psi^{\#}({}_1f_i^p) \circ {}_1c_p^i = u \circ \Sigma\, i(p) b_i^r(p) a_s^i\, \psi^{\#}(f_r^p) \circ c_p^s = u \circ \Sigma\, i(p)\psi^{\#}(f_r^p) \circ c_p^r. $$

The basis $\{{}_1c_p^i\}$ can be partitioned into the collections (32.5)

$$ \{\rho_p^m\}, \qquad \{j_p^m\} \text{ and } \{b_p^m\} \text{ where } \partial j_p^m = t_{p-1}^m\, b_{p-1}^m $$

with t_{p-1}^m the torsion coefficient and ρ_p^m the basis for the nonbounding cycles. The dual basis is then $\{F_m^p\}$, $\{B_m^p\}$ and $\{J_m^p\}$ with $\{F_m^p\}$ the basis for the nonbounding cocycles and $dJ_m^{p-1} = t_{p-1}^m\, B_m^p$.

(3.8c)
$$ \Gamma(\psi, \omega) = u \circ \Sigma\, i(p)\psi^{\#}(F_i^p) \circ c_p^i + u \circ \Sigma\, i(p)\psi^{\#}(B_m^p) \circ j_p^m + u \circ \Sigma\, i(p-1)\psi^{\#}(J_m^{p-1}) \circ b_{p-1}^m. $$

Since $\psi^{\#}$ is allowable

$$ i(p)\, d\psi^{\#}(J_m^{p-1}) \circ j_p^m = i(p) t_{p-1}^m\, \psi^{\#}(B_m^p) \circ j_p^m. $$

Moreover

$$ i(p-1)\psi^{\#}(J_m^{p-1}) \circ dj_p^m = i(p-1)\, t_{p-1}^m\, \psi^{\#}(J_m^{p-1}) \circ b_{p-1}^m. $$

Since $i(p)i(p-1) = (-1)^{p-1}$, when $R = \mathrm{Q}$, the contribution of the last two sums in (3.8c) is,

$$ d\left(u \circ \frac{1}{t_{p-1}^m}\, i(p)\psi^{\#}(J_m^{p-1}) \circ j_p^m\right). $$

Accordingly $\Gamma(\psi, \omega) = u \circ \Gamma'(\psi, \omega)$ where $\Gamma'(\psi, \omega) = i(p)\psi^{\#}(F_i^p) \circ \rho_p^i$ in $A \circ \psi^{\#}(E) \circ C$ and hence by (3.7)

$$\Gamma'(\psi, \omega) = L(\psi, \omega)v^0 \circ \sigma_0' \tag{3.8d}$$

in $E \circ C$ with $v^0 = \Sigma_j f_j$ the unit of E and σ_0' an arbitrary vertex.

We proceed to a more convenient form for $L(\psi)$. Note then that for X a smooth space, (3.8d) amounts to replacing cocycles $\{F_i^p\}$ and cycles $\{\rho_p^i\}$ by the generators of the omology groups of w and $\psi^{\#}$ can be replaced by ψ^*. By (2.3) these can be identified with the groups of X. Let

$$\psi^* \mathbf{F}_i^h = \Sigma_j a_i^j(p)\mathbf{F}_j^p. \tag{3.8e}$$

It is natural to define the dual of $E \circ C$ as $C \circ F$ since E and C are duals. Accordingly the Kronecker index of both sides of (3.8d) with respect to $\gamma = \Sigma_{j,p} i(-p),\ \rho_r^j \circ F_j^p$ must be the same by obvious extension of (72.4). Specifically taking account of (3.8d) and (3.8e)

$$\begin{aligned}
\mathrm{In}(\Gamma(\psi, \omega), \gamma) &= \Sigma_p \Sigma_j\, i(p)i(-p)(\psi^{\#}(F_k^p)(\rho_p^k))F_j^p(\rho_p^j) \\
&= \Sigma\, (-1)^p\, a_j^j(p) \\
&= L(\psi, \omega) In(v^0 \circ \sigma_0', \gamma) \\
&= L(\psi, \omega)\, \Sigma_j\, v^0(\sigma_0^j) \cdot F_j^0(\sigma_0'), \\
&= L(\psi, \omega).
\end{aligned}$$

In view of (2.2) this result is independent of ω.

Lemma 3.9. *Let ψ be a proper self map of X and let Y, V be a compact set and a containing open set respectively such that $F \cap (V - Y) = \varnothing$. If u_Y and $'u_Y$ are two identities associated with Y, V then for some ω taken from Q*

$$\Lambda = \Lambda(\psi, Y; u_Y, \omega) = \Lambda(\psi, Y, 'u_Y, \omega) = '\Lambda.$$

This is an easy application of (3.4).

Lemma 3.10. *Let G be an open set containing no fixed point of ψ on its boundary. For a residual collection of open sets $\{V_\alpha\}$ containing $\bar{G}$ where $\alpha < \alpha' \Leftrightarrow V_{\alpha'} \subset V_\alpha$, $\Lambda_\alpha = \Lambda(\psi, \bar{G}, u(\alpha), \omega)$ is invariant, when $u(\alpha)$ is any partial identity associated with $\bar{G}$ and V_α.*

The fixed point set, F, is compact and hence $F \cap \dot{G} = \varnothing$ implies $F \cap W = \varnothing$ where W is an open set containing $\dot{G}$. Let $\bar{G} \subset V_\alpha \subset \bar{V}_\alpha \subset W \cup G$. Then $F \cap \dot{V}_\alpha = \varnothing$. Let $u(\alpha)$ be the partial identity associated with $\bar{G}$ and V_α. Hence $\|du(\alpha)\| \cap F = \varnothing$. Choose ω to satisfy (3.4a) with $Y = \bar{G}$. Then with this simple cover or any refinement, $\Lambda(\psi, \bar{G}, u(\alpha), \omega)$ is defined, (3.5). Moreover by (3.9) the value is independent of α.

Definition 3.11. The common value of Λ_α in (3.10) is denoted by $\Lambda(\psi, G)$ and is called the **index**. If $F \cap V$ is the fixed point set in the closure of V then $\Lambda(F \cap V)$ is sometimes written for $\Lambda(\psi, V)$ and is termed the **index** of $F \cap V$. In particular if $F \cap V = \bar{x}$ we refer to the *index of* $\bar{x}$.

Theorem 3.12. *If $\psi_1 \simeq \psi_2$ and during the homotopy no fixed points enter the boundary of G, then $\Lambda(\psi_1, G) = \Lambda(\psi_2, G)$.*

Fix t as t_0. If $\omega = \{w_i \mid I\}$ let $\nu_{t_0} = \{\psi_{t_0}^{-1}(\psi_{t_0}(X) \cap w_i) = v_i\}$. It is possible that $v_i = \varnothing$ for some i values. The nerve of ν is isomorphic to that of the cover of $\psi_{t_0}(X)$ by ω and hence ν_t is a simple cover. We can assume ω sufficiently fine so that $\Lambda(\psi_{t_0}, \bar{G}, u_\alpha, \omega) = \Lambda(\psi_{t_0}, G)$ for some u_α. Thus referring to the demonstration of (3.4)

$$\|du_Y\| \cap \textstyle\bigcap_{\pi(j)} v_i \cap \bigcup_{\pi(j)} w_k = \varnothing$$

where $\pi_{(j)}$ is a collection of $m + 1$ distinct scripts in I for which

$$\varnothing \neq \textstyle\bigcap_{\pi(j)} v_i = \psi_{t_0}^{-1} \| f_j^m \|.$$

We swell ν_t to an open cover $\{U_i\}$. This cover is swelled to a closed cover ν' which in turn is swelled to an open cover $\{W_i\}$. Thus $v_i \subset U_i \subset v_i' \subset W_i$. Then ν' determines a swelling of $\psi^{\#}(\mathrm{E})$. The sets U_i and W_i can be chosen so that

$$\text{(3.12a)} \qquad \|du_Y\| \cap \textstyle\bigcap_{\pi(i)}^m W_i \cap \bigcup_{\pi(j)}^m w_k = \varnothing.$$

Let E' be a cochain grating determined by ν' with elements $\{F_j^m\}$. Thus $\|F_j^m\| = \bigcap_{\pi(j)}^m v_i'$. Clearly E' is a swelling of $\psi^{\#}(\mathrm{E})$. According to (3.12a) $u_Y \circ \Sigma\, F_j^m \circ \sigma_m^j$ is a zero cycle and is therefore equivalent to a cycle λc_0 in $C(3.5)$. From (2.11) follows that $\lambda = \Lambda(\psi_{t_0}, G)$. There is an open t interval Δt_0 such that $\psi_t^{-1}(\psi_t(X) \cap w_i) \subset W_i$ for all $t \in \Delta_{t_0}$. Hence $\Lambda(\psi_t, G) = \Lambda(\psi_t, G)$, for $t \in \Delta_{t_0}$. Plate the unit t interval with a finite number of open intervals Δ_{t_i} on each of which Λ is constant.

Let the homotopy be given by $h: X \times I \to X$. Since $\bar{G}$ is compact, all fixed points of h lie in the complement of $W \times I$ where W is an open neighborhood of $\dot{G}$.

From now on X and Y are understood to be compact smooth spaces with G an open subset. The cochains are written f_i^r and F_j^w respectively, and the elementary chains σ and e. For the next few propositions we deal with ψ: $W \to X$ where $W \subset X \times Y$ and is closed. Then F_x shall denote in this part $\{(x, y) \mid x = \psi(x, y)\}$.

Lemma 3.13. *Let X and Y be smooth spaces. Let V be a neighborhood of F. For some simple cover* ω *of X*

(3.13a) $$\bigcup \psi^{-1} \|f_i^p\| \cap (\|\sigma_p^i\| \times Y) \subset V.$$

PROBLEM

11-6. Show this.

Theorem 3.14. *Let X and Y be smooth and let* ψ *and* Θ *map the closed set A in* $X \times Y$ *into X and into Y respectively. Suppose G is open in* $X \times Y$*. Then* $\Lambda(x \times y = \psi(x, y) \times \Theta(x, y) \cap G)$ *is unchanged if* Θ' *replaces* Θ *where* Θ' *agrees with* Θ *on* $\bar{G} \cap F_x$.

Thus for suitable finite covers ω_1 and ω_2 chosen from the smooth families on X and on Y,

(3.14a) $$\Lambda(G) \leftarrow \Sigma\, i(p + q)\, u_G \circ \Theta^{\#}(F_j^q) \circ \psi^{\#}(f_i^p) \circ (\sigma_p^i \otimes e_q^j) = \gamma_0.$$

The cut homomorphism $F_x \cap \bar{G}$ yields the grating $(F_x \cap \bar{G})\Theta^{\#}E(\omega_2)$ over $F_x \cap \bar{G}$. Let V be an open neighborhood of $F_x \cap \bar{G}$ with $\bar{V} \subset G$. The normality of the spaces concerned allows us to first swell the cover $\omega_2 \cap F_x \cap \bar{G}$ to a cover ω_2' and then to extend ω_2' to ν a compact cover of $\bar{V}$ so that sets of ν intersect only if they meet in $F_x \cap \bar{G}$. Thus the nerve of $\omega_2 \cap F_x \cap \bar{G}$ is isomorphic to that of ν.

The grating determined by ν, $\mathrm{E}(\nu) = \{F_j'^p\}$, is abstractly isomorphic to $F_x \cap \bar{G}\, \Theta^{\#}\mathrm{E}(\omega_2)$ with $\Theta^{\#}F_j'^p$ corresponding to $F_j'^p$. Let ω_1 be the cover described in (3.13). Denote the right hand side of (3.14a) by $d\gamma_0' = 0$. Now (2.12) applies to assure us $\gamma_0 \sim \gamma_0'$. Hence the same Λ is determined by γ_0 and by γ_0'. We need only observe that $F_j'^p$ depends on the values of Θ on $F_x \cap \bar{G}$, alone.

Theorem 3.15. *Let G be open in X and suppose U open and connected in Y. Let* $\psi\colon \bar{G} \times Y \to X$ *and let* $\theta\colon \bar{U} \to Y$*. Suppose* $\dot{G} \times Y \cap {}_1F = \varnothing$ *and suppose* $\dot{U} \cap {}_2F = \varnothing$*, where* ${}_1F = \{(x, y) \mid \psi(x, y) = x\}$ *and* ${}_2F = \{y \mid \theta(y) = y\}$*. Then*

$$\Lambda(\psi \times \theta, G \times U) = \Lambda(\psi, G \times \bar{U})\Lambda(\theta, U).$$

With u and v referring to units defined in full gratings on X and Y,

(3.15a)

$$\Lambda(\psi \times \theta, G \times U) \leftarrow \Sigma\, i(p + q)(u_G \otimes v_U) \circ (u \otimes \theta^{\#}(F_i^p)) \circ \psi^{\#}(f_j^q) \circ (\sigma_q^j \otimes e_p^i)$$

(where of course $\circ$ implies reduction by taking cosets with respect to 0 support elements while $\otimes$ indicates gratings over different spaces are involved.) It can then be verified that the right hand side of (3.15a) can be written as $\gamma \otimes \mu$ where

$$\gamma = \Sigma\, i(q)(u_G \otimes v) \circ \psi^{\#}(f^{\,q}_{\,j}) \circ (\sigma^j_q \otimes v)$$

$$\mu = \Sigma\, i(p)(u \otimes \Sigma\, v_U \circ \theta(F^p_i) \circ e^i_p).$$

According to (3.13) for a suitable cover ω_1 of X,

$$\dot{G} \times Y \cap \psi^{-1} \|f^q_j\| \cap (\|\sigma^j_q\| \times Y) = \varnothing$$

and so γ is a cycle. By definition $\mu \sim \Lambda(\theta, U)(u \otimes e^1_0)$ and hence

(3.15b) $$\gamma \otimes \mu = \Lambda(\theta, U)\rho$$

where the cycle $\rho = \Sigma\, i(q)(u_G \otimes v) \circ \psi^{\#}(f^q_j) \circ (\sigma^j_q \otimes e^1_0) \to N\sigma^1_0 \otimes e^1_0$ for some integer N. Since $\theta^{\#}$ does not enter, ρ is a cycle independent of $\theta^{\#}$. Hence the value of N is unaffected by modification of θ. Thus if $\check{\theta}\colon U \to y_0$, $\Lambda(\check{\theta}, U) = 1$ (Example 11-1) so, since there are no fixed points of $\check{\theta}$ on $\bar{U} - y_0$, $\Lambda(\psi \times \theta, \bar{G} \times (\bar{U} - y_0)) = 0$ and accordingly

(3.15c) $$\Lambda(\psi \times \check{\theta}, G \times U) = \Lambda(\psi, G).$$

Then (3.15b) and (3.15c) imply $\rho \to \Lambda(\psi, G)$.

The next result is central in all index applications.

Theorem 3.16. Commutativity. *Let X_0 and Y_0 be closed subsets of the smooth spaces X and Y. Suppose $\alpha\colon Y_0 \to X$ and $\beta\colon X_0 \to Y$. Let G be an open set on which $\alpha\beta$ is defined. Then*

(3.16a) $$\Lambda(\alpha\beta, G) = \Lambda(\beta\alpha, \alpha^{-1} G)$$

Identify $\beta\alpha$ with θ and α with ψ in (3.15). Thus $\alpha(y) = \psi(x, y)$ independently of $x \in G$. Hence

(3.16b) $$\Lambda(\alpha \times \beta\alpha, G \times \alpha^{-1} G) = \Lambda(\alpha, G \times \alpha^{-1} G)\Lambda(\beta\alpha, \alpha^{-1} G).$$

(It is understood that the notation $(\psi \times \theta, A \times B)$ means the domain of *both* ψ and θ is $A \times B$.) If we set $y = y_0$, α or ψ can be considered a map of $G \times \alpha^{-1} G$ into the single point x_0. Hence $(\alpha, G \times \alpha^{-1} G) = 1$. Therefore the right hand side of (3.16b) reduces to $\Lambda(\beta\alpha, \alpha^{-1} G)$. This is to say the left hand side of (3.16b) refers to the fixed points

$$\{\bar{x} \times \bar{y} \mid \bar{x} = \alpha(\bar{y}), \bar{y} = \beta\bar{x}\} \subset G \times \alpha^{-1} G$$

and hence can be written $\Lambda(\alpha \times \beta, G \times \alpha^{-1} G)$ according to (3.14).

However these fixed points must also constitute the fixed points in $\beta^{-1} H \times H$ where $H = \alpha^{-1} G$ and so the left hand side of (3.16b) can be written also $\Lambda(\alpha \times \beta, \beta^{-1} H \times H)$. This, on reversing the argument above, is the same as $\Lambda(\beta \times \alpha\beta, \beta^{-1} H \times H)$ which in turn is the same as

$$\Lambda(\alpha\beta, \beta^{-1} H) \quad \text{or} \quad \Lambda(\alpha\beta, G).$$

A wider field for application of index and fixed point notions is afforded by noting that omology characteristics do not change under deformations.

Definition 3.17. A **smooth retract**, X, is a retract of a smooth space Z called the super space. The natural extension to neighborhood smooth retracts does not really add much.

PROBLEM

11-7. Show a connected compact retract of an open set in a smooth space is a smooth retract.

Definition 3.18. Let X be a smooth retract under r of the smooth super space Z and let G be an open subset with $\dot{G} \cap F = \varnothing$ where ψ is on X to X. Let $\Lambda(\psi, G) = \Lambda(\psi r, r^{-1} G)$ defined for Z.

For this index to be of value we must have the following result:

Lemma 3.19. *If Z and Z' are smooth superspaces for the smooth retract X, then $\Lambda(\psi r, r^{-1}G) = \Lambda(\psi r', r'^{-1}G)$.*

Since $X \subset Z$, ψ can be considered on X to Z. Thus consider the map $r' r\psi$. Then by (3.16) using $r\psi = \psi$ and $r' r = r$

$$\Lambda(r\psi r', r'^{-1} G) = \Lambda(\psi r' r, (r' r)^{-1} G),$$

$$\Lambda(\psi r', r'^{-1} G) = \Lambda(\psi r, r^{-1} G).$$

Lemma 3.20. *If $G_1 \subset \bar{G}_1 \subset G_2$ and $\overline{G_2 - \bar{G}_1}$ has no fixed points, then $\Lambda(\psi, G_1) = \Lambda(\psi, G_2)$.*

Let u_{G_1} be a unit of A for $\bar{G}_1$. Then for a sufficiently fine cover, ω,

$$\overline{G_2 - \bar{G}_1} \cap \bigcup \psi^{-1} \|b_i\| \cap \|b_i\| = \varnothing, \quad (3.4),$$

so $(u_{G_2} - u_{G_1}) \circ \Sigma\, \psi^{\#} f_i^p \circ \sigma_p^i = 0.$

This amounts to the assertion of the lemma.

Theorem 3.21. *If $\{G_\alpha\}$ constitutes a collection of pairwise disjoint open sets, then if $\overline{\bigcup G_\alpha} - \bigcup G_\alpha$ contains no fixed point*

$$\Lambda(G) = \Sigma\, \Lambda(G_\alpha).$$

X compact ensures that except for a finite number of α values, $G_\alpha \cap F = \emptyset$. Pick $G_1' \subset \bar{G}_1' \subset G_1$ such that

$$F \cap ((\bar{G}_1 - G_1') \cup \dot{G}_2) = \emptyset.$$

Choose $u = u_{G_1'} + u_{G_2}$ where $\|u_{G_1'}\| \cap \|u_{G_2}\| = \emptyset$. Then

$$\Lambda(G_1 \cup G_2) = \Lambda(G_1' \cup G_2) = \Lambda(G_1') + \Lambda(G_2) = \Lambda(G_1) + \Lambda(G_2).$$

Corollary 3.22. *If $\Lambda(\psi, G) \neq 0$ there is a fixed point of ψ in G.*

Otherwise there would be a simple cover ω and a unit $u_{\bar{G}}$ satisfying (3.4a). However, (3.4a) yields $\Lambda(\psi, G) = 0$.

Theorem 3.23. *Let X be an absolute retract and suppose $\{Y_i \mid i = 1, \ldots, n, n > 1\}$ are n open sets whose closures $\{\bar{Y}_i\}$ are pairwise disjunct absolute retracts. Let $G = \bigcup_{i=1}^{i=n} Y_i$ and let θ map $X - G$ to X subject to θ: $\dot{Y}_i \subset \bar{Y}_i$. Then θ has a fixed point in $X - G$.*

Consider θ applied to $\dot{Y}_i$. Let r_i be the retracting function of some parallelotope P containing $\bar{Y}_i$. Since θ_i: $\dot{Y}_i \to P$, the Tietze theorem guarantees an extension to θ_i' on $\bar{Y}_i$ to P. Then $\psi_i = r_i\,\theta_i'$ maps $\bar{Y}_i$ into $\bar{Y}_i$. Define Ψ as θ on $X - G$ and ψ_i on $\bar{Y}_i$. If Ψ is fixed point free on each $\dot{Y}_i$ it is fixed point free on $\dot{G}$. Accordingly (3.6), (3.11), and (3.21) yield

$$\Lambda(\Psi, G) + \Lambda(\Psi, X - G) = L(\Psi). \tag{3.23a}$$

Since $\bar{Y}_i$ is an absolute retract it is acyclic and hence

$$\Lambda(\Psi, Y_i) = L(\Psi, \bar{Y}_i) = 1.$$

Furthermore, since $\bar{Y}_i \cap \bar{Y}_j = \emptyset$, $i \neq j$ we can apply (3.21) whence

$$\Lambda(\Psi, G) = \Sigma\, \Lambda(\psi, Y_i) = n. \tag{3.23b}$$

Then (3.23a) and (3.23b) yield

$$\Lambda(\psi, X - \bar{G}) = 1 - n \neq 0.$$

This assures the presence of a fixed point for Ψ in $X - \bar{G}$ whence in view of the definition of Ψ, θ has a fixed point in $X - G$.

We shall need presently a slight generalization of (3.12).

Lemma 3.24. *Let G be open in $X \times I$. Assume $\psi((x, t) \mid G) \subset X \times t$ has no fixed points in $\dot{G}$. Write $G_{t_0} = \{(x, t_0) \mid (x, t_0) \in G\}$. Denote by ψ_{t_0} the restriction $\psi \mid G_{t_0}$. Then $\Lambda(\psi_{t_0}, G_{t_0})$ is independent of t_0 in I.*

It is easy to find an open set V in X and an open interval Δ in I such that

$$F \cap \bigcup_{t \in \Delta} G_t \subset V \times \Delta.$$

Then (3.12) applies to $V \times \Delta$. A finite number of intervals Δ cover I.

The utility of the index extends beyond smooth spaces if a simple artifice is employed. Till the end of this section we shall use the following terminology. Z is an arbitrary space (merely T_2) and Z_0 is a closed subset, X is a smooth space. Let $\psi: Z_0 \to X$, $\theta: X \to Z$. Suppose z_0 is a fixed point of $\theta\psi$. Let $\psi(z_0) = x_0$. Then $\theta(x_0) = z_0$. Therefore $\psi\theta(x_0) = x_0$. The converse is also valid if $\theta(x_0)$ is in Z_0. This motivates the following definition.

Definition 3.25. With Z, Z_0, X, θ and ψ as described, if G is open in Z the *index* $\Lambda(\theta\psi, G)$ *is defined as* $\Lambda(\psi\theta, \theta^{-1} G)$. (If $\mu: W \to X$, then there is an apparent difficulty with this definition, for presumably one should have the two interpretations $\Lambda(\mu(\psi\theta), \theta^{-1} G)$ and $\Lambda((\psi\theta)\mu, \mu^{-1}\theta^{-1} G)$. However, since both $(\psi\theta)$ and μ are on smooth spaces, our commutativity result (3.16) shows both indices coincide.)

We can now generalize some of our earlier results.

Theorem 3.25. *Let Z be an arbitrary T_2 space and let X be smooth. Let G be open in $Z \times I$. Suppose $\psi: \bar{G} \longrightarrow X$ and furthermore $X \times I \xrightarrow{\theta} Z \times I$ where $\theta: X \times t \longrightarrow Z \times t$. Let $\mu: \bar{G} \longrightarrow Z \times t$, be defined by $\mu(z, t) = \theta(\psi(z, t), t)$. Let $G_t = G \cap Z \times t$ and write $\dot{G}_t$ for its boundary in $Z \times t$. Let $\mu_t = \mu \mid \bar{G}_t$. Suppose μ_t is fixed point free on $\dot{G}_t$. Finally assume $\Lambda(\psi\theta, \theta^{-1} G_0) \neq 0$. The fixed point set of μ in G is denoted by F. Then F contains a connected set joining $Z \times 0$ and $Z \times 1$.*

Everything depends on the fact that F is compact. Indeed $\theta^{-1} F$ is compact since it is the fixed point set of $(\psi\theta)$ in $\overline{\theta^{-1}(G)}$. Let $\{K_i\}$ be the components of F which meet $Z \times 0$ and $\{L_j\}$ those which meet $Z \times 1$. If the theorem is false, $\bigcup K_i \cap \bigcup L_j = \varnothing$. Since K_i is a component of a compact set, $K_i = \bigcap_j U_i(j)$ where $U_i(j)$ is open and closed in F. Hence for some j, $U_i(j) = U_j \subset Z \times \Delta_i(0) \cap G$ where $\Delta_i(0) = \{t \mid 0 \leq t < t_i < 1\}$. Similarly there is an open and closed set W_k satisfying

$$L_k \subset W \subset Z \times \Delta_k(1) \cap G, \quad \Delta_k(1) = \{t \mid t_k < t \leq 1\}.$$

Hence $\{U_i\} \cup \{W_k\}$ constitutes an open cover of F and therefore admits a finite subcover whose typical element is now denoted by V_i. Let F_0 be the union of the elements $\{V_i\}$ meeting $Z \times 0$ and let F_1 be the union of the others. Then $F_0 \subset \Delta(0) \times Z$, while $F_1 \cap \Delta(0) \times Z = \varnothing$. Since V_i is open and closed F_0 and F_1 are disjunct compact subsets of F. Let A and B be disjoint open sets of $Z \times I$ with $F_0 \subset A \subset \Delta'(0) \times Z$, $F_1 \subset B$, where

$\Delta(0) \subset \Delta'(0) \neq I$. Now $\bar{A} \cap F = F_0 \subset B^{\sim}$ whence $\dot{F}_0 \cap F = \varnothing$. Let $A_0 = \{(z, 0) \mid (z, 0) \in A\}$. Hence μ_0 has no fixed points on $G_0 - A_0$. It follows that $\psi\theta$ has no fixed points on $\theta^{-1} G_0 - \theta^{-1} A_0$. Since

$$\Lambda(\psi\theta, \theta^{-1} G) \neq 0$$

$\Lambda(\psi\theta, \theta^{-1} A_0) \neq 0$ by (3.21).

We now assume tacitly that ψ and μ are restricted to A. Then μ has no fixed point on $\dot{A}$. Moreover $\Lambda(\psi\theta, \theta^{-1} A_0) \neq 0$. According to (3.25) $\Lambda(\mu_t, A_t) = \Lambda(\psi\theta, \theta^{-1} A_t)$. The right hand side is nonzero by (3.24). Hence the left hand side is nonzero for all t, that is to say there is a fixed point of μ_t in A_t which contradicts the fact that $A_t = \varnothing$ for $t \in \Delta_1$.

4. COMPACTIFICATION AND LOCAL RINGS. We propose now to combine the information afforded by A and by its compact subgrating $^{\bullet}$A. We assume X is locally compact and paracompact and take A to be the Alexander R grating. Let $\mu = \{U_a\}$ be the directed family of all open sets with compact closure, where $a < b$ is defined by $\bar{U}_a \subset U_b \subset X$.

Theorem 4.1. (**a**) $0 \longrightarrow {}^{\bullet}\mathrm{A}^p \xrightarrow{i} \mathrm{A}^p \longrightarrow \mathrm{A}^p/{}^{\bullet}\mathrm{A}^p \longrightarrow 0$ *is an exact sequence.*

If X is an open subset of a compact set $\check{X}$, then

(**b**) $$\longrightarrow H^p(\check{X}, X) \xrightarrow{j^*} H^p(\check{X} - X) \xrightarrow{i^*} I^p(X) \longrightarrow$$

is an exact sequence. The terms entering are described below.

Evidently $^{\bullet}$A is an ideal of A. Hence A/$^{\bullet}$A is an R grating.

Consider the exact sequence

(4.1c) $$0 \to {}^{\bullet}\mathrm{A}^p(U) \to \mathrm{A}^p \to \mathrm{A}/{}^{\bullet}\mathrm{A}^p(U) \to 0$$

where $^{\bullet}\mathrm{A}^p(U)$ refers to the Alexander grating with compact supports over U. Thus (**a**) is the direct limit, for $U \in \{U_a\}$, of (4.1c). $H^*(X)$ is obtained from the complete grating A and $H^*(X - U)$ comes from A/$^{\bullet}$A(U). Thus (4.1c) yields the cohomology exact sequence

(4.1d) $$\longrightarrow {}^{\bullet}H^*(U) \longrightarrow H^p(X) \longrightarrow H^p(X - U) \xrightarrow{d} H^{p+1}(U)$$

We derive (**b**). Let $U \subset X$ and let $\mathrm{A}(X, U) = \{a \mid \|a\| \cap U = \varnothing\}$. The associated cohomology ring is written $H^*(X, U)$. Write $\mathrm{A}(U) = \mathrm{A}/\mathrm{A}(X, U)$. Then the cohomology sequence for the pair $\check{X} - U, X - U$ is

$$\longrightarrow H^p(\check{X} - U, X - U) \xrightarrow{j^*} H^p(\check{X} - U) \xrightarrow{i^*} H^p(X - U) \xrightarrow{d} .$$

The direct limits over $\{U\} \in \mu$ furnish the sequence (4.1b) where the continuity theorem is used to get $H^p(\check{X} - X)$ (91.2).

An interpretation of $I^p(X)$ is in order. Suppose $\check{X}$ is the closure of an open concrete simplicial manifold X. Then $H^*(\check{X}, X) = 0$. Accordingly $i^*\ H^*(\hat{X} - X) \to I^*(X)$ is a ring isomorphism, so $I^*(X)$ in this case is the cohomology ring of a boundary $\dot{X} = \check{X} - X$ associated with a compactification of X in which X emerges as an open subset. For instance, this is the 1 point compactification for R. (More generally I^p is linked to the so-called Freudenthal compactification.)

Another justification for the introduction of $I^*(X)$ follows.

Definition 4.2. Let Y be closed in X. Let $\mu = \{U_a\}$ be the directed family in (4) with $Y \subset U_a$. If $Y \subset V \subset U$ then $(V - Y)$ acts on $(U - Y)$A. (The effect is to restrict the cochain f^p defined over $U - Y$ to arguments in $V - Y$.) It is convenient then to write this homomorphism $r_{V-Y}^{U-Y\#}$. Then

(4.2a) $$I_Y^m(X) = \underset{\rightarrow}{\mathsf{L}}\ \{H^m(U - Y),\ r_{V-Y}^{U-Y*}\}$$

is called the **local cohomology ring of X over Y.**

If $Y \subset W \subset X$ where $X - Y$ is paracompact, then

(4.2b) $$I_Y^m(X - W) = \underset{\rightarrow}{\mathsf{L}}\, H^m(U - U \cap W)$$

when F is the family of subsets of $U - (U \cap W)$ which are closed in U.

Lemma 4.3. *In the notation of* (4.2a) *and* (4.2b) *there is an exact sequence*

$$\longrightarrow I_Y^m(X - W) \longrightarrow I_Y^m(X) \longrightarrow I_Y^m(W) \xrightarrow{d} I_Y^{m+1}(X - W) \longrightarrow$$

This is immediate from the observation that "direct limits and exact sequences commute" (77.15).

chapter 12

PRODUCTS

1. EXISTENCE OF MAPPINGS. It is not new to us that the algeb aic relationships of the omology groups on a fixed space or on different spaces are not exhausted by their group associations. Indeed this has already been established in Section 61 and in the definition of a grating as first of all an algebra. In (85.1), (84.1), and (86.1), for instance, we have made explicit the notion of a product in connection with the singular and Alexander cohomology algebras, and this product is the cup product referred to below. Moreover in (113) we have used what will appear later as the cap product. We propose now to put these matters in a more general setting, and below we use the simplicial or singular complex as model.

Among the various relations between omology groups that have been discovered, the linear or bilinear ones are the natural ones to investigate first, and among these the situations to which we restrict ourselves are roughly the following: Suppose ${}_1H$, ${}_2H$, and ${}_3H$ are omology groups over the complexes or spaces ${}_1X$, ${}_2X$, and ${}_1X \times {}_2X$, respectively. It develops that certain nontrivial correspondences can be defined between pairs of elements, ${}_1h$, ${}_2h$ in (**a**) ${}_1H^i$ and ${}_2H^j$ and elements in ${}_3H^k$ or (**b**) between the pair in ${}_1H_i$ and ${}_2H^j$ and an element in ${}_3H_k$. Such a correspondence is a group homomorphism when either ${}_1h$ or ${}_2h$ is held fast. Moreover, the group homomorphisms are to map corresponding triples of omology groups into corresponding triples. In this, and in the next section we shall deal exclusively with the case that $k = \pm 1 + j$, but more general correspondences are noted incidentally and from a different viewpoint in (136). When ${}_1X = Y = {}_2X$, homomorphisms on $H^*(X \times X)$ to $H^*(X)$ exist and may be composed with the correspondences mentioned above and then the bilinear homomorphisms are referred to as **multiplications** or **products** and comprise the **cross product**, **cup product**, and **cap product** and when $k \neq j \pm i$, other types of products enter.

The existence of these interrelations restricts the possibilities for the omology groups and their homomorphisms. Moreover, an immediate application is to duality relations, like those of Alexander (8.2), between cohomology and homology groups. Another is to the problems of extensions of mappings or retractions of spaces. We remark parenthetically that both of these problems are included in the following formulation:
Let A, B, and C be complexes or spaces and suppose maps $f\colon A \to B$ and $g\colon A \to C$ are known. Our concern is whether or not a map, k, exists on $B \to C$ such that $kf = g$.

Lemma 1.1. *The given maps induce homomorphisms f^* and g^* on the cohomology groups. A necessary condition for the existence of k is that a homomorphism k^* exist so that*

(1.1a) $$f^*\, k^* = g^*.$$

However, further independent necessary conditions proceed from (1.1a) when one invokes the property that these homomorphisms must take products into products.

Lemma 1.2. *No map ψ of the Euclidean $n+1$ disk, E^{n+1}, $\{x \mid \Sigma\, x_i^2 \leq 1\}$ onto the n sphere, $S^n = \{x \mid \Sigma\, x_i^2 = 1\}$ exists if points on S^n are to be held fast.*

Let j be the identity map of $S^n \to S^n$. Let i be the inclusion map of $S^n \to E^{n+1}$. Suppose the map ψ existed. Then $\psi i = j$ whence (a) $\psi_*\, i_* = j_*$. However, since $H_*(E^{n+1}) = 0$, $i_* = 0$ whereas j_* is the identity isomorphism and therefore is nontrivial on $H^n(S^n) \to H^n(S^n)$. Hence (1.1a) cannot be satisfied.

The proof has been selected to illustrate (1.1a). The result is equivalent to the Brouwer theorem (Example 7-6). It is noteworthy that if D^{n+1} and S^n are replaced by the infinite dimensional Banach space disk D and sphere S, a map ψ as described in the lemma invariably exists. By compounding this map with the antipodal map a there results a fixed point free map $a\psi$ of $D \to D$. Besides the fact that the image S of $a\psi$ is infinite dimensional, $a\psi$ has invariant sets, namely the pairs of antipodal points of S. The result stated in the following problem may therefore be of interest.

PROBLEM

12-1. Show there is a self-map of the unit disk in a nonfinite dimensional Banach space, with no proper invariant set. *Hint:* Since S is not conditionally compact, there is a denumerable collection $\{x_i \mid x_i \in s\}$ with mutual distances $\geq \epsilon > 0$. Map onto the homeomorph L of the nonnegative real axis consisting of the chords frnm x_i to x_{i+1} in such wise that the map of $L \to L$ has no invariant proper subset.

2. PRODUCTS. The primitive notions of $\times$ products extend at once to pairs and for spaces are merely the expected Cartesian products.

Definition 2.1. If the space ${}_iA$ is contained in ${}_iX$ then

$$({}_1X, {}_1A) \times ({}_2X, {}_2A) = ({}_1X \times {}_2X, {}_1X \times {}_2A \cup {}_1A \times {}_2X)$$

while for complexes

$$(K_1, L_1) \times (K_2, L_2) = (K_1 \times K_2, K_1 \times L_2 \cup L_1 \times K_2).$$

For clarity we focus first on some notions for the special case $L_1 = L_2 = 0$. In any case the substitutions (K_1, L_1) for K_1 and (K_2, L_2) for K_2 may be made directly in (2.2).

Definition 2.2. If K_1 and K_2 are cell complexes with cells $\{e_r^i\}$ and $\{E_m^j\}$ respectively then $K_1 \times K_2$ is the product complex consisting of cells $\{e_r^i \times E_m^j\}$. So far this merely asserts that $K_1 \times K_2$ represents the collection of pairs $\{e_r^i, E_m^j\}$. It becomes a cell complex on the addition of the properties

(2.2a) $e_r^i \times E_m^j$ is a face of $e_p^a \times {}_2E_n^b$ provided e_r^i, E_m^j are faces of e_p^a, E_n^b respectively.

(2.2b) The degree of $e_r^i \times E_m^j$ is $r + m$.

(2.2c) The incidence numbers for $K_1 \times K_2$ are defined in terms of those for K_1 and K_2. Specifically

$$[e_r^i \times E_n^j, e_r^i \times E_{m-1}^b] = (-1)^r[E_m^j, E_{m-1}^b],$$

$$[e_r^i \times E_m^j, e_{m-1}^a \times E_m^j] = [e_r^i, e_{r-1}^a].$$

All other incidence numbers are to be 0.

Similarly we can define $K_1 \times \cdots K_s$ by induction.

Definition 2.3. The chain modules, $C(K_1 \times K_2)$ admit a boundary operator defined as in (64.13). Thus for the elementary chains

$$d(ge_r^i \times E_m^j) = \Sigma_{a,b}\, g[e_r^i \times E_m^j, e_p^a \times E_n^b]e_p^a \times E_n^b,$$

where the sum is over all product cells for which the incidence number entering as coefficient is not 0. The sum is finite after (2.1) and it may be verified that $d^2 = 0$.

An interesting case arises when the cells are simplexes, either ordered or oriented. Thus using the vertex representations,

$$e_r = {}_1\sigma_r = \{u_i \mid i = 0, \ldots, r\},$$

$$E_m = {}_2\sigma_m = \{v_j \mid j = 0, \ldots, m\},$$

$$E_r \times E_m = u_0 \cdots u_r \times v_0 \cdots v_m.$$

Evidently, except for $r = 0$ or $m = 0$, the product of two simplexes is not a simplex. Then

$$\begin{aligned}\partial g(u_0 \cdots u_r \times v_0, \ldots, v_m) &= \Sigma\,(-1)^i\, gu_0 \ldots \hat{i} \ldots u_r \times v_0 \cdots v_m \\ &\quad + \Sigma\,(-1)^{r+j}\, gu_0 \cdots u_r \times v_0 \ldots \hat{j} \ldots v_m \\ &= \Sigma\,(-1) g^i({}_1\sigma_{r-1}(i) \times {}_2\sigma_m) \\ &\quad + \Sigma\,(-1)^r\, g(-1)^j\, {}_1\sigma_r \times {}_2\sigma_{m-1}(j) \\ &= \partial g\, {}_1\sigma_r \times {}_2\sigma_m + (-1)^r\, g({}_1\sigma_r \times \partial\, {}_2\sigma_m). \end{aligned} \tag{2.3a}$$

The apparently unsymmetric roles played by ${}_1\sigma_r$ and ${}_2\sigma_m$ in this analogue of the derivation of a product are fundamental in all ordered pair notions to be met with as, for example, the cup and cap products and the tensor products, and account for the entrance of $(-1)^r$ in (2.2c).

If $K_1 = K_2 = K$ we shall write K^2 and then naturally K^n for the corresponding iterated product. In general $\sigma_r \times \sigma_p$ is different from $\sigma_p \times \sigma_r$.

From 2.3a it follows that

$$\partial g({}_2\sigma_m \times {}_1\sigma_r) = (-1)^m\, g\, {}_2\sigma_m \times \partial\, {}_1\sigma_r + g\partial\, {}_2\sigma_m \times {}_1\sigma_r. \tag{2.3b}$$

Let $'T$ be the map $'T\, {}_1\sigma_n \times {}_2\sigma_m = {}_2\sigma_m \times {}_1\sigma_n$. Then $'T_\#$ is not allowable, i.e., $'T_\#\, \partial \neq \partial\, 'T_\#$ on $C(K_1 \times K_2)$. It is necessary in view of (3.3a) and (2.3b) to use instead

$$T = (-1)^{rm}\, 'T.$$

Definition 2.4. The **reversal map** T is defined by

$$T = (-1)^{rm}\, 'T$$

and its carrier function Q is $Q(e_n \times E_m) = E_m \times e_n$. In view of (2.3a) and (2.3b) $T_\#$ commutes with ∂. and in $T_\#(v \times V) = 1$ where v and V are vertices of ${}_1K$ and of ${}_2K$ respectively.

Definition 2.5. Let R_1 and R_2 be paired to R. Let X_i, A_i, $i = 1$, and 2 be simplicial complexes. To avoid formulae bursting with symbols we write W_1 for X_1, A_1, and R_1 and W_2 for X_2, A_2, R_2, and naturally $W_1 \times W_2$ for $(X_1, A_1) \times (X_2, A_2)$, R. *Until* (8.11) A_i, A *refer to closed subsets.*

The elementary chains over W_1 and over W_2 are indicated by e and by E respectively. The cochains are designated by f and F. A **cross product pairing**, $\times$, or **cross homomorphism** on chain modules is a bihomomorphism on

$$\times : C_p(W_1) \otimes C_q(W_2) \rightarrow C_{p+q}(W_1 \times W_2)$$

defined by

$$\times : r_1\, e_p \otimes r_2\, E_q \rightarrow r_1\, r_2(e_p \times E_q). \tag{2.5a}$$

The bihomorphism assertion means, that if either factor in the tensor product is fixed, a homomorphism is defined. We indicate the image of $\times$ by $C_p(W_1) \times C_q(W_2)$. The cross product for cochains is a bihomomorphism on

$$\times: C^p(W_1) \otimes C^q(W_2) \to C^{p+q}((W_1 \times W_2), R)$$

where the image under $\times$ of $f^p \otimes F^q$ is $f^p \times F^q$ which can take on non 0 values only on products of a p-cell and a q-cell,

$$(2.5b) \qquad (f^p \times F^q)(e_p \times E_q) = f^p(e_p)F^q(E_q) \in R.$$

Then, by (45.4a) and (2.3),

$$(2.5c) \qquad d(f^p \times F^q) = d_1 f^p \times F^q + (-1)^p f^p \times d_2 F^q.$$

Unless specific contrary indications are given this section assumes the complexes are finite.

We emphasize the implication of $\times$ by putting down explicitly

$$(2.5d) \quad \times\, C_p(W_1) \otimes C_q(W_2) = C_p(W_1) \times C_q(W_2) \subset C_{p+q}(W_1 \times W_2).$$

$$(2.5e) \quad \times\, C^p(W_1) \otimes C^q(W_2) = C^p(W_1) \times C^q(W_2) \subset C^{p+q}(W_1 \times W_2).$$

We replace $\times$ by $\times^\#$ and $\times_\#$ for the next result,

$$(f^p(W_1) \times^\# g^q(W_2)(C_p(W_1) \times_\# C_q(W_2)) = (f^p(W_1)C_p(W_1))(g^q(W_2)C_q(W_2)).$$

If the cells are cubes, then $\{e_p \times E_q\}$ constitutes an elementary chain basis. This yields at once

$$(2.5f) \qquad \Sigma_{p+q=n} C_p\,|K_1| \otimes C_q\,|K_2| = C_{p+q}\,|K_1 \times K_2|,$$

and

$$(2.5g) \qquad \Sigma_{p+q=n} H_p\,|K_1| \otimes H_q\,|K_2| = H_n\,|K_1 \times K_2|$$

which are of use in interpreting the Kunneth theorem.

We can put matters in proper context by writing down the general homomorphism on $C(W_1) \times C(W_2) \to C(W_3)$

$$(2.5h) \qquad \theta^\#: f_r^p \times F_s^q \to \Sigma\, \mu_{rs}^m(p, q) g_m^{p+q}$$

$$(2.5i) \qquad \theta^\#: e_p^r \times E_q^s \to \Sigma\, \mu_m^{rs}(p, q) c_{p+q}^m,$$

where e, E, and c are now to be considered base chains rather than cells. The particular case that $c = e \times E$ is an elementary chain is included, but in the simplicial case for instance $e \times E$ is generally nonavailable. The key conditions are that $\theta_\#$ and $\theta^\#$ be allowable; i.e., $\theta_\# d = d\theta_\#$, $\theta^\# d = d\theta^\#$. Whenever this is true the conclusions of (2.6), (2.7), and (2.8) remain valid and accordingly we may view $\theta^{\#}$ and $\theta_{\#}$ as cross-product homomorphisms. In the cell case where $e_p^i \times E_q^j = c_{p+q}^{m=i,j}$, the choice $\mu_m^{rs} = \delta_i^r \delta_j^s$ is that used in (2.5a), but (2.5h) suggests that other choices of μ_m^{rs} may also be available. As will appear later, at the omology level the induced cross-homomorphisms are equivalent.

Lemma 2.6. *If* $f^p \in Z^p(W_1)$ *and* $g^q \in Z^q(W_2)$ *then*

(2.6a) $$f^p \times g^q \in Z^{p+q}(W_1 \times W_2).$$

(2.6b) *If* $$f^p \in B^p(W_1) \quad \text{and} \quad g^q \in Z^q(W_2),$$

then $$f^p \times g^q \in B^{p+q}(W_1 \times W_2).$$

Similar relations are valid with cocycles replaced by cycles.

Both conclusions are immediate consequences of (2.5c). In particular, with $f^p = dF^{p-1}$, there results

$$f^p \times g^q = d(F^{p-1} \times g^q).$$

Lemma 2.7. *The cross-product pairing induces a bihomomorphism written* $\times$ *also, on* $H^*(W_1) \otimes H^*(W_2) \to H^*(W_1 \times W_2)$.

This is a corollary of (2.6a) and (2.6b).

The natural questions concerning a homomorphism and in particular a pairing are whether paired elements stay paired under homomorphisms induced by maps, or by the coboundary homomorphism associated with a cohomology sequence. The following theorems answer these questions in the affirmative.

Theorem 2.8

(2.8a) *If* $\mathbf{f}_i^0$, $i = 1, 2$, *are generators for* $H^0(x_i, R_i)$, $i = 1, 2$, *then* $r_1 \mathbf{f}_1^0 \times r_2 \mathbf{f}_2^0 = r_1 r_2 \mathbf{f}^0 \in H^0(X_1 \times X_2, R)$.

(2.8b) *If* $h_1 \in H^*(L_1, R_1)$, $h_2 \in H^*(K_2, R_2)$ *then* $\delta(h_1 \times h_2) = (\delta_1(h_1) \times h_2)$ *where* δ *and* δ_1 *are the homomorphisms entering the cohomology sequences for the pairs* $K_1 \times K_2$, $L_1 \times K_2$ *and for* K_1, L_1 *respectively.*

(2.8c) *Let* ψ_i *be a simplicial map on* K_i, $L_i \to$ *to* M_i, N_i, $i = 1, 2$. *Let* ψ *be defined by*

$$\psi\colon (K_1, L_1) \times (K_2, L_2) \to \psi_1(K_1, L_1) \times \psi_2(K_2, L_2).$$

Then for ${}_1\mathbf{f}^p \in H^p(M_1, N_1, R_1)$, ${}_2\mathbf{f}^q \in H^q(M_2, N_2, R_2)$,

$$\Psi^*({}_1\mathbf{f}^p \times {}_2\mathbf{f}^q) = \Psi_1^*({}_1\mathbf{f}^p) \times \Psi_2^*({}_2\mathbf{f}^q).$$

The verification of (2.8a) and (2.8b) requires merely the observation of validity for the representative cocycles. For (2.8b) we use the commutative diagram

$$\begin{array}{ccc} H^*(L_1) \otimes H(K_2) & \xrightarrow{\delta_1 \otimes 1} & H^*(K_1) \otimes H(K_2) \\ \downarrow \times & & \downarrow \times \\ H^*(L_1 \times K_2 \cup K_1 \times L_2) & \xrightarrow{\delta} & H^*(K_1 \times K_2, L_1 \times K_2 \cup K_1 \times L_2) \end{array}$$

where the upper row is from the exact cohomology sequence for K_1, L_1 tensored with $H(W_2)$ and the lower row is that for $W_1 \times W_2$.

Since Ψ_i is simplicial, $\Psi_i({}_i\sigma)$ can be taken as an acyclic carrier ${}_iQ({}_i\sigma)$, $i = 1, 2$. Thus ${}_iQ$ is an acyclic carrier function for $\Psi_{i\#}$. Then $\Psi = \Psi_1 \times \Psi_2$: ${}_1\sigma \times \sigma_2 = \Psi_1\,{}_1\sigma \times \Psi_2\,{}_2\sigma$ yields $Q({}_1\sigma \times {}_2\sigma) = {}_1Q({}_1\sigma) \times {}_2Q({}_2\sigma)$, an acyclic carrier for Ψ. Hence $\Psi_\#$, and ${}_1\Psi_\# \times {}_2\Psi_\#$ have the acyclic carrier function Q. Therefore $\Psi^* = \Psi_1^* \times \Psi_2^*$. This is (2.8c).

PROBLEMS

12-2. If $f^p \sim g^p \in Z(K, L, R)$ show $f^p \times f^p \sim g^p \times g^p$.

12-3. Let $K = \{e\}$ and $L = \{E\}$ be cell complexes. Relate *Cl*, *St* and *boundary* of $e \times E$ to those of e and E. Show $K \times L$ is closure finite (star finite) if K and L are closure finite (star finite). What are the components of $K \times L$?

If X and Y are triangulable, it is natural to define a cross product $f \times F$ by the transfer from the complexes.

Lemma 2.9. *If (X_i, A_i), $i = 1, 2$, are triangulable, a cross-product homomorphism exists independent of the triangulation.*

Suppose, then T_i and S_i are homeomorphisms from concrete simplicial complexes,

$$K_i, L_i \xrightarrow{T_i} X_i, A_i \xleftarrow{S_i} M_i, N_i.$$

Assume provisionally that a simplicial approximation to $S_i^{-1} T_i$ exists. Designate it by α_i. Define β_i as $S_i\, \alpha_i T_i^{-1}$. Then

$$\beta_i^* = T_i^{*-1} \alpha_i^* S_i^* \approx 1$$

where 1 is the identity isomorphism on $H(X, A) \to H(X, A)$. Let $\times_t$ be the cross product on $H(K_1 \times K_2)$ and $\times_s$ that on $H(M_1 \times M_2)$. Define $\times_T$, ($\times_S$ is defined analogously) by

(2.9a) $$f \times_T F = (T_1 \times T_2)^{*-1} (T_1^* f \times_t T_2^* F).$$

By (2.8c), $(\alpha_1 \times \alpha_2)^* (S_1^* f_1 \times_s S_2^* F) = (\alpha_1^* S_1^* f_1 \times_t \alpha_2^* S_2^* F)$, and so the right hand side of (2.9a) can be written

$$= (T_1 \times T_2)^{*-1} (\alpha_1 \times \alpha_2)^* (S_1^* f \times_s S_2^* F)$$

$$= (\beta_1 \times \beta_2)^* (f \times_s F).$$

Since $(\beta_1 \times \beta_2)^*$ is evidently the identity isomorphism,

$$f \times_T F = f \times_S F. \tag{2.9b}$$

We have yet to take care of the possibility that barycentric subdivisions of K_1 and K_2 are required before simplicial approximations α_1 and α_2 can be defined. Replace K_i by $Sd\, K_i$ and M_i by K_i. where Sd indicates some repeated order of subdivision. In this case simplicial approximations α_i plainly exist and (2.9b) asserts that the induced cross product on X_i, A_i is unchanged when printed K_i, L_i stands for $Sd(K_i, L_i)$. That is to say, with any M_i, N_i we can replace K_i, L_i by $Sd(K_i, L_i)$ and so there was no loss in generality in assuming the existence of α_i.

A distressing weakness of simplexes is that in general the topological product of two simplexes is not a simplex. With cubes or hypercubes as the base cells, we can avoid this failing. If e_p and E_q are singular cubes, then $e_p \times E_q$ is a map of I_{p+q} defined by $(e_p\, I_p, E_q\, {}_qI) \subset W_1 \times W_2$ where I_p has the first p coordinates and ${}_qI$ the last q of I_{p+q}.

Thus (2.5a) and (2.5b) hold as they stand for the singular chains and cochains built on singular cubes. However, if we stay with singular simplexes, then the extension of (2.5a) and (2.5b) presents the difficulty that if e_p and E_q are interpreted as singular simplexes, their product is not a singular simplex in $W_1 \times W_2$.

We accomplish other objectives as well in presenting the following existence proof. The first is that a firm foundation is provided for a general form of the Kunneth theorem, when $K_1 \times K_2$ below is interpreted as a topological product. The second is that it illustrates the typical technique of the important *method of acyclic models*. The idea of this method can be described simply for a restricted situation. The problem is to exhibit a homomorphism, satisfying certain relations valid for *every pair* X and Y, for each ${}_SC(X)$ to ${}_SC(Y)$. One of these relations (Cf. (2.10b)) yields h for any space pair once h can be defined for a preferred space pair. In the applications the preferred space pair is acyclic and the construction of h may be relatively easy. Since we make no other applications of the method, we have not framed it in the more natural language of categories and functors.

Later we show the existence of the cross product follows from that of the cup product which we have already defined (85.1). Let K replace ${}_SC$.

Definition 2.10. For every pair of spaces, X, Y there is a homomorphism $\chi(X, Y): K(X) \otimes K(Y) \to K(X \times Y)$ where the chain modules are over the integers, subject to

(2.10a) $$\chi(X, Y)(e_0 \otimes E_0) = (e \times E)_0.$$

(2.10b) If $\psi: X \to X'$, $\theta: Y \to Y'$ are maps, then

$$(\psi \times \theta)_{\#}\chi(X, Y) = \chi(X', Y')(\psi_{\#} \times \theta_{\#}).$$

and for $X = X'$, $Y = Y'$ and for ψ and θ the identity maps, $\chi(X, Y)$ $(\psi_{\#} \otimes \theta_{\#}) = \chi(X, Y)$.

(2.10c) $$\partial\chi = \chi\partial.$$

We can call such χ's *cross-products.*

Lemma 2.11. *χ exists.*

The proof is by induction. Let $(K(X) \otimes K'(Y))_{-1}$ have the basis element ϵ_{-1}. Let γ_{-1} be the basis element for $K_{-1}(X \times Y)$. Define $\chi_{-1}(X, Y)\, \epsilon_{-1} = \gamma_{-1}$. Then (2.10a), (2.10b), (2.10c) are trivially satisfied. Suppose then that χ_n can be defined for $n < m$ for all space pairs and therefore in particular on $K(\Delta_r) \otimes K'(\Delta_s)$ where $r + s = m$ (64.13). Let u_r, u_s be the identity self-maps of Δ_r and Δ_s. Then u_r and U_s are singular simplex generators of $K(\Delta_r)$ and of $K'(\Delta_s)$. Then $\chi_{n-1}(\Delta_r, \Delta_s)$, abbreviated χ, is defined on $\partial(u_r \otimes U_s)$. Moreover, in view of (2.10c)

$$\partial\chi_{n-1}\,\partial(u_r \otimes U_s) = \chi_{n-2}\,\partial^2(u_r \otimes U_s) = 0.$$

Hence $\chi_{n-1}\,\partial(u_r \otimes U_s) \in Z_{n-1}\,(X \times Y)$.

Since $\Delta_r \times \Delta_s$ is convex, it is locally connected in all dimensions and contractible, so its singular homology groups are trivial (112.4) (95.4). (Thus $\Delta_r \times \Delta_s$ is an acyclic model.) Hence $Z_n(\Delta_r \times \Delta_s) = B_n(\Delta_r \times \Delta_s)$ according to which $\chi_{n-1}\,\partial(u_r \times U_s) = \partial c_n$ for $c_n \in C_n(\Delta_r \times \Delta_s)$. Define $\chi(\Delta_n \times \Delta_s)$ as c_n. For arbitrary X and Y, if v_r and V_s are singular simplexes corresponding to maps from Δ_r to X and Δ_s to Y, note that $v_r = v_r\,u_r$, $V_s = V_s\,U_s$. Define $\chi_n(X, Y)(u_r \times u_s)$ as $(v_r \times V_s)_{\#}\,c_n$. Then (2.10b) is automatically satisfied for X, $Y = \Delta_r$, Δ_s and X', $Y' = X$, Y and hence for every pair (X, Y), (X', Y'). Besides $\partial\chi(\Delta_r \times \Delta_s) = \partial c_n = \chi\partial(\Delta_r \times \Delta_s)$ and therefore it is easy to deduce that (2.10c) holds always.

Definition 2.12. For the chain homomorphisms $\chi^{-}(X, Y)$ on $K_n(X \times Y) \to$ $(K(X) \times K(Y))$ (64.13) with

(2.12a) $\chi_0^{-}\, w_0 = u_0 \times v_0$ where $w_0(\Delta_0) = (x, y) \in X \times Y$, and u_0 and v_0 are defined by $u_0(\Delta_0) = x$, $v_0(\Delta_0) = y$.

(2.12b) For maps $\psi: X \to X'$, $\theta: Y \to Y'$, $(\psi_{\#} \times \theta_{\#})\mathrm{X}^{-}(X, Y) = \mathrm{X}^{-}(X', Y')$ $(\psi \times \theta)_{\#}$.

(2.12c) $$\partial_{+}\chi^{-} = \chi^{-}\partial.$$

Definition 2.13. Let R_1 and R_2 be paired to R by λ: $R_1 \times R_2 \to R$. Define $\chi(X, Y)$: $K^p(X, R_1) \otimes K^q(Y, R_2) \to K^{p+q}(X \times Y, R)$ by

$$(\chi(f^p \otimes F^q))(c_{p+q}(X \times Y, \text{J})) = \lambda(f^p \otimes F^q)(c_{p+q}(X \times Y, \text{J}))$$
$$= \lambda(f^p\, c_p \otimes F^q\, c_q) \in R.$$

Theorem 2.14. *χ exists as defined in* (2.13).

We need merely establish that χ^- exists following the pattern of (2.11). Thus χ^-_{-1} is easily defined by making the ideal generators of dimension -1 correspond. We take the special case $X = \Delta_n$, $Y = \Delta_n$. The induction argument goes through as in (2.11) if we start with u_n the diagonal map on Δ_n to Δ_n to $\Delta_n \times \Delta_n$ defined by $u_n(t) = (t, t)$. Again we show $X^{-1}\partial u_n$ is a cycle in $K(\Delta_n) \otimes K(\Delta_n)$ and observe that $K(\Delta_n) \otimes K(\Delta_n)$ is acyclic.

PROBLEM

12-4. If X and Y are acyclic spaces, show $K(X) \otimes K(Y)$ is acyclic.

For use in establishing a wide application for (104.11) we add a few results. Evidently χ can be considered on $\Sigma_{r+s=n} K_r(X) \otimes K_s(Y) \to K_n(X \times Y)$ in (2.11). When this is done we refer to the *modified* (2.11a), (2.11b), (2.11c).

Definition 2.15. $\chi(X, Y) \sim \chi'(X, Y)$ adds to the requirement that the homomorphisms $D_n(X, Y)$, $n = -1, 0, \ldots$ satisfy also the commutativity condition

(2.15a) $$(\psi_\# \times \theta_\#)_{j+1}\, D_j(X, Y) = D_j(X', Y')(\psi_\# \otimes \theta_\#)$$

For $\chi^-(X, Y) \simeq \chi'^-(X, Y)$, $\times$ and $\otimes$ are reversed in (2.11a).

Lemma 2.16. (a) *If χ and χ' satisfy* (2.11), *then* $\chi \simeq \chi'$.
(b) *If χ^- and χ'^{-1} satisfy* (2.12), *then* $\chi^- \simeq \chi'^-$.

The method of acyclic models again applies. Suppose X, $Y = X'$, Y' and Θ and Ψ are identity maps. Define $D_{-1}(\Psi_\# \otimes \Theta_\#) = 0$ for all X, Y. Make the induction hypothesis that homomorphisms D_j have been defined for all space pairs satisfying (2.11a) and also that

$$D_{j-1}\, \partial + \partial\, D_j = \chi_j - \chi'_j \qquad \text{for } j < n.$$

Fof the acyclic model we take X, Y as Δ_r and Δ_s, with u_r and u_s just as in the proof of (2.11). We proceed as in (71.5) or (84.2). Thus

$$\partial c_{n-1} = \chi(\Delta_r, \Delta_s) - \chi'(\Delta_r, \Delta_s) - \partial D_{n-1}(\Delta_r, \Delta_s)$$

yields $D_n(\Delta_r, \Delta_s)u_n = c_{n+1}$.

Lemma 2.17

(a) $\chi^{-}(X, Y)\chi(X, Y) \simeq 1\colon \Sigma_{r+s=n} K_r(X) \otimes K_s(Y) \to \Sigma_{r+s=n} K_r(X) \otimes K_s(Y)$

(b) $\chi(X, Y)\,\chi^{-}(X,Y) \simeq 1\colon K(X \times Y) \to K(X \times Y)$

(c) ${}_SH_*(X \times Y) \simeq H_*({}_SC(X) \otimes {}_SC(Y))$

In the correspondent of (2.15a) either $\otimes$ or $\times$ appears on both sides, depending on whether (2.17a) or (2.17b) is considered. The acyclic model arguments of (2.11) and (2.16) are direct. The key result (2.17c) is the obvious consequence of (2.17a) and (2.17b).

3. OTHER PRODUCTS. Definition 3.1. The **diagonal map,** Δ on X to $X \times X$ is defined by

$$\Delta\colon x \to x \times x.$$

The part of the diagonal in $X \times A_2 \cup A_1 \times X$ is in 1–1 correspondence with $A_1 \cup A_2$.

The **cup product,** $\cup$, is a homomorphism

$$\cup\colon\ C^p(X, A_1, R_1) \otimes C^q(X, A_2, R_2) \to C^{p+q}(X, A_1 \cup A_2, R)$$

indicated by $C^p(X, A_1, R_1) \cup C^q(X, A_2, R_2)$ and is defined by compounding the cross product with the diagonal map homomorphism. Thus

$$f^p(X, A_1, R_1) \cup f^q(X, A_2, R_2) = \Delta^{\#}(f^p \times f^p)$$
$$= (\Delta^{\#} \times\ )f^p \otimes f^q.$$

The induced pairing of the cohomology groups is again denoted by $\cup$, thus

$$H^p(X, A_1, R_1) \cup H^q(X, A_2, R) = \Delta^*(H^p(X, A_1, R_1) \times H^p(X, A_2, R)$$
$$= (\Delta^* \times\ )\, H^p(X, A_1, R_1) \otimes H^p(X, A_2, R)$$

or, considering the elements,

$$\mathbf{f}^p(X, A_1, R_1) \cup \mathbf{f}^q(X, A_2, R_2) = \Delta^*(\mathbf{f}^p \times \mathbf{f}^q)$$

We often write Δ for $\Delta^{\#}$ and for Δ^*.

Lemma 3.2. *Let ψ map X, A_1, A_2 into Y, B_1, B_2 and let the induced maps on the pairs $X, A_i \to Y, B_i$ be denoted by ψ_i. Let that on $X, A_1 \cup A_2 \to Y, B_1 \cup B_2$ be denoted by ψ_3. Then*

$$\psi_3^*(\mathbf{f}_1 \cup \mathbf{f}_2) = (\psi_1^*\, \mathbf{f}_1) \cup (\psi_2^*\, \mathbf{f}_2).$$

In particular with $A_i = \varnothing$, $B_i = \varnothing$, $i = 1, 2$, ψ^* is a ring homomorphism.

Since the homomorphisms in the diagram below are all induced by maps, there is commutativity in

$$\begin{array}{ccc} H((X_1\ A_1) \times (X, A_2)) & \xleftarrow{(\psi_1 \times \psi_2)^*} & H((Y, B_1) \times (Y_1\ B_2)) \\ \downarrow{\scriptstyle \Delta^*} & & \downarrow{\scriptstyle '\Delta^*} \\ H(X, A_1 \cup A_2) & \xleftarrow{\psi_3{}^*} & H(Y, B_1 \cup B_2) \end{array}$$

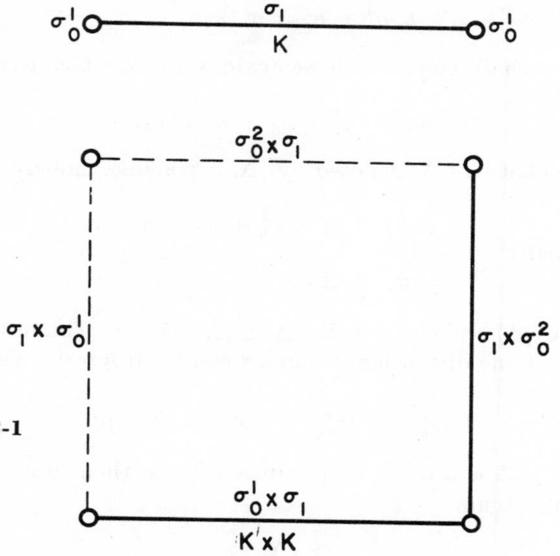

Figure 12-1

so, starting with an element $\mathbf{f}_1 \times \mathbf{f}_2$ in $H((Y, B_1) \times (Y_1\ B_2))$,

$$(\psi_1 \times \psi_2)^*(\mathbf{f}_1 \times \mathbf{f}_2) = (\psi_1^* \mathbf{f}_1) \times (\psi_2^* \mathbf{f}_2)$$
$$\Delta^*(\psi_1 \times \psi_2)^*(\mathbf{f}_1 \times \mathbf{f}_2) = \Delta^*(\psi_1^* \mathbf{f}_1) \times (\psi_2^* \mathbf{f}_2)$$
$$= (\psi_1^* \mathbf{f}_1) \cup \psi_2^* \mathbf{f}_2.$$

This is also the value of

$$\psi_3^* \Delta^* (\mathbf{f}_1 \times \mathbf{f}_2) = \psi_3^*(\mathbf{f}_1 \cup \mathbf{f}_2).$$

It may have struck the reader as strange that the factorization of the cup product as $\Delta \times$ should have been presented first for the singular theory rather than for the simplicial complex case. There is an immediate stumbling block in defining the diagonal chain map. With $K^2 = K \times K$ (2.3), the diagonal, space map Δ has no correspondent as a cell map since the point set diagonal generally does not constitute a concrete subcomplex of $K \times K$. Consider, for instance, the special case, K a closed 1 simplex.

$$K = \sigma_0^1, \sigma_0^2, \sigma_1$$
$$K \times K = \sigma_0^1 \times \sigma_0^2, \sigma_0^2 \times \sigma_0^1, \ldots, \sigma_0^1 \times \sigma_1, \sigma_0^2 \times \sigma_1, \sigma_1^2 \times \sigma_0, \sigma_1 \times \sigma_1$$

Definition 3.3
Note

(3.3a)
$$\|\Delta\sigma_1\| \subset \|\sigma_1\| \times \|\sigma_1\| = Q(\sigma_1).$$

We note also that the cyclic permutation group, T, on $K \times K$ has generators 1 and t. Thus

(3.3b)
$$t\colon \sigma_i^j \times \sigma_r^s = \sigma_r^s \times \sigma_i^j.$$

Then Q carries a chain map, which we again write Δ, which can be taken as

(3.3c)
$$\Delta\sigma_1 = \sigma_0^1 \times \sigma_1 + \sigma_1 \times \sigma_0^2.$$

An alternative choice of Δ, denoted by ${}_1\Delta$, is possible, namely

$${}_1\Delta\sigma_1 = \sigma_1 \times \sigma_0^1 + \sigma_0^2 \times \sigma_1.$$

Note that formally

$${}_1\Delta\sigma_1 = t\Delta\,\sigma_1.$$

Since $Q(\Delta) = Q({}_1\Delta)$ and Q is acyclic, $\Delta \simeq {}_1\Delta$ (71.1). The restriction of K to a single closed one dimensional simplex can be dropped. We need merely replace (3.3a) by

$$\|\Delta\sigma_m^r\| \subset \|\sigma_m^r\| \times \|\sigma_m^r\| = Q(\sigma_m^r),$$

and once more if Δ is a chain map induced by Δ, then so is $t\Delta$, where t is given by (3.3b). Again

(3.3d)
$$\Delta \simeq {}_1\Delta.$$

Thus the cup product for $\mathbf{f}^p \in H^p(K)$, $\mathbf{g}^q \in H^q(K)$ can be defined as in (3.1) by using representatives

$$(f^p \cup g^q)\sigma_{p+q} = (f^p \times g^q)\Delta\,\sigma_{p+q}.$$

For the sake of completeness, as well as to indicate how the diagonal approximations, or rather deviations, are behind other pairings as well, we denote Δ for the moment as ${}_0\Delta$. Let ${}_1\Delta$ be the endomorphism establishing the homotopy in (3.3d) and heretofore indicated by D,

$$d\,{}_1\Delta + {}_1\Delta\,d = t\,{}_0\Delta - {}_0\Delta.$$

Then we can define

$$(f^p \cup_1 g^q)\,\sigma_{p+g} = (f^p \times g^q)\,{}_1\Delta\,\sigma_{p+q}.$$

Proceeding, we get, with the endomorphism ${}_2\Delta$ satisfying

$$d\,{}_2\Delta - {}_2\Delta\,d = {}_1\Delta + t\,{}_1\Delta,$$

$$(f^p \cup_2 g^q)\,\sigma_{p+q} = (f^p \times g^q)\,{}_2\Delta\,\sigma_{p+q}.$$

This gives the $\cup_i$ products by induction for all i, when

$$d\ {}_{2i}\Delta - {}_{2i}\Delta\, d = {}_{2i-1}\Delta + t\ {}_{2i-1}\Delta,$$
$$d\ {}_{2i+1}\Delta + {}_{2i+1}\Delta\, d = {}_{2i}\Delta - t\ {}_{2i}\Delta.$$

The pairings, indicated by $\cup_i$, extend to the cohomology groups. What is at the heart of their derivation is the group of cyclic permutations T, here of $K \times K$, and more generally of $K \times \cdots \times K$. The key is the observation that ${}_i\Delta$ decreases the grade by i and hence induces homomorphisms in $H^p \to H^{p+i}$.

The development of this type of homomorphism is taken up in much more detail from a somewhat different point of view in (136).

4. RELATIONS OF PRODUCTS. We present some comments bearing on the order assumptions for the classical cup product definitions for simplicial complexes. Let w be a fixed partial ordering of the vertices of K, which is a simple ordering on each simplex. The ordered simplex, complex and pair are temporarily designated by ${}_w\sigma_p$, ${}_wK$ and ${}_wK$, ${}_wL$ while the oriented entities are intended when the script, w, is absent.

Definition 4.1. Let $\sigma_p = A_0 \cdots A_p$ be an oriented simplex. Let $A_{i_0} \cdots A_{i_p}$ be the vertex ordering imposed by w. Then

$$w_\# \sigma_p = {}_w\sigma_p \quad \text{or} \quad -{}_w\sigma_p, \tag{4.1a}$$

according as $A_0 \cdots A_p$ is an even or an odd permutation of $A_{i_0} \cdots A_{i_p}$. By linearity $w_\#$ extends to

$$w_\#\colon C(K, L) \to C({}_wK, {}_wL).$$

Lemma 4.2. *$w_\#$ is an allowable homomorphism.*

Let the oriented simplex σ_{p+1} be represented by $A_0 \cdots A_{p+1}$ which is the ordering prescribed by w (otherwise we should choose $-\sigma_{p+1}$). This implies that the face of σ_{p+1} opposite A_j has the w ordering $A_0 \cdots \hat{A_j} \cdots A_{p+1}$. Thus

$$\begin{aligned}\partial w_\#\sigma_{p+1} &= \partial A_0 \cdots A_{p+1} = \Sigma\,(-1) A_0 \cdots \hat{A_j} \cdots A_{p+1}\\ &= \Sigma\,(-1)^i\, w_\#\, A_0 \cdots \hat{A_j} \cdots A_{p+1} = w_\#\, \partial\sigma_{p+1}.\end{aligned}$$

Definition 4.3. Let $f^p \in C^p(K, L_1)$, $g^q \in C^q(K, L_2)$. Then $(f^p \cup g^q)(\sigma_{p+q})$ is defined by $(f^p \cup g^q)w_\#(\sigma_{p+q})$, whence

$$(f^p \cup g^q)(A_0 \cdots A_{p+q}) = f^p(A_{i_0} \cdots A_{i_p})g^q(A_{i_p} \cdots A_{i_{p+q}}).$$

Alternatively we can write

$$(w^\#(f^p \cup g^q)(\sigma_{p+q}).$$

PROBLEM

12-5. Show $\delta w^{\#}(f^p \cup g^q) = w^{\#}\,\delta(f^p \cup g^q)$.

The constructive definition of the cup product given in (2.13) allows proofs of associativity by direct computation. For example:

Lemma 4.4. *If* $R_1 = R_2 = R$ *and if* f^r, g^s, h^t *are elements of* $H^*(X, A)$, *then*

$$(f^r \cup g^s) \cup h^t = f^r \cup (g^s \cup h^t).$$

Let f^r, g^s, h^t be representative cocycles of the obvious cosets. Then with u_{r+s+t} a singular simplex with forward face u_{r+s} and back face u_t, etc.,

$$((f^r \cup g^s) \cup h^t)u_{r+q+s} = (f^r \cup g^s)u_{r+s}\, h^t\, u_t$$
$$= (f^r\, u_r)(g^s\, u_s)(h^t\, u_t).$$

Since coefficient rings have been assumed associative, the assertion of the theorem follows.

For the following lemma suppose the restriction $G_1 = G_2 = G_3 = G$ is put on the Abelian groups or rings paired (actually the condition $g_1 g_2 = g_2 g_1$ is sufficient).

Lemma 4.5. *Let* X *be a simplicial complex. Let* $\mathbf{f}^r \in H^r(X, A_1)$ *and let* $\mathbf{g}^s \in H^s(X, A_2)$. *Then* $\mathbf{f}^r \cup \mathbf{g}^s = (-1)^{rs}\, \mathbf{g}^s \cup \mathbf{f}^r \in H^{r+s}((X, A_1) \times (X, A_2))$.

Let f^r and g^s be representative cocycles of $\mathbf{f}^r$ and $\mathbf{g}^s$. Let $wA^p \cdots A^q = A^q \cdots A^p$ and denote $w^{\#}F$ by $\bar{F}$.

$$\overline{(f^r \cup g^s)}A^0 \cdots A^{r+s}$$
$$= \bar{f}^r(A^0 \cdots A^r)\bar{g}^s(A^r \cdots A^{r+s})$$
$$= \bar{g}^s(A^r \cdots A^{r+s})\bar{f}^r(A^0 \cdots A^r)$$
$$= (-1)^{\frac{s(s+1)}{2}}(-1)^{\frac{r(r+1)}{2}} g^s(A^{r+s} \cdots A^r) f^r(A^r \cdots A^0)$$
$$= (-1)^{\frac{s(s+1)+r(r+1)}{2}} (g^s \cup f^r)(A^{r+s} \cdots A^0)$$
$$= (-1)^{\frac{s(s+1)+r(r+1)+(r+s)(r+s+1)}{2}} (\bar{g}^s \cup \bar{f}^r)(A^0 \cdots A^{r+s}).$$

The proof is completed by the observation that

$$\frac{s(s+1) + r(r+1) + (r+s)(r+s+1)}{2} = rs \bmod 2$$

and appeal to (4.2) and (3.2).

PROBLEMS

12-6. Let K be a finite simplicial complex with $f^1 \in H^1(K, J)$. Show $\mathbf{f}^1 \cup \mathbf{f}^1 = 0$. *Hint:* If γ^i is the generator of $H^1(S^1, J)$, there is a simplicial map ψ on K to S^1 such that $\psi^*(\gamma^1) = \mathbf{f}^1$. (It is not necessarily true that $\mathbf{f}^m \cup \mathbf{f}^m = 0$, $m > 1$.)

12-7. Prove the result in Problem 12-4 with coefficient group J_p, $2 < p$, a prime. *Hint:* If f^1 is a representative of $\mathbf{f}^1$, use the condition $(\delta f^1)(\sigma_2 = (A_0A_1A_2)) = 0$ on $(f^1 \cup f^1)(A_0A_1A_2)$ and define $g^1(\sigma_1 \mid \sigma_1 < \sigma_2)$ as a quadratic function of $f^1(\sigma_1)$. Get $\delta g^1 = f^1 \cup f^1$.

12-8. Show there is no unit for the ring ${}_SH^*(X, A)$, $A \neq \varnothing$. *Hint:* Try the exact sequence. (For Alexander gratings, f^0, defined by $f^0(x \mid X - A)$ is a unit.)

Remark. The cross-products are of immediate interest in yielding generators in the Kunneth theorem. In view of applications of this theorem it is worthwhile emphasizing again that, except when $H(X)$ and $H(Y)$ are torsion free, the Kunneth relation is a group or module isomorphism and not a ring isomorphism. The following example illustrates this point.

EXAMPLE 12-1. Let $X = P^2 \vee S^1$ where $\vee$ indicates P^2 and S^1 have just one point in common. Let $Y = K^2$, the Klein bottle. Since $P^2 \vee S^1$ is nonorientable, $H^3(X) = 0$. The generators of $H^i(X)$ are $\mathbf{f}^0$, $\mathbf{f}^1$, and $\mathbf{f}^2$ where $\mathbf{f}^2$ is a torsion element with $2\mathbf{f}^2 = d\mathbf{g}^1$. The generators are the same for $H^i(Y)$. The cup products are indicated by

	$\mathbf{f}^0$	$\mathbf{f}^1$	$\mathbf{f}^2$
$\mathbf{f}^0$	$\mathbf{f}^0$	$\mathbf{f}^1$	$\mathbf{f}^2$
$\mathbf{f}^1$	$\mathbf{f}^1$	0	0
$\mathbf{f}^2$	$\mathbf{f}^2$	0	0

The generators of $H(X \times X)$ and $H(Y \times Y)$ are $\mathbf{f}^0 \times \mathbf{f}^0$, $\mathbf{f}^0 \times \mathbf{f}^1$, $\mathbf{f}^1 \times \mathbf{f}^2$, $\mathbf{f}^2 \times \mathbf{f}^1$ and, since $d\mathbf{g}^1 \times \mathbf{g}^1 = 2(\mathbf{f}^2 \times \mathbf{g}^1 - \mathbf{g}^1 \times \mathbf{f}^2)$, $\mathbf{f}^3 = \mathbf{f}^2 \times \mathbf{g}^1 - \mathbf{g}^1 \times \mathbf{f}^2$, a torsion element with torsion coefficient 2. The products are, however, different according as we take $X \times X$ or $Y \times Y$. The table below lists some of these products in these two complexes.

	$\mathbf{f}^1 \times \mathbf{f}^0$		$\mathbf{f}^0 \times \mathbf{f}^1$	
	$X \times X$	$Y \times Y$	$X \times X$	$Y \times Y$
$\mathbf{f}^1 \times \mathbf{f}^0$	0	0	0	0
$\mathbf{f}^2 \times \mathbf{f}^1$	0	0	0	0
$\mathbf{f}^3$	0	$(\mathbf{f}^2 \times \mathbf{f}^2)$	0	$(\mathbf{f}^2 \times \mathbf{f}^2)$

5. INTERRELATIONS OF PRODUCTS. The close liaison between cross- and cup products will be apparent from the converse process of deriving a cross-product from a cup product.

Definition 5.1. Suppose

(5.1a) $H^*((X_1, A_1) \times X_2) \cup H^*(X_1 \times (X_2, A_2) \subset H^*((X_1, A_1) \times (X_2, A_2))$.

Let the projections p and q be defined by

$$p: X_1, A_1 \times X_2 \to X_1, A_1 \qquad (5.1b)$$

$$q: X_1 \times (X_2, A_2) \to X_2, A_2.$$

Then, with ${}_ih \in H^*(X_1, A_1)$, $i = 1, 2$, $p^* \, {}_ih \in H^*((X_1, A_1) \times X_2)$ $q^* \, {}_2h \in H^*(X_1 \times (X_2, A_2))$. Define ${}_1h \times {}_2h$ by

$$ {}_1h \times {}_2h = (p^* \, {}_1h) \cup (q^* \, {}_2h). \qquad (5.1c)$$

Thus (82.17) and (5.1c) obviate the need for (2.10–2.14).

PROBLEM

12-9. Show that the homomorphism θ defined by $\theta \, {}_1h \otimes {}_2h = {}_1h \times {}_2h$ of (5.1c) satisfies conditions (b) and (c) of (2.5) and hence may be termed a cross-product.

The natural question as to whether the cross-product defined by starting with the cup product recovers the same cup product when substituted in (3.1) is answered in the affirmative in the following lemma.

Lemma 5.2

(5.2a) *If* $\cup$ *is a cup product homomorphism and* $\times$ *is determined by* (5.1c), *and if the cup product* $\cup_1$ *is defined by* (3.1), *then* $\cup = \cup_1$.

(5.2b) *If* $\times$ *is a cross-product and* $\cup$ *is determined by* (3.1) *and if* $\times_1$ *is then found from this* $\cup$ *by* (5.1c), *then* $\times = \times_1$.

Since $X \times X$, $A_1 \times X = (X, A_1) \times X$, and $X \times X$, $X \times A_2 = X \times (X, A_2)$, we can write

$$X, A_1, A_2 \xrightarrow{\Delta} X \times X, A_1 \times X, X \times A_2 \begin{matrix} \xrightarrow{p} X, A_1 \\ \xrightarrow{q} X, A_2 \end{matrix} \qquad (5.2c)$$

Write Δ_i for $\Delta \mid X, A_i$. Observe $p\Delta \mid X, A_1$ is the identity map and so is $q\Delta \mid X, A_2$. Accordingly $\Delta^* p^*$ and $\Delta^* q^*$ are identity automorphisms.

Let $f^m \in H^m((X_1, A_1) \times X)$ and let $g^n \in H_n(X \times (X, A_2))$. Then

$$\begin{aligned} f^m \cup_1 g^n &= \Delta^* f^n \times g^n \qquad (3.1) \\ &= \Delta^*(p^* f^m \cup q^* g^n) \\ &= (\Delta_1^* p^* f^m) \cup (\Delta_2^* q^* g^n) \qquad (3.2) \\ &= f^m \cup g^n, \end{aligned} \qquad (5.2d)$$

where for the indicated application of (3.2) we replace X, A_1, A_2 by $X \times X$, $A_1 \times X$, $X \times A_2$ and Y, B_1, B_2 by X, A_1, A_2 and use Δ_i for ψ_i. Hence $\cup$ and $\cup_1$ agree.

We turn to (5.2b).

$$\begin{aligned} f^m \times_1 g^n &= p^*f^m \cup q^*g^n \\ &= \Delta^*(p^*f^m \times q^*g^n) \qquad (3.1) \\ &= \Delta^*(p^*f^m) \times (\Delta^*q^*g^n) \\ &= f^m \times g^n \end{aligned}$$

so $\times_1$ and $\times$ agree.

6. CAP PRODUCTS.

The cup product is analogous to a vector product of two contravariant vectors or tensors and the cap product to the contraction of a contravariant and a covariant tensor. The cap product enters for dual gratings and has been extensively used in (113).

Definition 6.1. Let K be a simplicial complex with a prescribed vertex ordering w. We deal with replete simplexes and tacitly assume throughout that $p \leq m$. If $f^p \in C^p(K, G)$ and $c_m \in C_m(K, \mathrm{J})$,

(6.1a) $$A_0 \cdots A_m \cap f^p = f^p(A_0 \cdots A_p)(A_p \cdots A_m).$$

More generally with $c_m = \Sigma\, g\sigma^i_m$, where $\sigma^i_m = \sigma^i_{p\ m-p}\, \sigma^i$,

$$c_m \cap f^p = \Sigma\, g_i f^p(\sigma^i_p)_{m-p}\sigma, \qquad p \leq m.$$

$$\begin{aligned} A_0 \cdots A_m \cap \delta f^p &= (\delta f^p)(A_0 \cdots A_{p+1})(A_{p+1} \cdots A_m) \\ &= \Sigma_0^{p+1} (-1)^j f^p(A_0 \cdots \hat{A}_j \cdots A_{p+1})A_{p+1} \cdots A_m). \end{aligned}$$

$$\begin{aligned} (\partial(A_0, \cdots, A_m)) \cap f^p &= \Sigma_0^p(-1)^j f^p(A_0 \cdots \hat{A}_j \cdots A_{p+1})A_{p+1} \cdots A_m + \\ &\quad + \Sigma_p^n(-1)^j f^p(A_0 \cdots A_p)A_p \cdots \hat{A}_j \cdots A_m \\ &= A_0 \cdots A_m \cap \delta f^p + \partial(-1)^p(A_0 \cdots A_m) \cap f^p. \end{aligned}$$

This extends immediately by linearity to

$$(\partial c_m) \cap f^p = c_m \cap \delta f^p + (-1)^p\, \partial(c_m \cap f^p).$$

Remark. In the literature sometimes a sign factor is introduced in (6.1a), namely, $i(-p)$ (64.14d).

Definition 6.2. Assume G_1 and G_2 paired to G below. Replace simplexes by singular simplexes and get the **cap pairing**,

$$\cap\colon {}_SC_m(X, G_1) \otimes {}_SC^p(X, G_2) \to {}_SC_{m-p}(X, G)$$

where if $c_m = \Sigma_i g_i u^i_m \in {}_SC_m(X, G_1)$ and $f^p \in {}_SC^p(X, G_2)$, then, with $u^i_m = u^i_p{}_{m-p}u^i$, $c_m \cap f^p = \Sigma_1 g_i f^p(u^i_p)_{m-p}u^i$, where ${}_1g_i f^p(u^i_p) \in G$ by the assumed pairing.

(6.2a) $$\partial(c_m \cap f^p) = (-1)^p((\partial c_m) \cap f^p - c_m \cap \delta f^p).$$

Lemma 6.3. *If* $\psi: X \to Y$ *and* $c_m \in {}_SC_m(X, G_1)$ *and* $f^p \in {}_SC^p(Y, G_2)$, *then* $\psi_\#(c_m \cap \psi^\# f^p) = (\psi_\# c_m) \cap f^p$.

We need check this for a singular simplex u_m only. Then

$$\psi_\#(gu_m \cap \psi^\# f^p) = \psi_\#(g(\psi^\# f^p)(u_p)_{m-p}u) = gf^p(\psi_\# u_p)\psi_{\#\, m-p}u$$
$$= g\psi_\#(u_m \cap f^p).$$

Our cap pairing involves the absolute groups $C^p(X, G)$ and $C_m(X, G)$. In order to bring in the relative groups we observe that $C^p(X, A, G) \subset C^p(X, G)$. On the other hand, $C_p(X, A, G)$ and its subgroups $Z_p(X, A, G)$ and $B_p(X, A, G)$ are quotient groups of $C_p(X, G)$. We therefore replace these quotient groups by isomorphic images in the absolute chain group $C_p(X, G_2)$ analogously to the prescription (43.10a). For generality we replace the pair in (43.10a) by triples and the chain complex by a singular chain complex.

Definition 6.4. Let ${}_1i: A_1 \to X$, ${}_2i: A_2 \to X$, be inclusion maps. Then, dropping the script S, and the group symbol, G,

$$C_m(X, A_1, A_2) = C_m(X)/{}_1i_\# C_m(A_1) \cup {}_2i_\# C_m(A_2),$$

(6.4a) $$\bar{Z}_{m+1}(X, A_1, A_2) = \partial^{-1}({}_1i_\# C_m(A_1) \cup {}_2i_\# C_m(A_2)),$$

$$\bar{B}_m(X, A_1, A_2) = B_m(X) \cup {}_1i_\# C_m(A_1) \cup {}_1i_\# C_m(A_2),$$

are *subgroups of* $C_m(X, G_1)$. Just as in (44.7) we can establish

(6.4b) $$\bar{H}_m(X, A_1, A_2, G) \approx H_m(X, A_1, A_2, G).$$

Lemma 6.5. *If* $\bar{z}_m \in \bar{Z}_m(X, A_1, A_2, G_1)$ *and* $f^p \in Z^p(X, A_1, G_2)$, *then*

(6.5a) $$\bar{z}_m \cap f^p \in \bar{Z}_{m-p}(X, A_2)$$

(6.5b) *If either* $\bar{z}_m$ *or* f^p *is bounding, then the right hand side of* (6.5a) *can be substituted by* $\bar{B}_{m-p}(X, A_2)$.

From (6.2a), noting $f^p \mid C_p(A_1) = 0$, and

$$\partial\bar{z}_m \in {}_1i_\# C_m(A_1) \cup {}_2i_\# C_m(A_2),$$

$$\partial(\bar{z}_m \cap f^p) = (-1)^p(\partial\bar{z}_m) \cap f^p \in {}_2i_\# C_{m-p-1}(A_2),$$

as required by (6.5a).

If $z_m \in B_m(X, A_1, A_2)$ (6.4a), then write

$$\bar{z}_m = \partial c_{m+1}(X, G_1) + {}_1i_{\#}\, c_m(A_1, G_1) + {}_2i_{\#}\, c_m(A_2, G_1)$$

and

$$\bar{z}_m \cap f^p = \partial c_{m+1}(X, G_1) \cap f^p + {}_2i_{\#}\, c_m(A_2, G_1) \cap f^p$$
$$\subset \bar{B}_{m-p}(X, G_1) + {}_2i_{\#}\, C_{m-p}(A_2, G_1) \subset \bar{B}_{m-p}(X, A_2).$$

Lemma 6.6. *The cap pairing defined in* (6.1) *and* (6.2) *induces a cap pairing again denoted by*

$$\cap: H_m(X, A_1, A_2, G_1) \otimes H^p(X, A_1, G_2) \to H_{m-p}(X, A_2, G).$$

This is a consequence of (6.5a) when account is taken of (6.4b).

Lemma 6.7. *If* $\psi: X, A_1\, A_2 \to Y, B_1, B_2$ *and if* $\mathbf{h}_m \in H_m(X, A_1, A_2)$ *and* $\mathbf{f}^p \in H^p(Y, B_1)$ *then*

$$\psi_*(\mathbf{h}_m \cap \psi^* \mathbf{f}^p) = (\psi_* \mathbf{h}_m) \cap \mathbf{f}^p \subset H_{m-p}(Y, B_2).$$

It is only necessary to combine (6.3), (6.5), and (6.6).

Lemma 6.8. *If* $c_m \in {}_SC_m(X, G_1)$, $f^p \in {}_SC^p(X, G_2)$, $t^p \in {}_SC^q(X, G_3)$ *where*

$$(g_1\, g_2)\, g_3 = g_1(g_2\, g_3),$$

then

(6.8a) $$(c_m \cap f^p) \cap t^q = c_m \cap (f^p \cup t^q).$$

Thus with $u_m = u_p\, u_{m-p} = u_{p+q}\, u_{m-(p+q)}$, $u_{m-p} = u_q\, u_{m-(p+q)}$,

$$\begin{aligned}(u_m \cap f^p) \cap t^q &= f^p(u_p) t^q(u_q) u_{m-(p+q)}\\ &= (f^p \cup t^q)(u_{p+q}) u_{m-(p+q)}\\ &= u_m \cap (f^p \cup t^q)\end{aligned}$$

(where heretofore the back faces have been written ${}_{m-p}u$ and ${}_{m-(p+q)}u$.)

Definition 6.9. The **scalar product** of elements in ${}_SC_m(X, G_1)$ and in ${}_SC^m(X, G_2)$ is written $c_m f^m$ for

$$c_m f^m = \operatorname{In}(c_m \cap f^m), \qquad (71.3),$$

which coincides with the index $\operatorname{In}(c_m, f^m)$ (72.2b). For the omology classes there is an induced scalar product, $\cdot$, defined by the commutative triangle

$$\begin{array}{ccc} H_m(X, A, G_1) \otimes H^m(X, A, G_2) & \longrightarrow & G \\ \downarrow \cap & \nearrow & \\ H_0(X, G) & & \end{array}$$

PROBLEMS

12-10. Show $c_m \cdot f^p \cup t^q = c_m \cap f^p \cdot t^q$ if $m = p + q$. Observe that this gives a means of defining the cap product in terms of the cup product and the scalar product in the absolute case.

12-11. Show $(f \times g^r) \cup (F^s \times G) = (-1)^{rs}(f \cup F) \times (g \cup G)$.

12-12. Let $\underline{\times}$ and $\overline{\times}$ refer to chain and to cochain products respectively, as well as to the induced products on the omology groups. Show that

$$(a \underline{\times} b^r) \cap (f^s \overline{\times} g) = (-1)^{rs}(a \cap f) \times (b \cap g).$$

Remark. The considerations in (47) connected with K^* are in point for the geometric setting for cap products. Suppose K is a concrete simplicial manifold. It is then clear that $\|\sigma_p^i\| \cap \|E_j^q\| = \varnothing$ if $q > p$. If $q = p$, then $\|\sigma_p^i\| \cap \|E_i^p\|$ consists of precisely one point, and when $q < p$ the intersection if nonvoid is a $p - q$ dimensional simplex.

7. TOPOLOGICAL COEFFICIENT GROUPS. We now turn attention to topological, Abelian coefficient groups. Such a group G considered as a space is written $|G|$ and is a Hausdorff space (and even completely regular). Unless otherwise stated, *a homomorphism is also an open* (*always continuous*) *map.* It is understood that a quotient group $G/G' = \{[g]\}$ presupposes G' is a closed subgroup of G and that an open set in G/G' is of the form $\{[g] \mid g \in U, |U| \text{ open in } |G|\}$.

The topological interpretation to be given the chain groups over complexes is clear from the remark in (31.2). The complexes may be simplicial or singular. Thus, the infinite chain group $C_m(K, G)$ refers to direct products and, as a point set, is the topological product $\mathbf{P}_{\sigma_m \in K^{(m)}} |G_{\sigma_m}|$. If L is a subcomplex of K, then $i_\# C_m(L, G)$ is the subspace $\mathbf{P}_{\sigma_m \in L^{(m)}} |G_{\sigma_m}| \times \mathbf{P}_{\sigma_m \bar{\in} L^{(m)}} |0_{\sigma_m}|$. The topology of $|C_m(K, L, G)|$ is that of the group $C_m(K, G)/i_\# C_m(L, G)$. Similar remarks hold for the infinite cochain groups. If the complex is infinite, the finite chain groups are direct sums and are given the discrete topology. If the complex is finite, either the product topology or the discrete topology may be chosen.

The groups $Z^m(K, G)$, $Z_m(K, G)$, $B_m(K, G)$, $B^m(K, G)$, etc., are subgroups of the chain and cochain groups and have the relative topology.

Definition 7.1. A little care is required in defining the homology group. Thus if $B_m(K, G)$ is not a closed subgroup, i.e., not a closed subspace of the space $|C_m(K, G)|$ then $Z_m(K, G)/B_m(K, G)$ would not be a topological group in our sense, since points would not be closed sets. Accordingly we define $H_m(K, G)$ by

$$H^m(K, G) = Z^m(K, G)/\overline{B^m}(K, G), \tag{7.1a}$$

where $\bar{B}$ indicates topological closure.

Another problem arises when direct and inverse limits intervene, as in the case of the Cech groups. The inverse limit group considered as a space is a subspace of a product space (77.1). Thus if $H_m(X, G) = \underleftarrow{\mathsf{L}}\{H_m(a, G), p_{b*}{}^a, a$ the nerve of the finite open cover α, of $X\}$, then

$$(7.1b) \qquad |H_m(X, G)| \subset \mathbf{P}_\alpha\, |H_m(a, G)|.$$

Usually the direct limit is untopologized (but see (7.6)). Hence the Cech or Alexander cohomology groups are taken discrete. The situation for singular omology is the reverse of the above. Since finite singular chains have compact support, any singular chain is on some compact subset X_a of X. Hence one expects ${}_SH_*(X)$ would be at least isomorphic to $\underrightarrow{\mathsf{L}}\, {}_SH_*(X_a)$ and similarly that ${}_SH^*(X)$ would be $\underleftarrow{\mathsf{L}}\, {}_SH^*(X_a)$. The singular homology groups then are to be discrete, so the coefficient group is to be taken discrete while the cohomology groups may be topologized. In particular the coefficient group can be taken compact. This view of the singular groups is the basis for understanding (8.2).

Our interest is restricted to the case that G is either discrete, compact, or locally compact. The first division is that comprised, say by J and J_p or the rational or real numbers taken in the discrete topology. The second division is illustrated by the group P, the multiplicative group of complex numbers of modulus 1 taken in the topology of the circle: Thus

$$\text{P} \approx \{z \mid z = e^{i\theta}\}.$$

This is (topologically) isomorphic, on taking logarithms, to the representation as the *additive group of the real numbers mod* 1. The latter interpretation is that used below. The last division is illustrated by the real or complex numbers in their usual topology, or in their discrete topology.

We assume the elements of the *character theory* of groups are known or are available. For convenience we cite the specific aspects we shall use. All coefficient groups are understood to be locally compact for the moment.

Definition 7.2. The collection of homomorphisms $\{g^*\}$ of G to P with addition defined by

$$(g^* + g'^*)(g) = g^*(g) + g'^*(g),$$

and with the co-open topology (**A**), make up the **character group** G^*. The correspondence $g^* \otimes g' \to g^*(g) \in \text{P}$ constitutes a **pairing** in the topological case.

We need

(a) $(G^*)^* \approx G$.

(b) If G is discrete, G^* is compact, and by **(a)** if G^* is discrete, G is compact.

(c) If $g \neq 0$, then for some g^*, $g^*(g) \neq 0$. Similarly if $g^* \neq 0$, $g^*(g) \neq 0$ for some g. Thus pairing of G and G^* is **orthogonal** (72).

Remark. A slight generalization of character theory is possible. If, for instance, G is Q, R, or C, then the results above retain their validity when we replace P by G and take $G^* = G$ in the discrete topology. Thus, if Q is taken in the discrete topology, it is orthogonal to R with respect to R.

PROBLEM

12-13. If A and B are discrete groups, show $A \otimes B \approx (Hom(A, B))^*$ and $Hom(A \otimes B, C) \approx Hom(B, Hom(A, C))$.

The introduction of topological groups necessitates a slight modification in the results of (72)—by reason of (7.1a), for instance. We take cognizance of some modifications in the following:

Definition 7.3. If G_1 and G_2 are paired to G and $G_1' \subset G_i$, then $0(G_1'; G_2) = \{g_2 \mid G_1' g_2 = 0\}$ is the **annihilator** of G_1' in G_2. Similarly, $0(G_2'; G_1) = \{g_1 \mid g_1 G_2' = 0\}$ is the **annihilator** of G_2' in G_1.

In the next lemma the chain and cochain groups have arguments (K, G^*) and (K, G) respectively.

Lemma 7.4. *Under scalar pairing* (6.9),

(7.4a) $Z^m = 0(B_m; C^m)$

(7.4b) $\bar{B}_m = 0(Z^m, C_m)$

(7.4c) $Z_m = 0(B^m, C_m)$

(7.4d) $B^m = 0(Z_m, C^m)$.

The argument for (7.4a) is that of (72.7) for, by continuity, $0(\bar{B}_m; C^m) = 0(B_m; C^m)$. That for (7.4d) is (72.6) since B^m and $\bar{B}^m$ are here the same.

Lemma 7.5. *If K is a finite complex, then, for G locally compact,*

$$H_m(K, L, G) \otimes H^m(K, L, G^*) \to \mathrm{P}$$

is an orthogonal pairing.

Denote an element of $H_m(K, L, G)$ by $\mathbf{z}_m$ and that of $H^m(K, L, G^*)$ by $\mathbf{z}^m$. Then, independently of the representative chosen, $\mathbf{z}_m \cdot \mathbf{z}^m = z_m \cdot z^m$ (6.5b). Hence $z_m \cdot z^m = 0$ implies $z_m \in \bar{B}_m$ or $\mathbf{z}_m = 0$.

We have already found it convenient to introduce topological closures of the usual groups arising in omology (7.1a). Similarly introducing closure of a quotient group of the formal direct limit yields topologized direct limits and extends duality between direct and inverse limits. (Indeed from the viewpoint of category theory what we are about to do is covered by the dual category concept.)

Definition 7.6. Let $\Sigma^+ = \{G_a, p^a{}_b\}$ where G_a is compact. Then G_a^* is discrete (7.2b) and dual homomorphisms $\{p_a{}^b\}$ exist so that $\Sigma^- = \{G_a^*, p_a{}^b\}$ constitutes an inverse system. Here $p_a{}^b$ satisfies the condition that the pairing of G_a and $p_a{}^b G_b^*$ is that of $p^a{}_b G_a$ and G_b^*. More precisely for $g_a \in G_a$ and $g_b^* \in G_b^*$

$$(7.6a) \qquad (p_a{}^b\, g_b^*)(g_a) = g_b^*(p^a{}_b g_a) \in \mathrm{P}.$$

$\underleftarrow{\mathsf{L}}\, \Sigma^-$ is denoted by G^* and is contained in the Cartesian product ΠG_a^*. We assign ΠG_a^*, and therefore G^* also, the discrete topology. (This will generally not be the Tychonoff topology notwithstanding G_a^* is discrete.)

The untopologized direct limit $\underrightarrow{\mathsf{L}}\, \Sigma^+$ is indicated by G'. In view of (7.6a) the pairing of G' and G^* is defined by

$$(7.6b) \qquad g^*(g') = g_a^*(g_a)$$

where g_a is a coordinate of g^* and $g' = [g_a] \in G'$. Write $G'' = 0(G^*, G')$ (7.3). We define a typical member of the neighborhood basis at the neutral element of G'/G''. Thus let $\{{}_ig^* \mid i \in \pi\}$ be a finite subset of G^* and let U be a neighborhood of the neutral element of P. Then $\{h \mid {}_ig^*(h) \in U\}$ constitutes a neighborhood. (According to (7.2a), ${}_ig^*(h)$ can be written $h({}_ig^*)$.) Moreover since G^* is discrete, a compact subset is a finite subset. Hence the topology just defined for G'/G'' is the compact open topology for this subspace of the space of maps of G^* to P.

It is clear that G'/G'' is a subgroup of the compact group $G = (G^*)^*$(7.2b). Moreover it is dense in G. We therefore define the topologized direct limit of Σ^+ to be $G = \overline{G'/G''}$ a compact group which is dual to G^*.

Definition 7.7. Let K be an infinite complex and let $\{K_m\}$ be the directed system of its finite closed subcomplexes ordered by inclusion. Then $\{C_r(K_m, G)\}$ is a direct system. There are two ways of defining the limit homology groups. The **projective** homology groups are

$$(7.7a) \qquad H_r\, \underrightarrow{\mathsf{L}}\, C_*(K_m, G)$$

and the **expanded** groups are

$$(7.7b) \qquad \underrightarrow{\mathsf{L}}\, H_r(K_m, G).$$

Similarly $H^r \underleftarrow{\mathsf{L}} (C^*(K_m)$ and $\underleftarrow{\mathsf{L}}\, H^r(C^*(K_m\cdot G)$ are the projective and the expanded cohomology groups.

Theorem 7.8. *For G discrete the projective and the expanded homology groups are isomorphic. For G compact the projective and the expanded cohomology groups are isomorphic.*

8. ALEXANDER DUALITY THEOREM. The accomplishment of the Poincare Duality theorem (51.4) is to relate the omology groups of complementary dimension of the whole manifold. It does not add much to our understanding of the separation properties of point sets in the manifold. For the latter type of information one turns to the Alexander Duality theorem which concerns the omology properties of sets and their complements in a manifold, and has been immensely successful in settling deep point set theoretical problems.

Let K be a finite simplicial manifold (51) and suppose L is a closed subcomplex which, in view of (76.4), we assume total. Denote the barycentric subdivision by $(Sd\, K, Sd\, L)$ or $('K, 'L)$ and the dual complex to K, L by K^* (46.2). The base cycle of $Z_n('K, 'L, \mathrm{J})$ (43.10a) is denoted by $\gamma_n = \Sigma_{'K-'L}\, '\sigma_n^i$. An order is understood on the vertices of K.

Lemma 8.1.

(8.1a) $$H^p(K, L, G) \approx H_{n-p}(K - L, G).$$

(8.1b) *If* $K = S^n$, $H^p(L, G) \approx {}_SH_{n-p-1}(S^n - L, G)$, *For* $p \neq 0, n - 1$

Let f_i^p be an elementary cochain in $C^p(K, L, G)$ with $f_i^p(\sigma_p^j) = \delta_i^j$ and $f_i^p \mid L = 0$. Let E_j^p be the cell of K^* dual to σ_p^j. A simplex of its simplicial decomposition into simplexes of $'K$ is written $'\sigma_{n-p}$. Let $\sigma_n = A_0 \cdots A_n$ or $(0) \cdots (1)$ and suppose $'\sigma_n \in Sd\, \sigma_n$ and, more specifically, suppose $'\sigma_n = ((\pi_0), \ldots, (\pi_n))$ (22.2). Then (71.2)

$$'\sigma_n \cap p^\# f_i^p = ((p^\# f_i^p)((\pi_0), \ldots, (\pi_p)))((\pi_p), (\pi_n))$$
$$= (f_i^p p_\#((\pi_0), \ldots, (\pi_p)))((\pi_p), \ldots, (\pi_n)).$$

The righthand side vanishes unless $p_\#((\pi_0) \cdots (\pi_p)) = \sigma_p^i$. Accordingly if $\sigma_p^i = (i_0), \ldots, (i_p)$, then $(\pi_j) = (i_0, \ldots, i_j)$, $j \leq p$. This is denoted by $'\sigma_p^i$. It is then immediate that

(8.1c) $$\gamma_n \cap p^\# f_i^p = \Sigma \{'\sigma_{n-p} \mid {'\sigma_{n-p}} \in E_i^p\}, \quad (46.2).$$

Suppose $E^p \in K^*$. Define $j^\#$ by $j^\# E^p = \{'\sigma_{n-p} \mid {'\sigma_{n-p}} \in E^p\}$. Then $j_\#$ defines a monomorphism of $C_{n-p}(K^*, \mathrm{J}) \to C_{n-p}('K, \mathrm{J})$ and hence, by (8.1c)

$h_{\#} = j_{\#}^{-1}(\gamma \cap p^{\#})$ defines an isomorphism on $C^p(K, L, \text{J}) \to C_{n-p}(K^*, \text{J})$ on making the correspondence

(8.1d) $$f_i^p \leftrightarrow E_i^p.$$

From (6.2a)

(8.1e) $$\partial(\gamma \cap p^{\#}f^p) = (-1)^{p+1}\, \gamma \cap p^{\#}\delta f^p.$$

The integers can be replaced by the torsion free coefficient group G by tensoring with G, i.e.,

$$C^p(K, L, \text{J}) \otimes G \approx C^p(K, L, G) \approx C_{n-p}(K^*, \text{J}) \otimes G \approx C_{n-p}(K^*, G).$$

By the definition of $j_{\#}$, $\partial j_{\#} = j_{\#}\, \partial$ whence, combining with (8.1e) we have

(8.1f) $$\partial h_{\#} f^p = (-1)^{p+1}\, h_{\#}\, \delta f^p.$$

The isomorphism $h_{\#}$ of degree $-n$ (6.4) is allowable according to (8.1f), if we neglect a nonimportant sign factor. (Compare (53.11).) It follows that

(8.1g) $$H^p(K, L, G) \approx H_{n-p}(K^*, G).$$

Since L is total, $|K^*|$ is a deformation retract of $|K - L|$. Since $|K - L|$ is an open set we cannot get through with simplicial chains on the finite complex K or on $'K$. Any omology theory connected with full gratings will serve, but for convenience we choose the singular theory which is available to us, since $|K - L|$ is lc^{∞} (85.6). We infer then

(8.1h) $${}_SH_{n-p}(K^*, G) \approx {}_SH_{n-p}(K - L, G).$$

Consider the exact sequence for the pair K, L,

$$\longrightarrow H^p(K, G) \xrightarrow{i^*} H^p(L, G) \xrightarrow{\delta} H^{p+1}(K, L, G) \xrightarrow{j^*} H^{p+1}(K, G) \longrightarrow.$$

If $K = S^n$ is the triangulated n-dimensional sphere, $H^{p+1}(S^n, G) = 0$ for $p \neq n - 1$. Hence,

(8.1i) $$H^p(L, G) \approx H^{p+1}(S^n, L, G), \quad p \neq 0\ n - 1.$$

Combining (8.1g), (8.1h), and (8.1i) yields the assertion of the lemma.

Theorem 8.2. Alexander Duality Theorem. *Let A be a closed subset of the n sphere S^n. Then for, say, the Cech or Alexander homology group on the left and the singular group on the right:*

(8.2a) $$H^p(A, G) \approx {}_SH_{n-p-1}(S^n - A, G).$$

Let $\{{}^iK\}$ be a cofinal collection of barycentric subdivisions of a triangulation ${}^0K = K$ of S^n. In ${}^iK$ let ${}^i\sigma_r$ be an r-dimensional concrete open simplex. ${}^iL$ is $\{{}^i\sigma \mid |{}^i\sigma_r| \cap A \neq \varnothing\}$. Thus $|{}^iL|$ is made up of closed simplexes. Then

$$|{}^0L| \supset |{}^1L| \supset \cdots \supset A,$$

and indeed $A = \bigcap |^iL|$. Let $^iK^*$ be the dual complex to $(^iK, {}^iL)$ (46.2). Then $S^r - A = \bigcup |^iK^*|$. Let $r^i_{\ j}$ be the inclusion map: $|^iK|, |^iL| \to |^jK|, |^jL|$, $j < i$, and $q^i_{\ j}$ and $p^i_{\ j}$ the restrictions to $|^iK^*| \to |^jK^*|$ and to $|^iL| \to |^jL|$ respectively. Let $\Sigma^+(L)$ and $\Sigma^+(K)$ be the direct systems $\{H^p(^iL, g); p^{i*}_{\ j}\}$ and $\{H_{n-p-1}(^iK^*, G), q^{i*}_{\ j}\}$ respectively. The isomorphisms $^i\lambda^* = \{\lambda^i(p)^*\}$ then induce an isomorphism of $\Sigma^+(L)$ onto $\Sigma^+(K)$ according to

$$\begin{array}{ccccc} H^p(^0L, G) & \xrightarrow{p} & H^p(^1L, G) & \xrightarrow{p} & H^p(^2L, G) \longrightarrow \\ {\scriptstyle ^0\lambda^*}\downarrow\approx & & {\scriptstyle ^1\lambda^*}\downarrow\approx & & \downarrow \\ H_{n-p-1}(^0K^*, G) & \longrightarrow & H_{n-p-1}(^1K^*, G) \longrightarrow & & \end{array}$$

We need show only that each square is commutative. This stems from the fact that both

$$\text{(a)}\qquad \begin{array}{ccc} H^p(^mL, G) & \xrightarrow{p^{m\,*}_{\ m-1}} & H^p(^{m+1}L, G) \\ \downarrow \delta & & \downarrow \delta \\ H^{p+1}(^mK - {}^mL, G) & \xrightarrow{r^{m\,*}_{\ m+1}} & H^{p+1}(^{m+1}K - {}^{m+1}L, G) \end{array}$$

and

$$\text{(b)}\qquad \begin{array}{ccc} H^{p+1}(^mK - {}^mL; G) & \xrightarrow{r^{m\,*}_{\ m+1}} & H^{p+1}(^{m+1}K - {}^{m+1}L, G) \\ \downarrow {}^mh_* & & \downarrow {}^{m+1}h_* \\ H_{n-p-1}(^mK^*; G) & \xrightarrow{g^{m\,*}_{\ m+1}} & H_{n-p-1}(^{m+1}K^*, G) \end{array}$$

are commutative squares. For (**a**) this is obvious since $p^m_{\ m+1}$ and $r^m_{\ m+1}$ are inclusion maps. For (**b**) the result follows from the observation that there is commutativity at the cochain and chain level because of (8.1d),

$$\begin{array}{ccc} ^mf^p & \longrightarrow & ^{m+1}f^p \\ \downarrow h^\# & & \downarrow h^\# \\ ^mE^p & \longrightarrow & ^{m+1}E^p \end{array}$$

Hence the direct limits of $\Sigma^+(L)$ and $\Sigma^+ K^*$ are isomorphic.

We see that

$$H^p(^mL, G) = H^p(A, G),$$

as a direct consequence of the continuity theorem (91.2). We pause to point out that any compact set of $S^n - A$ lies ultimately in some $|^mK^*|$. A singular cell, u, on $S^n - A$ can therefore be considered restricted to $|^mK^*|$ when $u(\overline{\Delta_{n-p}}) \subset |^mK^*| \subset S^n - A$ and we then write ^mu for u. Let $p(m)$ be the inclusion map of $^mK^* \to S^n - A$. Evidently $q^r_{\ s}\,{}^ru(t) = {}^ru(t)$,

$t \in \Delta_{n-p}$, whence $p(r)^* = p(s)^* q^{r*}_{s}$. If ${}^r\mathbf{w} \in H_{n-p}({}^rK^*)$, denote by $[{}^r\mathbf{w}]$ or by $\mathbf{w}$ the coset or element of $\underrightarrow{\mathsf{L}}\, \Sigma^+ K^*$. Let

$$p_*(\underrightarrow{\mathsf{L}}\, \Sigma^+ K^*) \to H_{n-p-1}(S^n - A, G)$$

be defined by

$$p_*[{}^r\mathbf{w}] = p(r)_* \, {}^r\mathbf{w}. \tag{8.2b}$$

Our objective is to show that p_* is an isomorphism. First, p_* is onto. Let $\mathbf{z} \in H_{n-p-1}(S^n - A, G)$ have a representative $z(S^n - A) = \Sigma_\pi g_i u^i \in Z_{n-p-1}(S^n - A)$ with $\|u^i\| = u^i(\bar{\Delta}_{n-p-1}) \subset {}^mK^*$ for all $i \in \pi$. Then ${}^mz = \Sigma_\pi g_i \, {}^mu^i \in Z_{n-p-1}({}^mK^*, G)$, or $p(m)_* \, {}^m\mathbf{z} \in \mathbf{z}(S^n - A)$.

We have left to show $ker\, p_* = 0$. With full awareness of (8.2b) suppose then ${}^m\mathbf{w} \in ker\, p(m)_*$ with representative ${}^mw = \Sigma_\pi g_i \, {}^mu^i \in Z({}^mK^*, G)$. Note that $p(m)$ replaces ${}^mu^i$ by u^i, which refers to the same point set map, but with its range in $S^n - A$ rather than in $|{}^mK^*|$ and that we are supposing

$$p(m) \, {}^mw = w = \Sigma \, g_i u^i = \partial v,$$

for some singular chain v on $S^n - A$. Let $\|v\| \subset |{}^sK^*|$, $s \geq m$. Then v can be considered on ${}^sK^*$. Thus ${}^sw = q^m{}_s \, {}^mw - \partial^s v$. Therefore, $[{}^m\mathbf{w}] = [{}^s\mathbf{w}] = 0$.

Remark. If finite covers are used to define the Čech group,

$$H_{n-p-1}(S^n - A, G),$$

the result is not generally isomorphic to the singular homology group and (8.2) will not be valid. Similarly the singular cohomology group cannot always replace $H^p(A, G)$, (since the singular grating is not full). In fact the choice of the set in the remark after (86.3) for A shows this. Another point is that in the case $p = 0$ the augmented groups are implied.

A preliminary observation is in order if topological coefficient groups (7.1) are introduced in (8.2). When direct limits are untopologized we consider G discrete in (8.2). Then the character group of, say $H^p(A, G)$ is $H_p(A, G^*)$ where G^* is compact. Thus variations of (8.2) arise from

$$(H^p(A, G))^* \approx H_p(A, G^*) \approx ({}_SH_{n-p-1}(S^n - A, G))^*$$

$$\approx {}_SH^{n-p-1}(S^n - A, G^*) \tag{8.2c}$$

and from (8.2a). In particular when $G = \mathrm{J}_p$ or Q, G is orthogonally paired to itself and G^* may be taken as J_p, or Q also.

Corollary 8.3. *For the Betti numbers over* J,

$$R_{q-1}(A, \mathrm{J}_p) = R_{n-q}(S^n - A, \mathrm{J}_p) + \varepsilon\,(q)$$

where $\varepsilon(1) = 1$, $\varepsilon(n) = -1$, *and otherwise* $\varepsilon(q) = 0$.

The entrance of ε is occasioned by the fact that the augmented groups $\tilde{H}_0$ and $\tilde{H}^0$ must be understood in (8.2a) and (8.2c) (Cf (8.1b)).

Theorem 8.4. Jordan-Brouwer. *If A is the homeomorph under h of S^{n-1}, then A separates S^n into two components with A as the common boundary.*

From (7.3)

$$R_0(S^n - A, J_2) = R_{n-1}(A, J_2) + 1 = 2,$$

in other words $S^n - A$ has two components, say C_1 and C_2. Plainly the boundaries $\dot{C}_1 \cup \dot{C}_2$ are in A. Suppose $x_0 \in A - \dot{C}_1$. Since $B = A - \dot{C}_1$ is open in the relative topology of A, there is a homeomorph of σ_{n-1}; call it e_{n-1}, in B. Hence $A - e_{n-1}$ is the homeomorph, say E_{n-1}, of a closed disk on S^{n-1}. Therefore

$$R_0(S^n - E_{n-1}, J_2) = R_{n-1}(E^{n-1}, J_2) + 1 = 1,$$

that is to say, $S^n - E_{n-1}$ consists of a single component. Now $\bar{C}_1 \cap \bar{C}_2 \cap (A - E_{n-1}) = \varnothing$ since $\bar{C}_1 \cap e_{n-1} = \varnothing$. Hence

$$S^n - E_{n-1} = C_1 \cup (C_2 \cup e_{n-1})$$

where C_1 and $(C_2 \cup e_{n-1})$ are closed in $S^n - E_{n-1}$, that is to say, $S^n - E_{n-1}$ admits a dissection in contradiction with the fact that it is connected.

Once again we fix attention on a pair S^n, A with A closed in S^n. We reemploy the complexes $|{}^iL|$ entering the demonstration of (8.2). Thus ${}_Sw_p(S^n, A) = \underrightarrow{\mathsf{L}}\, [{}^rw_p]$ and $z^p(A) = [{}^rz^p] = \underrightarrow{\mathsf{L}}\, [{}^rz^p]$. We can define the representative cycles and cocycles by

$${}_Sw_p(S^n, A) = \underrightarrow{\mathsf{L}}\, [{}^tw_p] \quad \text{and} \quad z^p(A) = \underrightarrow{\mathsf{L}}\, [{}^tz^p]$$

Lemma 8.5. *In the notation of* (6.9)

$$\mathrm{In}({}^rw_p, {}^rz^p) = \mathrm{In}({}^r\mathbf{w}_p, {}^r\mathbf{z}^p) = {}^rw_p \cdot {}^rz^p = {}^sw_p \cdot {}^sz^p = \mathrm{In}({}^s\mathbf{w}_p, {}^s\mathbf{z}^p).$$

The common value can be written $In({}_Sw_p, z^p)$ or $In({}_S\mathbf{w}_p, \mathbf{z}^p)$.

PROBLEM

12-14. Demonstrate (8.5). Extend the result to the case ${}_Sw_p \cap z^q$ with $q < p$. Compare (6.6).

Compactify R^n by adding a point to get $R^n \cup \infty$ or S^n with its north pole corresponding to ∞. Let A be a compact subset of R^n. Then A is closed in $R^n \cup \infty$. By exactness in the omology sequences it is elementary that ∂ and δ are isomorphisms for $p < n$ in

$$_S\tilde{H}_p(S^n, A, Q) \xrightarrow{\partial} {_S}H_{p-1}(A, Q)$$
$$H^{p-1}(A, Q) \xrightarrow{\delta} H^p(S^n - A, Q)$$

We make use of these facts in the following definition.

Definition 8.6. Let A be a compact subset of R^n. Suppose $w_{p-1}(A) \in {_S}H_{p-1}(A, Q)$ and $w_p(S^n, A) \in {_S}H_p(S^n, A, Q)$ correspond under the isomorphism ∂ and suppose $z^p(S^n - A)$ and $z^{p-1}(A)$ correspond under the isomorphism δ. Let $z^{p-1}(A)$ correspond to ${_S}z_{n-p}(S^n - A) \in {_S}H_{n-p}(S^n - A, Q)$ under (8.2). The **linking coefficient** is expressed variously as

$$\begin{aligned} Lk({_S}w_{p-1}(A), z^p(S^n - A)) &= Lk({_S}w(S^n - A), z^{p-1}(A)) \\ &= Lk({_S}w_{p-1}(A), {_S}z_{n-p}(S^n - A)) \\ &= \text{In}\,({_S}w_p(S^n, A), z^p(S^n - A)). \end{aligned}$$

In the special case of A a point x_0 and $p = 1$, $Lk({_S}w_0(x_0), {_S}z_{n-1}(S^n - x_0))$ is called the **order** of x_0 with respect to the cycle z_{n-1} and is usually written $v(x_0, z_{n-1})$.

PROBLEM

12-15. Let ${_S}w_{p-1}(A; t)$ and ${_S}z_{p-1}(S^n - A; t)$ be disjunct cycles for every value of t in $0 \le t \le 1$ and constitute deformations. Show $Lk({_S}w_{p-1}(A; 0), {_S}z_{n-p}(S^n - A; 0)) = Lk({_S}w_{p-1}(A, 1), {_S}z_{n-p}(S^n - A, 1))$.

Lemma 8.7. *Let λ be an arc from x_0 to ∞ in R^n. Then $v(x_0, z_{n-1}) = In(\lambda, z_{p-1})$.*

We can assume $\|\lambda\| \cap \|z_{n-1}\|$ is finite. This can be achieved if necessary by small homotopic deformations of either the initially given λ or of z_{n-1} which do not disturb $In(\lambda, z_{n-1})$. Hence (8.7) states that the order of x_0 with respect to z_{n-1} is the *algebraic number of intersections* of L and z_{n-1}.

Remark. In R^3 two cycles z_1 and z_1' which are irreducible in the obvious sense, for which $Lk(z_1', z_1) = 0$ can be deformed without introducing intersections so that ultimately they lie in disjunct disks.

Theorem 8.8. Poincaré-Bohl. *Let Q be a compact carrier of the singular $n - 1$ dimensional cycle, z_{n-1}, in $R^n - 0$. Suppose ψ and ψ' map Q so that for each $x \in Q$ the segment $[\psi(x), \psi'(x)]$ misses the origin, 0. Then*

$$v(0, \psi(z_{n-1})) = v(0, \psi'(z_{n-1})).$$

Let $\psi_t(x)$ be the point on the segment $[\psi(x), \psi'(x)]$ dividing it in the ratio $t/1 - t$. This defines a homotopy in $R^n - 0$.

Definition 8.9. Let $\psi: R^n \to R^n$. Extend ψ to ψ' on $R^n \cup \infty$ to $R^n \cup \infty$ by requiring $\psi'(\infty) = \infty$. Let x_0 be an isolated fixed point. Suppose the sphere $S_r^n(x_0) = \{x \mid \|x - x_0\| = r\}$ contains no other fixed points of ψ. Let

$$\Psi(x) = x_0 + r\,\frac{\psi(x) - x}{\|\psi(x) - x\|}\,.$$

This maps a sphere with center x_0 and radius r into itself. Denote the image by $z_{n-1}(\psi)$. The **order** of ψ at the fixed point x_0 is written $o_\psi(x_0)$ and has the value $v(x_0, z_{n-1}(\psi))$. The **multiplicity** of the fixed point is $(-1)^n\, v(x_0, z_{n-1}(\psi))$. Some advantage of the multiplicity is suggested by the next lemma.

Lemma 8.10. *Let p be a projection or a retraction of R^n onto R^{n-1}. Let $\theta: R^{n-1} \to R^{n-1}$ and let $\psi = \theta p: R^n \to R^n$. If x_0 is an isolated fixed point of θ, then $v(x_0, z_{n-1}(\psi)) = -v(x_0, z_{n-2}(\theta))$.*

PROBLEM

12-16. Demonstrate (8.10).

We take up the extension of the Alexander Duality theorem (8.2) in two directions. First A is now an unrestricted subset of S^n, and second, the coefficient group R can be either discrete or compact. It will be convenient *to indicate* M is N^* *by writing* $N \mid M$.

If A is neither open nor closed, we approximate it by an expanding sequence of compact subsets $\{A_i\}$ ordered by inclusion. Let B_i be a triangulation necessarily infinite of $A_i^\sim$. We modify the notation of (8.3) and (8.4) slightly. For fixed i let K be a finite subcomplex of B_i and denote by L the infinite triangulated complex of $S^n - |K|$. Next the typical finite subcomplex of L is denoted by L_s and N_s is the open set $S^n - |L_s|$. In the diagrams below the arrows pointing to right or left indicate whether direct limits or inverse limits are to be taken as we proceed from L_s to A or from N_s to $S^n - A$ in 3 stages.

$$L_s \to \quad L \leftarrow \quad A_i \to \quad A$$

$$N_s \leftarrow \quad K \to \quad B_i \leftarrow \quad S^n - A.$$

Thus for instance

$$H_r(A, G) = \underset{\to}{\mathsf{L}}\ \underset{\leftarrow}{\mathsf{L}}\ \underset{\to}{\mathsf{L}}\ H_r(L_s, G),$$

$$H^r(A, G^*) = \underset{\leftarrow}{\mathsf{L}}\ \underset{\to}{\mathsf{L}}\ \underset{\leftarrow}{\mathsf{L}}\ H^r(L_s, G^*).$$

Theorem 8.11. *For G either discrete or compact and A arbitrary the following diagram is valid.*

(8.11a)
$$\frac{H_r(A, G)}{H^r(A, G^*)} \begin{array}{c} \mid \\ \mid \end{array} \frac{H_{n-r-1}(S^n - A, G^*)}{H^{n-r-1}(S^n - A, G)}$$

Moreover the groups along the two diagonals are isomorphic.

The Alexander theorem (8.2) covers the case G discrete and A closed. Suppose G is compact. Then for the expanded groups we have

$$H_r(L, G) = \underset{\rightarrow}{\mathsf{L}} \{H_r L_s, G), p^{s*}{}_t\}$$

with the limit in the sense of (7.6). We can, of course, write $|L_s|$ and $|L|$ for L_s and for L. We apply (87.3) to attain

$$\begin{aligned} \underset{\leftarrow}{\mathsf{L}} \{H_{n-r-1}(N_s, G^*), p_s{}^t{}_*\} &= \underset{\leftarrow}{\mathsf{L}} \{H_{n-r-1}({}_s v, G^*), p_s{}^t{}_*\} \\ &= H_{n-r-1}(K, G^*) \end{aligned}$$

where ${}_s v$ is a denumerable star finite open cover of K and the last group is the Čech homology group (87.4a).

At each stage $H_r(|L_s|, G) \mid H_{n-r-1}(|N_s|, G^*)$ where the left hand group is compact and the right hand group is discrete. Thus (7.6) implies

(8.11c)
$$H_r(L, G) \mid H_{n-r-1}(K, G^*).$$

By (7.2a) this is tantamount to

(8.11d)
$$H_r(L, G) \approx H^{n-r-1}(K, G)$$

and again we point out the right hand group is in the sense of Čech. Accordingly (8.11c) and (8.11d) yield the assertions of the theorem for the special case that A is the closed subcomplex of the triangulated sphere. Replace A and $S^n - A$ in (8.11a) by L and by K and alternate direct and inverse limits in moving clockwise around the modified diagram, starting with

$$H_{n-r-1}(B_i, G^*) = \underset{\rightarrow}{\mathsf{L}} \{H_{n-r-1}(K, G^*), p_k{}^{k'*}\}.$$

We need to appraise the groups $H_r(L, G)$ and $H^r(L, G^*)$. Since $|L|$ is the complement of a finite complex K, it is locally connected in all dimensions. Accordingly its omology groups with compact supports are the same for the singular and the Čech groups. This implies that the inverse limit $\underset{\leftarrow}{\mathsf{L}}\, H_r(L, G)$ is taken over Čech groups on the neighborhoods of A_i. Therefore in view of (87.3), $H_r(A_i, G)$ and $H^r(A_i, G^*)$ are the usual Čech groups for a compact set.

Our last set of limits consists of direct limits on $H_r(A_i, K)$ and inverse limits on its nieghbors. Hence the terms in the left column of (8.11a) are expanded groups obtained as direct limits of the Čech groups on A_i while those in the right column are given as inverse limits of expanded groups taken over neighborhoods of $A^{\sim}$.

PROBLEMS

12-17. If $z_p^1 \sim 0$ in $R^n - z_{n-p}^2$ then $Lk(z_p^1, z_{n-p}^2) = 0$.

12-18. In R_3 show $Lk(z_1^1, z_1^2) \neq 0$ only for the first of the classical cases illustrated in the figures. *Hint:* Fig. 12.2d shows that the situation is that of the previous problem.

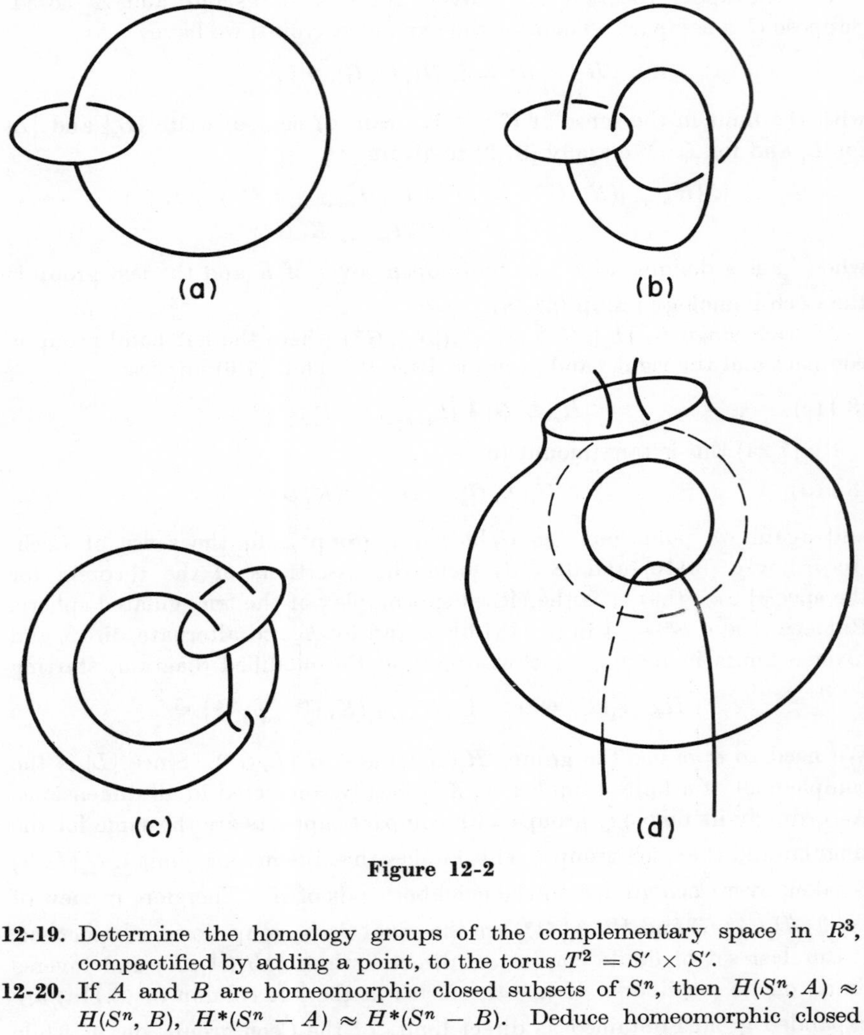

Figure 12-2

12-19. Determine the homology groups of the complementary space in R^3, compactified by adding a point, to the torus $T^2 = S' \times S'$.

12-20. If A and B are homeomorphic closed subsets of S^n, then $H(S^n, A) \approx H(S^n, B)$, $H^*(S^n - A) \approx H^*(S^n - B)$. Deduce homeomorphic closed sets separate S^n into the same number of components. Show the extension to the sphere in Hilbert space is false.

9. APPLICATIONS OF PRODUCTS An elegant application of cup and cap products is the characterization of the cohomology ring of a manifold admitting a multiplication. As a preliminary, we recall that the obstacle to defining a multiplication for homology classes is that for unspecialized complexes or spaces, no natural homomorphism on $H_*(X \times X)$ to $H_*(X)$ comparable to a dual of the diagonal homomorphism (3.1), can be set up to follow the cross product. However, for the manifolds defined below, such homomorphisms can be introduced, though as a matter of convenience, we shall prefer to deal with their counterparts in the cohomology ring. Reference may be made to the Pontrjagin multiplication defined in Problem (12.21). We return to these questions in 158.

Definition 9.1. A semigroup manifold is an n-dimensional, connected, oriented simplicial manifold $X = \{x\}$ admitting a map, μ, on $X \times X$ to X with $\mu(e, x) = \mu(x, e) = x$ for some fixed element e called the identity. If $\mu(x, \mu(y, z)) = \mu(\mu(x, y), z)$ for all $x, y, z \in X$, and if an inverse exists, i.e., for each $x \in X$, there is a $y \in X$ such that $\mu(x, y) = e = \mu(y, x)$, then X is a group manifold. The product $\mu(x, y)$ is sometimes written $x \cdot y$ also. A semigroup manifold is essentially a special instance of an H **space** (158.3).

Until (9.12) is reached the coefficient ring is tacitly understood to be Q and is generally omitted from the omology groups.

A **Hopf manifold** is a finite, simplicial, oriented, connected closed n manifold, $X = \{x\}$ which admits a map $\mu\colon X \times X \to X$, where it is required that if $i(x_0)$ and $j(x_0)$ are the inclusion maps of $x_0 \times X$ and $X \times x_0$ into $X \times X$, then ${}_1\mu = \mu i(x_0)$ and ${}_2\mu = \mu j(x_0)$ induce homomorphisms independent of x_0,

$$ {}_i\mu_* \; H_*(X \times X) \to H_*(X), \qquad i = 1, 2 $$

with

(9.1b) $$ {}_1\mu_*(\mathbf{1}_0 \times \mathbf{z}_n) = c_e \mathbf{z}_n,\ c_e \neq 0, $$

(9.1c) $$ {}_2\mu_*(\mathbf{z}_n \times \mathbf{1}_0) = c_r \mathbf{z}_n,\ c_r \neq 0. $$

Here $\mathbf{z}_n$ is the generator of $H_n(X)$ and $\mathbf{1}_0$ is the 0 cycle coset of a vertex.

Remark. It is no great trick to introduce multiplication on manifolds. For instance the trivial multiplication $(x \times y) = \bar{x}$ where $\bar{x}$ is fixed is such a multiplication. The difficulty comes in satisfying the condition $c_l c_r \neq 0$.

To avoid a time consuming extraneous diversion, we require also that

(9.1d) $$ 0 = \mathbf{f}^p \cap \mathbf{z}_n \Rightarrow \mathbf{f}^p = 0, $$

though this is derivable from the other conditions by way of the Poincaré duality theorem.

PROBLEM

12-21. For the group manifold X let $\gamma_r = \Sigma a^i\, {}_iu_r$, and $\gamma_s = \Sigma b^j\, {}_ju_s$ be non-bounding singular cycles. Let Δ_r and ${}_s\Delta$ be the forward r face and the back s face of Δ_{r+s} (21.2). Define a map ${}_{ij}u_{r+s}$ by ${}_{ij}u_{r+s}(x, y) = {}_iu_r(x) \cdot {}_ju_s(y)$, $x \in \Delta_r$, $y \in {}_s\Delta$, and as usual denote $(\Delta_{r+s}, {}_{ij}u_{r+s})$ by ${}_{ij}u_{r+s}$. Let $\Gamma_{r+s} = \Gamma(\gamma_r, \gamma_s) = \Sigma a^i b^j\, {}_{ij}u_{r+s}$. Show $\Gamma(\gamma_r, \gamma_s)$ is a cycle. Show further that if $\gamma_r' \sim \gamma_r$ and $\gamma_s' \sim \gamma_s$, then $\Gamma(\gamma_r, \gamma_s) \sim \Gamma(\gamma_r', \gamma_s')$ so that Γ_{r+s} depends on $\boldsymbol{\gamma}_r$ and $\boldsymbol{\gamma}_s$. Show Γ_{r+s} depends linearly on each argument and hence defines a product (known as the Pontrjagin product), under which $H_*(X)$ becomes a homology ring (equivalent to the ring using μ_*).

Lemma 9.2. *The multiplication μ induces a ring homomorphism μ^* on $H^*(X)$ to $H^*(X) \times H^*(X)$ of the form*

(9.2a) $$\mu^*\mathbf{f}^p = \mathbf{1} \times (\lambda\mathbf{f}^p) + (\rho\mathbf{f}^p) \times \mathbf{1} + \Sigma_{\substack{r+s=p\\ 0<r,\, s<p}} \mathbf{h}^r \times \mathbf{g}^s$$

where ρ and λ are ring homomorphisms on $H^*(X)$.

Since the semigroup manifold is lc^∞ the cohomology rings defined by the simplicial, singular, or Alexander gratings are isomorphic (111.9). We carry the argument through using Alexander cochains. We need only establish the commutativity of

$$\begin{array}{ccc} C(X) \otimes C(X) & \xrightarrow{\mu^\# \otimes \mu^\#} & C(X \times X) \otimes C(X \times X) \\ \downarrow \cup & & \downarrow \cup \\ C(X) & \xrightarrow{\mu^\#} & C(X \times X) \end{array}$$

Hence let $f^p \otimes g^q \in C(X) \times C(X)$. Then $\cup\, \mu^\# f^p \times g^q = \mu^\# f^p \otimes \mu^\# g^q$. Write w_i for $x_i \times y_i$,

$$(\mu^\# f^p \cup \mu^\# g^q)(w_0, \ldots, w_{p+q}) =$$
$$= (\mu^\# f^p)(w_0, \ldots, w_p)(\mu^\# g^q)(w_p, \ldots, w_{p+q})$$
$$= f^p \mu_\#(w_0 \cdots w_p) g^q(\mu_\#(w_p \cdots w_{p+q}))$$
(9.2b) $$= f^p(\mu(w_0)\, \mu(w_1) \cdots \mu(w_p)) g^q(\mu(w_p) \cdots \mu(w_{p+q})$$
$$= (f^p \cup g^q)(\mu(w_0) \cdots \mu(w_{p+q})$$
$$= \mu^\#(f^p \cup g^q)(w_0 \cdots w_{p+q}).$$

One deduces directly that $\mu^* f^p \cup \mu^* g^q = \mu^*(f^p \cup g^q)$.

Let us write

(9.2c) $$\mu^*\, \mathbf{f}^p = \sum_{a+b=p} \mathbf{h}_i^a \times \mathbf{g}_j^b.$$

Since X is connected, $H^0(X)$ is a one-dimensional vector space with base vector 1, the coset of the 0-dimensional cocycle taking on the value 1 on every vertex. Let $\lambda\mathbf{f}^p = \Sigma\,\mathbf{g}_i^p$, $\rho\mathbf{f}^p = \Sigma\,\mathbf{h}_i^p$. Insertion of these expressions in (9.2c) gives (9.2a).

We assert λ and ρ are ring homomorphisms. Consider λ and note that since μ^* is of course a module homomorphism

$$\begin{aligned}\mu^*(\mathbf{f}+\mathbf{f}') &= (\mathbf{1}\times\Sigma\,\mathbf{g}_i^p) + (\mathbf{1}\times\Sigma\,\mathbf{g}_i^{p'}) + \cdots\\ &= (\mathbf{1}\times\Sigma\,(\mathbf{g}_i^p+\mathbf{g}_i^{p'})) + \cdots = (\mathbf{1}\times\lambda(\mathbf{f}+\mathbf{f}')\cdots.\end{aligned}$$

Moreover from (9.2a)

$$\begin{aligned}\mu^*\,\mathbf{f}\cup\mathbf{f}' &= (\mathbf{1}\times\Sigma\,\mathbf{g}_i^0)\cup(\mathbf{1}\times\Sigma\,\mathbf{g}_i^{p'})) + \cdots\\ &= \mathbf{1}\times(\Sigma\,\mathbf{g}_i^p\cup\Sigma\,\mathbf{g}_i^{p'}) + \cdots\\ &= \mathbf{1}\times(\lambda\mathbf{f}\cup\lambda\mathbf{f}) + \cdots.\end{aligned}$$

Similarly ρ is demonstrated to be a ring homomorphism.

Definition 9.3. Let p and q be projections on $X\times Y$ defined, as in (5.1b), by $p\colon x\times y = x$, $q\colon x\times y = y$. Then, using cup products on $H(X\times Y)$ (5.1c),

$$\mathbf{h}_i^a\times\mathbf{g}_j^b = p^*\mathbf{h}_i^a\cup q^*\mathbf{g}_j^b. \tag{9.3a}$$

Write $\mathbf{l}(X)$, $\mathbf{l}(Y)$, and $\mathbf{l}(X\times Y)$ for the units in $H^*(X)$, $H^*(Y)$, and $H^*(X\times Y)$. Since $q^*\mathbf{l}(Y)$ is obviously $\mathbf{l}(X\times Y)$,

$$p^*\,\mathbf{f}^p = p^*\,\mathbf{f}^p\cup\mathbf{l}(X\times Y) = p^*\,\mathbf{f}^p\cup q^*\,\mathbf{l}(Y) = \mathbf{f}^p\times\mathbf{l}(Y),\ (5.1\text{c}).$$

Similarly, $q^*\,\mathbf{f}^p = \mathbf{l}(X\times Y)\cup q^*\,\mathbf{f}^p = \mathbf{l}(X)\times\mathbf{f}^p$.
In particular, if $X = Y$, $p^*\,\mathbf{f}^p = \mathbf{f}^p\times\mathbf{l}$ and $q^*\,\mathbf{f}^p = \mathbf{l}\times\mathbf{f}^p$.

Lemma 9.4. *If X is a semigroup manifold, λ and ρ are identity isomorphisms.*

Let i and j be maps on X to $X\times X$ defined by $ix = x\times e$, $jx = e\times x$. Then μi, μj, and pi are the identity maps of X on X (9.1) while qi maps X into e. Accordingly $i^*\mu^*$, $j^*\mu^*$, and i^*p^* are identity isomorphisms while $i^*q^*\colon H^*(X)\to H^*(e)$. If

$$\begin{aligned} p>0,\quad \mathbf{f}^p &= i^*\mu^*\,\mathbf{f}^p,\\ &= i^*(\rho\mathbf{f}^p\times\mathbf{l}+\mathbf{l}\times\lambda\mathbf{f}^p+\Sigma\,\mathbf{h}^a\times\mathbf{g}^b)\\ &= i^*(p^*\rho\mathbf{f}^p+q^*\lambda\mathbf{f}^p+\Sigma\,\mathbf{h}^q\times\mathbf{g}^b) \qquad (9.4\text{a})\\ &= \rho\mathbf{f}^p+0+i^*\,\Sigma\,\mathbf{h}^a\times\mathbf{g}^b.\end{aligned}$$

Note for a and b positive, $i^*q^*\,\mathbf{g}^b = 0$ whence

$$i^*\,\mathbf{h}^a \times \mathbf{g}^b = i^*(p^*\,\mathbf{h}^a \cup q^*\,\mathbf{g}^b) = (i^*\,p^*)\mathbf{h}^a \cup (i^*\,q^*)\mathbf{g}^b = 0.$$

Hence (9.4a) can be expressed

$$\mathbf{f}^p = \rho\mathbf{f}^p$$

Similarly

$$\mathbf{f}^p = \lambda\mathbf{f}^p$$

For completeness we note generalization is possible to the case of a Hopf manifold. Since the defining condition is on the n-dimensional generator, it stands to reason that a demonstration that λ and ρ are isomorphisms in this case, will involve this generator. Hence (just as in the case of the Alexander duality theorem), intervention of the cap product is to be expected.

Lemma 9.5. *If X is a Hopf manifold, λ and ρ are isomorphisms.*

The proof is given for λ. We establish that ker $\lambda = 0$. Thus let $\lambda\mathbf{f}^p = 0$. Since $\mathbf{h}^a \cap \mathbf{1}_0 = 0, \quad a > 0,$

$$\begin{aligned}\mu^*\,\mathbf{f}^p \cap \mathbf{1}_0 \times \gamma_n &= (\mathbf{1}_0 \underline{\times} \gamma_n)(\mathbf{1} \overline{\times} \lambda\mathbf{f}^p)\\ &= \mathbf{1}_0 \underline{\times} (\lambda\mathbf{f}^p \cap \gamma_n) = 0.\end{aligned}$$

Therefore

$$0 = \mu^*(\mu^*\,\mathbf{f}^p \cap \mathbf{1}_0 \times \gamma_n) = c_e\,\mathbf{f}^p \cap \gamma_n$$

whence $\mathbf{f}^p = 0$ (9.1d). Since $H^p(X)$ is a finite dimensional vector space, λ can be viewed as a linear self-map of $H^p(X) \to H^p(X)$ so λ is onto in consequence of *ker* $\lambda = 0$.

PROBLEM

12-22. If n is even, either ${}_1\mu_*\,\gamma_n = 0$ or ${}_2\mu_*\,\gamma_n = 0$. *Hint:* $\mu^*\,\mathbf{f}^m = c_e\,\mathbf{f}^n \times \mathbf{1} + c_r\,\mathbf{1} \times \mathbf{f}^n$ implies $0 = \mu^*(\mathbf{f}^n \cup \mathbf{f}^n) = 2c_e\,c_r\mathbf{f}^n \times \mathbf{f}^n$.

As a vector space, trivial for $r > n$, $H^r(X)$ admits a vector basis, a subcollection of which constitutes a ring basis. Thus the base vector for $H^0(X)$ is 1. Suppose $V^1 = \{\mathbf{f}_i^1 \mid i = 1, \ldots, N_1\}$ is a vector basis for $H^1(X)$ and $\{\mathbf{f}_j^2 \mid j = 1, \ldots, M\} = V^2$ is one for $H^2(X)$. Retain only those elements in V^2 which cannot be expressed in the form $\Sigma\, a_{rs}\,\mathbf{f}_r^1 \cup \mathbf{f}_s^1$. The elements left over constitute $B^2 = \{\mathbf{f}_r^2 \mid r = 1, \ldots, N_2\} \subset V^2$. The elements of V^3 which are independent of those of V^2 and of B^2 under the ring operators constitute B^3, etc.

Denote the ring bases, that is to say the elements of $\bigcup B^i$, by $\mathbf{b}^0 = \mathbf{1}$; $\mathbf{b}_2^1, \ldots, \mathbf{b}_n^1$; $\mathbf{b}_{N+1}^2, \ldots, \mathbf{b}_{N+M}^2, \ldots,$ where $\mathbf{b}_i^J \in B^J$. Thus any element of $H^m(X)$ is a polynomial in the base elements, i.e.,

$$\mathbf{h} = \Sigma_{n_1+n_2+\cdots\, n_s=m}\, c^{i_1\cdots i_s}\,\mathbf{b}_{i_1}^{n_1} \cup \cdots \cup \mathbf{b}_{i_s}^{n_s}.$$

We write H^* for the ring $H^*(X)$. Let J be an ideal of H^*, that is to say, a subring of H^* with $\mathbf{j}_1 + \mathbf{j}_2 \in J$ if $\mathbf{j}_i \in J$, $i = 1, 2$ and $\mathbf{j} \cup H^*$ and $H^* \cup \mathbf{j} \subset J$.

Lemma 9.6

(9.6a) *If J is an ideal of H^*, then $H^* \times J$ is a two sided ideal of $H^* \otimes H^* \approx H^* \times H^* \approx H^*(X \times X)$ and*

(9.6b) *If $\mathbf{f} \times \mathbf{g} \in H^* \times J$, with $\mathbf{f} \neq 0$, then $\mathbf{g} \in J$.*

For (9.6a) it is sufficient to show that if $\mathbf{h} = \mathbf{f} \times \mathbf{g} \in H^*(X \times X)$ then, with $\mathbf{j} \in J$,

(9.6c) $$(\mathbf{f} \times \mathbf{g}) \cup (\mathbf{f}' \times \mathbf{j}) \in H^* \times J.$$

This is substantiated by

(9.6d) $$\begin{aligned}(\mathbf{f} \times \mathbf{g}) \cup (\mathbf{f}' \times \mathbf{j}) &= p^*\,\mathbf{f} \cup q^*\,\mathbf{g} \cup p^*\,\mathbf{f}' \cup q^*\,\mathbf{j} \quad (4.5), (4.4)\\ &= \pm p^*\,\mathbf{f} \cup p^*\,\mathbf{f}' \cup q^*\,\mathbf{g} \cup q^*\,\mathbf{j}.\\ &= \pm p^*(\mathbf{f} \cup \mathbf{f}')q^*(\mathbf{g} \cup \mathbf{j})\\ &= (\mathbf{f} \cup \mathbf{f}') \times (\mathbf{g} \cup \mathbf{j})\end{aligned}$$

and $\mathbf{g} \cup \mathbf{j} \in J$ since J is an ideal.

From the vector space viewpoint J is a vector subspace or direct summand of the vector space H^*, thus $H^* = J \oplus K$. Hence, $H^* \otimes H^* = H^* \otimes J \oplus H^* \otimes K$. Accordingly, $\mathbf{g} = \mathbf{j} + \mathbf{k}$ with $\mathbf{j} \in J$ and $\mathbf{k} \in K$ wherefore $\mathbf{f} \times \mathbf{g} = \mathbf{f} \times \mathbf{j} + (\mathbf{f} \times \mathbf{k})$. We may assume $\mathbf{f}$ and $\mathbf{k}$ are finite sums of basis elements $\{\mathbf{f}_i\}$ and $\{\mathbf{h}_j\}$ respectively (112). Thus, $\mathbf{k} = \Sigma\, c^i\, \mathbf{k}_i$ and $\mathbf{f} = \Sigma\, d^j\, \mathbf{f}_j$ so (8.6h)

(9.6e) $$\Sigma_{i,j} d^j\, \mathbf{f}_j \otimes c^i\, \mathbf{k}_i = 0$$

and since this is a direct sum,

$$c^i\, d^j\, \mathbf{f}_j \otimes \mathbf{k}_i = 0.$$

Since $\mathbf{f}_j \otimes \mathbf{k}_i$ constitute elements of the basis for $H^* \otimes K$,

(9.6f) $$c^i\, d^j = 0.$$

We have assumed $\mathbf{f} \neq 0$ and so some $d^j \neq 0$ whence $c^i = 0$ for all i, or $\mathbf{k} = 0$.

Remark. It is in the inference (9.6f) from (9.6e) alone that the nature of Q enters throughout (9). Thus this inference is valid for R any field of characteristic 0.

Lemma 9.7. *The cup product of all the elements of the basis B is nonzero.*

The proof is by induction. Drop the dimension index on elements of B, but assume the order is such that

$$\mathbf{b}_i < \mathbf{b}_j \Rightarrow \dim \mathbf{b}_i \leq \dim \mathbf{b}_j.$$

Note the highest dimensional elements come last. We lay down the induction hypothesis that

$$\mathbf{M}_s = \Pi_{i=2}^{i=s} \mathbf{b}_i \neq 0,$$

where $\mathbf{b}_i \mathbf{b}_j$ is written for $\mathbf{b}_i \cup \mathbf{b}_j$. We define an ideal J, generated by $\mathbf{b}_2, \ldots, \mathbf{b}_s$. Thus

$$J = \{\Sigma_{j \geq 2} \mathbf{b}_j H^*\},$$

when cognizance is taken of the commutativity relation $\mathbf{b}_j \cup \mathbf{h} = \pm \mathbf{h} \cup \mathbf{b}_j$ (4.5).

Then $H^* \times J$ is a two-sided ideal in $H^*(X \times X)$ (9.6). We have

$$\mu^* \mathbf{b}_m = \mathbf{b}_m \times \mathbf{1} + \mathbf{1} \times \mathbf{b}_m + \Sigma\, \mathbf{h}_i \times \mathbf{g}_j, \quad m \leq s, \quad \dim \mathbf{g}_j < \dim \mathbf{b}_m.$$

Hence $\mathbf{g}_j^t \in J$ and

$$\Sigma\, \mathbf{h}_i^r \times \mathbf{g}_j^t \in H^* \times J.$$

This inclusion is valid for $\mathbf{1} \times \mathbf{b}_m$, of course, since $\mathbf{b}_m \in J$. Thus

(9.7a) $$\mu^* \mathbf{b}_m = \mathbf{b}_m \times \mathbf{1}, \quad \operatorname{mod} H^* \times J, \quad m > 1.$$

Then (9.2) builds on (9.6d) to establish, for instance,

$$\begin{aligned}\mu^*(\mathbf{b}_m \cup \mathbf{b}_n) &= \mu^* \mathbf{b}_m \cup \mu^* \mathbf{b}_n \\ &= (\mathbf{b}_m \times \mathbf{1}) \cup (\mathbf{b}_n \times \mathbf{1}) = (\mathbf{b}_m \mathbf{b}_n \times \mathbf{1}) \operatorname{mod} H^* \times J,\end{aligned}$$

whence

(9.7b) $$\mu^* \mathbf{M}_s = \mathbf{M}_s \times \mathbf{1} \operatorname{mod} H^* \times J$$

and

$$\begin{aligned}\mu^* (\mathbf{M}_s \cup \mathbf{b}_{s+1}) &= (\mathbf{M}_s \times \mathbf{1}) \cup (\mathbf{I} \times \mathbf{b}_{s+1} + \mathbf{b}_{s+1} \times \mathbf{1}) \operatorname{mod} H^* \times J \\ &= (\mathbf{M}_s \cup \mathbf{b}_{s+1}) \times \mathbf{1} + \mathbf{M}_s \times \mathbf{b}_{s+1} \operatorname{mod} H^* \times J.\end{aligned}$$

Suppose $\mathbf{M}_s \cup \mathbf{b}_{s+1} = 0$, then $0 = 0 + \mathbf{M}_s \times \mathbf{b}_{s+1} \operatorname{mod} H^* \times J$, or $\mathbf{M}_s \cup \mathbf{b}_{s+1} \in H^* \times J$, or since $\mathbf{M}_s \neq 0$, $\mathbf{b}_{s+1}$ must be in J at variance with the definition of J. Hence the supposition $\mathbf{M}_s \cup \mathbf{b}_{s+1} = 0$ is untenable. The theorem follows.

Lemma 9.8. *For any basic element* $\mathbf{b}$, $d = \dim \mathbf{b}$ *is odd, and* $\mathbf{b} \cup \mathbf{b} = 0$.

Let J be the ideal generated by $\{\mathbf{b}_i \mid \mathbf{b}_i \neq \mathbf{1}, \dim \mathbf{b}_i \neq d\}$. Then $H^* \times J$ is an ideal in $H^*(X \times X)$ (9.6). Hence $\mu^* \mathbf{b} = \mathbf{b} \times \mathbf{1} + \mathbf{1} \times \mathbf{b} \bmod H^* \times J$ whence, by (3.2) for an arbitrary positive integer m,

(9.8a)
$$\mu^* \mathbf{b}^m = (\mu^* \mathbf{b})^m$$
$$= (\mathbf{b} \times \mathbf{1} + \mathbf{1} \times \mathbf{b})^m \bmod H^* \times J$$

where the products are cup products. Note

(9.8b)
$$(\mathbf{b} \times \mathbf{1}) \cup (\mathbf{1} \times \mathbf{b}) = (\mathbf{b} \cup \mathbf{1}) \times (\mathbf{1} \cup \mathbf{b})$$
$$= \mathbf{b} \times \mathbf{b}$$
$$= (-1)^{d^2}(\mathbf{1} \times \mathbf{b}) \cup (\mathbf{b} \times \mathbf{1}) \qquad (4.5).$$

If d could be even, (9.8b) would ensure commutativity of $\mathbf{b} \times \mathbf{1}$ and $\mathbf{1} \times \mathbf{b}$ in their cup product with the neat consequence

(9.8c)
$$(\mathbf{b} \times \mathbf{1} + \mathbf{1} \times \mathbf{b})^m = (\mathbf{b} \times \mathbf{1})^m + m(\mathbf{b} \times \mathbf{1})^{m-1}(\mathbf{1} + \mathbf{b}) + \cdots$$
$$= \mathbf{b}^m \times \mathbf{1} + m\, \mathbf{b}^{m-1} \times \mathbf{b} + \Sigma$$
$$= \mathbf{b}^m \times \mathbf{1} + m\, \mathbf{b}^{m-1} \times \mathbf{b} \bmod H^* \times J.$$

Indeed the terms in the residue Σ are, except for numerical coefficient, of the form $\mathbf{b}^r \times \mathbf{b}^s$, $s > 1$, and hence $\dim \mathbf{b}^s \neq d$, i.e., $\Sigma \in H^* \times J$. Since $H^p(X)$ is trivial for sufficiently large p, we can specify m so that $\mathbf{b}^{m-1} \neq 0$, $\mathbf{b}^m = 0$. Hence $0 = \mu^* 0 = m\, \mathbf{b}^{m-1} \times \mathbf{b} \bmod H^* \times J$, and so

(9.8d)
$$\mathbf{b}^{m-1} \times \mathbf{b} = 0, \quad \bmod H^* \times J.$$

Since $\mathbf{b}^{m-1} \neq 0$, $\mathbf{b} \in J$ (9.6) which contradicts the definition of J.

Corollary 9.9. $\mathbf{b}_i \cup \mathbf{b}_j = \mathbf{b}_j \cup \mathbf{b}_i$.

Theorem 9.10. *A Hopf manifold has a cohomology ring over the rationals, isomorphic to that of a product of odd dimensional spheres.*

Let $\mathbf{P}_{i=1}^{i=N} S^{n_i} = S$ be the topological product of odd dimensional spheres. Since $H^*(S^{n_i})$ has no torsion subgroup, the Kunneth theorem asserts

(9.10a)
$$H^*(S) \approx \mathbf{P}_{i=1}^{i=N} H^*(S^{n_i}) \approx H^*(S^{n_1}) \cdots \otimes H^*(S^{n_N}).$$

A ring basis for $H^*(S)$ is given by the elements

(9.10b)
$$\mathbf{B}_j = \mathbf{P}_{i \neq j} \{\mathbf{f}_i^0 \mid 0 \neq \mathbf{f}_i^0 \in H^0(S^{n_i})\} \otimes \{\mathbf{f}_j^{n_j} \in H^{n_j}(S^{n_j})\}$$

and

(9.10c)
$$\mathbf{B}_0 = \mathbf{P}\{\mathbf{f}_i^0 \mid 0 \neq \mathbf{f}_i^0 \in H^0(S_i^{n_i})\}.$$

(9.10d)
$$\dim \mathbf{B}_j = n_j.$$

The rule for multiplication in $H^*(S)$, is

(9.10e) $(\mathbf{f}_1 \times \cdots \times \mathbf{f}_N) \cup (\mathbf{g}_1 \times \cdots \times \mathbf{g}_N) =$

$$= (-1)^{\dim \mathbf{f}_N \dim (\mathbf{g}_1 \times \cdots \times \mathbf{g}_{N-1})}(\mathbf{f}_1 \times \cdots \times \mathbf{f}_{N-1}) \cup$$
$$\cup (\mathbf{g}_1 \times \cdots \times \mathbf{g}_{N-1}) \times (\mathbf{f}_N \cup \mathbf{g}_N) =$$
$$= \pm(\mathbf{f}_1 \cup \mathbf{g}_1) \times (\mathbf{f}_2 \cup \mathbf{g}_2) \times \cdots$$

Hence the relations satisfied by $\{\mathbf{b}_i\}$ namely (9.7), (9.8), and (7.9) are satisfied by $\{\mathbf{B}_i\}$ also. Accordingly the correspondence $\mathbf{b}_i \leftrightarrow \{\mathbf{B}_i\}$ establishes a ring isomorphism between $H^*(X, R)$ and $H^*(S, R)$.

Remark. The theorem retains its validity if Q is replaced by a perfect field of characteristic p, i.e., a field in which each element has a pth root.

Theorem 9.11. *S^{2n+1} is a Hopf manifold.*

If $x, y \in S^{2n+1}$, let $\mu(x, y)$ be the reflection of x in the diameter through y. Denote the antipode of x by $\bar{x}$. In the exceptional case, $y = \bar{x}$, let $\mu(x, \bar{x}) = x$. This is a continuous multiplication. If $x = x_0$, then, as a function of y, two antipodal y values yield the same ${}_1\mu(y)$ values, that is to say the map covers S^{2n+1} twice, neglecting the two exceptional points. This is perhaps clearer if a coordinate system centered at x_0 is chosen. One coordinate, s, is great circle arc length, while the others are angle coordinates singling out a unique great circle. Hence, if y has the s coordinate $s(y)$, then $\mu(x_0, y)$ has the s coordinate $2s(y)$. With x_0 the north pole, the open upper and lower hemispheres are mapped homeomorphically by $\mu(x, y)$ onto $S^{2n+1} - (\bar{x}_0)$. Thus $\mu(x_0, y) = \mu(x_0, \bar{y})$. The equatorial sphere maps onto $\bar{x}_0$. The induced homomorphism ${}_1\mu^*$ takes the base element $\mathbf{f}^{2n+1}$ into $2\mathbf{f}^{2n+1}$. With the rational field this is an isomorphism of $H^{2n+1}(S^{2n+1}) \to H^{2n+1}(S^{2n+1})$. Similarly ${}_2\mu^*$ is an isomorphism. Hence c_e and c_r are 2 and 1 respectively, and so S^{2n+1} is a Hopf manifold.

PROBLEM

12-23. Show that the topological product of two Hopf manifolds, X_1 and X_2 is a Hopf manifold. Hence, if μ and ν are the multiplications, $\mu \times \nu$: $(X_1 \times X_1) \times (X_2 \times X_2) \to X_1 \times X_2$ has $c_e = {}_1c_e\, {}_2c_e$, $c_r = {}_1c_r\, {}_2c_r$.

Remark. A group manifold is plainly a Hopf manifold. We have shown that in particular S^{2n+1} is a Hopf manifold. However, the extra condition that inverses exist strains out all but the spheres S^1 and S^3. For the semi group manifold some other (but not all) odd dimensional spheres are available, also. Thus S^7 is a semi group manifold though S^5 is not. The verification for S^7 is settled by citation of the Cayley sections which have a norm satisfying $|xy| = |x|\,|y|$.

The semi group multiplication on S^1, S^3, S^7 is not that defined above. For instance on S^1 the semi group or group multiplication is given by $e^{i\theta}\, e^{i\phi} = e^{i(\theta+\phi)}$ so $c_l = c_r = 1$.

Because of its vast importance, as well as its implications for say (158), we continue with an abstract reformulation of some of the ideas developed above. We assume at first that R is a fixed commutative ring with unit and later specialize R to be a field of characteristic either 0 or $p \neq 0$. We shall understand that $\otimes$ and *Hom* refer to $\otimes_R$ and Hom_R. We begin by making precise the sense in which algebra is understood until the end of this section.

Definiton 9.12. An **algebra** A is a graded R module, $A = \otimes A_i$ which is of **finite type** if each A_i is finitely generated. It is equipped with a module bihomomorphism $m\colon A \otimes A \to A$ of degree 0, called **multiplication**. We shall assume it is **connected**, that is to say, there is an assigned isomorphism $h\colon A_0 \to R$. It is **augmented** if there is a homomorphism $A \xrightarrow{\varepsilon} R$ which we view as the composition of the projection $p\colon \oplus A_i \to A_0$ and h. A has a **unit** or **base point homomorphism** η if $\eta\colon R \to A$. We shall require η to be the composition of h^{-1} and the injection $i\colon A_0 \to A$. Thus ϵ and η are given by

(9.12a) $$A \xrightarrow{p} A_0 \xrightarrow{h} R,$$

(9.12b) $$R \xrightarrow{h^{-1}} A_0 \xrightarrow{i} A.$$

The algebra is **associative** if

(9.12c) $$\begin{array}{ccc} A \otimes A \otimes A & \xrightarrow{1 \otimes m} & A \otimes A \\ \downarrow{\scriptstyle m \otimes 1} & & \downarrow{\scriptstyle m} \\ A \otimes A & \xrightarrow{m} & A \end{array}$$

is commutative.

The algebra has a **unit** if the composition of the homomorphisms in each of the next two lines yields the identity map of A.

(9.12d) $$\begin{array}{l} A \xrightarrow{\approx} R \otimes A \xrightarrow{\eta \otimes 1_A} A \otimes A \xrightarrow{m} A. \\ A \xrightarrow{\approx} A \otimes R \xrightarrow{1_A \otimes \eta} A \otimes A \xrightarrow{m} A. \end{array}$$

Let T be the permutation homomorphism

(9.12e) $$T\colon a \otimes a' = (-1)^{rs}\, a' \otimes a, \quad a' \in A_r, \quad a \in A_s.$$

The algebra A is **commutative** (the classical terminology was anti-commutative) if

(9.12f) $$\begin{array}{ccc} A \otimes A & \overset{m}{\searrow} & \\ \downarrow{\scriptstyle T} & & A \\ A \otimes A & \underset{m}{\nearrow} & \end{array}$$

is commutative. Thus $a_r \otimes a_s$ and $(-1)^{rs} a_r \otimes a_s$ yield the same product under m. This is a familiar concomitant of all the earlier products defined in this chapter.

The **dual** algebra, or **coalgebra**, is defined by reversing all homomorphisms. We write A in place of the expected A^*. The grading is generally taken as upper grading. In more detail, ε and η reverse roles, thus the augmentation is now η. There is a **diagonal homomorphism** Δ written

(9.12g) $$A \xrightarrow{\Delta} A \otimes A.$$

The existence of a unit is the requirement that the compositions in the next two lines yield identity maps,

(9.12h) $$\begin{gathered} A \xrightarrow{\Delta} A \otimes A \xrightarrow{\varepsilon\otimes 1} R \otimes A \xrightarrow{\approx} A. \\ A \xrightarrow{\Delta} A \otimes A \xrightarrow{1\otimes \varepsilon} A \otimes R \xrightarrow{\approx} A. \end{gathered}$$

The associative condition is now

(9.12i) $$\begin{array}{ccc} A \otimes A \otimes A & \xleftarrow{1\otimes\Delta} & A \otimes A \\ \uparrow{\scriptstyle \Delta\otimes 1} & & \uparrow{\scriptstyle \Delta} \\ A \otimes A & \xleftarrow{\quad\Delta\quad} & A \end{array}$$

and (9.12e) and (9.12f) are taken over with the arrows reversed.

Remark. The correspondence with earlier work in this section is made by relating the algebra to $H_*(-, -)$ and the coalgebra to $H^*(-, -)$. The homomorphism Δ corresponds to μ^*. Connectivity, augmentation, and the unit homomorphism reflect the fact that for a connected space $H_0(-, R) \approx R$, that the Poincare axiom or R simplicity is valid, and the existence of the unit under the map $x \rightarrow \mu(x, \bar{x})$ or $\mu(\bar{x}, x)$. (The diagonal homomorphism enters the cup products as well, and so does T).

Definition 9.13. If A and B are algebras with multiplications m_1 and m_2, then $A \otimes B$ is an algebra with multiplication m defined by imposing commutativity in the following diagram

$$\begin{array}{ccc} A \otimes B \otimes A \otimes B & \xrightarrow{1\otimes T\otimes 1} & A \otimes A \otimes B \otimes B \\ & \searrow & \downarrow{\scriptstyle m_1\otimes m_2} \\ & & A \otimes B \end{array}$$

Reversal of arrows and replacement of m_i by Δ_i defines the product of two coalgebras.

Definition 9.14. If C and D are algebras, the homomorphism $f\colon C \to D$ is an **algebra homomorphism**, or simply a homomorphism if its degree is 0, and if the following diagram is commutative.

$$\begin{array}{ccc} C \otimes C & \xrightarrow{f \otimes f} & D \otimes D \\ \downarrow{\scriptstyle m} & & \downarrow{\scriptstyle m_1} \\ C & \xrightarrow{\quad f \quad} & D \end{array}$$

If C and D are coalgebras, homomorphisms must satisfy

$$\Delta_1 f = (f \otimes f)\Delta.$$

Definition 9.15. Let the coalgebra be the dual of an algebra. Specifically if $A = \oplus A_n$ we write $A^* = \oplus A^n$ with $A^n = Hom(A_n, R)$. If $\psi\colon A \to B$ is a homomorphism of algebras, then $\psi^*\colon B^* \to A^*$ is a homomorphism of coalgebras defined by $\psi^*(b^*)(a) = b^* \psi(a)$. The homomorphism $\lambda\colon A^* \otimes B^* \to (A \otimes B)^*$ is defined by

$$(\lambda(a^* \otimes b^*))(a \otimes b) = a^*(a) b^*(b) \in R.$$

Definition 9.16. A **Hopf algebra** is both an algebra and a coalgebra. Thus A is a graded R module equipped with homomorphisms m and Δ and with ε and η with ε acting as an augmentation for the algebra and as a unit for the co-algebra, and the reverse for η. Either upper or lower grading can be assumed. The following diagram is required to be commutative.

(9.16a)
$$\begin{array}{ccccc} A \otimes A & \xrightarrow{m} & A & \xrightarrow{\Delta} & A \otimes A \\ \downarrow{\scriptstyle \Delta \otimes \Delta} & & & & \uparrow{\scriptstyle m \otimes m} \\ A \otimes A \otimes A \otimes A & & \longrightarrow & & A \otimes A \otimes A \otimes A \end{array}$$

Unless contrary statement is made, *we shall understand that our Hopf Algebras are associative and commutative as well.*

The following relation is valid,

$$\varepsilon\eta = 1, \quad \text{the identity on } R.$$

Hence

(9.16b)
$$A = Im\,\eta \oplus ker\,\varepsilon = R \oplus A'.$$

where $A' = \oplus_{i>0} A^i$ is an ideal of A.

Theorem 9.17. *If A is a Hopf algebra, then*

(9.17a) $\Delta 1 = 1 \otimes 1$

(9.17b) $\Delta a = a \otimes 1 + 1 \otimes a + \Sigma\, b_r \otimes b_s, \quad 0 < r, \quad 0 < s, \quad r + s = n,$

where $a \in A^n$, $n > 0$ and grade $b_i = i$.

This is an immediate consequence of (9.12g), (9.12h), and (9.16b) since

$$\Delta A = R + A' \otimes R + R \otimes A' + A' \otimes A'.$$

Lemma 9.18. *If R is a field, or if A and B are projective modules, then* (a) λ *in* (9.14) *is an isomorphism,* (b) *Dual A^* is a Hopf co-algebra with $\Delta = m^*$ if A is an algebra and conversely.*

The isomorphism

$$Hom(A, R) \otimes Hom(A, R) \xrightarrow{\lambda} Hom(A \otimes A, R)$$

is immediate if A and B have a single generator and hence is valid if A and B are R free modules. Since projective modules are direct summands of free modules, the general case follows easily.

Definition 9.19. Let δ: $A \to A \otimes A$ be defined by

(9.19a) $\delta a = \Delta a - a \otimes 1 - 1 \otimes a = \Sigma_{r+s=n} b_r \otimes b_s$, grade $b_i = i$, (9.17b).

Let Δ' indicate Δ restricted to A'. Then

$$\Delta' \colon A' \to A' \otimes A'$$

Designate $ker\ \Delta'$ by $P(A)$. The elements in $P(A)$ are said to be **primitive**. Thus if $a \in P(A)$, $\delta(a) = 0$ or $a \in A'$ and

(9.19b) $$\Delta' a = 1 \otimes a' + a' \otimes 1.$$

If m' is m restricted to $A' \otimes A'$, then $Im\ m'$ is a two-sided ideal which is written $(A')^2$ (since it consists of products). Then

$$Q(A) = A'/(A')^2 = cok\ m' (= Tor^A(R, R))$$

is somewhat inaccurately referred to as the collection of **indecomposable** elements of A. However, when R is a field, this usage is perhaps justified. Indeed A is then a vector space and $P(A)$ and $Q(A)$ can be viewed as vector subspaces.

If R is a field, A is a vector space. Then not only $P(A)$, but $Q(A)$ also, is a vector subspace.

Lemma 9.20. *If R is a field, a vector basis $\{b_i\}$ for the vector space for $Q(A)$ constitutes a minimal basis for the Hopf algebra A.*

We may assume $\{b_i\}$ partially ordered by ascending grade. Let $a \in A'$ be the element of lowest grade which is not in the algebra A'' generated by

$(1, \{b_i\})$. Let $[a] = a \bmod (A')^2$ be the element of $Q(A)$ determined by a. Since the b's constitute a vector basis for $Q(A)$

$$[a] = \Sigma_\pi r_i b_i = a'' \in A''$$

or

$$a - a'' = \Sigma c_r d_s \in (A')^2$$

where c_r and d_s are in A'. Since $\sup r, s < n$, c_r and d_s are in A''. Hence $a \in A''$ a contradiction.

We shall assume throughout that A is of finite type (9.12). This restriction is not important since it can be established that taking a direct limit of Hopf algebras of finite type yields the general case.

Lemma 9.21. *Suppose that the Hopf algebras A and B are projective modules, or that R is a field. Let $f: A \to B$ be an algebra homomorphism. The induced homomorphisms are written $P(f)\colon P(A) \to P(B)$ and $Q(f)\colon Q(A) \to Q(B)$. Then f is a monomorphism or an epimorphism if $P(f)$ is a monomorphism or $Q(f)$ is an epimorphism.*

If f is a monomorphism, then so is $P(f)$ by restriction. Suppose $P(f)$ is a monomorphism. The assertion of the theorem is trivially valid for $n = 1$. We make the induction hypothesis that $f \mid A^i$ is a monomorphism for $i < n$. Plainly $f \otimes f\colon A^r \otimes A^s \to B^r \otimes B^s$, $\sup r, s < n$ is a monomorphism since $f \otimes f$ is the composition of $f \otimes 1$ and $1 \otimes f$. Suppose that $a \in A^n$ and that $f(a) = 0$. We will show $a = 0$. Thus

$$0 = \Delta 0 = \Delta f(a) = (f \otimes f)\Delta a \qquad (9.16)$$
$$= (f \otimes f)\,\Sigma.$$

Since $f \otimes f$ is a monomorphism, $\Sigma = 0$. Accordingly $a \in P(A)$. Since $f(a) = Pf(a) = 0$ and $P(f)$ is a monomorphism, $a = 0$.

Theorem 9.22. *If R is a field, and A is a Hopf algebra, then*

$$P(A^*) = (Q(A))^* \quad \text{and} \quad Q(A^*) = (P(A))^*.$$

The key is that under duality Δ' and m' are interchanged and so are *ker* and *coker*.

From now on R *will invariably be understood to be a field.*

Theorem 9.23. *If A is a Hopf algebra over the field R of characteristic p, p a prime, the homomorphism λ given by composition*

(9.23a) $$P(A) \to A' \to Q(A)$$

is a monomorphism iff $a'^p = 0$ *for all* $a' \in A'$. *The composition is always a monomorphism if char* $p = 0$.

Let $\{b_i \mid b_i \in Q(A)\}$ be a minimal basis for the algebra A (9.20).

Let B_n be the subalgebra generated by $(1, \{b_i\} \mid i \leq n)$. This is a Hopf algebra. For instance if $\Delta' = \Delta \mid B_n$, then $\Delta' \colon B_n \to B_n \otimes B_n$. Indeed

$$\Delta b_i = 1 \otimes b_i + b_i \otimes 1 + \Sigma \tag{9.23b}$$

where, since the elements entering Σ are of grade inferior to grade b_i, $\Sigma \in B_{n-1}$.

Let J be the two-sided ideal of B_n generated by B_{n-1}. Let $D_n = B_n/J$. Evidently Δ' induces a diagonal map

$$\Delta_n \colon D_n \to D_n \otimes D_n. \tag{9.23c}$$

Thus D_n is readily seen to be a Hopf algebra.

Since there is one generator b_n only, it must be primitive. We shall establish the correspondence $P(D_n) \to Q(D_n)$ is an isomorphism. First if $n = 2m + 1$, $b_n^2 = 0$ (9.12f). Hence $Q(D_n) \approx D_n$. Since b_n is primitive $P(D_n) = D_n$.

If $n = 2m$, then

$$b_{2m} = b_{2m} \otimes 1 + 1 \otimes b_{2m}. \tag{9.23d}$$

Let $A = B$ in (9.13). It is plain from $m(b \otimes b^{n-1}) = b^n$ that

$$\Delta b^j = b^j \otimes 1 + 1 \otimes b^j + \Sigma\, cb^n \otimes b^s, \quad r + s = j, \quad \text{grade } b = 2m, \tag{9.23e}$$

where c is the appropriate binomial coefficient. Plainly then, if $p = 0$, $b^j \neq 0$ and b^j is not primitive for $j > 1$. Accordingly

$$P(D_{2m}) = \{rb_{2m} \mid r \in R\}.$$

Since $b_{2m}^j \in (D'_{2m})^2$ for $j > 0$, it follows $Q(D_{2m}) = \{rb_{2m} \mid r \in R\} = P(D_{2m})$.

If $p \neq 0$, the binomial coefficients $\{c\}$ for $j = p$ are divisible by p, so (9.23d) implies b^j is nonprimitive for $1 < j < p$ only. Hence if $b^p \neq 0$, $P(D_m)$ includes b^p while $Q(D_m)$ does not.

If $a \in P(A)$, then for n sufficiently large, $a \in P(B_n)$. We assert that with the homomorphism λ applied on $P(B_n)$ to $P(B_n)$, $\lambda(a) \neq 0$. This is certainly true for $n = 0$. We make the induction hypothesis that n is the lowest grade for which $\lambda(a) = 0$. Write $[a]$ for the class of a in $P(D_n) \subset D_n$. Then $\lambda[a] = 0$ in $Q(D_n)$. We have already shown λ is an isomorphism for D_n and so $[a] = 0$. Therefore $a \in B_{n-1}$ in contradiction with our induction hypothesis.

Suppose now that $p \neq 0$ and that λ is a monomorphism. There must follow $a^p = 0$ for $a \in A'$. This is trivial for grade $a = 1$. Suppose the assertion true for grade $a < n$. If $a \in A^n$, then a^p is primitive. Since $a^p \in (A')^2$, $\lambda a^p = 0$. However, since λ is a monomorphism, $a^p = 0$.

Definition 9.24. Let E be a graded vector space over R, $E = \oplus E_m$. If $e \in E_m$, it is **homogeneous** and $deg\, e = m$. Let $T(E)$ be the **tensor algebra** or **free associative algebra** generated by E. Thus if $E^r = E \otimes \cdots \otimes E$, then

$$T(E) = \oplus E^r. \tag{9.24a}$$

We write ee' for $e \otimes e'$. An element of E^r is a finite sum of terms of the form $t = \Pi_{i=1}^{i=r} e_i$, where each e_i is homogeneous and $deg\, t = \Sigma\, deg\, e_i$. Multiplication in $T(E)$ yields $E^r \otimes E^s \approx E^{r+s}$.

Let e and e' be homogeneous with $deg\, e = m$, $deg\, e' = n$. Let

$$ee' - (-1)^{mn}\, e'e$$

be a relation R and let $\{R\}$ indicate the totality of such relations. Then

$$C(E) = T(E)/\{R\}$$

is the **free associative commutative algebra** generated by E. Write c for $[e]_{\{R\}}$ and c' for $[e'']_{\{R\}}$ in $C(E)$. Then $deg\, c = deg\, e = m$, $deg\, c' = deg\, e' = n$. Then $cc' = (-1)^{mn}\, c'c$.

For completeness we add the following information. Let S be the ideal generated by squares in $T(E)$. (Then the typical element of S is of the form $rt'\, t^2\, t''$ where t' or t'' may be absent and t', t and $t'' \in T(E)$.) If $E_m = 0$ whenever m is odd, then $C(E)$ is the **symmetric algebra** $U(E)$. If $E_m = 0$ for m even, then $V(E) = T(E)/S$ is the **external algebra** or Grassman algebra generated by E.

If $E = E' \oplus E''$ then $T(E)$ is the free product of $T(E')$ and $T(E'')$ while $C(E) = C(E') \otimes C(E'')$. In particular, if $E^+ = \oplus E_{2i}$ and $E^- = \oplus E_{2i+1}$, then

$$C(E) = C(E^+) \otimes C(E^-).$$

Lemma 9.25. *If E has just one element, e, in its basis and either $deg\, e$ is even or R has characteristic 2, then $T(E) = C(E)$ is the polynomial algebra generated by e. If $E_m = 0$ for m even and char $R \neq 2$, then $C(E) = V(E)$. If char $R \neq 2$, then $C(E) = U(E) \otimes V(E)$.*

For the second conclusion we need only that for homogeneous elements e and e', $[e]_S\, [e']_S = -[e]_S\, [e]_S$. This follows at once from

$$0 = [(e + e')^2]_S = [ee']_S + [e'\, e]_S.$$

Lemma 9.26. *Let B be an associative commutative algebra and let E be a vector space, both over the same field R. If f is a linear map or vector space homomorphism of E to B then f has an extension g'' to an algebra homomorphism of $C(E)$ to B.*

The facts alluded to here are obtained by gaining the extension g'' in two stages. Thus

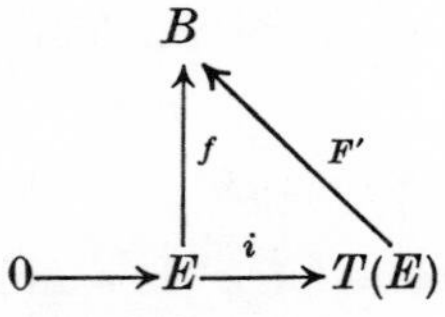

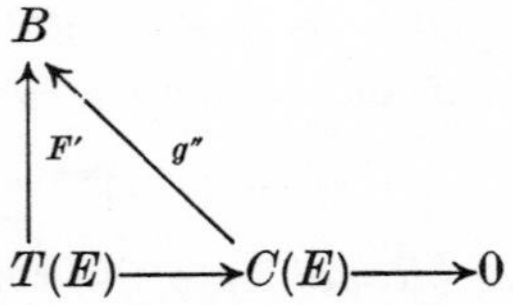

Lemma 9.27. *Let f be a linear map of the vector space $Q(A)$ into the Hopf Algebra A. Let g'' be the extension to $CQ(A)$ to A guaranteed by (9.26). Then g'' is onto and $Q(g'')\colon QCQ(A) \to Q(A)$ is an isomorphism.*

The first assertion is an immediate consequence of (9.20). Since Q singles out the indecomposable elements, the second assertion is obvious.

Our last result is a generalization of (9.10). Write g for g of (9.26) applied to $CQ(A)$ to A.

Theorem 9.28. Hopf-Leray. *If char $R = 0$, then g'' is an isomorphism of graded algebras.*

Write E for $Q(A)$. That $C(E)$ is a Hopf algebra follows easily once it is known there is a diagonal homomorphism.

$$(9.28a) \qquad\qquad \Delta_1\colon C(E) \to C(E) \otimes C(E).$$

We proceed to define Δ_1. Let $C' = C(E)'$ be the ideal in $C(E)$ generated by elements whose grade is non-0. Let $g' = g \,|\, C'$. In view of (9.27) g' is an epimorphism on C' to A' and hence $g' \otimes g'$ is an epimorphism on $C' \otimes C'$ to $A' \otimes A'$. From

$$Q(A) \xrightarrow{\;f\;} A' \xrightarrow{\;\delta\;} A' \otimes A', \qquad (9.19a)$$

there arises the diagram

$$
\begin{array}{c}
Q(A) \\
\downarrow{\scriptstyle \delta f} \\
C' \otimes C' \xrightarrow{\;g' \otimes g'\;} A' \otimes A' \longrightarrow 0
\end{array}
$$

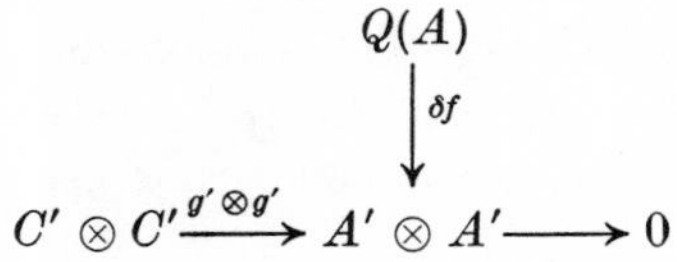

Since R is a field, $Q(A)$ is free. Hence there is a homomorphism h on $Q(A)$ to $C' \otimes C'$ such that $\delta f = (g' \otimes g')h$. We define Δ_2 on $Q(A)$ to $C \otimes C$ by

$$\Delta_2 a = a \otimes 1 + 1 \otimes a + h(a).$$

We call on (9.26). The correspondence is Δ_2 with f, $C \otimes C$ with B and Δ_1 will be written for g'' (and is the homomorphism required in (9.28a)). Thus g is a homomorphism of Hopf algebras. For instance, one verifies easily that $\Delta\, \mathrm{g} = (\mathrm{g} \otimes \mathrm{g})\, \Delta$.

The following diagram is evidently commutative.

$$\begin{array}{ccc} PC(E) & \longrightarrow & QC(E) \\ \downarrow{\scriptstyle P(g)} & & \downarrow{\scriptstyle Q(g)} \\ P(A) & \longrightarrow & Q(A) \end{array}$$

The horizontal lines are monomorphisms according to (9.23) and $Q(g)$ is an isomorphism (9.27). Accordingly $P(g)$ is a monomorphism. In concert with the first part of (9.27) this shows g is an isomorphism.

The **height** h or $h(b)$ of an element b is the lowest vanishing power of b and may be infinite. The next result is due to Borel.

Theorem 9.29. *Let R be a perfect field of characteristic p (each element of R has a pth root). Then a minimal base $\{b_i\}$ of a Hopf algebra A can be chosen so that*

(9.29a) $$h(b_i) \le h(b_i + w(b_1, \ldots, b_{i-1}))$$

for every homogeneous polynomial w with $\deg b_i = \deg w$. Moreover ker f'': $CQ(A) \to A$ is the ideal generated by $\{(b_i)^{h_i} \mid h_i < \infty\}$ where the height h_i is a power of p except when $p \ne 2$ and $\deg b_i$ is odd, in which case $h_i = 2$.

That (9.29a) can be satisfied is easily seen.

Assume each monomial M is ordered as in (9.7) so that

(9.29b) $$M = (b_n)^r \cdot (b_{n-1})^s \cdots (b_1)^t.$$

Further the monomials can be ordered lexicographically. Thus $M > M'$ if $n > n'$ or if $n = n'$, then the first nonzero difference $r - r'$, $s - s'$ determines the order.

Let J_m be the ideal generated by $(b_1, \ldots, b_m)$. Let I_m be the ideal $J_m \otimes A$ in $A \otimes A$. Then

(9.29c) $$\begin{aligned} \Delta\, b_m &= b_m \otimes 1 + 1 \otimes b_m \mod I_{m-1} \\ \Delta\, b_i &= 1 \otimes b_i \qquad\qquad\qquad \mod I_{m-1}. \end{aligned}$$

Let $N_1 = (b_{m-1})^s \cdots (b_1)^t$ and let $M_1 = (b_m)^q N_1$. Then

(9.29d) $$\Delta M_1 = (b_m)^q \otimes N_1 + 1 \otimes M_1 + + \Sigma_{0<i<r} c(b_m)^i \otimes (b_m)^{q-i} N_1 \bmod I_{m-1}.$$

where c refers to the appropriate binomial coefficient.

That these monomials generate A is plain. What is required is a demonstration that these monomials are linearly independent. If $n = 1$, this is trivial. We make the induction hypothesis that this linear independence is valid for the degree i inferior to n. Thus for two monomials, M and M', if $\deg M$, $\deg M' < n$, then $M = M'$ only if the monomials are identical. This applies also to the monomials $M \otimes N$ in $A \otimes A$ for sup $(\deg M, \deg N) < n$ and hence $\{M \otimes N \mid \deg M = \deg N < n\}$ are linearly independent.

Write the polynomial relation

(9.29e) $$w(b_m, \ldots, b_1) = \Sigma r_i M_i, \quad \deg M_i = n, \quad r_i \in R$$
$$= (b_m)^q u(b_{m-1}, \ldots, b_1) + v(b_m, \ldots, b_1)$$

where b_m enters with an exponent inferior to q in v.

Assume $w = 0$.

Let $\deg u > 0$. Then from (9.29d) and (9.29e) it is plain that no term in Δv can balance a non-0 term $c(b_m)^i \otimes (b_m)^{q-i} N_i$. Accordingly $\deg u = 0$ and we may as well write $u = 1$. Thus $q \deg b_m = n$.

We assert q is either 1 or p^k for some $k > 0$. Otherwise the binomial coefficients c in (9.29d) do not vanish and therefore $\Delta(b_m)^q$ cannot be balanced by Δv (to yield $\Delta w = 0$). However, manifestly $q = 1$ is not admissible since then $b_m = -v(b_{m-1}, \ldots, b_1)$.

We now show

(9.29f) $$w(b_m, \ldots, b_1) = (b_m + \rho(b_{m-1}, \ldots, b_1))^q, \quad q = p^k, \quad k \geq 1.$$

We make the induction hypothesis that the right hand side of (9.29e) is representable as

(9.29g) $$(b_m + \rho(b_{m-1}, \ldots, b_1))^q + (b_j)^t \mu(b_{j-1}, \ldots, b_1) + \tau(b_j, \ldots, b_1)$$

where $j \leq m$ and the degree of b_j in τ is inferior to t. This is certainly valid for $\rho = 0$. Then

(9.29h) $$\Delta(b_m + \rho)^q = (b_m + \rho)^q \otimes 1 + 1 \otimes (b_m + \rho)^q + \Sigma r_i M_i^q \otimes N_i^q$$

where M_i and N_i are monomials and $q = p^k$, $k \geq 1$. Suppose $\deg \mu > 0$. Then $\Delta((b_j)^t \mu + \tau)$ contains a term $d(b_j)^t \otimes M$ where M is the first monomial in μ in the sense of our earlier ordering and $d \in R$. If this is to be balanced in (9.29h), we must have for some i, neglecting signs, $M_i^q = (b_j)^t$,

$N_i{}^q = M$. Hence $(b_j)^t M = (\theta M_i N_i)^q$ where θ is a qth root of -1. In case $\mu =$ constant we can, of course, assume $j < m$ and therefore, since $t \deg b_j = q \deg b_m = n$ and $\deg b_j = \deg b_m$, $q \leq t$. If then $t = p^r$, t is divisible by q and $(b_j)^t = (b_j{}^s)^q$. If $t \neq p^r$ for any r, then $\Delta(b_j)^t$ contains a term $c(b_j)^i \otimes (b_j)^{t-i}$ which must be balanced by a term in (9.29h). Thus neglecting signs for some i, $M_i{}^q = (b_j)^i, N_i{}^q = (b_j)^{t-i}$. Hence $(b_j)^t = (\theta M_i N_i)^q$. Hence for $\deg \mu \geq 0$, $((b_j)^t\mu) = d(M')^q + \boldsymbol{\nu}$ so ρ can be replaced by $\rho + eM'$. The induction validation of (9.29f) is thus complete. However, if $w = 0$ (9.29f) is in contradiction with (9.29a). We have, therefore, shown the assumption $w = 0$ is untenable.

Suppose finally either $p = 2$, or that $\deg b_j$ is even, and that the height h of b_j is not a power of p. Then $h = \infty$. Indeed otherwise $(b_j)^{h-1} \neq 0$ and $(b_j)^h$ contains $c((b_j)^i \otimes (b_j)^{h-1})$, $0 < i < h$ which cannot be balanced off, so $(b_i)^h \neq 0$.

chapter 13

GROUPS OF HOMEOMORPHISMS

A vast territory is catalogued under the central idea of a map of one space X, into another, B, under a mapping function p, with the sets $p^{-1}b = F_b$ somehow related. The space X is the **superspace**, B is the **base space**, and F_b is the **fiber** over b. We write (X, B, F_b, p) or sometimes the triple (X, B, p). Presently we take up in their proper places as illustrations the group, normal subgroup, quotient group, spaces admitting groups of homeomorphisms, covering spaces and fiber bundles and sheaves.

1. HOMOTOPY TYPE. The invariance of omology characteristics under homotopy indicates that omology arguments cannot establish the existence of a homeomorphism, but merely equivalence in some sense under homotopy.

Definition 1.1. If α maps X into Y and β maps Y into X, then, if $\beta a \simeq 1$, β is a **left homotopy inverse** of α, and α is a **right homotopy inverse** of β. (If $= 1$ replaces $\simeq 1$ the qualifying term homotopy is dropped.) If β is both a right and a left homotopy inverse of α, then β is a **homotopy inverse** of α. If some α admits a homotopy inverse, X and Y are of the same **homotopy type.** For X and Y fixed, it is possible that some maps have right homotopy inverses and others left homotopy inverses, yet no map has a homotopy inverse; i.e., X and Y are not of the same homotopy type. A case in point is illustrated.

Example 13-1. Let $X = Z \times Z \times Z \times, \ldots,$ where Z is the figure 8 set of Fig. 13-1, and $Y = C \times X$ where C is a circle. Let α_1 take the first Z space of X into Y by "folding" the 8 to give the doubly covered circle, and let β_1 take C into the lower half of the Z above. Then $\alpha_1 \beta_1 \simeq 1$, i.e., β_1 has a left inverse. Next let α_2: $(t_1, t_2, \ldots) = (a_0, t_1, t_2, \ldots)$ where a_0 is fixed. Let $\beta_2(a_0, t_1, \ldots) = (t_1, t_2, \ldots)$. Hence $\beta_2 \alpha_2 \simeq 1$ or β_2 has a right inverse.

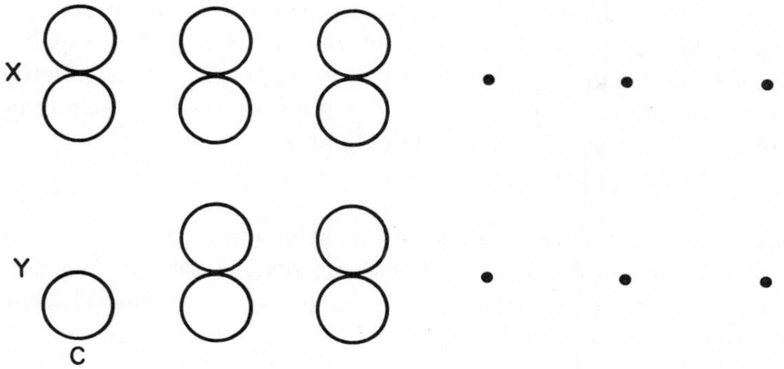

Figure 13-1

Before raising anchor for omological seas we announce some of our objectives in the remainder of this chapter. A translation is a simple enough example of a self map of the plane with no fixed points. The plane admits several groups of homeomorphisms. Let t be a homeomorphism of the plane with t^2 the identity, or more generally with t^k the identity. Let ψ commute with t. For such maps there is always a fixed point. (That this is reasonable is suggested by taking for t the reflection in the origin.) The striking feature is that the compactness restriction usually imposed on fixed point theorems does not come in. The Borsuk problem is whether for the cover of a 2-sphere by 3 closed sets one of the sets must contain an antipodal pair. The answer is yes and is part of the group T_2, theory. A seemingly different type of question is whether every convex set in R^3 admits a circumscribing cube. Again this is an application of the same T_2 theory. What is the nature of the fixed point set for a homeomorphism of order k? The answer, which depends strongly on the fact that k is at worst the power of a prime, is that this fixed point set is of sphere type. Other significant applications merely mentioned at the end of this chapter involve relations to certain products entering omology theory and to the question of imbedding one space in another.

There are some slight deviations from our earlier practice, as for instance the use of black face letters. These will mitigate the strain of complicated formulae.

2. TRANSFORMATION GROUPS. Definition 2.1. The space X **admits** the topological or continuous transformation group G of homeomorphisms, or admits the topological group G as operators on the left if there is a map (therefore continuous) $G \times \boldsymbol{X} \to \boldsymbol{X}$ which for fixed g is a homeomorphism defined by $(g, x) = g \times \boldsymbol{x} \to \boldsymbol{x}'$ where $\boldsymbol{x}'$ is written $g\boldsymbol{x}$ with $g_2(g_1\, \boldsymbol{x}) = (g_2\, g_1)\boldsymbol{x}$ and $e\boldsymbol{x} = \boldsymbol{x}$. The correspondence $g\boldsymbol{x} = g\boldsymbol{x}'$ implies $\boldsymbol{x} = \boldsymbol{x}'$.

The group G is **transitive** or operates transitively if for any assigned pair $\boldsymbol{x}_1$, $\boldsymbol{x}_2$ in $\boldsymbol{X}$ there is an element of G such that $\boldsymbol{x}_2 = g\boldsymbol{x}_1$. The **stability group** at $\boldsymbol{x}_0$ is the subgroup, $G_{\boldsymbol{x}_0}$, for which $g\boldsymbol{x}_0 = \boldsymbol{x}_0$, $g \in G_{x_0}$. G is **effective** if the identity is the only element leaving X pointwise fixed. G **acts freely** if no point of X is fixed under all the elements of G.

Similar definitions hold for G an operator group on the right.

Remark. We can elect to write an operator group on the left, or on the right, depending on the order of operation desired for gg'. To change we can replace gx by xg^{-1}. When two such groups are available, then it is convenient to have one on the right and the other acting on the left.

Definition 2.2. If G_1 is a closed subgroup of G, the **left cosets** are the sets of form gG_1. The cosets constitute a **homogeneous** space G/G_1 with the point $[g]$ corresponding to gG_1. The group G acts as a transitive operator group (on the left) according to $[g] \xrightarrow{g'} [g'\, g]$ with the projection $p\colon G \longrightarrow G/G_1$. Open sets in G/G_1 are those whose inverses, under p, are open. Since, for open U, $p^{-1}(pU\, G_1) = UG_1$, p is open.

Let N be the largest subgroup of G_1 which is invariant in G. Then G/N is the effective left operator group on G/G_1. Write (g) for the coset gN in G/N. Then $(g)[g']$ corresponds to the coset $gNg'\, G_1 = gg'\, NG_1$ whence $[gg'] = (g)[g']$. If $g'\, gG_1 = gG_1$, for every g in G, then $g^{-1}\, g'\, g \in G_1$, so $g' \in N$, that is to say *G/N is effective on G/G_1* and is easily verified to be a continuous group of transformations.

Let G be a transitive topological operator group on X and let G_0 be the stability subgroup of x_0. Then if $p\colon g \to gx_0$, we factor p by

$$G \xrightarrow{\mu} G/G_0 \xrightarrow{\nu} X$$

The transitivity of G implies ν is single valued, whence ν is continuous (**A**). On the other hand ν^{-1} need not be continuous.

Lemma 2.3. *ν^{-1} is continuous if and only if p is open.*

If V is open in G then, since μ is open, $\mu(V)$ is open and the continuity of ν^{-1} implies $(\nu^{-1})^{-1}V = \nu\mu(V)$ is open, but this is $p(V)$. If p is open and U is open in G/G_0 then $\nu U = p\mu^{-1}U$ is open, so ν^{-1} is continuous.

Definition 2.4. We denote by $\boldsymbol{F}_t$ the fixed point set $\boldsymbol{F}_t = \{\boldsymbol{x} \mid t\boldsymbol{x} = \boldsymbol{x}\}$ with T an operator group on the left. The set fixed for all $t \in T$ is denoted by

$F = \bigcap_T F_t$. A set A is **invariant** under t if $tA = A$, $t \in t$, but the points of A need not be fixed. For instance, under the group of rotations of the plane about the origin, every circle with θ as center is an invariant set, but $F = \theta$. If $F_t = \varnothing$, X is fixed point free, *fpf*, relative to t, we also refer to t as *fpf*. If every t is *fpf*, T is *fpf*.

Definition 2.5. If X admits T, an equivalence relation, $x \sim x'$ is defined if $x = tx'$, $t \in T$ and the **orbit** of x is defined as $\{x' \mid x \sim x'\}$. The equivalence class Tx of x is denoted by x. The identification topology $(A, 2)$ on the space with elements $\{x\}$ the orbits of X yields the **orbit space** denoted by X or by X/T. Define $X \xrightarrow{p} X$ by

(2.5a) $$px = x.$$

Definition 2.6. If X admits T, and $F = \varnothing$, a **fundamental set** D in X is any set satisfying

(2.6a) $$tD \cap D = \varnothing, \qquad t \in T,$$

(2.6b) $$\bigcup_T tD = X.$$

Denote elements of D by a stroke before the letter, i.e., $'x \in D$, $x \in X$.

Example 13-2. Let X be the circle S^1. Let t be the rotation by π so $T = (1, t)$. Then, writing x for the arc length mod 2π on S^1, $D = \{x \mid 0 \leq x < \pi\}$. Note D is neither open nor closed.

Definition 2.7. A concrete finite complex K with all closed vertex stars disjunct admits the operator group T on the left if each t in T is a dimension preserving cell map, t: $e'_m = e''_m$. If $te_m \cap e_m \neq \varnothing$ then in fact e_m is pointwise invariant under t. (The simplexes or cells are here to be considered open sets.) K is *fpf* if $F = \varnothing$ and a fundamental set, D, for such a K is a subcomplex of K generally non-closed such that

(2.7a) $$tD \cap D = \varnothing$$

(2.7b) $$\bigcup tD = K.$$

When $F \neq \varnothing$, D consists of the union of F and the fundamental set for $K - F$. Analogously to the notation $'x$, $'e \in D$. The fundamental set for m chains is the collection of m cells in D, namely $D^{[m]}$.

Definition 2.8. Let T be a multiplicative not necessarily Abelian group. Denote by T_k the cyclic group $\{t^i \mid i = 0, \ldots, k-1\}$. The **group algebra**

J(T) is an algebra whose elements, r, are the formal sums, $r = \Sigma_\pi n_i t_i, n_i$ an integer, $t \in T$, subject to the rules of combination:

$$\Sigma_\pi n_i t_i \Sigma_\pi m_j t_j = \Sigma_\pi n_i m_j t_i t_j \qquad \in \text{J}(T), \tag{2.8a}$$

$$\Sigma_\pi n_i t_i + \Sigma_\pi m_i t_i = \Sigma_\pi (n_i + m_i) t_i. \tag{2.8b}$$

Note n_i, or m_i may be 0. The neutral element 1 of T yields the unit of J(T). In this chapter T will invariably be a finite group but this need not be the case in (149) for instance.

A special module over J(T) is determined by an additive Abelian group G. This module is denoted by $G(T)$ and consists of the elements $\Sigma n_i g_{ij} t_j = \Sigma g_j' t_j$ where $g_j' = \Sigma n_i g_{ij}$. A glance ahead at (2.12) will indicate the utility of these considerations.

It is important for our developments that there are 0 divisors in J(T). For instance, define (the **norm** homomorphism) τ and σ_i by

$$\tau = \Sigma_T t_i = t\tau \tag{2.8c}$$

$$\sigma_i = 1 - t_i,$$

$$\tau\sigma_i = \sigma_i \tau = 0. \tag{2.8d}$$

In this chapter σ_i is never a simplex. The excuse for the notation is that it is common (up to permutation of τ and σ). For T_k, $t_i = t^i$, $0 \leq i < k$, in (2.8c) and we introduce

$$\gamma = 1 + 2t + 3t^2 + \cdots + (k-1)t^{k-2}. \tag{2.8e}$$

Therefore

$$\sigma\gamma = \tau - kt^{k-1} \tag{2.8f}$$

$$= \tau \bmod k.$$

Definition 2.9. Let η be the **augmentation** homomorphism on J(T) to J defined by

$$\eta(r) = \eta \Sigma_\pi n_i t_i = \Sigma n_i, \tag{2.9a}$$

where $r = \Sigma n_i t_i$. We use the same symbol, η, for the analogous homomorphism on $G(T)$ to G defined by

$$\eta(\alpha) = \eta \Sigma g_i t_i = \Sigma g_i \tag{2.9b}$$

where $\alpha = \Sigma g_i t_i$.

Definition 2.10. Let I be the ideal of J(T) generated by $\{\sigma_i\}$. Thus

$$I = \{\Sigma_\pi n_i \sigma_i\}. \tag{2.10a}$$

If G is a $\mathrm{J}(T)$ module G^T or $F(G)$ is the set of fixed elements of $G(T)$ under T. Thus

(2.10b) $$F(G) = \{\alpha \mid \sigma_i\, \alpha = 0\}.$$

$IG \subset ker\, \tau$. $IG = ker\, \tau$, if T is the cyclic group T_k.

We introduce the first of our definitions of omology groups of groups. (Another approach is given in Chapter 17.) We shall write G for T in (2.11).

Definition 2.11. Let J be considered a two sided $J(G)$ module with the action of $\mathrm{J}(G)$ trivial. Then $t \cdot n = n$ for $t \in G$, $n \in \mathrm{J}$. For (117.3) let R be $\mathrm{J}(G)$. Suppose A is a left $\mathrm{J}(G)$ module. Define

(2.11a) $$H^n(G, A) = \mathrm{Ext}^n_{\mathrm{J}(G)}(\mathrm{J}, A) = H^n(Hom_{\mathrm{J}(G)}(K_*(\mathrm{J}), A)$$

(2.11b) $$H_n(G, A) = \mathrm{Tor}_n^{\mathrm{J}(G)}(\mathrm{J}, A) = H_n(K_*(\mathrm{J}) \otimes_{\mathrm{J}(G)} A).$$

With ε the augmentation (2.9),

(2.11c) $$0 \longrightarrow ker\, \varepsilon \longrightarrow \mathrm{J}(G) \xrightarrow{\varepsilon} \mathrm{J} \longrightarrow 0$$

is exact and hence so is

$$0 \to A \otimes_{\mathrm{J}(G)} ker\, \varepsilon \to A \otimes_{\mathrm{J}(G)} \mathrm{J}(G) \to A \otimes_{\mathrm{J}(G)} \mathrm{J} \to 0$$

Since ε: $ng = n$ for $g \in G$, $A \otimes ker\, \varepsilon \approx IA$. According to (107.9)

(2.11d) $$H_0(G, A) \approx \mathrm{J} \otimes_{\mathrm{J}(G)} A \approx A \otimes_{\mathrm{J}(G)} \mathrm{J}(G)/A \otimes_{\mathrm{J}(G)} ker\, \varepsilon \approx A/I(A).$$

If ψ is a $\mathrm{J}(G)$ homomorphism on J to A then $\psi(j) = \psi(gj) = g\psi(j)$. Hence $Hom_{\mathrm{J}(G)}(\mathrm{J}, A) = A^G$ where A^G consists of the fixed elements of A under G. Hence by (107.9)

$$H^0(G, A) \approx Hom_{\mathrm{J}(G)}(\mathrm{J}, A) \approx A^G.$$

Definition 2.12. If the finite complex $\boldsymbol{K}$ admits T and if G is a coefficient group, then the typical chain in $C(\boldsymbol{K}, G)$ is of the form

$$\boldsymbol{c}_m = \Sigma\, \alpha_j\, '\boldsymbol{e}_m^j, \quad \alpha_j = \Sigma_i\, g_{ij}\, t_i, \quad g_{ij} \in G, \quad t_i \in T.$$

Since $\tau = \tau t$ for all $t \in T$,

$$\begin{aligned} \tau_\#\, \boldsymbol{c}_m &= \Sigma_j \Sigma_i\, g_{ij}\, \tau\, '\boldsymbol{e}_m^j \\ &= \Sigma_j\, \eta(\alpha_j)\, \tau\, '\boldsymbol{e}_m^j. \end{aligned}$$

(If $'\boldsymbol{e}_m \in \boldsymbol{F}$, then, of course, α_i reduces to an element of G.)

Definition 2.13. We generalize p, p^{-1} to the case of pairs; that is to say, to the relative theory. Let $\boldsymbol{Z} = \{\boldsymbol{z}\}$, $\boldsymbol{Z}_0 = \{\boldsymbol{z}_0\}$ refer *either* to $\boldsymbol{X}$, $\boldsymbol{X}_0$ or to

$\boldsymbol{K}$, $\boldsymbol{K}_0$, with $\boldsymbol{Z}_0$ invariant under each t in T. (If $\boldsymbol{Z}$ refers to $\boldsymbol{K}$, $\boldsymbol{z}$ is a cell, $\boldsymbol{e}$). Then $p(\boldsymbol{Z}, \boldsymbol{Z}_0) = Z, Z_0$ is defined by

(2.13a) $$p(\boldsymbol{z}, \boldsymbol{z}_0) = (p\boldsymbol{z}, p\boldsymbol{z}_0) = z, z_0.$$

Write $\boldsymbol{D}_0 = \boldsymbol{D} \cap \boldsymbol{Z}_0$. Then

(2.13b) $$p^{-1}(z, z_0) = (\tau\, '\boldsymbol{z}, \tau\, '\boldsymbol{z}_0)$$

where $\tau\, '\boldsymbol{z}$ may not have $\eta(\tau)$ different elements. For instance, if $'\boldsymbol{z}_0 \in \boldsymbol{F}(T)$, then $\tau\, '\boldsymbol{z}_0 = {}'\boldsymbol{z}_0$. Thus if $\boldsymbol{Z}_0 = \boldsymbol{F}$ even though $\tau\; {}_0\boldsymbol{e}_m = {}_0\boldsymbol{e}_m$, nevertheless $\tau_{\#}\; {}_0\boldsymbol{e}$ is the chain $\Sigma\, t\; {}_0\boldsymbol{e}_m = \eta(\tau)\; {}_0\boldsymbol{e}_m$.

Remark. Change to the barycentric subdivisions $'\boldsymbol{Z}, '\boldsymbol{Z}_0$ if necessary insures p is simplicial when simplicial complexes are involved.

The notation in earlier chapters would be cumbersome here. For the induced homomorphisms connecting $C(Z, Z_0, G)$ and $C(\boldsymbol{Z}, \boldsymbol{Z}_0, G)$ we agree in this chapter that the homomorphism $\boldsymbol{\pi}$ will represent both $p^{\#}$ and p^* and that $\boldsymbol{\omega}$ will stand for both $p_{\#}$ and for p_*. (The reader will not, of course, confuse $\boldsymbol{c}_m$ or $\boldsymbol{f}^m$ which refer to chains or cochains for spaces $\boldsymbol{X}$ or $\boldsymbol{X}$, $\boldsymbol{X}_0$ with $\mathbf{c}_m$ or $\mathbf{f}^m$ which invariably denote elements of omology algebras.)

Lemma 2.14

(2.14a) $\boldsymbol{\omega}[\Sigma_\pi\, \alpha_i\, '\boldsymbol{e}^i_m] = [\Sigma_\pi\, \eta(\alpha_i) e^i_m]$ *where the brackets indicate cosets relative to* $\boldsymbol{K}_0$ *or to* K_0. *Thus* $\boldsymbol{\omega}$: $C_m(\boldsymbol{K}, \boldsymbol{K}_0, G) \to C_m(K, K_0, G)$

(2.14b) $$\boldsymbol{\omega}^{-1}\colon [\Sigma_\pi\, g_i\, e^i_m] \to [\Sigma\, g_i\, \tau_{\#}\, '\boldsymbol{e}^i_m] = \tau_{\#}[\Sigma\, g_i\, '\boldsymbol{e}^i_m]$$

(2.14c) $$\boldsymbol{\omega}^{-1}\, \boldsymbol{\omega}\colon [\Sigma_\pi\, \alpha_i\, '\boldsymbol{e}_m] \to [\Sigma\, \eta(\alpha_i)\, \tau_{\#}\, \boldsymbol{e}^i_m]$$

(2.14d) $$\boldsymbol{\omega}\boldsymbol{\omega}^{-1}\colon [c_m] \to \eta(\tau)[c_m], \to k[c_m] \text{ for } T = T_k.$$

PROBLEM

13-1. Demonstrate these relations.

We develop the analogue of (2.14) for the cochain case.

Lemma 2.15

(a) $\boldsymbol{\pi}\colon C^m(K, K_0, G) \to C^m(\boldsymbol{K}, \boldsymbol{K}_0, G)$

(b) $\boldsymbol{\pi}^{-1}\colon C^m(\boldsymbol{K}, \boldsymbol{K}_0, G)$ *onto* $C^m(K, K_0, G)$

(c) $\boldsymbol{\pi}\boldsymbol{\pi}^{-1} = \tau^{\#}$

(d) $\boldsymbol{\pi}^{-1}\, \boldsymbol{\pi} = \eta(\tau)$.

If $f^m \in C^m(K, K_0, G)$, the induced homomorphism $\boldsymbol{\pi}$ acts by $(\boldsymbol{\pi} f^m) = \boldsymbol{f}^m$ where $(\boldsymbol{\pi} f^m)[\boldsymbol{e}^i_m] = f^m(\boldsymbol{\omega})[\boldsymbol{e}^i_m]$. Thus $\boldsymbol{f}^m$ takes on the value 0 on $\boldsymbol{K}_0$ and so

$\boldsymbol{f}^m \in C^m(\boldsymbol{K}, \boldsymbol{K}_0, G)$ as expected. Below we drop the brackets and understand the $\boldsymbol{K}_0$ or K_0 cosets when ω^{-1} or ω enter.

The homomorphism

$$\boldsymbol{\pi}^{-1}\colon C^m(\boldsymbol{K}, \boldsymbol{K}_0, G) \to C^m(K, K_0, G)$$

is defined by

$$(\boldsymbol{\pi}^{-1}\, \boldsymbol{f}^m)e^i_m = \boldsymbol{f}^m(\boldsymbol{\omega}^{-1}\, e^i_m) = \boldsymbol{f}^m(\tau_{\#}\, {}'\boldsymbol{e}^i_m) = \tau^{\#}\, \boldsymbol{f}^m({}'\boldsymbol{e}^i_m).$$

To check $(\boldsymbol{\pi}^{-1}\boldsymbol{f}^m)e^i_m = 0$ for $e^i_m \in K_0$, note that then $\boldsymbol{e}^i_m \in \boldsymbol{K}_0$ so $\tau^{\#} \boldsymbol{f}(\boldsymbol{e}^i_m) = \tau^{\#}\, 0 = 0$. In particular, for assigned f^m, $\boldsymbol{f}^m$ exists to satisfy $\boldsymbol{\pi}^{-1}\boldsymbol{f}^m = f^m$. For instance, define $\boldsymbol{f}^m$ by

$$\boldsymbol{f}^m({}'\boldsymbol{e}^i_m) = f^m e(^i_m)$$
$$\boldsymbol{f}^m(t\, {}'\boldsymbol{e}^i_m) = 0, \qquad (t \neq 1).$$

Thus (2.15a) and (2.15b) are valid.

We establish (2.15c) and (2.15d). Indeed

$$\begin{aligned}(\boldsymbol{\pi}\boldsymbol{\pi}^{-1}\boldsymbol{f}^m)(\boldsymbol{e}_m) &= \boldsymbol{f}^m(\boldsymbol{\omega}^{-1}\,\boldsymbol{\omega}\boldsymbol{e}_m)\\ &= \boldsymbol{f}^m(\tau_{\#}\, \boldsymbol{e}_m)\\ &= (\tau^{\#}\, \boldsymbol{f}^m)\boldsymbol{e}_m\end{aligned}$$

while

$$\begin{aligned}(\boldsymbol{\pi}^{-1}\, \boldsymbol{\pi} f^m)e_m &= f^m\, \boldsymbol{\omega}\, \boldsymbol{\omega}^{-1}\, e_m\\ &= f^m(\eta(\tau)e_m)\\ &= \eta(\tau) f^m(e_m).\end{aligned}$$

3. SMITH GROUPS. We exploit the ideas in (62.1) where M is taken as $C(K, K_0, G)$. For the cyclic group T_k, $\psi\#$ in (62.1) is customarily replaced by the symbol ρ which refers either to $\tau\#$ or to $\sigma\#$. It is customary also to introduce the homomorphism $\bar{\rho}$, where $\rho\bar{\rho} = 0$. For example, if ρ is $\sigma\#$ or $\tau\#$ then $\bar{\rho}$ is $\tau\#$ or $\sigma\#$. We write ${}^{\rho}C(\boldsymbol{K}, \boldsymbol{K}_0, G)$ for *ker* ρ and ${}^{\rho^{-1}}C(\boldsymbol{K}, \boldsymbol{K}_0, G)$ for *Im* ρ. However, we write ${}^{\sigma}C$ and ${}^{\tau}C$ for the case $\rho = \sigma\#$ or $\tau\#$.

Lemma 3.1. *If* $\boldsymbol{K}_0 \supset \boldsymbol{F}$ *and* $T(\boldsymbol{K}_0) = \boldsymbol{K}_0$, *then for* $\rho = \tau$ *or* σ

$${}^{\rho}C(\boldsymbol{K}, \boldsymbol{K}_0, G) = {}^{\bar{\rho}^{-1}}C(\boldsymbol{K}, \boldsymbol{K}_0, G)$$

We treat the chain module first. By (44.1) we can choose as a representative of $[c_m]$ the chain of $C_m(\boldsymbol{K}, G)$ with no terms involving $\boldsymbol{e}_m$'s in $\boldsymbol{K}_0$. Our hypothesis is $\rho[c_m] = 0$ from which we are to show $[\boldsymbol{c}_m] = \bar{\rho}[\boldsymbol{c}'_m]$. Since $t(\boldsymbol{K}_0) = \boldsymbol{K}_0$, only the cells in $\boldsymbol{D} - \boldsymbol{K}_0 \cap \boldsymbol{D} = \boldsymbol{D}_1$ need enter in the representative, $\boldsymbol{c}_m$, of $[\boldsymbol{c}_m]$. [Application of the boundary operator to such representatives would generally introduce cells in $\boldsymbol{K}_0$, but fortunately the boundary operator does not enter in (3.1)]. Thus for $[\boldsymbol{c}_m]$, choose

(3.1a) $$\boldsymbol{c}_m = \Sigma\, \alpha_i\, {}'\boldsymbol{e}^i_m, \quad \alpha_i \in G(T), \quad {}'\boldsymbol{e}^i_m \in D_1, \quad (2.11),$$

as the representative. Then $\rho[\boldsymbol{c}_m] = 0$ implies for $\rho = \tau_{\#}$, using exactness,

(3.1b) $$\tau_{\#}\, \boldsymbol{c}_m = \Sigma\, \eta(\alpha_i)\tau\, '\boldsymbol{e}^i_m \quad \epsilon\; i_{\#}\, C_m(\boldsymbol{K}_0, G)$$

However, $\tau \boldsymbol{D}_1 = \boldsymbol{K} - \boldsymbol{K}_0$. Therefore $\tau\, '\boldsymbol{e}^i_m \in \boldsymbol{K} - \boldsymbol{K}_0$ so $\tau_{\#}\,(\boldsymbol{c}_m) = 0$. Accordingly $\eta(\alpha_i) = 0$ (2.11) whence noting $\sigma_j = 1 - t^j$, $\alpha_i = \Sigma_j\, g_{ij}(1 - t^j)$ (2.8c). Therefore $\boldsymbol{c}_m = (1 - t)\boldsymbol{c}'_m$ where $\boldsymbol{c}'_m = \sigma_{\#}\, \Sigma\, \beta_i\, '\boldsymbol{e}^i_m$. Consequently

(3.1c) $$[\boldsymbol{c}_m] = \sigma_{\#}[\boldsymbol{c}'_m].$$

Since, on the other hand (3.1c) implies $\tau_{\#}[\boldsymbol{c}_m] = 0$, the $\rho = \tau_{\#}$ case is settled.

If $\rho = \sigma_{\#}$, then $\sigma_{\#}[\boldsymbol{c}_m] = 0$ implies $\sigma_{\#}\, \boldsymbol{c}_m \in i_{\#}\, C_m(\boldsymbol{K}_0, G)$. Choose the representative $\boldsymbol{c}_m$ as in (3.1a) whence $\sigma_{\#}\, \boldsymbol{c}_m = 0$, i.e., $\alpha_i = t_{\#}\, \alpha_i$ or

(3.1d) $$\Sigma_{j=0}^{j=k-1}\, g_{ij}\, t^j = \Sigma_{j=0}^{j=k-1}\, g_{ij}\, t^{j+1}$$

On comparing coefficients of t^j there results

$$g_{i0} = , \ldots , = g_{ik-1}$$

or each α_i in the representation (3.1d) satisfies $\alpha_i = g_{i0}$. This is to say $\boldsymbol{c}_m = \tau_{\#}\, \Sigma\, g_{i0}\, '\boldsymbol{e}_m$, whence

(3.1e) $$[\boldsymbol{c}_m] = \tau_{\#}[\boldsymbol{c}'_m].$$

Had we started with (3.1e) $\sigma_{\#}[\boldsymbol{c}_m] = 0$ would have been a consequence. Sic transit $\rho = \sigma_{\#}$.

PROBLEM

13-2. Show (3.1) is true for general ρ, $\bar{\rho}$ subject to $\rho\bar{\rho} = 0$. For example, try $\rho = \sigma^m$, $\rho = \sigma^{k-m}$.

${}^{\rho}C^m$ can be defined directly as $Hom({}^{\rho}C_m(\boldsymbol{K}, \boldsymbol{K}_0, J), G)$ whence the analogue of (3.1) for the cochain modules or rings follows at once. It is instructive, though, to carry through the basic argument.

The cochain $\boldsymbol{f}^m \in C^m(\boldsymbol{K}, \boldsymbol{K}_0, G)$ takes on 0 values on the cells of $\boldsymbol{K}_0$. Suppose then $(\rho\, \boldsymbol{f}^m)(\boldsymbol{e}_m) = \boldsymbol{f}^m(\rho \boldsymbol{e}_m) = 0$. If $\rho = \tau^{\#}$, define $\boldsymbol{F}^m$ by

$$\boldsymbol{F}^m(t^i\, '\boldsymbol{e}_m) = \Sigma_{j=i}^{j=k-1}\, \boldsymbol{f}^m(t^j\, '\boldsymbol{e}_m).$$

Let $\boldsymbol{e}_m$ be arbitrary. Then $\boldsymbol{e}_m = t^i\, '\boldsymbol{e}_m$ for some i and for some $'\boldsymbol{e}_m \in D$. Since $F^m('e_m) = \tau^{\#}\, f^m('e_m) = 0$

$$\boldsymbol{f}^m(\boldsymbol{e}_m) = \boldsymbol{f}^m(t^i\, '\boldsymbol{e}_m) = \sigma^{\#}\, \boldsymbol{F}^m(t^i\, '\boldsymbol{e}_m)$$
$$= \sigma^{\#}\, \boldsymbol{F}^m(\boldsymbol{e}_m).$$

Moreover $\boldsymbol{F}^m$ is 0 on $\boldsymbol{e}_m \in \boldsymbol{K}_0$ and therefore is in $C^m(\boldsymbol{K}, \boldsymbol{K}_0, G)$. Indeed since $(D \cap K_0) = K_0$, if $e_m \in K_0$, $e_m = t^i('e_m)$ implies $'e_m \in D \cap K_0$. Hence $F^m(t^i\,'e_m) = 0$. We have shown

$$f^m = \sigma^{\#} F^m,\ F^m \in C^m(K, K_0, G). \tag{3.1f}$$

Conversely (3.1f) implies $\tau^{\#} f^m = 0$, so the case $\rho = \tau^{\#}$ is disposed of.

If $\rho = \sigma^{\#}$, then $f^m(e_m) = , \ldots , = f^m(t^{k-1}\, e^m)$. Define F^m by

$$F^m('e_m) = f^m('e_m)$$

$$F^m(t^i\,'e_m) = 0, \qquad i \neq 0 \bmod k.$$

Evidently $F^m \in C^m(K, K_0, G)$ and

$$f^m = \tau^{\#} F^m \tag{3.1g}$$

From (3.1e) follows $\sigma^{\#} f^m = 0$. Therefore we are through with the case $\rho = \sigma^{\#}$ also.

Lemma 3.2. *The exact sequences of* (62.1) *may be written*

$$\begin{array}{l} {}^{\rho}H_m(K, K_0, G) \xrightarrow{i_*} H_m(K, K_0, G) \xrightarrow{\rho_*} {}^{\bar\rho}H_m(K, K_0, G) \xrightarrow{'\partial} {}^{\rho}H_{m-1} \\ {}^{\rho}H^m(K, K_0, G) \xrightarrow{i^*} H^m(K, K_0, G) \xrightarrow{\rho^*} {}^{\bar\rho}H^m(K, K_0, G) \xrightarrow{'\delta} {}^{\rho}H^{m+1} \end{array} \tag{3.2a}$$

Suppose below that $F \neq \varnothing$. Write kG for $\{g' \mid g' = kg, g \in G\}$ and G_k for G/G_k.

Lemma 3.3. ${}^{\rho}C_n(K, G_k) = {}^{\bar\rho^{-1}}C_n(K, G_k) \oplus C_n(F, G_k)$.

Designate chains in $C_n(F, G_k)$ by the subscript 0, i.e., ${}_0c_m \in C_m(F, G_k)$. Suppose $\tau_{\#}\, c_m = 0$ where $c_m = \Sigma\, \alpha_i\, 'e^i_m + {}_0c_m$. The restriction to the group G_k is forced to ensure $\tau_{\#}\, {}_0c_m = kc_m = 0$. Hence

$$0 = \tau_{\#}\, c_m = \Sigma\, \eta(\alpha_i)\tau_{\#}\, 'e^i_m$$

so $\eta(\alpha_i) = 0$. Following the argument in (3.1), $\alpha_i = \sigma\beta_i$. Thus

$$c_m = \sigma_{\#} \Sigma\, \beta_i\, 'e^i_m + {}_0c_m.$$

PROBLEM

13-3. Give the demonstration of (3.3) for $\rho = \tau$.

Lemma 3.4. *The sequence.*

$$\longrightarrow {}^{\rho}H_n(K, G_k) \xrightarrow{i_*} H_n(K, G_k) \xrightarrow{\rho} {}^{\bar\rho}H_n(K, F, G_k) \xrightarrow{'\partial} {}^{\rho}H_{n-1} \longrightarrow \tag{3.4a}$$

is exact.

In view of (3.3)

$$^{\rho^{-1}}C_n(\boldsymbol{K}, G_k) = {}^{\bar{\rho}}C_n(\boldsymbol{K}, G_k)/C_n(\boldsymbol{F}, G_k)$$
$$= {}^{\bar{\rho}}C_n(\boldsymbol{K}, \boldsymbol{F}, G_k).$$

We combine this with the developments in (62.1).

Reference to (61.2e) makes plain the interpretation to be attached to $'\partial$ or to $'\delta$ both of which we indicate for the moment by $'d$. Thus the fact that ${}^{\bar{\rho}}\boldsymbol{z} = \rho \boldsymbol{u}$ is a cycle or cocycle means $d\rho\boldsymbol{u} = \rho\, d\boldsymbol{u} = 0 \mod C(K_0, G)$. Since the set of elements mapping onto ρu by ρ is $(\boldsymbol{u} + Im\ \bar{\rho})$ we have $'d\, {}^{\bar{\rho}}\boldsymbol{z} = d\boldsymbol{u} + d(\bar{\rho}C(\boldsymbol{K}, \boldsymbol{K}_0, G)) = d\boldsymbol{u} + {}^{\bar{\rho}}B$. Accordingly

$$'d\langle {}^{\bar{\rho}}\boldsymbol{z}\rangle_{\rho_B} = \langle d\boldsymbol{u}\rangle_{\bar{\rho}_B}.$$

From now on $_{\bar{\rho}}\partial$ and $_{\bar{\rho}}\delta$ acting on ${}^{\bar{\rho}}H$ will replace $'\partial$ and $'\delta$ in omology sequences.

EXAMPLE 13-1. Suppose $k = 2$ and K is the symmetrically triangulated S^n. Take $\boldsymbol{D}$ as the open upper hemisphere plus half the equatorial sphere S^{n-1}. Then ${}^{\sigma}\boldsymbol{z}$ is the chain sum of the n simplexes of S^n and $\boldsymbol{u}$ the chain sum of those of the upper hemisphere. Then $d\boldsymbol{u}$ is in $Cl\ \boldsymbol{D}$. However since

$$(1 + t)(t\boldsymbol{u}) = (1 + t)\boldsymbol{u} = {}^{\sigma}\boldsymbol{z},$$

$d\boldsymbol{u}$ must also be in $Cl\ t\boldsymbol{D}$. That is to say $d\boldsymbol{u} = \partial\boldsymbol{u}$ is in $Cl\boldsymbol{D} \cap Cl\ t\boldsymbol{D} = S^{n-1}$.

Lemma 3.5. *${}^{\rho}H*(\boldsymbol{K}, G_k) \approx {}^{\rho}H*(\boldsymbol{K}, \boldsymbol{F}, G_k) \oplus H*(\boldsymbol{F}, G_k)$ for both homology and cohomology.*

We restrict ourselves to the cohomology case. Let $\boldsymbol{f}$ be a cocycle representative of an element in ${}^{\rho}H(\boldsymbol{K}, G_k)$. We assert

(3.5a) $$^{\rho}\boldsymbol{f}^m = \bar{\rho}\boldsymbol{f}_1^m + \boldsymbol{f}_0^m.$$

Specifically let $\boldsymbol{f}_0^m \in C^m(F, G_k)$ be defined by $\boldsymbol{f}_0^m \mid \boldsymbol{F} = {}^{\rho}\boldsymbol{f}^m \mid \boldsymbol{F}$, with $\boldsymbol{f}_0^m = 0$ elsewhere. Set ${}^{\rho}\boldsymbol{f}^m - \boldsymbol{f}_0^m = \boldsymbol{f}_2^m$. Then $\rho\boldsymbol{f}_2^m = 0$, and $\boldsymbol{f}_2^m \mid \boldsymbol{F} = 0$, which is equivalent to the statement $\boldsymbol{f}_2^m \in {}^{\rho}C(\boldsymbol{K}, \boldsymbol{F}, G_k)$. We may, therefore, write $\boldsymbol{f}_2^m = \bar{\rho}\boldsymbol{f}_1^m$ where $\boldsymbol{f}_1^m \in C(\boldsymbol{K}, \boldsymbol{F}, G_k)$ and (3.5a) is established.

Since ${}^{\rho}\boldsymbol{f}^m$ is a cocycle

(3.5b) $$0 = \delta\, {}^{\rho}\boldsymbol{f}^m = \delta(\bar{\rho}\boldsymbol{f}_1^m) + \delta\boldsymbol{f}_0^m.$$

Then from $\bar{\rho}\boldsymbol{f}^m(\partial\boldsymbol{e}_{m+1} \cap \boldsymbol{F}) = 0$ and (3.5b) and the fact that $\boldsymbol{f}_0$ is nonzero only on $\boldsymbol{F}$ at best,

$$\boldsymbol{f}_0^m\, \partial\boldsymbol{e}_{m+1} = 0.$$

Accordingly $\delta\bar{\rho}f_1^m\, e_{m+1} = 0$. Therefore

$$\bar{\rho}f_1^m \in {}^{\rho}Z^m(\boldsymbol{K}, \boldsymbol{F}, G_k) \tag{3.5c}$$

$$f_0^m \in Z^m(\boldsymbol{F}, G_k). \tag{3.5d}$$

If ${}^{\rho}f^m \in {}^{\rho}B(\boldsymbol{K}, G)$, then

$$\begin{aligned} {}^{\rho}f^m &= \delta(\bar{\rho}f_1^{m-1} + f_0^{m-1}) \\ &= {}^{\bar{\rho}}\delta\, f_1^{m-1} + \delta\, f_0^{m-1}. \end{aligned}$$

Observe $\bar{\rho}\delta f_1^{m-1} \in {}^{\rho}B^m\,(\boldsymbol{K}, \boldsymbol{F}, G_k)$ and $\delta f_0^{m-1} \in B^m\,(\boldsymbol{F}, G_k)$. Add this information to (3.5c) and (3.5d).

Corollary 3.6. *The following sequence is exact:*

$$\longleftarrow {}^{\rho}H(\boldsymbol{K}, \boldsymbol{F}, G_k) \xleftarrow{\bar{\rho}\delta} {}^{\bar{\rho}}H(\boldsymbol{K}, \boldsymbol{F}, G_k) \oplus H(\boldsymbol{F}, G_k) \xleftarrow{i^*} H(\boldsymbol{K}, G_k) \xleftarrow{\rho^*} \tag{3.7a}$$

Combine (3.4a) and (3.5).

Theorem 3.7. $\boldsymbol{\pi}$ *induces an isomorphism denoted by* $\boldsymbol{\lambda}$ *of* $H^m(K, K_0, G) \to {}^{\sigma}H^m(\boldsymbol{K}, \boldsymbol{K}_0, G)$.

To $f^m \in C^m(K, K_0, G)$ make correspond $\boldsymbol{F}^m$ satisfying

$$\boldsymbol{F}^m\, {}'\boldsymbol{e}_m = f^m(\boldsymbol{\omega}\, {}'\boldsymbol{e}_m) = f^m(\boldsymbol{e}_m)$$

$$\boldsymbol{F}^m\, \boldsymbol{e}_m = 0, \quad \boldsymbol{e}_m \bar{\in} D.$$

The correspondence is $1 - 1$ and, in view of (3.1f), yields the isomorphism $\boldsymbol{\lambda}$ in

$$C^m(K, K_0, G) \xrightarrow{\lambda} {}^{\sigma}C^m(\boldsymbol{K}, \boldsymbol{K}_0\, G) \xrightarrow{i^{\#}} C^m(\boldsymbol{K}, \boldsymbol{K}_0, G).$$

PROBLEM

13-4. Show π induces the epimorphism $H^m(F, G) \to H^m(\boldsymbol{F}, G)$.

Lemma 3.8. $\boldsymbol{\gamma}^*$ *is a monomorphism of* ${}^{\tau}H(\boldsymbol{K}, K_0, G)$ *into* ${}^{\sigma}H(\boldsymbol{K}, \boldsymbol{K}_0, G_k)$ *and maps* $\langle\sigma \boldsymbol{f}\rangle$ *onto* $\langle\tau \boldsymbol{f}\rangle$. *We write* $\boldsymbol{\gamma}$ *for* r^*.

Since all elements of $\text{J}(T)$ are allowable homomorphisms of the chain and cochain groups, the lemma is an immediate consequence of

$$\begin{aligned} \gamma^{\#}(\sigma^{\#}\, \boldsymbol{f}) &= (\sigma\gamma)^{\#}\, \boldsymbol{f}_m \quad (2.8e) \\ &= (\tau^{\#} - k\, t^{\#k-1})\, \boldsymbol{f} \\ &= \tau^{\#}\, \boldsymbol{f} \bmod kG. \end{aligned}$$

Lemma 3.9. *There is a homomorphism, μ, of ${}^{\sigma}H(\boldsymbol{K}, \boldsymbol{K}_0, G)$ into ${}^{\tau}H(\boldsymbol{K}, \boldsymbol{K}_0, G_k)$.*

Thus $\tau^{\#} f^m = (\sigma^{\#} \gamma^{\#} + kt^{\#k-1})f^m = \sigma^{\#} \gamma^{\#} f^m \bmod kG$ implies that the correspondence $\tau^{\#} f^m \to \gamma^{\#} f^m$ induces a homomorphism denoted by $\mu^{\#}$ carrying the coset $\langle \tau^{\#} f^m \rangle_{\sigma}$ in ${}^{\sigma}H$ onto the coset $\langle \tau^{\#} f \rangle_{\tau}$ considered now in ${}^{\tau}H$. (In short $\mu^{\#}$ preserves the representative element $(\tau^{\#} f)$ but merely changes the coset specification.) Henceforth $\boldsymbol{\mu}$ and $\boldsymbol{\gamma}$ will be written both for μ^*, γ^*, and for $\mu^{\#}$, $\gamma^{\#}$.

Lemma 3.10. *The two squares in the following diagram are commutative, that is*

(3.10a) $${}_{\tau}\delta\boldsymbol{\mu} = \boldsymbol{\gamma}\, {}_{\sigma}\delta$$

(3.10b) $${}_{\sigma}\delta\boldsymbol{\gamma} = \boldsymbol{\mu}\, {}_{\tau}\delta$$

$$\begin{array}{ccccc}
{}^{\tau}H^m(-, G_k) & \xrightarrow{\tau\delta} & {}^{\sigma}H^{m+1}(-, G_k) & \xrightarrow{\sigma\delta} & {}^{\tau}H^{m+2} \\
\uparrow \mu & & \uparrow \gamma & & \uparrow \mu \\
{}^{\sigma}H^m(-, G) & \xrightarrow{\sigma\delta} & {}^{\tau}H^{m+1}(-, G) & \xrightarrow{\tau\delta} & {}^{\sigma}H^{m+2}
\end{array}$$

where γ and μ are defined in (3.8) *and* (3.9) .

We demonstrate (3.10a). For ease in reference we denote the cohomology class by $\langle - \rangle_n$, where $n = 1, 2, 3, 4$. The numbering starts with ${}^{\sigma}H^m$ and proceeds clockwise. Let ${}^{\sigma}\boldsymbol{f} = \tau^{\#} \boldsymbol{f}$ be a representative cocycle of $\langle {}^{\sigma}\boldsymbol{f} \rangle_1$. Then

$$\begin{aligned} \boldsymbol{\mu} \langle {}^{\sigma}\boldsymbol{f} \rangle_1 &= \boldsymbol{\mu} \langle \tau^{\#} \boldsymbol{f} \rangle_1 \\ &= \langle \tau^{\#} \boldsymbol{f} \rangle_2 = \langle \sigma^{\#}(\boldsymbol{\gamma f}^m) \rangle_2. \end{aligned}$$

Hence

(3.10c) $${}_{\tau}\delta\boldsymbol{\mu} \langle {}^{\sigma}\boldsymbol{f} \rangle_1 = \langle \delta\boldsymbol{\gamma f} \rangle_3.$$

On the other hand

$$\boldsymbol{\gamma}\, {}_{\sigma}\delta \langle {}^{\sigma}\boldsymbol{f} \rangle_1 = \boldsymbol{\gamma} \langle \delta\boldsymbol{f} \rangle_4$$

(3.10d) $$= \langle \boldsymbol{\gamma}\delta\boldsymbol{f} = \delta\boldsymbol{\gamma f} \rangle_3$$

since $t^{\#}$, and therefore $\boldsymbol{\gamma}$ commutes with δ. The conclusions in (3.10a) and (3.10b) follow from (3.10c) and (3.10d).

PROBLEM

13-5. Demonstrate (3.10b).

4. SMITH HOMOMORPHISMS. Definition 4.1. Let $s(2j+1)$ be the homomorphism on $H^m(K, K_0, G)$ to $H^{m+2j+1}(K, K_0, G_k)$ defined by

$$s(2j+1)\langle f^m\rangle = \boldsymbol{\lambda}^{-1}\boldsymbol{\gamma}\,{}_\sigma\delta\cdots{}_\tau\delta\,{}_\sigma\delta\boldsymbol{\lambda}\langle f^m\rangle$$

Similarly $s(2j)$ is a homomorphism on $H^m(K, K_0, G)$ to $H^{m+2j}(K, K_0, G)$, $s(2j)\langle f^m\rangle = \boldsymbol{\lambda}^{-1}\,{}_\tau\delta\cdots{}_\sigma\delta\boldsymbol{\lambda}\langle f^m\rangle$.

Theorem 4.2

(4.2a) $s(1)\,s(1) = 0$ *for k odd and* $-k/2\; s(2)$ *for k even.*

(4.2b) $$s(1)\,s(2) = s(2)\,s(1).$$

(4.2c) $$s(2)^j = s(2j).$$

For (4.2a) $\boldsymbol{\lambda}^{-1}\boldsymbol{\gamma}\,{}_\sigma\delta\boldsymbol{\lambda}\boldsymbol{\lambda}^{-1}\boldsymbol{\gamma}\,{}_\sigma\delta\boldsymbol{\lambda} = \boldsymbol{\lambda}^{-1}\boldsymbol{\gamma}\,\boldsymbol{\mu}\,{}_\tau\delta\,{}_\sigma\delta\boldsymbol{\lambda}$ in view of (3.10b). Straightforward computation based on (3.8) and (3.10) shows

$$\begin{aligned}\boldsymbol{\gamma\mu}\langle{}^\sigma F\rangle_1 &= \boldsymbol{\gamma\mu}\langle\tau^{\#} f\rangle_1\\ &= \langle\boldsymbol{\gamma}\tau^{\#} f\rangle_3 \quad (3.8)\\ &= \left\langle\frac{k(k-1)}{2}\,\tau^{\#} f\right\rangle_3\\ &= 0, \quad k \text{ odd},\\ &= -\frac{k}{2}\,\langle\tau^{\#} f\rangle_3 \quad k \text{ even}.\end{aligned}$$

For (4.2b), we have

$$\boldsymbol{\lambda}^{-1}\boldsymbol{\gamma}\,{}_\sigma\delta\boldsymbol{\lambda}\boldsymbol{\lambda}^{-1}\,{}_\tau\delta\,{}_\sigma\delta\boldsymbol{\lambda} = \boldsymbol{\lambda}^{-1}\boldsymbol{\gamma}\,{}_\sigma\delta\,{}_\tau\delta\,{}_\sigma\delta\boldsymbol{\lambda},$$

whence by alternate use of (3.10a) and (3.11b) there is a reduction to

$$\begin{aligned}\boldsymbol{\lambda}^{-1}\,{}_\tau\delta\,{}_\sigma\delta\boldsymbol{\gamma}\,{}_\sigma\delta\boldsymbol{\lambda} &= \boldsymbol{\lambda}^{-1}\,{}_\tau\delta\,{}_\sigma\,\delta\boldsymbol{\lambda}\,\boldsymbol{\lambda}^{-1}\boldsymbol{\gamma}\,{}_\sigma\delta\boldsymbol{\lambda}\\ &= s(2)\,s(1)\end{aligned}$$

The proof of (4.2c) amounts to interpolating $\boldsymbol{\lambda}\boldsymbol{\lambda}^{-1}$ at the obvious places. By reason of (3.6), if we start with the cocycle f^n a representative of $\langle f^n\rangle$ then $\boldsymbol{\lambda}$ is, of course, replaced by $\lambda^{\#}$, etc., and at each stage of the homomorphism defining $s(n)$, we have a cocycle, i.e., ${}_\rho\delta\cdots{}_\sigma\delta\lambda^{\#} f^n$ is a cocycle, etc. By combining (4.2a), (4.2b), and (4.2c) it is clear that

$$s(2j+1) = s(1)\,s(2)^j = s(2)^j\,s(1) = s(2m)\,s(2j+1-2m) \quad \text{for } 2m \leq 2j.$$

We have need for the cup product. For the application below the coefficient group pairing is either $G \otimes J_k \to G_k$ or $J_k \otimes J_k \to J_k$.

Lemma 4.3. *Let $f^p \in C^p(K, J_k)$ and $F^q \in C^q(K, G)$, then:*

(4.3a) $$\tau^{\#}(f^p \cup \tau^{\#} F^q) = \tau^{\#} f^p \cup \tau^{\#} F^q$$

(4.3b) $$f^p \cup F^q = \pi^{-1}(f^p \cup \tau^{\#} F^q)$$

(4.3c) $$\sigma^{\#}(f^p \cup \tau^{\#} F^q) = \sigma^{\#} f^p \cup \tau^{\#} F^q.$$

Note ${}^{\sigma}C^q(K, G)$ can be considered a submodule of $C^q(K, G)$ so

$$(f^p \cup \tau^{\#} f^q) = f^p \cup {}^{\sigma}f^q \in C^{p+q}(K, G_k).$$

Observe next that if the vertex scheme of e_{p+q} is $v^0 \cdots v^{p+q}$, then with $e_p = v^0 \cdots v^p$, and $e_q = v^p \cdots v^{p+q}$ for the back face there results

$$te_{p+q} = t(e_p\, e_q) = (te_p)\,(te_q).$$

Hence

$$\begin{aligned} t^{\#}(f^p \cup F^q)e_{p+q} &= f^p\,(t_{\#}\, e_p)\, F^q(t_{\#}\, e_q) \\ &= (t^{\#} f^p)(e_p)(t^{\#} F^q)e_q \\ &= (t^{\#} f^p \cup t^{\#} F^q)e_{p+q}. \end{aligned}$$

Moreover

$$p(e_{p+q}) = pe_p\, pe_q.$$

For (4.3a): According to (4.3d)

$$\begin{aligned} \tau^{\#}(f^p \cup \tau^{\#} F^q) &= \Sigma\, t^{\# i}\,(f^p \cup \tau^{\#} F^q) \\ &= \Sigma\, t^{\# i} f^p \cup (t^i\, \tau)^{\#} F^q \\ &= \Sigma\, t^{\# i} f^p \cup \tau^{\#} F^q \\ &= \tau^{\#} f^p \cup \tau^{\#} F^q. \end{aligned}$$

For (4.3b): $$\begin{aligned} \pi^{-1}(f^p \cup \tau^{\#} F^q)e_{p+q} &= (f^p \cup \tau^{\#} F^q)\tau_{\#}\, e_{p+q} \quad (2.14\text{b}), \\ &= \tau^{\#}(f^p \cup \tau^{\#} F^q)e_{p+q}, \\ &= (\tau^{\#} f^p) \cup (\tau^{\#} F^q)e_{p+q} \\ &= f^p\,(\omega\, e_p)\, F^q\,(\omega\, e_q) \\ &= (\pi^{-1} f^p \cup \pi^{-1} F^q)e_{p+q}. \end{aligned}$$

The argument for (4.3c) is precisely that for (4.3a).

Let $I(0)$ be the cocycle in $C^0(K, K_0, G)$ which is 1 on every 0-simplex, e_0^i, in K, that is to say on every vertex in K where G may in particular be G_k. For the cohomology elements write $\mathbf{I}(m) = s(m)\mathbf{I}(0)$. Let $E(0)$ take on the value 1 on vertices of D and 0 elsewhere. Similarly $E(2\,m)$ is non-0 on

D-simplexes alone. Indeed $d\tau^{\#}\, E(0) = 0$ so $dE(0) = \sigma E(1)$ whence by induction $dE(m) = \rho E(m+1)$ with $\rho = \tau^{\#}$ or $\sigma^{\#}$ according as m is even or odd. Hence $\tau^{\#}\, E(m) = \boldsymbol{\lambda} I(m)$.

Theorem 4.4

(4.4a) $$s(m)\mathbf{f}^n = \mathbf{I}(m) \cup \mathbf{f}^n$$

(4.4b) $$\mathbf{I}(2j) = (\mathbf{I}(2))^j$$

(4.4c) $$\mathbf{I}(2j+1) = \mathbf{I}(2)^j \cup \mathbf{I}(1).$$

For $m = 0$, representatives $I(0)$ and f^n are chosen. Then, using the vertex representation of e_m

$$(I(0) \cup f^n)(v^0 \cdots v^n) = (I(0)v^0)f^n(v^0 \cdots v^n)$$
$$= f^n(v^0 \cdots v^n).$$

In short

$$\mathbf{I}(0) \cup \mathbf{f}^n = \mathbf{f}^n.$$

Suppose

$$(\mathbf{I}(2r) \cup \mathbf{f}^p) = s(2r)\mathbf{f}^p.$$

Recall $\boldsymbol{\pi} = i^*\boldsymbol{\lambda}$ (3.7). Hence (2.15c) implies $\boldsymbol{\lambda}\boldsymbol{\pi}^{-1} = \tau^*$. By (4.3b) (on changing from $\mathbf{F}^q$ to $\mathbf{f}^q$ in the notation),

$$\boldsymbol{\pi}^{-1}(\langle E(2r) \cup \tau^{\#} f^q \rangle) = \mathbf{I}(2r) \cup \mathbf{f}^q$$

whence using the cohomology form of (4.3a)

(4.4d) $$s(2)(\mathbf{I}(2r) \cup \mathbf{f}^q) = \boldsymbol{\lambda}^{-1}\, {}_{\tau}\delta\, {}_{\sigma}\delta\, \boldsymbol{\lambda}\boldsymbol{\pi}^{-1}\langle E(2r) \cup \tau^{\#} f^q \rangle$$
$$= \boldsymbol{\lambda}^{-1}\, {}_{\tau}\delta\langle \delta(E(2r) \cup \tau^{\#} f^q)\rangle.$$

Since $\delta\tau^{\#}\, E(2r) = 0$, $\delta E(2r) = \sigma^{\#}\, E(2r+1)$. Moreover $\delta\tau^{\#} f^q = 0$. Hence with proper regard for (4.3c), the right hand side of (4.4d) becomes

$$\boldsymbol{\lambda}^{-1}\, {}_{\tau}\delta\langle \delta E(2r) \cup \tau^{\#} f^q\rangle = \boldsymbol{\lambda}^{-1}\, {}_{\tau}\delta\langle \sigma^{\#}(E(2r+1) \cup \tau^{\#} f^q)\rangle$$
$$= \boldsymbol{\lambda}^{-1}\langle \delta(E(2r+1) \cup \tau^{\#} f^q)\rangle$$
$$= \boldsymbol{\lambda}^{-1}(\langle \delta E(2r+1)\rangle \cup \langle \tau^{\#} f^q\rangle.$$

Evidently

(4.4e) $$s(2)\mathbf{I}(2r) = \boldsymbol{\lambda}^{-1}\langle \delta E(2r+1)\rangle = \mathbf{I}(2r+2).$$

Thus the induction starting with (4.4a) establishes (4.4e) for $r \geq 0$, $q \geq 0$. The choice $\mathbf{f}^q = \mathbf{I}(2)$ together with $r = 0, 1, 2, \ldots$ yields (4.4b) while (4.4c) arises from the conjunction of (4.4b) and (4.2b).

5. EQUIVARIANT MAPS. Definition 5.1. Refer to the pair, $\boldsymbol{X}$, T when T is a group of homeomorphisms of $\boldsymbol{X}$ as an **operator couple** or simply **couple.** Let $\boldsymbol{X}$, T and $\boldsymbol{X}'$, T' be couples and let h be a homomorphism on T to T'. p and p' are the projections $\boldsymbol{X} \to X$ and $\boldsymbol{X}' \to X'$ respectively. The map Ψ: $\boldsymbol{X} \to \boldsymbol{X}'$ is an equivariant map if for $t' = h(t)$,

$$t'\,\Psi = \Psi t. \tag{5.1a}$$

We shall use only the special case $T' = T$ with h an automorphism, and we shall assume all maps are simplicial. The point about an equivariant map apart from its beguiling symmetry is that it induces a map ψ on the orbit spaces X to X'. More precisely

$$\psi x = p'\,\Psi\boldsymbol{x}; \quad \boldsymbol{x} \in p^{-1}\,x. \tag{5.1b}$$

If $t^j\,\boldsymbol{x} \in p^{-1}\,x$ had been chosen, ψ would not have been affected for

$$p'\,\Psi t^j\,\boldsymbol{x} = p'\,t^j\,\Psi\boldsymbol{x} = p'\,\Psi\boldsymbol{x}$$

The definitions for complexes are immediate with the understanding that Ψ is a simplicial map.

For the next few lemmas Ψ is an equivariant map on $\boldsymbol{K}$, T to $\boldsymbol{K}'$, T'. Again we use $\boldsymbol{\pi}$ and $\boldsymbol{\omega}$ and $\boldsymbol{\pi}'$, $\boldsymbol{\omega}'$ for $p^{\#}$, $p_{\#}$ and for $p'^{\#}$, $p'_{\#}$ respectively.

Lemma 5.2. *$\Psi^{\#}$ and $\Psi_{\#}$ commute with the homomorphism induced by t. Moreover*

$$\Psi^{\#}\,\boldsymbol{\pi}' = \boldsymbol{\pi}\psi^{\#} \tag{5.2a}$$

$$\boldsymbol{\omega}'\,\Psi_{\#} = \psi_{\#}\,\boldsymbol{\omega} \tag{5.2b}$$

$$\Psi^{\#}\,\boldsymbol{\lambda}' = \boldsymbol{\lambda}\psi^{\#} \tag{5.2c}$$

$$\Psi^{\#}\,{}_{\rho}\delta' = {}_{\rho}\delta\Psi^{\#} \tag{5.2d}$$

$$(\boldsymbol{\lambda}\psi^{\#}(f'^m))\boldsymbol{e}_m = \psi^{\#}(f'^m)\boldsymbol{\omega}\,\boldsymbol{e}_m = \psi^{\#}(f'^m)e_m = f'^m(\psi_{\#}(e_m)) \tag{5.2e}$$

$$(\psi^{\#}\,\boldsymbol{\lambda}'\,f'^m)\boldsymbol{e}_m = (\boldsymbol{\lambda}'\,f'^m)(\Psi_{\#}\,\boldsymbol{e}_m) = f'^m(\boldsymbol{\omega}'\,\psi_{\#}\,\boldsymbol{e}_m). \tag{5.2f}$$

The identity of (5.2c) and (5.2f) follows from (5.2b).

Theorem 5.3. *If Ψ is an equivariant map on $\boldsymbol{K}$, T to $\boldsymbol{K}'$, T' and $s(m)$ and ${}_1s(m)$ are the associated Smith homomorphisms, then*

$$s(m)\psi^* = \psi^*\,{}_1s(m) \tag{5.3a}$$

We have written ${}_1s(m)$ in place of $s(m)'$. The proofs are largely mechanical in view of (5.2). We set down the operations in $s(m)$ and ${}_1s(m)$ and proceed to build up (5.3a) operation by operation. Thus let F^m be a representative cocycle of $\langle F^m \rangle \in H^m(K', \text{J})$. Then by (5.2) (5.2c), (5.2d) in this order

$$(5.3b) \qquad {}_\sigma\delta\boldsymbol{\lambda}\psi^{\#} F^m = \Psi^{\#}\, {}_\sigma\delta'\, \boldsymbol{\lambda}' F^m.$$

We observe that $\boldsymbol{\gamma}\psi^{\#} = \Psi^{\#}\boldsymbol{\gamma}'$ by virtue ultimately of (5.1). The relation $\boldsymbol{\lambda}^{-1}\Psi^{\#} = \psi^{\#}\boldsymbol{\lambda}'^{-1}$ arises from (5.2c) by operating on both sides by $\boldsymbol{\lambda}^{-1}$ on the left and $\boldsymbol{\lambda}'^{-1}$ on the right, which is legitimate since these are isomorphisms. The rest of the verification of (5.2a) proceeds by operating on the left of both sides of (5.2c) by $\boldsymbol{\lambda}^{-1}\boldsymbol{\gamma}$, by $\boldsymbol{\lambda}\delta$ or by preceding these operations by $({}_\tau\delta\, {}_\sigma\delta)^j$.

Definition 5.4. The **index** of the couple $(\boldsymbol{K}, T)$ is the largest integer, m, for which $s(m)$ is not trivial that is to say $\mathbf{I}(m) \neq 0$, and is denoted by $\nu(\boldsymbol{K}, T)$ or by $\nu(\boldsymbol{K})$ when T is understood.

We now state a result whose proof is trivial in view of what has gone before, but which is crucial for applications.

Theorem 5.5. *If Ψ is an equivariant map of $\boldsymbol{K}$, T to ${}_1\boldsymbol{K}$, T, then*

$$\nu({}_1K) \geq \nu(K).$$

Since Ψ is a simplicial, equivariant map, ψ is defined on K to ${}_1K$. Then $\psi_{\#}\, e_0$ is an elementary chain ${}_1e_0$. Since ${}_1I(0)$ assigns the value 1 to every vertex

$$(\psi^{\#}\, {}_1I(0))e_0 = {}_1I(0)(\psi_{\#}\, e_0) = {}_1I(0){}_1e_0 = 1.$$

Thus

$$\psi^{\#}\, {}_1I(0) = I(0).$$

Therefore

$$\psi^*\, s_1(m)\, {}_1\mathbf{I}(0) = s(m)\psi^*\, {}_1\mathbf{I}(0) = s(m)\mathbf{I}(0)$$

Accordingly $s(m)\,\mathbf{I}(0) \neq 0$ implies its antecedent under $\psi^{\#}$ namely ${}_1s(m)\, {}_1\mathbf{I}(0)$ cannot be 0. The assertion of the theorem follows.

We now consider the question of existence of equivariant maps. We remark that the results here are valid for any homology grating. For simplicity $T' = T$.

Definition 5.6. Define the action of T on $\boldsymbol{X} \times \boldsymbol{X}'$ by $g(\boldsymbol{x}, \boldsymbol{x}') = (g\boldsymbol{x}, g\boldsymbol{x}')$. Let $(\boldsymbol{X} \times \boldsymbol{X}')/T$, (2.5) be written $X \times X'$. Write Q for the projection $\boldsymbol{X} \times \boldsymbol{X}' \to \boldsymbol{X}$, while q is the induced projection on $X \times X'$ to X. Write $E_T(X, X')$ for the collection of equivariant maps $\{\Psi\}$ on $\boldsymbol{X}$ to $\boldsymbol{X}'$.

Lemma 5.7. (a) *If S is a subgroup of T, $E_T(X, X') \subset E_S(X, X')$.* (b) *If the subspace F is invariant in the sense $tF \subset F$, for all $t \in T$, $E_T(F, X') = \varnothing$ implies $E_T(X, X') = \varnothing$.*

For (5.7b) observe that if $\Psi \in E_T\,(X, X')$, then $\Psi \mid F \in E_T\,(F, X')$.

Definition 5.8. If ψ is a map on X to Y, not necessarily equivariant, then $R(\psi)$ is the collection of all right inverses of ψ (1.1).

Lemma 5.9. *If $R(\psi) \neq \varnothing$, then $H_m(Y)$ is isomorphic to a direct summand of $H_m(X)$.*

Indeed $\psi\beta = 1$ implies $(\psi\beta)_* = \psi_* \beta_*: H_m(Y) \to H_m(Y)$ is the identity. We refer now to (101.1). Incidentally, though ψ must be onto in order that $R(\psi) \neq \varnothing$, this is not enough; witness $\psi = p: S^n \to P^n$.

Lemma 5.10. *A necessary condition that $E_T(X, X') \neq \varnothing$ is that $R(q) \neq \varnothing$.*

Let $\Psi \in E_T(X, X')$. Define $\Theta \in E_T(X, X \times X')$ by $\Theta \mathbf{x} = (\mathbf{x}, \Psi\mathbf{x})$. The situation is then plain from the commutative diagram below. Evidently $Q\Theta = 1$. Therefore $p = pQ\Theta = q\theta p$. Since p is onto, $q\theta$ is the identity on X. Hence $\theta \in R(q)$.

$$\begin{array}{ccccc} \mathbf{X} & \xrightarrow{\Theta} & \mathbf{X} \times \mathbf{X}' & \xrightarrow{Q} & \mathbf{X} \\ \downarrow p & & \downarrow & & \downarrow p \\ X & \xrightarrow{\theta} & X \times X' & \xrightarrow{q} & X \end{array}$$

Example 13-2. Let $\{Y_i \mid i = 1, \ldots, k\}$ be disjoint copies of a fixed complex Y. Let β_i map Y_i homeomorphically onto Y. Write $\mathbf{X} = \bigcup Y_i$ and define t as $\beta_{i+1}^{-1} \beta_i(y_i)$ noting $\beta_{k+1} = \beta_1$. Then $\mathbf{X}/T = X$ is homeomorphic to Y and $p: \mathbf{X} \to X$ is defined by $p \mid Y_i = \beta_i\ Y_i$. Then $\mathbf{I}(m) = 0$ for $m > 0$.

Example 13-3. Let $\mathbf{X}$ be the unit sphere S^n with t the antipodal map, $t\mathbf{x} = -\mathbf{x}$ so $t^2 = 1$. Thus $X = S^n/T_2$ is P^n the projective n space and $H^i(X, \mathrm{J}_2) \approx \mathrm{J}_2$ for $i \leq n$. A cell division consistent with T yields $\mathbf{I}(m) \neq 0$, $m \leq n$, while $\mathbf{I}(m) = 0$ for $m > n$ or $\nu(\mathbf{S}^n, T_2) = n$.

Example 13-4. Let $\mathbf{X}_n$ be the space of unit tangent vectors to S^n. Thus $x = (y, w)$ where y is a point of S^n and w a unit tangent vector at y $t(y, w) = (y, -w)$. Then $\mathbf{I}(m) \neq 0$ for $m < n$ or $m \leq n$ according as n is odd or even and $\mathbf{I}(m) = 0$ for larger m. Hence

$$\nu(\mathbf{X}_{2k+1}, T_2) = 2k = \nu(\mathbf{X}_{2k}, T_2).$$

PROBLEM

13-6. Prove the assertions about $\nu(\mathbf{S}^n, T_2)$ using the results in Example 13-2 and Example 13-3.

Example 13-5. Let $\mathbf{X}$ be the subspace of $S^n \times S^n$ consisting of

$$\{(u, v) \mid u \in S^n, v \in S^n; 0 < \measuredangle (u, v) = a < \pi\}.$$

Let $t(u, v) = (v, u)$. Then $\nu(X, T_2) = n - 1$ or n according as n is odd or even.

PROBLEM

13-7. Prove the assertion about $\nu(X, T_2)$ in Example 13-5 by reducing to Example 13-4, by letting y be the midpoint of the shorter great circle arc through $(u, v) \in X$ considered a space of point pairs on S^n and defining w as the tangent at y pointing towards v in the diametral plane of (u, v).

The developments in this chapter have presupposed suitable triangulations. The generalization to singular omology is immediate and amounts to assuming the simplexes singular. Indeed if the space X admits t then t induces $\bar{t}$ on SX to SX according to $\bar{t}(\Delta_n, u) = (\Delta_n, tu)$ for the singular simplexes. This frees us from the restriction to simplicial maps. However, there is the defect, though, that conclusions regarding dimensions of fixed sets, as in (7) are difficult to establish because $A \subset R^n$, $n \geq 3$ does not bar $H_m(SA) \neq 0$ for a nonfinite collection of values of m. This is a pity since the algebra goes through so well for the singular theory. The generalization to Čech and Alexander gratings would therefore seem more important. The methods of Chapters 16 and 17 have recently been used also. To reflect the requisite openness of cells (2.7) we may assume that if, for instance, T acts freely on X then for each x and some open $U(x)$, the translates $\{tU(x)\}$ are disjunct.

In dealing with omology results for spheres and their closed subsets we can assume sufficiently fine symmetric triangulations, so that the subset is now replaced by an approximating subcomplex. This requires that any equivariant maps be replaced by equivariant simplicial approximations. The validation is stereotyped. We therefore refer to sets rather than to complexes.

We present the basic facts for application of the Čech theory.

Definition 5.10. Let T be a finite group and suppose X_0 is a closed T invariant subspace of X. Let $(\alpha, \alpha \cap X_0)$ be a cover pair (82.4) satisfying (i) if $\alpha = \{a_i\}$ then $ta_i \in \alpha$ and (ii) if $a_i \in \alpha \cap X_0$ then $ta_i \in \alpha \cap X_0$. We term such a covering an **invariant** covering. An invariant cover is **primitive** if it satisfies $a_i \cap (ta_i) = \varnothing$ if $ta_i \neq a_i$.

Theorem 5.11. (a) *Every invariant cover α of (X, X_0) admits a primitive refinement β. There is an equivariant projection on β to α (taking b_j into a_i where $a_i \supset b_j$).*

(b) *If P and P' are two equivariant projections in (a), they are equivariantly chain homotopic.*

(c) *If every point of X is either fixed under T or all its transforms are disjunct then the simplexes of b are either fixed under T or are all distinct.*

(d) *If Ψ is an equivariant map of X, X_0 to Y, Y_0 and if α is a primitive cover of Y, Y_0 then so is $\beta = \{\Psi^{-1}(a_i) \mid a_i \in \alpha\}$.*

(e) *If F and F_0 are the fixed point sets of X and X_0 under T, the induced covers of F, F_0 by primitive covers of X, X_0 are cofinal in the directed set of covers of F, F_0 induced by open covers of X.*

For (a) we need only the T_2 character of X.

For (b) note the orbits of the open sets in β under G section the index set of β into disjunct collections called orbit sets. Simply order the orbit sets and order the indices in each orbit set. Hence there is obtained an ordering of the indices. Since β is primitive any simplex of the nerve b of β will have its vertices simply ordered. Let $(b_0), \ldots, (b_n)$ be an ordered set of vertices of a simplex $\sigma \in b$. Define D by

$$D(b_0 \cdots b_n) = \Sigma_{i=0}^{i=n} (-1)^i (P(b_0) \cdots P(b_i)P'(b_i) \cdots P'(b_n))$$

Then D is equivariant and satisfies the conditions required for (63.1).

Next (c) and (d) are immediate since T obviously acts simplicially on the nerve of an invariant cover.

Accordingly the equivariant Čech homology groups arise by taking inverse limits over primitive covers. When X is compact only finite covers enter and the proof of (5.10) is even simpler.

6. SPHERE MAPS. In various sphere mappings use is made of a line of reasoning which we proceed to describe.

Definition 6.1. Let $z = (z_1, \ldots, z_k)$ denote a point of the k fold topological product of $R^l, l \geq 1$, thus $z \in R^l \times \cdot \times R^l = R^{lk}$. Define t' by $t'(z_1, \ldots, z_k) = (z_2, \ldots, z_k, z_1)$ so $\{t'^r \mid 0 \leq r \leq k-1\} = T'_k \approx T_k$. Let Δ denote the diagonal of R^{lk} namely $\{z \mid z_1 = z = \cdots = z_k\}$ and let P be the hyperplane through the origin orthogonal to Δ. Thus P is given analytically by $\Sigma\, z_i = 0$. Let p project R^{lk} parallel to Δ onto P. Then $pz = z - \dfrac{\Sigma\, z_i}{k}$. Since Δ is the homeomorph of R^l, P has dimension $lk - l$. The unit sphere about the origin in P is then $S^{l(k-1)-1}$ and is defined by $\Sigma\, |z_i|^2 = 1$. Let q be the radial projection of $P - 0$ onto $S^{l(k-1)-1}$. Note T'_k acts freely on the complement of Δ in R^{lk} and also on $S^{l(k-1)-1}$ to itself.

Let $e^1, \ldots, e^n$ be the unit vectors along a fixed orthogonal frame in R^n. Suppose $w = (w', \ldots, w^k)$ is an orthogonal k tuple on S^{n-1}. Let M_k be the $k \times k$ matrix

$$\begin{matrix} 0 & 1 & 0 & \cdots & 0 \\ 0 & 0 & 1 & \cdots & 0 \\ \cdots & \cdots & \cdots & \cdots & \cdots \\ 0 & 0 & 0 & \cdots & 1 \\ 1 & 0 & 0 & \cdots & 0 \end{matrix}$$

and let I_r be the r dimensional identity matrix. Then

$$t = \left(\begin{array}{c|c} M_k & 0 \\ \hline 0 & I_{n-k} \end{array}\right)$$

induces a permutation of $e^1, \ldots, e^n$ keeping $e^{k+1}, \ldots, e^n$ fixed. Write T_k for the cyclic group of order k with generator t. Remark that the space W, of k-tuples of orthogonal points $w^1, \ldots, w^k$ on S^{n-1}, is in 1–1 correspondence with the cosets of orthogonal transformation moving $e^1, \ldots, e^k$ to $w^1, \ldots, w^k$ where two orthogonal transformations are in the same coset if and only if they differ on $e^{k+1}, \ldots, e^n$ alone.

Theorem 6.2. Borsuk-Ulam. *If Θ maps S^n into R^n, then for some $\bar{x}$, $\Theta(\bar{x}) = \Theta(-\bar{x})$.*

Let $tx = -x$. Let $\Psi(x) = (\Theta(x), \Theta(-x)) = z$. Then $\Psi(tx) = (\Theta(-x), \Theta(x)) = t'\,\Psi(x)$. Hence Ψ is equivariant on (S^n, T_2) to $(R^n \times R^n, T_2')$. If the theorem is false $\Psi(S^n) \cap \Delta = \varnothing$. Accordingly $p\Psi S^{n-1} \in P - 0$. Since Δ is homeomorphic to S^n the dimension of Δ is n and that of P is n. Hence it is easy to see $qp\Psi$ is an equivariant map of $(S^n, T_2) \to (S^{n-1}, T_2')$. By (5.5), $\nu(S^{n-1}) \geq \nu(S^n)$. To show the absurdity of this conclusion the exact value of $\nu(S^n)$ is not needed (Example 13-3). It is sufficient that $\nu(S^m)$ is strictly monotone in m.

Corollary 6.3. *If S^n is covered with $n + 1$ closed sets, at least one of these sets contains an antipodal pair of points.*

Remark. Notwithstanding its appearance in the literature, the following plausible generalization of (6.3) is false. If S^n is covered with n closed sets, at least one of these sets contains a closed connected set which is invariant under involution. The cover of a tennis ball yields an immediate counter example.

PROBLEMS

13-8. Demonstrate (6.3).

13-9. Show that if Ψ is equivariant with respect to involutions of $S^n \to R^n$, then for some $x_0 \in S^n$, $\Psi(x_0) = 0$ and derive another proof of (6.2) from this result.

Lemma 6.4. *Let Y be a closed subset of S^n. Let T_2 be the group of involutions of S^n. Let $H_m(Y \cup tY/T_2, \mathrm{J}_2) \neq 0$. Then $\tilde{H}_{m-1}(Y \cap tY/T_2, \mathrm{J}_2) \neq 0$, $0 < m < n$.*

An easy argument depends on the commutativity of

$$\begin{array}{ccc} H_m(Y \cup tY/T_2, \mathrm{J}_2) & \xrightarrow{\partial} & H_{m-1}(Y \cup tY/T_2, \mathrm{J}_2) \\ \Big\downarrow i_* & & \Big\downarrow i_* \\ H_m(P^n, \mathrm{J}_2) & \underset{\approx}{\xrightarrow{\partial}} & H_{m-1}(P^n, \mathrm{J}_2) \end{array}$$

where P^n is the projective n space and $H_m(P^n, \mathrm{J}_2) \approx \mathrm{J}_2$ for all $m \leq n$.

We can now establish a generalization of the Borsuk-Ulam Theorem.

Theorem 6.5. *Let θ map S^n into R^j, $j < n$. Let $\mathbf{X}_j = \{x \mid \theta(x) = \theta(tx)\}$. Then $\tilde{H}_{n-j}(\mathbf{X}_j/T_2, \mathrm{J}_2) \neq 0$* **(Bourgin-Yang).**

The case $j = n$ is the Borsuk-Ulam Theorem and a different proof is thus afforded for (6.2). Let $\theta(x)$ have the coordinates $z_i = \theta_i(x)$, $i = 1, \ldots, j$. Let $\mathbf{Y}_1 = \{x \mid \theta_1(x) \geq \theta_1(tx)\}$. The hypothesis of (6.4) is evidently satisfied with $\mathbf{Y}_1$ taken as Y. Proceed inductively with $\mathbf{Y}_r = \{x \mid \theta_r(x) \geq \theta_r(tx)\} \cap \mathbf{Y}_{r-1}$.

Lemma 6.6. *If ψ is equivariant with respect to a fixed point free involution t of S^n, then the degree of ψ^* is odd.*

We give two proofs. For the first we start with $\psi S^n \to S'^n$. Then

$$\psi^* \mathbf{I}'(0) = \mathbf{I}(0).$$

The generator f'^n of $H(S'^n/T_2, \mathrm{J}_2)$ is ${}_1s(n)\mathbf{I}'(0)$. By (5.3)

$$\psi^*(f'^n) = \psi^* \, {}_1s(n)\mathbf{I}'(0) = s(n)\, \mathbf{I}(0)$$

the generator of $H^n(S^n/T_2, \mathrm{J}_2) = H^n(P^n, \mathrm{J}_2) \approx H^n(S^n, \mathrm{J}_2)$ (6.2b). In short ψ^* has degree 1 mod 2.

We sketch a second proof which is an instructive derivation of this theorem for $k = 2$ from the Lefschetz number. For this assume a homotopic equivariance-preserving deformation if necessary to ensure ψ: $S^n \to S^n$ has a finite number of fixed points each of index ± 1. Then $L(\psi) = 1 + (-1)^n d$ where d is the degree of ψ. Let us label the sum of the fixed points with index $+1$ by n_+ and the sum of those of index -1 by n_-. Then $N = n_+ + n_-$ is the total number of fixed points. Therefore $L(\psi) = n_+ - n_- = N$ mod 2. The equivariance condition implies the fixed points occur in antipodal pairs since for a fixed point $\bar{x}$, $-\bar{x} = -\psi(\bar{x}) = \psi(-\bar{x})$. Hence N and therefore $L(\psi)$ are even. This means d must be odd.

7. FIXED POINTS. Write ρ, $\bar{\rho}$ for σ^m, σ^{k-m} so that again $\rho\bar{\rho} = 0$. Observe too that $\sigma^{k-1} = \tau \bmod k$. Define $\Psi^\#$ on ${}^{\sigma^m}C^*(\boldsymbol{K}, \boldsymbol{F}, J_k)$ to ${}^{\sigma^{m-1}}C^*(\boldsymbol{K}, \boldsymbol{F}, J_k)$ by $\sigma^{k-m}\boldsymbol{f} \to \sigma^{k-m+1}\boldsymbol{f}$. Then,

$$\begin{aligned}\ker \Psi^\# &= \{\boldsymbol{F} \mid \boldsymbol{F} = \sigma^{k-m}\boldsymbol{f}, \quad \sigma\boldsymbol{F} = 0\} \\ &= {}^{\sigma}C^*(\boldsymbol{K}, T, I_k) \cap {}^{\sigma m}C^*(\boldsymbol{K}, F, I_k).\end{aligned}$$

However $\sigma\boldsymbol{F} = 0 \Rightarrow \sigma^m\boldsymbol{F} = 0$, whence ${}^{\sigma}C^*(K, F, \mathrm{J}_k) \subset {}^{\sigma m}C^*(\boldsymbol{K}, \boldsymbol{F}, \mathrm{J}_k)$, so $\ker \Psi^\# = {}^{\sigma}C^*(\boldsymbol{K}, \boldsymbol{F}, \mathrm{J}_k)$.

Accordingly

$$0 \longrightarrow \ker(\Psi^\#) \xrightarrow{i^\#} {}^{\sigma m}C^*(\boldsymbol{K}, \boldsymbol{F}, \mathrm{J}_k) \xrightarrow{\Psi^\#} {}^{\sigma^{m-1}}C^*(\boldsymbol{K}, \boldsymbol{F}, \mathrm{J}_k) \longrightarrow 0,$$

and so by (61.12) and (62.1e) we have fabricated the exact sequences (where d is $'\partial$ or $'\delta$)

$$\text{(7.1)} \qquad {}^{\sigma}H(\boldsymbol{K}, F, \mathrm{J}_k) \longrightarrow {}^{\sigma^m}H(K, F, \mathrm{J}_k) \longrightarrow {}^{\sigma^{m-1}}H(K, F, \mathrm{J}_k) \xrightarrow{d}.$$

We understand below that the coefficient group is J_k, k prime. Moreover we go to homology and write S^n for $\boldsymbol{X}$ and S^n/T_k for X.

PROBLEM

13-10. If $\rho = \Sigma\, a_i\, t^i$, $a_i \in \mathrm{J}$ or $a_i \in \mathrm{J}_k$ derive exact cohomology sequences.

Theorem 7.2

$$\text{(7.2a)} \qquad {}^{\rho}H_m(S^n, F) = H_m(F) = 0, \qquad m > n$$

$$\text{(7.2b)} \qquad {}^{\bar{\rho}}H_n(S^n) \approx {}^{\bar{\rho}}H_n(S^n, F) \oplus H_n(F) \approx H_n(S^n) \approx \mathrm{J}_k$$

$$\text{(7.2c)} \qquad {}^{\rho}H_n(S^n, F) \approx {}^{\bar{\rho}}H_{n-1}(S^n, F) \oplus H_{n-1}(F)$$

Since S^n is finite dimensional, all homology groups are trivial for $m \geq N$. By exactness in (3.4a) with $N > n + 1$,

$$0 \approx H_N(S^n) \approx {}^{\rho}H_N(S^n, F) \approx {}^{\bar{\rho}}H_{N-1}(S^n).$$

However, ${}^{\rho}H_{N-1}(S^n, F) \oplus H_{N-1}(F) \approx 0$ (3.5) has as consequences

$$H_{N-1}(F) \approx 0 \quad \text{and} \quad {}^{\rho}H_{N-1}(S^n, F) \approx 0.$$

Evidently ρ and $\bar{\rho}$ can be interchanged. This settles (7.2a).

For (7.2b) and (7.2c) suppose $\boldsymbol{z}^n$ is the base cycle of S^n. Then $t\boldsymbol{z}^n \sim m\boldsymbol{z}^n$, m an integer mod k and t the generator of T_k. Then $t^k\,\boldsymbol{z}^n \sim m^k\,\boldsymbol{z}^n \sim \boldsymbol{z}^n$. Hence $m^k = 1 \bmod k$ or, since k is prime, $m = 1$. Then

$$\tau\boldsymbol{z} \sim k\boldsymbol{z} \sim 0 \bmod k,$$

$$\sigma\boldsymbol{z} \sim 0.$$

Accordingly $\rho\gamma \sim 0$ and consequently $\rho H_n(S^n) = 0$. We shall use the exactness of (3.4a) and also (3.5). The isomorphisms obtained depend on the fact that $H_{n\pm 1}(S^n) = 0$. Thus since $ker\ i_n = Im\ \partial = 0$ and $ker\ \rho_n = Im\ i_n$ there results first

$$\mathrm{J}_k = H_n(S^n) \approx {}^\rho H_n(S^n),$$

and then the relation (6.2b) for

$${}^\rho H_n(S^n) \approx {}^\rho H_n(S^n, F) \oplus H_n(F) \approx H_n(S^n), \quad (3.5).$$

Further $0 = Im\ \rho_n = ker\ '\partial$ together with (3.5) yields (6.2c) according to

$${}^\rho H_n(S^n, F) \overset{'\partial}{\approx} {}^{\bar\rho} H_{n-1}(S^n) \approx {}^{\bar\rho} H_{n-1}(S^n, F) \oplus H_{n-1}(F)$$

Theorem 7.3. *The fixed point set F for a homological J_k, n-sphere under the cyclic group, T_k, k prime is either vacuous or a homological J_k, r-sphere, $r \leq n$.*

Suppose r is the largest integer such that $H_r(F, \mathrm{J}_k) \neq 0$. If no such integer exists, take $r = -1$. Assume $r < n$. Then from (7.2b)

$$\text{(7.3a)} \qquad {}^\rho H_n(S^n, F) \approx \mathrm{J}_k.$$

If $r < n - 1$, then, from (7.3a) and (7.2c),

$$\text{(7.3b)} \qquad {}^\rho H_n(S^n, F) \approx {}^\rho H_{n-1}(S^n, F) \approx \mathrm{J}_k.$$

Since $H_{n-1}(S^n) = H_{n-2}(S^n) = 0$, use of (3.5) in (3.4a) yields

$$\text{(7.3c)} \qquad {}^\rho H_s(S^n, F) \approx {}^{\bar\rho} H_{s-1}(S^n, F) \oplus H_{s-1}(F),$$

for $r < s \leq n$. It thus follows, by proceeding as for (7.3a) and (7.3b), that

$$\text{(7.3d)} \qquad {}^\rho H_m(S^n, F) \approx \mathrm{J}_k, \qquad m > r.$$

In view of the definition of r, the choice $s = r + 1$, in (7.3c), and reference to (7.3d), yields

$$\text{(7.3e)} \qquad {}^{\bar\rho} H_r(S^n, F) \approx 0,$$

$$\text{(7.3f)} \qquad H_r(F) \approx \mathrm{J}_k.$$

The use of (7.3c) and (7.3e) guarantees that for the augmented groups

$${}^\rho H_s(S^n, F) \approx 0, \qquad H_s(F) \approx 0,$$

successively for $s = r - 1, r - 2, \ldots, 0$.

Theorem 7.4. *If T is cyclic of order k^m, $m \geq 1$ and k prime, operating on the homological J_k, n-sphere, then the fixed point set is a homological J_k, r-sphere.*

The case $m = 1$ has just been settled. We make the induction hypothesis that the theorem holds for $n \leq m - 1$. Let T' be the subgroup of T with generator $t^{k^{m-1}} = s$. Then T' is cyclic of order k. Denote its fixed point set by F'. By our induction hypothesis, this is a homological I_k, r-sphere. Observe F' is invariant under T. Indeed $t^j F' = t^j sF' = st^j F'$.

Hence $t^j F' \subset F'$ and actually $t^j F' = F'$. Evidently $F' \supset F$. Suppose that F' is not only invariant as a set, but is actually pointwise fixed. In this case $F' = F$ and we are through. If F' is not pointwise fixed, let T''' be the largest subgroup of T leaving F' pointwise fixed. Then

$$T/T' \supset T/T''' \approx T'' \subset T,$$

is a cyclic group of period u, $u \leq m - 1$, taking F' into F'. Denote by F''' the fixed point set in F' under T''. Since F' has been established as a homological I_k sphere, F'' is a homological $I_k\, r''$ sphere. Since F is fixed under T, it is fixed under T''. On the other hand, for any $g \in T$, $g = t''' t''$, so if $x'' \in F''$

$$\begin{aligned} gx'' &= t''' t'' x'' \\ &= x''. \end{aligned}$$

Thus $F'' \subset F$. This shows $F = F''$.

PROBLEM

13-11. If I^n is a J_k omological closed cell, i.e., $\tilde{H}_m(I^n, J_k) = 0$, $m = 0, 1, \ldots, k$ a prime, show $F = F(T_k) \neq \varnothing$ and that $\tilde{H}_m(F, J_k) = 0$, all m.

Remark. Theorems 7.3 and 7.4 are *best possible* in the sense that they are no longer necessarily valid if k is not a prime. Neither theorem is valid if the finite dimensional sphere S^n is replaced by the sphere in a nonfinite Banach space. Moreover any preassigned closed set can be the fixed point set of the closed cell $\{x \mid \|x\| \leq 1\}$ of a nonfinite dimensional Banach space under T_k.

Theorem 7.5. *If θ is an equivariant self map of R^n with respect to T_k, k a prime, then θ has a fixed point. If $k = 2$ and the fixed point set is finite there can be only 1 fixed point.*

Compactify R^n to a sphere S^n by adding ∞. Extend θ, T_k to θ^+, T_k^+ on $R^\infty \cup \infty$ by $\theta^+(\infty) = \infty = T^+(\infty)$. Then θ^+ is equivariant with respect to T_k. Moreover $F(\theta^+) \supset \infty$ and so is nonempty. Hence $F(\theta^+)$ is a homological sphere of dimension r, (6.3). Accordingly $F(\theta^+)$ contains a point $x \neq \infty$ and x is therefore a fixed point of θ. For the last conclusion $F(\theta^+)$ being finite must be S^0 with ∞ one of the two points in S^0.

The Smith homomorphisms can be used to give a straightforward proof of the next well known result.

Theorem 7.6. *If S^n is triangulated, n odd, with the fixed point free group of simplicial transformations T_k, k a prime, then the equivariant map ψ of S^n, $T_k \to S^n$, T_k induces an isomorphism ψ^* on $H^n(S^n, J_k) \to H^n(S^n, J_k)$.*

By (7.3) with $r = -1$, ${}^{\sigma}H^{m-1}(S^n, J_k) \approx {}^{\tau}H^m(S^n, J_k) \approx J_k$, $0 \leq m \leq n$. (In all accuracy (7.3) makes this assertion for the homology groups, but the argument is plainly valid in detail for cohomology.) Since $H^m(S^n, J_k) \approx 0$ for $0 < m < n$ it follows from the exact sequence (3.6) that ${}_{\sigma}\delta$ and ${}_{\tau}\delta$ in (4.1) are isomorphisms and so is γ. Therefore, by reason of (3.8) and (4.1), $I(n) = s(n)\, I(0) \neq 0$. Since (3.8) shows $H^n(S^n/J_k, J_k) \approx J_k$, we know $I(n)$ is the generator of $H^n(S^n/J_k, J_k)$ and hence $\psi^*\, I(n) = I(n)$, (5.5). Then the isomorphisms $H^n(S^n, J_k) \approx J_k \approx {}^{\sigma}H^n(S^n, J_k) \approx H^n(S^n/J_k, J_k)$ are the grounds for our conclusion that ψ^* is an isomorphism.

The demonstration of (7.6) has incidentally established an important result which generalizes Example 13-3.

Corollary 7.7. $\nu(S^n, T_k) = n$.

We add two results connecting the order of a finite transformation group and the Lefschetz number.

Lemma 7.8. *Let K admit the finite group G of order m. Let ψ be a self map of K with $\psi g = g\psi$ for all $g \in G$ and suppose $F(\psi) \cap F(g) = \varnothing$, $g \neq 1$, where $F(\psi)$ and $F(g)$ stand for the fixed point sets of ψ and of g. Suppose $F(\psi)$ and $F(g)$ are finite. Then $L(\psi)$ is a multiple of m.*

In the trivial case that $F(\psi) = \varnothing$ the assertion is evidently valid. Let $x_0 \in F(\psi)$. Then $\psi(g(x_0)) = g(\psi(x_0)) = g(x_0)$. Hence $G(x_0) = \{g(x_0)\} \subset F(\psi)$. These points are distinct for if $g(x_0) = g'(x_0)$, then x_0 would be a fixed point for $g'^{-1} g \neq 1$. Evidently if $x_1 \in F(\psi) - G(x_0)$, $G(x_0) \cap G(x_1) = \varnothing$. The fixed point index of $g(x_0)$ is the same as that for x_0. Hence $G(x_0)$ contributes $m\nu(x_0)$ to the algebraic sum of all the indices. Our final observation is that $L(\psi)$ is just this sum.

Theorem 7.9. *Let K admit the finite group G of order m. Let ψ be a self map of K with $\psi g = g\psi$ for all g in G. Let G_1 of order n be the smallest subgroup generated by elements g_i of G for which $F(\psi) \cap F(g_i) = \varnothing$. Then G_i is an invariant subgroup of G and $L(\psi)$ is a multiple of m/n.*

Let $x_i \in F(\psi)$. Let G_{1i} be the subgroup of G_1 of order n_i generated by elements admitting x_i as a fixed point. If $gx_i = g'\, x_i$ where g and g' are in

G_1, then $g^{-1} g' \in G_{1i}$ and hence there are as many distinct points in $\{g_1(x_i) \mid g_1 \in G_1\}$ as there are cosets of G_1 with respect to G_{1i} namely n/n_i. The same conclusion follows from a choice of $g\, G_1$, $g \in G$, instead of G_1 for if $g\, g_1\, x_i = g\, g_1'\, x_i$ then $g_1\, x_i = g_1'\, x_i$. It is impossible that $g\, x_i = g'\, x_i$ for $g' \bar{\in} g\, G_1$. Hence there are $m/n \cdot n/n_i$ distinct points generated by x_i. Since $\psi(g(x_i)) = g(\psi(x_i))$ each of these points is in $F(\psi)$. The index for each of these is the same and hence in the algebraic sum of the indices of the fixed point the contribution is $m/n\; \nu(x_i)$. Thus

$$L(\psi) = \Sigma_i\, m/n_i\; \nu(x_i) = m/n\; \Sigma\; n/n_i\; \nu(x_i)$$

8. GENERAL APPLICATIONS OF SMITH HOMOMORPHISMS. So far it has seemed that only complexes or spaces admitting a finite group of operators can take advantage of the Smith homomorphisms. We wish to disabuse the reader of this notion. We will sketch two different applications. For quite general spaces there is, in fact, an equivalence between the generalizations of the cup product namely the Steenrod reduced powers and the Smith homomorphisms. The second application is to the homeomorphic imbedding problem.

The Steenrod reduced powers for a prime k are certain homomorphisms $\{St_k(m)\}$ of the form

(**a**) $$St_k(m)\colon H^n(K, J_k) \to H^{n+m}(K, J_k).$$

We have shown in (4.1) that Smith homomorphisms also exist for a prime k in the parallel form

(**b**) $$Sm_k(m)\colon H^n(K, J_k) \to H^{n+m}(K, J_k)$$

Since we make no use of these products in this book we shall not prove that $\{St_k(m)\}$ is determined by $\{Sm_k(m)\}$ and, instead, we content ourselves with a formal plausible indication of the genesis of (**b**).

Though our developments have stressed simplicial complexes the discussion after (5.10) makes it clear that the results are valid for general spaces using say the singular omology groups except as regards dimensional considerations.

Let Z^k be the topological product $Z \times Z \times \cdots \times Z$. The diagonal map $\Delta\colon Z \to Z^k$ is defined by $\Delta z = (z, z, \ldots, z)$. Let t be the permutation operator

$$t\colon (z^1, \ldots, z^k) \to (z^2, \ldots, z^k, z^1)$$

Then $T_k = \{t^i \mid i < k\}$ acts on Z^k. For complexes a little more needs to be said. Thus z^i is some simplex $\sigma^{j_i}_{n_i}$ say. The elements of Z^k are then the cells $\sigma^{j_1}_{n_1} \times \sigma^{j_2}_{n_2} \times \cdots \times \sigma^{j_k}_{n_k}$. Furthermore we assume such triangulations that ΔZ is isomorphic to Z and is a subcomplex of Z^k. The fixed elements under t are constituted by ΔZ.

Accordingly consider $\mathbf{X} = Z^k - \Delta Z$. Plainly T_k acts on $\mathbf{X}$ without fixed points. Thus for any Z there is determined a pair $\mathbf{X}$, T_k. We can then proceed to $X = \mathbf{X}/T_k$ and can define the Smith homomorphism attached to X. It is plausible that the omology groups for X and $\mathbf{X}$ are characteristic of Z. That is to say omology elements of Z and omology elements of $\mathbf{X}$ and of X are correlated (Cf. also (46.5)). Accordingly the Smith homomorphisms over X induce homomorphism of the omology groups of Z. For each prime, then, these homomorphisms are of the type (**b**).

We turn to the next and perhaps clearer application of the pair $\mathbf{X} = Z^k - \Delta Z$, T_k. Suppose h is a homeomorphism of Z into Z'. Then h induces a map Ψ of $\mathbf{X} \rightarrow \mathbf{X}'$ where $\mathbf{X}' = Z'^k - \Delta Z'$. Since t is a permutation operator it is plain that Ψ is an equivariant map on $\mathbf{X}$, T_k into $\mathbf{X}'$, T_k. Let $\nu(X)$ and $\nu(X')$ be the indices defined in (135.4). By (135.5), $\nu(X) \leq \nu(X')$. Accordingly this is a necessary condition for imbedding Z homeomorphically in Z'.

chapter 14

FIBERINGS

1. FIBER SPACE CONCEPTS. Various conditions can be placed on the triple X, B, p, with the projection p depending on the properties desired in an investigation and for easy designation one lumps these together as various types of **fiber spaces**. We shall define those of prime utility. For instance the notion of local sections may be central or the fact that the fibers are of the same homotopy type or that locally the super space is a product space or finally that some form of the covering homotopy theorem is satisfied. In current usage the last type of defining property dominates fiber space studies.

A further basis for classification arises with the introduction of an operator group, G, which is a subgroup of the group of automorphisms on the fibers. The term **fiber bundle** is then used. In a sense one may assume of course that a group is always present, namely the group of all homeomorphisms of the fibers. If adjunction of a group be made to the first types of fiber spaces we may choose between requiring that the group be topological or not.

Now, although the traditional definition and view of fiber spaces is in partial eclipse, the ideas involved here and cognate notions such as that of slicing function enter naturally in mapping problems. We therefore start with a brief account of these ideas.

Definition 1.1. Let $\mu = \{U_i\}$ be an open cover of B. A **local slicing function,** ψ is a collection of maps $\{\psi_i \mid \psi_i\colon U_i \times p^{-1} U_i \text{ to } p^{-1} U_i\}$ where for each fixed x in $p^{-1} U_i$, $\psi_i(b, x \mid b \in U_i)$ is a section over U_i passing through x (81.25). Thus

(1.1a) $$p\psi_i(b, x) = b, \qquad (b, x) \in U_i \times p^{-1} U_i$$

and

(1.1b) $$\psi_i(px, x) = x.$$

The slicing functions are **coherent** if the natural consistency condition is satisfied, namely

(1.1c) $\quad \psi_i(b, x) = \psi_j(b, x), \quad (b, x) \in U_i \cap U_j \times p^{-1}(U_i \cap U_j).$

Thus the prisms $U_i \times p^{-1} U_i$ are sectioned into paper thin wafers by $\psi_i(b, x)$ as x moves along the fiber $p^{-1}(b_0)$. A **fiber space** is the triple X, B, p which for some open cover $\mu = \{U_i\}$ of B admits coherent local slicing functions. The fibers are the sets $p^{-1}(b)$.

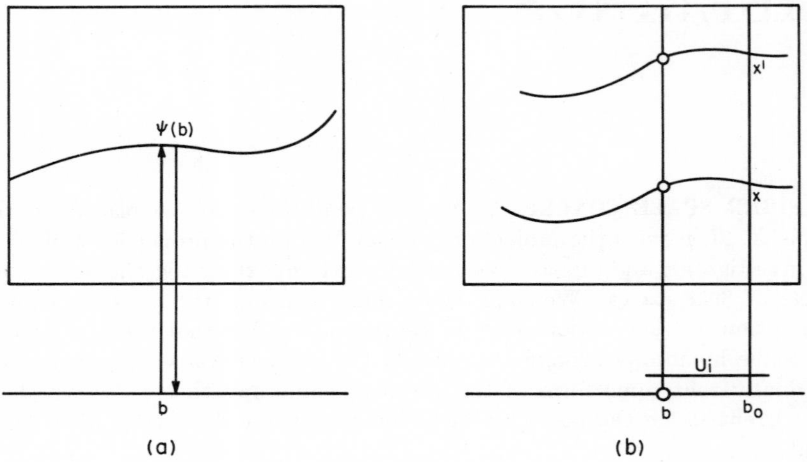

Figure 14-1

It is not to be inferred that (1.1b) implies a local section can be continued over all B by passing from one U_i to another even if $\mu = \{U_i\}$ is a finite cover. The rub is of course that in the process of continuation one may come back to a different section over U_i. For instance consider X to be an infinite spiral over the circle B. Then in passing around the circle clockwise one lands on the next higher coil so no global single valued map is defined on B to X though locally there is a section (Fig. 14.2).

The clarity and precision in statement that the fiber space lends geometrical analysis is illustrated by the remainder of this section.

Definition 1.2. Let M_n be an n dimensional closed manifold of class C^1 admitting a family of special rectifiable paths, that is to say, a path distance is defined for every pair of points on the path, but the paths may be self intersecting or even overlapping. For each assignment of a point and a vector, there is to be a unique special path containing the assigned point with the vector as initial tangent. We shall use the designation **quasi**

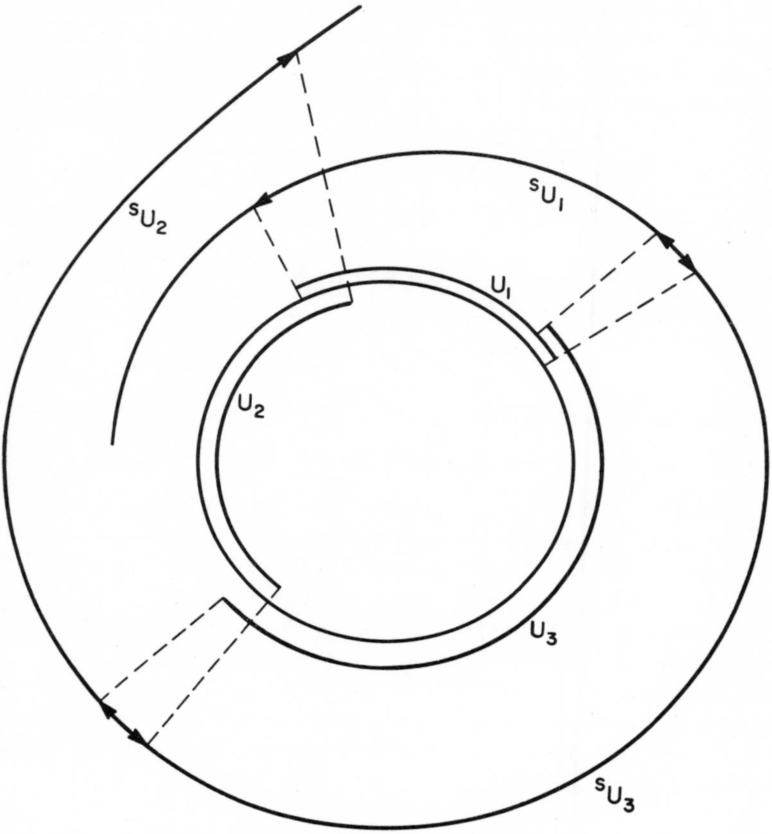

Figure 14-2

geodesic manifold. For instance, the special family may be that of geodesics if there is a nonsingular Riemannian metric. More specially M may be a Euclidean sphere and then one may wind round and round along a great circle.

Theorem 1.3. *Let ψ map the n dimensional quasi geodesic manifold M_n into R^n. Then for every positive a, there is a point pair x_0, x_1 whose distance apart along some path is a and $\psi(x_0) = \psi(x_1)$.*

Write B for M_n, and r for a unit tangent to B. Let $x = (b, r)$. Accordingly $X = \{x\}$, B, $F = S^{n-1}$, p constitutes a fiber space. In particular $p(b, r) = b$. Let t: $(b, r) \to (b, -r)$. Let $C(b, r)$ be the unique path on B determined by (b, r). Let s be the distance parameter along $C(b, r)$ increasing from 0 in the direction of r. The *tangent* to $C(b, r)$ at the *point* x specified by s is determined by (b, r) and the pair is designated by $\theta_s(b, r)$. For each s, θ_s is a homeomorphism of X and in particular θ_0 is the identity. Note that $\theta_s t = t\theta_{-s}$. Define μ_s on X to X by $\mu_s x = \psi p \theta_s x \subset \psi(B)$. If $x \in p^{-1} b$ then $\mu_0 x = \psi(b)$. Denote by $v_s(x)$ the vector from $\mu_s(x)$ to $\mu_{s+a}(x)$. Continuity in s and in x is easy to establish. The assertion of the theorem is equivalent to the statement $v_s(\bar{x}) = 0$ for some $\bar{x}$ and some s.

Observe

$$\mu_s t = \psi p \theta_s t = \psi p t \theta_{-s}.$$

For the special choice $s = -a/2$, $\psi p \theta_{-a/2} tx = \mu_{-a/2} tx = \mu_{a/2} x$. This is an equivalence condition,

(1.3a) $$v_{-a/2}\, tx = -v_{-a/2}\, x.$$

Suppose the theorem is false. Then $v_s(x)$ is never a zero vector; that is to say $v_s(x)$ always prescribes a unique direction. The map λ_s: $v_s(x) \to \dfrac{v_s(x)}{|v_s(x)|} = w_s(x)$ takes $\{v_s(x)\}$ into the unit sphere Σ^{n-1} with center at the origin in R^n. In particular λ_s maps each fiber $p^{-1} b$ into Σ^{n-1}. By reason of (1.3a), $\lambda_{-a/2}$ is an equivariant map of S^{n-1}, t into Σ^{n-1}, t' where t' is antipodal. Hence $\lambda_{-a/2}$ has degree 1 mod 2 (136.6). Since λ_s is homotopic to $\lambda_{-a/2}$, λ_s^* has degree 1 mod 2, and so is nontrivial. We finish up the proof by establishing a contradiction with this conclusion.

The point $\psi(b)$ has coordinates we can write $\psi_1(b), \ldots, \psi_n(b)$. Since M_n is compact, for some $\bar{b}$, $\psi_n(\bar{b}) = \max \{\psi_n(b) \mid b \in M_n\}$. Accordingly if $x \in p^{-1} \bar{b}$, the nth component of $v_0(x)$ is nonpositive. Thus λ_0 takes the sphere $p^{-1} \bar{b}$ into a proper subset of Σ^{n-1} and therefore $\lambda_0^* = 0$.

Remark. It seems plausible (in analogy with (136.5)) that $H_{n-1}(Y, \mathfrak{J}_2)$ is not trivial when $Y = \{(b, r) \mid \psi(b) = \psi(b')$, distance b, b' along $C(b, r)$ is $a\}$.

2. FIBER BUNDLES. We present the more or less traditional definition of the fiber bundle with a view to later applications.

Definition 2.1. $P = (X, B, G, p)$ is a **principal fiber bundle** or a **principal bundle** if G is a topological group and there is an open cover $\mu = \{U_i\}$ for which the conditions below are valid. (All spaces are supposed T_2.)

(2.1a) p is an open map on X onto B.

(2.1b) (Local triviality) $U_i \times G$ is homeomorphic to $p^{-1} U_i$ under a homeomorphism ϕ_i where $\phi_i(b \times G) = p^{-1}(b)$. Local coordinates (b, g) are assigned each $x \in p^{-1} U_i$ according to the rule $(b, g) = \phi_i^{-1}(x)$.

(2.1c) For each $b \in U_i \cap U_j \neq \varnothing$ there is a unique **bridging** element $g_{ij}(b) \in G$ and $g_{ij}(b)$ can be considered a map of $U_i(b) \cap U_j(b)$ into G. The local coordinates $(b, g_i) \in p^{-1}(U_i)$ and $(b, g_j) \in p^{-1}(U_j)$ represent the same point of X if $g_i = g_{ij}(b)g_j$. Then $g_{ik}(b) = g_{ij}(b)g_{jk}(b)$. The multiplication by $g_{ij}(b)$ is *left multiplication* in G.

Remark. One does not solve for $g_{ij}(b)$ as $g_{ij}(b) = g_i\, g_j^{-1}$. The right-hand side by itself is meaningless until g_i is translated into the U_j local G coordinates or g_j into the U_i local coordinate. This is precisely what the bridging function $g_{ij}(b)$ does.

The fiber over b, designated by G_b is $p^{-1}(b)$. *Right multiplication* or translation applies not only to the fiber but to X. Thus in $p^{-1}(U_i)$, $x = (b, g) \to xg'$ where $xg' = (b, g\, g')$.

There are sections over each U_i. For instance such a section s_i is defined by $s_i(b) = \phi_i(b, g)$ for fixed $g \in G$. Recall this means $ps_i(b) = b$ for all b in U_i. Evidently $g_{ij}(b)$ is the element $\phi_i^{-1}\, \phi_j(b, g)$.

Definition 2.2. Let $\boldsymbol{P}' = \{X', B, G, p'\}$ and $\boldsymbol{P} = \{X, B, G, p\}$ be principal fiber bundles. The cover μ may be assumed the same for both since otherwise, intersecting two covers would lead to this situation. Then $\boldsymbol{P}$ is **equivalent** to $\boldsymbol{P}'$ if there is a homeomorphism ψ on X to X' such that $px = p'\, \psi x$ (so fibers correspond) and there exist maps t_i on U_i to G such that

$$g'_{ij}(b) = t_i(b)^{-1}\, g_{ij}(b)t_j(b). \tag{2.2a}$$

Strictly speaking it is the *equivalence class of* $\boldsymbol{P}$ *that is the principal fiber bundle,* but we shall use the imprecise terminology which confounds the representative $\boldsymbol{P}$ and the coset determined by $\boldsymbol{P}$.

$\boldsymbol{P}$ is **trivial** or a **product bundle** if for arbitrary b, i, j, $g_{ij}(b) = e$. This implies X is homeomorphic to $B \times G$. A **general principal fiber bundle** is defined if (2.1b) and (2.1c) are replaced by the requirements that for each b there is a homeomorphism $\phi(b)$ of G onto $p^{-1}(b)$, continuous in b and that G acts on $p^{-1}(b)$ by $(b, \phi(b))g = (b, g\phi(b))$. (The French terminology is principal fiber bundle and locally trivial fiber bundle, for our general principal fiber bundle and our fiber bundle respectively.) Thus the fibers are the orbits.

The existence of a section over all of B is of importance. The nature of the impediment is brought out in Fig. 14-2.

Lemma 2.3. *The principal fiber bundle* $\boldsymbol{P}$ *is equivalent to a product bundle iff* (a) *there are maps* t_i *on* U_i *to* G *such that*

$$g_{ij}(b) = t_i(b)\, t_j(b)^{-1} \tag{2.3a}$$

or (b) *iff there is a section.*

For (a) *take* g'_{ij} *as* e *in* (2.2a).

For (*b*) if $s\colon B \to X$ is a section, let $t_i(b)$ be the G coordinate relative to U_i of $s(b)$.

If $\boldsymbol{P}$ is equivalent to a product bundle, then by (2.3a) we can define $s_i(b)$ as the point of X with local coordinates $(b, t_i(b))$ relative to U_i. In $U_i \cap U_j$, $s_i(b)$ and $s_j(b)$ have the local coordinates $(b, t_i(b))$ and $(b, t_j(b))$. These represent the same point according to (2.1c). Thus a section exists over $U_i \cup U_j$ and so evidently over B.

The group G plays a double role in the principal fiber bundle, for it is simultaneously an operator group and a fiber (or rather a homomorph of the fibers), on which G acts as a set of automorphisms. Allied with the (general) principal fiber bundle there are various other fiber bundles in which the fiber is no longer required to be the space G, but merely a space, Y, on which G acts as an operator group.

Definition 2.4. As a guide to the definition of a fiber bundle with fiber Y, we note that in the case of product spaces we should have formally, with $X = B \times G$,

(2.4a) $$W = B \times Y = \frac{B \times G \times Y}{G} = \frac{X \times Y}{G}.$$

With (2.4a) at the masthead, suppose Y is a space admitting G as an effective group of operators on the left. Let $\boldsymbol{P} = (X, B, G, p)$ be a (general) principal fiber bundle where X admits G on the right. For the product space $X \times Y$ define the operations of the group G acting on the right by

(2.4b) $$(x, y)g = (xg, g^{-1}y).$$

Let

(2.4c) $$\tilde{p}(x, y) = x.$$

Write $w_0 = [x_0, y_0]$ for the equivalence class]

(2.4d) $$\{(x, y) \mid x = x_0 g, \quad y = g^{-1} y_0, \quad g \in G\}$$

and let W be the identification space of these equivalence classes; thus $W = (X \times Y)/G$. Define the projection $p_1\colon W \to B$ (identified with X/G) by

(2.4e) $$p_1[x_0, y_0] = [x_0].$$

If (x, y_0) is any other representative of the class denoted by $[x_0, y_0]$ then $x = x_0 g$, $y_0 = g^{-1} y_0$ whence $[x] = [x_0 g] = [x_0]$.

With η the natural map $\eta\colon (x, y) \to [x, y]$ and p defined above, we can show the following square is commutative

(2.4f) $$\begin{array}{ccc} X \times Y & \xrightarrow{\ \eta\ } & \dfrac{X \times Y}{G} = W \\ {\scriptstyle \tilde{p}}\big\downarrow & & \big\downarrow{\scriptstyle p_1} \\ X & \xrightarrow{\ p\ } & B = X/G \end{array}$$

$Q = (W, B, Y, G, p_1)$ is a (general) fiber bundle with fiber Y and group G **associated** with the (general) principal bundle $\boldsymbol{P}$. We often refer to the super space, W, as the **bundle space**. (The role of X and of Y can be interchanged and we shall understand by p_2 the projection of W on Y/G.)

We check that $p_1^{-1}(b)$ can be identified with Y. Indeed if we fix x at x_0 then $p_1^{-1}(b) = [x \times Y]_G$. It is then immediate that this is in 1-1 correspondence with Y/G_0 where G_0 is the collection of elements of G for which $gx_0 = x_0$; that is to say $g(b, g_0) = (b, gg_0) = (b, g_0)$ or $gg_0 = g_0$. The last relation implies $g = e$ so $G_0 = e$.

Left and right translations may be distinguished. For simplicity we take $Y = G$ so that W is again X. Let $x_0 = (b, e)$ though any fixed g would serve as well as e. If x is fixed at x_0 then

$$x \times g' = (b, g) \times g' \sim (b, g)g^{-1} \times gg' = x_0 \times gg'$$

This is a *left translation* of G_b by g. If g is held fast at e then $x \times g = (b, g') \times g \sim (b, g')g \times e$. Now a *right translation* on X has been defined. Again the fibers are preserved.

If $\boldsymbol{P}$ is a principal fiber bundle the procedure just described yields a fiber bundle. An independent specification of a fiber bundle is obtained by replacing G by Y in (2.1a) and (2.1b) and usually G is required to act effectively on Y on the left. In (2.1c) $g_{ij}(b)$ is again in G and the local coordinates (b, y_i) relative to U_i and (b, y_j) relative to U_j refer to the same point if $y_i = g_{ij}(b)y_j$. The fiber $p^{-1}(b)$ will often be designated by $\boldsymbol{F}_b$ or Y_b.

PROBLEM

14-1. Show in the notation of (2.4f) that $p_1^{-1}\, b = X/G_y$.

Examples of Fiber Bundles: Actually all the general fiber bundles in the examples below are fiber bundles, but we do not prove this.

EXAMPLE 14-1. Let $B = S^1$, $Y = G = \mathrm{J}_2 = (e, g)$, $X = \mathrm{J}_2 \times S^1$ and $p(g \times b) = b$. Then $P = (X, B, \mathrm{J}_2, p)$ is a general principal fiber bundle, namely the trivial or product bundle, $\mathrm{J}_2 \times S^1$.

EXAMPLE 14-2. Let $X = S^2$, the unit sphere with the origin as center. Let $G = \mathrm{J}_2 = (e, g)$ act on X by $xe = x$, $xg = -x$. Identify the pair $(x, -x)$ and write it $[x]$ or b. Then $B = \{[x]\}$ is the projective plane, P^2. Let $p(x) = p(-x) = [x]$. Hence $p^{-1}[x] = (x, -x)$ is a homeomorph of J_2. Thus (S^2, P^2, J_2, p) is a general principal fibre bundle.

EXAMPLE 14-3. The bundle $(S^n, P^n, \mathrm{J}_2, p)$, with P^n the n dimensional projective space, is a general principal fiber bundle with $p(x) = p(-x)$.

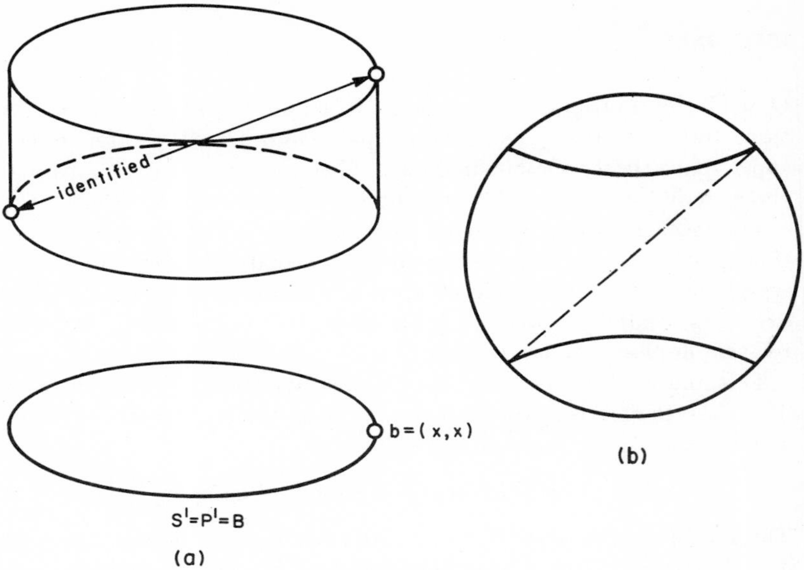

Figure 14-3

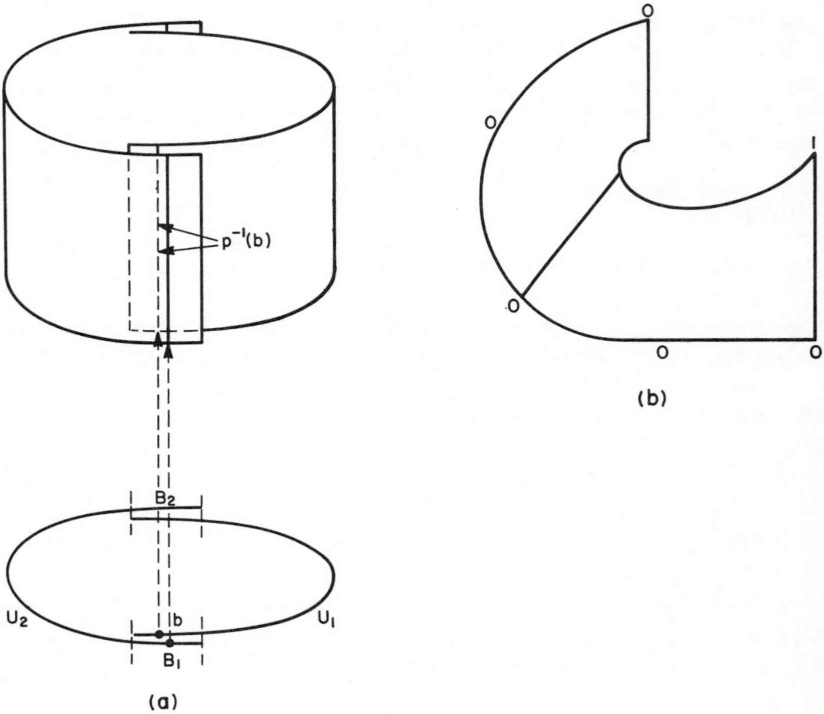

Figure 14-4

For $n = 1$, P^1 is homeomorphic to S^1. Thus $\boldsymbol{P}^1 = (S^1, S^1, J_2, p)$ is a (general) principal fiber bundle. This is different from $\boldsymbol{P}_1 = (S^1 \times J_2, S^1, J_2, p)$ which has the same G and B but is a product bundle.

Example 14-4. Take $Y = \{-1 \leq y \leq 1\} = I$. Start with P_1. Let J_2 act on I by $gy = -y$. A typical point in the bundle space $W = (S^1 \times I)/J_2$ is the coset consisting of (x, y) and $(-x, -y)$. The bundle space can be considered the equatorial belt of the sphere with antipodal points identified, i.e., a band in the projective plane and hence a Mobius Band.

Example 14-5. If we had used $\boldsymbol{P}_1$, then $W = (S^1 \times J_2 \times I)/J_2$ would have as points the coset $(b \times e, y)$, $(b \times g, -y)$. This is an identification of the rings $(S^1 \times e) \times J$ and $(S^1 \times g) \times J$ and therefore W is a ring.

Example 14-6. Suppose now $Y = S^1$. We need to specify how J_2 acts on Y. Since $g^2 = e$ there are essentially only two choices: (**a**) g advances each point by π radians or (**b**) g reflects each point in the horizontal axis. Again we start with $\boldsymbol{P}_1$ and use (2.2f). Hence for (**a**) the typical point of W is the identified (x, θ) and $(-x, \pi + \theta)$. For (**b**) the identification is for (x, θ) and $(-x, 2\pi - \theta)$. Two general fiber bundles are represented by

$$Q = (W, S^1, S^1, J_2, p)$$

thus (**a**) yields the **twisted torus** for W while (**b**) yields the **Klein bottle**.

Example 14-7. Mobius Band. $\boldsymbol{P} = (M, S^1, I, J_2, p)$. Let U_1 and U_2 be an open cover of $B = S^1$ by two arcs: Let B_1 and B_2 be the disjunct arcs in $U_1 \cap U_2$. Let $g_{12}(b) = g_{21}(b)$ with $g_{12}(b, B_1) = e$ and $g_{12}(b \mid B_2) = g$ and $g_{ii}(b) = e$. The identification in (2.4b) amounts to twisting the part above U_2 in B_1 through π radians as illustrated in (a') before matching with its counterpart above U_1 in B_1.

Lemma 2.5. *Let B and Y be arbitrary spaces and let $U = \{U_j \mid j \in J\}$ be an open cover of B. Let G be an operator group acting on the left on $Y = \{y\}$, thus $g\colon\ y \to gy \in Y$, and let $g_{ij}(b \mid b \in U_i \cap U_j)$ be elements of G satisfying the conditions $g_{ij}(b)g_{jk}(b) = g_{ik}(b)$ and depending continuously on b. A fiber bundle is specified by this data.*

Let $Z = \bigcup U_i \times Y \times J$. The relation between points in $(U_i \cap U_j) \times F$ considered as points of $U_i \times F$ or as points of $U_j \times F$ is defined through the intermediation of $g_{ij}(b)$ as follows: Let R denote the equivalence relation $\sim$, where

(2.5a) $$z = (b, y, i) \sim (b, g_{ij}(b)\, y, j), \quad b \in U_i \cap U_j, \quad y \in F.$$

Let $X = Z/R$ so x is a coset with respect to R, namely $[z] = [b, y, j]$. Define p by $p[(b, y, i)] = b$. Let $\lambda: z \to [z]$ and take the identification topology in X, that is to say V is open in X if $\lambda^{-1} V$ is open in Z. Accordingly $\phi_j(b, y) = [b, y, j]$ can be verified to be continuous in b. Then $(X, B, Y, G, p) = \boldsymbol{Q}$ is a fiber bundle.

Definition 2.6. If Y is changed in the construction described in (2.5) an **associated** fiber bundle is obtained. In particular, replacement of Y by G yields the associated principal fiber bundle. Evidently the bridging functions $\{g_{ij}(b) \mid U_i \cap U_j\}$ are the same for associated fiber bundles. Let $\boldsymbol{Q}$ and $\boldsymbol{Q}'$ be fiber bundles with the same B, Y, and G. Then $\boldsymbol{Q}$ and $\boldsymbol{Q}'$ are **equivalent** if (2.2a) is satisfied. Thus equivalence of fiber bundles amounts to equivalence of their associated principal bundles. The fact that the fiber Y does not enter explicitly in this equivalence condition indicates that it is the nature of the action of G on the fiber rather than the fiber itself that is central here. Suppose now G_1 and G_2 are closed subgroups of G and that G acts effectively on Y on the left. Suppose too that $\boldsymbol{Q}$ and $\boldsymbol{Q}'$ have Y and B in common and that the group for $\boldsymbol{Q}$ is G_1 and that for $\boldsymbol{Q}'$ is G_2. Therefore $\{g_{ij}(b)\} \subset G_1$ and $\{g'_{ij}(b)\} \subset G_2$. Then $\boldsymbol{Q}$ is equivalent to $\boldsymbol{Q}'$ over G if (2.2a) holds with $t_j(b)$ allowed to be an element of G. The special case $G_2 = G$ and principal bundles merits consideration. We then say $\boldsymbol{P}$ with G is an **enlargement** of $\boldsymbol{P}'$ with G' and that $\boldsymbol{P}'$ is a **reduction** of $\boldsymbol{P}$. It is then trivial that $\boldsymbol{P}'$ is an enlargement of $\boldsymbol{P}$ if and only if the associated fiber bundles with fiber Y are equivalent over G.

It is of interest to formulate these concepts for the general bundles. Then (2.2a) is no longer available.

Definition 2.7. Let $\boldsymbol{P} = (X, B, G, p)$ and $\boldsymbol{P}_1 = (X(1), B, G_1, p_1)$ be general fiber bundles with G_1 a closed subgroup of G. Require that f be a homeomorphism of $X(1)$ into X, i.e., onto $fX(1)$, inducing the identity map on B. Thus,

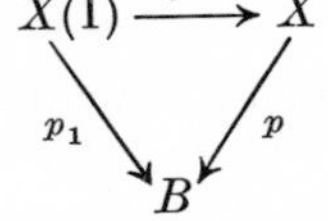

subject to $f(g_1 g) = g_1 f(g)$ for g_1 and g in G_1. Write $f\boldsymbol{P}_1 = (fX(1), B, G, p)$. Call $f\boldsymbol{P}_1$ the **image** of $\boldsymbol{P}_1$ in $\boldsymbol{P}$ and $\boldsymbol{P}$ the **enlargement** of $\boldsymbol{P}_1$. Then $\boldsymbol{P}_1$ is the **reduction** to G_1 of $\boldsymbol{P}$. Since f defines a homeomorphism we may consider $X(1)$ imbedded as a subset of X. (Evidently a general homomorphism $j: G_1 \to G$ can replace the inclusion $i\, G_1 \subset G$ to give j enlargement and j reduction if $f(g_1 g) = j(g_1) f(g)$.) If G_1 is a closed subgroup of G the left cosets are meant in G/G_1 (namely $\{g\, G_1\}$). We write $[g]_1$ for the element of G/G_1 corresponding to $g \in G$. G acts on G/G_1 according to $g'[g]_1 = [g'\, g]_1$.

However it need not act effectively in general. Let G_0 be the maximal subgroup of G_1 which is invariant in G. Then $G' = G/G_0$ is effective on G/G_1 (132.1).

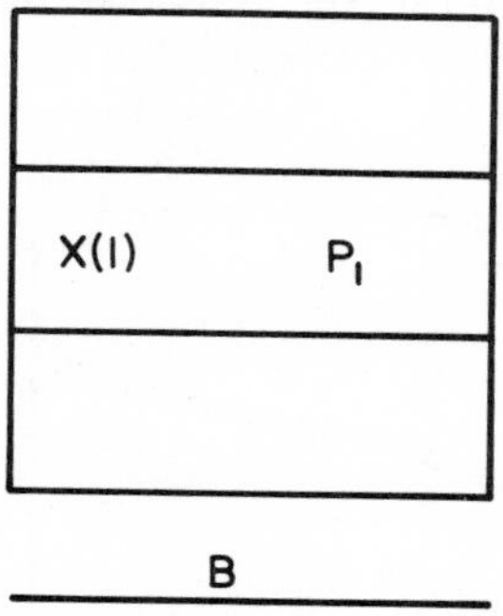

Figure 14-5

A **bundle map** ψ on the fiber bundles $\boldsymbol{Q}$ to $\boldsymbol{Q}'$ is a pair ψ_X, ψ_B on X to X' and on B to B' respectively with $p'\psi_X = \psi_B p$. Furthermore if $b \in U_i \cap \psi_B^{-1}(V_j)$ and (b, y_i) are the local coordinates of $x \in X$ and $(\psi_B(b), y_j')$ of $\psi_X(x)$ then $y_j' = \bar{g}_{ij}(b)y_i$ where $\bar{g}_{ij}(b) \in G$ and is continuously dependent on b.

Lemma 2.8. *Let G_1 be a closed subgroup of G. A sufficient condition that a reduction of $\boldsymbol{P} = (X, B, G, p)$ to $\boldsymbol{P}_1 = (X(1), B, G_1, p_1)$ exist is that the bundle, $\boldsymbol{Q} = (X/G_1, B, G/G_1, G, p_1)$, have a section. This condition is also necessary.*

The diagram for $\boldsymbol{Q}$ is easily seen to be

(2.8a)
$$\begin{array}{ccc} X \times G/G_1 & \xrightarrow{\bar{p}} & [X \times G/G_1]_G \\ \downarrow & & p_1 \downarrow \uparrow s \\ X & \xrightarrow{p} & X/G \end{array}$$

Define λ by $x \to [g]_1$ according to

(2.8b)
$$x \xrightarrow{p} [x] \xrightarrow{s} [x, [g]_1]$$

where s is the section predicated and $[-]$ and $[-]_1$ are cosets with respect to G and G_1 respectively. Let e be the neutral element of G. Define

(2.8c)
$$X(1) = \lambda^{-1}[e]_1.$$

This yields $X(1)$ as a subspace of X. It is immediate, since the correspondence X/G and $s(X/G)$ is $1 - 1$, that X/G and $X(1)/G_1$ are homeomorphs of B. Thus $\boldsymbol{P}(1) = (X(1), B, G_1, p(1))$ is a reduction of $\boldsymbol{P} = (X, B, G, p)$.

On the other hand if there is a reduction, ηf maps $X(1)$ into X/G_1 where $X(1) \xrightarrow{f} X \xrightarrow{\eta} X/G_1$. According to (2.7), $\eta f(g_1 x_1) = \eta(g_1 f(x_1)) = \eta f(x_1)$ where $g_1 \in G_1$ and $x_1 \in X(1)$. Hence ηf induces a map s on $B = X(1)/G_1$ to X/G_1. Plainly s is a section in $\boldsymbol{Q}$.

Remark. It is easily verified that (2.8) is valid for fiber bundles if G/G_1 has a local section in G; compare (2.9).

The next lemma seems intuitively obvious and not only furnishes an interesting application of some earlier results, but finds later application in (152.11). (Section and cross section are used interchangeably below.)

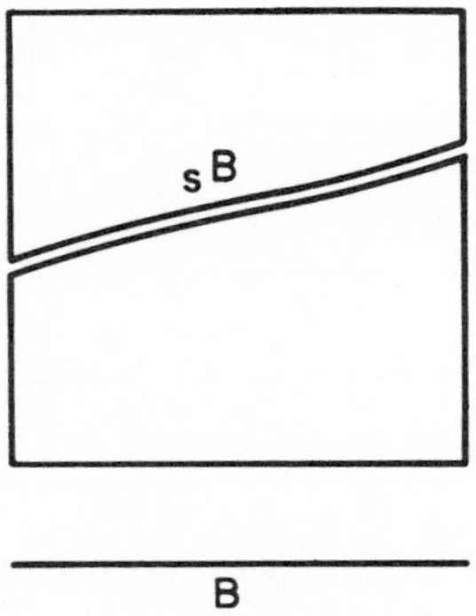

Figure 14-6

Lemma 2.9. *Suppose G_1 is a closed subgroup of G and has a local cross section, t, in G. Let Q be a fiber bundle $(W, B, Y = G/G_1, G, p)$ and suppose there is a cross section, s. Write: $W' = W - sB$. Let p' be the restriction of p to W'. Then $Q' = (W', B, Y - [e], G_1, p')$ is a fiber bundle.*

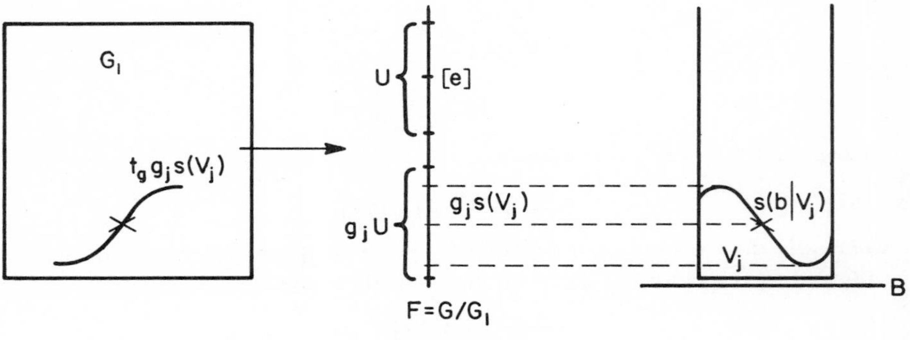

Figure 14-7

The idea of this demonstration is that an equivalent bundle Q_1 exists with sB pointwise invariant under G_1, so sB can be dropped. The quickest proof of this involves (2.8). We present an alternative argument giving more details, which is, besides, of independent interest. Let $\{V_j\}$ be an open cover of B. Let U be a neighborhood of $[e] \in Y = G/G_1$ for which the section $t: U \to G$ is defined. An open cover of Y is $\mu = \{gU \mid g \in G\}$. Let η be the projection on G to Y defined by $g \to [g]$. By straightforward computation we confirm $t_g y = gtg^{-1} y$ defines a section t_g over gU. Let q_j be the projection of $p^{-1}V_j$, onto Y, q_j: $[x, y] = y$. There is no loss of generality in requiring that $q_j a(V_j) \subset g_j U$ for some $g_j \in G$. Write

$$\rho_j(b) = t_g q_j s(b) \in G$$

and define $g'_{ij}(b)$ by using $\{g_{ij}(b)\}$ associated with $\boldsymbol{P}$ (2.6).

(2.9a) $$g'_{ij}(b) = \rho_i(b)^{-1} g_{ij}(b)\rho_j(b).$$

We assert that $\eta g'_{ij}(b) = [e]$ and hence that $g'_{ij}(b) \in G_1$. Indeed, since η is a homomorphism, and $g[h] = [gh]$.

$$\begin{aligned} \eta g'_{ij}(b) &= \rho_i(b)^{-1} g_{ij}(b)\eta\rho_j(b) \\ &= \rho_i(b)^{-1} g_{ij}(b)g_j s(b) \\ &= \rho_i(b)^{-1} g_i s(b) = [e]. \end{aligned}$$

or $g'_{ij}(b) \in G$.

The construction in (2.5) using $g'_{ij}(b)$ yields the fiber bundle $\boldsymbol{Q}_1$ with group G_1. That $\boldsymbol{Q}_1$ is equivalent to $\boldsymbol{Q}$ follows from (2.9a) and (2.1). Thus $W = W(1)$. Moreover, $g'_{ij}(b)\,[g] = [g]$ for $[g] \in G/G_1$ and in particular $g'_{ij}(b)\,[e] = [e]$. Of course $[g]$ is a left coset corresponding to gG_1 (so $g_1[g]_1$ corresponds to $g_1 gG_1$ and is not necessarily $[g]_1$). Since $W - sB = W(1) - sB = \{[b, [g], i] = [b, [g], j]$ for $b \in U_i \cap U_j$, $[g] \neq [e]\}$ it follows that $W(1) - s(B)$, B, $G/G_1 - [e]$, G_1, p' constitutes a fiber bundle.

3. LIFTING. A partial sharpening of the section concept will now be studied.

Definition 3.1. Let X, B, p be a triple as defined in (1.1). Let Y be a topological space mapped to B by ψ. If f is a map on Y to X with $pf(y) = \psi(y)$ then ψ is said to be **lifted** to f. Similar concepts hold for homotopy. Thus let ψ map Y to B and suppose ψ is lifted to f. Let h be on $Y \times I$ to B with $h(y, 0) = \psi(y)$. If $\bar{h}$ exists on $Y \times I$ to X with

$$h(y, t) = p\bar{h}(y, t),$$
$$h(y, 0) = p\bar{h}(y, 0),$$

the homotopy h is lifted to $\bar{h}$. The homotopy h is **stationary** over an interval, Δ, if $h(x, t) = h(x, t')$ for t and t' in Δ.

The covering homotopy theorems like (3.2) refer to such lifting. The general situation is that of maps or homotopies which can be lifted locally for instance over simplexes or arcs. The difficulty resides in the choice of matching maps to extend the local lifting to a global lifting. When this choice is unique, much stronger statements can be made. This is the case when the fibers are discrete or totally disconnected, as in the case of covering spaces, for instance.

Theorem 3.2. *Let $Q = (X, F, G, p)$ be a fiber bundle or fiber space* (1.1) *over the arcwise connected base space B where* (**a**) *B is either paracompact or denumerably locally compact or* (**b**) *F is discrete. If ψ maps a space Y to B, and f maps Y to X so that $pf = \psi$, then any homotopy h of ψ can be lifted to a homotopy, $\bar{h}$, of f and $\bar{h}$ is stationary when h is stationary. Under* (3.2a) *the homotopy $\bar{h}$ need not be unique.*

A particular case is that of Y a single point so the map by h is a **path**. Thus

Corollary 3.3. *Let l be the path with initial point $b_0 = l(b_0;\ 0)$ and points $l(b_0; t)$. Suppose $px_0 = b_0$. Then the path l can be lifted to a path $\tilde{l} = \{\tilde{l}(x_0; t)\}$.*

This is one of the few theorems for whose proof the reader is directed to the literature since, except for using the notion of local triviality, the demonstrations are aside from our interest.

4. EXTENSION. A dual action to that of lifting is extension. Thus with the notation of (3.1) if f is inclusion and ψ is assigned then p is an **extension** of ψ. We shall have immediate use for the following extension result.

Theorem 4.1. Borsuk-Dowker. *Let C be a closed subset of the normal denumerably paracompact space X (or assume $X \times I$ is normal). Suppose Y is a compact ANR and let f_0 and f_1 be homotopic on C to Y under the homotopy $\{f(c, t) \mid (c, t) \in C \times I\}$. Suppose also that f_0 admits an extension F_0 on X to Y. Then f_1 admits an extension F_1 with $F_0 \simeq F_1$.*

The set $A = X \times 0 \cup C \times I$. is closed in $X \times I$. Define a map h on A to Y by

$$h(x, 0) = F_0(x)$$
$$h \mid C \times I = f(c, t)$$

The assumption of normal denumerable paracompactness for X guarantees $X \times I$ is normal (**A**) so Tietze's theorem may be invoked to ensure there is an extension of h to $H\colon\ X \times I \to T$ where T is a Tychonoff parallelotope containing Y. Let r be the retracting function on the open neighborhood N in T of Y to Y. Note $X \times I \supset V = H^{-1} N \supset A$. Accordingly for each point (c, t_0) in $C \times I$, there is an open interval $\Delta(t_0)$ and an open neighborhood $U_{t_0}(c) \subset X$ such that

(4.1a) $$U_{t_0}(c) \times \Delta(t_0) \subset 0.$$

The compactness of I implies there is a finite collection of neighborhoods $\{\Delta(t_i) \mid i = 1, \ldots, n\}$ each satisfying (4.1a) (with t_0 replaced by t_i of course). Hence with $U(c) = \bigcap U_{t_i}(c)$, $U(c) \times I \subset 0$. Let $U = \bigcup_c U(c)$, whence $C \times I \subset U \times I \subset V$. Since rH is on V to Y, $rH \mid U \times I \cup X \times 0 \to Y$. Since C and $U^{\sim}$, are disjunct closed sets there is a Urysohn function $\mu(U^{\sim}, C)$. Define F by $F(x, t) = rH(x, t\mu(x))$ then $F\colon X \times I \to Y$ and $F(x, 0) = rH(x, 0) = F_0(x)$,

$$F(x, 1) = rH(x, \mu(x)) = F_1(x),$$

with F_1 an extension of f_1 since on C,

$$F(-, 1) \mid C = rH(c, 1) = H(c, 1)$$
$$= f_1(c).$$

Instead of the restriction that $X \times I$ be normal, a condition on Y may be imposed or the homotopies considered may be restricted.

Definition 4.2. If Y is metric then a homotopy h on $X \times I \to Y$ is a **uniform homotopy** if for assigned $\varepsilon > 0$, and some δ, $d(h(\ , t), h(\ , t')) < \delta$ for $|t - t'| < \varepsilon$ in the metric topology of Y^X. If the metric of Y is replaced by an equivalent one the property of being a uniform homotopy may be lost except when Y is a compactum. If, besides, X is compact, homotopy and uniform homotopy coincide.

PROBLEM

14-2. Prove these statements.

Theorem 4.3. *Theorem* 4.1 *is valid for X merely normal provided Y is a compact metric ANR and all homotopies are uniform.*

PROBLEM

14-3 Demonstrate (4.3).

5. FIBER SPACE EXTENSIONS. The wide utility of the covering homotopy theorem (3.2) suggests giving a name to the class of spaces satisfying it.

Definition 5.1. A **Serre Fiber Space** is a triple (X, B, p) which satisfies the homotopy covering theorem for any finite polyhedron. (Actually the conclusions derived in this book would be valid under lighter conditions also than are tacitly implied in this chapter so far. Thus B need not be a T_2 space, nor need the topology of B be the identification topology defined by

p. Moreover, p need not be open nor need $p^{-1}(b)$ be closed.) If finite polyhedron is replaced by paracompact space and the requirement that the lifted cover be stationary is added, the result is a **Hurewicz Fiber Space** or without the stationary property, a **deficient** Hurewicz Fiber Space.

Lemma 5.2. *If the finite polyhedron K is contractible, it is a retract of every denumerably paracompact normal space X containing it.*

Let h be the contraction of K where for convenience we replace t by $1 - t$. Thus h: $K \times I \to K$, $h \mid K \times 1$ is the identity map and $h \mid K \times 0 = x_0 \in K$. Let f map X into x_0 so h on $K \times 0$ may be viewed as the restriction of f to K. As a finite polyhedron K is an ANR of some Euclidean cube I^n. Accordingly the hypotheses of (4.1) are met and there must exist an extension of $h(\ , 1)$ to X. Moreover the extension of an identity map is, of course, a retraction map.

Remark. It is not true in general that K is also a deformation retract of X.

Theorem 5.3. *Suppose the contractible finite polyhedron A is imbedded in a contractible finite polyhedron K. Suppose that f maps K into B and that g maps A into X so that $pg = f$. Then the necessary and sufficient condition that the triple X, B, p constitute a Serre fiber space is that there is an extension of g to a map G: $K \to X$ satisfying $pG = f$.*

We take up the necessity. We may assume A shrunk to a_0 by the contraction D; that is to say we identify the points of A. This turns K into a space $\check{K}$ and determines a map j: $K, A \to \check{K}$, a_0 with j a homeomorphism on $K - A$ onto $K - a_0$, for suitable n, K, as well as $\check{K}$ can be assumed a subset of I^n and both are countably compact. There is a retracting function on K to A. Thus by (5.2)

$$\begin{array}{l} K = \{u\} \to \check{K} \\ \downarrow \\ A \to K, a_0 \subset I_n, \tau_0 \end{array}$$

for some point $\tau_0 (\neq a_0)$ in I^n. Designate the points of K by $\{u\}$. Then define ψ by $u \xrightarrow{\psi} r(u), j(u)$. Note ψ maps A homeomorphically into $A \times I^n$ by $a \to a, \tau_0$. Since K is contractible also we invoke (46.3) again to assert K is a retract of $A \times K^n$ with retracting function r'. Hence f on K to B can be extended to F on $A \times I^n \to B$ defined by $F = fr'$. If $n = 1$ the assertion of the theorem with K replaced by $A \times I$ is simply the defining property of a Serre Fiber Space. Since $A \times I^n = (A \times I^{n-1}) \times I$ a trivial induction guarantees that there is a map $G: A \times I^n \to X$ extending g and satisfying $pG \doteq F$. The restriction of G to K yields the assertion of the theorem.

PROBLEM

14-4. Prove sufficiency.

For completeness it is worthwhile to indicate some generalizations of the fiber space notions.

Definition 5.4. A **singular fiber space over** B with **singular patch** A is a triple X, B, p with $p^{-1}(B - A)$, $B - A$, p a fiber space in some sense, as say a Serre or Hurewicz fiber space. Fibers, $\{p^{-1}(a) \mid A)\}$, are termed **singular fibers.** Two special cases enter, namely the case, **(a)**, in which the singular fibers each consists of a single point and that, **(b)**, in which each non-singular fiber consists of a single point. The compass of these two special cases is summed up in the following:

Lemma 5.5. *If A is closed in B and X, B, p is a singular fiber space with A a singular patch, then p is the composition*

$$X \xrightarrow{p_2} Y \xrightarrow{p_1} B, \qquad p = p_1 p_2$$

where X, Y, p_2 is a singular fiber space of type (5.4b) *and Y, B, p_1 is of type* (5.4a).

PROBLEM

14-5. Prove this lemma. *Hint:* Let Y be the identification space of X, A where each singular fiber $p^{-1}(a)$, is identified to a point.

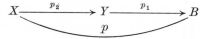

6. FUNDAMENTAL GROUP. Definition 6.1. A **path,** or **sensed path** in B starting at b_0 is the image of the segment $I_t = \{t \mid 0 \leq t \leq 1\}$ under a map ψ with $\psi(0) = b_0$. (This requires some arcwise connectivity condition on B, of course.) We often denote the path by the same symbol as that for the map, namely ψ. Let A_1 and A_2 be subsets of B. Then the space of paths B^{I_t} with $\psi(0) \in A_1$ and $\psi(1) \in A_2$ and topologized by the co-open topology is *denoted by* $\Omega(A_1, A_2)$. If $A_1 = b_0$ and $A_2 = B$, then the symbol $\Omega_{b_0}(B)$ or $\Omega(b_0)$ is frequently used. If $A_1 = A_2 = B$ then the symbol is simply $\Omega(B)$. The **loop space** with $A_1 = A_2 = b_0$ is *denoted by* Λ_{b_0}. Later we shall consider Ω and Λ as bundle spaces of a fiber bundle over B. A multiplication can be introduced in the path spaces and loop spaces. If ψ_1 is a path starting at $b_1 = \psi_0(1)$ then the path $\psi_0\,\psi_1 = \psi$ is obtained intuitively by a promenade at twice the normal rate from b_0 to $\psi(1)$ *first* along ψ_0 and *then* along ψ_1. Analytically

$$(6.1a)\qquad (\psi_0\,\psi_1)t = \psi_0(2t) \qquad 0 \le t \le \tfrac{1}{2},$$
$$= \psi_1(2t-1) \qquad \tfrac{1}{2} \le t \le 1.$$

The path ψ^{-1} is defined by $\psi^{-1}(t) = \psi(1-t)$. If $\psi(0) = b_0 = b_1 = \psi(1)$, the path is a **loop** at b_0. It may be verified that the multiplication defined in (6.1a) is continuous (considered as a map on $\Lambda_{b_0} \times \Lambda_{b_0} \to \Lambda_{b_0}$). However, neither Ω or Λ is a group under the multiplication defined in (6.1a) because this multiplication is not associative, i.e., $(\psi_0\,\psi_1)\psi_2 \neq \psi_0(\psi_1\,\psi_2)$ because the parametrizations are different.

We indicate that the loops l_1 and l_2 both at b_0 are **homotopic** by $l_1 \sim l_2$. If ψ and θ are paths joining b_0 and b_1 we say ψ is homotopic to θ, $\psi \sim \theta$ or $\psi \simeq \theta$, if the loop $\theta^{-1}\psi \sim b_0$ the trivial loop.

Lemma 6.2. *If $l_1 \sim l_1'$, $l_2 \sim l_2'$ with all loops at b_0, then $l_1 l_2 \sim l_1'\,l_2'$.*

For the homotopy class of the loop l_1, at b_0 write $\boldsymbol{l}_1$. If $l_3 \sim l_1\,l_2$ define $\boldsymbol{l}_1\boldsymbol{l}_2$ as $\boldsymbol{l}_3$ in keeping with (6.2). Then $(\boldsymbol{l}_1\,\boldsymbol{l}_2)\boldsymbol{l}_3 \sim \boldsymbol{l}_1(\boldsymbol{l}_2\,\boldsymbol{l}_3)$. Accordingly with $\boldsymbol{b}_0$ the neutral element, $\{\boldsymbol{l}\}$ constitutes a multiplicative group.

This is the **fundamental** or **Poincaré group** and is denoted by $\pi_1(B, b_0)$. It is generally nonAbelian. If B is not arcwise connected the fundamental group refers to the arcwise connected component containing b_0. We tacitly assume hereafter that B is this component unless the contrary is clear from the context.

Figure 14-8

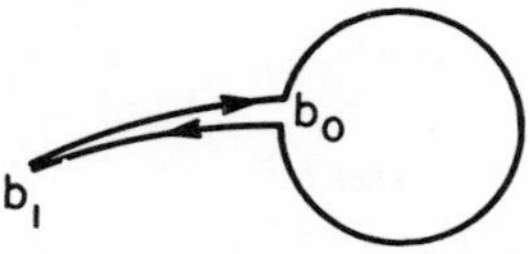

Definition 6.3. If b_0 and b_1 are distinct points in B, let C be an arbitrary (sensed) path from b_1 to b_0. Then, for every loop l based at b_0 there corresponds the loop $l' = C\,l\,C^{-1}$ based at b_1 and conversely. Moreover $l_1 \sim l_2$ implies and is implied by $l_1' \sim l_2'$, and $l_1'\,l_2' = C\,l_1\,C^{-1}\,C\,l_2\,C^{-1}$. Accordingly, then, there is an isomorphism determined by the choice of path C and indicated by

$$(6.3a)\qquad C_*\colon \pi_1(B, b_0) \approx \pi_1(B, b_1).$$

If now b_0 and b_1 coincide, then C becomes a loop and C_* becomes the inner automorphism

$$C\,\pi_1(B, b_0)C^{-1}. \tag{6.3b}$$

Remark. If X is a concrete simplicial complex, $|K|$, paths and loops may be restricted to those on the 1 skeleton K^1 because of the obvious local connectivities. Then $\pi_1(|K|, k_0)$ depends on K^2 alone.

There is obviously a relationship between $\pi_1(X, x_0)$ and $H_1(X, \text{J})$. As a matter of record, and as an indication of the subtler discrimination achieved by the homotopy group, we remark that with the notation $[G]$ for the commutator subgroup of G,

$$\pi_1(X, x_0)/[\pi_1(x, x_0)] \approx H_1(SX, \text{J}).$$

Thus ${}_SH_1(X, \text{J})$ is the result of imposing commutativity on $\pi_1(x, X_0)$ products.

We shall have use for some local connectivity concepts and for certain standard notation. It is assumed that connectivity is in an **arcwise** sense.

Definition 6.4. B is **simply connected** if $\pi_1(B, b_0) = 0$. If $A \subset B$, then A is **relatively simply connected** (with respect to B) if for every $a \in A$, every loop in A based at a is homotopic to a over B. B is **semisimply locally connected,** or **semilocally 1-connected** if each point associates a neighborhood of itself which is relatively simply connected with respect to B. Such spaces are referred to as *semi* $1 - LC$. An arcwise locally connected space is $0 - LC$ or simply LC. If B is LC and semi $1 - LC$, it is **semi** LC^1. If every neighborhood $U(b)$ associates a neighborhood $V(b)$ which is relatively simply connected with respect to $U(b)$, then B is **locally simply connected,** written $1 - LC$. Again B is LC^1 if it is both LC and $1 - LC$.

7. MONODROMY AND DECK TRANSFORMATION GROUPS.

In the next two sections we take up some of the minutiae of a particular but vastly important class of principal fiber bundles, namely the covering spaces.

Definition 7.1. In the mapping triple X, B, p with $pX = B$, a subset B_0 is **evenly** covered if each component of $p^{-1}\,B_0$ is mapped homeomorphically onto B_0 by p.

We say that X, p, or sometimes X, is a **covering space** of B if B is connected and locally connected and each point in B has a neighborhood which is evenly covered. The connectivity demanded need not be arcwise connectivity. However, except in (7.2), we shall understand all connectivity assertions to refer to arcwise connectivity. The next lemma might have been made a part of the definition.

Lemma 7.2. *In a covering space, B also is connected and locally connected.*

PROBLEMS

14-6. In a mapping triple show that if $B_1 \subset B_0$ where B_0 is evenly covered, then if B_1 is connected it is evenly covered.

14-7. If B_0 and B_1 are open, connected subsets of B with $B_0 \cap B_1$ nonempty and connected, then $B_0 \cup B_1$ is evenly covered.

Definition 7.3. Let l be a loop at b_0 and let $\tilde{l}(x_0; t)$ denote the covering path starting at x_0. Then $\tilde{l}(x_0, t)$ covers $l(b_0, t)$. Write $x_0 l$ for $\tilde{l}(x_0; 1)$ and simply $\tilde{l}$ when $\tilde{l}$ is a loop.

Lemma 7.4. *If* $l_1 \sim l_2$ *then* $x_0 l_1 = x_0 l_2$ *for* $x_0 \in p^{-1}(b_0)$.

Let h be the homotopy on $B \times I$ to B taking l_1 to l_2. Then b_0 is stationary. Accordingly the lifted homotopy taking $\tilde{l}_1(x_0, t)$ to $\tilde{l}_2(x_0, t)$ has the points covering b_0, stationary and so $\tilde{l}_1(x_0, 1) = \tilde{l}_2(x_0, 1)$ (3.2). Hence we may write $x_0 \boldsymbol{l}$ from now on.

Theorem 7.5. *The map p induces a monomorphism*

$$p_*\colon \pi_1(X, x_0) \to \pi_1(B, b_0).$$

The representative loop $\tilde{l}$ of $\tilde{\boldsymbol{l}} \in \pi_1(X, x_0)$ takes x_0 into x_0 and corresponds to $l = p\tilde{l}$. If $\tilde{h}$ is a homotopy between $\tilde{l}_1$ and $\tilde{l}_2$, $h = p\tilde{h}$ is a homotopy between $l_1 = p\tilde{l}_1$ and $l_2 = p\tilde{l}_2$. Accordingly the correspondence

$$\tilde{\boldsymbol{l}} \xrightarrow{p_*} \boldsymbol{l}$$

is defined by $\tilde{l} \to p\tilde{l} = l$. Note $p\tilde{l}_2 \tilde{l}_1 = p\tilde{l}_2 \, p\tilde{l}_1$. Hence p_* defines a homomorphism. If $l(t) \equiv b_0$, then $\tilde{e} = \tilde{l}(t) \equiv x_0$ is the covering loop at x_0. Accordingly the kernel of p_* consists of $\tilde{\boldsymbol{e}}$ alone. Therefore p_* is an injection.

Write

$$H(x_0) = p_* \pi_1(X, x_0). \tag{7.5a}$$

As in (6.3a) $\pi_1(X, x_1) = \tilde{C}_* \pi_1(X, x_0)$, where $\tilde{C}$ joins x_0 and x_1 and may be replaced by $\tilde{C}_1 \simeq \tilde{C}$. Thus $p\tilde{C} = l$ is a loop at b_0 if $b_0 = px_0 = px_1$. In short

$$\boldsymbol{l}^{-1} H(x_0) \boldsymbol{l} \approx H(x_1) = p_* \pi_1(X, x_1). \tag{7.5b}$$

Define H by

(7.5c) $$H = \bigcap H(x)$$

for $x \in p^{-1}(b_0)$. Clearly $x\boldsymbol{l} = x$ for each $x \in p^{-1}(b_0)$ only if $\boldsymbol{l} \in H$.

Lemma 7.6. *H is a normal subgroup of $\pi_1(B, b_0)$.*

Let l be chosen arbitrarily and suppose

$$\boldsymbol{l}_1 \in \boldsymbol{l}^{-1}H\boldsymbol{l}.$$

Then for each $x \in p^{-1}b_0$, with $y = x\boldsymbol{l}^{-1}$, and with l_1 and h representatives,

$$\begin{aligned} x(l_1) &= (x\boldsymbol{l}^{-1}h\boldsymbol{l}) \\ &= yh\boldsymbol{l} = y\boldsymbol{l} = x. \end{aligned}$$

Accordingly $\boldsymbol{l}_1 \in H$ and so $H = \boldsymbol{l}^{-1} H\boldsymbol{l}$.

Definition 7.7. $M(X, B, b_0) = \pi_1(B, b_0)/H$ is the **monodromy group.** Denote by χ the natural homomorphism

$$\pi_1(B, b_0) \xrightarrow{\chi} M(X, B, b_0) = M.$$

Theorem 7.8. *If X is a covering space then $\boldsymbol{Q} = (X, B, F, G = M, p)$ is a fiber bundle.*

Let F be identified with F_{b_0} where b_0 is arbitrary but fixed. There may be several homeomorphisms $h(b_1)$: F_{b_0} on F_{b_1}. Some selection principle must be followed that will yield continuity in b of the homeomorphism $h(b)$. Our procedure founds the choice ultimately on the uniqueness of the lifted covering paths. Specifically choose $b_i \in U_i$ and paths λ_i from b_0 to b_i arbitrarily after which they are considered fixed. For each $b \in U_i$ choose a path $\rho_i(b)$ in U_i from b_i to b. The points of F_{b_0} may be denoted by y in place of x with $px = b_0$. As before let $y\lambda_i$ be the end point over pb_i of the lifted path starting with y. Then

(7.8a) $$h_i(b)\colon y \to y\lambda_i\rho_i(b)$$

defines a homeomorphism of F_{b_0} onto F_b. Then for $V(y\lambda_i)$ connected and in $p^{-1}U_i$

$$p^{-1}(b) \cap V(y\lambda_i)$$

is a unique point whence if $\rho_i'(b)$ were another path in U_i, the end point $y\lambda_i\rho_i'(b)$ would again be $y\lambda_i\rho_i(b)$. Define yl or $y(l)$ by

(7.8b) $$\begin{aligned} g_{ij}(b) \cdot y &= h_i^{-1}(b)h_j(b)y \\ &= y(\lambda_j\rho_j(b)\rho_i^{-1}(b)\lambda_i^{-1} = l) \end{aligned}$$

where l is a loop at b_0 so $l \in \pi_1(B, b_0)$. Since $\boldsymbol{l} \in H$ implies $y\boldsymbol{l} = y$, $g_{ij}(b) \cdot y = y\chi(\boldsymbol{l})$.

For each $\bar{b} \in U_i \cap U_j$ choose a locally arcwise connected neighborhood $W(\bar{b})$ in $U_i \cap U_j$. Let μ be a path in $W(\bar{b})$ from $\bar{b}$ to b. Then $\rho_i(\bar{b})$ is to be replaced by $\mu\rho_i(\bar{b})$ and $\rho_j(\bar{b})$ by $\mu\rho_i(\bar{b})$. Evidently l as defined above (but with $\bar{b}$ replacing b) is unaffected since $\rho_j(\bar{b})\mu\mu^{-1}\rho_i^{-1}(b) \sim \rho_j(\bar{b})\rho_i^{-1}(\bar{b})$. Thus $g_{ij}(b \mid W(\bar{b})) = g_{ij}(\bar{b})$. Since G is discrete, a neighborhood of g is g itself, so $g_{ij}(b)$ has been demonstrated continuous.

Besides the monodromy group there is another natural group connected with a covering space.

Definition 7.9. The **translation** or **deck transformation group** D of a covering space is a group of right translations or homeomorphisms defined by $x \to x\boldsymbol{l}$ ((2.1) and (2.4)). The distinction between the monodromy group and the deck transformation group is that the first acts on *a* single fiber while the second is global, (2.1). Hence it is to be expected that the first may be a larger group than the second.

Definition 7.10. The covering space is **regular** if $H(x_0) = H(x)$ whenever $p(x_0) = p(x)$. It is m-**leaved**, m-**sheeted** or is an m-**fold covering** if $p^{-1}(b)$ has m points for every b.

Lemma 7.11. *If* $\boldsymbol{P}$ *is a principal fiber bundle where* B *is arcwise connected and locally arcwise connected and* G *is totally disconnected and in particular may be a discrete group* g *then*

(7.11a) If $x_0\boldsymbol{l} = x_0$ *then* $x_1\boldsymbol{l} = x_1$ for $px_1 = px_0$

(7.11b) X *is a regular covering space of* B.

We assert

$$(gx_0)\boldsymbol{l} = g(x_0\boldsymbol{l})$$

or

$$\tilde{l}(gx_0, 1) = g\tilde{l}(x_0, 1).$$

Indeed, suppose

(7.11c) $$\tilde{l}(x_0, t_0) = x_1; \qquad \tilde{l}(gx_0, t_0) = gx_1, g \neq e.$$

No generality is lost by assuming the neighborhoods $\{U_i\}$ chosen in B are arcwise connected. Since G is discrete $U_i \times g$ is an open component of a neighborhood in $U_i \times G$. Then for g running through G, $\{V_i(g) = gs_i(bU)\}$ constitute disjunct arcwise connected homeomorphs of U_i.

Let $l(b_0)$ be a path in B starting with b_0 and suppose $\tilde{l}(x_0, t)$ is a lifted path. Let $(\bar{x}, \bar{t}) = \tilde{l}(x_0, t)$. Then $\bar{x}, \bar{t} \in V_i(g_1)$ for some g_1, and $(g\bar{x}, \bar{t}) \in V_i(gg_1) = gV_i(g_1)$. Then for some positive δ

(7.11d) $$\tilde{l}(gx_0, t) = g\tilde{l}(x_0, t) \in gV_i(g_1) \quad \text{for} \quad |t - \bar{t}| < \delta.$$

Let $\tau = \sup \{t \mid \tilde{l}(gx_0, t) = g\tilde{l}(x_0, t)\}$. Since (7.11d) is valid for $t_0 = 0, \tau > 0$. However, if $\tau \neq 1$, then, by continuity, $(\tilde{l}(gx_0, \tau) = g\tilde{l}(x_0, \tau)$. This contradicts the existence of a two sided interval of validity asserted in (7.11d).

To show (7.11b), let $x_1 = gx_0$. Then according to (7.11a) if $\tilde{l}(x_0)$ is a loop,

$$\tilde{l}(x_1) = g\tilde{l}(x_0) = gx_0 = x_1.$$

Definition 7.12. If G_1 is a subgroup of the group G, then the **normalizer** of G_1, denoted by $N(G_1)$, is

$$N(G_1) = \{g \mid g^{-1} G_1 g = G_1\}.$$

We make immediate use of this concept.

Lemma 7.13. *The deck transformation group, D, is isomorphic to* $N(H(x_0))/H(x_0)$.

If the covering space is *regular*,

$$N(H(x_0)) = \pi_1(B, b_0), \quad (7.8)\ (7.12).$$

As representatives of D, l_1 and l_2 take x_0 into $x_0\, l_1\, l_2$. This is the translation corresponding to $(l_2\, l_1)$. Thus $\boldsymbol{l_2\, l_1}$ represents the element of M which corresponds to the element represented by $\boldsymbol{l_1\, l_2}$ in D, an anti-isomorphism. Considering the covering space as a principal bundle (7.11) the correspondence of M and D is that of left and right multiplication. If the covering space is *not regular* let $x_0 l = x_i$ for some $i \neq 0$. If $\boldsymbol{l} \in NH(x_0)$, a loop at x_0 is taken into a loop at x_i where $x_i = x_0$ only if $\boldsymbol{l} \in H(x_0)$. If $\boldsymbol{l} \bar{\in} N(H(x_0))$ then some loop at x_0 is taken by $\boldsymbol{l}$ into a nonloop starting at x_i. Accordingly in the latter case no element of D can take x_0 into x_i.

PROBLEM

14-8. Finish up the proof.

Lemma 7.14 Suppose B is an n dimensional complex, Let X, p be an m leaved covering space. Then

(7.14a) $$\chi(X) = m\, \chi(B),$$

Recall

$$\chi(X) = \Sigma_0^n (-1)^i \alpha_i$$

where α_i is the number of i dimensional faces. Since there are m leaves, each α_i become $m\alpha_i$ for X.

Remark. Similarly for a fiber space over the polyhedron B, $\chi(X) = \chi(F)\chi(B)$.

EXAMPLE 14-8. Suppose $X = S^n$ is a covering space for some B. If n is even $\chi(S^n) = 2$ which together with (7.14a) implies $\chi(B)$ is either 1 or 2 and that m is then either 2 or 1. The 1 sheeted cover is, of course, simply the cover of S^n by itself, and is of no interest. Hence $\pi_1(B, b_0)$ has at most one generator of order 2. It is immediate that S^n is a 2 sheeted universal covering space for the n dimensional projective space P^n and hence P^n is the unique space admitting a nontrivial cover by S^n when n is even.

Theorem 7.15. *B is an arcwise connected, semi LC^1 space. Let $\{H_i\}$ be all the conjugates of some fixed subgroup H_1 of $\pi_1(B, b_0)$, i.e., $H_i = \mathbf{l}^{-1}H_1\mathbf{l}$ for some $\mathbf{l}$. Then there is a covering fiber bundle with fiber F homeomorphic to $\pi_1(B, b_0)/H_1$ and group $G = \pi_1(B, b_0)/H$ where $H = \bigcap H_i$. Let χ be the natural homomorphism $\chi\colon\ \pi_1(B, b_0) \rightarrow G$. Moreover G is the monodromy group and $H_i = p_*\pi_1(X, x_i)$ for $x_i = F_{b_0}$;* Cf. (7.5a).

Let $\mu = \{U_i\}$ be an open cover of B by arcwise connected relatively arcwise simply connected sets. The procedure is analogous to that in (7.8). Thus fix b_0 in B and a b_i in each U_i. Fix also the paths λ_i joining b_0 and b_i and the paths $\rho_i(b)$ in U_i (b_i) connecting b_i and b.

$$g_{ij}(b) = \chi(\lambda_i\rho_i(b)\rho_j^{-1}(b)\lambda_j^{-1}) = \chi(l), \quad b \in U_i \cap U_j. \tag{7.15a}$$

If $\rho_i(b)$ were replaced by $\rho_i'(b)$ then by the $1 - LC$ property, $\rho_i'(b)\rho_i^{-1}(b) \sim 0$, or $\rho_i'(b) \sim \rho_i(b)$ so l in (7.15a) is unaffected. In particular, if $\rho'(b) = \rho_i(\bar{b})\mu(\bar{b}, b)$ where $\mu(\bar{b}, b)$ is a path in $U_j \cap U_i$ from $\bar{b}$ to b, then l is unaffected, and so $g_{ij}(b) = g_{ij}(\bar{b})$. This is valid for all points $\bar{b}$ in the component of $U_j \cap U_i$ containing b, i.e., in an open set since the LC property ensures components of open sets are open. Consequently $g_{ij}(b)$ is continuous.

The matching relations (2.1c) are a matter of mechanical combination of paths. Accordingly, a fiber bundle is determined by choosing the left cosets of $\pi_1(B, b_0)$ by H_1, as fiber and applying the procedure of (2.5).

Denote by $y_m = [\mathbf{l}_m]_1$ and $g = [\mathbf{l}]$ the left coset class of $\pi_1(B, b_0)/H_1$ and the element of the quotient group $\pi_1(B, b_0)/H$ respectively. Then the prescription

$$\begin{aligned} gy_m &= [\mathbf{l}]\,[\mathbf{l}_m]_1 \\ &= [\mathbf{l}\,\mathbf{l}_m]_1 \end{aligned} \tag{7.15b}$$

is a consistent description of the action of G on the fiber, since evidently the particular representatives chosen for $[\mathbf{l}]$ or $[\mathbf{l}_n]_1$ are unimportant.

Consider the loop l. Let $\{U_j \mid j \in \mathrm{J}\}$ be a finite open cover of l by open sets in μ. Reorder the j's so that as the parameter t for l increases, i increases also. (In general any U will then have several different i's attached to it if the loop does any doubling back). Then l can be broken up into a succession of paths $\nu_i(c_i, d_i) \subset U_i$, $w_{i+1}(d_i, c_{i+1}) \subset U_{i+1}$, where $c_i \in U_i$ and $d_i \in U_i \cap U_{i+1}$. By introducing paths connecting c_i and b_i and using the semi LC^1 property, the paths ν_i, w_{i+1} may be replaced by $\rho_i(d_i)$ and l by $l' \sim l$ where

(7.15c)
$$\begin{aligned} l' &= \Pi l_{i\,i+1} \\ &= \Pi(\lambda_i \rho_i(d_i)\rho_{i+1}^{-1}(d_i)\lambda_{i+1}^{-1}). \end{aligned}$$

It must be shown that the change in x_1, say, on passing around l, namely $x_1\boldsymbol{l}$ is, as we expect, given by $\chi(\boldsymbol{l})x_1$. Indeed $\chi(\boldsymbol{l})$ is the product of terms $\chi(\boldsymbol{l}_{i\;i+1})$, that is to say, using (7.15a)

(7.15d)
$$\chi(\boldsymbol{l}) = g_{01}(d_1) \cdots g_{n-1\;0}\,(d_n).$$

Refer now to (7.8a) and (7.8b). With $x_i \in F_{b_i}$

(7.15e)
$$\begin{aligned} x_i\rho_i(d_i)\rho_{i+1}^{-1}(d_i) &= y\lambda_i\rho_i(d_i)\rho_{i+1}^{-1}(d_i)\lambda_{i+1}^{-1}\lambda_{i+1} \\ &= (g_{i+1i}(d_i)y)\lambda_{i+1} \\ &= x_{i+1} \in F_{b_{i+1}}. \end{aligned}$$

Then piecing together the contributions of $l_{i\;i+1}$ there arises from (7.15d) and (7.15e)

$$x_1\boldsymbol{l} = \chi(\boldsymbol{l})x_i.$$

Definition 7.16. If $\pi_1(X, x_0) = 0$ the covering space is regular and is called the **universal covering space**. Alternatively the universal covering space is one which admits itself as the only covering space.

PROBLEM

14-8. Show the universal covering space has a topology equivalent to the compact-open topology.

Remark. In recapitulation of (7.13) the universal covering space, for instance, may be thought of as one whose points are the pairs $(\boldsymbol{C}, b)$ where $\boldsymbol{C}$ is a homotopy class of paths from b_0 to b and b is the terminal point. Let $\boldsymbol{C}_1$ be a representative path of $\boldsymbol{C}$, then a neighborhood of $(\boldsymbol{C}_1, b_1)$ is the collection of all homotopy classes $(\boldsymbol{C}, b)$ whose representative paths are homotopic to $\boldsymbol{C}_1\rho(b)$ where $\rho(b)$ is a path in $U(b_1)$ from b_1 to b.

Example 14-9. Let $B = S^1$. Then $X = R$ is the universal covering space. It is noncompact and is regular since $\pi_1(S^1, b_0)$ is infinite cyclic. S^1 is its own m fold covering space under the projection $z \xrightarrow{p} z^m$ since any cyclic group of order m is a subgroup of $\pi_1(S^1, b)$.

8. ILLUSTRATIONS. We assemble some immediate consequences of the results above. Denote the elements of the monodromy group M by q and those of the deck transformations by d.

Lemma 8.1. *Suppose the covering space (X, p) has m leaves. If it is regular, then,* **(a)** *the order or number of elements of M is m,* **(b)**. *If (X, p) is nonregular, then δ the order of M is greater than m,* **(c)** *the order of D is less than m.*

Let Y_b be the fiber over b.
For (**a**): The definition of H guarantees distinct elements of M map x_0 into distinct points of Y_b. Any point of Y_b can be joined to x_0 by a path whose projection is a loop in B and hence yields an element of $\pi_1(B, x_0)$ and so of $N(H(x_0))$. Therefore this element represents a coset in D and so also in M, (7.15). In short, M and Y_b are in $1 - 1$ correspondence.
For (**b**): If X is nonregular, some $\boldsymbol{l} \in H(x_0)$ yet $\boldsymbol{l} \bar{\in} H$. Hence the coset of $\boldsymbol{l}$ in M occurs besides those cited in (8.1a).
For (**c**): If X is nonregular, suppose $x_1 \boldsymbol{l} = x_1$ and $x_2 \boldsymbol{l} = x_3$. Suppose L represents an element of D taking x_1 to x_2. Then $l \in H(x_1)$, $L \in N(H(x_1))$ so $x_2 = x_1 \boldsymbol{lL} = x_1 \boldsymbol{Ll} = x_2 \boldsymbol{l} = x_3$, a contradiction. Hence D cannot take x_1 to x_2.

Example 14-10. An example where $H(x_0)$, $H(x_1)$, and $H(x_1)$ are not the same and where in consequence the covering space is *not regular* is that of the pretzel or double anchor ring. This covering space may be constructed in principle by taking 3 copies of B one inside the other, and cutting through the two sheaves at l_1 and l_2 respectively. The lips are then reconnected so that in passing around l_1, the sheet branching follows the scheme in Fig. 14-9b, so that one passes from layer 1 to layer 2 and conversely but one skates round and round on layer 3. At l_2 the lips are welded according to Fig. 14-9c. The minor difficulty that in 3 dimensions the various skin layers must intersect is met by plunging the pretzel (and perhaps the welder) in a 4-dimensional Euclidean space. The cover so obtained is not regular. This follows from the fact that, $x_1 \boldsymbol{l}_1 = x_2$, $x_2 \boldsymbol{l}_1 = x_3$, and $x_3 \boldsymbol{l}_1 = x_3$. Accordingly $\boldsymbol{l}_1 \in H(x_3)$ but $\boldsymbol{l}_1 \bar{\in} H(x_2) \cup H(x_3)$.

Assume $\pi_1(B, b_0)$ has a finite number of generators $\boldsymbol{l}_1, \ldots, \boldsymbol{l}_k$. Suppose too that X is a covering space with m leaves. Thus write $\{x_i \mid i = 0, \ldots, m\} = p^{-1}(b_0)$. Suppose $x_i \boldsymbol{l}_j = x_{q=q(i,j)}$, $i = 1, \ldots, m$, $j = 1, \ldots, h$. Hence for j fixed, $\boldsymbol{l}_j$ induces the permutation on $p^{-1}(b_0)$ indicated by the script correspondence

$$\boldsymbol{l}_j \leftrightarrow \begin{pmatrix} 1 & \cdot\cdot & m \\ (q(1,j) & \cdot\cdot & q(m,j)) \end{pmatrix}$$

Then the product $\boldsymbol{l}_i \boldsymbol{l}_j$ is indicated by the permutation associated with $\boldsymbol{l}_j$ followed by that associated with $\boldsymbol{l}_1$. This yields the representation of $\pi_1(B, b_0)$ as a permutation group on $p^{-1}(b_0)$.

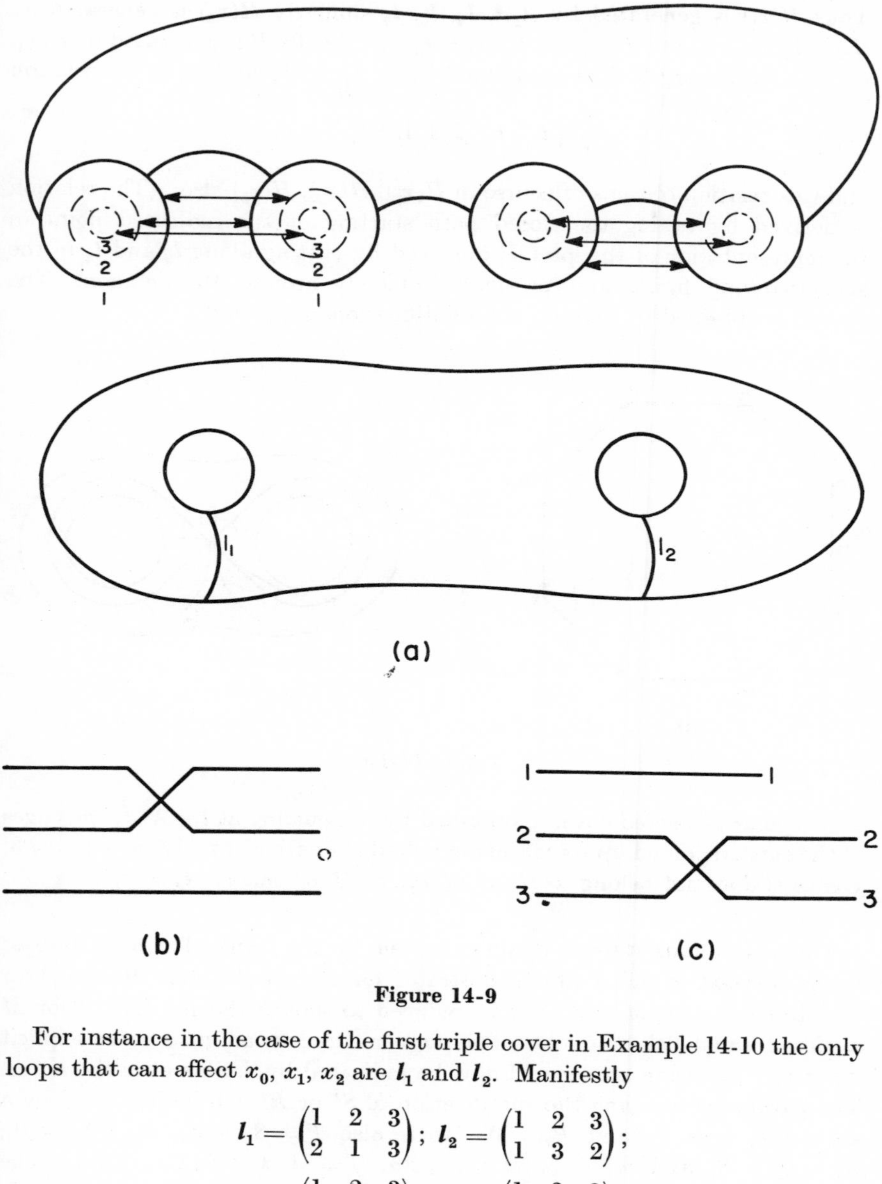

Figure 14-9

For instance in the case of the first triple cover in Example 14-10 the only loops that can affect x_0, x_1, x_2 are $\boldsymbol{l}_1$ and $\boldsymbol{l}_2$. Manifestly

$$\boldsymbol{l}_1 = \begin{pmatrix} 1 & 2 & 3 \\ 2 & 1 & 3 \end{pmatrix}; \ \boldsymbol{l}_2 = \begin{pmatrix} 1 & 2 & 3 \\ 1 & 3 & 2 \end{pmatrix};$$

$$\boldsymbol{l}_3 = \begin{pmatrix} 1 & 2 & 3 \\ 1 & 2 & 3 \end{pmatrix}; \ \boldsymbol{l}_4 = \begin{pmatrix} 1 & 2 & 3 \\ 1 & 2 & 3 \end{pmatrix};$$

$$(\boldsymbol{l}_2)^2 = (\boldsymbol{l}_1)^2 = \begin{pmatrix} 1 & 2 & 3 \\ 1 & 2 & 3 \end{pmatrix}.$$

Thus $H(x_1)$ is generated by $(l_1)^2$, l_2, l_3, l_4 similarly $H(x_2)$ is generated by $(l_1)^2$, $(l_2)^2$, l_3, l_4 and $H(x_3)$ by l_1, $(l_2)^2$, l_3, l_4. Finally H is generated by l_3, l_4, l_1^2, l_2^2. Observe $\pi_1(B, b_0)$ is generated by l_3, l_4, l_1, l_2 subject to the relation

$$l_2\, l_4\, l_2^{-1}\, l_4^{-1}\, l_1\, l_3\, l_1^{-1}\, l_3^{-1} = \mathrm{e},$$

and this relation obtains of course in $H(x_1)$, $H(x_2)$, $H(x_3)$ also. (The relation is derived by taking the closed path starting at the indicated point in the representation of the pretzel obtained by cutting along l_3 and l_4 in the accompanying figure and passing completely around the octagon. The pretzel is obtained by making the identifications suggested.)

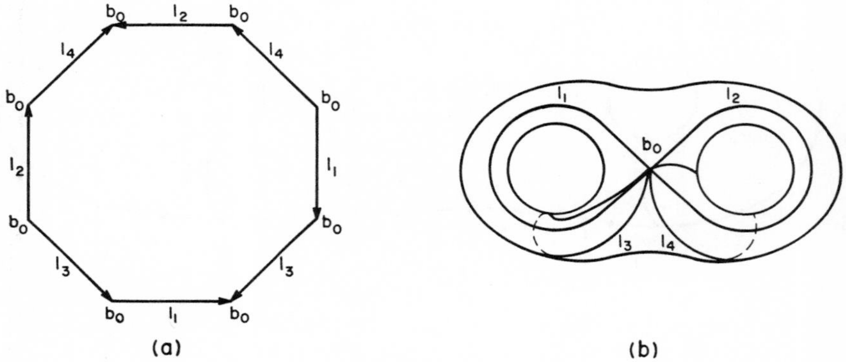

Figure 14-10

A regular 3-sheeted cover is obtained by not cutting at l_1. At l_4 the edges of the cuts are joined up by matching left edge i with right edge $i + 1 \; mod \; 3$. Hence l_4 does not belong to $H(x_1)$, $H(x_2)$, or $H(x_3)$ since $x_i\, l_4 \neq x_1$.

The next lemma states a duality theorem for the torus. Its main interest is the method of proof which illustrates for the special case $M = S^1$ how certain results for $M \times S^1$ can be reduced to those valid for $M \times I$ for M a closed simplicial manifold. For convenience we adopt a more explicit notation. Covering spaces will now be indicated by a tilde over the letter. The parameter entering the specification of S^1 or R^1 will be indicated by a subscript, thus S_x and R_t. We write also $T = S_x \times S_t$, $S_1 = S_x \times 0_t$, $S_2 = 0_x \times S_t$ and $mI = \{y \mid 0 \leq t \leq 2\pi,\ y = kt,\ k = 0, 1, \ldots, m\}$. The coefficient group for the cycles is J.

Lemma 8.2. *Suppose that A is a closed subcomplex of the triangulated torus T, then* **(a)** *if A carries no nonbounding cycle of T homologous to $aS_1 + bS_2$,*

$b \neq 0$, the complement of A carries a cycle $\sim S_1$; **(b)** *if A does not carry a non-bounding cycle of T, the complement of A carries cycles homologous respectively to the fundamental cycles S_1 and S_2 on T.*

Let N be the number of vertices of T. Choose $m > N$. The cylinder $S_x \times R_t = \tilde{T}$ is a covering space for T and contains the finite cylinder $Q = S_x \times mI_t$. Let p project $\tilde{T}$ onto T by $p(x, y) = (x, t = y (mod\ 2\pi))$. Let $\tilde{A} = p^{-1} A \cap Q$. Evidently $\tilde{A}$ has no component containing both (x, y) and $(x, y + 2\pi j)$, $j \neq 0$ an integer, for this component would carry an arc, $\tilde{C}$, with $p\tilde{C} \sim aS_1 + jS_2$ for some integer a. On the other hand, if there were a component $\tilde{L}$ of $\tilde{A}$ joining $y = 0$ and $y = 2\pi m$, since the number of vertices on $\tilde{L}$ is at least m, there would needs be at least two distinct representatives of some vertex of A. Thus $\tilde{L}$ would contain a pair (x, y) and $(x, y + 2\pi j)$, $j \neq 0$. Accordingly there is no continuum in $\tilde{A}$ joining $y = 0$ and $y = 2\pi m$. Therefore by (97.1) there is a separating (polygonal) arc $\tilde{K} \sim S_1$ on Q. Thus $K = p\tilde{K}$, considered on T is disjoint from the original A. This establishes (8.2a). For (8.2b) we need merely consider $mI_x \times S_t$ also, besides Q.

PROBLEMS

14-10. Let ψ be a real valued doubly periodic continuous function on the plane $R_x \times R_t$ with period 2π in each of x and t. Show, using (8.2), that for any positive real number α there is a parallelogram with base parallel to the x axis and of length π and of height α on the four vertices of which ψ assumes the same value.

14-11. Let S^2 be the metric sphere of radius 1 with map ψ to R^1. Let α be an arbitrary real number between 0 and π. Show ψ takes on the same value on four points x_1, x_2 and y_1, y_2 such that either (a) x_1, x_2 are the extremities of a diameter D, y_2 is the reflection of y_1 in D and the distance (on the sphere) from y_1 to x_1 is α or, for some diameter D, x_2 and y_2 are the reflections in D of x_1 and y_1 respectively and the distance between the latitude circles, orthogonal to D, through x_1, x_2 and y_1, y_2 respectively is (b) α or (c) $\pi - \alpha$.

9. FIXED POINT CLASSES. We shall restrict ourselves to the semi LC^1 spaces (6.4) which admit a special family of paths with unique representative for point pairs in some vicinity ν of the diagonal of $X \times X$. Our spaces will be assumed completely regular. As ν is a vicinity of the diagonal it defines a neighborhood at each point of x by $\nu(x) = \{x' \mid (x, x') \in \nu\}$. For a vicinity ε there is to exist a vicinity δ such that if $x \times y \in \mu$ and $x' \times y' \in \delta(x) \times \delta(y)$ then $x'(s) \times y'(s) \in \varepsilon x(s) \times \varepsilon y(s)$ where $x(s) \times y(s)$ is the point of parameter s on the unique preferred path joining x and y. This is referred to as the **path continuity** condition.

We can suppose that the smooth spaces (and their retracts) have these properties added to their definitions. We restrict our statements, however, to absolute neighborhood retracts which conform to our specifications without further assumption as will appear directly.

Lemma 9.1. *Suppose B is an ANR. Then there is a path family, Ω, which for each finite open cover of B, $\alpha = \{a_j\}$ admits a finite refinement $\mu = \{u_i\}$ such that each pair of points in u_i is joined by a unique path of Ω in a_j and the path continuity condition is satisfied.*

Let B be the retract of the open set G in the Tychonoff paralleotope **P**. The proof is carried out by taking a finite cover of B consisting of retracts of convex neighborhoods in G. The preferred paths are then retracts of straight line paths in G.

Corollary 9.2. *Let α and μ be as in* (9.1). *Let θ_1 and θ_2 be self maps of B. If for each b, $\theta_1(b)$ and $\theta_2(b)$ are in the same u_i of μ, then θ_1 is homotopic to θ_2 with homotopy function $\theta\colon B \times I \to B$ and for each b, $\theta(b, t)$ is in some $a_j \in \alpha$ for all t.*

For each b let $\omega(\theta_1(b), \theta_2(b); s)$ be the unique path whose existence is established in (9.1). Define $\theta(b, s)$ as the point of parameter s on this path. The path continuity condition ensures the continuity of θ.

Definition 9.3. Let X be the universal covering space for B. Let p be the projection of X to B, and let $C(b)$ be a path from the base point b_0 to b in B. The generic point in X is the pair $\lceil C, b\rceil$ where $\lceil C, b\rceil$ is the homotopy or path class, assuming b_0 and b are held fast during the homotopy. Then $p(x = \lceil C, b\rceil) = b$.

Let t map $B \to B$. Denote an element of $\pi_1(B, b_0)$ by $\boldsymbol{l}$ or $[l]$ where l is a loop based on b_0 in B. Let D be a path from b_0 to $t(b_0)$. For every path class $\lceil D\rceil \equiv \lceil D, t(b_0)\rceil$ we introduce a self map of X by $\tau_D\lceil C, b\rceil = \lceil Dt(C), t(b)\rceil$, where $Dt(C)$ is a product of the paths D and $t(C)$. We define H_D on $\pi_1(B, b_0)$ to $\pi_1(B, b_0)$ by

$$\text{(9.3a)} \qquad \mathrm{H}_D(\boldsymbol{l}) = \mathrm{H}_D[l] = [Dt(l)D^{-1}].$$

We collect some obvious relations.

Theorem 9.4

(a) $\tau_D(\boldsymbol{l})\, x = \mathrm{H}_D(\boldsymbol{l})\, \tau_D x$ (equivariance).

(b) *If $D' = \gamma D$, then $\mathrm{H}_{D'}(\boldsymbol{l}) = [\gamma]\mathrm{H}_D(\boldsymbol{l})[\gamma]^{-1}$ and is written $t_\gamma \mathrm{H}_D(\boldsymbol{l})$.*

(c) *H_D is a homomorphism of $\pi_1(B, b_0)$ to $\pi_1(B, b_0)$*

and is an automorphism if t is a homeomorphism or is homotopic to one.

Thus

$$\begin{aligned}\tau_D(\boldsymbol{l})x &= \tau_D[lC, b] \\ &= [Dt(l)t(C), t(b)] \\ &= [Dt(l)D^{-1}Dt(C), tb] \\ &= \text{H}_D(\boldsymbol{l})\tau_D x.\end{aligned}$$

Assertion (9.4b) follows immediately from $\lceil \gamma D \rceil^{-1} = D^{-1}[\gamma]^{-1}$ since $\text{H}_D(\boldsymbol{l}) = [\gamma D t(l)(\gamma D)^{-1}]$.

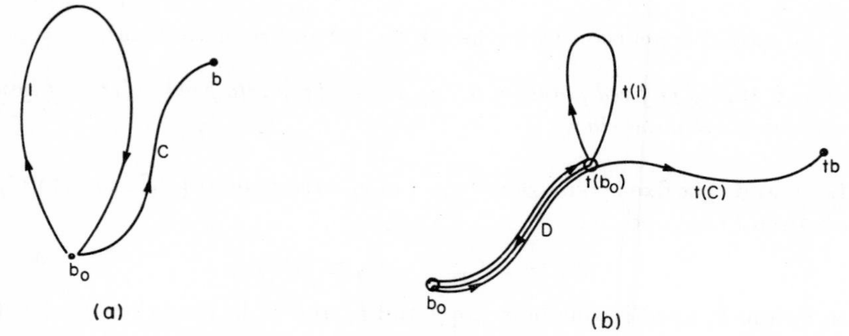

Figure 14-11

For (9.4c): $\text{H}_D[lm] = \text{H}_D(l)\text{H}_D(m)$ is immediate. If t is a homeomorphism, any $\boldsymbol{l}'$ is the H_D image of $[l = t^{-1}\, D^{-1}\, l'\, D]$. If $\boldsymbol{l} \in \ker \text{H}_D$, then $Dt(l)D^{-1} \simeq b_0$ so $t(l) \simeq D^{-1}\, b_0\, D \simeq tb_0$ whence, since t is a homeomorphism, $l \simeq b_0$.

Definition 9.5. For a fixed homeomorphism t the collection $\{\text{H}_D(\boldsymbol{l}) \mid D \text{ variable}\}$ is the **automorphism family** of $\boldsymbol{l}$.

Definition 9.6. Let b_1 and b_2 be in F (the fixed point set of t). They are **equivalent** if for a C in $\Omega(b_1, b_2)$, $tC \simeq C$, b_i held fast. The collection of equivalent fixed points constitutes a **fixed point class** F_i. If $b_1 \in F$, then each arbitrary choice of $C \in \Omega(b_0, b_1)$ and $D \in \Omega(b_0, tb_0)$ defines $\boldsymbol{\alpha} \in \pi_1(B, b_0)$ according to

(9.6a) $$\boldsymbol{\alpha} = [Dt(C)C^{-1}]$$

and $\boldsymbol{\alpha}$ and the fixed point b_1 are **associated.**

Lemma 9.7. *If* $\lceil C \rceil$ *is replaced by* $\boldsymbol{\gamma}\lceil C \rceil$, $\boldsymbol{\gamma} \in \pi(B, b_0)$, *then the associated homotopy class to* b_1 is $\boldsymbol{\beta} = \text{H}_D(\boldsymbol{\gamma})\boldsymbol{\alpha}\boldsymbol{\gamma}^{-1}$.

PROBLEM

14-12. Prove (9.7).

Definition 9.8. For fixed $\boldsymbol{\alpha}$ the elements $\{\boldsymbol{\beta}\}$ in (9.7) as $\boldsymbol{\gamma}$ runs through $\pi_1(B, b_0)$ are **conjugate** with respect to H_D. Hence there is a partition of $\pi_1(B, b_0)$ into disjunct (conjugate) H_D classes designated by H_i.

Lemma 9.9. *Suppose $\bar{x}$ stands for $\lceil C \rceil$ where $p\bar{x} = \bar{b}$ is a fixed point. Then $\bar{x}$ is a fixed point of $\boldsymbol{\alpha}^{-1}\tau_D$ for any D where α is defined by (9.6a) using C. If $p\bar{x}' = p\bar{x}$, then $\bar{x}' = \boldsymbol{\beta}^{-1}\tau_D\bar{x}'$ where $\boldsymbol{\beta}$ is a conjugate of $\boldsymbol{\alpha}$ with respect to H_D.*

Thus

$$\tau_D\bar{x} = \lceil D\, t(C)\, C^{-1}\, C \rceil = \boldsymbol{\alpha}\lceil C \rceil = \boldsymbol{\alpha}\bar{x}\ .$$

For the second conclusion we replace $\bar{x}'$ by $\boldsymbol{\gamma}\bar{x}$ and refer to (9.4a).

Lemma 9.10. *The fixed points of $\boldsymbol{\alpha}^{-1}\tau_D$ project by p into fixed points of t lying in a single fixed point class.*

Let x_1 and x_2 be fixed points of $\boldsymbol{\alpha}^{-1}\tau_D$. Let x_1 correspond to $\lceil C_1 \rceil$ and x_2 to $\lceil C_2 \rceil$. Then from (9.6a) and (9.8)

$$\alpha C_1 \simeq DtC_1, \qquad \alpha C_2 \simeq DtC_2$$

with b_0 and b_1 fixed in one homotopy and b_0 and b_2 in the other, that is to say $C_1\ C_2^{-1}$ can be taken as C in (9.6).

We drop the subscript D on H_D and on τ_D

Lemma 9.11. *Two fixed points are in the same fixed point class if and only if their associated elements are in the same* H *class.*

Let $\boldsymbol{\alpha}$ and $\boldsymbol{\beta}$ be associated with the fixed points b_1 and b_2 with $\boldsymbol{\beta} = \mathrm{H}(\boldsymbol{\gamma})\boldsymbol{\alpha}\boldsymbol{\gamma}^{-1}$. Then $\boldsymbol{\alpha}x_1 = \tau x_1$ and $\boldsymbol{\beta}x_2 = \tau x_2$ for x_1 and x_2 in X. However

$$\begin{aligned}\tau(\boldsymbol{\gamma}^{-1}\,x_2) &= \mathrm{H}(\boldsymbol{\gamma}^{-1})\tau x_2 \quad (9.4\mathrm{a})\\ &= \mathrm{H}(\boldsymbol{\gamma}^{-1})\mathrm{H}(\boldsymbol{\gamma})\boldsymbol{\alpha}\boldsymbol{\gamma}^{-1}\,x_2\\ &= \boldsymbol{\alpha}(\boldsymbol{\gamma}^{-1}\,x_2).\end{aligned}$$

Hence $x_3 = \boldsymbol{\gamma}^{-1}\,x_2$ satisfies $px_3 = b_2$ and $\tau x_3 = \boldsymbol{\alpha}x_3$ and so b_2 is in the same fixed point class as b_1 by (9.10).

The converse is trivial.

Definition 9.12. Let ψ: $B \times I \rightarrow B$ constitute a homotopy with $\psi(b, 0) = t(b)$ and $\psi(b, 1) = t'(b)$. Then b_1, a fixed point of t and b_2, a fixed point of t', correspond under ψ if there is a path γ in $\Omega(b_1, b_2)$ with $\psi(\gamma) = \psi(\gamma(s), s) \simeq \gamma$.

Lemma 9.13. *The correspondence of fixed points induced by a homotopy yields a 1-1 correspondence of subsets of the fixed point classes of t and t'.*

We need only show that if b_1 and b_2 are in the same fixed point class, say F_1, under t, and if b_1' and b_2' are correspondents under ψ, then b_1' and b_2' are in the same fixed point class under t'. The proof carries out the indications in Fig. 14-12a.

Our goal is the relation $t'(C_1^{-1}CC_2) \simeq C_1^{-1}CC_2$. Let $E_1 = \psi(b_1, w)$ and $E_2 = \psi(b_2, w)$ for $0 \leq w \leq 1$. Our hypotheses are that $\psi(C_1) \simeq C_1$, $\psi(C_2) \simeq$

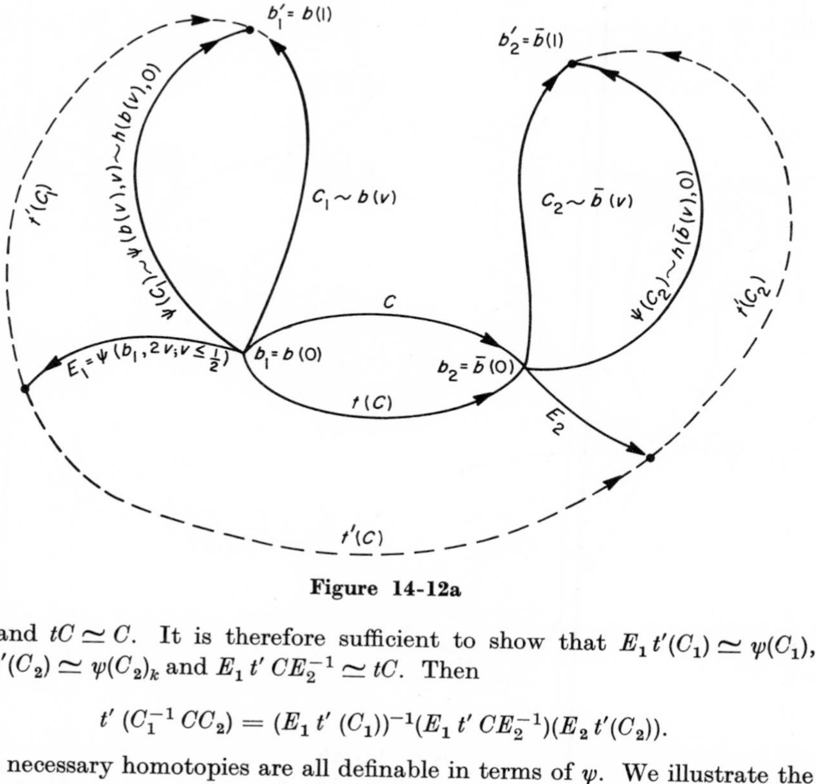

Figure 14-12a

C_2 and $tC \simeq C$. It is therefore sufficient to show that $E_1 t'(C_1) \simeq \psi(C_1)$, $E_2 t'(C_2) \simeq \psi(C_2)_k$ and $E_1 t' CE_2^{-1} \simeq tC$. Then

$$t' (C_1^{-1} CC_2) = (E_1 t' (C_1))^{-1}(E_1 t' CE_2^{-1})(E_2 t'(C_2)).$$

The necessary homotopies are all definable in terms of ψ. We illustrate the procedure. Let $0 \leq v \leq 1$, $0 \leq u \leq 1$, $b(v \mid I) = C_1$, $b_1 = b(0)$, $b_1 = b(1)$. Then the first homotopy for instance is defined by

$$\text{(9.13a)} \qquad \begin{aligned} h(b(v), u) &= \psi(b_1, 2v), & 0 &\leq v \leq u/2, \\ &= \psi(b(v - u/2), v + u/2), & u/2 &\leq v \leq 1 - u/2, \\ &= \psi(b(2v - 1), 1), & 1 - u/2 &\leq v \leq 1. \end{aligned}$$

Theorem 9.14. **(a)** *To every F class there corresponds an* H *class, and to every* H *class there corresponds either one or no F class.* **(b)** *The correspondence is preserved under the deformations of t and D which preserve the F classes.*

Since (9.14)(a) is covered by (9.11), we pass to (9.14b). The argument is clear from Fig. 14-12. The deformation is $\psi: B \times I \to B$. Let $\bar{b}$ and $\bar{b}'$ be the corresponding fixed points for t and t', that is to say the path $C_1 = \{C_1(s \mid I)\}$ is homotopic to $\{\psi(C_1(s), s)\} = \psi(C_1)$. Associated with $\bar{b}$ is $\boldsymbol{\alpha} = Dt(C)C^{-1}$ which we proceed to prove is in the same H class as

$$\boldsymbol{\beta} = [(DE)(t'(C)t'(C_1)C_1^{-1}\,C^{-1}] \tag{9.14c}$$

the associated element to $\bar{b}'$. Note $t(C)\psi(C_1) \simeq \psi(t(C))t'(C_1)$ and $\psi t(C) \simeq$

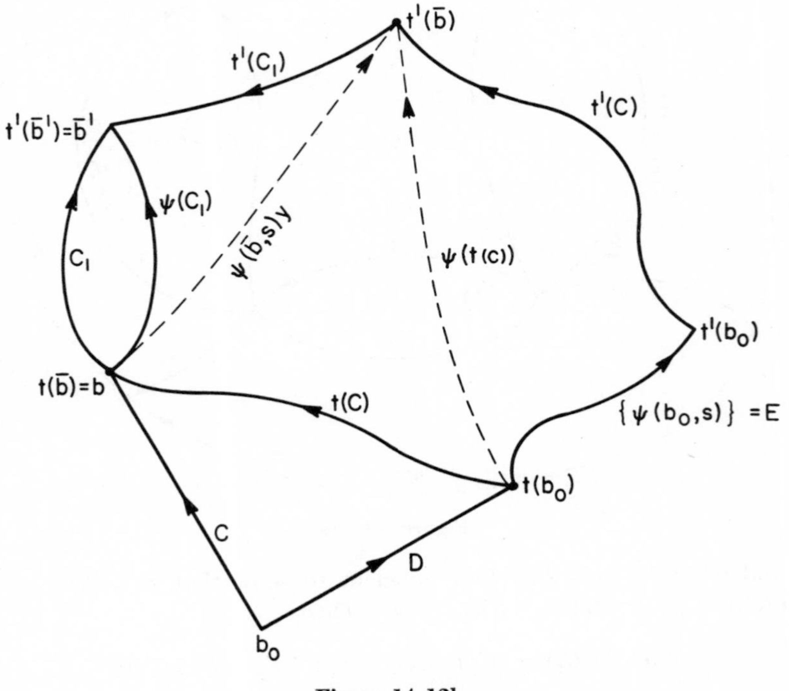

Figure 14-12b

$Et'(C)$. Accordingly $t(C)C_1 \simeq Et'(C)t'(C_1)$ or $t(C) \simeq Et'(C)t'(C_1)C_1^{-1}$. On substituting on the right hand side (9.14c) there results $\boldsymbol{\alpha}$, that is to say $\boldsymbol{\beta}$ and $\boldsymbol{\alpha}$ are identical.

It is now clear that the correspondence of fixed point classes under ψ is independent of the paths. That is to say, if F_1 corresponds to F_1' under a path C_1 and to F_2' under a path C_2, $(\psi(C_i) \simeq C_i)$, then F_1' and F_2' associate the same H class and so are identical.

Theorem 9.15. *For every* $\boldsymbol{\alpha} \in \pi_1(B, b_0)$ *there is a fixed point* $\bar{b}$ *of a map* t', $t' \simeq t$, *with associated element,* $\boldsymbol{\alpha}$.

In fact b_0 can be made this fixed point. Let D join b_0 and $t(b_0)$ and let C be a path from $t(b_0)$ to b_1 with $[DC] = \boldsymbol{\alpha}$. Introduce a homotopy, ψ, satisfying $\{\psi(b_0, s)\} = C$. Let $t' = \psi$ for $s = 1$. Then $t'(b_0) = b_0$. Let C_1 be the degenerate path consisting of b_0 alone. The associated π_1 element is

$$[(DC)t'(C_1)C_1^{-1} = [DC] = \boldsymbol{\alpha}.$$

We have only to verify such a ψ exists.

PROBLEM

14-13. Show the desired ψ exists when B is an ANR. *Hint:* Use (144.1).

Lemma 9.16. *The number of fixed point classes is finite.*

Suppose there were a nonfinite collection $\{F_\alpha\}$ of such classes. Pick a point, b_α, in F_α. Since B is compact let $\bar{b}$ be a cluster point. The LC^1 property of B (the semi LC^1 property is enough) indicates that for assigned $U(\bar{b})$ there are neighborhoods $V(\bar{b})$, $W(\bar{b})$, and $N(\bar{b})$ with $N(\bar{b}) \cup tN(\bar{b}) \subset W(\bar{b})$ and such that point pairs in $W(\bar{b})$ can be joined by a path in $V(\bar{b})$ and loops in $V(\bar{b})$ are contractible to a point over $U(\bar{b})$. Hence for b_α and b_β in $N(\bar{b})$, $\alpha \neq \beta$, there is a path from b_α to b_β for which $C(tC)^{-1} \simeq 0$, a contradiction. This argument shows incidentally that fixed points "close enough together" lie in the same class.

Evidently F_i, a fixed point class is a compact set. By the compactness of B, open sets, G_i, exist with $F_i \subset G_i$ and $\bar{G}_i \cap \bar{G}_j = \varnothing$ for arbitrary $i \neq j$.

Definition 9.17. The **index** of F_i, written $\lambda(F_i)$ or λ_i, is defined as $\Lambda(G_i)$. We say F_i is an **essential class** or **nonessential class** according as $\lambda_i \neq 0$ or $\lambda_i = 0$.

Theorem 9.18. *If $t \simeq t'$ and the fixed point class F_i for t goes into the fixed point class F_j' for t', then $\lambda(F_i) = \lambda(F_j')$.*

Denote $\psi(-, s)$ by t_s and indicate the fixed point classes by $F_j(s)$. For $s = \bar{s}$ there is an open interval $I_{\bar{s}}$: $|s - \bar{s}| < \varepsilon$, such that $F_j(s) \subset G_j(\bar{s})$ and $\lambda(\psi(s), G_i(\bar{s}))$ is independent of s. Since I is compact we need piece together a finite number of such open intervals.

Our scripts will be assumed to order the fixed point classes so that $\lambda_j < \lambda_k$ implies $k > j$. By reason of (9.11) and (9.14a) we denote the H class for F_i by H_i. The remaining H classes, namely those for which the corresponding fixed point class is empty, are given higher scripts.

Consider a **cyclic homotopy** that is to say $\psi(-, 0) = \psi(-, 1)$. It is not true that F_i always corresponds to itself under ψ.

Theorem 9.19. *In order that F_1 correspond to F_2 under a cyclic homotopy, it is necessary that:* **(a)** $\lambda_1 = \lambda_2$, **(b)** *there be a nontrivial element,* $\boldsymbol{\gamma}$, *in* $\pi_1(B, b_0)$ *which commutes with all elements of* $\mathrm{H}_D(\pi_1(B, b_0))$ *and furthermore,* **(c)** $\boldsymbol{\gamma}\mathrm{H}_1 = \mathrm{H}_2$.

Under the action of ψ, tb_0 is taken into a loop $E = \{\psi(b_0, s)\}$ so $[DE] = \boldsymbol{\gamma}^{-1}[D]$ with $\gamma = DED^{-1}$. However both H_1 and $\boldsymbol{\alpha}$ are preserved (9.13) due cognizance being taken of the replacement of D by $\gamma^{-1}D$. Hence $\boldsymbol{\alpha} = \boldsymbol{\gamma\beta}$ where $\boldsymbol{\beta}$ is in H_2. This is (9.19c). On the one hand H_D goes to $t_\gamma \mathrm{H}_D$ (9.4b) while on the other H_D is unaffected by a homotopy of t. Accordingly $t_\gamma \mathrm{H}_D = H_D$. This is to say $\boldsymbol{\gamma}\mathrm{H}_D(\boldsymbol{l})\boldsymbol{\gamma}^{-1} = \mathrm{H}_D(\boldsymbol{l})$ which is the same as (9.19b).

PROBLEM

14-14. If H_D is an automorphism of $\pi_1(B, b_0)$ and if the center of $\pi_1(B, b_0)$ consists only of the neutral element, then each fixed point class of t is unchanged by a cyclic homotopy.

For each cyclic homotopy, ψ, γ is determined as $\psi(b_0, s)$. The totality of possible γ's evidently constitutes a subgroup M of $\pi_1(B, b_0)$. However no permutation $\{F_i\}$ may attach to a particular γ. Those elements of M for which a nontrivial permutation of fixed point classes obtains, constitute a group M'.

PROBLEMS

14-15. Prove M' is an invariant subgroup of M and that the group of permutations of $\{F_i\}$ is M/M'.

14-16. Let $\{\mathrm{H}_i\}$ constitute a basis for a module over J. Show $\Sigma\, \lambda_i \mathrm{H}_i$ is invariant under homotopy (but depends on D).

EXAMPLE 14-11. Let B be the circle represented as the reals, $\{b\}$, mod 1. Let t be the reflection in $\frac{1}{2}$ and let $\psi(b, s) = s - b \bmod 1$, $0 \leq s \leq 1$, with fixed points $s/2$, $(s + 1)/2$. Then $\psi(b, 0) = t = t' = \psi(b, 1)$. Here 0, $\frac{1}{2}$ are in different fixed point classes for t, yet 0 goes into $\frac{1}{2}$ and $\frac{1}{2}$ into 0 by ψ.

We can now state a significant conclusion as a consequence of (9.18).

Corollary 9.20. *The minimum number of fixed points is the number of essential fixed point classes at least.*

EXAMPLE 14-12. Let t map S^1 into itself with $L(t) = -k$. Here S^1 is represented by the reals mod 1. The Lefschetz number by itself permits only the conclusion there is at least 1 fixed point, though it implies that the base 1-cycle z goes into $(k + 1)z$. Accordingly a homotopy takes t into t' defined by $t'(b) = (k + 1)b$. Note $\pi_1(S^1, b_0)$ is the cyclic group with 1 generator, γ, so $\text{H}_D \gamma = \gamma^{k+1}$. The conjugate class for

$$\alpha = \gamma^p \text{ is } \text{H}_D(\gamma^m)\alpha\gamma^{-m} = \{\gamma^{mk+p} \mid m = 0, 1, 2, \ldots\}.$$

Hence there are k such classes, i.e., $\text{H}_1, \ldots, \text{H}_k$. Moreover M contains γ which induces a cyclic permutation of $\text{H}_1, \ldots, \text{H}_k$. This means that $\lambda_1 = \lambda_2 = \cdots \lambda_k$. From $L(t) = \Sigma \lambda_i$ there follows $\lambda_i = 1$. Thus there are k essential classes of fixed points, whence by (9.20) there are at least k fixed points.

The bound in (9.20) may be too low.

Example 14-13. Let K be a graph with $R_1 = n + 1$ and at most $m + 1$ 1-simplexes meeting at each vertex. For the identity map ψ there is just one fixed point class. Nevertheless every map homotopic to ψ must have at least $[n/m] + 1$ fixed points, where $[r]$ is the integer part of r. Indeed the index, Λ, (113.11) of a point not a vertex is ± 1, that of a vertex is at most $1 - m$. We now refer to the relation $L(\psi) = -n = \Sigma \Lambda_i$ (113.21).

Example 14-14. Let X be a retract of Y with retracting function r. Let $X \subset \psi(X) \subset Y$. Then ψ and $r\psi$ have the same fixed points. It follows at once that, if the even dimensional spheres, $S_i^{2m_i}$, $i = 1, 2, 3$ have their centers on a line and meet in two points, there must be at least two fixed points for every map homotopic to the identity. (One need only take S_1 or S_3 as X and $\bigcup S_i$ as Y.)

Relations 9.21. We remark that the developments in this section can be phrased in terms of special modules $G(T)$ (132.8), except that T is no longer necessarily finite, but can be taken as $\pi_1(X, x_0)$. We therefore write $G(\pi)$ with G the coefficient group for chains. We write also $J(\pi)$. Thus let X be a finite simplicial complex and suppose x_0 is a fixed vertex. $\boldsymbol{X}$ is now the universal covering complex. Since our chains involve $\boldsymbol{X}$ alone, we shall write σ^i instead of $\mathbf{e}^i$ for a simplex of $\boldsymbol{X}$. The chains are of the form given in (132.12) and (132.13). Allowability includes our earlier equivariance.

For simplicity let t be a homeomorphic simplicial self map of X. This induces a simplicial self map τ (really τ_D) of $\boldsymbol{X}$ of the form

$$\text{(9.21a)} \qquad \tau\sigma^i = \Sigma\, \alpha_j^i \sigma^j, \qquad \alpha_j^i \in G(\pi).$$

We define T' on $G(\pi)$ to $G(\pi)$ by

$$\text{(9.21b)} \qquad T'(ng\gamma + mg'\,\rho) = ng\text{H}(\gamma) + mg'\,\text{H}(\rho),$$

where γ and ρ are elements of π and H (an abbreviation for H_D) is defined in (9.3a). Thus $T'(\gamma) = \text{H}(\gamma)$. Write $[\rho]$ for the H conjugacy class of ρ (9.8) and let

$$\text{(9.21c)} \qquad [\Sigma\, n_i\rho_i] = \Sigma\, n_i[\rho_i].$$

Then with $\beta_i \in G(\pi)$,

$$\tau(\Sigma\, \beta_i \sigma^i_m) = \Sigma\, T'(\beta_i)\tau(\sigma^i_m). \tag{9.21d}$$

When t and τ are homeomorphisms, (9.4c) shows τ is equivariant with respect to π. We understand throughout that τ is allowable. This means as usual

$$\partial\tau = \tau\partial. \tag{9.21e}$$

Let $\mathbf{A} = (\alpha^i_j)$ be the matrix for (9.21a). Let $\mathbf{U}$ be a unimodular matrix (integers as entries) and let $\mathbf{V}$ be the matrix with the elements $\gamma_1, \ldots, \gamma_n$ on the main diagonal and zero's elsewhere. Let $Tr\,\mathbf{A}$ be the trace of $\mathbf{A}$, thus

$$Tr(\mathbf{A}) = \Sigma\, \alpha^i_i \in G(\pi).$$

Then $\mathbf{U}\; Tr\; \mathbf{A}\mathbf{U}^{-1} = Tr\; \mathbf{A}$,

$$\mathbf{V}\; Tr\; \mathbf{A}\mathbf{V}^{-1} = T'(\gamma_i)\alpha^i_i\, \gamma_i^{-1}. \tag{9.21f}$$

If instead of $Tr\,\mathbf{A}$ we introduce $\bar{T}r\,\mathbf{A} = \Sigma\, [\alpha^i_i]$, then

$$\mathbf{V}\; \bar{T}r\; \mathbf{A}\mathbf{V}^{-1} = \bar{T}r\; \mathbf{A}. \tag{9.21g}$$

If $\mathbf{A}(k)$ is the matrix attached to the k-dimensional chains, we can define

$$L(\mathbf{A}) = \Sigma\, (-1)^k\, \bar{T}r\; \mathbf{A}(k), \tag{9.21h}$$

the analogue of the Lefschetz number.

The transformations induced by $\mathbf{U}$ and $\mathbf{V}$ amount to changing the chain basis. The invariance of $L(\mathbf{A})$ under these changes does not exhaust all possibilities by tampering with the basis $\{\sigma^i_k\}$. Thus suppose $\boldsymbol{X}$ is augmented by the addition of two base chains c'_k and c''_{k-1} satisfying

$$\partial c'_k = c''_{k-1} \tag{9.21i}$$

$$\partial c''_{k-1} = 0.$$

(The contrary process, namely that of reduction of the basis is also possible by removal of pairs of chains satisfying (9.21i).) There is no difficulty in establishing that under an adjunction, or a reduction of type (9.21i), $L(\mathbf{A})$ is unchanged.

PROBLEMS

14-17. Demonstrate the last statement. *Hint:* Use the allowability condition (9.21e).

14-18. Suppose $\alpha^i_j \in \pi$ for each pair i and j. Show $\xi\, \sigma^i_m$ is fixed under τ in the sense $\tau(\xi\, \sigma^i_m) \supset \xi\, \sigma^i_m$, is equivalent with $T'(\xi)\, \alpha^i_i\, \xi^{-1} = 1$ the neutral element of π. Hence show that if $T'(\gamma) = \text{H}(\gamma) = \gamma$ has the unique solution 1, then $L(\boldsymbol{A})$ is the algebraic number of fixed simplexes in $\boldsymbol{X}$.

chapter 15

HOMOTOPY

1. THE HIGHER HOMOTOPY GROUPS. The fundamental group consists of mapping classes of the pairs S^1, y_0 into X, x_0. Two natural generalizations would seem to be the mapping classes of the n-torus pair $S^1 \times \cdots \times S^1$, y_0 into X, x_0 or those of S^n, y_0 into X, x_0. Both generalizations can in fact be carried out to yield groups, but because of its more natural definition of a group product, the second has been the more fruitful.

Definition 1.1. Let I^n be the cube $\mathbf{P}_{i=1}^{i=n} I_{t_i}$, $I_t = \{t \mid 0 \leq t \leq 1\}$. The boundary is

(1.1a) $$\dot{I}^n = \bigcup_j \mathbf{P}_{i \neq j} I_{t_i} \times 0_{t_j} \cup \bigcup_j \mathbf{P}_{i \neq j} I_{t_i} \times 1_{t_j}.$$

The base is

(1.1b) $$I^{n-1} = \mathbf{P}_{i \neq n} I_{t_i} \times 0_{t_n} = I^n \cap \{t \mid t_n = 0\}$$

and J^{n-1} consists of all the other closed faces in $\dot{I}^n$,

(1.1c) $$J^{n-1} = \bigcup_{j=1}^{j=n-1} (\mathbf{P}_{i \neq j} I_{t_i} \times (0_{t_i} \cup 1_{t_j})) = \overline{\dot{I}^n - I^{n-1}}.$$

Definition 1.2. The space of maps into the triple X, $A \subset X$, $x_0 \in A$, is F_n or in a more precise notation $\mathrm{F}_n(X, A, x_0) = (X^{I^n}, A^{\dot{I}^n}, x_0^{J^{n-1}})$, that is to say $f \in \mathrm{F}_n(\ )$ if the map f restricted to $\dot{I}^n$, maps it into A and restricted to J^{n-1} maps it into x_0. In order to view the procedure in proper perspective, and also because of some inherent interest, we introduce the spaces X, A_1, A_2, x_0; where $A_1 \cap A_2 \supset x_0$ and the function space $\mathrm{G}_n(X, A_1, A_2, x_0) = (X^{I^n}, A_1^{I_+^n}, A_2^{I_-^n}, x_0^{J^{n-1}})$ where $I_+^n = I^{n-1} \cap \{t \mid t_2 \leq \frac{1}{2}\}$, $I_-^n = I^{n-1} \cap \{t \mid t_2 \geq \frac{1}{2}\}$. X^{I^n} has the co-open topology and its subsets F_n and G_n have the relative, or induced, topology.

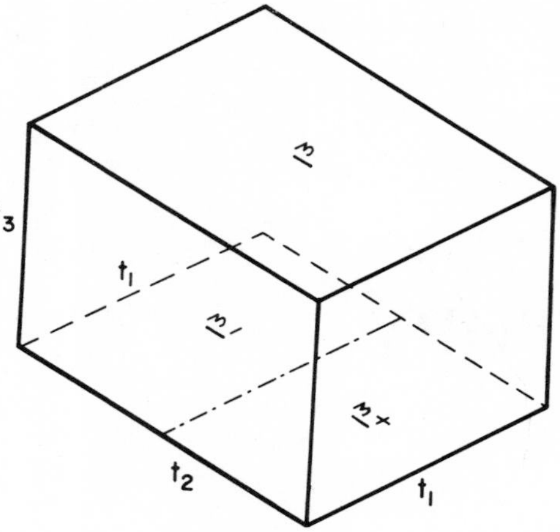

Figure 15-1

Let $\pi_n(X, A, x_0)$ or $\pi_n(X, A_1, A_2, x_0)$ consist of the homotopy classes of elements in F_n or in G_n, where $\boldsymbol{f}$ or $[f]$ is the homotopy class of f. Thus $\boldsymbol{f}_1 = \boldsymbol{f}_2$ if for some $h(-, t)$ with $h(-, 0) = f_1$ and $h(-, 1) = f_2$

$$h(x, t) \in X^{I^n \times I_t}, A^{\dot{I}^n \times I_t}, x_0^{J^{n-1} \times I_t}$$

or

$$h(x, t) \in X^{I^n \times I_t}, A_1^{I_-{}^n \times I_t}, A_2^{I_+{}^n}, x_0^{J^{n-1} \times I_t}$$

Thus h is an element of $\Omega(\mathrm{F}_n)$ the space of paths on $\mathrm{F}_n(X, A, x_0)$. The path must, of course, be in a single arcwise connected component. The converse implication is equally direct. Hence $\pi_n(X, A, x_0)$ may be viewed also as the set of *arcwise connected components of* F_n. Similar remarks hold for $\pi_n(X, A_1, A_2, x_0)$ and for G_n. Note

$$X^{I^n}, A^{\dot{I}^n}, x_0^{J^{n-1}} = X^{I^k \times I_k{}^n}, A^{\dot{I}^k \times I_k{}^n \cup I^k \times \dot{I}_k{}^n}, x_0^{J^{n-1}} \tag{1.2a}$$

$$I_k^n = \mathbf{P}_{i=k+1}^{i=n} I_{t_i}$$

In $\dot{I}^n$ only points with $t_n = 0$ can map into points of A other than x_0. Since $\dot{I}^k \subset J^{n-1}$, $\dot{I}^k$ maps into x_0. Accordingly,

$$(X^{I^n}, A^{\dot{I}^n}, x_0^{J^{n-1}}) = (\mathrm{F}_{n-k}(X, A, x_0))^{I^k}, x_0^{\dot{I}^k}, x_0^{J^{k-1}}$$

so that in particular with $k = 1$,

$$\pi_n(X, A, x_0) = \pi_1(\mathrm{F}_{n-1}(X, A, x_0), x_0, x_0).$$

Definition 1.3. $\Omega(X; x_0, A)$ is the space of paths in X, starting at x_0 and ending in A, with the co-open topology (146.1). Thus

$$\Omega(X; x_0, A) = X^{I_t}, A^{I_t}, x_0^{t=0}$$

$$= \mathrm{F}_1(X, A, x_0),$$

whence another definition of the elements of $\pi_n(X, A, x_0)$ is given by

(1.3a) $$\pi_n(X, A, x_0) = \pi_{n-1}((\Omega(X; x_0, A), x_0).$$

Yet another interpretation arises if we replace t_n by t. This (1.1b) and (1.1c) show a representative, f, of an element of $\pi_n(X, A, x_0)$ yields a homotopy between $f(t_1 \cdots t_{n-1}; t = 0)$ representing an element of $\pi_{n-1}(A, x_0)$ and the trivial map $f(t_1 \cdots t_{n-1}, t = 1)$, where the *homotopy is over* X.

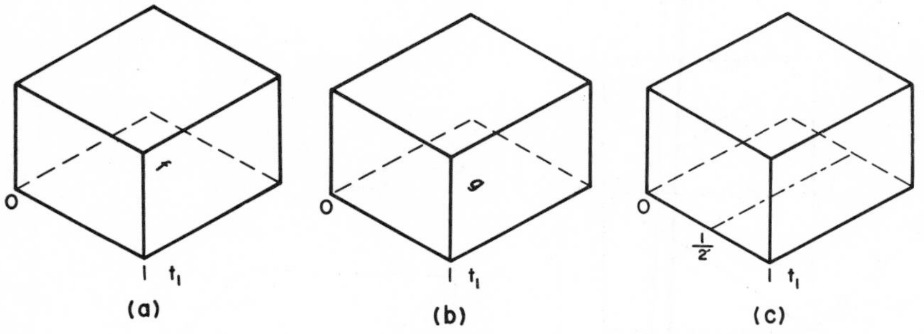

Figure 15-2

Definition 1.4. We provide a multiplication for elements of $\pi_n(X, A, x_0)$. Since the elements of $\pi_n(X, A, x_0)$ are classes of maps, we need to define a map denoted by (fg) in terms of the maps f and g respectively. The way to do this is clear from the diagram, and indicates the wearisome analytical formulation. Thus,

(1.4a) $$(fg)(t_1, \ldots, t_n) = f(2t_1, t_2, \ldots, t_n),\ t_1 \leq \tfrac{1}{2},$$
$$= g(2t_1 - 1, t_2, \ldots, t_n),\ t_1 \geq \tfrac{1}{2}.$$

Denote by f^{-1}, $\{f^{-1}(t_1, \ldots, t_n) = f(1 - t_1, t_2, \ldots, t_n)\}$. One can evidently replace representatives by their homotopy classes and so get $\boldsymbol{fg}$ as the homotopy class of fg.

Associativity is proved by routine translation into formulas of the homotopy diagrams below.

Definition 1.5. For the homotopy classes occurring as elements of $\pi_n(X, A, x_0)$, points in $\dot{I}^n$ cannot escape being mapped into A and J^{n-1} points into x_0 throughout the homotopy. If this predestination is relaxed as regards J^{n-1} and the base point is permitted to move on the path $e(t)$, $e(0) = x_0$ where $e(t) \subset A$, then a **relatively free** homotopy results and there is a correspondence between a map f representing an element $\boldsymbol{f}$ in $\pi_n(X, A, x_0)$ and the relatively free homotopic map to it, g, representing an element $\boldsymbol{g}$ in $\pi_n(X, A, x_1 = e(1))$. Evident homotopies show the correspondence is independent of the particular representative chosen as the particular representative of the homotopy

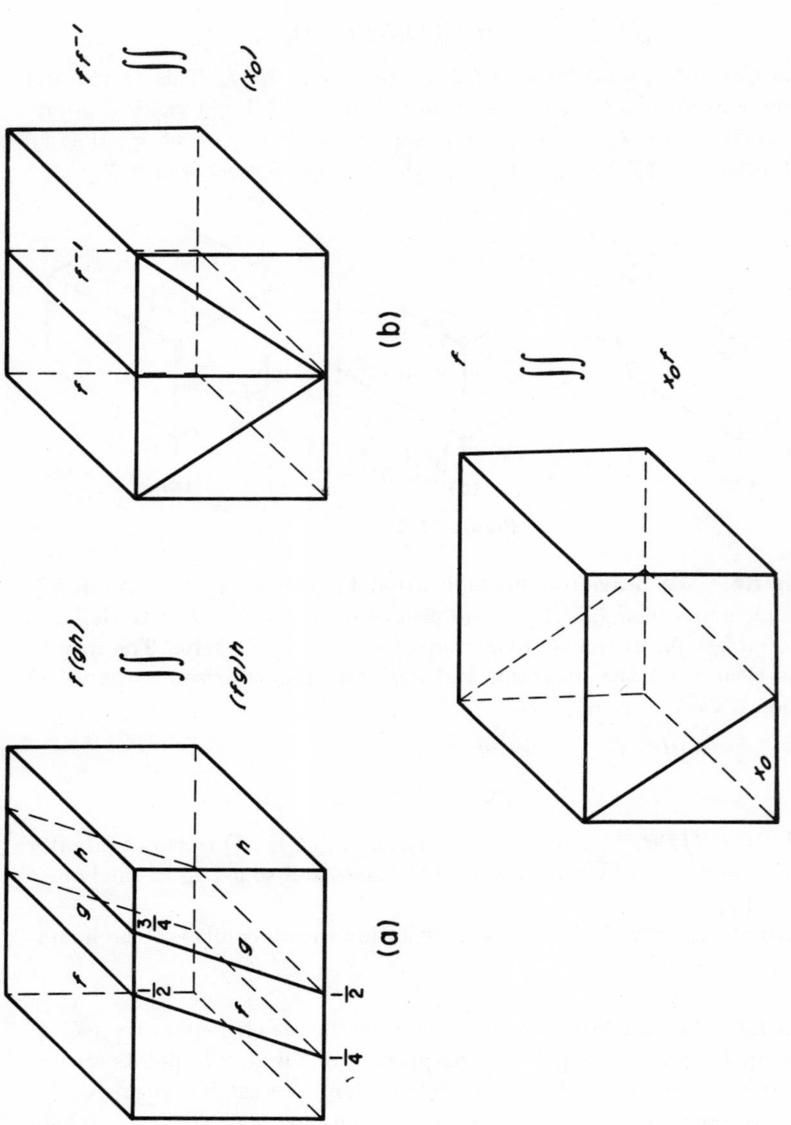

Figure 15-3

class of the path e and a homomorphism is defined on the corresponding homotopy groups as indicated by

(1.5a) $$f \to f^e.$$

The case of special interest is that when $e \in \Lambda(x_0)$, that is to say $e \in \pi_1(X, x_0)$. As usual e^{-1} is represented by $e^{-1}(t) = e(1 - t)$ and $\pi_1(X, x_0)$ becomes an operator group on $\pi_n(X, A, x_0)$. If the action of $\pi_1(X, x_0)$ is trivial, that is to say if f^e in (1.5a) is f, then X, A is n-**simple.** In particular, if $\pi_1(X, x_0) = 0$,

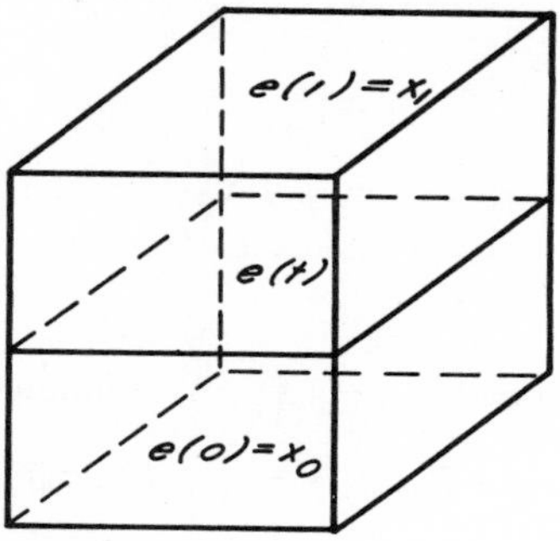

Figure 15-4

X, A is **simple in all dimensions.** If $n = 1$, then $f^e = efe^{-1}$. An example of nontrivial action of $\pi_1(X, x_0)$ is illustrated by the projective plane taken as X, Fig. 15-4.

The introduction of a product or pairing of two groups to a third adds to the relations involved in transferring a mapping problem to its algebraic sublimation. A general viewpoint is the following: Suppose $f \in \pi_n(X, x_0)$ and $g \in \pi_m(X, x_0)$, $n \neq m$. Turning to representatives, a first step in defining a product (fg) would be to cover a cube I^r by two sets A, B with $A \cap B \neq \varnothing$ so that fg coincides with f on A and with g on B and f and g are to map $A \cap B$ into x_0. Dimensional considerations preclude such a cover of I^r with dim $A = n$ and dim $B = m$. This difficulty is easily turned, however, by defining f not on A, but on a map of A onto a set of dimension n and similarly for g. We make the discussion specific for the *Whitehead product* with $r = m + n - 1$.

Definition 1.6. Let ψ be a map $\psi\colon I^{m+n-1}, \dot{I}^{m+n-1} \to \dot{I}^{m+n} = S^{m+n-1}, \tau_0$ of degree 1. Then, with $t \in I^{m+n-1}$, $\psi(t) = \psi_1(t), \psi_m(t), \psi_{m+1}(t), \ldots, \psi_{m+n-1}(t)$. Write, following (1.2a), $I^{m+n} = I^m \times I_m^{m+n}$, $\dot{I}^{m+n} = \dot{I}^m \times I_m^{m+n} \cup I^m \times \dot{I}_m^{m+n}$. Define

$$\psi^m(t) = \psi_1(t), \ldots, \psi_m(t) \subset I^m$$
$$\psi_m^{m+n}(t) = \psi_{m+1}(t), \ldots, \psi_{m+n}(t) \subset I_m^{m+n}.$$
$$A = \psi^{-1} I^m \times \dot{I}_m^{m+n}$$
$$B = \psi^{-1} \dot{I}^m \times I_m^{m+n}.$$

Thus, $(fg)\colon I^{m+n-1}, \dot{I}^{m+n-1} \to X, x_0$ is defined by

(1.6a) $$\begin{aligned}(fg)t &= f\psi^m(t) \qquad \text{for } t \in A\\ &= g\psi_m^{m+n}(t) \qquad \text{for } t \in B.\end{aligned}$$

It is easy to see that homotopies on f and g respectively yield a homotopy of (fg) as defined in (1.6a) so that the homotopy class of (fg) depends solely on the homotopy classes f and g and not on the representative chosen. We write $\boldsymbol{f} \circ \boldsymbol{g}$ for the product and call it the **Whitehead product.**

PROBLEM

15-1. For $m = n = 1$ verify $f \circ g = fgf^{-1}g^{-1}$. Since $\pi(X, x_0)$ is Abelian for $n \geq 2$ (Problem 15-3 and Problem 15-4 below) show $\boldsymbol{f}\,\boldsymbol{g} = (\boldsymbol{g} \circ \boldsymbol{f})^{(-1)^{mn}} = \boldsymbol{f}\,\boldsymbol{g}^{-1}$ for $m = 1, n > 1$.

With $\boldsymbol{f}$ fixed and $\boldsymbol{g}$ arbitrary in $\pi_n(X, x_0)$ a homomorphism $f_\#$ on

$$\pi_n(X, x_0) \to \pi_{m+n-1}(X, x_0)$$

is determined by the correspondence

$$\boldsymbol{g} \xrightarrow{f_\#} \boldsymbol{f} \circ \boldsymbol{g}.$$

The case of a Whitehead Product over relative groups is handled by reducing to the case of the absolute groups by (1.3a).

PROBLEMS

15-2. If $f \in \mathrm{F}_n(A, A, x_0)$ show $\boldsymbol{f}$ is the neutral element of $\pi_n(X, A, x_0)$.

15-3. Show $\pi_2(X, x_0)$ is Abelian. *Hint:* A geometrical proof may be based on twisting I^2, represented as a cylinder, through 180 degrees, Fig. 15-5. The general case is covered by (8.16).

15-4. Show $\pi_n(X, A, x_0)$ is Abelian for $n \geq 3$. *Hint:* $\pi_n(X, A, x_0) \approx \pi_2(F_{n-2}(X, A, x_0), x_0)$.

EXAMPLE 15-1. The following illustrates a nontrivial isomorphism induced by $\pi_1(P^2, b_0)$ acting on $\pi_2(P^2, b_0)$ by relatively free homotopy. P^2 is the sphere with antipodal points identified. Antipodal pairs of points are designated a, a'; b, b', etc. The nontrivial element α of $\pi_1(P^2, b_0)$ is the loop class of $o\epsilon o'$ in Fig. 15-6. Then for f defined in Fig. 15-6 for $t = 0$, $\alpha f = f^{-1}$ according to the diagram for $t = 1$.

The map of $S^n \to S^1$ is always trivial for $n > 1$. This is not necessarily the case for $S^n \to S^2$, $n \geq 2$.

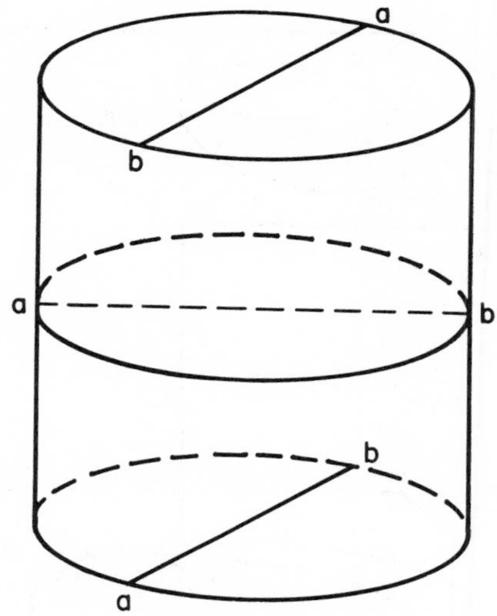

Figure 15-5

EXAMPLE 15-2. Hopf Map: Let S^3 be represented by $w_1\bar{w}_1 + w_2\bar{w}_2 = 1$ where $w_1 = x + iy$ and $w_2 = z + iv$. Thus $x^2 + y^2 + z^2 + v^2 = 1$, and an arbitrary point of S^3 is denoted by (w_1, w_2). Introduce the equivalence relation $(w_1, w_2) \sim (\mu w_1, \mu w_2)$ for $(w_1, w_2) \neq (0, 0)$ and μ any nonzero complex number. The cosets so determined are denoted by $[w_1, w_2]$ and represent the sphere S^2 as is clear on taking the representation of $[w_1, w_2]$ with $\mu = (w_1\bar{w}_1 + w_2\bar{w}_2)^{-1/2}$. Define the projection

$$(w_1, w_2) \xrightarrow{p} [w_1, w_2].$$

Evidently $p^{-1}[w_1,w_2] = \{(e^{i\varphi} w_1, e^{i\varphi} w_2)\}$. Hence great circles on S^3 project into points on S^2. Thus S^2 is the orbit space of S^3 under the obvious group. More generally we can get arbitrary degrees by

$$(w_1, w_2) \xrightarrow{p} [w_1^n, w_2], \quad n \geq 1.$$

EXAMPLE 15-3. Let q denote a quaternion $y + x_1 i + x_2 j + x_3 k$. Then $S^3 = \{q \mid |q|^2 = y^2 + x_1^2 + x_2^2 + x_3^2 = 1\}$ and $S^2 = \{q \mid y = 0, |q|^2 = 1\}$. Moreover S^3 acts as a group, G, on S^2. Thus with $w \in S^2$ and $q \in S^3$, $q \cdot w$ is given by $q \cdot w \cdot q^{-1}$. In particular $w = \pm 1$ is invariant, whence follows that the equatorial sphere, S^2, must also be left invariant. Hence under G, $S^2 \to S^2$.

That G is the rotation group, $SO(3)$, is patent on consideration of say the point $w = i$. Then $q = e^{i\theta}$ yields $q \cdot i = e^{i\theta} ie^{-i\theta} = i$, while $q \cdot j = e^{i\theta} je^{-i\theta} = e^{2i\theta} j$, since $ij = -ji$. Similarly for k. Thus $q = e^{i\theta}$ rotates the jk plane by 2θ around i. It is easy to see that any point can be moved to any other by compounding rotations about i, about j, and about k. This shows G is

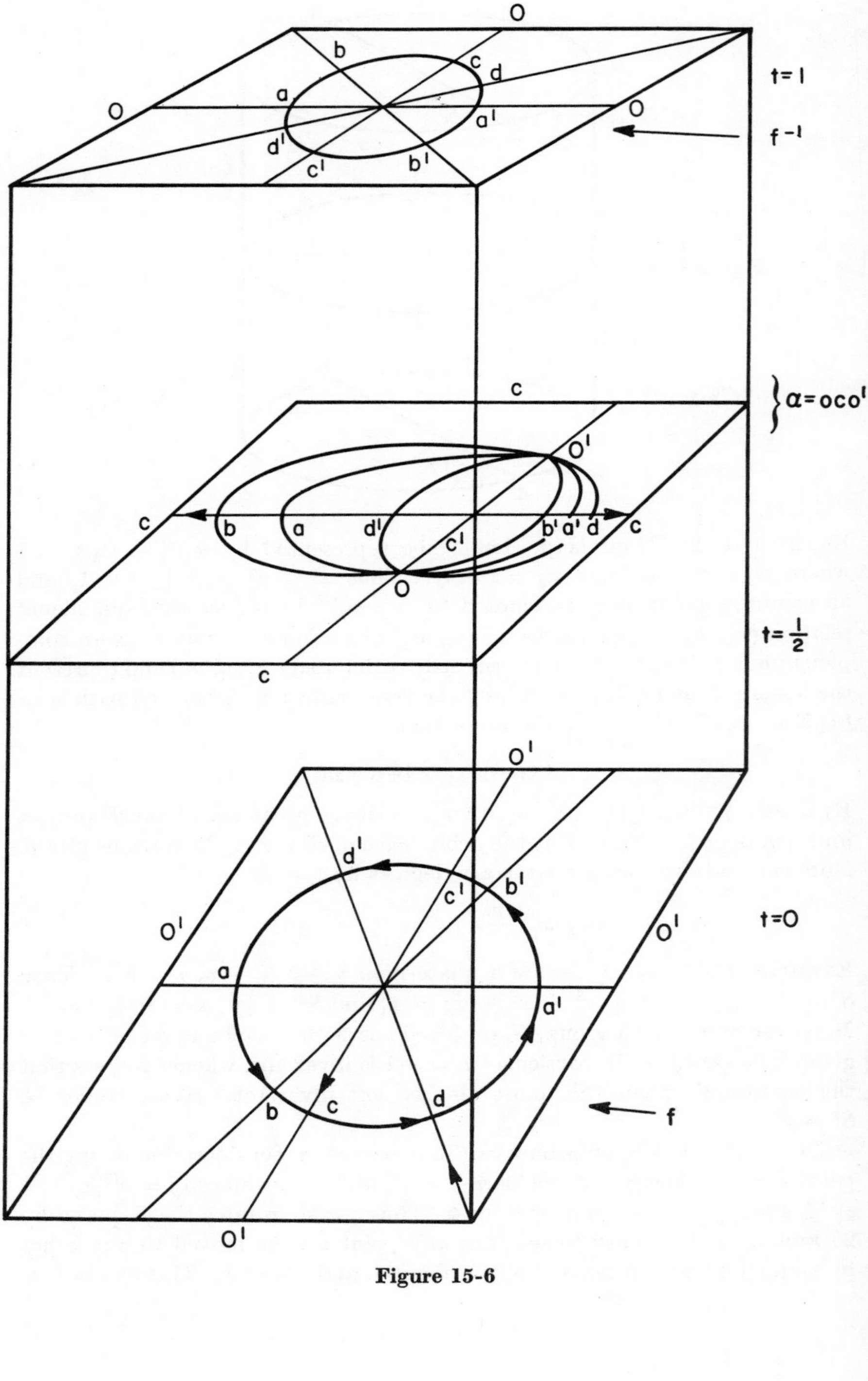
O
b
c
d
t=1
a
O
O
a'
f⁻¹
d'
c'
b'
c
α=oco'
O'
c
b
a
d'
c'
b' a' d
c
O
t=1/2
c
O'
d'
c'
b'
O'
O'
t=0
a
a'
b
c
d
f
O'

Figure 15-6

transitive. Thus to every element, q, in S^3 corresponds a rotation r of S^2. Moreover this correspondence, denoted by p, is a homomorphism on G to $SO(3)$ because $(qq') \cdot w = q(q' \cdot w)$ since $q'\, q \cdot w \cdot (q'\, q)^{-1} = q'(q \cdot w \cdot q^{-1})q'^{-1}$ and so if q, q' correspond to r, r', then $q'\, q$ corresponds to $r'\, r$. If e is the identity of $SO(3)$ then $p^{-1}(e) = \pm 1 \in G = S^3$. It is then immediate that S^3 is the covering space of $SO(3)$ and thus $SO(3)$ *is topologically the projective 3-space*, P^3.

PROBLEMS

15-5. Let a be a fixed point on S^2. Let $\pi = tp$, thus

$$S^3 \xrightarrow{p} SO(3) \xrightarrow{t} S^2$$

where p is clear from Example 15-3 and t is defined by $t(r) = ra$ where $r \in SO(3)$. Prove π is the Hopf map of Example 15-2.

15-6. Show $(S^3, F = S^1, B = S^2, G = S^3, \pi)$ is a fiber bundle.

15-7. Show π in Problem 15-5 is not homotopic to a constant. *Hint:* Any homotopy of $S^3 \to S^2$ is obtained by taking πh where h is a homotopy of $S^3 \times I \to S^3$.

It is inevitable that the question be raised of defining homotopy groups as suitable inverse limits attached to nerves of covers. Weakening of conditions of arcwise connectivity of the space can be attained by such limiting processes. Various schemes for introducing the inverse limits may be defined. We content ourselves with the following instance.

Let X be a compact subset of a parallelotope $\mathbf{P}$.

Definition 1.7. Let $\alpha(\nu) = a_1(\nu), \ldots, a_N(\nu)$ (N depending on ν), $a_i(\nu) \subset \mathbf{P}$, be a finite open cover of X. Write $A(\nu) = \bigcup_i a_i(\nu)$. Define the **concrete nerve**, $a(\nu)$, by choosing the vertex $(a_i(\nu))$ in $a_i(\nu)$ and using the convex extension of the vertices of a simplex as the concrete simplex in the nerve. Fix a point x_0. Let $\sigma(\nu)$ be the maximal simplex in $a(\nu)$ that contains x_0. Let

$$\psi_\nu\colon S^n, s_0 \to a(\nu), \sigma(\nu). \tag{1.7a}$$

Let $p_\mu{}^\nu$ be the projection, mapping the concrete nerve $a(\nu)$ into $a(\mu)$, $\alpha(\mu) < \alpha(\nu)$. If $\psi_\mu \simeq p_\mu{}^\nu\, \psi_\nu$, then $\psi = \{\psi_\nu, p_\mu{}^\nu\}$ is a **cover map** of S^n, s_0 to X, x_0. A homotopy class $[\psi]$, is defined by $\psi \simeq \psi'$ if $\psi_\nu \simeq \psi'_\nu$ so that during the homotopy s_0 is mapped into $\sigma(\nu)$. The classes, $\{[\psi]\}$ constitute a group under the following interpretation of multiplication. Let ψ_ν and ϕ_ν satisfy (1.7a). Since $\psi_\nu(s_0)$ can be connected to $\phi_\nu(s_0)$ inside $\sigma(\nu)$, we may replace ϕ_ν by a homotopic map ϕ'_ν where $\psi_\nu(s_0) = \phi'_\nu(s_0)$ and so we drop the prime. The product $\lambda_\nu = \psi_\nu \cdot \phi_\nu$ is defined satisfying (1.7a), and $[\lambda]$ is defined as

$[\psi][\phi]$. The details are as in (1.4). The group so determined may be designated by $\boldsymbol{\pi}_n(X, x)$. That it is not the same as $\pi_n(X, x)$ is evidenced by the case of Example 8-4a. Here $\pi_1(X, x_0) = 0$, while $\boldsymbol{\pi}_1(X, x_0)$ is infinite cyclic since for covers of small enough mesh, the nerve is essentially an annulus. Another example is afforded by reflecting the part B in Example 8-4a—in the y axis, and replacing D by a concave curve connecting $-\frac{2}{\pi}, 0$. Again $\pi_1(X, x_0) = 0$ while $\boldsymbol{\pi}_1(X, x_0)$ is infinite cyclic. Notice that in the first example X is not locally connected, in the second, X is not connected. This suggests that so far as $\boldsymbol{\pi}_1$ is concerned, at least, arcwise connectivity is weakened to the property that (with c_ν denoting a contraction $a(\nu) \to x_\nu$) there exist contractions $\{c_\nu\}$ which must, of course, satisfy $p_\mu{}^\nu c_\nu \simeq c_\mu p_\mu{}^\nu$.

The text of this section and the examples just given make it possible to add a few results to the discussion of equivariant maps in Chapter 13.

A necessary condition for the existence of equivariant maps was stated in (135.10). We now present constructive sufficient conditions having in mind the extension of equivariant maps to skeletons of successively higher dimensions. (Ordinary type replaces the **black** face used in Chapter 13.)

Lemma 1.8. *Let K be an n dimensional concrete finite complex, and suppose X is a space with $\pi_i(X, x_0) = 0$, $i < n$ and in particular X may be $|K|$. Let t and t' be fixed point free self maps of $|K|$ and of X respectively of prime period k, where t is simplicial. Then there is an equivariant map Ψ: $|K|, T_k \to X, T'_k$ i.e., $\Psi t = t'\Psi$.*

We sketch the proof. Let D be the fundamental domain for $|K|, T_k$ and write D^m for the m skeleton. Since D^0 consists of isolated vertices $\{v^i\}$ define $\Psi v^i = x^i$ arbitrarily and $\Psi t v^i$ as $t'\Psi v^i$. More generally $\Psi t^j v^i$ is defined as $t'^j \Psi v^i = t'^j x^i$, $j < k$. Proceed by induction. Thus suppose Ψ has been defined on K^r, $r \leq m < n$. Hence Ψ is known on $\|\partial' \sigma^i_{m+1}\|$ where $'\sigma^i_{m+1} \in D^{m+1}$. The points of $\|'\sigma^i_{m+1}\|$ can be given the coordinates (y, s) where $0 \leq s \leq 1$. The points with $s = 0$ constitute $\|'\dot{\sigma}_{m+1}\|$ or $\|\partial\,'\sigma^i_{m+1}\|$ while for $s = 1$ there is a unique point described by $(y, 1)$ independently of y. Since $\|\partial\,'\sigma^i_{m+1}\|$ is a topological sphere, $\Psi \|\partial\,'\sigma^i_{m+1}\| \simeq x_0$ by the assumption that $\pi_m(X, x_0) = 0$. Let h: $\Psi \|\partial\,'\sigma^i_{m+1}\| \times I \to X$ be the homotopy in question. Thus $h(x, 0) = x$ and $h(x, 1) = x_0$. Define $\Psi(y, s)$ by $h(\Psi(y), s)$. This gives Ψ over $\|'\sigma^i_{m+1}\|$. Then $\Psi t^j \|\sigma^i_{m+1}\|$ is defined as $t'^j \Psi \|'\sigma^i_{m+1}\|$.

Lemma 1.9. *Suppose $\pi_i(X, x_0) = 0$, $i < n$. Let S^n be the triangulated sphere. Let θ be an equivariant map of X, T'_k to S^n, T_k, then θ_*: $H_n(X, \mathrm{J}_k) \to H_n(S^n, \mathrm{J}_k)$ is nontrivial.*

Indeed using the Ψ guaranteed by (1.8) there results $t\theta\Psi = \theta t' \Psi = \theta\Psi t$. That is $\theta\Psi$ is an equivariant self map of S^n, T_k. Accordingly $(\theta\Psi)_* = \theta_*\Psi_*$ is not trivial (137.6) whence θ_* cannot be trivial.

We return to sphere to Euclidean-space maps. A triple of points is **equilateral** if the three distances between pairs are the same.

Theorem 1.10. *Let x_1, x_2, x_3 be an equilateral triple on S^3 and suppose $\psi\colon S^3 \to R^2$. Then some congruent triple maps into a single point, that is $\psi(\bar{r}x_1) = \psi(\bar{r}x_2) = \psi(\bar{r}x_3)$.*

A point of R^2 is denoted by z or by y_1, y_2. Since a congruent triple may replace the original one and $-\psi$ can replace ψ we can suppose $y_1(x_1) = \max_{x \in S^3} y_1(x) > 0$, neglecting the trivial case ψ a constant. For some $r_0 \in SO(4)$, r_0^3 is the identity and $r_0 x_1 = x_2$, $r_0 x_2 = x_3$. Since r_0 is a homeomorphism on a sphere of odd dimension, there is a fixed point $x = \xi$. The stability group at any point x is denoted by $SO(4)_x$. Define $t\colon SO(4) \to SO(4)$ by $tr = rr_0$ and $t'\colon R^6 \to R^6$ by $t'(z_1, z_2, z_3) = z_3, z_1, z_2$. Then

$$qp\psi t = t' qp\psi\colon SO(4) \to S^3.$$

Note $tSO(4)_\xi = SO(4)_\xi$ because $r_0 \in SO(4)_\xi$. Write μ for $qp\psi$ restricted to $SO(4)_\xi$. Then $\mu t = t' \mu\colon SO(4)_\xi \to S^3$, that is to say μ is an equivariant map. We can make use of (1.9) by noting $SO(4)_x \approx SO(3)$ and $SO(3)$ is homeomorphic to P^3 the projective 3 space according to Example 15-3. We can therefore identify X with $SO(4)_\xi$ and K with S^3. Accordingly μ_* is nontrivial. On the one hand, if $r \in SO(4)_{x_1}$ then

$$\psi(r) = \psi(rx_1), \psi(rx_2), \psi(rx_3) = (y_1, y_2), (y_3, y_4), (y_5, y_6)$$

satisfies $0 < y_1 \geq y_3$ and $y_1 \geq y_5$. Hence the first coordinate in $\mu' = qp\psi\colon SO(4)_{x_1}$ is nonnegative, and so μ' cannot be onto S^3 whence μ'_* is trivial on $H_3(SO(4)_{x_1}) \to H_3(S^3)$. On the other hand all stability subgroups of $SO(4)$ are conjugates, so a homotopy can be defined taking μ to μ' by using a suitable path of elements in $SO(4)$ from x_1 into ξ. Accordingly there is the contradiction $D = \mu'_* = \mu_* = 0$.

We place on record two important theorems providing a link between homotopy and omology considerations. The proofs are long and are omitted. A full discussion and extension of the ideas to cases involving more than one critical dimension would involve us in considerations (obstruction theory) not developed in this book.

Theorem (Hopf) 1.11. *If K is a concrete n dimensional complex, $n \geq 1$, then the homotopy classes of maps of $|K|$ into S^n are in 1-1 correspondence with the elements of $H^n(K, J)$.*

Theorem (Hurewicz) 1.12. *If X is connected and simply connected and $H_m(X, \mathrm{J}) = 0$ for $0 < m < n$, then $\pi_n(X, x_0)$ is in 1-1 correspondence with $H_n(X, \mathrm{J})$.*

2. HOMOTOPY SEQUENCE. An exact sequence for homotopy can be set up just as in the case of the homology modules (61.12) on properly interpreting the homomorphisms $i\#, j\#, \partial$.

Definition 2.1. Let i, j be the inclusion maps for the triple X, A, p, $i\colon A, x_0 \subset X, x_0$, $j\colon X, x_0, x_0 \subset X, A, x_0$. Let ∂ be the homomorphism defined as follows: If $f \in \mathrm{F}_n(X, A, x_0)$, let $f' = f \mid I^{n-1}, \dot{I}^{n-1}, J^{n-2}$. Since $\dot{I}^{n-2} \cup I^{n-2} \subset J^{n-1}$, f maps $I^{n-1}, \dot{I}^{n-1}, J^{n-2}$ into A, x_0, x_0. If the homotopy $f \simeq g$ is defined by h, then h maps $I^{n-1} \times I_t$, $J^{n-1} \times I_t$, $J^{n-2} \times I_t$ into A, x_0, x_0 so f' is homotopic to g' *over* A, x_0, x_0. Thus $f' \in \pi_{n-1}(A, x_0)$. Define ∂f as f' and call ∂ the **boundary homomorphism.** In the case of the triad X, A_1, A_2, x_0, there are two boundary operators *denoted by* ∂_+ *and* ∂_- respectively acting on the elements $\{f\}$ of $\pi_n(X, A_1, A_2, x_0)$. Thus

$$\partial_+ f = (f \mid I_+^{n-1}, \dot{I}_+^{n-1}, J^{n-2}) \in \pi_n(A_1, A_1 \cap A_2, x_0)$$

and

$$\partial_- f = (f \mid I_-^{n-1}, \dot{I}_-^{n-1}, J^{n-2}) \in \pi_n(A_2, A_1 \cap A_2, x_0).$$

For f and g in $F_n(X, A, x_0)(fg) \mid I^{n-1}, \dot{I}^{n-1}, J^{n-2}$ is in $\mathrm{F}_{n-1}(A, x_0, x_0)$ whence

$$\partial fg = \partial f\, \partial g.$$

On the other hand if f and g are in $\mathrm{G}_n(X, A_1, A_2, x_0)$, then

$$\partial_+ fg = \partial_+ f\, \partial_+ g$$

$$\partial_- fg = \partial_- g\, \partial_- f.$$

Thus ∂_+ is a homomorphism while ∂_- is an **anti** homomorphism. The reason is that in the definition of the homotopy groups of pairs an orientation relation between I^{n-1} and I^n is central and since ∂_+ and ∂_- yield elements of the pair group, this relation is maintained for ∂_+ and reversed for ∂_-. The appended Fig. 15-7a and Fig. 15-7b and especially Fig. 15-7c, may illuminate the point. Of course, for Abelian groups (for $n > 3$, $\pi_n(Z, A, x_0)$ is Abelian), ∂_- can be considered a homomorphism.

The induced homomorphisms i_* and j_* are special cases of the induced homomorphism ψ_* where ψ is the map, $\psi\colon X, A, x_0 \to Y, B, y_0$. Let $f\colon I^n, \dot{I}^n, J^{n-1} \to X, A, x_0$. Then $(\psi f)\colon I^n, \dot{I}^n, J^{n-1} \to Y, B, y_0$. Again $f \simeq g$ induces $\psi f \simeq \psi g$. Hence we may define ψ_* by

(2.1a) $$\psi_* f = [\psi f]_* \in \pi_n(Y, B, y_0)$$

to give

$$\pi_n(X, A, x_0) \xrightarrow{\psi_*} \pi_n(Y, B, y_0).$$

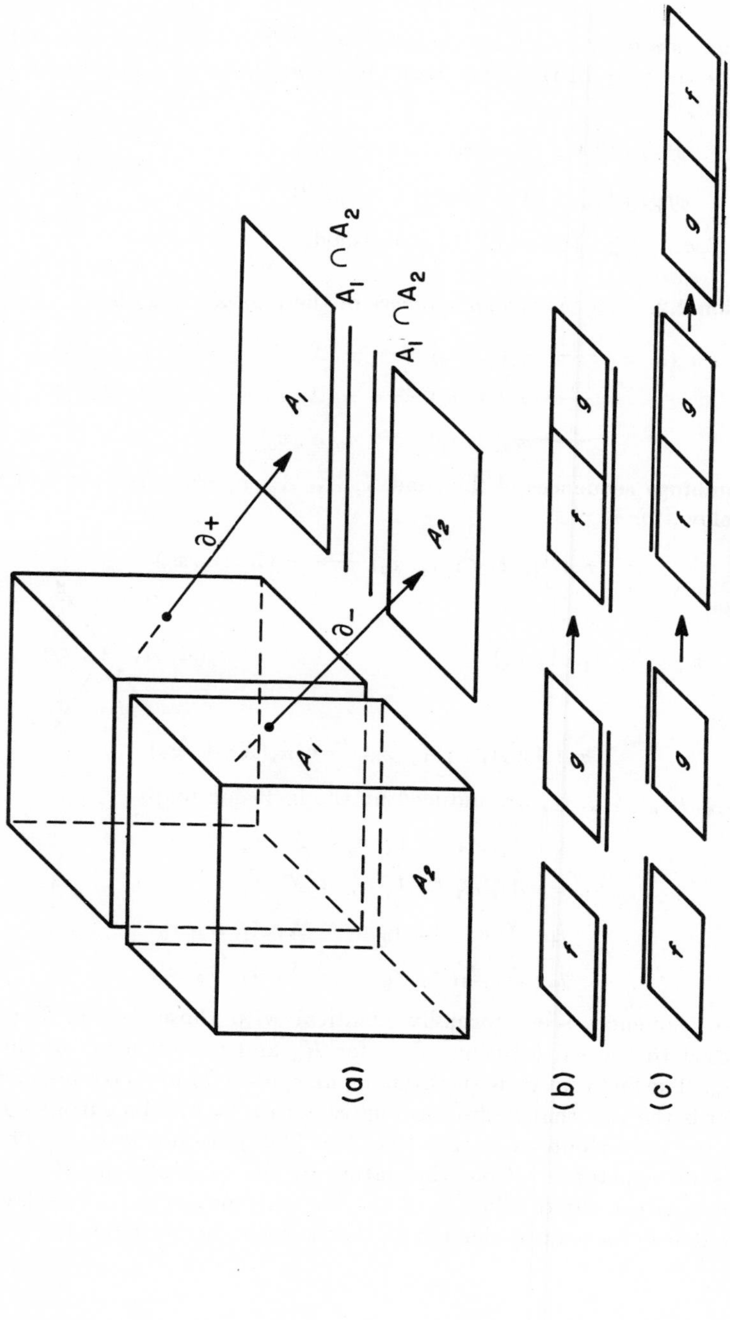

Figure 15-7

We need only verify that

(2.1b) $$\psi_* fg = \psi_* f\, \psi_* g.$$

The definition of fg uses f for the map of half the cube sectioned at $t_1 = \frac{1}{2}$ and g for the map of the other half. Replacing f by ψf and g by ψg yields $\psi f \psi g$.

Note. $\psi f \psi g\{t \mid t_1 \leq \frac{1}{2}\} = (\psi f)(t) = \psi(fg)(t).$

$\psi f \psi g\{t \mid t_1 \geq \frac{1}{2}\} = (\psi g)(t) = \psi(fg)(t).$

Thus, $\psi f \psi g = \psi fg$. Hence (2.1b) is satisfied.

Definition 2.2. The *homotopy sequence* of the pair X, A, x_0 is

(2.2a)
$$\begin{aligned}\pi_n(A, x_0) \xrightarrow{i_*} \pi_n(X, x_0) \xrightarrow{j_*} \pi_n(X, A, x_0) \xrightarrow{\delta} \pi_{n-1}(A, x_0)\\ \xrightarrow{\delta} \pi_1(A, x_0) \xrightarrow{i_*} \pi_1(X, x_0) \xrightarrow{j^*} \pi_1(X, A, x_0)\\ \xrightarrow{\delta} \pi_0(A, x_0) \longrightarrow \pi_0(X, x_0)\end{aligned}$$

The **homotopy sequences of the triad** X, A_1, A_2, x_0 are the upper and lower lines below, for $n \geq 1$.

(2.2b)
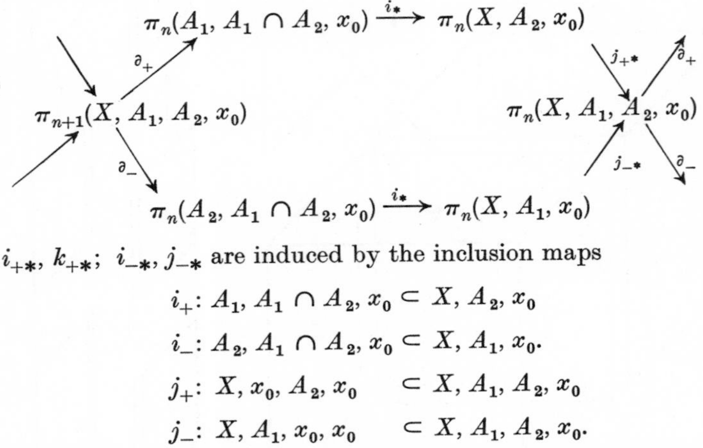

Here i_{+*}, k_{+*}; i_{-*}, j_{-*} are induced by the inclusion maps

$$\begin{aligned} i_+ &: A_1, A_1 \cap A_2, x_0 \subset X, A_2, x_0\\ i_- &: A_2, A_1 \cap A_2, x_0 \subset X, A_1, x_0.\\ j_+ &: X, x_0, A_2, x_0 \quad \subset X, A_1, A_2, x_0\\ j_- &: X, A_1, x_0, x_0 \quad \subset X, A_1, A_2, x_0.\end{aligned}$$

These sequences seem formally identical with those for the homology modules with the substitution of π_n for H_n and the inclusion of the base point x_0. The fact that ∂_- is an anti homomorphism for low n is one difference. Another is the fact that (2.2b) terminates with $n = 1$ and a surprising third is that the lowest entries in (2.2a) (and in (2.2b) are not groups. This last receives its explanation from the nature of the exactness proof for these sequences as presented below in (2.3). The only property really relevant is the existence of a neutral element so that kernels can be defined.

The symbol $\pi_0(X, x_0)$ represents the arcwise connected components of X, with the component containing x_0 considered the neutral element.

$$\pi_0(X, A, x_0),\ A \supset x_0,$$

arises from $\pi_0(X, x_0)$ by identifying all the components meeting A and this identified set is now the neutral element. The symbol $\pi_1(X, A, x_0)$ refers to the homotopy classes of the maps

$$I, \dot{I}, t_1 = 0 \to X, A, x_0.$$

The convenient group terminology is, therefore, to be interpreted as indicated for these nongroups. The neutral element in $\pi_1(X, A, x_0)$ is the class of paths from x_0 to $a_1 \in A$ deformable into a path on A under a homotopy keeping a_1 in A_1. This is equivalent to the apparently stronger requirement that the deformation be to the trivial path x_0 keeping a_1 constantly in A.

Theorem 2.3. *The sequences in* (2.2a) *and* (2.2b) *are exact for the values of n indicated.*

From the interpretations of the nth homotopy groups given in (1.2) in connection with (1.2d) as arcwise connected components

$$\pi_{n-1}(X, x_0) \leftrightarrow \pi_0(\mathrm{F}_{n-1}(X, x_0), x_0),$$
$$\pi_{n-1}(A, x_0) \leftrightarrow \pi_0(\mathrm{F}_{n-1}(A, x_0), x_0).$$

Write $X' = \mathrm{F}_{n-1}(X, x_0)$ and $A' = \mathrm{F}_{n-1}(A, x_0)$. There results also

$$\pi_n(X, A, x_0) \approx \pi_1(X', A', x_0).$$

Accordingly, the squares in the following diagram are commutative.

$$\begin{array}{ccccccc}
\xrightarrow{\partial} & \pi_n(A, x_0) & \longrightarrow & \pi_n(X, x_0) & \longrightarrow & \pi_n(X, A, x_0) & \longrightarrow, \\
 & \downarrow & & \downarrow & & \downarrow & \\
\xrightarrow{\partial} & \pi_1(A', x_0) & \xrightarrow{i_*} & \pi_1(X', x_0) & \xrightarrow{j_*} & \pi_1(X', A', x_0) & \longrightarrow
\end{array}$$

(2.3a)

$$\begin{array}{ccccc}
\xrightarrow{\partial} & \pi_{n-1}(A', x_0) & \longrightarrow & \pi_{n-1}(X, x_0) & \longrightarrow \\
 & \downarrow & & \downarrow & \\
\xrightarrow{\partial} & \pi_0(A', x_0) & \longrightarrow & \pi_0(X', x_0). &
\end{array}$$

The proof of (2.3) is now reduced to demonstration of the exactness of the lower lines of (2.3a) where we drop the primes.

At $\pi_1(X, x_0)$: $Im(i_*)$ consists of homotopy classes of loops in A centered at x_0. An element of $\pi_1(X, x_0)$ mapping into the neutral element e of

$\pi_1(X, A, x_0)$ is represented by a loop, l, centered at x_0 which may be cut at x_0 to give a path $P(a_1, 0)$ with end points x_0 and $x_0^+ = a_1$. (Note the entity written l is a loop and written $P(a_1, 0)$ is a path.) It is then required that $P(a_1, 0)$ can be deformed homotopically into x_0; holding a_1 in A. We, therefore, write $P(a_1(t))$ with $P(a_1(1))$ consisting of x_0 alone. Consider the path Q traced out by a_1 during this deformation. Let the part of Q traced by a_1 from $t = 0$ to $t = t$ be added to $Pa_1(t)$. This gives a loop denoted by $l(t)$ which is evidently homotopic to l. Hence $\boldsymbol{l} = \boldsymbol{e}$ if $l(t)$ is ultimately in A for some $0 \leq t \leq 1$. We have shown $ker\, j_* = Im\, i_*$.

At $\pi_1(X, A, x_0)$: $Im\, j_*$ consists of the classes of loops in X containing x_0. $ker\, \partial$ comprises classes of those paths in X whose end points lie in the path component of A determined by x_0. Evidently $ker\, \partial \supset Im\, j_*$. Let p be a path in X with end points x_0 and $a \in A$, and suppose x_0 and a can be joined by a path μ in A. Then p may be deformed so that a traverses μ to yield a loop l containing x_0. Thus p and 1 are homotopic. Hence $ker\, \partial \subset Im\, j_*$.

At $\pi_0(A, x_0)$: $Im\, \partial$ consists of the arcwise connected components, A_i, of A, when $A_i \in Im\, \partial$ if there is a path in X from x_0 to A_i. Since the neutral element of $\pi_0(X, x_0)$ is the arcwise connected component of x_0, $A_j \in ker\, i$ if there is a path in X joining x_0 and $a_j \in A_j$. Hence $ker\, i = Im\, \partial$.

Remark. The exact sequences of type (2.2a) and (2.2b) extend directly. Thus take $X, A_1, \ldots, A_m, x_0$, $m \leq n - 1$. There are then homomorphisms ∂_k, i_k, j_k with $k = 1, \ldots, m$ so that *each line with fixed k is exact* where

$$\xrightarrow{j_k} \pi_n(X, A_1, \ldots, A_n, x_0) \xrightarrow{\partial_k} \pi_{n-1}(A_k, A_k \cap A_1, \ldots, A_k \cap A_m, x_0)$$

$$\xrightarrow{i_k} \pi_{n-1}(X, A_1, \ldots{}_k \ldots A_m, x_0) \xrightarrow{j_k}$$

The homotopy sequence is no less a powerful tool than the homology sequence. We give some characteristic applications.

First, we indicate an equivalent formulation of the higher homotopy groups.

Definition 2.4. Denote the metric $n - 1$ dimensional disk or closed cell by E^{n+1} and the boundary by S^n. These are, of course, homeomorphs of I^{n+1} and $\dot{I}^{n+1}$. Let the closed upper hemisphere of S^n be denoted by E^n_+ and the closed lower hemisphere by E^n_-. Then $E^n_+ \cap E^n_- = S^{n-1}$, the *equatorial* sphere. Designate some point of it as s_0. This configuration can be achieved by deforming the two halves of $\{t \mid t_{n+1} = 0\}$ into E^n_+ and E^n_- respectively while carrying J^{n-1} into a point. Thus maps from S^n, E^n_+ s_0 to X, A, x_0, or from E^{n+1}_+, S^n, s^0 can equally well be used to define $\pi_n(X, A, x_0)$. Moreover, either of these triples may substitute for S^n, t_0 in the homotopy groups of

S^n, t^0 as we proceed to show as a simple application of the homotopy sequences,

$$\begin{array}{ccccccc} \pi_{m+1}(E_+^{n+1}, s_0) & \longrightarrow & \pi_{m+1}(E_+^{n+1}, S^n, s_0) & \xrightarrow{\partial} & \pi_m(S^n, s_0) & \longrightarrow & \pi_m(E_+^{n+1}, s_0) \\ \| & & & & & & \| \\ 0 & & & & & & 0 \end{array}$$

$$\pi_{m+1}(S^{n+1}, E_-^{n+1}, s_0) \xrightarrow{\partial} \pi_m(E_-^{n+1}, s_0) \xrightarrow{i} \pi_m(S^{n+1}, s_0) \xrightarrow{j}$$

whence

$$\pi_{m+1}(E_+^{n+1}, S^n, s_0) \approx \pi_m(S^n, s_0) \approx \pi_m(S^{n+1}, E_-^{n+1}, s_0).$$

Theorem 2.5. *If ψ is a map of X, A, x_0 into Y, B, y_0 or of X, A_1, A_2, x_0 into Y, B_1, B_2, y_0 the induced homomorphism* (2.1a) *yields commutative squares in* (2.5a) *or* (2.5b), *respectively*

(2.5a)
$$\begin{array}{ccccc} \longrightarrow \pi_{n+1}(X, A, x_0) & \xrightarrow{\partial} & \pi_n(A, x_0) \longrightarrow \\ \downarrow \psi_* & & \downarrow \psi_* \\ \pi_{n+1}(Y, B, y_0) & \xrightarrow{\partial} & \pi_n(B, y_0) \longrightarrow \end{array}$$

(2.5b)
$$\begin{array}{ccc} \pi_{n+1}(X, A_1, A_2, x_0) & \xrightarrow{\partial_u} & \pi_n(A_u \cap A_1, A_2, x_0) \longrightarrow \\ \downarrow \psi_* & & \downarrow \psi_* \\ \pi_{n+1}(Y, B_1, B_2, y_0) & \xrightarrow{\partial_u} & \pi_n(B_u, B_1 \cap B_2, y_0) \longrightarrow \end{array}$$

where for $u = 1$, ∂_u, i_u, j_u, $= \partial_+$, i_{+*}, j_{+*} and for $u = 2$, these are ∂_-, i_{-*}, j_{-*} respectively.

Theorem 2.6. *Let Q be the fiber space W, B, F, p and suppose B_0 is a subset of B. Write $W_0 = p^{-1}B_0$, $w_0 \in p^{-1}(b_0)$. Then*

(2.6a)
$$p_*: \pi_n(W, W_0, w_0) \approx \pi_n(B, B_0, b_0), \qquad n \geq 2$$

$$p_*: \pi_n(W, F, w_0) \simeq \pi_n(B, b_0), \qquad n \geq 2$$

and p_* is a monomorphism for $n = 1$ if $W_0 = w_0$, $B_0 = b_0$.

Note first that *ker* $p_* = 0$. The tilde refers to the bundle space. Indeed, if for $[\tilde{f}] \in \pi_n(W, W_0, w_0)$, $\quad n \geq 1$, with representative $\tilde{f}$,

$$0 = [p\tilde{f}] \in \pi_n(B, B_0, b_0),$$

then $p\tilde{f}$ is homotopic under h to the trivial map, f_0, where $f_0(I^n) = b_0$. Thus h: $I^n \times I_t$, $\dot{I}^n \times I_t$, $J^{n-1} \times I_t \to B$, B_0, b_0 with

$$h(\ ,0) = p\tilde{f}$$

$$h(\ ,1) = f_0.$$

The covering homotopy theorem guarantees the existence of the homotopy H where $pH\colon I^n \times I_t \to W$, with

(2.6b) $$H(\ ,0) = \bar{f}$$
$$H(I^n, 1) = w_0,$$

and $pH = h$. The stationary property asserts

(2.6c) $$H(J^{n-1}, I_t) = w_0.$$

Moreover, $pH(\dot{I}^n, I_t) \subset h(\dot{I}^n, I_t) = B_0$, so

(2.6d) $$H(\dot{I}^n, I^t) \subset W_0 = p^{-1} B_0.$$

Thus (2.6c), (2.6d) in conjunction with (2.6b) show $[\bar{f}] = [H(\ ,1)] = 0$.

To show p_* is onto for $n \geq 2$, recall (1.2). Thus any representative, f, of an element of $\pi_n(B, B_0, b_0)$ can be considered an element of

$$\mathrm{F}_{n-1}(B, B_0, b_0)^{I_t}, b_0^{I_t}.$$

Hence f is a homotopy over B between maps on $I^{n-1}, \dot{I}^{n-1}, J^{n-2}$ to B, B_0, b_0. Write $\bar{t} = 1 - t_n$. From its original definition $f \mid \dot{I}^n \subset B_0$ and $f(I^{n-1}, \bar{t} = 1) \subset B_0$. Since $f(J^{n-1}) = b_0$,

(2.6e) $$f(\dot{I}^{n-1}, \bar{t}) = b_0 \quad \text{and} \quad f(I^{n-1}, \bar{t} = 0) = b_0.$$

Define F_0 on I^{n-1} to W by $F_0(I^{n-1}) = w_0$. The covering homotopy theorem provides $\bar{f}\colon I^{n-1} \times I_{\bar{t}} \to W$,

(2.6f) $$p\bar{f} = f,$$

satisfying $f(\ ,0) = F_0$. Then the stationary property, with due cognizance of (2.6e), ensures that

(2.6g) $$\bar{f}(\dot{I}^{n-1}, I) = w_0.$$

Since $J^{n-1} = \dot{I}^{n-1} \times I_t \cup I^{n-1} \times (\bar{t} = 0)$, the combined assertions of (2.6f) and (2.6g) may be expressed by $\bar{f}(J^{n-1}) = w_0$. From (2.6f) there results $\bar{f}(\dot{I}^{n-1}) \subset p^{-1} B_0 = w_0$. Hence, $\bar{f}$ maps into $[f]$ under p_*.

PROBLEM

15-8. Show $\pi_n(S^1, x_0) = 0$, $n \geq 2$. *Hint:* Apply the fact that the covering space of S^1 is the real line.

Theorem 2.7. *In the fiber space* Q, *with* $b_0 = px_0$,

$$\longrightarrow \pi_{n+1}(B, b_0) \xrightarrow{\partial p_*^{-1}} \pi_n(F_{b_0}, x_0) \xrightarrow{i_x} \pi_n(X, x_0) \xrightarrow{\dot{p}_* = (pj)_*} \pi_n(B, b_0)$$
$$\xrightarrow{i_*} \pi_0(X, x_0) \xrightarrow{\dot{p}_*} \pi_0(B, b_0) \longrightarrow 0$$

is an exact sequence.

The basic sequence is again (2.2). Note (2.6) allows the replacement of $\pi_n(X, p^{-1}(b_0), b_0)$ by its isomorph under p_*^{-1}, namely $\pi_n(B, b_0)$. The only other difference with (2.2) lies in the last two terms.

At $\pi_0(X, x_0)$: $Im\ i_*$ consists of path components of X meeting F_{b_0}. $ker\ \dot{p}_*$ consists of arc components in X which project into arc component of B determined by b_0. Since p preserves connectedness, $\dot{p}_* i_* = 0$. Also, any component X_i of X with $pX_i \supset b_0$ must satisfy $X_i \cap F_{b_0} \neq \varnothing$, so $ker\ \dot{p}_* \subset Im\ (i_*)$.

At $\pi_0(B, b_0)$: $Im\ \dot{p}_*$ consists of these arc components of B which meet the projections of the arc components of X. Since $B = pX$, $\dot{p}_*$ is onto.

The combination of (101.1) and either (2.3) or (2.6) produces a variety of direct sum results.

Theorem 2.8. *If M and N are topological spaces and p, p' are the projections of $M \times N$ onto M and onto N respectively, then*

(2.8b) $$\pi_n(M \times N, m_0 \times n_0) \xrightarrow{\approx} \pi_n(M, m_0) \oplus \pi_n(N, n_0).$$

$M \times N$ is the superspace of the fiber spaces $M \times N$, M, p_1 and $M \times N$, N, p_2. A section is given by

$$s_1\colon m = m \times \bar{n} \qquad \text{for } \bar{n} \text{ fixed},$$

$$s_2\colon n = \bar{m} \times n \qquad \text{for } \bar{m} \text{ fixed}.$$

Then $(p_1 s_1)_*$ and $(p_2 s_2)_*$ are identity isomorphisms and so since the absolute homotopy groups are Abelian for $n \geq 2$ (101.1) applies. For $n = 1$ note $s_1{}^*\pi_1(M, m_0) = ker\ (p_2{}^*)$. Thus $s_1{}^*\pi_1(M, m_0)$ is a normal subgroup of $\pi_1(M \times N, m_0 \times n_0)$ and again (101.1) applies.

PROBLEM

15-9. Show (2.8) is valid for the infinite product $\Pi_{a \in A} M_a$.

A useful, necessary condition for the existence of a section may now be given.

Theorem 2.9. *If the bundle Q has a section then*

(2.9a) $$\pi_n(W, w_0) \approx \pi_n(F_{b_0}, w_0) \oplus \pi_n(B, b_0 = pw_0), \qquad n \geq 2.$$

(2.9b) $\pi_1(W, x_0)$ *contains G_1 and G_2*

where $G_1 \approx \pi_1(F_{b_0}, w_0)$ and $p_* G_2 \approx \pi_1(B, b_0)$. Though G_2 need not be a *normal subgroup yet every element* $[f] \in \pi_1(W, w_0)$ *admits a unique decomposition* $[f] = g_1 g_2$, *with* $g_i \in G_i$.

Choose $w_0 = s(b_0) \in F_{b_0}$. Then, since $ps(b) = b$,

$$p_* : \pi_n(W, w_0) \to \pi_n(B, b_0)$$
$$s_* : \pi_n(B, b_0) \to \pi_n(W, w_0)$$

with $p_* s_*$ the identity automorphism of $\pi_n(B, b_0)$. Hence (2.2) and (101.1) apply as in the immediately preceding theorems.

Remark. That (2.9a) is not necessarily valid for $n = 1$ is illustrated by the case of the Klein bottle for which with α, β the generators of $\pi_1(F_{b_0}, w_0)$ and $\pi_1(B, b_0)$ respectively, the fundamental relation is $\alpha\beta\alpha\beta^{-1} = e$ whereas according to (2.9a) it would need to be $(\alpha\beta)(\alpha\beta^{-1}) = \alpha^2$.

Lemma 2.10. *Let* Q' *be a subbundle of* Q *over the base space* B, *i.e.*, $X \supset X' \supset x_0$, $p' = p \mid X'$, $F' \subset F$, $G' = G$. *Let* $x_0 \in p'^{-1}b_0 = F'_0 \subset p^{-1}b_0 = F_0$. *Then the inclusion map* $i_+ \colon F_0, F'_0, x_0 \subset X, X', x_0$ *induces the isomorphism* $\pi_m(F_0, F'_0, x_0) \xrightarrow{i_{+*}} \pi_m(X, X', x_0)$.

Remark. Actually Q and Q' need only be fiber spaces or quasi fiber spaces (2.12).

The upper and lower levels of the sequence for the triad X, F_0, X' levels are exact (2.2b). Thus, since $F_0 \cap X' = F'_0 = p'^{-1}\, b_0$,

$$\begin{array}{ccccc}
 & \partial_+ \, \pi_m(F_0, p'^{-1}\, b_0, x_0) & \xrightarrow{i_{+*}} & \pi_m(X, X', x_0) & \\
 \overset{\partial_+}{\nearrow} & & & & \searrow \\
\pi_{m+1}(X, F_0, X', x_0) & & & & \pi_m(X, F_0, X', x_0) \\
 \underset{\partial_-}{\searrow} & & & & \nearrow \\
 & \pi_m(X', p'^{-1}\, b_0, x_0) & \xrightarrow{i_{-*}} & \pi_m(X, F_0, x_0) &
\end{array}$$

Moreover the triangle below is commutative,

$$\begin{array}{ccc}
\pi_m(X', p'^{-1}\, b_0, x_0) & \xrightarrow{i_{-*}} & \pi_m(X, F_0, x_0) \\
 {\scriptstyle p'_*} \searrow & & \swarrow {\scriptstyle p_*} \\
 & \pi_m(B, b_0, b_0) &
\end{array}$$

Both p_* and p'_* are isomorphisms (2.6). Accordingly i_{*-} in (2.10b), and hence in (2.10a), is an isomorphism. Then by exactness of the lower level there results

$$\pi_m(X, F_0, X', x_0) = 0, \qquad m \geq 1.$$

Accordingly i_{+*} is an isomorphism.

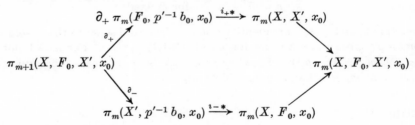

Theorem 2.11. *Let M be a connected n manifold and let m_0 be arbitrarily chosen. The inclusion map*

$$i: (M \times m_0, (M - m_0) \times m_0) \subset M \times M, M \times M - D, x_0 \times m_0$$

induces an isomorphism

$$\pi_m(M, M - m_0, m_0) \xrightarrow{i*} \pi_m(M \times M, U \times M - D, x_0 \times m_0),$$

where D is the diagonal of $M \times M$ and $x_0 \neq m_0$.

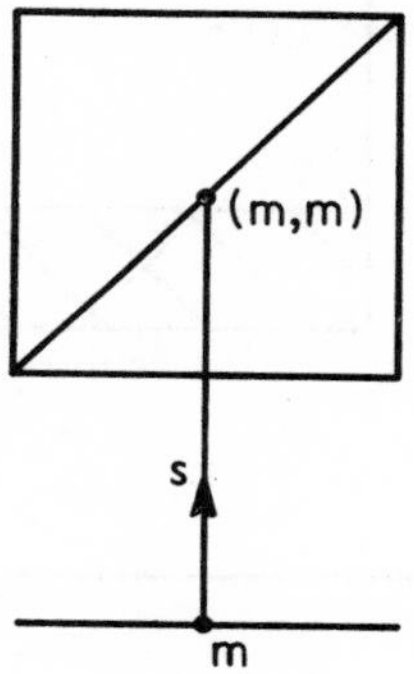

Figure 15-8

Take $M \times M$ and $M \times M - D$ as W, W' and write F and F' for M and $M - m_0$ respectively. According to (96.3) $G/G_1 \approx M$. Then $Q = \{W = M \times M, B = M = G/G_1 = F, G, p\}$ is a product bundle. The diagonal map is a section s in Q,

$$s: b = m \to (m, m).$$

(96.3) asserts that G_1 has a local section in G. Hence the conditions of (132.8) are met. Thus, $Q' = \{W' = W - sB = M \times M - D, M, F_0', G_1, p'\}$ is a fiber bundle where F_0' is taken as the fiber over m_0, i.e., $F_0' = p'^{-1} m_0 = p^{-1} m_0 - m_0 = M - m_0$. The proof is completed by applying (2.10) to Q and Q'.

Remark. Two of the notable differences between omology and homotopy groups are often cited. Thus in (2.6) π_n cannot be replaced by H_n nor by H^n. On the other hand the excision theorem (92.1) is generally invalid for homotopy groups.

Definition 2.12. A **quasi fiber space** is a triple X, B, p with p merely a map of X onto B and the induced homomorphism p_* is an isomorphism

(2.12a) $$p_*: \pi_m(X, p^{-1} px, x) \approx \pi_m(B, px), \qquad m \geq 0.$$

The isomorphism for $m = 0, 1$ is interpreted as a $1 - 1$ correspondence of the sets and a group structure is then assigned to $\pi_1(X, p^{-1}px, x)$ by the isomorphism (2.12a).

The earlier fiber spaces are also quasi fiber spaces. However, the appended diagram shows the converse is not true. The path $f(b) = b$ cannot be lifted to X so this is not a fiber space in our previously understood sense.

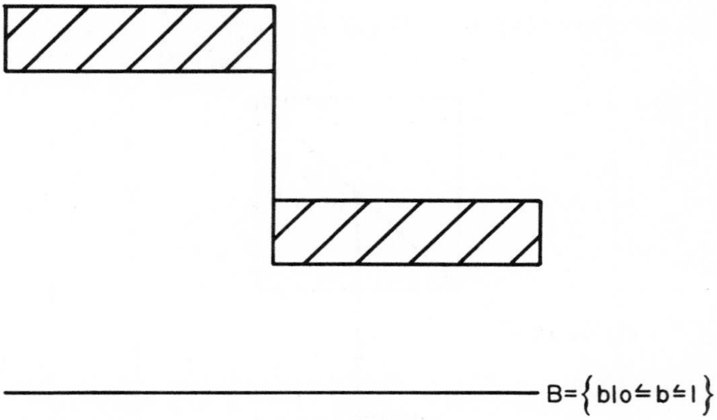

Figure 15-9

3. ATTACHING MAPS. An intuitive picture of a nontrivial element f in $\pi_n(B, b_0)$ is provided by a B exterior to a tube T, either bored completely through the space or like an $n + 1 -$ torus, which links the set $f(S^n)$. (It is to be borne in mind that the complement of S^2 in R^4 is connected and hence the inside and outside of S^2 may be joined by a path or tube disjunct from S^2.) When $n = 1$ for instance, T may be taken as a torus and $f(S^1)$ as a curtain ring which can slide around but cannot be shrunk past the boundary of T. It appears plain if an $n + 1$ dimensional disk D were introduced transversely to T that then $f(S^n)$ could be displaced to this disk and collapsed over the disk. Thus if $f(S^n)$ links only this one tube, f, would be trivial in $\pi_n(B \cup D, b_0)$ or in more drastic terminology, f would be *killed*. The figure indicates the $n = 1$ situation. I and II show the original and the collapsed positions. The attachment of D above will be given a more precise formulation.

Definition 3.1. Let σ^n be a homeomorph of an open n-simplex which is disjunct from X. Let f be continuous on $\dot{I}^n$ to X and a homeomorphism on $I^n - \dot{I}^n$ onto σ^n. Let Z be the set $X \cup \sigma^n$ topologized by keeping the topology of X intact as well as that of σ^n and defining $\overline{\sigma^n}$ as $f(I^n)$. Then $f \mid \dot{I}^n$ is an **attaching map** for σ^n and f is called a **characteristic map** for σ^n.

In the appended Fig. 15-11a the dots refer to a sequence converging to $\dot{t} \in \dot{I}^2 = S^1$ so that the limit of the corresponding sequence in σ^n is the point $f(\dot{t})$. Note that, $f(S^1)$ winds around twice (just to show another possibility).

Suppose X is S^1 then using angle parameters the map f on $\dot{I}^2 = S^1$ is defined by $f(\theta) = 2\theta$ giving 2 points of $\dot{I}^2 = S^1$ mapping into one point of S^1 and the result is a well known model of the projective plane P^2, Cf Fig. 15-11b.

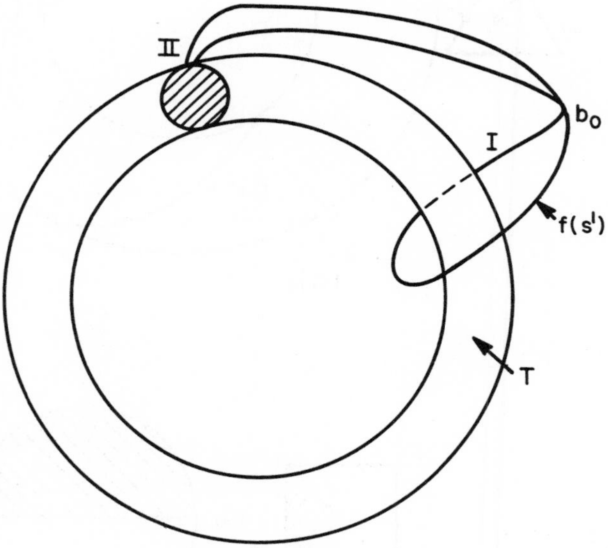

Figure 15-10

4. CW COMPLEXES. Since all cells and simplexes are understood to be concrete in this section we write $\bar{\sigma}_n$, $\bar{e}_n$ for $\|\bar{\sigma}_n\|$, $\|\bar{e}_n\|$ as well as σ_n for the open simplex and generally use the same letter for the abstract and the correlated topological entity.

Definition 4.1. The closure, $\bar{e}_n$, of an n cell, e_n, is defined by a map f of a closed simplex $\bar{\sigma}_n$ (or hypercube I^n) subject to

(a) $f\colon \sigma_n \to e_n$ is a homeomorphism,

(b) $f\dot{\sigma}_n = \dot{e}_n$,

where $\dot{e}_n$ is the boundary set of e_n and $\dot{\sigma}_n$ that of σ_n. Accordingly e_n is a T_2 space and $\dot{e}_n$ and $\bar{e}_n$ are compact.

The identification topology (**A**) is understood for $\bar{e}_n$. (Thus if $fX = Y \subset e_n$, then Y is closed if X is closed and $f^{-1}fX = X$.)

Remark. We may view e_n as being the attachment of a cell to $\dot{e}_n$ (3.1).

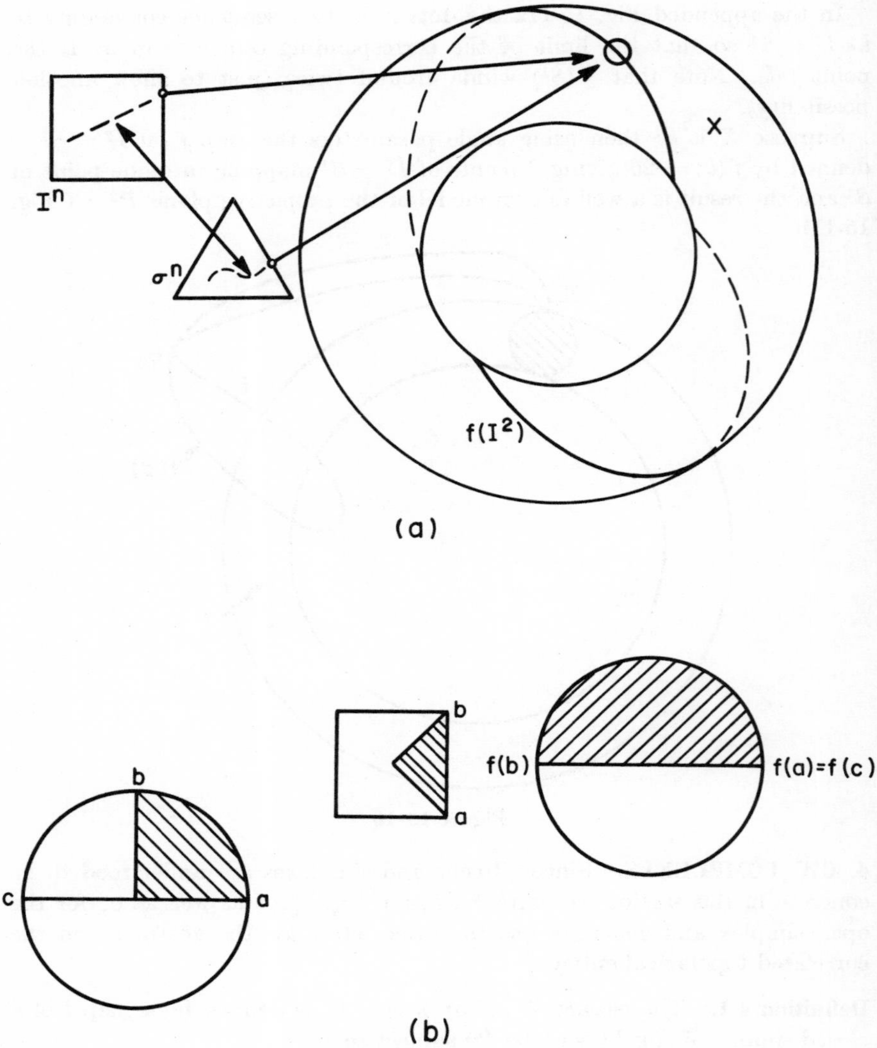

Figure 15-11

EXAMPLE 15-4. Identify $\dot{\sigma}_n$ with a point x_0 and let f be a homeomorphism on σ_n to $S^n - x_0$. Thus $e_n = S^n - x_0$ and $\dot{e}_n = e_0 = x_0$.

Definition 4.2. A **cell complex** K consists of a collection of disjunct cells $\{e_n\}$. The cells, $\{e_r\}$ such that $e_r \cap \bar{e}_n \neq \varnothing$, $r < n$ are called faces of e_n. Supplanting (21.7a) we require of K that the point set union of the faces of e_n contain $\dot{e}_n$. A **cell subcomplex**, L, of K is a subcollection $\{e_n'\}$ of the cells of K and is closed in K in the sense that if $e'_n \subset L$, then all the faces of e'_n are in L. This does not mean that L is a closed subset of K, but only that it may be represented as the union of closed sets of the form $\{e_n\}$. Note $\bar{e}_n$ need not be the point set of any subcomplex L.

Figure 15-12

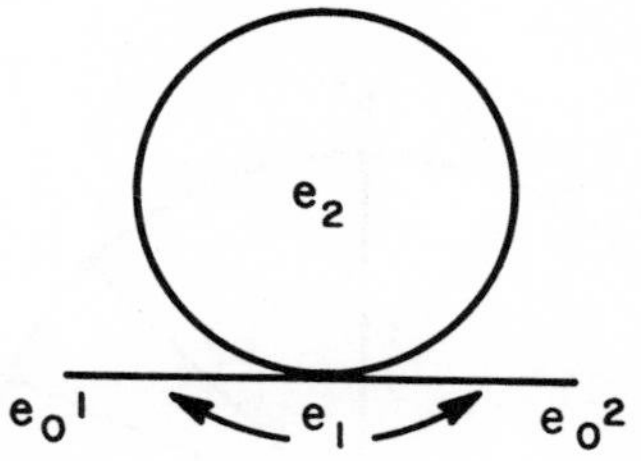

EXAMPLE 15-5. Let $K = e_2 \cup e_1 \cup e_0^1 \cup e_0^2$ where e_2 is $S^2 - x_0$, e_1 is the open segment bisected by x_0 tangent to S^2 at x_0, and e_0^1 and e_0^2 are the end points of this segment. Then $\bar{e}_2 = e_2 \cup x_0$ *is not the point set of a subcomplex* because x_0 is not a cell (but merely the map of the circle bounding σ_2, (4.1b)) and indeed the smallest complex containing $\bar{e}_2$ is K. The faces of e_2 are e_1, e_0^1, and e_0^2.

Lemma 4.3. *If L_a is a subcomplex of K for each $a \varepsilon A$ then $L = \bigcap_A L_a$ is a subcomplex of K.*

Definition 4.4. If X is a subset of K, then with L denoting a subcomplex of K

(4.4a) $$K(X) = \bigcap \{L \mid L \supset X\}$$

is the *smallest complex* or **hull** containing X. If X is a single point p let $e_n(p)$ be the unique cell containing p whence, by (4.4a),

$$K(p) = K(e_n(p)) = K(\bar{e}(p)).$$

If e_n is a simplex then $K(e_n)$ is the union of e_n and all its r dimensional faces, $0 \leq r < n$.

K is closure finite if each cell has only a finite number of faces, i.e., if $K(e_n)$ is a finite subcomplex. K is **locally finite** if every point p is an inner point of some finite subcomplex L (bear in mind e_n is not necessarily a subcomplex).

Definition 4.5. The **weak topology** for K is defined by the requirement that a point set A in K is closed (open) if and only if $A \cap \bar{e}_n$ is closed in $\bar{e}_n$ (open in $\bar{e}_n$) for the closure, $\bar{e}_n$, of every cell in K. A closure finite cell complex with the weak topology is termed a **CW complex**.

Example 15-6. Let e_1^{n+1} be the open ray from the origin to the circle of radius 1 making an angle $\pi/2^n$ with the positive x axis. Let e_1^1 be the open interval (0, 1) on the axis and let e_0^0 be the origin and e_0^n the other end point of e_1^n, $n > 1$, and let e_0^1 be the other end point of e_1^1. Let the complex K consist of these cells. The set $A = \bigcup_{n>1} e_0^n$ considered in the Euclidean

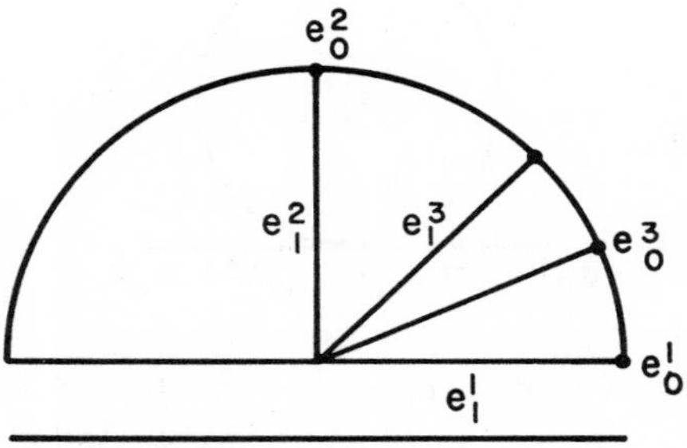

Figure 15-13

metric would have e_0^1 as a limit point and hence A would not be closed. However in the weak topology $A \cap \bar{e}_1^n = e_0^n$ is a closed set and so A is closed.

PROBLEMS

15-10. If K is a CW complex then A is closed $\Leftrightarrow A \cap L$ is closed for every finite subcomplex L.

15-11. If K is a locally finite cell complex (4.2), then K is a CW complex.

Lemma 4.6. *If K is CW and contains either an open or a closed subset X, then a transformation on X to Y where Y is an arbitrary space is continuous $\Leftrightarrow f \mid X \cap \bar{e}$ is continuous for each cell in K.*

The following refer to complexes or cells which are *not CW* cells or complexes.

Example 15-7. The boundary of an n-simplex, $n > 1$, considered a 0 complex K^0 with each point of the boundary a 0 cell. The weak topology here would imply that every set is closed, i.e., the weak topology here would be the discrete topology. Hence K^0 must contain every subset of $\dot{\sigma}_n$.

Example 15-8. The set $\bar{\sigma}_n$ considered as the complex $\underset{K^0}{\underset{\parallel}{\dot{\sigma}_n}} \cup \underset{e_n}{\underset{\parallel}{\sigma_n}} = K^n$.

Here K^0 is defined as in Example 15-7. The weak topology is consistent for $\bar{e}_n = K^n$ but this is not closure finite since $K(e_n) = e_n \cup K^0$, an infinite number of cells.

EXAMPLE 15-9. The Hilbert parallelotope is not a CW complex.

It is now possible to extend the concrete realization of abstract complexes.

Theorem 4.7. *If K is a star finite simplicial complex it has a concrete realization.*

Index the vertices of K. Suppose the simplex σ has the vertices $\{v^i \mid i \in \pi\}$. Let $\{t_i \mid i \in \pi\}$ be real numbers subject to $0 \leq t_i$, $\Sigma_\pi t_i = 1$. We topologize this set by say the Euclidean metric, thus

$$d(\{t_i\}, \{t_i'\} \mid i \in \pi\}) = (\Sigma_\pi |t_i - t_i'|^2)^{1/2}.$$

Thus we have a concrete simplex which we designate by $e(\sigma)$. Then $\{e(\sigma)\}$ is the concrete realization of K when $\bigcup e(\sigma)$ is assigned the weak topology (4.5).

5. SUSPENSION HOMOMORPHISM. Definition 5.1. Let $t_1, \ldots, t_{n+1}$ be the Cartesian coordinates of R^{n+1}. Let K be contained in the hyperplane R^n defined by $t_{n+1} = 0$. Let $\pm v^0$ be the points $(0, \ldots, 0, \pm 1)$. Connect v^0 to each point of K by a segment. The **join** so obtained is a **cone** designated by K^+. The join of $-v^0$ and K is K^-. (Evidently each segment contains only one point of K.) Then $K^+ \cup K^-$ is a double cone over K with vertices $\pm v^0$. We write this $\Sigma\, K$. More generally let I_1 be $\{t \mid |t| \leq 1\}$ and let X be an arbitrary space. Then $X \times I_1 = \{(x, t) \mid x \in X, t \in I_1\}$. Identify all points $(x, 1)$ and write v^0 and similarly identify the points $(x, -1)$ and write $-v^0$, and call the resulting space $\Sigma\, X$ the **suspension** of X. It is understood that the identification topology is used for $\Sigma\, X$. Thus if $p(x, t) = (x, t)$, $t \neq \pm 1$, and $p(x, \pm 1) = \pm v^0$ then a set A in $\Sigma\, X$ is open iff $p^{-1} A$ is open in $X \times I_1$. We shall identify X and Y with $X \times 0$ and $Y \times 0$. Suppose $\psi: X \to Y$. Let $\Sigma\, X$ have the vertices $\pm a$ and $\Sigma\, Y$ the vertices $\pm b$. We define an extension of ψ to $\Sigma\, X$ to $\Sigma\, Y$ by $\Psi(\pm a) = \pm b$ and $\Psi(x, t) = (\psi(x), t)$ otherwise. For the pair X, x_0 the suspension $\Sigma\,(X, x_0)$ is defined as the pair $\Sigma\, X$, $x_0 \times 0$ where $\Sigma\, X$ results from $X \times I_1$ by identifying $X \times \dot{I}_1 \cup x_0 \times I_1$ with $x_0 \times 0$. X, x_0 is imbedded in $\Sigma\,(X, x_0)$ as $X \times 0$, $x_0 \times 0$.

If $X = S^m$ and $Y = S^n$ *then* Ψ *induces a homomorphism called the* **suspension homomorphism** *denoted by* Σ *also*

$$\pi_m(S^n, x_0) \xrightarrow{\Sigma} \pi_{m+1}(S^{n+1}, y_0).$$

We use the inclusion maps

$$E_+^{n+1}, S^n, x_0 \xrightarrow{k} S^{n+1}, E_-^{n+1}, x_0 \xleftarrow{j} S^{n+1}, x_0, x_0.$$

The following diagram is required to be commutative:

$$\begin{array}{ccc} \pi_m(S^n, x_0) & \xrightarrow{\Sigma} & \pi_{m+1}(S^{n+1}, x_0) \\ \uparrow{\scriptstyle \partial} & & \downarrow{\scriptstyle j_*} \\ \pi_{m+1}(E_+^{m+1}, S^n, x_0) & \xrightarrow{k_*} & \pi_{m+1}(S^{n+1}, E_-^{n+1}, x_0) \end{array}$$

Since the homotopy groups of E^{m+1} are trivial it is immediate using (2.2) that ∂ and j_* are isomorphisms. Thus

$$\Sigma = j_*^{-1}\, k_*\, \partial^{-1}.$$

As a product of homomorphisms, Σ itself must be a homomorphism.

Theorem 5.2. *If X is compact, $H_n(X) \approx H_{n+1}(\Sigma X)$ for an arbitrary coefficient group.*

Let C be a cone over X. Let i and j be the inclusion maps of X into C and of C into Σ. Let e be the excision map (or relative homeomorphism) of C, X to ΣX. The exact homology sequence for C, X yields the ∂ isomorphism of $H_{n+1}(C, X)$ and $H_n(X)$. Since $e_* = \Sigma\ \partial$ the proof is complete. The cohomology counterpart is again only a group isomorphism by trivial dimensional considerations applied to products.

An associated notion in the spirit of suspension is that of the path and loop spaces.

6. PATH SPACES AS FIBER SPACES.

Till further notice it is assumed that Z is an arcwise connected space.

Definition 6.1. Let $A \cup B \subset Z$ and let $p_{A,B}$ transform $\Omega(A, B)$ (146.1). to $A \times B$ by

$$p_{A,B}(\psi) = \psi(0), \psi(1) \quad \text{for} \quad \psi \in \Omega(A, B).$$

Then $p_{A,B}$ is an onto map. The fiber is of course $p^{-1}(a, b) = \Omega(a, b)$. The fundamental importance of this path space is illustrated by the following result.

Theorem 6.2. *The triple $\Omega(A, B)$, $A \times B$, $p_{A,B}$ is a deficient Hurewicz fiber space.*

Thus let W be an arbitrary topological space and let h be a homotopy

$$W \times I_t \xrightarrow{h = h_1 \times h_2} A \times B,$$

where $h_i(W \times I) \to A$ or B accordingly as $i = 1$ or 2.

Let f map W into $\Omega(A, B)$ with $p_{A,B}f(w) = (h_1(w, 0) \times h_2(w, 0))$. That is to say

(6.2a) $$f(w) \in (Z^{I_s}, A^0, B^1)$$

or $(f(w))(s) \in Z$ subject to $(f(w))(0) \in A$, $(f(w))(1) \in B$.

We define a map $\hat{f}$ on $W \times I_s$ to Z by

(6.2b) $$\hat{f}(w, s) = (f(w))(s)$$

so $f(w, 0) = h_1(w, 0)$ and $\hat{f}(w, 1) = h_2(w, 0)$. Our problem is to find a lifted homotopy $\tilde{h}$ where $\tilde{h}$: $W \times I_t \to \Omega(A, B)$ with $\tilde{h}(w, 0) = f(w)$ and

$$p_{A,B}\,\tilde{h}(w, t) = h(w, t), h_2(w, t).$$

Hence we have the equivalent formulation of our problem as the quest for a map

(6.2c) $$\hat{h}: (W \times I_t) \times I_s \to Z$$

defined by $\hat{h}(w, t, s) = (\hat{h}(w, t))(s)$, where we know

(6.2d) $$\hat{h}(w, 0, s) = \hat{f}(w, s),\quad \hat{h}(w, t, 0) = h_1(w, t),\quad \hat{h}(w, t, 1) = h_2(w, t).$$

The set

$$K = \{0\}_t \times I_s \cup I_t \times \{0\}_s \cup I_t \times \{1\}_s$$

is a retract of $I_t \times I_s$. A retracting function, r, projects $I_t \times I_s$ onto K from the point $t, s = \frac{3}{2}, \frac{1}{2}$. Then note (6.2d) gives the definition of $\hat{h}$ on $W \times K$ to Z. Write this known map as $\hat{h}_0$. Define the extension of $\hat{h}$ required in (6.2c) by $\hat{h}(w, t, s) = \hat{h}_0(w, r(t, s))$.

If for fixed $\bar{w}$ and $t \in U(t_0)$, $h_i(\bar{w}, t)$ is constant, the stationary property would require that the same be true of $h(\bar{w}, t, s)$ for each $s \in I_s$, but the mode of definition gainsays this for $s \times U(t_0)$ does not map into a single point under r.

On changing the projection other fiber spaces are obtained from the path space. Thus if $pf = f(0)$, $f \in \Omega(Z, A)$, the fiber is $\Omega(z, A)$ and the fiber triple is $\Omega(Z, A)$, Z, p. A similar remark obtains if $pf = f(1)$.

Lemma 6.3. $\Omega(z_0) = \Omega(z_0, Z)$ *is contractible.*

Again we shall use z_0 not only as a point, but as a point path or map $z_0(t \mid I_t) = z_0$. The points of a path from z_0 to z are denoted by $f(t; z)$ where $\{f(t; z) \mid t \in I_t$ or $f(\ \ ; z) \in \Omega(z_0)$. A contraction h on $\Omega(z_0) \times I_s$ to the point map z_0 is defined by $h(f(\quad; z), s) = f(st, z)$. Thus the new end point when $s \neq 0$ is $f(s, z)$. Intuitively each path is shrunk over itself to z_0. (Of course nothing is implied here about contractibility of Z to z_0.)

Lemma 6.4. *$\Omega(A, Z)$ is a deformation retract of Z.*

PROBLEMS

15-12. If z is locally arcwise connected, and $pf = f(1)$ where $f \in \Omega(z_0)$, then p is open.

15-13. If X_1 and X_2 are 1-connected, $\Lambda(X_1 \times X_2)$ is homeomorphic to $\Lambda X_1 \times \Lambda X_2$.

The path spaces furnish a natural perquisite for treating local properties and imbedding concepts.

Definition 6.5. Suppose X is arcwise connected. The **tangent space** at x_0, $T(x_0)$, is the subset of $\Omega(x_0)$ consisting of paths with initial point x_0, never crossing x_0 thereafter. The **local omology modules at** x_0 are defined as the omology modules of $T(x_0)$, thus $H(T(X, x_0), T(A, x_0), R)$ for A a closed subset of X, for instance. A quite different definition is that in (114.2a).

If $Y \subset X$, the **enveloping space** of Y in X, $E(Y, X)$, is the subset of $\Omega(Y, X)$ consisting of paths in X, whose initial point only, is in Y.

We can apply these ideas in an alternate exposition of the Smith homomorphisms (Cf. 138). Thus with Z a space, k a prime and Δ the diagonal map of $Z \to Z^k$ we define $E_k(Z)$ as $E(\Delta Z, Z^k)$. Let μ be an element of $E_k(Z)$, that is to say μ is a certain map of I. Then the permutation operator t on Z^k induces an operator $\dot{t}$ on $E_k(Z)$ according to $(\dot{t}\mu)(s) = t(\mu(s))$. A fixed point would be a μ such that $t(\mu(s)) = \mu(s)$, but t has no fixed points in $Z^k - \Delta Z$ and so except for $s = 0$, $t\mu(s) \neq \mu(s)$ or $\dot{t}$ is fixed point free on $E_k(Z)$. We can therefore write $\boldsymbol{X}$ for $E_k(Z)$. Let $\mu \sim \nu$ for elements of $E_k(Z)$ iff $\mu = \dot{t}^i\nu$ for some $i < k$. The orbit space is $E_k(Z)/\dot{T}_k$ or $\boldsymbol{X}/\dot{T}_k = \{\dot{t}\}$. This is the basic situation in Chapter 13. If triangulations are introduced, we can therefore carry over the results from that chapter. We can use singular omology instead and avoid triangulations. We therefore add the following comments: Suppose now $E(Z, W)$ is an arbitrary enveloping space of Z. We assume t is a homeomorphism of W of period k. A singular simplex of $E(Z, W)$ is the pair (Δ_n, u) where u: $\bar{\Delta}_n \to E(Z, W)$. Define the induced action of t on u by writing $(\bar{t}u)(\Delta_n) = t(u(\Delta_n))$. Thus we are led to the singular complex $SE(Z, W)$ admitting the group of order k generated by $\bar{t}$. Write $\boldsymbol{X}$ for $SE(Z, W)$ and X for $SE(Z, W)/T_k$. The parallelism with (138) is clear.

7. COVERING SPACE GENERALIZATIONS. One view of the space-covering space relation is that the fundamental group is modified, but the other homotopy groups remain the *same* for both. Such a relation can be extended by replacing the fundamental group by the first m homotopy groups. The way of making the extension must be different from that involved in going to the usual covering space, and utilizes a variety of concepts occurring in the preceding two chapters. Parenthetically we may remark that a homology counterpart can evidently be formulated.

Definition 7.1. Let f be a representative of a nontrivial element $f \in \pi_m(B, b_0)$ where B is considered arcwise connected. Then f maps S^m, s_0 into B, b_0. Identify σ^{m+1} with $E^{m+1} - S^m$ where $S^m = \dot{E}^{m+1}$ and write $f(s \mid s \in E^{m+1} - S^m) = s$. Then f is a characteristic map for σ^{m+1} and attaches it to B. Observe that f is homotopic to s_0 in $B \cup \sigma^{m+1}$. Accordingly, f has been **killed.** The group $\pi_m(B, b_0)$ can be killed by killing all its generators by adding disjoint (open) cells to get a space $B_1 = B \cup \bigcup \sigma^{m+1}$ where the union refers to all the added cells. Note B is closed in B_1. Moreover

(7.1a)
$$\pi_i(B_1, b_0) \approx \pi_i(B, b_0), \qquad i < m,$$
$$\pi_m(B_1, b_0) = 0.$$

It is not necessarily true that

(7.1b)
$$\pi_{m+j}(B_1, b_0) \approx \pi_{m+j}(B, b_0), \qquad j > 0.$$

Indeed, suppose $B = S^2$. Then $\pi_3(S^2, s_0) \neq 0$ by Example 15-2. On the other hand, if a cell σ^3 is attached to S^2, the result is a solid sphere or disk for which not only π_2 but, π_3 also, vanishes.

If B_n is the space obtained by killing $\pi_{n+m-1}(B_{n-1}\, b_0)$, $B_0 = B$ then

(7.1c)
$$\hat{B} = \bigcup B_n$$

contains B as a closed subset and satisfies

(7.1d)
$$\pi_i(\hat{B}, b_0) \approx \pi_i(B, b_0), \qquad i < n,$$

under the inclusion map of B in $\hat{B}$ and

(7.1e)
$$\pi_i(\hat{B}, b_0) = 0, \qquad i \geq n.$$

Theorem 7.2. *If B is arcwise connected, a space X and a projection p can be defined to constitute a fiber space. Furthermore*

$$\pi_i(X, x_0) \approx \pi_i(B, b_0), \qquad i \geq m,$$
$$\pi_i(X, x_0) \approx 0, \qquad i < m.$$

With $\hat{B}$ given by (7.1c), let $\hat{p}$ be defined on $\Omega = \Omega(b_0, \hat{B})$ to $\hat{B}$ by $\hat{p}f = f(1)$. Let $\Omega^1 = \Omega^1(b_0, B) = p^{-1}\, B$ and let $p^1 = \hat{p} \mid \Omega^1(b_0, B)$. Then $\Omega^1(b_0, B)$, B, p^1 and $\Omega(b_0, \hat{B})$, $\hat{B}$, $\hat{p}$ yield deficient Hurewicz fiber spaces. Moreover a fiber $p^{-1}(b) = F_b$ is $\Omega(b_0, b)$ which is of the same homotopy type as $F = \Lambda(b_0)$ the loop space in $\hat{B}$. The homotopy sequences of these two fiber spaces are indicated in a common diagram in which the upper and lower lines represent exact sequences, and the central square is commutative.

$$\begin{array}{ccccccc} & & \pi_q(\Omega^1, b_0) & \xrightarrow{p^1} & \pi_q(B, b_0) & & \\ & \nearrow^{i} & \big\downarrow j & & \big\downarrow k & \searrow^{\partial^1} & \\ \rightrightarrows \pi_q(F, b_0) & & & & & & \pi_{q-1}(F, b_0) \\ & \searrow_{i} & & & & \nearrow_{\hat{\partial}} & \\ & & \pi_q(\Omega, b_0) & \xrightarrow{\hat{p}} & \pi_q(\hat{B}, b_0) & & \end{array}$$

Note b_0 is the trivial loop based at b_0 in $F = \Lambda(b_0)$ and in Ω and in Ω^1 and is also used as a point of B or of $\hat{B}$ for $\pi_q(B, b_0)$ and for $\pi_q(\hat{B}, b_0)$. Since $\Omega(b_0, \hat{B})$ is contractible (6.3), for all q, $\pi_q(\Omega, b_o) = 0$. Hence ∂^1 is an isomorphism. For $q \geq m$,

$$\pi_q(F, b_0) = \pi_{q-1}(F, b_0) = 0,$$

by reason of (7.1e). Therefore

$$\pi_q(\Omega^1, b_0) \approx \pi_q(B, b_0). \tag{7.2a}$$

If $q < m$, then k is an isomorphism according to (7.1d). Hence ∂^1 is an isomorphism. Accordingly for $q < m$,

$$\pi_q(\Omega^1, b_0) = 0. \tag{7.2b}$$

The assertion of the theorem is, therefore, valid for $X = \Omega^1(b_0, B)$.

A special consequence is that passage from a space to its universal covering space does not affect the higher homotopy groups. Hence investigations involving these last named groups can be carried out under the assumption that the space is simply connected with no loss of generality.

We shall describe a general situation reminiscent of Hopf Algebras as treated in (129). However, our exposition does not demand previous reading of (129).

8. EXTENDED HOMOTOPY GROUPS. **Definition 8.1.** We restrict attention to the category of based spaces X, x_0 (Example 10-9). We suppress the base point generally and write X for X, x_0. Recall if $f \in G(X, Y)$ then $f(x_0) = y_0$. A homotopy satisfies

$$\begin{aligned} &\psi((X, x_0) \times I) \to Y, y_0, \\ &\psi(x_0, t) = y_0, t \in I. \end{aligned} \tag{8.1a}$$

The map functor M on $\mathfrak{A}_0 \times \mathfrak{A}_0$ to $\mathfrak{A}_0$ assigns to each pair of based spaces X, Y the based space $Y^X, y_0^{x_0} = W, w_0$ topologized by the compact open topology (Example 10-22). Here w_0 is the map taking all of X into y_0.

The homotopy classes are the path components of $M(X, Y)$ and constitute $\pi(X, Y)$. If $\mathfrak{B}_0$ is the category of based sets and N is the functor on $\mathfrak{A}_0$ to $\mathfrak{B}_0$ which assigns to each based space its underlying set, then the composition NM yields the *hom* functor defined in (108.4). It is clear either directly from the definition of M or by the analogy with *Hom*, that M is covariant in the second variable and contravariant in the first.

Definition 8.2. The **wedge product,** $X \vee Y$, of two based spaces is the subset of $X \times Y$ consisting of $X \times y_0 \cup x_0 \times Y$. If $X \xrightarrow{\tau} X'$ and $Y \xrightarrow{\theta} Y'$ we define $\theta \vee \psi\colon X \vee Y \to X' \vee Y'$ by

$$\theta \vee \psi\,(x \times y_0) = \theta(x) \times y_0',$$

$$\theta \vee \psi\,(x_0 \times y) = x_0' \times \psi(y).$$

The dual of the diagonal map Δ, is written ∇, with $\nabla\colon X \vee X \to X$ defined by

$$\nabla(x, x_0) = \nabla(x_0, x) = x.$$

Remark. If i_1 and i_2 are the injections of X, x_0 onto the first or onto the second member of $X \vee X$ and if p_i and p_2 are the projections of $X \times X$ onto the first or onto the second member then $\nabla\, i_j =$ identity and $p_j\, \Delta =$ identity.

Definition 8.3. Y is an H **space** if there is a pairing or map $\mu\colon Y \times Y \to Y$ which is like a group multiplication up to homotopy equivalence. More precisely we postulate also the existence of $i\colon Y \to Y$ such that with 0 the collapsing map $Y \to y_0$ there maintains

$$\mu \in \pi(Y \times Y, Y) \quad \text{and} \quad i \in \pi(Y, Y)$$

with

(8.3a) Associativity: $\mu(\mu \times 1) \simeq \mu(1 \times \mu)$.

(8.3b) Right unit: Up to homotopy

$$y \xrightarrow{\Delta} y \times y \xrightarrow{1\times 0} y \times y_0 \xrightarrow{\mu} y.$$

That is to say $\mu(1 \times 0)\Delta$ yields the homotopy class of the identity map.

(8.3c) Right inverse: $\mu(1 \times i)\Delta \simeq 0$.

Definition 8.4. X is a co-H space if there are maps ν on X to $X \vee X$ and j on X to X with

(8.4a) $$(1 \vee \nu)\nu \simeq (\nu \vee 1)\nu,$$

(8.4b) $$\nabla(1 \vee 0)\nu \simeq 1,$$

(8.4c) $$\nabla(1 \vee j)\nu \simeq 0.$$

If X is a co-H **space** or Y is an H **space** one can define a multiplicative structure in $\pi(X, Y)$ where if α is the map, $[\alpha]$ or $\boldsymbol{\alpha}$ is the homotopy class.

Definition 8.5. Let Y be an H space and suppose α and α_1 are elements of $\pi(X, Y)$. Since $\alpha \simeq \alpha', {}_1\alpha \simeq \alpha_1'$ implies $\alpha \times \alpha_1 \simeq \alpha_1' \times \alpha_1'$ we define $\circ$ by

$$\boldsymbol{\alpha} \circ \boldsymbol{\alpha}_1 = [\alpha \circ \alpha_1 = \mu(\alpha \times \alpha_1)\Delta] \in \pi(X, Y).$$

If X is a co-H space and β and β_1 are elements of $\pi(X, Y)$ we define the operation $+$ by

$$\boldsymbol{\beta} + \boldsymbol{\beta}_1 = [\beta + \beta_1 = \nabla(\beta \vee \beta_1)\nu] \in \pi(X, Y).$$

Theorem 8.6. *If Y is an H space then $\pi(X, Y)$ is a group under the operation $\circ$ and is contravariant in the first variable. Thus if $\tau\colon X \to X'$ then the induced map $\pi(X', Y) \to \pi(X, Y)$ is a homomorphism. (i.e. the group structure is natural).*

For associativity observe

$$(\alpha \circ \beta) \circ \gamma = \mu(\mu(\alpha \times \beta)\Delta \times \gamma)\Delta \simeq \mu(\mu \times 1)(\alpha \times \beta \times \gamma)\Delta^3$$

where Δ^3 is the homotopy class of the diagonal map

$$y \to y \times y \times y.$$

Similarly

$$\alpha \circ (\beta \circ \gamma) = \mu(1 \times \mu)(\alpha \times \beta \times \gamma)\Delta^3.$$

We now invoke (8.3a). Similarly the existence of a right unit namely 0 and a right inverse are immediate consequences of (8.3b) and (8.3c). If τ maps X into X' then we define $\tau\, \boldsymbol{\alpha}$ by $[\alpha\tau]$. Accordingly

$$\begin{aligned}\tau\,[\alpha \circ \beta] = [(\alpha \circ \beta)\tau] = [\mu(\alpha \times \beta)\Delta\tau] &= [\mu(\alpha \times \beta)(\tau \times \tau)\Delta] \\ &= \mu(\alpha\tau \times \beta\tau)\Delta \\ &= \tau\,(\alpha) \circ \tau\,(\beta).\end{aligned}$$

That is to say τ is a homomorphism so subsequently we may write $\tau^{\#}$.

Remark. If homotopy *equivalence* is replaced by *equality* an H-space becomes a topological group.

For a co-H space we find it convenient to bring in the base point in the notation

$$(x, x_0) \xrightarrow{\nu} (x, x_0) \vee (x, x_0) \xrightarrow{0 \vee 1} (x_0, x_0) \vee (x, x_0) \xrightarrow{\nabla} (x_0, x).$$

If *equality* replaces *homotopy* we get $\nabla(0 \vee 1)\nu = 1$. This means $(x, x_0) = (x_0, x)$. Hence $X = x_0$ or only the one point space is possible.

Remark. An alternative designation of the two products would be μ^* and ν_*. In any case, for comparison with similar concepts treated in the latter part of 129, the correspondents are $\circ$ and m, and $+$ and Δ.

Theorem 8.7. *If X is a co-H space then $\pi(X, Y)$ is a group under the operation $+$ and is covariant in the second variable. Thus if $\theta\colon Y \to Y'$ then the induced map $\pi(X, Y) \to \pi(X, Y')$ is a homomorphism (the composition $+$ is natural on Y).*

The situation is the dual of that for (8.6).

Theorem 8.8. *If $\pi(X, Y)$ is a group with contravariance in the first variable then its structure is induced by an H-space structure on Y.*

First let $\tau\colon X \to Y$. Then since $\tau^{\#}$ is a homomorphism, if e is the identity of $\pi(Y, Y)$, $\tau^{\#}(e)$ is the identity of $\pi(X, Y)$. However with τ the 0 map $X \to y_0$, $\tau^{\#}(\alpha) = 0$ for every $\alpha \in \pi(Y, Y)$ and in particular for $\alpha = e$. In short 0 is the identity of $\pi(X, Y)$.

As a trick for exposition we denote somewhat inaccurately by $p \otimes \phi$ and $\phi \otimes p$ the obvious projections on $Y \times Y$ to Y. Effectively ϕ acts as a "space annihilator," $\otimes$ as an indexing device and p is used for 1. Let $\tau\colon X \to Y \times Y$. Then since $\tau^{\#}$ is a homomorphism

$$\tau^{\#}([p \otimes \phi] \circ [\phi \otimes p]) = [(p \otimes \phi)\tau] \circ [(\phi \otimes p)\tau].$$

Denote by μ the element $(p \otimes \phi) \circ (\phi \otimes p)$. Then with $\tau = \mu \times 1$ and $X = Y \times Y \times Y$

$$\begin{aligned}\mu(\mu \times 1) &= (p \otimes \phi)(\mu \times 1) \circ (\phi \otimes p)(\mu \times 1)\\ &\simeq (p\mu \otimes \phi) \circ (\phi \otimes \phi \otimes p)\end{aligned}$$

using $(p \otimes \phi)(\mu \times 1) = (p\mu \otimes \phi)$ and $(\phi \otimes p)(\mu \times 1) = (\phi\mu) \times p = \phi \otimes \phi \otimes p$. Next

$$(p\mu \times \phi) \simeq (p \otimes \phi \otimes \phi) \circ (\phi \otimes p \otimes \phi)$$

so

$$\begin{aligned}\mu(\mu \times 1) &\simeq (p \otimes \phi \otimes \phi) \circ (\phi \otimes p \otimes \phi) \circ (\phi \otimes \phi \otimes p)\\ &\simeq \mu(1 \times \mu).\end{aligned}$$

Accordingly μ satisfies (8.3a).

Similarly we can show (8.3b) and (8.3c). For instance for (8.3b)

$$\begin{aligned}\mu(1 \times 0)\,\Delta &= (p \otimes \phi) \circ (\phi \otimes p)(1 \times 0)\,\Delta\\ &\simeq (p \otimes \phi)(1 \times 0)\,\Delta \circ (\phi \otimes p)(1 \times 0)\,\Delta \simeq 1 \circ \phi \simeq 1.\end{aligned}$$

Theorem 8.9. *If $\pi(X, Y)$ is a group and the composition is natural on Y then this composition is induced by a co-H structure on X.*

The argument will be clear from that for (8.8).

One of the notably useful results is the commutativity theorem.

Theorem 8.10. *If α_i and β_i are elements of $\pi(X, Y)$, $i = 1, 2$, then*

(8.10a) $$(\alpha_1 + \alpha_2) \circ (\beta_1 + \beta_2) = \alpha_1 \circ \beta_1 + \alpha_2 \circ \beta_2.$$

The multiplications $+$ and $\circ$ are the same and are commutative.

We observe first that

$$\pi(X_1 \vee X_2, Y) \approx \pi(X_1, Y) \oplus \pi(X_2, Y).$$

The key to our proof is that $\circ$ and $+$ are natural transformations on

$$\pi(X, Y) \oplus \pi(X, Y) \text{ to } \pi(X, Y).$$

We introduce the permutation isomorphism T, namely

$$T\colon \pi(X_1, Y) \oplus \pi(X_2, Y) \xrightarrow[\approx]{} \pi(X_2, Y) \oplus \pi(X_1, Y).$$

Since $\circ$ is natural, the following diagram commutes.

$$\begin{array}{ccc} \pi(X_1 \vee X_2, Y) \oplus \pi(X_1 \vee X_2, Y) & \approx & \pi(X_1, Y) \oplus \pi(X_2, Y) \oplus \pi(X_1, Y) \oplus \pi(X_2, Y) \\ \Big\downarrow \circ & & \approx \Big\downarrow 1 \oplus T \oplus 1 \\ & & \pi(X_1, Y) \oplus \pi(X_1, Y) \oplus \pi(X_2, Y) \oplus \pi(X_2, Y) \\ & & \Big\downarrow \circ \oplus \circ \\ \pi(X_1 \vee X_2, Y) & \approx & \pi(X_1, Y) \oplus \pi(X_2, Y). \end{array}$$

In particular, suppose α_i and β_i are in $\pi(X_i, Y)$, $i = 1, 2$. Then

(8.10c) $$\begin{aligned}(\alpha_1 \vee \alpha_2) \oplus (\beta_1 \vee \beta_2) &\to (\alpha_1 \vee \alpha_2) \circ (\beta_1 \vee \beta_2) \\ &\to (\alpha_1 \circ \beta_1) \oplus (\alpha_2 \circ \beta_2)\end{aligned}$$

The following diagram commutes:

(8.10d) $$\begin{array}{ccc} \pi(X \vee X, Y) \oplus \pi(X \vee X, Y) & \xrightarrow{+\oplus+} & \pi(X, Y) \oplus \pi(X, Y) \\ \Big\downarrow \circ & & \Big\downarrow \circ \\ \pi(X \vee X, Y) & \xrightarrow{\quad + \quad} & \pi(X, Y) \end{array}$$

Let α_i and β_i be elements of $\pi(X, Y)$, $i = 1, 2$. The down and then over path may be interrupted at the end of the $\circ$ homorphism to take account of (8.10c). There results

$$(\alpha_1 \vee \alpha_2) \oplus (\beta_1 \vee \beta_2) \to (\alpha_1 \circ \beta_1) \oplus (\alpha_2 \circ \beta_2) \to (\alpha_1 \circ \beta_1) + (\alpha_2 \circ \beta_2).$$

The over and down path yields

$$(\alpha_1 \vee \alpha_2) \otimes (\beta_1 \vee \beta_2) \to (\alpha_1 + \alpha_2) \vee (\beta_1 + \beta_2) \to (\alpha_1 + \alpha_2) \circ (\beta_1 + \beta_2)$$

and the two end results just obtained must be the same (8.10d).

Let us differentiate between the unit of $\circ$ and that of $+$ by writing 0 and 0^+. Take -0 as the inverse of 0 under the group multiplication $+$. Thus

(8.10e) $$0 + (-0) = 0^+.$$

If $\alpha_2 = \beta_1 = 0$, $\alpha_1 = -0$ and $\beta_2 = 0^+$, then (8.10a) yields $0^+ = -0$.

Hence substituting in (8.10e),

$$0 = 0 + 0^+ = 0^+.$$

We were therefore justified in not making a distinction between 0 and 0^+. Let $\alpha_2 = \beta_1 = 0$ and let $\alpha_1 = \alpha$, $\beta_2 = \beta$. Then from (8.10a)

$$\alpha \circ \beta = \alpha + \beta.$$

Let $\alpha_1 = \beta_2 = 0$ and let $\alpha_2 = \alpha$, $\beta_1 = \beta$. Then

$$\alpha \circ \beta = \beta + \alpha.$$

Hence $+$ is a commutative multiplication and is identical with $\circ$ (for instance let $\alpha_1 = \beta$, $\beta_2 = \alpha$ and $\alpha_2 = \beta_1 = 0$).

Definition 8.11. Let $\mathfrak{A}_0$ be the category of based locally compact spaces. We write X and Y for X, x_0 and Y, y_0. Let I be the unit segment. Let $h: X \times I \to Y$. We define the map $h': X \to Y^I$ by $h'(x)$ is a function $h_x \in Y^I$ such that

(8.11a) $$h'(x)(t) = h_x(t) = h(x, t).$$

It is well known that since I is metric, continuity of h and of h' are equivalent. Accordingly $Y^{I \times X}$ and $(Y^I)^X$ are homeomorphic. Then $Y^{\Sigma X} = M(\Sigma X, Y)$ is a subspace of the first and $(\Lambda Y)^X = M(X, \Lambda Y)$ of the second, where ΛY comprises the maps for which $\dot{I}$ goes to y_0 and Y is assumed path connected. Moreover these spaces are homeomorphic under (8.11a). Denote this correspondence by L.

Let $\psi: X' \to X$ and $\theta: Y \to Y'$. Define $\Sigma\,\psi: \Sigma\, X' \to \Sigma\, X$ and $\Lambda\theta: \Lambda Y \to \Lambda Y'$ by

Lemma 8.12

(8.12a) $$(\Sigma\,\psi)(x', t) = (\psi(x'), t)$$

(8.12b) $$(\Lambda\theta)(\omega) = \theta\omega.$$

Suppose h and $k \in M(\Sigma X, Y)$. Then $L(h \Sigma \psi) = (Lh) \psi$. Thus

$$\begin{aligned} L(h \Sigma \psi)(x')(t) &= (h \Sigma \psi)(x', t) \\ &= h(\psi(x'), t) \\ &= (Lh)(\psi(x'))(t). \end{aligned}$$

Similarly $L(\theta h) = \Lambda\theta L(h)$. Also $L(h + k) = L(h) \circ L(k)$.

Remark. Let N be the functor taking a space into its (untopologized) set. Then (8.12a) implies that there is a natural equivalence ϕ on $hom(\Sigma X, Y) = NM(\Sigma X, Y)$ to $NM(X, \Lambda Y) = hom(X, \Lambda Y)$, that is to say ΣX is the left adjoint of ΛY. We can introduce E and E' (with S, T corresponding to Σ, Λ) (108.4) and then pass to the homotopy groups.

Theorem 8.13. *The transformation L defines a natural equivalence again denoted by L on $\pi(\Sigma X, Y)$ to $\pi(X, \Lambda Y)$.*

It is plain that homotopic elements of $M(\Sigma X, Y)$ correspond to homotopic elements of $M(X, \Lambda(Y))$. That is to say with ψ^* and θ_* constricted by (8.12a) and (8.12b),

$$\psi^* L = L(\Sigma \psi)^*$$

$$(\Lambda\theta)_* L = L\theta_*.$$

Definition 8.14. Denote $\pi(\Sigma^n X, Y)$ by $\pi_n(X, Y)$.

Evidently

Lemma 8.15. $\pi_n(X, Y) = \pi(\Sigma^{n-k} X, \Lambda^k Y), \qquad 0 \leq k \leq n,$

$$= \pi_{n-k}(X, \Lambda^k Y).$$

An important consequence (Problem 15-3) is

Lemma 8.16. $\pi_n(X, Y)$ *is Abelian for* $n \geq 2$.

Thus $\pi_n(X, Y) = \pi_{n-1}(\Sigma X, \Lambda Y)$. Then (8.10) applies.

Example 15-10. Let $X, x_0 = S^n, s_0$. Then $\pi_n((S^n, s_0), (Y, y_0))$ is the usual homotopy group $\pi_n(Y, y_0)$ (151.2). Since

$$S^n, s_0 = \Sigma(S^{n-1}, s_0), \quad \pi_n(Y, y_0) = \pi_{n-k}(\Lambda^k(Y, y_0)).$$

Example 15-11. If X is a topological space its suspension ΣX (5.1) is a co-H space. Indeed the natural map $\nu\colon \Sigma X \to \Sigma X \vee \Sigma X$ can be defined by

$$\begin{aligned} \nu(x, t) &= ((x, 2t), x_0), \quad 0 \leq t \leq \tfrac{1}{2}, \\ &= (x_0, (x, 2t - 1)), \quad \tfrac{1}{2} \leq t \leq 1. \end{aligned}$$

The loop space $\Lambda(X, x_0)$ (146.1) is an H space. Then the 0 element is the trivial loop $\omega(s \mid I) = x_0$. The natural map μ on $\Lambda \times \Lambda$ to Λ is defined by

$$\begin{aligned}\mu(\omega_1, \omega_2)(t) &= \omega_1(2t), & 0 \leq t \leq \tfrac{1}{2}\\ &= \omega_2(2t-1), & \tfrac{1}{2} \leq t \leq 1.\end{aligned}$$

Continuity of ν and ω is a routine inference, the latter because the coopen topology is used for Λ.

EXAMPLE 15-12. In the category $\mathfrak{A}_o$ (8.11) if $[\psi] \in \pi(X, Y)$ identify $\Sigma[\psi] \in \pi(\Sigma X, \Sigma Y)$ with $[\Sigma \psi]$ where $\Sigma \psi$ is the Ψ of (5.1). Since ΣX is a co-H space $\pi(\Sigma^k X, \Sigma^k Y)$ is a group for $k \geq 1$ and is Abelian for $k \geq 2$ (8.10) so for $k \geq 1$, Σ is a homomorphism. The **stable homotopy group** $\{X, Y\}$ is $\underrightarrow{\mathrm{L}}\{[\Sigma^k X, \Sigma^k Y]$ and is Abelian. The **suspension** or **Σ category** has based spaces as objects and the elements of the stable homotopy groups as maps.

chapter 16

SPECTRAL SEQUENCES

1. FILTRATIONS. The physical separation of suspensions, by passage through media of decreasing size of interstices has its counterpart for the modules and rings of interest to us. We use the term filtration for the succession of residual modules.

Definition 1.1. Write $J^+ = J \cup \infty$ and $\bar{J} = J^+ \cup -\infty$, referring to the script range of the integers in their usual order together with the final and initial ideal elements $\pm\infty$. R is invariably a commutative ring with a unit. A **decreasing filtration** of a group or a module is indicated by encasing indices in parentheses and is an ordered collection of groups or modules

$$A = \{A^{(p)} \mid A = \bigcup A^{(p)},\ p \in \bar{J} \text{ (or } J^+)\}$$

subject to

(1.1a) $A^{(p)} \supset A^{(p+1)}$,

(1.1b) $A^{\infty} = 0,\ A^{-\infty} = A.$

In most of the developments in this chapter the stronger restriction is made

(1.1b′) $A^{(m)} = A, \qquad m < 0.$

If A is a ring or an algebra (over R), then the modules $A^{(p)}$ satisfy besides,

(1.1c) $A^{(p)}A^{(q)} \subset A^{(p+q)}.$

If A is a d-module,

(1.1d) $dA^{(p)} \subset A^{(p)},\ d^2 = 0.$

A is a d-ring if there is an involution α on A to A such that

(1.1e) $d(a^{(p)}\, a^{(q)}) = da^{(p)}\, a^{(q)} + \alpha(a^{(p)})\, da^{(q)}.$

The decreasing filtration finds use in cohomology developments and will be assumed unless contrary statement is made. For homology treatments an ascending filtration can be defined in an obvious way. A bifiltration $\{A^{(pq)}\}$ will later be of use.

EXAMPLE 16-1. Duality relations such as (126.4) suggest that if A is endowed with an increasing filtration, i.e., $A_{(m)} \subset A_{(m+1)}$, then $B = Hom(A, G)$, where G is an arbitrary Abelian group, can be given a decreasing filtration according to

$$B^{(m+1)} = 0(A_m, G) \quad (126.3).$$

If J is the script range, let the f, on A to J^+ be defined by

$$f(a) = \sup \{p \mid a \in A^{(p)}\}.$$

Then (1.1a), (1.1b), (1.1c) imply

(1.1f) $f(a - b) \geq \inf (f(a), f(b))$.

Indeed suppose $a \in A^{(p)}$, $b \in A^{(q)}$. Assume $p \leq q$. Then a and $b \in A^{(p)}$ and so $a - b \in A^{(p)}$ whence $f(a - b) \geq p$.

(1.1g) $f(ab) \geq f(a) + f(b)$.

This follows from (1.1c).

(1.1h) $f(0) = \infty$,

(1.1i) $f(ra) \geq f(a)$ (if A is a module or an algebra over R),

(1.1j) $f(\alpha a) = f(a)$.

By a **filtration function** on A to J^+ is meant one satisfying (1.1f), . . . , (1.1j). If such a function is given, $A^{(p)}$ is defined by

$$A^{(p)} = \{a \mid f(a) \geq p\}.$$

For application to cohomology we need the following:

Definition 1.2. If J is a two-sided ideal (42.8), of the ring A with filter function f, then a filter function for A/J is defined by

$$f'([a]) = \sup \{f(b) \mid [b] = [a]\}.$$

Definition 1.3. If A is a filtered ring or filtered module, $A^{(p)}/A^{(p+1)}$ is a module and the graded ring associated with the filtered ring A is the direct sum

(1.3a) $$GA = \oplus A^{(p)}/A^{(p+1)}$$

where if $[a^{(p)}]^p$ is the coset of $A^{(p)}/A^{(p+1)}$, then products are defined by $[a^{(p)}]^p [b^{(q)}]^q = [a^{(p)}b^{(q)}]^{p+q}$.

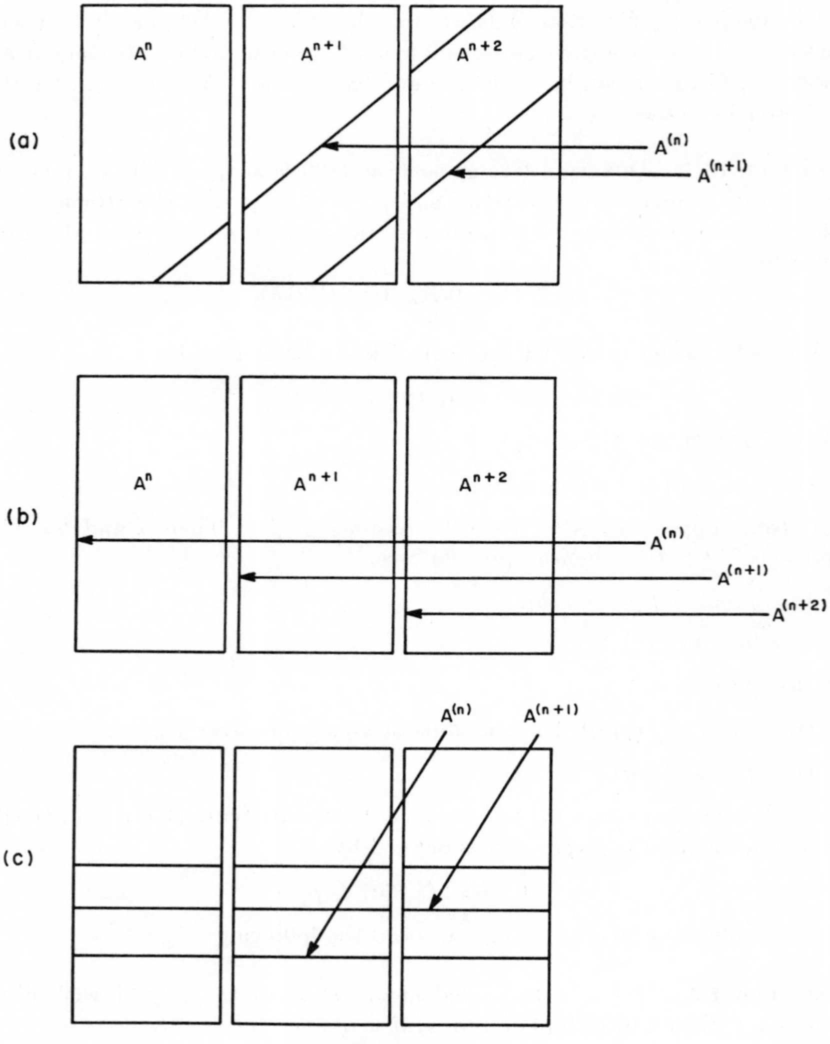

Figure 16-1

PROBLEM

16-1. If GA has no elements of finite order, i.e., no torsion, prove A has none.

Definition 1.4. If A is graded, $A = \oplus {}^nA$, and is also filtered, then the grading and filtration are **compatible** if

$$A^{(p)} = \oplus({}^nA \cap A^{(p)}).$$

Example 16-2. Let $\{K_i\}$ denote a denumerable collection of concrete complexes simply ordered by inverse inclusion so that $K_{-m} = K_0 = \bigcup K_i$, $m \geq 0$. Then the grading of the upper complex is given by ${}^pK = C^p(K_0, R)$ while a filtration of this upper complex is defined by $K^{(p)} = C(K_p, R) = \oplus_m C^m(K_p, R)$. Let $i(p): C(K_p, R) \to C(K, R)$ be defined by $i(p)f = F$ where $F \mid K - K_p = 0$, $F \mid K_p = f$. More generally

$$i(p, p - j): C(K_p, R) \to C(K_{p-j}, R)$$

where

$$i(p, p - j)f = F$$

with

$$F \mid (K_p - K_{p-j}) = 0, F \mid K_p = f.$$

Thus $K^{(p)} \supset K^{(p+1)} \supset \dots$.

Example 16-3. Not every dimension index can be interpreted as a grade of course. Thus let A consist of the functions of a complex variable analytic in the unit disk. "Grade" by ${}^nA = \{rz^n \mid r \in R\}$. Filter by $A^{(q)} = \{a \mid a = \Sigma_q^\infty r_n z^n\}$. However, unless a represents a polynomial, A is not a direct sum of homogeneous elements. Hence A is *not a graded ring*. (A boundary homomorphism d can be defined either with d trivial or defined by $dz^n = 0$, $n \neq m$ and $dz^m = z^{m+1}$.)

Example 16-4. Let A be the ring of polynomials with integer coefficients. Let $A^{(1)}$ be the special polynomials $\{n(z + z^2) \mid n \in J\}$ (an ideal). Filter by $A = A^{(0)} \supset A^{(1)} \supset A^{(2)} = 0$. Grade by ${}^nA = \{mz^n \mid m \in J\}$. Then ${}^nA \cap A^{(1)} = \varnothing$ for all n. Hence the grade and the filtration are not compatible. This can be made into a nontrivial d ring by

$$dmz = mz^2, d^nA = 0, \qquad n \neq 1.$$

Definition 1.5. If A is graded, then a filtration function f **associated** with the grading is defined by

$$f(a = \oplus {}^pa) = \inf \{p \mid {}^pa \neq 0\}, \tag{1.5a}$$

and the filtered ring so determined is written FA.

Lemma 1.6. *If A is a graded ring, then the passage A to FA to GFA yields an isomorph of A.*

PROBLEM

16-2. Prove this.

EXAMPLE 16-5. A is J_4. It is filtered by $A^{(0)} = A$, $A^{(1)} = 2J_4$, $A^{(2)} = 0$; ${}^0(GA) = J_4/2J_4 = J_2$, ${}^1(GA) = J_2$. The associated filtered group (1.6) is $F(GA)^{(0)} = J_2 \oplus J_2$, $(FGA)^{(1)} = J_2$. Thus $FGA \approx A$ here. A trivial differential can be introduced here (and elsewhere).

PROBLEMS

16-3. If A is a graded, filtered ring, show the filtration function f of (1.5a) gives a compatible filtration (1.4).

16-4. If f is a filtration function satisfying Problem 16-3, f' is a filtration function satisfying (1.6) where $f'(a = \oplus {}^p a) = inf\,\{l_r + f\,({}^p a)\}$, l a fixed integer.

Definition 1.7. If A and B are filtered differential rings with filtration functions f_1 and f_2 respectively, an **allowable homomorphism** h on A to B is understood to satisfy, besides commutativity with d, the added requirement

$$f_2 h(a) \geq f_1(a). \tag{1.7a}$$

Remark. This guarantees when $A = B$ that $hA^{(p)} \subset A^{(p)}$.

We take account of a small blemish, namely that the category of filtered Abelian groups with homomorphisms satisfying (1.7a) do not constitute an exact category (106.7). As a consequence wherever filtrations enter in the next two chapters, generality prescribes assertions of bijection rather than isomorphism in many cases.

EXAMPLE 16.6. Let A and B refer to the same underlying Abelian group under two different filtrations. Thus let $A = A^{(0)} \supset A^{(1)} \supset A^{(2)} = 0$ where $A^{(1)}$ is a proper subgroup of A. Let $B = B^0 = B^1 = A \supset B^{(2)} = 0$. Let h be the identity map of $A \to B$ as groups. Then h satisfies (1.7a) but h^{-1} does not, so no allowable inverse of h exists. Accordingly h is a bijection, but not an isomorphism.

We shall make frequent reference to the following example:

EXAMPLE 16-7. Let C be a torsion free DG group. So $C = \oplus\, {}^nC$, ${}^nC$ a free group. Let D be a differential group. For instance, C can be a cochain group with ${}^nC = C^n(K, G)$ for some complex K over the coefficient group R. Introduce $C^{(m)} = \oplus_{n \geq m} {}^nC$. Hence C is filtered by $C^0 \supset C^1 \supset \cdots$ and, recalling $i(n)$ is an injection Example 16-2,

$$C^{(n)} = {}^nC + i(n)\, C^{(n+1)}.$$

Consider $A = C \otimes D$. Then

$$C^{(n)} \otimes D = {}^nC \otimes D + (i(n)C^{(n+1)}) \otimes D.$$

(Variations can be introduced. Thus with D a filtered group $\{D^{(t)}\}$ we can define $(C \otimes D)^{(p)} = \oplus_{r+s \geq p} {}^rC \otimes D^{(s)}$.)

2. DERIVED MODULES. Definition 2.1. Let Z (or $Z(A)$), B and H be the usually so designated rings for the filtered, differential ring A, i.e., $Z = ker\, d$, $B = Im\, d$, $H = Z/B$. Write $Z^{(p)} = Z \cap A^{(p)} = Z(A^{(p)})$. There are two contenders for bounding cycles associated with $A^{(p)}$, to wit: $D^{(p)} = dA^{(p)}$ and $B^{(p)} = B \cap A^{(p)} = dA \cap A^{(p)}$. Then

$$H(A^{(p)}) = Z(A^{(p)})/D^{(p)} = \{\langle z^{(p)} \rangle_{D^{(p)}}\}.$$

Let $H^{(p)}(A)$ or $(HA)^{(p)}$ be the image in $H(A)$ of $H(A^{(p)})$ under the homomorphism i^* induced by the injection $A^{(p)} \xrightarrow{i} A$. Thus $H^{(p)}(A)$ comprises the cosets of $H(A)$ containing cocycles of $A^{(p)}$. In general $H^{(p)}(A) \not\approx H(A^{(p)})$. ($H^{(p)}(A)$ is a submodule of $H(A)$ and is not to be confused with a p dimensional cohomology module of H which we write $H^p(A)$ or ${}^pH(A)$ to indicate p is a grade, Cf. 2.2).

Lemma 2.2. $H^{(p)}(A) = Z^{(p)}(A)/B^{(p)}(A)$.

Indeed with i defined above $i \mid D^{(p)} \subset B \cap Z^{(p)} = B^{(p)}$. Hence

$$i^*\langle z^{(p)} \rangle_{D^{(p)}} = \langle z^{(p)} \rangle_{B^{(p)}} \tag{2.2a}$$

and i^* is evidently an epimorphism.

Thus $H(A)$ is filtered by $\{H^{(p)} = H^{(p)}(A)\}$. This is a decreasing filtration. The associated graded ring is then

$$GH(A) = \oplus((H^{(p)}(A)/H^{(p+1)}(A)) = {}^p(GH(A)). \tag{2.2b}$$

Of course ${}^pGHA$ is not the same as $Z^{(p)}(A)/B^{(p)}(A)$. The spectral sequence to be developed links $G(A)$ and $GH(A)$ by a series of approximations.

EXAMPLE 16-8. Let A be an upper complex $\{{}^nA = {}^nC(K, R), d\}$. Define a filtration by $A^{(p)} = \oplus_{p \leq i} {}^iA$. Then

$$z^{(5)} = d\, {}^4a + {}^5z + {}^7z + {}^8z \in Z^{(5)}(A) = Z(A^{(5)})$$

where ${}^iz \in {}^iZ(A)$, ${}^4a \in {}^4A$. Then $\langle z^{(5)} \rangle_{D^{(5)}}$ denotes the coset

$$z^{(5)} \oplus \oplus_{5 \leq n} d\, {}^nC(K, R).$$

The image of this element in $H(A)$ is $\langle z^{(5)} \rangle_{B^{(5)}}$ and denotes the coset $z^{(5)} + \oplus_{4 \leq n} d\, {}^nC(K, R)$, an element of $H^{(5)}(A)$ where $d\, {}^4a$ has been swallowed up in $d\, {}^4A$. The cocycles ${}^7z$ and ${}^8z$ are in $A^{(6)}$ also. Since $D^{(6)} \subset D^{(5)}$, this means $\langle {}^7z \rangle_{D^{(5)}} \neq 0$ implies $\langle {}^7z \rangle_{D^{(6)}} \neq 0$. It follows that $i^*\langle {}^7z + {}^8z \rangle_{D^{(6)}} \in H^{(6)}(A)$. Accordingly $\langle {}^5z \rangle_{B^{(5)}}$ is the representative of a coset of

$$H^{(5)}(A)/H^{(6)}(A) = {}^5GH(A).$$

On the other hand

$$\langle {}^5z \rangle_{B^{(5)}} \in \frac{{}^5Z(A)}{B^{(5)}(A)} \approx \frac{{}^5Z(A) + B^{(5)}}{B^{(5)}} \approx \frac{{}^5Z(A)}{{}^5Z(A) \cap B} \approx {}^5H(A),$$

so that in this case ${}^5GHA \approx {}^5H$.

Example 16-8 may be misleading. One cannot deduce from (2.2b) that ${}^rH(A) \approx {}^r(GH(A))$. This is because the filtration introduced in (1.5a) applied to $H(A)$ is not generally the filtration in (2.1).

EXAMPLE 16-9. Let A be graded with ${}^nA = 0$ for $n \geq q - 1$. Let

$$A = A^{(0)} = \cdots = A^{(q)} = \oplus_{i<q}\, {}^iA \supset A^{(q+1)} = 0.$$

Suppose ${}^jH(A) = H(A^{(j)}) \neq 0$ for some $0 < j < q - 1$. Then

$$0 \neq {}^jH(A) \neq {}^j(GH(A)) = 0.$$

Definition 2.3

(2.3a) $Z_r^{(p)} = \{a \mid a \in A^{(p)}, da \in A^{(p+r)} \quad , r \geq 0\}$. $Z_r^{(p)}/A^{(p+r)}$ is equivalent to $Z(A^{(p)}/A^{(p+r)})$. In particular, in view of (1.1d)

(2.3b) $$Z_0^{(p)} = A^{(p)},$$

(2.3c) $$B_r^{(p)} = A^{(p)} \cap dA^{(p-r)} = d\,Z_r^{(p-r)}.$$

Lemma 2.4

(2.4a) $$\subset B_r^{(p)} \subset B_{r+1}^{(p)} \subset \cdots \subset B^{(p)} \subset Z^{(p)} \subset \cdots \subset Z_{r+1}^{(p)} \subset Z_r^{(p)} \subset \cdots \subset A^{(p)},$$

$r\uparrow$ $\qquad$ $r\uparrow$

(2.4b) $$Z_{r-1}^{(p+1)} = Z_r^{(p)} \cap A^{(p+1)} \subset Z_r^{(p)},$$

(2.4c) $$B_{r+1}^{(p+1)} \subset B_r^{(p)},$$

(2.4d) $$Z_r^{(p)}\, Z_{r+t}^{(q)} \subset Z_r^{(p+q)},\ t \geq 0,$$

(2.4e) $$Z_{r+1}^{(p)}\, B_r^{(q)} \subset Z_r^{(p+q+1)} + B_r^{(p+q)}.$$

PROBLEM

16-5. Verify these important inclusions.

3. SPECTRAL SEQUENCES. The grading achieved by (1.3a) suggests that in $Z^{(p)}$ we ought to take cosets with respect to elements in $A^{(p+1)}$, that is to say, in view of (2.4b), with respect to Z_{r-1}^{p+1}. The cohomology module requires cosets of cocycles with respect to coboundaries. It seems natural therefore that the following rings should be central in spectral sequence theory:

Definition 3.1. $E_r = \oplus E_r^p$ is a graded ring, with

(3.1a) $$E_r^p = Z_r^{(p)}/(Z_{r-1}^{(p+1)} + B_{r-1}^{(p)}) = Z_r^{(p)}/\Gamma_{r-1}^{(p)},$$

where $\Gamma_{r-1}^{(p)} \doteq Z_{r-1}^{(p+1)} + B_{r-1}^{(p)}$ is also written $\Gamma(p, r-1)$. (Observe p in E_p^r denotes a grade, not a filtration.) The graded ring E_∞, is defined by

(3.1b) $$E_\infty = \Sigma E_\infty^p = \oplus Z^{(p)}/Z^{(p+1)} + B^{(p)} = \oplus Z^{(p)}/\Gamma^{(p)},$$

Remark. To set this result off we sketch an extension. Let p, q, r, s be indices in increasing order. The relative theory for pairs then yields

$$E(p, q) = H(A^{(p)}/A^{(q)}) = Z(A^{(p)}/A^{(q)})/B(A^{(p)}/A^{(q)})$$
$$= Z_{q-p}^{(p)}/(dA^{(p)} + A^{(q)}).$$

Let π be the inclusion homomorphism on $E(q, s)$ to $E(p, r)$ induced by

$$A^{(q)}/A^{(s)} \to A^{(p)}/A^{(r)}.$$

Then

$$E(p, q, r, s) = Im\ \pi$$
$$= E(q, s)/ker\ \pi$$
$$\approx \frac{Z_{s-q}^{(q)}/(dA^{(q)} + A^{(s)})}{Z_{s-q}^{(q)} \cap (dA^{(p)} + A^{(r)})/(dA^{(q)} + A^{(s)})}$$

(3.1*c*) $$\approx Z_{s-q}^{(q)}/(Z_{s-q}^{(r)} + B_{q-p}^{(q)}).$$

In particular

$$E(p, p+t-1, p+t, p+2t-1) \approx Z_t^{(q)}/(Z_{t-1}^{(q+1)} + B_{t-1}^{(q)})$$
$$\approx E_t^q.$$

PROBLEM

16-6. Using (2.4d) and (2.4e) verify E_r is a ring.

Definition 3.2. In view of (2.3a) and (2.4a), with d induced by the boundary operator of A,

(3.2a) $$Z_r^{(p)} \xrightarrow{d} B^{(p+r)} \subset Z^{(p+r)} \xrightarrow{i} Z_r^{(p+r)},$$

where i is an injection. Also

(3.2b) $$Z_{r-1}^{(p+1)} + B_{r-1}^{(p)} \xrightarrow{d} dZ_{r-1}^{(p+1)} + 0 = B_{r-1}^{(p+r)} \xrightarrow{i} Z_{r-1}^{(p+r+1)} + B_{r-1}^{(p+r)}.$$

The composition, (id), therefore induces the important homomorphism denoted by

$$d_r = \{d_r^p\colon E_r^p \longrightarrow E_r^{p+r}\}, \text{ viz}$$

(3.2c)
$$d_r\langle z_r^{(p)}\rangle_{\Gamma_{r-1}^{(p)}} = \langle idz_r^{(p)}\rangle_{\Gamma_{r-1}^{p+r}},$$

and since $(id)^2 = 0$, $d_r^{p+r}\, d_r^p = 0$. Thus $d_r = \{d_r^{p+r}\}$ can be considered the coboundary operator for the cochain complex E_r (61.4) and

(3.2d)
$$\longrightarrow E_r^p \xrightarrow{d_r} E_r^{p+r} \xrightarrow{d_r} E_r^{p+2r} \longrightarrow \cdots.$$

The cohomology module is given by

(3.2e)
$$H(E_r^p) = \frac{ker(d_r^p)}{d_r^{p-r}\, E_r^{p-r}}.$$

The notable relationship between the graded rings $\{E_r\}$ constitutes the next theorem.

Theorem 3.3. $H(E_r^p) = E_{r+1}^p$.

In view of (3.2c), $\langle d_r^p\, z_r^{(p)}\rangle = 0$, if $idz_r^{(p)} \in \Gamma_{r-1}^{(p+r)}$, i.e., if $dz_r^{(p)} \in Z_{r-1}^{(p+r+1)} + B_{r-1}^{(p+r)} \subset Z_{r+1}^{(p+r+1)} + B_{r-1}^{(p+r)}$. Accordingly $z_r^{(p)} \in (Z_{r+1}^{(p)} + Z_{r-1}^{(p+1)}) \in Z^{(p)} \subset Z_{r+1}^{(p)}$. That is to say

(3.3a)
$$ker(d_r^p) = (Z_{r+1}^{(p)} + Z_{r-1}^{(p+1)})/\Gamma_{r-1}^{(p)} \subset E_r^p,$$

(3.3b)
$$\begin{aligned} d_r^{p-r}\, E_r^{p-r} &= id(Z_r^{(p-r)}/Z_{r-1}^{(p-r+1)} + B_{r-1}^{(p-r)}) \\ &= id(Z_r^{(p-r)} + \Gamma_{r-1}^{(p)})/\Gamma_{r-1}^{(p)} \\ &= (B_r^{(p)} + d(\Gamma_{r-1}^{(p-r)}) + \Gamma_{r-1}^{(p)})/\Gamma_{r-1}^{(p)} \\ &= (B_r^{(p)} + \Gamma_{r-1}^{(p)})/\Gamma_{r-1}^{(p)}. \end{aligned}$$

Hence by (42.11) and (42.12),

$$\begin{aligned} H(E_r^p) &\approx \frac{(Z_{r+1}^{(p)} + Z_{r-1}^{(p+1)})/\Gamma_{r-1}^{(p)}}{(B_r^{(p)} + B_{r-1}^{(p)} + Z_{r-1}^{(p+1)})/\Gamma_{r-1}^{(p)}} \\ &\approx \frac{Z_{r+1}^{(p)} + Z_{r-1}^{(p+1)}}{Z_{r-1}^{(p+1)} + B_r^{(p)}} \\ &\approx Z_{r+1}^{(p)}/((Z_{r-1}^{(p+1)} + B_r^{(p)}) \cap Z_{r+1}^{(p)}) \quad (11.7). \end{aligned}$$

Since $B_r^{(p)} \subset Z_{r+1}^{(p)}$, the reduction of the denominator needs only

(3.3c)
$$Z_{r-1}^{(p+1)} \cap Z_{r+1}^{(p)} = Z_r^{(p+1)}.$$

Indeed from (2.4b) the left hand side is

$$\begin{aligned} &A^{(p+1)} \cap d^{-1}\, A^{(p+r)} \cap A^{(p)} \cap d^{-1}\, A^{(p+r+1)} = \\ &\qquad = A^{(p+1)} \cap d^{-1}\, A^{p+r+1} = Z_r^{(p+1)}. \end{aligned}$$

These facts being so,

$$H(E_r^p) = Z_{r+1}^{(p)}/Z_r^{(p+1)} + B_r^{(p)}$$
$$= E_{r+1}^p.$$

Definition 3.4. If A is a filtered differential ring, a collection of graded differential rings $\{E_r\}$ with $H(E_r^p) \approx E_{r+1}^p$, $r \geq 0$, is called a **spectral sequence** of A. Some authors do not include (the spectres) $\{E_r \mid r < 2\}$, in the spectral sequence.

Remark. In practically all our developments we restrict ourselves to the group aspect of E_r.

Lemma 3.5. $GH(A) \approx E_\infty$.

Indeed

(3.5a) $$E_\infty = \oplus\, Z^{(p)}/(Z^{(p+1)} + B^{(p)})$$
$$\approx \oplus \frac{Z^{(p)}/B^{(p)}}{(Z^{(p+1)} + B^{(p)})/B^{(p)}}.$$

We need the relation

$$Z^{(p+1)} \cap B^{(p)} = A^{(p+1)} \cap Z \cap A^{(p)} \cap B = A^{(p+1)} \cap B = B^{(p+1)}.$$

In view of (11.7), $(Z^{(p+1)} + B^{(p)})/B^{(p)} \approx Z^{(p+1)}/Z^{(p+1)} \cap B^{(p)} \approx Z^{(p+1)}/B^{(p+1)}$. Reference to (2.2b) and to (2.2a) settles matters.

Lemma 3.6

(3.6a) $$\bigcup_r B_r^{(p)} = B^{(p)},$$

(3.6b) $$\bigcap_r Z_r^{(p)} \supset Z^{(p)}.$$

Let $a^{(p)} = db \in B^{(p)}$. Suppose $b \in A^{(q)}$. Then $a^{(p)} \in B_r^{(p)}$ for $r = p - q$. Thus

$$B^{(p)} \subset \bigcup B_r^{(p)}.$$

The reverse implication as well as (3.6b) is part of (2.4a).

Definition 3.7. Define p_{r+1}^r as the natural map or projection of the cocycles $Z(E_r)$ (3.3a) under d_r onto $H(E_r) = E_{r+1}$. Thus in view of (3.3a)

$$p_{r+1}^r(w \mid w \in \ker d_r^p) = \langle w \rangle_{d_r} E_r^{p-r}$$

where $d_r E_r^{p-r}$ is given explicitly (3.3b). Define p_s^r by the composition,

(3.7a) $$p^r{}_s = p^{s-1}{}_s \cdots p_{r+1}^r, \quad r < s.$$

For (3.7a) to be meaningful, it is necessary that $p^r{}_{r+1}\, w$ be an element of $ker\, d_{r+1}$. Then, granting this, that $p^{r+1}{}_{r+2}\, p^r{}_{r+1}\, w \in ker\, d_{r+2}$, etc.

Definition 3.8. p^r_∞ is defined on a subring of E_r onto E_∞ by

$$p^r_\infty \langle z^{(p)}\rangle_{\Gamma^{(p)}{}_{r-1}} = \langle z^{(p)}\rangle_{\Gamma^{(p)}},\ z^{(p)} \in Z^{(p)}.$$

Write W_r for the subring of E_r for which $p^r{}_s$ is defined for all $s > r$. Write D_r for $\{h_r \mid h_r \in W_r,\ p^r{}_s\, h_r = 0 \text{ for some } s, \quad s > r\}$.

Lemma 3.9

(3.9a) *D_r is an ideal of W_r,*

(3.9b) $p^r{}_s \mid D_r \to D_s$,

(3.9c) *$p^r{}_s$ induces an isomorphism $\pi^r{}_s$ on $W_r/D_r \to W_s/D_s$.*

Assertions (3.9a), . . . , (3.9c) are plain.

Although the matching conditions are satisfied, in general $\{E_r, p^r{}_s\}$ is not a direct system since $p^r{}_s$ is not defined on all of E_r. To appreciate what is going on, note that w_r determines a coset in

$$W_r = \{w_s \mid w_s = p^r{}_s\, w_r,\ w_s \in Z(E_s) = ker\, d_s\}$$

so that W_r is *analogous* to a direct limit of cocycle groups $\{Z(E_s), p^s{}_t\}$ where the indexing starts with r. Of course here we do not have a direct system. In the same way $b_r \in D_r$ determines a coset $\{b_s \mid b_s = p^r{}_s\, b_r,\ b_s \in B(E_s)\}$, so that D_r is analogous to a direct limit of coboundary groups $\{B(E_s), p^r{}_s\}$. With (77.10) as guide it is natural to take advantage of (3.9c) to define the **quasi-direct limit** indicated by a half arrow $\rightharpoondown$.

Definition 3.10

(3.10a) $$\underset{\rightharpoondown}{\mathsf{L}}\{E_r, p^r{}_s\} \quad \text{or} \quad \underset{\rightharpoondown}{\mathsf{L}}\, E_r = W_s/D_s, \qquad s \geq r.$$

Lemma 3.11. *$p^r{}_\infty\, e_r = 0$ for $e_r \in W_r$ if for some $s \geq r$, $p^r{}_s\, e_r = 0 \in W_s$.*

If $p^r{}_s e_r = 0$, then $p^r{}_\infty\, e_r = p^s{}_\infty (p^r{}_s e_r) = 0$.

If $e^p_r = z^p/\Gamma^p_{r-1}$ satisfies $p^r{}_\infty e^p_r = 0$, then $z^{(p)} \in Z^{(p+1)} + B^{(p)}$ or, for some $s \geq r$,

$$z^{(p)} \in Z^{(p+1)} + B^{(p)}_{s-1} \subset Z^{(p+1)}_{s-1} + B^{(p)}_{s-1}$$

whence $p^r{}_s\, e_r = 0$.

Lemma 3.12. $GH(A) \subset \underset{\rightharpoondown}{\mathsf{L}}\, E_r$.

Let $e^p = z^{(p)}/\Gamma^{(p)} = \langle z^{(p)}\rangle \in E^p_\infty$ where $z^{(p)} \in Z^{(p)}_{r+1}$ for every r. By (3.3b) $\langle z^{(p)}\rangle \in ker\ d^p_s$. Hence

$$p^s{}_{s+1}\langle z\rangle \in ker\ d^p_{s+1}.$$

Then $w_r = z^{(p)}/\Gamma^{(p)}_{r-1} \in W_r$. We show that if e^p is not trivial, neither is w_r. First $p^r{}_\infty\, z^{(p)}/\Gamma^{(p)}_{r-1} = \langle z^{(p)}\rangle$, (3.7). That $w_r \bar{\in} D_r$ follows from (3.11) for $0 \neq p^r{}_\infty\, w_r = p^s{}_\infty(p^r{}_s\, w_r)$.

Remark. In practice for each r, $E^p_r = 0$ except for a finite p set. However we enunciate somewhat weaker restrictions.

Definition 3.13. The filtration is **convergent** if $Z^{(p)} = \bigcap_r Z^{(p)}_r$. *In all our applications the filtration will be convergent.*

Theorem 3.14. *If the filtration is convergent, then* $GHA \approx \underrightarrow{\mathsf{L}}\, E_r$.

Let $w_r \in W_r$ be a representative of a nontrivial element of $\underrightarrow{\mathsf{L}}\, E_r$, so that $w_r \bar{\in} D_r$. Then $w_r = \dfrac{z^{(p)}}{\Gamma_{r-1}}$, where $z^{(p)} \in Z^{(p)}_{r+1}$. Since $A^\infty = 0$, we may assume $z^{(p)} \bar{\in} Z^{(p+m)}_{r+1}$, $m \geq 1$ (for otherwise we could replace p by $p + m$ in the demonstration). Accordingly, $p^r{}_s\, w_r = \dfrac{z^{(p)}}{\Gamma^{(p)}_{s-1}}$ so $z^{(p)} \in Z^{(p)}_{s+1}$ for all $r \leq s$. Therefore $z^{(p)} \in \bigcap_{r\leq s} Z^{(p)}_{s+1} = Z^{(p)}$. Hence $p^r{}_\infty\, w_r = (z^{(p)})_{\Gamma^{(p)}}$ corresponds to w_r. In view of (3.11), if $p^r{}_\infty\, w_r = 0$, then $0 = w_s = p^r{}_s\, w_r$ or $w_r \in D_r$ a contradiction. We have shown then that to a nontrivial element of $\underrightarrow{\mathsf{L}}\, E_r$ corresponds a nontrivial element of E_∞ and in conjunction with (3.12) this asserts (3.14).

Definition 3.15. If K is a differential ring which is graded and filtered compatibly (1.4), we define, with $q = n - p$,

(3.15a)

$$\begin{aligned} {}^nK^{(pq)} &= K^{(pq)} = {}^nK \cap K^{(p)}, \\ {}^nZ^{(pq)}_r &= Z^{(pq)}_r = {}^nK \cap Z^{(p)}_r, \\ {}^nB^{(pq)}_r &= B^{(p)}_r \cap {}^nK, \\ {}^nE^{pq}_r &= Z^{(pq)}_r / B^{(pq)}_{r-1} + Z^{(p+1\ q-1)}_{r-1}. \end{aligned}$$

The analogues of (2.3), (2.4), (3.2a), (3.2b), (3.2), etc., are maintained, bearing in mind

(3.15b)

$${}^nE^{pq}_r \xrightarrow{d_r} {}^{n+1}E^{p+r\ q-r+1}_r.$$

Remark. More general double filtrations can be introduced, not relating to grading, but we shall have no concern with them. Moreover, doubly graded rings ensue by setting

$$^{n}A^{pq} = {}^{n}H(K^{(p)}),$$

where n reflects the grading of K.

We can now replace (3.13) by more convenient restrictions.

Definition 3.16. The *filtration* of J is **strongly regular** if for every n an integer $P(n)$ exists for which

(3.16a) $$J^{(p)} \cap {}^{n}J = 0, \qquad p > P(n).$$

It is **regular** if for every n there is a $P(n)$ with

(3.16b) $$^{n}H(J^{(p)}) = 0, \qquad p > P(n).$$

It is bounded from above (or from below) if for some integer P, (P'),

$$J^{(p)} = 0, \qquad p \geq P \text{ (or if } J^{(p)} = J, \qquad p \leq P').$$

In all our applications one of the restrictions in (3.16) is *invariably satisfied.*

Remark. Since $n = p + q$ the condition $p > P(n)$ is equivalent to $q < Q(n)$. Strong regularity implies regularity.

EXAMPLE 16-10. In Example 16-7 suppose both C and D are upper complexes and let $A = C \otimes D$ have the grading $^{n}A = \oplus_{r+s=n} C^{r} \otimes D^{s}$ and filtration $A^{(p)} = \oplus_{p \leq r} \oplus_{s}(C^{r} \otimes D^{s})$. The grading and filtration are compatible. Since $D^{s} = 0$ $s < 0$, the filtration is strongly regular. Indeed for $p \geq n + 1 = P(n)$, $^{n}A \cap A^{(p)} = \oplus_{\substack{r+s=n \\ s \leq 0}} C^{r} \otimes D^{s} = \oplus C^{r} \otimes 0 = 0$.

Theorem 3.17. *If the filtration is regular, then* $\varinjlim E_{r} = E_{\infty}$.

PROBLEM

16-7. Demonstrate (3.17) by showing regularity implies

$$\bigcap Z_{r}^{(p)} = Z^{(p)} \bmod (dA^{(p)} + A^{(p+1)}).$$

Hint: Show regularity implies $\bigcap_{s \geq r} \underline{Z}_{r}^{(p)} = \underline{Z}_{r}^{(p)}$ (cf. (4.1a) below).

EXAMPLE 16-11. That regularity does not imply convergence is revealed by taking the graded module with $^{n}A = J_{4}$ (the integers mod 4). Let

$A^{(p)} = \mathrm{J}, p \neq \infty$ and let $A^{(\infty)} = 0$. Define d as multiplication by 2. Hence $d^nA \approx \mathrm{J}_2$. Thus ${}^nA \xrightarrow{d} (d^nA) \approx \mathrm{J}_2 \subset {}^{n+1}A$. Then ${}^nZ^{(p)} \approx {}^nB^{(p)} \approx {}^nD^{(p)} \approx \mathrm{J}_2$. Incidentally $H^{(p)}({}^nA) = H(A^{(p)}) = 0$ for all p. On the other hand ${}^nZ_r^{(p)} = {}^nA \cap d^{-1}A^{(p+r)} = {}^nA = \mathrm{J}_4$. Therefore $\bigcap_r {}^nZ_r^{(p)} = \mathrm{J}_4$.

Corollary 3.18. *If the filtration of A is bounded from above and from below, then $GH(A) = E_r$, $r \leq r_0$ and $GH(A) = E_r$, $r \geq r_1$, and $H^{(p)}(A) = 0$ for all sufficiently large or all sufficiently small p.*

4. OTHER VIEWPOINTS. We present some variants of the development of spectral sequences. We restrict ourselves to groups and modules, though products can be defined and the ideas can be extended to spectral rings. One direct approach is by way of reduction of the cohomology modules (and rings) of pairs and triples (61.12), (62.4).

Definition 4.1. Using the pair A, $A^{(p)}$ one obtains the relation $H^{(p)}(A) = ker((H(A) \to H(A/A^{(p)}))$. With the pair $A^{(p)}$, $A^{(p+1)}$ we define $\underline{Z}^{(p)}$ as $ker\ d$. With Problem 6-1 as a guide,

$$\underline{Z}^{(p)} = \frac{Z^{(p)} + A^{(p+1)}}{dA^{(p)} + A^{(p+1)}}. \tag{4.1a}$$

The triple A, $A^{(p)}$, $A^{(p+1)}$ gives

$$\begin{array}{ccccc} H(A/A^{(p)}) & \xrightarrow{\delta} & H(A^{(p)}/A^{(p+1)}) & \xrightarrow{\lambda} & H(A/A^{(p+1)}) \\ & {\scriptstyle d}\searrow & \nearrow{\scriptstyle \eta} & & \\ & & H(A^{(p)}) & & \\ & & \searrow & & \end{array}$$

Define $\underline{B}^{(p)}(A)$ as $Im\ \delta$,

$$\underline{B}^{(p)}(A) = \frac{d^{-1}A^{(p+1)} \cap A^{(p)} \cap (dA + A^{(p+1)})}{dA^{(p)} + A^{(p+1)}}$$

$$\approx \frac{B^{(p)}(A) + A^{(p+1)}}{dA^{(p)} + A^{(p+1)}} = ker\ \lambda. \tag{4.1b}$$

Similarly using $A^{(p)}$, $A^{(p+1)}$, $A^{(p+r)}$ we define $\underline{Z}_r^{(p)}$ as $ker\ \delta$,

$$\begin{array}{ccc} H(A^{(p)}/A^{(p+1)}) & \xrightarrow{\delta} & H(A^{(p+1)}/A^{(p+r)}) \\ {\scriptstyle d}\searrow & & \nearrow{\scriptstyle \eta} \\ & H(A^{(p+1)}) & \end{array}$$

and with $A^{(p)}$, $A^{(p+1)}$, $A^{(p-r+1)}$ we define $\underline{B}_r^{(p)}$ as $Im\ \delta = ker\ \lambda$ in the exact sequence

$$\begin{array}{ccccc} H(A^{(p-r+1)}/A^{(p)}) & \xrightarrow{\delta} & H(A^{(p)}, A^{(p+1)}) & \xrightarrow{\lambda} & H(A^{(p-r+1)}/A^{(p+1)}) \\ & {\scriptstyle d}\searrow & & \nearrow{\scriptstyle \eta} & \\ & & H(A^{(p)}) & & \end{array}$$

Hence just as Problem 6-1 there results

$$\underline{Z}_r^{(p)} = (Z_r^{(p)} + A^{(p+1)})/(dA^{(p)} + A^{(p+1)}) \tag{4.1c}$$

$$\underline{B}_r^{(p)} = \frac{d^{-1}A^{(p+1)} \cap A^{(p)} \cap (dA^{(p-r+1)} + A^{(p+1)})}{dA^{(p)} + A^{(p+1)}} \tag{4.1d}$$

$$= \frac{B_{r-1}^{(p)} + A^{(p+1)}}{dA^{(p)} + A^{(p+1)}}.$$

PROBLEM

16-8. Show $E_\infty^p = \underline{Z}^{(p)}(A)/\underline{B}^{(p)}(A)$. *Hint*: Use (11.7) and (11.8). Show $E_r^p = \underline{Z}_r^{(p)}/\underline{B}_r^{(p)}$.

The next variant shows that the fundamental entities $\{E_r\}$ can be defined even when neither a filtration nor a grading is present. We illustrate one method of procedure below and follow later by another, (4.3). Let A be a differentiable module with α an allowable endomorphism of $A \to A$, i.e., $d\alpha = \alpha d$ and with λ an automorphism satisfying $\lambda\, da + d\lambda a = 0$,

$$dab = (da)b + \lambda(a)\, db.$$

EXAMPLE 16-11. In Example 16-7, define α by replacing $C^{(n)}$ by $i(n)C^{(n+1)}$ in A, i.e., $\alpha C^{(n)} \otimes D = i(n)C^{(n+1)} \otimes D$.

Definition 4.2.

$$Z_r = d^{-1}\,\alpha^r A, \quad Z_0 = Z_{-1} = A,$$

$$B_r = \alpha^{-r}\, dA, \quad B_{-1} = d\alpha A, \quad B_0 = dA, \tag{4.2a}$$

$$d_r = \alpha^{-r} d.$$

PROBLEM

16-9. Show $\alpha Z_r \subset Z_{r+1} \subset Z_r$, $\alpha B_{r+1} \subset B_r \subset B_{r+1}$, $B_r \subset Z_s$ for any r and s.

Write $C = \bigcap Z_r$, $D = \bigcup B_r$. The usual inferences then follow. For instance with $Z = d^{-1}0$

$$H(A) = Z/dA$$

$$\alpha H A = \frac{\alpha Z + dA}{dA}$$

whence

$$\frac{H(A)}{\alpha H(A)} \approx \frac{Z}{\alpha Z + dA}.$$

Similarly, if $\bar{H}(A) = Z/D$, then $\bar{H}(A)/\alpha\bar{H}(A) = Z/(\alpha Z + D)$. Let

$$E_r = Z_r/\alpha Z_{r-1} + B_{r-1},$$

$$E_\infty = C/\alpha C + D.$$

If subsidiary conditions guarantee $Z = C$, then

(4.2b) $$E_\infty \approx \bar{H}(A)/\alpha\bar{H}(A),$$

but it is noteworthy that weaker conditions may suffice.

PROBLEMS

16-10. Show $d_r Z_r = B_r$, $d_r B_r = 0$, $d_r \alpha Z_r \subset B_r$, $dA \subset D \subset Z \subset C$. If $d\alpha^r z = 0$, then $dz = 0$.

16-11. Show $Z(E_r) = \ker d_r = Z_{r+1}/\alpha Z_r + B_{r-1}$

$$dE_r = (B_r + \alpha Z_r)/\alpha Z_r + B_{r-1}$$

16-12. Show (4.2b) is valid if (a) there is an allowable submodule $L \subset \alpha A$ (with $dL \subset L$ and $\alpha L \subset L$), (b) $dL = dA \cap L$ and (c) $\bigcap \alpha^r A \subset L$.
Hint: Show $Z + L = C + L$ and $\alpha Z + L = \alpha C + L$ and use (11.7) and (11.8).

16-13. Show that even if conditions (a), (b), and (c) in Problem 16-13 are met it is not necessarily true that $Z = C$, by taking for A the ring of polynomials in two variables, x and y over J_9. Let $\alpha x = x^2$ and $\alpha y = y$. Let $d = 3\,\partial/\partial y$. Take L as the ring of polynomials over y. Then show y is in C, but not in Z.

Definition 4.3. A derivation of spectral sequences which is sometimes more general follows. Suppose then A and C are modules over a ring R, and assume the diagram

(4.3a)

$$\begin{array}{ccc} A & \xrightarrow{\ f\ } & A \\ {\scriptstyle h}\nwarrow & & \swarrow {\scriptstyle g} \\ & C & \end{array}$$

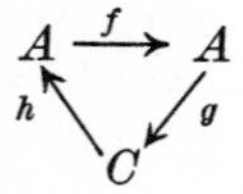

is exact for the homomorphisms f, g, h. It is possible that h is a derivation, δ, but in any case a new **derivation** denoted by d is introduced. Thus $d: C \to C$

is defined by $d = gh$. The association $(A, C; f, g, h)$ is called an **exact couple** of modules. Write $C_1 = H(C)$, and $A_1 = f(A)$. Furthermore let $f_1\colon A_1 \to A_1$, where $f_1\colon A_1 = f \mid A$.

We assert a homomorphism, h_1, on C_1 to A_1 is induced by h. Thus $Z(C) = \mathit{ker}\, d = \mathit{ker}(gh)$. Hence $ghZ(C) = 0$ whence $hZ(C) \subset \mathit{ker}\, g$ or, by exactness, $hZ(C) \subset f(A) = A_1$. Moreover $h(B(C)) = (hg)hC = 0)$ by exactness. Therefore

$$h_1\colon Z(C)/B(C) \to A_1/0 \approx A_1.$$

The definition of g_1 on A_1 to C_1 still remains. Let $a_1 \in A_1$, i.e., $a_1 = fa$. Evidently $dg(a) = g(hg)a = 0$ or $g(a) \in Z(C)$. Suppose a' is another element of $f^{-1}(a_1)$. Then $f(a - a') = 0$, so by exactness, for some c, $a - a' = h(c)$, whence $g(a - a') = ghc = dc$. In short, $gf^{-1}(a_1)$ is a coset of C with respect to $B(C)$. We therefore define the homomorphism

$$g_1\colon A_1 \to Z(A)/B(C)$$

by $g_1 a_1 = g(a)/B(C)$ where $a_1 = f(a)$.

Lemma 4.4. *The diagram* (4.4a) *is exact, and* $(A_1, C_1, f_1, g_1, h_1)$ *is an exact couple*:

(4.4a)

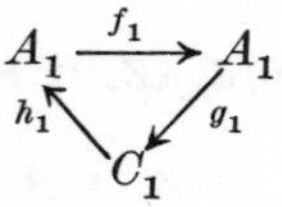

PROBLEM

16-14. Prove this.

The process continues. The collection $\{C_n, d_n\}$ constitutes a spectral sequence in consonance with (4.4).

Suppose A and C are bigraded modules over R,

$$A = \oplus A^{pq}, \qquad C = \oplus C^{pq}. \tag{4.4b}$$

(We remark parenthetically that just as in the case of single grading a submodule Q of A has a grading imposed by that of A. Thus $Q = \oplus(Q^{pq} = A^{pq} \cap Q)$. Similarly for C. Our earlier work involved homomorphisms of 0 degree, but in this section this will not be true in general. Bear in mind f is of degree (m, n) if $f(A^{pq}) \subset A^{p+m\; q+n}$ and similarly for h and for g.

Lemma 4.5. f *and* f_1 *are of the same degree and so are* h *and* h_1, *but* $\mathit{deg}\, g_1 = \mathit{deg}\, g - \mathit{deg}\, f$.

The last relation is an immediate consequence of the fact that $g_1 a_1$ is in the coset $gf^{-1} a_1$, noting that $\deg f^{-1} = -\deg f$.

Definition 4.6. A **homomorphism** of the couple $(A, C, f, g; h)$ to the couple $({}_0A, {}_0C, {}_0f, {}_0g, {}_0h)$ is a pair (u, v) where u is a homomorphism on A to ${}_0A$, v is a homomorphism on C to ${}_0C$ and the following diagram is commutative:

(4.6a)
$$\begin{array}{ccccccc} A & \xrightarrow{f} & A & \xrightarrow{g} & C & \xrightarrow{h} & A \\ {\scriptstyle u}\downarrow & & {\scriptstyle u}\downarrow & & {\scriptstyle v}\downarrow & & {\scriptstyle u}\downarrow \\ {}_0A & \xrightarrow{{}_0f} & {}_0A & \xrightarrow{{}_0g} & {}_0C & \xrightarrow{{}_0h} & {}_0A \end{array}$$

Lemma 4.7. *The homomorphism (u, v) induces homomorphisms (u_n, v_n) of the derived couples.*

We assert first that v is allowable. Indeed from (4.6a) $vd = vgh = {}_0guh = {}_0g\,{}_0hv = {}_0dv$. Allowability implies $v_1\colon C_1 \to {}_0C_1$. Moreover from the first square in (4.6a) follows $uA_1 = ufA = {}_0f\,uA \subset {}_0f\,{}_0A = {}_0A_1$, so $u_1\colon A_1 \to {}_0A_1$.
It is a straightforward matter to verify that (4.6a) remains valid when the derived couples replace the rows and u_1, v_1 replace u, v. Iteration of this procedure yields homomorphisms u_n, v_n of the nth derived couples.

Definition 4.8. The homomorphisms $({}_0u, {}_0v)$ and $({}_1u, {}_1v)$ are **homotopic**, $({}_0u, {}_0v) \simeq ({}_1u, {}_1v)$, if there is a homomorphism, D, on C to ${}_0C$ for which

(4.8a) $${}_1vc - {}_0vc = Ddc + {}_0dDc, \qquad c \in C,$$

and

(4.8b) $${}_1ua - {}_0ua = {}_0hDg, \qquad a \in A.$$

Lemma 4.9. $({}_0u, {}_0v) \simeq ({}_1u, {}_1v) \Rightarrow {}_0u_n = {}_1u_n,\ {}_0v_n = {}_1v_n, \qquad n \geq 1.$

We now show that the exact couple yields the spectral sequence except for a trivial change in indexing.

Definition 4.10. Let (J, δ) be a filtered differential group. Then, (61.12),

(4.10a)
$$\begin{array}{ccc} H(J^{(p+1)}) & \xrightarrow{\quad j \quad} & H(J^{(p)}) \\ & {\scriptstyle \delta}\nwarrow \quad \swarrow{\scriptstyle \eta} & \\ & H(J^{(p)}/J^{(p+1)}) & \end{array}$$

is exact. Write $A^p = H(J^{(p)})$ and $C^p = H(J^{(p)}/J^{(p+1)})$. Note

(4.10b) $$A = \oplus A^p, \quad C = \oplus C^p$$

are graded groups and since j, η, δ have the degrees -1, 0, and 1 respectively, so therefore do the induced homomorphisms f, g, h in (4.1a).

Theorem 4.11. *The spectral sequence* (C_r, d_r) *is identical with* $(E_{r+1}(A); d_{r+1})$.

The symbols of (2.3) have their usual meaning except that the letters J and $J^{(p)}$ replace A and $A^{(p)}$. Let $F_r^p = Z^{(p+r)}/B_r^{(p+r)}$. Accordingly F_r and E_r are graded groups $F_r = \Sigma F_r^p$ and $E_r = \Sigma E_r^p$. Consider the diagram

(4.11a)

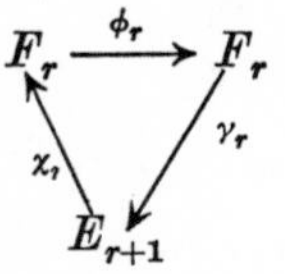

ϕ, γ, χ are the Greek-letter cousins of f, g, h and will now be defined. Let s be the injection s: $Z^{(p+r)} \to Z^{(p+r-1)}$. Then, by (2.4), s: $B_r^{(p+r)} \to B_r^{(p+r-1)}$.

Define ϕ_r as the homomorphism induced by s,

$$\phi_r\colon F_r \to F_r$$

where $\phi_r\colon F_r^p \to F_r^{p-1}$. That is to say, ϕ_r is of degree -1. The injection t: $Z^{(p+r)} \to Z_{r+1}^{(p+r)}$ yields

$$t\colon B_r^{(p+r)} \to B_r^{(p+r)} + Z_r^{(p+r+1)} = \Gamma_r^{(p+r)}.$$

Therefore t induces the homomorphism

$$\gamma_r\colon F_r \to E_{r+1},$$

where

$$\gamma_r\colon F_r^p \to E_{r+1}^{p+r}.$$

Thus γ_r is of degree r.

In view of (2.3a) and (2.3c), δ takes $Z_{r+1}^{(p)}$, $Z_r^{(p+1)}$, and $B_r^{(p)}$ into $Z^{(p+r+1)}$, $B_r^{(p+r+1)}$, and 0 respectively and so induces the homomorphism of degree 1, $\chi_r\colon E_{r+1}^p \to F_r^{p+1}$. Write $\Delta_{r+1} = \gamma_r\,\chi_r$.

It can be verified that the diagram (4.11a) is exact. Hence

$$\{F_r, E_{r+1}, \phi_r, \gamma_r, \chi_r\}$$

is an exact couple and $E_{r+1} = H(E_r)$. In view of (2.3a) and (2.3c), $E_0^p = J^{(p)}/J^{(p+1)}$ so

(4.11b)
$$E_1^p = H(J^{(p)}/J^{(p+1)}) = C^p.$$

Next, in view of (4.10a) and (4.10b),

(4.11c)
$$F_0^p = Z^p/B^p = A^p.$$

The E_{r+1} terms in the successively derived couples arising from (4.11b) are also given by (3.1a). From (4.11b) and (4.11c) we infer

$$(A, C, f, g, h) = (F_0, E_1, \phi, \gamma, \chi)$$

and so we can identify $(A_r, C_r, f_r, g_r, h_r)$ and $(F_r, E_{r+1}, \phi_r, \gamma_r, \chi_r)$ or $(C_r, d_r) = (E_{r+1}, \Delta_{r+1})$, $r \geq 0$, where Δ_{r+1} is to be identified with d_{r+1} of (3.2c).

Definition 4.12. Let now J be a filtered, DG group or module with

(4.12a) $$J^{(p)} = \oplus_n {}^nJ^{(p)}$$

$$\supset J^{(-1)} \supset J^{(0)} \supset J^{(+1)} \supset \ldots \supset J^{(p)} \supset$$

Consistently with (4.10b) we have the direct sums for the graded modules,

$$H(J^{(p)}) = \oplus\, ({}^nH(J^{(p)}) = {}^nH(J) \cap H^{(p)}(J) = {}^nA^{p,q}),$$

$$H(J^{(p)}/J^{(p+1)}) = \oplus\, {}^nH(J^{(p)}/J^{(p+1)}) = {}^nC^{p,q}.$$

In the first line the intersection assumes both ${}^nH(J)$ and $H^{(p)}(J)$ are injected in $H(J)$. Here n reflects the grading of J and is the analogue of the usual dimension script in cohomology while $q = n - p$. Then (bearing in mind only two grades are independent), we have the doubly graded modules

(4.12c) $$A = \Sigma\, {}^nA^{p,q}, \qquad C = \Sigma\, {}^nC^{p,q},$$

and the exact couple (A, C, f, g, h) in the notation of (4.3a) and (4.12c) is defined as in (4.10) or (4.11). Since (4.10a) is exact, by (61.13b) the effect of δ is to increase n by 1 while j and η leave n invariant. On the other hand, from (4.10) the effect of f is to decrease p by 1, that of g to leave p the same and that of h to increase p by 1. Since $q = n - p$, we infer

(4.12d) $$deg\, f = (0, -1, 1),$$

$$deg\, g = (0, 0, 0),$$

$$deg\, h = (1, 1, 0)$$

in terms of n, p, q.

5. CONVERGENCE. The applications of exact couples extend beyond omology groups. It is of interest to show that if regularity conditions are introduced, there is convergence of C_r to a specific limit, in the sense that C_r^{pq} is ultimately not dependent on r. In particular (3.14) is included. For convenience pick n and q as the independent grades. We write then ${}^nA^q$, ${}^nC^q$ for ${}^nA^{p,q} = {}^nA^{n-q,q}$ and ${}^nC^{n-q,q}$ respectively.

Theorem 5.1. *Let $A^{pq} = 0$ for $U(n) > q$ and let ${}^nC^{pq} = 0$ for $L(n) < q$. Then for each pq and large enough r,*

(5.1a) $$C_r = C_\infty,$$

(5.1b) $${}^nC^q_\infty \approx {}^n\mathbf{A}^q/{}^n\mathbf{A}^{q-1} \text{ (cf. italics below).}$$

${}^nA^q$ and ${}^{n+1}A^q$ are 0 for $q < \min(U(n), U(n+1)) = V(n)$. Exactness of the couple then implies ${}^nC^q = 0$, $q < V(n)$. Since $C_i = H(C_{i-1})$, ${}^nC^q_i = 0$ for $L(n) < q$, or $q < V(n)$. From d_r: ${}^nC^q_r \to {}^{n+1}C^{q-r}_r$ follows $d_r\,{}^nC^q_r = 0$ for $q - r < V(n+1)$, i.e., for $q - V(n+1) = W_1(n, q) \leq r$. Similarly the bounding cocycles under d_r in ${}^nC^{pq}_r$ arise from ${}^{n-1}C^{q+r}_r$ so we are assured there are none if $L(n-1) < q + r$ or if $L(n-1) - q = W_2(n-1, q) < r$. In short, if $r \geq \max(W_1(n+1, q), W_2(n-1, q)) = R(n, q)$, then ${}^nC^q_r$ consists of nonbounding cocycles so ${}^nC^q_r \approx Z({}^nC^q_r) = H({}^nC^q_r) \approx {}^nC^q_{r+1}$. We paraphrase this by writing ${}^nC^q_\infty$. Thus for assigned q and n,

(5.1c) $${}^nC^q_r \approx {}^nC^q_\infty \approx {}^nC^q_s, \qquad r, s > R(n, q).$$

By exactness of the couple (4.3a), in view of our hypotheses, for fixed n and q sufficiently large,

(5.1d) $$f\colon {}^nA^q \xrightarrow{\approx} {}^nA^{q+1}.$$

Hence for arbitrary but fixed n and q and for m sufficiently large,

(5.1e) $${}^nA^{q+m}_m = f^m\,{}^nA^q \approx f^{m+1}\,{}^nA^q = {}^nA^{q+m+1},$$

where $f^{m+1} = f(f^m)$. Denote ${}^nA^{q+m+1}$ by ${}^nA^\infty$ and *for these m values denote* $f^m\,{}^nA^q$ *by* ${}^n\mathbf{A}^q$. Plainly

$${}^n\mathbf{A}^q = {}^n\mathbf{A}^{q+1} \subset {}^nA.$$

The exactness condition for the rth derived couple with due regard for (4.3) takes the form

(5.1f) $${}^{n+r-2}C^{q+r-1}_r \xrightarrow{h_r} {}^{n+r-1}A^{q+r-1}_r \xrightarrow{f_r} {}^{n+r-1}A^{q+r}_r \xrightarrow{g_r} {}^{n+r-1}C^q_r \xrightarrow{h_r} {}^{n+r}A^{q+1}_r$$

Then for r large enough, our previous results guarantee

$${}^{n-r-2}C^{q+r-1}_r = 0,\ {}^{n+1}A^{q+1}_r = f^r(A^{q-r+1}) = 0,\ {}^{n+r-1}A^{q+r+\varepsilon}_r = {}^n\mathbf{A}^q,\ \varepsilon = 0, 1, \tag{4.13e}$$

and ${}^nC^q_r = {}^nC^q_\infty$, (5.1c), so (5.1f) becomes

$$0 \xrightarrow{h_r} \mathbf{A}^{q-1} \xrightarrow{f_r} \mathbf{A}^q \xrightarrow{g_r} {}^nC^q \longrightarrow 0.$$

Hence ${}^nC^q_\infty \approx {}^n\mathbf{A}^q/{}^n\mathbf{A}^{q-1}$ as asserted. The special case ${}^nA^{p,q} = {}^nH(J^{(p)})$, ${}^nC^{pq} = {}^nH(J^{(p)}/J^{(p+1)})$ yields ${}^n\mathbf{A}^q = {}^nH^{(n-q)}(J)$, or returning to $p = n - q$,

$$\underset{\rightarrow}{\mathsf{L}}\ {}^nC^{pq}_r \approx {}^nH^{(p)}(J) / {}^nH^{(p+1)}(J).$$

PROBLEMS

16-15. Establish a theorem analogous to (5.1) where n is replaced by p in the hypotheses.

16-16. If for every p, $A^{pq} = 0$ for $L(p) < q$ and $C^{pq} = 0$ for $q < U(p)$, show $ker\, f^r, f^r\colon A^{pq-r} \to A^{pq}$ is independent of r (up to isomorphism), for large values of r. Write K^{pq} for this common group. Show A^{pq} is independent of q (up to isomorphism) for q sufficiently small. Show $C^{pq}_\infty \approx K^{p+1\,q+1}/K^{p+1\,q}$.

6. HOMOMORPHISMS OF *DF* MODULES. We write $E_r.$ for $E_r.(A)$ and $'E_r.$ for $E_r.(A')$.

Lemma 6.1. *If h is an allowable homomorphism of the filtered differential modules $A \to 'A$, then h induces a homomorphism h^* of E_r to $'E_r$ with $r \leq \infty$ where A, $'A$ give rise to E_r, $'E_r$.*

We make use of

$$h\colon A^{(p)} \subset 'A^{(p)} \quad (1.7).$$

Since h is allowable, (61.3), h commutes with d,

$$id\, h\, Z_r^{(pq)} \subset h\, id\, Z_r^{(pq)} \quad (3.2a)$$
$$\subset h\, A^{(p+r\, q-r+1)} \subset 'A^{(p+r\, q-r+1)}.$$

Hence $h\, Z_r^{(pq)} \subset 'Z_r^{(pq)}$. Similarly, using (3.2b), $h\colon B_{r-1}^{(pq)} \to 'B_{r-1}^{(pq)}$. Accordingly h induces the homomorphism

(6.1a) $$h^*\colon E_r \to 'E_r,$$

defined by $h^*\langle z_r^{(p)}\rangle_{\Gamma_{r-1}^{(p)}} = \langle h\, z_r^{(p)}\rangle_{'\Gamma_{r-1}^{(p)}}$. Hence

$$'d_r\, h^*\langle z_r^{(p)}\rangle = \langle 'i\, 'd\, h\, z_r^{(p)}\rangle = h^* d_r \langle z_r^{(p)}\rangle.$$

Relations similar to (6.1a) subsist for $'Z^{(pq)}$ and $'B^{(pq)}$ whence $h^*\colon E_\infty \to 'E_\infty$. Incidentally,

(6.1b) $$'p^r{}_{r+1} h = h\, p^r{}_{r+1}.$$

The next theorem is central.

Theorem 6.2. *Let h be a homomorphism of the DF module J into $'J$. Suppose J and $'J$ are regular. Suppose for some r*

(6.2a) *$h^*\colon E_r \to 'E_r$ is a bijection;*

then

(6.2b) *$h^*\colon E_s \to 'E_s$, $s > r$, is a bijection and the induced $\bar{h}^*$ yields*

(6.2c) *$\bar{h}^*\colon H(J) \to H('J)$ is a bijection.*

Conclusion (6.2b) follows from the fact that d_r and h^* commute whence h^* induces a bijection

$$E_{r+1} \approx H(E_r) \to H('E_r) \approx 'E_{r+1}.$$

For the conclusion (6.2c) note, in view of (6.1b), that $h^* W_r \subset 'W_r$. Moreover, for each $W_r \in D_r$ and large enough s, $'p^r{}_s h^* W_r \approx h^* p^r{}_s W_r \approx 0$, so $h^* D_r \subset 'D_r$. Then h^* induces a homomorphism also denoted by h^*

(6.2d) $$h^*: \frac{W_r}{D_r} \to \frac{'W_r}{'D_r} \quad \text{or} \quad h^*: \underrightarrow{\mathsf{L}}\, E_r \to \underrightarrow{\mathsf{L}}\, 'E_r.$$

Actually h^* is a bijection. Thus if w_r is a representative of *ker* h^* in (6.2d), then $'p^r{}_s h^* w_r = 0$ implies $h^* w_s = 0$ where $w_s = p^r{}_s w_r \in E_s$. Then (6.2a) asserts $w_s = 0$ or $w_r \in D_r$. To show h^* is onto, observe that if $'w_r$ is a representative of a coset in $'W_r/'D_r$, $w_r = h^{*-1}\, 'w_r$ is unique (6.2a) and is in W_r, since $p^r{}_s w_r$ is meaningful according to $p^r{}_s w_r = h^{*-1}\, 'p^r{}_s\, 'w_r$. We invoke (3.17) and (3.5) as justification for the assertion h induces the bijections h^* on E_∞ to $'E_\infty$ and h''^*: $GH(J) \to GH('J)$.

To complete the proof of (6.2c) we show first that $\bar{h}^*$ *is onto*: If ${}_1^n a^{(p)} \in {}^n H^{(p)}('J)$ then since h''^* is a bijection, there is an antecedent

$$(h''^*)^{-1}[{}_1^n a^{(p)}]_1 = [{}^n a^{(p)}] \in {}^n H^{(p)}(J)/{}^n H^{(p+1)}(J).$$

Thus ${}_1^n a^{(p)} = \bar{h}^* ({}^n a^{(p)}) + {}_1^n a^{(p+1)}$. By induction

$${}_1^n a^{(p)} = \bar{h}^*({}^n a^{(p)} + {}^n a^{(p+1)} + \cdots {}^n a^{(p+t)}) + {}_1^n a^{(p+t+1)}.$$

Since $'J$ is regular, for fixed n and t large enough, ${}_1^n a^{(p+t+1)} = 0$, so ${}_1^n a^{(p)}$ is covered by $\bar{h}^*$.

We establish ker $\bar{h}^* = 0$. Remark that

(6.2e) $${}^n Z^{(p)} \xrightarrow{\eta^{(p)}} H^{(p)}(J) \xrightarrow{\lambda^{(p)}} H^{(p)}(J)/H^{(p+1)}(J),$$

where $\eta^{(p)}$ and $\lambda^{(p)}$ are the natural epimorphisms. Then $h''^* \lambda^{(p)} \eta^{(p)} {}^n z^{(p)} = \bar{h}^* \eta^{(p)}\, {}^n z^{(p)}$ *mod* $H^{(p+1)}('J)$. Suppose $0 \neq {}^n u \in$ *ker* $\bar{h}^*$ and let ${}^n z \in {}^n Z(J)$ be a representative of ${}^n u$. For some p, ${}^n z \in J^{(p)}$, ${}^n z \,\bar{\in}\, J^{(p+1)}$ and so ${}^n z \,\bar{\in}\, {}^n Z^{(p+1)}$, but ${}^n z \in Z_r^{(p)}$ (2.4a). Since ${}^n z \,\bar{\in}\, {}^n B(J)$, ${}^n z \,\bar{\in}\, {}^n B^{(p)}(J)$ (3.6). Thus ${}^n z^{(p)}/\Gamma_{r-1}^{(p)}$ is a nontrivial member of ${}^p(W_r/D_r) \approx {}^p GH(J)$, and accordingly its map by h^* is nontrivial (6.2b). It is then immediate that $h''^* \lambda^{(p)} \eta^{(p)}$ is nontrivial whence so is $\bar{h}^* \eta^{(p)}\, {}^n z^{(p)}$, a contradiction.

Lemma 6.3. *If* $0 \longrightarrow H(A^{(t)}) \xrightarrow{i(t)} H(A)$ *is exact for all* t, *then*

$$E_1 = E_s, \quad 1 < s.$$

First $w = id\, z_r^{(p)} \in B(A) \cap A^{(p+r)}$. By hypothesis $v = i(p + r)^{-1} w \in B(A^{(p+r)})$. Thus $v = du$, $u \in A^{(p+r)}$. In particular then, $u \in A^{(p+1)}$, $du \in$

$A^{(p+r)}$ so $u \in Z_{r-1}^{(p+1)} \subset \Gamma_{r-1}^{(p)}$. Accordingly $\eta_r^{(p)}(u) = 0$ and $d(u - z_r^{(p)}) = 0$, where $\eta_r^{(p)}$ is defined in (6.2e).

$$d_r \eta_r^{(p)} z_r^p = d_r \eta_r^{(p)}(u - z_r^{(p)}) = \eta_r^{(p)}(id(u - z_r^{(p)})) = 0.$$

Hence d_r is trivial for $r > 0$.

7. THE BASIC COMBINATIONS. At the center of things here is (3.3) and the fact that d_r advances p to $p + r$ and demotes q to $q - r + 1$. If $E_r^{p+r,q-r+1} = 0$, then $E_r^{pq} = Z(E_r^{pq})$ so there is an epimorphism $E_r^{pq} \to E_r^{pq}/B(E_r^{pq}) = E_{r+1}^{pq}$. If, however, $E_r^{p-r,q+r-1} = 0$, then $B(E_r^{pq}) = 0$ so there is a monomorphism $E_{r+1}^{pq} = Z(E_r^{pq}) \to E_r^{pq}$. The next lemmas amount to this and play various changes on these elementary observations. It will be sufficiently clear to give only two of the superscripts in ${}^nE^{pq}$. Thus E^{pq} or ${}^nE^{p\cdot}$ or ${}^nE^{\cdot q}$ since $p + q = n$.

In dealing with E_∞, in order to make use of (3.14) or of (3.17) in conjunction with (3.5) or of (6.2) we shall understand a *hypothesis of convergence or regularity* on the filtration throughout the remainder of this section. (This hypothesis would not be necessary if our conclusions were restricted to E_r, r finite or if ${}^nE_r^p = 0$ for all small enough p.) We list what corresponds to a table of integrals, though often in the sequel we prefer to derive the needed relation ab ovo.

Lemma 7.1. (a) *If $E_r^{pq} = 0$, then $E_{r+s}^{pq} = 0$, $0 \le s < \infty$.*

(7.1b) *If ${}^nE_\infty^{p\cdot} = 0$ for $p < P$, then ${}^nH \to {}^nE_\infty^P \to 0$ is exact.*

(7.1c) *If ${}^nE_\infty^{p\cdot} = 0$ for $p > P$, then ${}^nH^{(P+1)} = 0$ and $0 \to E_\infty^{P\cdot} \to {}^nH$ is exact.*

We shall consistently abbreviate $H^{(p)}(A)$ to $H^{(p)}$ below. Evidently, using the trivial conclusion (7.1a),

$${}^nH^{(P)} \to H^{(P)}/H^{(P+1)} \approx {}^nE_\infty^{P\cdot} \to 0.$$

Moreover, since the filtration is decreasing $H^{(p)} \approx H^{(p+1)}$ follows from (3.5), if $p > P$ and

$${}^nH = \bigcup {}^nH^{(t)} = \bigcup_P^\infty {}^nH^{(t)} = {}^nH^{(P)}.$$

The decreasing filtration and the fact that ${}^nH^{(p)} \approx {}^nH^{(p+1)}$, $p > P$, leads to

$$0 = \bigcap {}^nH^{(p)} = {}^nH^{(P+1)}.$$

Then ${}^nE_\infty^P \approx {}^nH^{(P)}/{}^nH^{(P+1)} \approx {}^nH^{(P)} \to {}^nH$.

Theorem 7.2. *If ${}^nE_r^{p\cdot} = 0$, $p \ne a$, $a + b$, where $b > 0$, then*

(a) $$0 \to {}^nE_\infty^{a+b\cdot} \xrightarrow{j^*} {}^nH \xrightarrow{k^*} {}^nE_\infty^{a\cdot} \to 0$$

is exact.

(b) *If ${}^nE_r^{p\cdot} = 0$, $p \ne a$, then ${}^nE_\infty^{a\cdot} \approx {}^nH$.*

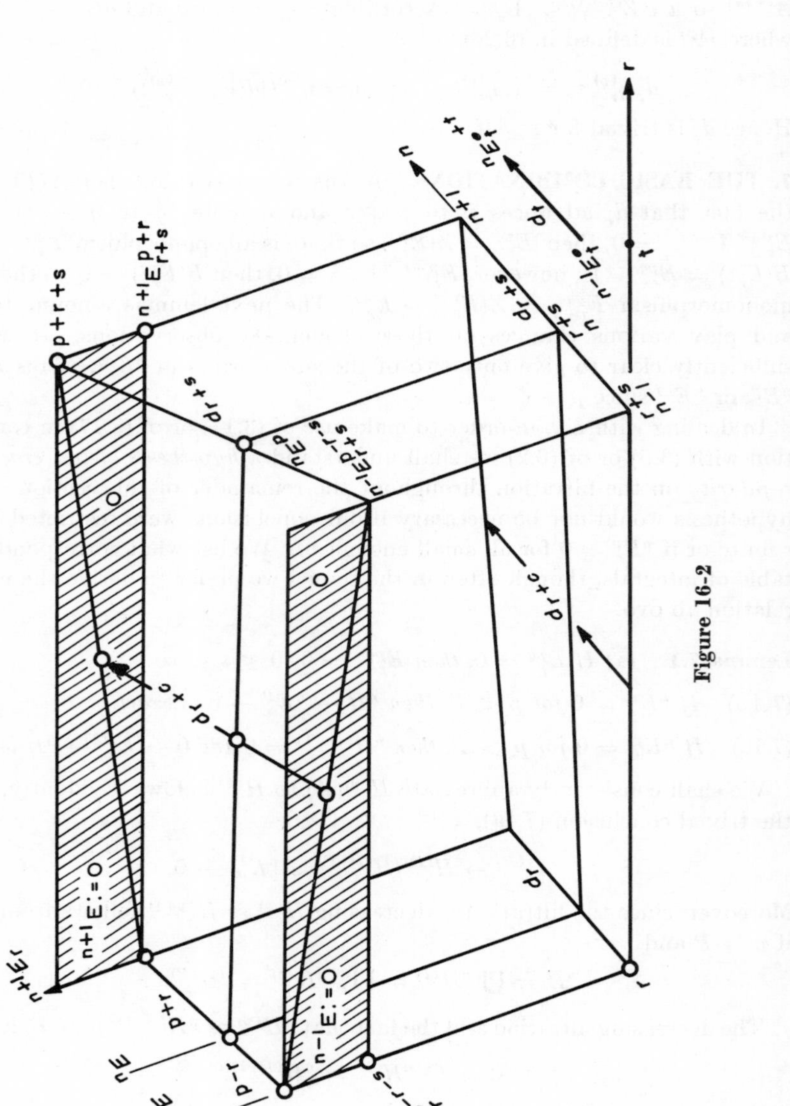

Figure 16-2

The homomorphisms j^* and k^* are those of (7.1b) and (7.1c). The hypotheses assure that for $a < p < p + b$, $E_\infty^{p,n-p} = 0$. From (3.5) we infer ${}^nH^{(a+1)} \approx \cdot \approx {}^nH^{(a+b)}$, and so

$$Im\, j^* = {}^nH^{(a+b)} \approx {}^nH^{(a+1)} = ker\, k^*.$$

Lemma 7.3.

(7.3a) *If*

$${}^nE_r^{t\cdot} = 0, p - (r + s) < t \leq p - r,$$

then for $0 < s \leq \infty$,

$$0 \to {}^nE_{r+s}^{p,q} \to {}^nE_r^{p,q}$$

is exact.

(7.3b) *If* ${}^{n+1}E_r^{t\cdot} = 0$, $p + r \leq t \leq p + r + s$, *then for* $0 < s \leq \infty$

$$E_r^{p,q} \to E_{r+s}^{p,q} \to 0$$

is exact.

For (7.3a): A bounding cocycle under d_{r+c} in $E_{r+c}^{p,q}$, $0 \leq c < s$ has an antecedent in $E_{r+c}^{p-(r+c),\, q+r+c-1}$ which vanishes in view of (7.1a) and the hypotheses for (7.3a). Hence

$$E_{r+c+1}^{pq} = H(E_{r+c}^{pq}) = Z(E_{r+c}^{pq}) \subset E_{r+c}^{p,q}.$$

For $s = \infty$, the argument is still valid.

For (7.3b), if $0 < s \leq c$, then $d_{r+c}\, E_{r+c}^{pq} = E_{r+c}^{p+r+c\; q-(r+c+1)} = 0$, that is to say $Z(E_{r+c}^{pq}) = E_{r+c}^{pq}$ whence follows by (3.3)

$$E_{r+c}^{pq} \to H(E_{r+c}^{pq}) = E_{r+c+1}^{pq} \to 0.$$

Theorem 7.4

(7.4a) *If* ${}^{n-1}E_r^{p\cdot} = 0$, $p \leq P - r$, *and if* ${}^nE_r^p = 0$, $p < P$, *there is a homomorphism,* ${}^nH \xrightarrow{j^*} {}^nE_r^{p\cdot}$.

(7.4b) *If* ${}^{n+1}E_r^{p\cdot} = 0$, $P + r \leq p$, ${}^nE_r^{p\cdot} = 0$, $P < p$, *there is a homomorphism* ${}^nE_r^{P\cdot} \xrightarrow{k^*} {}^nH$.

(7.4c) *Under the assumptions of* (7.4a) *and* (7.4b), $j^* = (k^*)^{-1}$.

For (7.4a), combine (7.3a) and (7.1b).
For (7.4b), combine (7.3b) and (7.1c).

Theorem 7.5. *If* ${}^nE_r^{p\cdot} = 0$, $p \neq P$, $P - a$, *where* $a > 0$, ${}^{n+1}E_r^{p\cdot} = 0$, $p \geq P + r$, ${}^{n-1}E_r^{p\cdot} = 0$, $p \leq P - a - r$, *then*

$${}^nE_r^{P\cdot} \to {}^nH \to {}^nE_r^{P-a\cdot}$$

is exact.

The hypotheses on the first line coincide with those of (7.2a), noting that $a + b$ is replaced by P and a by $P - a$. Next, the case $s = \infty$ in (7.3a) is applied to replace $E_\infty^{P-a\cdot}$ by $E_r^{P-a\cdot}$ and finally (7.3b) settles the demonstration.

Theorem 7.6

(7.6a) *If for some nonnegative a, (i)* ${}^{n-1}E_r^{t\cdot} = 0$ *for* $t \leq p - r$, *(ii)* ${}^{n}E_r^{t\cdot} = 0$, $p \neq t \leq p + a$, *(iii)* ${}^{n+1}E_r^{t\cdot} = 0$, $p + r \leq t \neq p + r + a$, *then the upper row in*

$$\begin{array}{ccccc} {}^nH & \longrightarrow & {}^nE_r^{p\cdot} & \xrightarrow{\delta} & {}^{n+1}E_r^{p+r+a\cdot} \\ & & \rho\downarrow & & \uparrow\lambda \\ & & {}^nE_{r+a}^{p\cdot} & \xrightarrow{d_{r+a}} & {}^{n+1}E_{r+a}^{p+r+a} \end{array}$$

is exact, where δ denotes the composition of the homomorphisms listed.

(7.6b) *If for some nonnegative a,* ${}^{n+1}E_r^{t\cdot} = 0$ *for* $t \geq p + r$, ${}^nE_r^{t\cdot} = 0$ *for* $p - a \leq t \neq p$, ${}^{n-1}E^{t\cdot} = 0$, $p - (r + a) \neq t \leq p - r$, *then the upper row in*

$$\begin{array}{ccccc} {}^{n-1}E_r^{p-(r+a)\cdot} & \xrightarrow{\delta} & {}^nE_r^{p\cdot} & \longrightarrow & {}^nH \\ \downarrow & & \uparrow & & \\ {}^{n-1}E_{r+a}^{p-(r+a)} & \xrightarrow{d_{r+a}} & {}^nE_{r+a}^{p} & & \end{array}$$

is exact, where δ is defined as the composition of the indicated homomorphisms.

We begin by showing ρ is an isomorphism and λ is a monomorphism. The first line of the hypothesis is that ${}^{n-1}E_r^{p-(r+b)\cdot} = 0$, for every nonnegative b, whence ${}^{n-1}E_s^{p-(r+b)\cdot} = 0$ for $s \geq r$. Thus ${}^nE_{r+a}^{p\cdot}$ has no bounding cocycles. Therefore

$${}^nE_{r+a+1}^{p\cdot} = H(E_{r+a}^{p}) = Z(E_{r+a}^{p}) = ker\ d_{r+a}.$$

Therefore

$$0 \longrightarrow {}^nE_{r+a+1}^{p\cdot} \longrightarrow {}^nE_{r+a}^{p\cdot} \xrightarrow{d_{r+a}} {}^{n+1}E_{r+a}^{p+r+a\cdot} \tag{7.6c}$$

is an exact sequence. Since $t \leq p - (r + a + 1)$ is included in $t \leq p - r$, $E_\infty^{p\cdot}$ injects into ${}^nE_{r+a+1}^{p\cdot}$ by (7.3a). However *(iii)* corresponds to (7.3b) with $p + r$ replaced by $p + r + a$, so ${}^nE_\infty^{p\cdot}$ includes ${}^nE_{r+a+1}^{p\cdot}$. Hence ${}^nE_\infty^{p\cdot} \approx {}^nE_{r+a+1}^{p\cdot}$. Similarly $E_{r+a}^{p\cdot} \approx E_r^{p\cdot}$. We use (7.3a) again for the monomorphism of ${}^{n+1}E_{r+a}^{p+r+a}$ into ${}^{n+1}E_r^{p+r+a\cdot}$. Hence (7.6c) can be written

$$0 \to {}^nE_\infty^{p\cdot} \to {}^nE_r^{p\cdot} \to {}^{n+1}E_r^{p+r+a\cdot}. \tag{7.6d}$$

By the second line of the hypothesis, (7.1b) is valid to ensure substituting ${}^pH$ for ${}^nE_\infty^{p\cdot}$ in (7.6d).

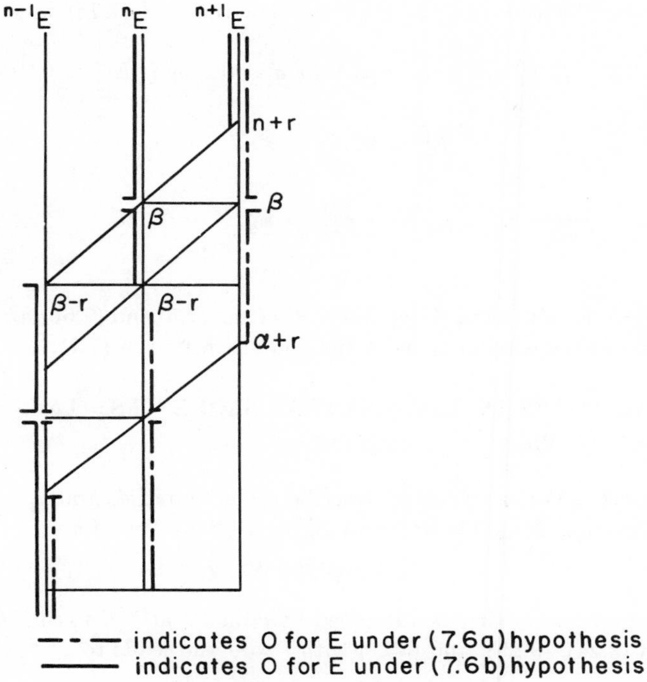

Figure 16-3

The following two theorems are of paramount importance. They bear hypotheses often encountered in applications and are corollaries of the preceding lemmas.

Theorem 7.7. *If* $E_r^{pq} = 0$ *for* $p \neq a, b$ *where* $b - a \geq r$, *then*

(7.7a) $$\to E_r^{b\cdot} \to {}^nH \to {}^nE_r^{a\cdot} \to {}^{n+1}E_r^{b\cdot} \to {}^{n+1}H \to$$

is exact.

In (7.6a) let p, $p + r + a$ be b, c. In (7.6b) let $p - (r + a)$, p be b, c. In (7.5) let P, $P - a$ be b, c. With the identifications listed, the hypotheses of (7.6a) and (7.6b) include those of (7.5). (The relations are transparent when one superposes the diagrams for (7.6a) and (7.6b) with the values above. The result could be listed as (7.6 $(a + b)$). Abutting the sequences in the conclusions of (7.6a) and (7.6b) at ${}^nH$ yields

(7.7b) $${}^{n-1}E^{a\cdot} \to {}^nE^{b\cdot} \to {}^nH \to {}^nE^{a\cdot} \to {}^{n+1}E^{b\cdot}.$$

Exactness at ${}^nH$ is covered by (7.5). Thus (7.7b) is an exact sequence. We close by remarking that the hypotheses of (7.6a) and (7.6b) are more than covered by those of (7.7), so the exactness of (7.7a) is guaranteed.

Theorem 7.8. *If* $E_2^{pq} = 0$ *for* $p < 0$ *or* $q < 0$ *and if* $E_2^{pq} = 0$, $0 < q < N$, *then*

(7.8a) $$E_2^{io} \approx {}^iH \qquad i < N$$

and

(7.8b) $$0 \to E_2^{No} \to {}^NH \to E_2^{oN} \to E_2^{n+1o} \to {}^{N+1}H$$

is exact.

Here (7.8a) follows from (7.4c) and (7.8b) from (7.5) and (7.6b) for sagacious adjustment of the constants, as in the demonstration of (7.7).

8. INITIAL TERMS IN THE SPECTRAL SEQUENCES. Let J be a DF module as in (4.10).

Definition 8.1. We are going to describe the action of d_0 and d_1. Evidently for nonpositive t, $Z_t^{(p)}(J) = J^{(p)}$ and $B_t^{(p)} \supset J^{(p+1)}$. Therefore

(8.1a) $$E_0 = \oplus J^{(p)}/J^{(p+1)} = GJ.$$

The boundary homomorphism induced by d on $J^{(p)}/J^{(p+1)}$ to $J^{(p)}/J^{(p+1)}$ is d_0 in view of (3.2a), (3.2b), and (3.2c) with $r = 0$ and leads to

(8.1b) $$E_1^p = H(E_0^p) = H(J^{(p)}/J^{(p+1)}).$$

Let h be the injection

$$h: J^{(p+1)} \to J^{(p)}.$$

Write $[j]_{p+m}$ for the coset with respect to $J^{(p+m)}$. Then

(8.1c) $$0 \longrightarrow J^{(p+1)}/J^{(p+2)} \xrightarrow{h^\#} J^{(p)}/J^{(p+2)} \xrightarrow{\eta^\#} J^{(p)}/J^{(p+1)} \longrightarrow 0,$$

is exact, where

$$h^\# [j^{(p+1)}]_{p+2} = [hj^{(p+1)}]_{p+2},$$
$$\eta^\# [j^{(p)}]_{p+2} = [j^{(p)}]_{p+1}.$$

Thus $J^{(p+1)}/J^{(p+2)}$, $J^{(p)}/J^{(p+2)}$ and $J^{(p)}/J^{(p+1)}$ play the roles of J, G, and G/J in (61.12) and this being so, the corresponding cohomology sequence is exact (61.13b),

(8.1d) $$\begin{array}{ccccc} \xrightarrow{\eta^*} & H(J^{(p)}/J^{(p+1)}) & \xrightarrow{\delta} & H(J^{(p+1)}/J^{(p+2)}) & \xrightarrow{h^*} . \\ & \| & & \| & \\ & E_1^p & & E_1^{p+1} & \end{array}$$

The definition of δ in (61.11) is precisely that of d_1 in (3.2c), so that we may identify d_1 and δ.

Thus a representative of $Z(J^{(p)}/J^{(p+1)})$ has the form $z^{(p)} = w^{(p)} + j^{(p+1)}$ where $dw^{(p)} = 0$ and $j^{(p+1)} \in J^{(p+1)}$. Then d_1 acting on the cohomology class of $z^{(p)}$ yields $dj^{(p+1)}/\Gamma_0^{(p+1)} \in E_1^{p+1}$.

Definition 8.2. Using d_1 we define $E_2^r = H(E_1^p)$. Moreover, to gain insight into the customary applications, we consider now a double (upper) complex

(8.2a) $$A = \oplus A^{pq},$$

with the two differentials

(8.2b) $${}_1d\colon A^{pq} \to A^{p+1\,q},$$

(8.2c) $${}_2d\colon A^{pq} \to A^{p\,q+1}.$$

This is the situation for the tensor product of complexes, or of gratings. We suppose

(8.2d) $${}_1d\,{}_2d = -{}_2d\,{}_1d.$$

The single complex associated with A, is graded by

(8.2e) $${}^nA = \oplus_{p+q\,=\,n}\, A^{pq},$$

and has the differential

(8.2f) $$d = {}_1d + {}_2d.$$

With $d^2 = 0$ we may filter A in two natural ways. The **first filtration** is defined by

(8.2g) $$A^{(p)} = \oplus_{i \geq p} \oplus_j A^{ij}.$$

Denote the spectral sequence of $A \supset \cdot \supset A^{(p)} \supset$ by $\{{}_1E_r\}$. According to (8.1b)

(8.2h) $${}_1E_1^p = H(A^{(p)}/A^{(p+1)}).$$

Write

(8.2i) $$A^{(p)}/A^{(p+1)} \approx \oplus_j A^{pj} = A^{p*},$$

whence

(8.2j) $$A^{(p)}/A^{(p+2)} \approx A^{p*} + A^{p+1*}.$$

The coboundary homomorphism d_0 arises as in (8.1d) from the differential taking $A^{(p)}$ into $A^{(p)}$ and $A^{(p+1)}$ into $A^{(p+1)}$. Since ${}_1d$ would affect (p), according to (8.2c), we must *identify* d_0 with ${}_2d$. Hence with ${}_1H$ and ${}_2H$ indicating the module determined by ${}_1d$ or by ${}_2d$,

(8.2k) $${}_1E_1^p = {}_2H(A^{p*}) = \oplus_j\, {}_2H(A^{pj}) = \oplus_j\, {}_2H^j(A^{p*})$$
$${}_1E_1 = \oplus\, {}_2H(A^{p*}) = {}_2H(A).$$

To compute d_1, use the fact that by (8.1d), ${}_2H(A^{p*}) \xrightarrow{\delta} {}_2H(A^{p+1*})$ where δ is defined by

$$\langle {}_2z^p \rangle_{{}_2d} \xrightarrow{\delta} \langle d({}_2z^{(p)}) \rangle_{{}_2d} = \langle ({}_1d + {}_2d)\, {}_2z^{(p)} \rangle_{{}_2d} = \langle {}_1d\, {}_2z^{(p)} \rangle_{{}_2d}.$$

Hence δ is induced by ${}_1d$. Thus

$$\text{(8.2l)} \qquad {}_1E_2{}^p = \oplus_j\, {}_1H\, {}_2H^j(A^{p*}),$$
$$ {}_1E_2^{pq} = {}_1H^p({}_2H^q(A)).$$

It will be instructive to establish this relation by a detailed study of individual terms. We repeat the definition of E_2 for ready reference.

$$\text{(8.2m)} \qquad E_2^{pq} = Z_2^{(pq)}/(B_1^{(pq)} + Z_1^{(p+1\,q-1)} = \Gamma_1^{(p\,q)}).$$

Recall

$$Z_2^{(pq)} = Z_2^{(p)}(A) \cap {}^nA \subset A^{(p)} \cap {}^nA = {}^nA^{(pq)},$$

where ${}^nA$ is given by (8.2e). The typical term, z, of $Z_2^{(pq)}$ may be represented as

$$\text{(8.2n)} \qquad z = z^{pq} + z^{p+1\,q-1} + z^{p+m\,q-m} + \cdots$$

with $z^{p+i\,q-i} \in A^{p+i\,q-i}$, where

$$dz \in A^{(p+2)} \cap {}^{n+1}A = {}^{n+1}A^{(p+2\,q-1)}.$$

We show every coset in ${}_1E_2^{pq}$ has as representative just the first two terms in (8.2n). The formal application of $d = {}_1d + {}_2d$ in (8.2n) yields some terms in ${}^{n+1}A^{p\,q+1}$ and in $A^{p+1\,q}$. Since neither of these is included in ${}^{n+1}A^{(p+2\,q-1)}$, the terms in question must be 0. Thus

$$\text{(8.2o)} \qquad {}_2d\, z^{pq} = 0$$
$$ {}_1d\, z^{pq} + {}_2d\, z^{p+1\,q-1} = 0.$$

We turn to representations of $\Gamma_1(p\,q)$ and first to *elements of* $B_1^{(pq)}$. By (2.4a) and (2.3a) $B_1^{(pq)}$ is included in $Z_2^{(pq)}$ and is given by $dA^{(p-1)} \cap A^{(p)} \cap {}^nA$. Hence turning to (8.2m) we require, since $A^{p-1\,q+1}$ is disjunct from $A^{(pq)}$,

$$\text{(8.2p)} \qquad z^{pq} = {}_2d\, w^{p\,q-1} + {}_1d\, w^{p-1\,q}$$
$$0 = {}_2d\, w^{p-1\,q}$$
$$z^{p+1\,q-1} = {}_2d\, w^{p+1\,q-2} + {}_1d\, w^{p\,q-1}$$
$$z^{p+m\,q-m} = \cdots.$$

The *representatives of* $Z_1^{(p+1\,q-1)}$ are of the form (8.2n), but lack z^{pq}. Moreover, though a term $a^{p+1\,q-1}$ may occur, it must satisfy ${}_2d\, a^{p+1\,q-1} = 0$ by (2o). A representative of E_2^{pq} is then

$$\text{(8.2q)} \qquad z = z^{pq} + z^{p+1\,q-1}.$$

If z represents the neutral element of (8.2o), then the first two relations in (8.2p) are satisfied. On the other hand, let z^{pq} and $z^{p+1\,q-1}$ satisfy (8.2n), (8.2m), and (8.2p). Write

$$z^{p+1\,q-1} - {}_1d\, w^{p\,q-1} = v^{p+1\,q-1}. \tag{8.2r}$$

Then

$${}_2d\, v^{p+1\,p-1} = {}_2d\, z^{p+1\,q-1} - {}_2d\, {}_1d\, w^{p\,q-1}.$$

Then (8.2p) and (8.2d) yield ${}_2d\, v^{p+1\,q-1} = 0$. Hence by (8.2q), (8.2p), and (8.2r)

$$z = v^{p+1\,q-1} + {}_2d\, w^{p\,q-1} + {}_1d\, w^{p-1\,q} + {}_1d\, z^{p\,q-1}$$
$$= v^{p+1\,q-1} + d(z^{p-1\,q} + z^{p\,q-1}),$$

i.e.

$$z \in Z_1^{p+1\,q-1} + B_1^{pq} = \Gamma_1^{pq}.$$

Let z in (8.2q) represent an element of E_2^{pq} (so that (8.2n) and (8.2m) are satisfied). Note z^{pq} is a cocycle under ${}_2d$, and hence represents an element $\langle z^{pq}\rangle_2$ of ${}_2H^q(A)$ where $\langle - \rangle_2$ indicates ${}_2d$ is used for coboundaries. By (8.2o)

$${}_1d\langle z^{pq}\rangle_2 = {}_1d\, \langle z^{pq}\rangle_2 = \langle {}_2d\, z^{p+1\,q-1}\rangle_2 = 0.$$

Hence $(z^{pq})_2$ is a representative of an element of ${}_1H^p\, {}_2H^q(A)$. Accordingly, to each z corresponds $\langle z^{pq}\rangle_2$. Let u be a ${}_2d$ cocycle with $\langle u\rangle_2 \in {}_2H^q(A)$. Suppose $\langle u\rangle_2$ is a ${}_1d$ cocycle of grade p. Then this amounts to saying ${}_2d\, u = 0$, ${}_1d\, u = {}_2dv$, so u can be designated as z^{pq}, and v as $z^{n+1\,q-1}$ with $z = u^q + v$ a representative of E_2^{pq}. Therefore to each element of ${}_1H^p\, {}_2H^qA$ there corresponds an element of E_2^{pq}. The neutral element of ${}_1H^p\, {}_2H^q(A)$ arises only when

$$\langle z^{pq}\rangle_2 = \langle {}_1d\, x^{p-1\,p}\rangle_2 = {}_1d\langle x^{p-1\,q}\rangle_2,$$

where ${}_2d\, x^{p-1\,q} = 0$. Thus, for some $x^{p\,q-1}$, $z^{pq} - {}_1d\, x^{p-1\,q} = {}_2d\, x^{p\,q-1}$. The last two equations constitute the first two lines of (8.2p). Therefore the elements of E_2^{pq} that correspond to the neutral element of ${}_1H^p\, {}_2H^q(A)$ are in the 0 coset (or cosets of elements in $Z^{(p+1\,q-1)} + B_1^{(pq)}$. In short ${}_1H^p\, {}_2H^q(A) \approx {}_1E_2^{pq}$.

PROBLEM

16-17. Let $\{A_\lambda, p^\lambda{}_\nu\} = \Sigma^+$ be a direct system of DF modules over a common ring R, where $p^\lambda{}_\nu$ is allowable (1.1d, 1.8). Let $A = \underrightarrow{\mathrm{L}}\,\Sigma^+$ and $A^{(p)} = \underrightarrow{\mathrm{L}}\{A_\lambda^{(p)}, p^\lambda{}_\nu\}$. Show $\{A^{(p)}\}$ is a filtration of the differential filtered module A,

$$A^{(p)}/A^{(p+1)} = {}^pA = \underrightarrow{\mathrm{L}}\{A_\lambda^{(p)}/A_\lambda^{(p+1)}\},$$
$${}^pH(A) = H^{(p)}(A)/H^{(p+1)}(A) = \underrightarrow{\mathrm{L}}\{H^{(P)}(A_\lambda)/H^{(p+1)}(A_\lambda), p^{\lambda *}{}_\nu\}$$
$$E_r = \underrightarrow{\mathrm{L}}\{E_r(A_\lambda), p^{\lambda *}{}_\nu\}.$$

The first filtration of the doubly graded d module has been given in (8.2g).

Definition 8.3. The **second filtration** is defined by

(8.3a) $$L^{(q)} = \oplus_{q \leq j} \oplus_i A^{ij}.$$

We get $$E_0^{*q} = L^{(q)}/L^{(q+1)} = \oplus_i A^{iq} = A^{*q}.$$

Then

(8.3b) $$\begin{aligned} {}_2E_1^{qp} &= \oplus_i {}_1H(A^{iq}) = {}_1H^p(A^{*q}) \\ {}_2E_2^{qp} &= {}_2H\ {}_1H^p(A^{*q}) \\ &= {}_2H^q\ {}_1H^p(A). \end{aligned}$$

The point to keep straight is that now d_2 advances q by 2 and regresses p by 1. (In the literature ${}_2E^{pq}$ is often written for our ${}_2E^{qp}$).

Lemma 8.4. *If $A^{ij} = 0$ for $j < 0$, then the first filtration* (8.2g), *is strongly regular. If $A^{ij} = 0$ for $i < 0$, then the second filtration* (8.3a) *is strongly regular, and actually $P(n) = n + 1$.*

Let ${}^nK = \Sigma_{i+j=n} A^{ij}$. The argument is now clear from the figure. In the sequel we often write ${}_1K$ *and* ${}_2K$ *for the first and for the second filtration respectively.*

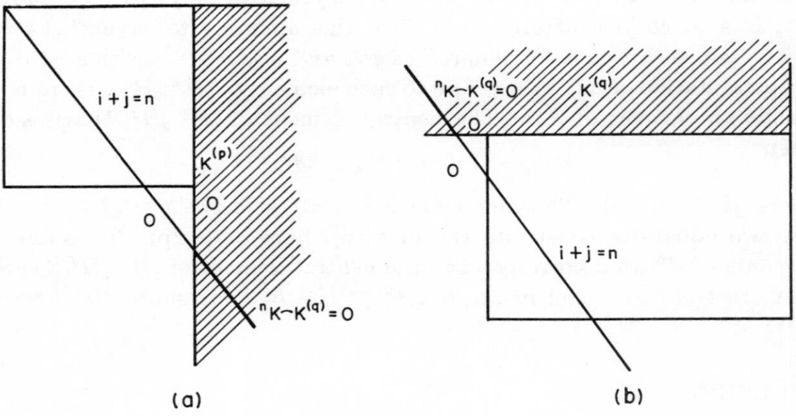

Figure 16-4

Lemma 8.5. *Let A be a doubly graded d module, $\{A^{ij}\}$, with $A^{ij} = 0$ when $i < 0$ or $j < 0$. There result the edge homomorphisms*

(8.5a) $${}_1E_2^{no} \to {}^nH \to {}_2E_2^{on}, \qquad {}_2E_2^{no} \to {}^nH \to {}_1E_2^{on},$$

and the spectral sequences of low degree

(8.5b) $$\begin{aligned} 0 \to {}_1E_2^{10} \to {}^1H \to {}_1E_2^{01} \to {}_1E_2^{20} \to {}^2H \\ 0 \to {}_2E_2^{01} \to {}^1H \to {}_2E_2^{10} \to {}_2E_2^{02} \to {}^2H \end{aligned}$$

Suppose $A^{ij} = 0$ for $j < 0$. Since ${}^nK \cap {}_1K^{(p)} = 0$ for $p \geq n + 1$ (8.4) and ${}^n_1Z^{pq}_r \subset {}^nK \cap {}_1K^{(p)}$, we infer ${}^n_1E^{pq}_r = 0$ for $p \geq n + 1$ and ${}^{n+1}_{\ \ 1}E^{pq}_r = 0$ for $p \geq n + 2$. These are the hypotheses of (7.4b) if $P = n$, $r \geq 2$. Hence

$$ {}^n_1E^{no}_2 \xrightarrow{k^*} {}^nH. $$

We also have

$$ {}_2E^{q\cdot}_1 = {}_1H({}_2K^{(q)}/{}_2K^{(q+1)}) = {}_1H(A^{*q}) = 0, \quad q < 0. $$

The hypotheses of (7.4a) are therefore satisfied for the grade $n - 1$, by $P - r < 0$ and for grade n by $P = 0$. Hence $r \geq 1$ is consistent. Accordingly

$$ {}^nH \xrightarrow{j^*} {}^n_2E^{on}_r, \quad r \geq 1. $$

Our hypotheses include those of (7.5) for $n = P = a = 1$, $r = 2$. Hence $E^{10}_2 \to {}^1H \to E^{01}_2$ is exact. Moreover, since

$$ d_2\, {}^1E^{10}_2 = {}^2E^{3-1}_2 = 0,\ B({}_1E^{10}_2) = d({}_1E^{-10}_2) = 0,\ {}^1E^{10}_2 \approx {}^1E^{10}_\infty, $$

whence by (7.1b), $0 \to {}^1E^{10}_2 \to {}^1H$ is exact. Our hypotheses cover $n = p = 2$, $r = a = 1$. Use the bottom row (consisting of E_{r+a} terms) to get

$$ {}^1E^{01}_2 \to {}_1E^{20}_2 \to {}^2H $$

is exact. On assembling these separate pieces of information, (8.5b) ensues. **Edge** refers of course to $p0$ or to $0q$. Similarly,

Corollary 8.6. *If $H(J^{(p)}/J^{(p+1)}) = 0$ for $p < n - a - 1$ and if ${}^nH(J^{(p)}) = 0$ for $p > n - a$,*

$$ {}^nE^{n-a}_2 \to {}^nH \to E^{n-a-1}_2 \to E^{n-a+1}_2 \to {}^{n+1}H \to {}^{n-a}E $$

is an exact sequence.

This is covered by (7.7) if the constants are adjusted.

Corollary 8.7. *If $H(J^{(p)}/J^{(p+1)}) = 0$ for $p < a$ and $H(J^{(p)}) = 0$ for $p > a + 1$, then*

$$ 0 \to {}^nE^{a+1}_2 \to {}^nH \to {}^nE^a_2 \to 0 $$

is exact.

The filtration is regular and because of (7.3a) and (7.3b) we can assert $E_\infty = E_2$, after which (7.2a) applies with $b = 1$.

Lemma 8.8. *Let $A = A^{ij}$ be a double upper complex, i.e., $A^{ij} = 0$ for $\inf(i, j) < 0$. Let ${}_1E^{pq}_2 = 0$ for $q > 0$. Write $W = \ker {}_2d \cap \Sigma_i A^{i0}$ and let $i^\#$ be the injection $0 \longrightarrow W \xrightarrow{i^\#} A$. Then $H(W) \underset{\approx}{\xrightarrow{i^\#}} H(A)$.*

View $W = \{W^{ij} = ker\ {}_2d \cap A^{ij}\}$ as a double upper complex with $W^{ij} = 0$ for $j \neq 0$ and with ${}_2d$ trivial on W. Then using the first filtration of W,

$$ {}_1E_2^{pq}(W) = {}_1H^p\ {}_2H^q(W) \quad (8.21)$$

$$ {}_2H^q(W) = \frac{{}_2Z(W) \cap \oplus_i W^{iq}}{{}_2B(W) \cap \oplus_i W^{iq}} = 0, \quad q \neq 0,$$

(8.8a)
$$ = W, \quad q = 0.$$

Accordingly ${}_1E_2^{p0}(W) = {}_1H^p(W)$.

By virtue of the hypothesis, using the first filtration of A,

(8.8b)
$$ {}_1E_2^{pq}(A) = {}_1H^p\ {}_2H^q(A) = 0, \quad q > 0,$$
$$ = {}_1H^p\ {}_2H^0(A), \quad q = 0.$$

Since A is an upper complex, there are no ${}_2d$ coboundaries in dimension 0. Hence

$$ {}_2H^0(A) = ({}_2Z(A) \cap \Sigma_i A^{i0})/0$$
$$ = W.$$

Therefore

(8.8c)
$$ {}_1E_2^{p0}(A) = {}_1H^p(W)$$

In sum, including common 0 values, $i^{\#}$ induces,

(8.1d)
$$ {}_1E_2^{pq}(W) \approx {}_1E_2^{pq}(A).$$

Since the modules A and W are bounded from below in both grades, the first filtration is regular. Hence (6.2c) applies.

9. FUNCTORS. Our discussion in this section makes explicit certain underlying functorial aspects.

Definition 9.1. Consider the *DG* module $C^* = \{C^i, \delta\}$ over a principal ideal ring R. Each C^i can be given an injective resolution

$$\begin{array}{ccccccccc}
 & & \downarrow & & \downarrow & & \downarrow & & \\
0 & \longrightarrow & C^i & \longrightarrow & A^{i0} & \xrightarrow{{}_2d} & A^{i1} & \xrightarrow{{}_2d} & ,\ldots, \\
 & & \downarrow{\scriptstyle\delta} & & \downarrow{\scriptstyle {}_1d} & & \downarrow{\scriptstyle {}_1d} & & \\
0 & \longrightarrow & C^{i+1} & \longrightarrow & A^{i+1\ 0} & \longrightarrow & A^{i+1\ 1} & \xrightarrow{{}_2d} & ,\ldots, \\
 & & \downarrow{\scriptstyle\delta} & & \downarrow{\scriptstyle {}_1d} & & \downarrow & &
\end{array}$$

${}_1Z^{im}, {}_1B^{im}, {}_1H^{im}$ denote $ker(A^{im} \xrightarrow{{}_1d} A^{i+1\ m})$, $Im(A^{i-1\ m} \xrightarrow{{}_1d} A^{im})$ and ${}_1Z^{in}/{}_1B^{in}$ respectively. Similarly $Z = Z(A)$, B, H ensue with δ. Suppose that for W, ${}_1W$ identified with Z, ${}_1Z$ or with B, ${}_1B$ or with H, ${}_1H$ the sequence

(9.1a) $$0 \longrightarrow W^i \longrightarrow {}_1W^{i0} \xrightarrow{{}_2d} {}_1W^{i1} \longrightarrow$$

is an injective resolution. We then say A or A^{**} or $\{A^{ij}\}$ is an **injective resolution** of C^*. (The usual module resolution is the special case $C^i = 0 = A^{iq}$ for $i \neq 0$, and $\delta = 0$, ${}_1d = 0$.) An important special case in all this is that of an upper complex, i.e., $C^i = 0$, $i < 0$.

The definition of an injective resolution may be stated without change of relation for the general case of C^* of order 2 in an exact category $\mathfrak{A}$ with enough injectives. A projective resolution is obtained by reversing arrows in all sequences of (9.1) and again an exact category with this time enough projectives will serve.

PROBLEM

16-18. Show every DG module over R, a principal ideal ring, admits an injective resolution unique up to homotopy. *Hint:* Use (103.7) as a guide together with (102.7).

Relations 9.2. Let T be a covariant functor on the category of DG modules over R to itself. Then with T written for the $\dot{T}$ of (107.6) we have $(TA)^{pq} = T(A^{pq})$ is a double complex with boundary operators ${}_1\Delta = (T\ {}_1d)$, ${}_2\Delta = (T\ {}_2d)$, $\Delta = {}_1\Delta + {}_2\Delta$. The omology consequences are not dependent on the resolution chosen and define **hyperhomology**.

Since A^{i*} is an injective resolution of C^i,

(9.2a) $${}_2H^q\, T(A^{i*}) = \mathrm{T}^q(C^i) \quad (107.8\text{c}).$$

Only the ${}_1\Delta$ part of Δ acts nontrivially on the modules of (9.2a) above, so by (8.2)

(9.2b) $${}_1E_2^{pq} = H^p\, \mathrm{T}^q C^*.$$

Again since A^{**} is an injective resolution of the upper complex $\{C^i\}$, A^{*q} and W^{*q} are injective (9.1). We infer from (103.2) and (102.4) that B^{*q} is a direct summand of Z^{*q} as well as of A^{*q} and that Z^{*q} is a direct summand of A^{*q}. Since T is additive when applied to a direct sum, it yields a direct sum. It then follows that so far as the sequences in (103.2) are concerned, at least, T is exact. Hence by (108.1c), ${}_1H^p(TA)^{*q} = T\ {}_1H^p(A^{*q})$. Since only the ${}_2\Delta$ part of Δ is nontrival on ${}_1H$, it follows from (9.1a) with $W^p = H^p(C^*)$ that

(9.2c) $${}_2E_2^{qp}\ (= {}_2H^q\ {}_1H^p\, TA) = \mathrm{T}^q\, H^p(C^*).$$

Both filtrations of A^{**} are regular when C is an upper complex (8.4). The edge homomorphisms (8.5a) are therefore here

$$\text{(9.2d)} \qquad H^n\, \mathrm{T}^0(C^*) \to H^n(TA) \to \mathrm{T}^0\, H^n(C^*)$$

and ${}_1E_\infty = GHTA = {}_2E_\infty$. Suppose C^* is an acyclic complex over the module R and $\mathrm{T}^q A = 0$ for $q > 0$. Then $H^0(C) \approx R$ and $H^n\, \mathrm{T}^0(C^*) \approx \mathrm{T}^n(R)$.

Definition 9.3. If $K^* = K^*(C)$ is an injective resolution of an object in an exact category $\mathfrak{C}$ and if T is a covariant functor on $\mathfrak{C}$ to $\mathfrak{C}'$, then $\mathfrak{C}$ is T **acyclic** if $H^m\, TK^*(C) = 0$ for $m > 0$, $\mathrm{T}^0 = T$.

We admit tacitly that *the exact categories mentioned below contain enough injectives* in the sense of the remark following (107.8). Let $\mathfrak{C}$ and $\mathfrak{C}'$ be exact categories with U a covariant functor on $\mathfrak{C}$ to $\mathfrak{C}'$. Since $K^*(C)$ is determined up to homotopy, (103.5), $UK^*(C)$ is in $\mathfrak{C}'$ and is determined up to homotopy (107.6). Hence the *cohomology modules below are independent of the particular $K^*(C)$ chosen.*

Theorem 9.4. *If $\mathfrak{C}$, $\mathfrak{C}'$, $\mathfrak{C}''$ are three exact categories, and if U and V are covariant functors on $\mathfrak{C}$ to $\mathfrak{C}'$ and on $\mathfrak{C}'$ to $\mathfrak{C}''$ respectively, and if V is left exact while $U(C)$ is V acyclic whenever $K^*(C)$ is an injective in $\mathfrak{C}$ then there is a spectral sequence whose elements are in $\mathfrak{C}$ with values in $\mathfrak{C}''$ and*

$$\text{(9.4a)} \qquad {}_2E_2^{pq} = \mathrm{V}^p\, \mathrm{U}^q(C), \quad H^p\, \mathrm{VU}\, K^*(C) = (\mathrm{VU})^p\, C.$$

We start then with K, an injective resolution of $C \in \mathfrak{C}$ and write $L = UK^*(C)$. Then V and L correspond to T and C in (9.3). Hence VL is a complex to which the considerations (9.2) apply. We assume A is an injective resolution of L. Then, following (9.2b),

$$\text{(9.4b)} \qquad {}_1E_2^{pq} = H^p\, \mathrm{V}^q(L) = H^p\, \mathrm{V}^q(UK^*(C)).$$

Similarly for (9.2c)

$$\text{(9.4c)} \qquad {}_2E_2^{pq} = \mathrm{V}^q\, H^p(L) = H^q\, H^p\, VU(K)$$
$$\|$$
$$\mathrm{V}^q(\mathrm{U}^p(C)).$$

From (107.9a) there follows $\mathrm{V}^0(UC) = V(UC)$. The hypotheses of the theorem yield using (7.8a) ${}_1E_2^{pq} = 0$, $q \neq 0$, ${}_1E_2^{po} = H^p\, \mathrm{V}^0(UK^*(C)) \approx H^p(VU)(K^*(C)) = (\mathrm{VU})^p\, C$.

Definition 9.5. Let T be a covariant left exact functor on the exact categories, $\mathfrak{A}$ to $\mathfrak{A}'$. A **resolvent functor** $\bar{T}^*$ of T on $\mathfrak{A}$ is an exact functor which associates a complex in $\mathfrak{A}'$ to each $A \in \mathfrak{A}$, thus $\bar{T}^*(A) = \{\bar{T}^n(A)\}$. There is exactness at $\bar{T}^0$ of the symbolic

(9.5a) $$0 \longrightarrow T \xrightarrow{\epsilon} \bar{T}^0 \xrightarrow{d} \bar{T}^1 \longrightarrow \cdots$$

Furthermore if A is injective, then $\bar{T}^n(A)$ is acyclic for $n > 0$. ($\bar{T}$ replaces $\bar{T}^*$ below.)

Theorem 9.6. *Let $\bar{T}$ be a resolvent functor for T. Let $K^* = K^*(A)$ be an upper resolution of $A \in \mathfrak{A}$ by T acyclic objects* (9.3). *Let i and j be the induced natural homomorphisms*

(9.6a) $$TK^* \xrightarrow{i} \bar{T}(K^*)$$

(9.6b) $$\bar{T}(A) \xrightarrow{j} \bar{T}(K^*)$$

defined by ϵ in (9.5a) *and by $A \to K^*(A)$. Then i^* and j^* are isomorphisms, where*

(9.6c) $$H^n\, T(K^*) = \mathrm{T}^n(A) \xrightarrow{i^*} H^n\, \bar{T}(K^*) \xleftarrow{j^*} H^n\, \bar{T}(A).$$

The two important sequences are

(9.6d) $$0 \longrightarrow T(K^*) \xrightarrow{\epsilon} \bar{T}^o(K^*) \xrightarrow{{}_2d} \bar{T}^1(K^*) \longrightarrow$$

(9.6e) $$0 \longrightarrow \bar{T}(A) \xrightarrow{\epsilon'} \bar{T}(K^0) \xrightarrow{{}_1d} \bar{T}(K^1) \longrightarrow \bar{T}(K^2) \longrightarrow$$

We shall view $\bar{T}(A)$ and $T(K^*)$ as doubly graded complexes with the first grade and then the second grade zero respectively. The doubly graded complex $D^{ij} = \bar{T}^j(K^i)$ then leads to ${}_2H^q\, \bar{T}(K^*) = 0$ for $q > 0$. For $q = 0$ evidently ${}_2H^o\, \bar{T}(K^*) = (ker\, {}_2d)/0 = Im\, \epsilon = T(K^*)$. Hence as a consequence of T acyclicity,

(9.6f) $${}_1E_2(\bar{T}(K^*)) = {}_1HT(K^*) = {}_1E_2(T(K^*)).$$

Similarly using (9.6e) we deduce ${}_1H\bar{T}(K^i) = 0$ for $i > 0$, and ${}_1H\bar{T}(K^0) = (ker\, {}_1d)/0 = Im\, \epsilon' = \bar{T}(A)$. This is because $\bar{T}$ is exact and K^* is a resolution. Accordingly

(9.6g) $${}_2E_2\, \bar{T}(K^*) = {}_2H(\bar{T}A) = {}_2E_2(\bar{T}A).$$

On the basis of (6.2c) we conclude that i^* and j^* in (9.6c) are isomorphisms.

EXAMPLE 16-12. Let $\mathfrak{A}$ be the category of left R modules and let $\mathfrak{A}'$ be the category of Abelian groups. Let $T(A) = Hom(B, A)$. Let $K_*(B)$ be a projective resolution of B. Then $\bar{T}^n(A) = Hom(K_n(B), A)$ defines a resolvent functor. Accordingly (9.6) provides the justification for our earlier assertion (107.11) that

$$\mathrm{Ext}^n(B, A) = H^n\, Hom(B, K^n) = H^n\, \Sigma_{i+j=n} Hom(K_i, K^j) \approx H^n\, Hom(K_n, A).$$

The equivalence for spectral sequence computation of $\bar{T}$ and T developments is established in (9.7) and (9.8).

Corollary 9.7. *Let $\bar{T}$ be a resolvent functor of T and let C^* be an upper complex. Let the double complex $J^{rs} = \bar{T}^s(C^r)$ be given the two filtrations* (8.2g) *and* (8.3a). *Then*

$$ {}_1E_2^{rs}(\bar{T}C^*) = H^r\mathrm{T}^s(C^*) = {}_1E_2^{rs}(TC^*), \quad {}_2E_2^{rs}(\bar{T}C^*) = \mathrm{T}^r H^s(C^*) = {}_2E_2^{rs}(TC^*) $$

and ${}_1E_\infty = {}_2E_\infty(\bar{T}C^*) = {}_mE_\infty(TC^*)$, $m = 1, 2$.

This is a direct consequence of (9.2b) and (9.2c) and the exactness of $\bar{T}$ combined with the isomorphism j^*i^{*-1} of (9.6c).

We assume the augmentation $0 \to C^* \to A^{**}$. (As usual, this can be interpreted as a monomorphism of double complexes by the artifice of identifying C^* with C^{**} where C^{*m} is trivial for $m > 0$.) Various derivatives enter, namely a derivative $d'\colon \bar{T}^n \to \bar{T}^{n+1}$, a derivative $d''\colon A^{rs} \to A^{r+1\,s}$ and $d'''\colon A^{rs} \to A^{r\,s+1}$. (In the terminology of (9.1) d'', $d''' = {}_1d$, ${}_2d$.) Write ${}_1d = d''$ and ${}_2d = (d', d''')$. Let $D^{pq} = \Sigma_{s+t=q}\, \bar{T}^t(A^{p\,s})$ with derivatives ${}_1d$ and ${}_2d$. Again D^{pq} yields two filtrations (8.2g) and (8.3a). Since resolutions are determined up to homotopy equivalence $\{D^{pq}\}$ is not unique. The important thing is that the two spectral sequences are uniquely determined by C^*.

Theorem 9.8

(9.8a) $\quad {}_mE_2(T(A^{**})) \xrightarrow{i} {}_mE_2(\bar{T}(A^{**})) \xleftarrow{j} {}_mE_2(\bar{T}(C^*)), \quad m = 1, 2$

(9.8b) $\quad H(T(A^*)) \xrightarrow{i'} H(\bar{T}(A^{**})) \xleftarrow{j'} H(\bar{T}(C^*))$

The analogue of (9.6a) and (9.6b) is

(9.8c) $\quad T(A^{**}) \longrightarrow \bar{T}(A^{**}) \longleftarrow \bar{T}(C^*).$

Consider the first filtration of $\{D^{pq}\}$ and recall ${}_2d = d', d'''$. If p is fixed, ${}_2d$ is therefore the *total* derivative of $\bar{T}(A^{p*})$. Since A^{p*} is the resolution of C^p, ${}_2H\bar{T}(A^{p*})$ is, except for the extra script p, precisely the same as the center term $H(TK^*)$ in (9.6c). Together with (9.7) we therefore have

(9.8d) $\quad {}_2H^q(\bar{T}A^{p*}) = \mathrm{T}^q(C^p)$

$$ {}_1E_2^{pq}(\bar{T}(A^{**})) = {}_1H^p(\mathrm{T}^q(C^*)) = {}_1E_2^{pq}(T(A^{**})) = {}_1E_2^{pq}(\bar{T}(C^*)). $$

From (9.1a) there follows that $K^*({}_1H^p) = \{{}_1H(A^{p*}) \mid * = 0, 1, 2 \cdots\}$ is an injective resolution of ${}_1H(C^p)$. Since $\bar{T}$ is exact

(9.8e) $\quad H^p(\bar{T}A^{*s}) = \bar{T}(H^p(A^{*s})) = \bar{T}K^*(H^p).$

We use (9.6e), (9.8e), and (9.7) to gain

(9.8f) $\quad {}_2E_2^{qp}(\bar{T}A^{**}) = H^q\,\bar{T}K^*H^p$

$$ = \mathrm{T}^q\, H^p(C^*) = {}_2E_2^{qp}(T(A^{**})) = {}_2E_2^{qp}(\bar{T}(C^*)). $$

(The demonstrations for (9.8d) and (9.8f) essentially establish also that the induced isomorphism i^* and j^* (9.8a) arrived at in (9.8d) and in (9.8f) are actually natural equivalences (108.2).)

Remark. To clarify the nature of the developments in this chapter we fix attention on a special case, the DF group, $A = \{A^{(p)}\}$. What is the totality of the information we can extract by applying a class of operations, designated as admissible operations, such as set intersections, group unions, injections and projections of groups, and perhaps group extensions? Our somewhat fuzzy question can be made more precise by interpreting it as asking for the largest category, $\mathfrak{C}$, of groups and homomorphisms generated by the DF groups under the admissible operations. Actually only certain of the elements of $\mathfrak{C}$ and the operations connecting them would have an invariant significance in any reasonable sense, so that we really seek a subcategory, $\mathfrak{C}'$, of $\mathfrak{C}$ consisting of invariant objects and maps and comprising what we view as significant information according to our criteria. It is then natural to demand: What is a basis for $\mathfrak{C}'$? One would expect the collection of all the relative omology groups $\{H(A^{(p)}/A^{(q)})\}$ and their homomorphisms might be all or a large part of such a basis. We have been concerned with another type of basis, or partial basis for $\mathfrak{C}'$ in this chapter, namely that afforded by the spectral sequence $\{E_r^p\}$ or by exact couples. One can connect the spectral sequences with the relative omology groups. Then in particular, if the DF group is determined by the chain groups of a space, X, all deductions can be made in terms of the spectral sequence or in terms of the relative omology groups with no need to go back to the chain groups.

We shall not enter into a discussion of how near the spectral sequence comes to being a basis for $\mathfrak{C}'$, except to remark that if A is bounded from above, then if group extensions are included as permissible operations, the spectral sequence does constitute a basis of $\mathfrak{C}'$. When A is bifiltered, the spectral sequence $\{E_r^{pq}\}$ is no longer a basis for $\mathfrak{C}'$ and indeed the facts are still obscure here.

chapter 17

SHEAF THEORY

1. SHEAVES AND PRESHEAVES. The most satisfactory answer to "was sind und sollen die Garben (sheaves)" is perhaps to be sought in the expansive view of sheaves as a chapter in the theory of functor categories. These aspects are presented in (1.9) and in various places later on. However, we have preferred to forego ultimate generality in favor of recognition of the type of sheaves entering in the omology and mapping considerations in this book. Thus from the start our exposition stresses the analogy with a sort of local product space with structure or with a principal fiber bundle with discrete group. (Except for structure a French equivalent is *l'espace etale*.)

The term **structure** is used below as an abbreviation for group, ring, ring with unit or R module, each of which is posited to be Abelian unless contraindicated. The term *general topological space* is used when separation restrictions of the T_0, T_1, or T_2 type may be absent. (We remind the reader that our neighborhoods are open unless otherwise stated.) The close ties between gratings and sheaves show up in (5.2).

Definition 1.1. A sheaf $\mathcal{A}$ or (A, p, X) consists of a topological **base space** X, a general topological **sheaf space** $A = \{a\}$ with structure and a continuous **projection** p on A onto X. For each $x \in X$ there is a structure called a **stalk** or **fiber** over x and denoted by $A(x)$. A is made up of the collection $\{A(x)\}$. The following conditions are imposed:

(1.1a) $$p^{-1}\,x = A(x).$$

Hence we may write $a(x)$ instead of a when $pa = x$.

(1.1b) p is a local homeomorphism, that is to say, for each $a \in A$ and some neighborhood $U(a)$ in A, p is a homeomorphism on $U(a)$ to $pU(a) \subset X$.

Hence the induced topology on $A(x)$ is the *discrete topology* and if X is T_1 or T_2, then A is T_1.

(1.1c) The operations on A, consequent on the structure of $A(x)$ are required to be continuous. Thus the homomorphism $a \to ra$ on $A(pa)$ to $A(pa)$ is continuous as a varies over A. Also algebraic addition is continuous. We spell this out. Suppose $pa = pb$ and suppose $W(a - b)$ is an assigned neighborhood in A of $a - b$. Then there exist neighborhoods $U(a)$ and $V(b)$ such that $pa' = pb' \in pU(a) \cap pV(b)$ and if $a' \in U(a)$ and $b' \in V(b)$, then $a' - b' \in W(a - b)$.

Remark. We have elected to include structure as well as topological aspects in the definition of the sheaf space and sometimes identify the sheaf and the sheaf space. This explains our writing $\mathcal{A} = \bigcup A(x)$ later. The neutral element in $A(x)$ is denoted by $o(x)$.

PROBLEM

17-1. Prove the assertion in (1.1b) that X a T_1 or a T_2 space implies only that A is T_1.

Remark. More general sheaves can be defined. For instance, suppose $\mathcal{R} = (R, \pi, X)$ is a sheaf of rings with a unit where in particular $\psi x = 1(x)$, the unit of the ring $R(x)$, is required to be continuous in x. Let $\mathcal{A} = (A, p, X)$ be a sheaf of left modules over R. Then $\mathcal{A} = (A, p, X)$ is a sheaf of $\mathcal{R}$ modules if every $A(x)$ is a module over $R(x)$ and the multiplication $r(x)\, a(x)$ for $r(x) \in R(x)$, $a(x) \in A(x)$, is continuous on $R \otimes A$ to A.

EXAMPLE 17-1. Let G be a module or a ring. The constant sheaf, denoted by $\mathcal{A} = G \times X$, satisfies $A(x) = G$ and the topology is the product topology of X and of G with G taken discrete.

EXAMPLE 17-2. Let X be the complex sphere. For each x let $A(x)$ be the additive group of functions, each analytic in some neighborhood of x. Then $\mathcal{A} = \bigcup A(x)$. If $a(x) \in A(x)$, a neighborhood of $a(x)$ in $\mathcal{A}$ is determined by the open set over which $a(x)$ can be analytically continued. Here A is T_2. The next two examples are modifications of 17-2.

EXAMPLE 17-3. If the analytic functions which do not vanish in some neighborhood of x are chosen, the operation on $A(x)$ can be taken as multiplication and again yields a sheaf with Abelian group structure.

EXAMPLE 17-4. If addition and multiplication of analytic functions is given by these operations on their power series about x, $A(x)$ is a ring with a unit and $\mathcal{A}$ is a sheaf of rings with a unit.

EXAMPLE 17-5. Let X be the real line. For each x let $A(x)$ be the additive group of functions in $C^\infty(x)$, i.e., functions which are continuous together with their derivatives of all orders in some neighborhood of x.

Lemma 1.2. *The map $x \to O(x)$ is continuous and $\Theta = \{O(x)\}$ is an open set in A.*

Let $WO(x_0)$ be an open neighborhood of $O(x_0)$ which maps homeomorphically under p, into X (1.1c). Since $a(x) - b(x)$ is continuous on $A \times A$

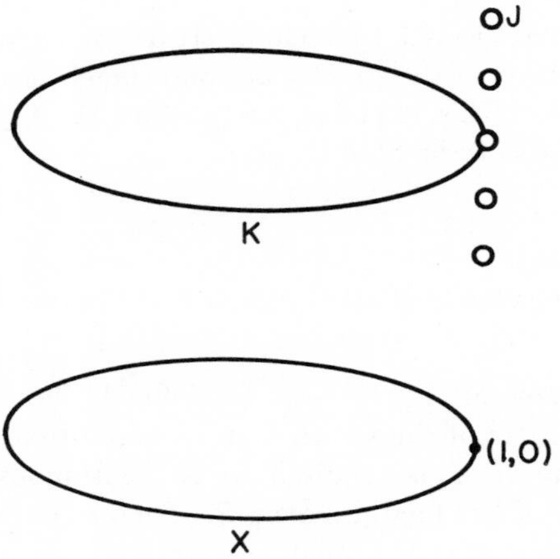

Figure 17-1

to A, there is an open set $Ua(x_0)$ for which $Ua(x_0) - Ua(x_0) \subset WO(x_0)$, where $Ua(x_0)$ maps homeomorphically onto $V(x_0)$ by p. Thus, since $Ua(x_0)$ and $WO(x_0)$ have at most one element on each fiber,

$$O(x \mid V(x_0)) = Ua(x_0) - Ua(x_0)$$
$$= p^{-1} V(x_0) \cap WO(x_0).$$

We shall often write 0 *for* Θ *especially in exact sequences.*

EXAMPLE 17-6. Let K be the unit circle about the origin, lacking the point $(1, 0)$. Let J be the additive group of integers as usual. Let A be $K \cup J$ (where K and J indicate K and J considered in the sheaf space) with the following topology: The neighborhoods of points of K are the usual open arc intervals. The typical neighborhood of the point $n \in$ J is the part of K to the left of $x = x_0$ plus the point n. Let X be the unit circle and let p, restricted to K, map $K \to X$ by $p(a, b) = (a, b)$, $a^2 + b^2 = 1$, $a \neq 1$. Let p map J into $(1, 0) \in X$. The fiber over x has the structure of the Abelian Group J if $x = (1, 0)$ and is the trivial group if $x = (a, b) \neq (1, 0)$. Though

X is T_2, A is merely T_1. The 0 set, $\Theta = K \cup 0$, is open as expected from (1.3), but because the point n cannot be separated from K, Θ is not closed.

Definition 1.3. Let $\mu = \{U\}$ be the *open subsets of* X ordered by inverse inclusion, i.e., $U \subset V \Leftrightarrow V < U$. A **section**, s or s_U is a map on U to A for which ps is the identity (81.25). Hence by (1.1b) a section is an open map. The set $s(U)$ is the **concrete section**. Define $r_1 s + r_2 s'$ by $(r_1 s + r_2 s')(x) = r_1 s(x) + r_2 s'(x)$ and ss' by $(ss')(x) = s(x) \cdot s'(x)$, so that $S(U, \mathcal{A})$, the collection of sections over U, is a structure. For the special case $U = X$ we often write $S(\mathcal{A})$ for $S(X, \mathcal{A})$. Define the **restriction homomorphism**,

$$r^U{}_V\colon S(U, \mathcal{A}) \to S(V, \mathcal{A}),\ U < V,$$

by

(1.3a)
$$r^U{}_V\, s = s \mid V,\ s \in S(U, \mathcal{A})$$
$$= 0 \text{ if } V = \varnothing.$$

Then $\mathcal{S}(\mu, \mathcal{A})$ or $\mathcal{S}(\mu) = \{S(U, \mathcal{A}), r^U{}_V\}$ constitutes a direct system of structures referred to as a **presheaf** of structures, where it is understood that $\mathcal{S}(\phi, \mathcal{A}) = 0$. More generally a pre-sheaf of structures is the direct system $\mathcal{P}(\mu) = \{P(U), r^U{}_V\}$ sometimes abbreviated to $\{P(U)\}$. Here $P(U)$ is a structure with $P(\phi) = 0$. In place of $\mathcal{P}(\mu)$ we can bring out the functorial character by writing $U \to P(U)$ and then we often write $\mathcal{P}(U)$ rather than $P(U)$. (For the justification see (1.9).)

We announce that $r^{U(x)}{}_{V(x)}$, as the letter r suggests, will *invariably* denote a homomorphism by restriction, $r^{U(x)}{}_{V(x)}\, P(U(x)) = P(V(x))$, (so in particular $r^{U(x)}{}_{U(x)}$ is the identity). (The notation $U(x)$, $V(x)$ has been introduced earlier and refers to open sets containing x.)

Example 17-7. If $\mathcal{A}$ is the sheaf in Example 17-4, then $S(U, \mathcal{A})$ is the ring of analytic functions over U and $S(\mathcal{A})$ is the ring of everywhere analytic functions and is therefore isomorphic to the ring of complex numbers.

Definition 1.4. The **supports** of elements of $S(U, \mathcal{A})$ are defined by

$$\|s\| = \{x \mid s(x) \neq 0(x),\ x \in U\}.$$

Lemma 1.5. *Supports of sections are closed and if* $s_1(x_0) = s_2(x_0)$, *then for some* $U(x_0)$, $s_1 \mid U = s_2 \mid U$.

Since s is an open map and Θ is an open set, if $s(x) = 0(x)$, then by continuity $sU(x) \subset \Theta$. Hence $\{x \mid s(x) \neq 0(x)\}$ is closed. The last half of (1.5) restates that $\|s_1 - s_2\|$ is closed. If $U \neq X$, closure is to be interpreted in the relative topology of U.

All sections agreeing at a point must agree on an open set (1.5) and also, if A is T_2, on a closed set. Accordingly in this case, sections agree on components. Since an analytic function is determined by its values in an open set, and since this is not true of C^∞ functions, we infer that the sheaf space for Example 17-1 can be (and actually is) T_2, while that in Example 17-4 is not T_2.

In analogy to the situation for gratings, we can define an F-**presheaf** or F-sheaf as one whose supports lie in the family F (81.5).

Definition 1.6. Let $\mathcal{S}(\mu) = \{P(U), r^U{}_V\}$ be a presheaf, and denote the typical elements of $P(U)$ by $g(U)$. The sheaf derived from $\mathcal{S}(\mu)$ will now be defined. The stalk

(1.6a) $P(x) = \{g(x) \mid g(x) = [g(W(x))]_x\} = \underrightarrow{\mathrm{L}}\{g(U(x)) \mid P(U(x)), r^{U(x)}{}_{V(x)}\}$

Write $\mathcal{S} = \bigcup P(x)$. This is called the **sheaf of germs** of $\mathcal{S}(\mu)$. The operations are defined by

$$\begin{aligned} g(x) + g'(x) &= [g(W(x))] + [g'(U(x))] \\ &= [r^{W(x)}{}_{V(x)}\, g(W(x)) + r^{U(x)}{}_{V(x)}\, g'(U(x))] \end{aligned}$$

for $V(x) = W(x) \cap U(x)$ and similarly for the other operations. If $y \in U(x)$, we indicate by $[g(U(x))]_y$ the coset of the direct limit, using open sets containing y. The topology of $\mathcal{S}$ is given by the neighborhood assignment

(1.6b) $N(g(x_0), g(x_0) = [g(U(x_0))]_{x_0}) = \{g(y) = [g(U(x_0))]_y \mid y \in U(x_0)\}$

Moreover

(1.6c) $$p\colon P(x) = x.$$

We write $r^{U(x)}{}_{V(x)}$ for the map $P(U)$ to $P(x)$.

Lemma 1.7. *The triple (P, p, X) is a sheaf derived from $\mathcal{S}(\mu)$ and is denoted by $\mathcal{S}$, (or $\mathcal{A}$, $\mathcal{B}$, etc.). If $S(U, \mathcal{A}) = P(U, \mathcal{A})$ this sheaf is $\mathcal{A}$.*

Definition 1.8. The sheaf may be considered a special type of presheaf, $\mathcal{S}(\mu)$ for which for any open set U and open cover $\alpha = \{a_i\}$ of U the following conditions are valid,

(1.8a) if g and g' are elements of $\mathcal{S}(\mu)$, then $g \mid a_i = g' \mid a_i$ for all a_i demands $g = g'$,

(1.8b) if $g_i \in P(a_i)$, and if $g_i \mid a_i \cap a_j = g_j \mid a_i \cap a_j$, then there is a unique element $g \in \mathcal{S}(\mu)$ such that $g_i = g \mid a_i$.

We now present the functorial aspects of these definitions. We state once and for all that in this chapter *if μ is a cover of a space, all finite intersections of elements of the cover are comprised in the elements of the cover.*

For convenience we start out with a resume of the essentials of Examples 10-8 and 10-9. Let X be a set. The category $\mathfrak{X}$ has as objects all subsets of X. The morphisms $G(X_0, X_1)$ consist of restriction maps. Thus $G(X_0, X_1)$ is empty unless $X_1 \subset X_0$ and in this case there is a unique morphism. (Compare the ordering by inverse inclusion in (1.3).) A topology $T(X)$ or μ is a collection of subsets including X and ϕ, closed under finite intersections and arbitrary unions. These assigned sets are referred to as open sets. (The **space** X indicates the set X plus an understood topology $T(X)$.) The category $\mathfrak{T}(X)$ has the sets of $T(X)$ as its objects and its morphisms are those of $\mathfrak{X}$, i.e., $\mathfrak{T}(X)$ is a full subcategory of $\mathfrak{X}$.

Definition 1.9. Let $\mathfrak{A}$ be an exact category. Then $\mathfrak{P}(X, \mathfrak{A}) = \mathfrak{A}^{\mathfrak{T}(X)}$ (Example 10-21) is the **category of presheaves** over the space X with values in $\mathfrak{A}$. A **presheaf** $\mathcal{P}$ is an object of $\mathfrak{P}(X, \mathfrak{A})$ and is therefore a functor on the objects U of $\mathfrak{T}(X)$ with values in $\mathfrak{A}$. Accordingly it is often indicated by $U \xrightarrow{\mathcal{P}} P(U) \subset \mathfrak{A}$. The morphisms are the natural transformations of one presheaf $\mathcal{P}$ to another, $\mathcal{P}'$, where both are in $\mathfrak{P}(X, \mathfrak{A})$.

The **category of sheaves** $\mathfrak{S}(X, \mathfrak{A})$ is the full subcategory of $\mathfrak{P}(X, \mathfrak{A})$ defined by imposing the conditions (1.8a), (1.8b) or (1.8c) on $\mathcal{P}$. An equivalent definition is that the presheaf $\mathcal{P}$ is a sheaf if for any open set G and every open cover $\nu = \{v_i\}$ of G, $P(G) = \underleftarrow{\mathrm{L}}\, P(v_i)$. The stalk at x of $\mathcal{P}(\mu)$ is defined as in (1.6a).

In order to make the subject comprehensible to the reader without extensive grounding in category theory, some of the key notions are given parallel discussion utilizing the description (1.1) and (1.8), and then utilizing the description (1.9). To call attention to the point of view of (1.9) as well as to the greater scope achieved, we shall use the terms **general presheaf** and **general sheaf**. Thus when $\mathfrak{A}$ is the category of Abelian groups, or modules over a ring with unit, the sheaves and presheaves defined in (1.1) and (1.8) constitute general sheaves and presheaves. In most of the exposition and proofs for the "general" presheaves we actually restrict ourselves to these two exemplars of $\mathfrak{A}$. However, it is worth while to list the restrictions sufficient to guarantee validity when the qualifying "general" enters.
(**a**) The collection of objects of $\mathfrak{A}$ constitute a set, and (**b**) $\mathfrak{A}$ is exact and satisfies VIII c. $\mathfrak{A}$ can be considered a subcategory of $\mathfrak{A}^{\mathfrak{B}}$ (Example 10-21) and we denote the inclusion functor by $I(\mathfrak{A}, \mathfrak{B})$. We require (**c**) that I have a right adjoint (108.5) for all choices of $\mathfrak{B}$ satisfying (**a**). Furthermore (**d**) $\mathfrak{A}$ has a family of **generators** $\{g_i\}$ defined by the property that if α and β are distinct morphisms in $G(A, A')$, then for some g_i, $\alpha g_i \neq \beta g_i$ and finally

(e) the generators satisfy $\underrightarrow{\bigsqcup} Hom(g, A_i) \to Hom(g, \underrightarrow{\bigsqcup} A_i)$ (Cf Problem 10-15) is a monomorphism for $\{A_i, -, -\}$ any direct system (106.12). These restrictions are not independent, but are listed in a form convenient for application. A useful concomitant is the fact that $\underrightarrow{\bigsqcup}$ is an exact functor (Problem 10-15). A category subject to the restrictions (a)—(e) can be referred to as a **sufficient category**. The Abelian groups or modules over a ring with unit yield sufficient categories. (Further generalizations of the sheaf and presheaf concepts are, of course, possible. For instance restriction (**a**) may be dropped or the category $\mathfrak{T}(X)$ may be replaced by some other category.)

Definition 1.10. $'\mathcal{A} \subset \mathcal{A}$ is a **subsheaf** of $\mathcal{A}$ over the same base space X, if the induced operations on $'A(x)$ make it a substructure of $A(x)$, if p' is p restricted to $'\mathcal{A}$ and if $'A$ is an open set in A.

If $s_U = s$ is a section over U, $s(U) \cap {'A}$ is an open set, N, of $'A$. Thus p and p' coincide on N. Moreover since projections are open maps and s is a section, p (and therefore p') maps N homeomorphically onto X or (1.1a) and (1.1b) are satisfied. The validation of (1.1c) for $'\mathcal{A}$ is immediate. In particular $\Theta(= {'A}) = \{0(x) \mid X\}$ is a subsheaf of $\mathcal{A}$.

Unless otherwise stated our sheaves are sheaves of modules over a commutative ring with unit. If $'\mathcal{A}$ is a subsheaf of $\mathcal{A}$, then the quotient sheaf $\mathcal{A}/{'\mathcal{A}} = \{[a]\}$ consists of cosets under the equivalence $a \sim b$ if $pa = pb$ and $a - b \in p'^{-1}\, x$. Q is open in $\mathcal{A}/{'\mathcal{A}}$ if $Q = \{[a] \mid a \in N, N \text{ open in } A\}$.

We wish to define homomorphisms. First we consider the sheaves and the ideas of (1.1). We then present a more general definition based on (1.9) which includes homomorphisms of presheaves.

Definition 1.11. If $\mathcal{A}_1$ and $\mathcal{A}_2$ are sheaves of R modules on X, the correspondence $h\colon \mathcal{A}_1 \to \mathcal{A}_2$ is a **homomorphism** if h is a map of the sheaf spaces such that $p_2 h = p_1$ and $h \mid A_1(x) \to A_2(x)$ is a homomorphism for each $x \in X$. The double use of h will lead to no confusion. The sequence

$$\longrightarrow \mathcal{A}_i \xrightarrow{h_i} \mathcal{A}_{i+1} \xrightarrow{h_{i+1}} \mathcal{A}_{i+2} \longrightarrow$$

is an **exact sequence** of sheaves if $Im\, h_i = ker\, h_{i+1}$.

PROBLEM

17-2. Show the homomorphism h takes sections into sections and is a local homeomorphism.

Lemma 1.12. *If h is a homomorphism on $\mathcal{A}_1$ to $\mathcal{A}_2$, $ker\ h$ and $Im\ h$ are subsheaves of $\mathcal{A}_1$ and of $\mathcal{A}_2$ respectively.*

The continuity of h ensures $h^{-1}(\Theta_2)$ is open, (1.2). Similarly $Im\, h$ is open in A_2 since h is an open map (Problem 17-2).

Definition 1.13. The homomorphisms in $\mathfrak{P}(X, \mathfrak{A})$ or in $\mathfrak{S}(X, \mathfrak{A})$ (1.9) are merely the morphisms in these categories; that is to say, the natural transformations. Thus if the functors $\mathcal{F}$ and $'\mathcal{F}$ are the general presheaves, or the general sheaves, then for each $U \in \mu$, $'P(U) \xrightarrow{h(U)} P(U)$ and for $U \supset V$

$$h(V)r^U{}_V = r^U{}_V h(U). \tag{1.13a}$$

Incidentally, if h is a general presheaf homomorphism, then $h(x)$ is a homomorphism on $'P(x)$ to $P(x)$ where $'r^U{}_x\, h(U) = h(x)r^U{}_x$ is supposed valid for all $x \in U$. Moreover $'\mathcal{F}$ is a general subpresheaf of $\mathcal{F}$ if $'P(U) \subset P(U)$ for every U and $'r^W{}_U = r^W{}_U \mid 'P(W)$. We drop the prefix "general" and obtain the definitions for presheaves and sheaves. Then the quotient presheaf is $\mathcal{F}/\mathcal{F}' = \{P(U)/'P(U)\}$.

If $h(U)$ is onto for all U, then h is onto. Then $Im\, h$, and $ker\, h$ are the direct systems $\{Im\, h(U), r^U{}_V\}$, $\{ker\, h(U), r^U{}_V\}$. In view of (1.13a), if $\mathcal{K}$ and $\mathcal{F}$ are the induced sheaves (1.7), there is an induced homomorphism $h\colon \mathcal{K} \to \mathcal{F}$ (compare 1.11). Moreover, when the meaning is clear, we may write h in place of $h(U)$.

Let $I = I^{\mathfrak{S}}{}_{\mathfrak{P}}$ be the inclusion functor on $\mathfrak{S}(X, \mathfrak{A})$ to $\mathfrak{P}(X, \mathfrak{A})$. If h is a homomorphism $\mathcal{L} \to \mathcal{M}$, where $\mathcal{L}$ and $\mathcal{M}$ are in $\mathfrak{S}(X, \mathfrak{A})$, it is not necessarily true that $\{P(U) = L(U)/M(U)\}$ is a sheaf, though it is a presheaf. This situation will be met later and shows I is not right exact (but is left exact).

Definition 1.14. If $\mathcal{A}$ is the sheaf derived from the presheaf $\mathcal{F}(\mu)$, then a **homomorphism** $h = \{h(U)\}$ of $\mathcal{F}(\mu)$ to $\mathcal{S}(\mu) = \{S(U, \mathcal{A})\}$ is defined by

$$h(U)\colon g = s_g,\ g \in P(U),.$$

where $s_g(x \mid U) = g(x) = [gU']_x$. That s_g is continuous follows from (1.6b). In general, h is neither a monomorphism nor an epimorphism.

Remark. The reason for not requiring a sheaf to be a T_2 space in (1.1) is once more endorsed, for points of the sheaf space of $\mathcal{A}/'\mathcal{A}$, for instance, are not closed in general, even when A is T_2 (since $'A$ is open in A).

Theorem 1.15. *Let Y be locally closed in X,* (**A**) *and suppose $\mathcal{A}$ is a sheaf of Abelian groups on Y. There is a unique sheaf of Abelian groups denoted by $\mathcal{F}_Y$, inducing a sheaf $\mathcal{F} \mid Y$ isomorphic to $\mathcal{A}$ on Y and to the zero sheaf on $X - Y$.*

Let $F \cap U$ designate a support family consisting of closed sets in U (81.12). Sections on $U \cap Y$ with such supports yield a subgroup $P(U)$ of

$S(U \cap Y, A)$ since a closed set in U is closed in $U \cap A$. If $Q \cap U$ is closed in U and $V \subset U$, $Q \cap V$ is closed in U, so the restriction map $r^U{}_V$, $V \subset U$, takes $P(U)$ into $P(V)$. Of course, if $U \cap Y = \varnothing$, $P(U)$ is the trivial group with a single element. Then $\{P(U), r^U{}_V\}$ is a presheaf $\mathcal{T}(\mu)$ (and is actually a sheaf (1.9)). In any case, $\mathcal{T}$ can be considered $\{P(x)\}$ the derived sheaf (1.7). Evidently $\mathcal{T}$ is the 0 sheaf on $X - \bar{Y}$. Let $x \in \dot{Y} = \bar{Y} - Y$. If $s \in P(U(x))$, s is a section over $U(x) \cap Y$ and hence $\|s\| \cap x = \varnothing$. Therefore, for some $V(x)$, $\|s\| \cap V(x) = \varnothing$, so $P(x) = \underrightarrow{\mathsf{L}}\, P(U(x)) = 0(x)$. Every section in $P(U)$ extends (i.e., continuously) to a section over U by defining $s(x \mid U - U \cap Y) = 0(x)$ since $U \cap Y$ is closed in U. Hence $S(U, \mathcal{T}) \approx S(U \cap Y, \mathcal{A})$, and for $x \in Y$, $P(x) = \underrightarrow{\mathsf{L}}\, P(U(x)) = A(x)$.

Lemma 1.16. *If*

(1.16a) $$0 \longrightarrow \mathcal{A}' \xrightarrow{h'} \mathcal{A} \xrightarrow{h} \mathcal{A}'' \longrightarrow 0$$

is an exact sequence of sheaves, then

(1.16b) $$0 \longrightarrow S(U, \mathcal{A}') \xrightarrow{\dot{h}'} S(U, \mathcal{A}) \xrightarrow{\dot{h}} S(U, \mathcal{A}'')$$

where $\dot{h}$ need not be onto in general.

The homomorphism $\dot{h}'$ is defined by $(\dot{h}'s)(x \mid U) = h'(s(x \mid U))$, $s \in S(U, \mathcal{A}')$ We can say only $\dot{h}(S(U, \mathcal{A})) \subset S(U, \mathcal{A}'')$. It may seem a little unfair that $\dot{h}$ is not onto in spite of the fact that h is. Generally speaking, the explanation is topological. For instance, either the topology of X must be restricted, or continuity of the sections must be abandoned, or the sheaves must be of a special type. The first two alternatives enter in the sequel (under the headings of paracompactness and serrations respectively). The last is taken up in (6.3).

2. COCHAINS AND COHOMOLOGY WITH COEFFICIENTS IN A SHEAF.

Definition 2.1. A **simple** or **constant sheaf** $\mathcal{A}$ (already described in Example 17-1) has the topological product $G \times X$, G an R module with the discrete topology, as sheaf space and p: $g \times x$, or pg_x, $= x$. Thus $s \in S(U, \mathcal{A})$ satisfies $s(x) = g$ independently of x in U.

The sheaf can replace the usual coefficient group or module or ring in the cochain and cohomology modules, as we proceed to show. The modules in earlier chapters may be considered the special cases for which the sheaves are simple. We give an Alexander grating type of definition:

Definition 2.2. Let $\omega = \{w_i\}$ and $\nu = \{v_j\}$ be open covers with w and v the corresponding nerves. The simplex $(w_{i_0}) \cdots (w_{i_q})$ is also denoted by $i_0 \cdots i_q$ and the nucleus is $N = \bigcap_{m=0}^{m=q} w_{i_m} \neq \varnothing$. Let $\mathcal{A}$ be a fixed sheaf.

We denote the presheaf $\mathcal{S}(U) = \{S(U, \mathcal{A}) \mid r^U{}_V\}$ by Σ. Then the cochain module $C^q(w, \Sigma)$ consists of the cochains $\{f^q\}$ where

(2.2a) $$f^q(i_0, \ldots, i_q) \in S(\textstyle\bigcap_{m=0}^{m=q} w_{i_m}, \mathcal{A})$$

with the obvious definition of $(f^q + 'f^q)$ and (rf^q). Define d on $C^q(w, \Sigma)$ to $C^{q+1}(w_1, \Sigma)$ by

(2.2b) $$(df^q)(i_0, \ldots, i_{q+1}) = \Sigma(-1)^k\, r^{N_k}{}_N f(i_0, \ldots, \hat{i_k}, i_{q+1})$$

where $N = \bigcap_{m=0}^{m=q+1} w_{i_m}$ and $N_k = \bigcap_{m\neq k} W_{i_m}$.
(Restriction to the subchains whose supports belong to a family F (81.4) is possible). Then

$$H^q(w, \mathcal{A}) = ker(d^q)/Im(d^{q-1}).$$

If $\nu = \{v_j \mid J\} > \omega = \{w_i \mid I\}$, a nonunique projection indicated by

(2.2c) $$p^w{}_v\colon C^q(w, \Sigma) \to C^q(v, \Sigma),$$

is defined by

(2.2d) $$(p^w{}_v^{\#} f^q)(j_0, \ldots, j_q) = r^M{}_N f^q(pj_0, \ldots, pj_q),$$

where $M = \bigcap_{j\in\pi} w_{i=pj}$ and $N = \bigcap_{j\in\pi} v_j$. Then $p^{w*}_v\colon H(w, \Sigma) \to H(v, \Sigma)$.

To establish that p^{w*}_v is not affected by a variation of $p^w{}_v$ (2.2c), we can cite the analogous homology argument in (71.5) and (71.6). However, to make the demonstration self-contained, we give the details. Thus if ${}_1p$ and p are choices in (2.2c), define the endomorphism D by

$$Df^q(j_0, \ldots, j_{q-1}) = \Sigma(-1^m) r^{M_m}{}_N f^q(pj_0, \ldots, pj_m, {}_1pj_m, \ldots, {}_1pj_{q-1}).$$

where $M_m = \bigcap_{i=0}^{i=m} w_{pj_i} \cap \bigcap_{k=m}^{k=q-1} w_{{}_1pj_k}$. This satisfies

$$Dd + dD = {}_1p^{\#} - p^{\#},$$

whence, just as in (81.1) and (81.2), ${}_1p^{\#} = p^{\#}$.

It follows easily that $\{H(w, \Sigma);\ p^{w*}_v\}$ constitutes a direct system (77.3). We write

Definition 2.3. $H^p(X, \mathcal{A}) = \underrightarrow{L}\{H^p(w, \Sigma);\ p^{w*}_v\}$.

The presheaf of sections $\mathcal{S}(\mu)$ may be replaced by other presheaves, $\mathcal{T}(\mu)$, to yield a direct limit definition for $H^p(X, \mathcal{T})$ but it is not necessarily true that this latter module is isomorphic to $H^p(X, \mathcal{A})$ as defined above.

An application to some fiber bundle classifications is possible. Thus, in connection with the fiber bundle maps, let $\mathcal{G}$ be the sheaf determined by the presheaf of sections $S(U, \mathcal{G}) = G^U$ for G a topological group.

Lemma 2.4. *If G is Abelian and $\mu = \{U_i\}$ is an open cover, then*

$$\{g_{ij}(b)\} \in Z^1(u, \mathcal{G})$$

and equivalent bundles yield the same element of $H^1(B, \mathcal{G})$.

Let Σ be the presheaf over $\mathcal{G}$ (1.3) and let $g^1 \in C^1(u, \Sigma)$ be defined by $(g^1(i, j))(b) = g_{ij}(b)$, $b \in U_i \cap U_j$. That g^1 is a cocycle as claimed is immediate from the Abelian form of the matching conditions (142.1c) and from (2.2b).

Equivalence of bundles $\boldsymbol{Q}$ and $\boldsymbol{Q}'$ is determined by equivalence of the associated principal bundles $\boldsymbol{P}$ and $\boldsymbol{P}'$, or more specifically by (142.2a). Let $g^0 \in C^0(u, \Sigma)$ be defined by $g^0(i)(b) = t_i(b)$ and let $g^i = \{g_{ij}(b)\}$, $g^1 = \{g_{ij}(b)\}$. Then

$$\begin{aligned}(dg^0)(i, j) &= t_i - t_j \\ &= g_{ij} - g'^{1}_{ij} \quad (142.2\text{a}) \\ &= (g^1 - g'^1)(i, j).\end{aligned}$$

Hence $g^1 \sim g'^1$ if $\boldsymbol{Q}$ and $\boldsymbol{Q}'$ are equivalent. Thus an element of $H^1(u, \mathcal{G})$ is the coset of equivalent bundles and in particular the 0 element corresponds to the product bundle class.

For the coefficient group or ring, G,

$$H^0(X, G) \approx \Pi_{R^0(G)}\, G_i$$

where $R^0(G)$ is the 0 dimensional Betti number and $G_i = G$. The following result will be recognized as a direct generalization.

Lemma 2.5. $H^0(X, \mathcal{A}) \approx S(\mathcal{A})$.

Note $f^0 \in C^0(w, \Sigma)$ satisfies $f^0(w_i) \in S(w_i, \mathcal{A})$ or $f^0(w_i) = s_i$, a section over w_i. If $df^0 = 0$, then $r^{w_i}{}_{w_j \cap w_i} f^0(w_i) = r^{w_j}{}_{w_j \cap w_i} f^0(w_j)$. Hence s_i agrees with s_j on $w_i \cap w_j$ and so $s_i \cup s_j$ constitutes a section over $w_i \cup w_j$ whence $\bigcup s_i$, is a section over X corresponding to f^0. Conversely each section defines a cocycle. The correspondence just discussed establishes a homomorphism of $Z^0(w, \Sigma) \to S(\mathcal{A})$ whose kernel is 0. Since there are no 0 dimensional coboundaries, there is a homomorphism h_w on $H^0(w, \Sigma)$ to $S(\mathcal{A})$ with $ker\ h_w^* = 0$. The requisite conditions in (77.4) are easily checked and we obtain a homomorphism h^* on $H^0(X, \mathcal{A})$ to $S(\mathcal{A})$. Moreover $ker\ h^* = 0$ since the generic element of $H^0(X, A)$ is $[f_w^0]$ where $f_w^0 \in Z^0(w, \Sigma)$.

3. ASSOCIATED SHEAVES. When the base spaces are different, (1.9) indicates the nature of the problem involved in defining homomorphisms. Since $\mathcal{S} \in \mathfrak{P}(X, \mathfrak{A})$ and $\mathcal{S}' \in \mathfrak{P}(Y, \mathfrak{B})$ are objects in different categories, a "homomorphism" is no longer a morphism (1.13). Therefore *the maps called ψ-homomorphisms (or ψ-cohomomorphisms) below may be logically different from those characterized in* (1.13). Let $\mathcal{A}$ and $\mathcal{B}$ be sheaves over X and over Y respectively below.

Definition 3.1. Suppose that $\psi: X \to Y$ and that h is a map on the sheaf space A to B. Then h is **compatible** with ψ, or is a ψ-**homomorphism** if $p_y\, ha = \psi p_x\, a$.

If λ is a map on the sheaf spaces B to A, then λ is **compatible** with ψ or is a ψ-**homomorphism** (sometimes called a ψ-**cohomomorphism**), if λ induces a homomorphism λ_x, continuous in x, on $B(\psi(x))$ to $A(x)$. Since sections determine the topology this condition can be made more specific. Suppose for $U(x_0)$ and $V(\psi(x_0))$ that $s_U(x_0) = t_V\, \psi(x_0)$ for sections s_U and t_V. Then there is a $W(x_0)$ with $\psi(W) \subset V$, and

$$s_U(x \mid W(x_0) = \lambda\, t_V\, \psi(x \mid W_0) \quad (1.5).$$

PROBLEM

17-3. In (3.1) show the continuity of h is tantamount to: $h\, s_U$ is a section over V, where U, V are open sets of X and Y.

Definition 3.2. Let $\psi: X \to Y$. Suppose $\mathcal{B}$ is a sheaf over Y. The **inverse sheaf,** denoted by $\psi^{\#}\mathcal{B}$ has base space X. If X and Y are discrete it is essentially the sheaf obtained by attaching a duplicate of the stalk over y at each x in $\psi^{-1}(y)$. More generally, let t_U map $U \subset X$ into B by $t_U(x) \in B(\psi(x))$. Then $r(t_U + t'_U)x = rt_U(x) + rt'_U(x)$ defines a module $P(U, \mathcal{B})$ over R. (The prescription $(t'_U\, t_U)x = t'_U(x)\, t_U(x)$ is added if ring structures are involved). As usual, ${r^{U(x)}}_{V(x)}$ is the restriction homomorphism. Then

$$\psi^{\#}(\mathcal{B}) = \underrightarrow{\mathsf{L}}\{P(U, \mathcal{B}), {r^U}_V\}.$$

An alternative exposition of $\psi^{\#}(\mathcal{B})$ is: Let $X \times B = \{(x, b)\}$. Let $Z = \{(x, b) \mid p(b) = \psi(x)\}$. This is closed in $X \times B$. Assume $q: Z \to X$ is given by $q(x, b) = x$. The operations in Z are on the b's and are those valid in B. Thus the fiber $Z(x) = \{(x, b) \mid p(b) = \psi(x)\} \approx B(\psi(x))$. Denote the isomorphism by ϕ_x. Let $\mathcal{Z} = (Z, q, X)$. Then $\phi = \{\phi_x\}: \mathcal{B} \to \mathcal{Z}$ is compatible with ψ. The sheaf (Z, q, X) is isomorphic to $\psi^{\#}(\mathcal{B})$.

PROBLEM

17-4. Show the relation $S(V, \mathcal{B}) \to S(\psi^{-1}(V), \psi^{\#}(\mathcal{B}))$ is injective, but is not onto. *Hint:* Let Y be a single point and X, two points.

If $\mathcal{C}$ is a sheaf over X, a presheaf over Y is defined by $\{S(\psi^{-1}(U), \mathcal{C}) \mid U$ open in $Y\}$. If V is an open subset of U, then

$$r^U{}_V\, s(\psi^{-1}(U), \mathcal{C}) = s(\psi^{-1}(U), \mathcal{C}) \mid \psi^{-1}(V)$$

is the restriction homomorphism. Then, taking direct limits, (1.6), there is defined a sheaf over Y, denoted by $\psi_{\#}(\mathcal{C})$ referred to as the **direct sheaf,** or **image sheaf.** Intuitively here when X and Y are discrete a replica of $C(x)$ is planted over $\psi(x)$.

Let $p^{\#}$ denote the projection in $\psi^{\#}(\mathcal{B})$. Write $y_0 = \psi(x_0)$. Let $V = V(y_0)$ and $U = U(x_0)$ be neighborhoods satisfying $\psi(U) = V$. Let s be a section in $S(U, \psi^{\#}(\mathcal{B}))$ and let t be a section on V to $\mathcal{B}$ with $s(x_0) = t(y_0)$. Then $W(x_0) = p^{\#}\, t(y \mid V) \cap U$ is open in X. Hence if σ is another section with $\sigma(x_0) = s(x_0)$, then σ and s would agree on a neighborhood $W'(x_0)$ in $W(x_0)$. Accordingly writing $[\ ]_{x_0}$ for the germs at x_0, $[s]_{x_0} = [\sigma]_{x_0}$. The correspondence ψ^- which assigns $[t]_{y_0}$ to $[s]_{x_0}$ is clearly a ψ homomorphism. Moreover if $[t]_{y_0} = [0]_{y_0}$ then $[s]_{x_0} = [0]_{x_0}$. Also for assigned $[t]_{y_0}$ there is a section s on $\psi^{-1}\, V(y_0)$ to $\psi^{\#}\, \mathcal{B}$ with $s(x_0) = t(y_0)$ so $[s]_{x_0} = [t]_{y_0}$. In short ψ^- is a bijection on $\psi^{\#}(\mathcal{B})(x_0)$ to $\mathcal{B}(y_0)$.

Example 17-8. Let X consist of two points x_0 and x_1 and let Y consist of one point, y_0. Let $\psi(X) = Y$. If $\mathcal{A}$ is a sheaf over X, then $\psi_{\#}\, \mathcal{A}$ is the sheaf over y_0 given by $\mathcal{A}(x_0) \oplus \mathcal{A}(x_1)$. If $\mathcal{B}$ is an assigned sheaf over y_0 then $\psi^{\#}(\mathcal{B})(x_0) = \mathcal{B}$, $\psi^{\#}(\mathcal{B})(x_1) = \mathcal{B}$. Thus ψ^- is not a global bijection on $\psi^{\#}(\mathcal{B})$ to $\mathcal{B}$.

If F is the support family for $\mathcal{C}$ the notation $F(U)$ will indicate supports in $\psi^{-1}(U)$. *The image sheaf now is written* $\psi_F(\mathcal{C})$. $\psi_{\#}(\mathcal{C})$ is reserved for the case that F consists of all closed subsets of X, and

$$\psi_F(\mathcal{C}) = \varinjlim \{S_{F(U)}(\psi^{-1}(U), \mathcal{C}), r^U{}_V\}.$$

Theorem 3.3. *If h is a ψ-homomorphism on $\mathcal{A}$ to $\mathcal{B}$* (3.1), *then $h = \psi^-\,\mu$ where μ is a homomorphism on $\mathcal{A}$ to $\psi^{\#}(\mathcal{B})$ and ψ^- is the ψ-homomorphism on $\psi^{\#}(\mathcal{B})$ to $\mathcal{B}$ defined in* (3.2).

Let $a \in A(x)$. Pick a section $s_U \in S(U, \mathcal{A})$ with $s_U(x) = a$. Note the germ $[s_U]_x = a$ (1.6a). Let t_U be given by $t_U(x) = h\, s_U(x) \in \psi^{\#}\, B(x)$. Define $\mu(U)$ by $\mu(U)\, s_U = t_U$. This yields the homomorphism μ on $\mathcal{A}$ to $\psi^{\#}(\mathcal{B})$, (1.13) according to

$$\mu\colon (a = [s_U]_x) = [\mu(U)\, s_U = t_U]_x.$$

Then with $pa = x$, $\psi^-\, \mu a = ha$.

EXAMPLE 17-9. If $X \subset Y$ and ψ is the inclusion map, $\mathcal{B}$ a sheaf over Y, then $\mathcal{B} \mid X = \psi^{\#} \mathcal{B}$.

The factorization by composition in (3.3) involves ψ^{-} which is independent of h and A and is termed a **universal factor.**

PROBLEM

17-5. If k is a ψ-homomorphism: $\mathcal{B} \to \mathcal{A}$ then $k = \rho\psi^{\#}$.

We present the functorial theory for the inverse and direct images of general presheaves. Again ψ: $X \to Y$. Then ψ' is a functor (and even a general presheaf) on $\mathfrak{T}(Y)$ to $\mathfrak{T}(X)$ defined by $\psi'(U) = \psi^{-1}(U)$. If $\mathcal{P} \in \mathfrak{P}(X, \mathfrak{A})$, then we define the functor Ψ_*

$$\Psi_* \, \mathcal{P} = \mathcal{P}\psi' \colon \mathfrak{T}(Y) \to \mathfrak{A}.$$

Let I and J refer to the inclusion functor on $\mathfrak{S}(X, \mathfrak{A})$ to $\mathfrak{P}(X, \mathfrak{A})$ and on $\mathfrak{S}(Y, \mathfrak{A})$ to $\mathfrak{P}(Y, \mathfrak{A})$ respectively. The relations which are our aim are indicated in the accompanying diagram:

$$\begin{array}{ccc} \mathfrak{P}(X, \mathfrak{A}) & \underset{\Psi_*}{\overset{\Psi^*}{\rightleftarrows}} & \mathfrak{P}(Y, \mathfrak{A}) \\ R \downarrow \quad \uparrow I & & S \downarrow \quad \uparrow J \\ \mathfrak{S}(X, \mathfrak{A}) & \underset{\psi_*}{\overset{\psi^*}{\rightleftarrows}} & \mathfrak{S}(Y, \mathfrak{A}) \end{array}$$

Define Ψ^* by

$$\Psi^* \, (\mathcal{P}) \, (U) = \underset{\to}{\mathsf{L}}_{\psi^{-1}(V) \supset U} P(V)$$

where $\mathcal{P} \in \mathfrak{P}(Y, \mathfrak{A})$.

Lemma 3.4. Ψ^* *is a functor which is a left adjoint of* Ψ_* (108.4).

For $W \subset U$, $\psi(W) \subset \psi(U)$, so there is a morphism $r^U{}_W \Psi^*(\mathcal{P})U \to \Psi^*(\mathcal{P})W$. Therefore $\Psi^*(\mathcal{P}) \in \mathfrak{P}(X, \mathfrak{A})$. If (3.4a) λ: $\mathcal{P} \to \mathcal{P}'$, then $\Psi^*(\lambda)$ is defined by $\Psi^*(\lambda)_U = \underset{\to}{\mathsf{L}}_{\psi(U) \subset V \in \mathfrak{T}(Y)} \lambda_V$. Hence Ψ^* is a functor.

To show Ψ^* and Ψ_* are adjoints, we propose first to define

$$\text{(3.4b)} \qquad \begin{aligned} E &\colon \Psi^* \Psi_* \to I(\mathfrak{P}(X, \mathfrak{A})) \quad (108.3\text{b}) \\ E' &\colon I'(\mathfrak{P}(Y, \mathfrak{A})) \to \Psi_* \Psi^* \quad (108.3\text{c}) \end{aligned}$$

where I and I' stand for the appropriate identity functors. Let $\mathcal{P} \in \mathfrak{P}(Y, \mathfrak{A})$. Then

$$\begin{aligned} (\Psi_* \Psi^*(\mathcal{P}))(V) &= \Psi^*(\mathcal{P})(\psi^{-1}(V)) \\ &= \underset{\to}{\mathsf{L}}_{\psi\psi^{-1}(V) \subset U} P(U) = P(V). \end{aligned}$$

Moreover $\Psi_* \Psi^*(\lambda) = \lambda$. Accordingly we take E' as the identity natural transformation (108.4) (since $\mathfrak{F}(V)$ and $P(V)$ are the same (1.3)).

We now define E. We start with

$$(\Psi^* \Psi_*(\mathfrak{F}))(U) = \underrightarrow{\mathsf{L}}_{\psi(U)\subset V} \Psi_* P(V) \tag{3.4c}$$
$$= \underrightarrow{\mathsf{L}}_{\psi(U)\subset V} P(\psi^{-1}(V))$$

Since the restriction morphism is unique on $P(\psi^{-1}(V))$ to $P(U)$, there is a unique E taking the right hand side of (3.4c) into $P(U)$.

We assert $\Psi_* E$ and $E\Psi^*$ take $\Psi_* \Psi^* \Psi_*$ into the identity functor $I(\Psi_* \mathfrak{F}(X, \mathfrak{A}))$ and $\Psi^* \Psi_* \Psi^*$ into $I(\Psi^* \mathfrak{F}(Y, \mathfrak{A}))$ respectively. Thus

$$(\Psi_*(\Psi^* \Psi_*)(\mathfrak{F}))V = (\Psi^* \Psi_*(\mathfrak{F}))(\psi^{-1}(V))$$
$$= \underrightarrow{\mathsf{L}}_{\psi\psi^{-1}W\subset V} P(\psi^{-1}(W))$$
$$= P(\psi^{-1}V) = (\Psi_* \mathfrak{F})(V)$$
$$((\Psi^* \Psi_*)\Psi^*(\mathfrak{F}))U = \underrightarrow{\mathsf{L}}_{U\subset\psi^{-1}(V)} \Psi^*(\mathfrak{F})(\psi^{-1}(V))$$
$$= \underrightarrow{\mathsf{L}}_{U\subset\psi^{-1}(V)} P(V) = (\Psi^*(\mathfrak{F}))(U)$$

Accordingly $E\Psi^* \cdot \Psi^* E'$ *and* $\Psi_* E \cdot E' \Psi_*$ *are identity natural transformations* on Ψ^* to Ψ^* and on Ψ_* to Ψ_* respectively.

Write $\mathfrak{A}'$ for $\mathfrak{P}(X, \mathfrak{A})$ and $\mathfrak{B}'$ for $\mathfrak{P}(Y, \mathfrak{A})$ and A and B for typical objects in $\mathfrak{A}'$ and in $\mathfrak{B}'$. Define ϕ and ϕ' on $hom(\Psi^*(-), -; \mathfrak{A}')$, to $hom(-, \Psi_*(-); \mathfrak{B}')$ and the reverse by

$$\phi(\lambda) = \Psi_*(\lambda)E'(A) \tag{3.4d}$$
$$\phi'(\mu) = E(B)\Psi^*(\mu)$$

where $\lambda \in hom(\Psi^*(B), A)$ and $\mu \in hom(B, \Psi_*(A))$. To finish the proof we need show that ϕ is an isomorphism (108.5), or equivalently that $\phi\phi'$ and $\phi'\phi$ are identities. This follows at once from the property of Ψ^*

$$\phi'\phi(\lambda) = E(B)\Psi^*(\phi(\lambda)) \tag{3.4e}$$
$$= E(B)\Psi^*(\Psi_*(\lambda) \cdot E'(A))$$
$$= E(B) \cdot \Psi^* \Psi_*(\lambda) \cdot \Psi^* E'(A)$$

because Ψ^* is a functor. According to (108.4) applied to E, the right hand side of (3.4e) can be written $\lambda \cdot (E\Psi^*)_A \cdot (\Psi^* E')_A$ which is $\lambda e_{\Psi^*(A)} = \lambda$. Similarly for $\phi\phi'(\mu)$.

To proceed we need the fact that the inclusion functor $i^{\mathfrak{S}}{}_{\mathfrak{P}}$ (or I or J) has a right adjoint. We prove this in (6.10). We label these adjoints to the inclusion functors I and J of (3.4) as R and S according as the spaces are X and Y.

Definition 3.5. $\psi^* = R\Psi^* J$

$$\psi_* = S\Psi_* I.$$

Lemma 3.6. *ψ^* is the left adjoint of ψ_*.*

It is easy to see by composition of obvious natural equivalences ϕ_1 and ϕ_2 that if T_1 and T_2 are left adjoints of S_1 and of S_2 respectively, then $T_2 T_1$ is a left adjoint of $S_1 S_2$. Hence $R\Psi^*$ is the right adjoint of $\Psi_* I$, which by commutativity of the diagram preceding (3.4) is the same as $J\psi_*$. Let $\mathcal{M}$ and $\mathcal{N}$ be sheaves on Y and on X respectively. Then

$$\begin{aligned} hom(\psi^* \mathcal{N}, \mathcal{M}; \mathfrak{S}(X, \mathfrak{A})) &= hom(J\mathcal{N}, J\psi_* \mathcal{M}); \mathfrak{P}(Y, \mathfrak{A})) \\ &= hom(\mathcal{N}, \psi_* \mathcal{M}; \mathfrak{S}(X; \mathfrak{A})) \end{aligned}$$

since J is inclusion of the full subcategory $\mathfrak{S}(Y, \mathfrak{A})$ in $\mathfrak{P}(Y, \mathfrak{A})$.

Remark. Later (6.9) we show that ψ^* is exact.

PROBLEM

17-6. Show that ψ_* and ψ^* are transitive, i.e. if $X \xrightarrow{\psi} Y \xrightarrow{\theta} Z$, then $(\theta\psi)_* = \theta_* \psi_*$ and $(\theta\psi)^* = \psi^* \theta^*$.

Remark. It is of interest that (1.15) illustrates the ideas in this section so that that result is valid for the general sheaf. We sketch the proof for the special case Y a closed subset of X. Let ψ be the inclusion map $Y \subset X$. Define $\mathcal{B} = \psi_* \psi^* \mathcal{A}$. Since $\psi^* \psi_* \psi^* \mathcal{A} = \psi^* \mathcal{A}$, $\mathcal{B}$ induces the same sheaf on Y as $\mathcal{A}$. If $x \bar{\in} Y$, for some open $U = U(x)$, $U \cap Y = \varnothing$. Hence

$$\begin{aligned} B(x) &= (\psi_* \psi^* \mathcal{A})(x) \\ &= \underset{\to x \in U}{\mathsf{L}} (\psi^* \mathcal{A})(U \cap Y) \end{aligned}$$

which is Θ since $A(\varnothing) = 0$. Therefore $B(x \mid X - Y) = 0$. Let θ be the inclusion $X - Y \subset X$. Then $(\theta^* \mathcal{A})(x) = B(x)$ for $x \in X - Y$. Therefore $\theta^* \mathcal{B} = \Theta$.

4. DG SHEAVES.

The introduction of grading and a differential for sheaves is natural. Until further notice, *all sheaves are sheaves of modules.*

Definition 4.1. $\mathcal{A}$ is a graded or G sheaf over X if $\mathcal{A} = \{\mathcal{A}^n \mid \mathcal{A}^n$ a sheaf over $X\}$. $S(\mathcal{A}) = \{S(\mathcal{A}^n)\}$. (Generally $\oplus S(\mathcal{A}^n)$ is not the same as $S(\oplus \mathcal{A}^n)$. A **homomorphism of degree** r of the graded sheaves $\mathcal{A}$ to $\mathcal{B}$ where the base space is the same for both, is the collection of homomorphisms $\{f^n\}$ with

$f^n\colon \mathcal{A}^n \to \mathcal{B}^{n+r}$. If $r = 0$, f is referred to simply as a homomorphism. A **differential sheaf** or D sheaf $\mathcal{A}$ is a sheaf admitting d with $d^2 = 0$. An **allowable sheaf homomorphism** is one that commutes with the d's. For DG sheaves the definition of $\mathcal{Z}^n(\mathcal{A})$ is $ker(d\colon \mathcal{A}^n \to \mathcal{A}^{n+1})$, that of $\mathcal{B}^n(\mathcal{A})$ is $d\mathcal{A}^{n-1}$ and $\mathcal{H}^n(\mathcal{A}) = \mathcal{Z}^n(\mathcal{A})/\mathcal{B}^n(\mathcal{A})$.

Remark. The homomorphisms on sheaves and differential sheaves constitute an Abelian group or a module and admit composition. Accordingly they are elements of additive categories and the differential sheaves are elements of an exact category.

Definition 4.2. Let T be an additive, covariant functor (76) on the category of D sheaves over X to the category of modules. If $\mathcal{A}$ is a DG sheaf, $T\mathcal{A}$ is graded by $(T\mathcal{A})^p = T\mathcal{A}^p$. Moreover $T(d)$ is the d homomorphism defined by the commutative diagram

(4.2a)
$$\begin{array}{ccc} \mathcal{A}^p & \xrightarrow{T} & T\mathcal{A}^p \\ {\scriptstyle d}\downarrow & & \downarrow{\scriptstyle T(d)} \\ \mathcal{A}^{p+1} & \xrightarrow{T} & T\mathcal{A}^{p+1} \end{array}$$

Since $0 = T(d^2) = (Td)^2$, $T(d)$ may be written d' to indicate it acts as a differential. Suppose further T is exact. We repeat the material in (108.1) for our special case. The exactness of

(4.2b) $$0 \longrightarrow \mathcal{Z}^n(\mathcal{A}) \xrightarrow{i} \mathcal{A}^n \xrightarrow{d} \mathcal{B}^{n+1}(\mathcal{A}) \longrightarrow 0$$

implies the exactness of

(4.2c) $$0 \longrightarrow T\mathcal{Z}^n \xrightarrow{T(i)} T\mathcal{A}^n \xrightarrow{T(d)} T\mathcal{B}^{n+1} \longrightarrow 0.$$

Of course $\mathcal{Z}^{(n)}$ and $\mathcal{B}^{(n+1)}$ are sheaves while $T\mathcal{Z}^n$, $T\mathcal{B}^{n+1}$ are modules. From

(4.2d) $$0 \longrightarrow \mathcal{B}^n(\mathcal{A}) \longrightarrow \mathcal{Z}^n(\mathcal{A}) \longrightarrow \mathcal{H}^n(\mathcal{A}) \longrightarrow 0$$

there arises the exact sequence

(4.2e) $$0 \longrightarrow T\mathcal{B}^n(\mathcal{A}) \longrightarrow T\mathcal{Z}^n(\mathcal{A}) \longrightarrow T\mathcal{H}^n(\mathcal{A}) \longrightarrow 0.$$

Write $Z(T\mathcal{A}) = ker T(d)$ and $B^{n+1}(T\mathcal{A}) = (Td)(T\mathcal{A}^n)$ in (4.2c). Then, by exactness, we get

$$Z^n(T\mathcal{A}) = TZ^n\,\mathcal{A}$$
$$B^n\,T\mathcal{A} = TB^n\,\mathcal{A}.$$

whence in conjunction with (4.2e) we get

(4.2f) $$H^n(T\mathcal{A}) = T\mathcal{H}^n(\mathcal{A}),$$

where $\mathscr{H}^n(\mathcal{A})$ is the quotient sheaf $\mathscr{Z}^n(\mathcal{A})/\mathscr{B}^n(\mathcal{A})$ (and $H^n(T\mathcal{A})$ is a module).

EXAMPLE 17-10. An instance of an exact functor is T: $\mathcal{A} = A(x)$ so (4.2f) becomes $H^n(A(x)) = (H^n(\mathcal{A}))(x)$.

5. FINE SHEAVES AND ASSOCIATED GRATINGS. Definition 5.1. If X is locally compact, the sheaf $\mathcal{A}$ over X is **fine** (compare (81.18) if for an arbitrary fine cover $\beta = \{b_i \mid b_i \text{ compact } 1 \leq N - 1,\ b_N^{\sim} \text{ compact}\}$ there are endomorphisms $\{e_i \mid i = 1, \ldots, N\}$ such that

(5.1a) $$\Sigma e_i\, a = a, \qquad a \in \mathcal{A}$$

(5.1b) $$e_i\, A_x = 0_x, \qquad x \bar{\in} b_i.$$

If X is paracompact, $\mathcal{A}$ is fine (or parafine), if for every locally finite cover $\beta = \{b_i\}$ (5.1a) and (5.1b) are valid, with $a(x)$ in place of a in (5.1a).

The section notion relates gratings and sheaves.

Definition 5.2. If $\mathcal{A}$ is a differential sheaf over X, the **associated grating** has sections as elements and is $\mathrm{A} = S(\mathcal{A})$ (1.4). If A is a grating, the **associated differential sheaf,** or, more succinctly, **associated sheaf,** is $\mathcal{A} = \bigcup(A(x))$ with $A(x) = x\mathrm{A} = \mathrm{A}/\mathrm{A}_x$, $p(x\mathrm{A}) = x$. We have to define the topology. Let $\bar{a} = [a]_x \in A(x)$ and suppose $b \in \mathrm{A}$ satisfies $xb = \bar{a}$. Then a neighborhood, $N(\bar{a}; U(x))$, of $\bar{a}$ in $\mathcal{A}$ is the collection $\{yb \mid y \in U(x)\}$. A neighborhood basis at $\bar{a}$ is constituted by $\{N(\bar{a}; U(x))\}$ (where b runs through all solutions of $xb = \bar{a}$ and $\{U(x)\}$ is a neighborhood basis at x).

If $\mathrm{A} = S(\mathcal{A})$ is the associated grating to the sheaf $\mathcal{A}$, then the associated sheaf to $\mathcal{A}$, $\{S(\mathcal{A})(x)\}$, is called the **constant sheaf associated with** $\mathcal{A}$ and is designated by ${}_c\mathcal{A}$.

PROBLEMS

17-7. If $\mathcal{A}$ is fine, show the associated grating $S(\mathcal{A})$ is fine, provided one defines the endomorphism e_i' on the element s in $(S(\mathcal{A}))$ by $(e_i'\, s)(x) = e_i\, s(x)$ where e_i is given in (5.1).

17-8. If A is fine, the associated $\mathcal{A}$ is fine.

Definition 5.3. Let A be a grating with associated sheaf $\mathcal{A}$. The **inclusion** homomorphism, or **injection** of A into the grating $S(\mathcal{A})$ is defined by $b \xrightarrow{i} \{xb \mid x \in X\}$, i.e. the section s with $s(x) = xb$. We write $i\mathrm{A} \subset S(\mathcal{A})$ That i does not increase supports is immediate for, by (1.4), $\|ib\| = \{x \mid xb \neq 0_x\} = \{x \mid \|b\| \cap x \neq \varnothing\} = \|b\|$. Hence i is an allowable homomorphism (81.8a).

Lemma 5.4. *If* A *is fine, the restricted injection* i_0: $x_0\mathrm{A} \to x_0\, S(\mathcal{A})$ *is an isomorphism.*

We need show i_0 is onto. Let $[s]_{x_0} \in [S(\mathcal{A})]_{x_0}$. Pick $b \in \mathrm{A}$ to satisfy $x_0\, b = s(x_0)$ and let $\alpha = (a_1, a_2)$ be a fine cover with $x_0 \bar{\in} a_2$. Hence $e_1(b) = c \in \mathrm{A}$. Then $\{xc \mid X\}$ is a section which we denote by s', where $[s']_{x_o} = [s]_{x_o}$. That is to say in some $U(x_0) \subset a_1$, s is of the form xc.

When the supports are compact the situation is as expected, namely

Theorem 5.5. *If* A *is a full grating, then* i: $\mathrm{A} \to S(\mathcal{A})$ *is an isomorphism.*

This follows from (5.4) since by (81.24) it is enough to establish the restricted injection i: $x_o\mathrm{A} \to x_o\, S(\mathcal{A})$ is an isomorphism for each $x \in X$.

It would be natural to term A **complete** if i is an isomorphism. Then $S(\mathcal{A})$ is the completion of A. This is consistent with (111.10).

Example 17-11. The elements of A are the cochains, f^p, with nonempty support. Those of $x\mathrm{A}$ are $\{[f^p]_x$ where f^p and g^p are in the same coset if $\|f^p - g^p\| \cap x \neq \varnothing$. This is to say, for some $U(x)$, $f^p(x_0, \ldots, x_p) = g\,(x_0, \ldots, x_p)$ when $\{x_i\} \subset U$ or f^p and g^p agree on some neighborhood of x. Hence each coset is a germ of cochains. To see that i is an isomorphism, let s be an arbitrary, but fixed section in $S(A)$ with $s(x_0) = [f^p]_{x_0} \in A(x_0)$. Denote this f^p by ${}_0f^p$. A section s' over $V(x_o)$ can be defined by the assignment $s'(x \mid Vx_0) = {}_0f^p$. Since agreement of two sections at x_0 implies agreement in an open set $U(x_0)$, (1.5), there results

(a) $$s(x \mid U(x_0)) = \{[{}_0f^p]_x \mid U(x_0)\}.$$

Hence x_0 can be paired to a $U(x_0)$ satisfying (a) for each $x_0 \in X$. Well order the points of X. Define F^p, an Alexander cochain and therefore in A, by $F^p(x_1, \ldots, x_{p+1}) = 0$ if no $U(x_0)$ includes this $p + 1$ tuple of points and $F^p(x_1, \ldots, x_{p+1}) = {}_0f^p(x_1, \ldots, x_{p+1})$, if x_0 is the first element for which $U(x_0)$ contains this $p + 1$ tuple. Then $iF^p = s$.

PROBLEM

17-9. If A is fine, show the associated sheaf to $S(\mathcal{A})$ is again A. *Hint:* Since A is fine, only sections with compact support need be taken.

Definition 5.6. If $\mathcal{A}$ and $\mathcal{B}$ are sheaves over X, their **tensor product** is a sheaf $\mathcal{A} \otimes \mathcal{B}$ defined as $\underrightarrow{\mathrm{L}}\ \{S(U), r^U{}_V\}$ where $S(U) = S(U, \mathcal{A}) \otimes S(U, \mathcal{B})$

is a presheaf with $r^U{}_V$ interpreted as the restriction to V, $V \subset U$. Note the fiber is given by

$$(\mathcal{A} \otimes \mathcal{B})(x) = A(x) \otimes B(x), \tag{5.4a}$$

since

$$\varinjlim (S(U(x)), r^{U(x)}{}_{V(x)}) = \varinjlim (S(U(x), \mathcal{A}), r^{U(x)}{}_{V(x)}) \otimes \varinjlim (S(U(x), B), r^{U(x)}{}_{V(x)}).$$

(Of course, the three entries of $r^{U(x)}{}_{V(x)}$ refer to different homomorphisms.)

If A is a grating and $\mathcal{B}$ is a sheaf, both over X, then a grating is defined by $S(X, \mathcal{A} \otimes \mathcal{B})$ where $\mathcal{A}$ is the associated sheaf to A (5.2). For the subgrating of elements of compact support we use the notation $A \circ \mathcal{B} = {}^{\bullet}S(X, \mathcal{A} \otimes \mathcal{B})$ where ${}^{\bullet}S$ indicates sections with compact supports.

PROBLEM

17-10. Show $A \circ \mathcal{B}$ is fine if A is fine.

6. SECTIONS, SERRATIONS, AND SPECIAL SHEAVES.

A troublesome point in dealing with maps, and in particular with sections, is that the domains cannot always be extended. This difficulty vanishes if the continuity requirement is dropped and in this way $\to 0$ can be added on the right of (1.16b). Moreover, noncontinuous sections yield capacious presheaves into which the usual presheaves can be packed. The development for general presheaves will use such considerations.

Definition 6.1. A **serration** on U is a single valued, not necessarily continuous, transformation $t: U \to \mathfrak{I}$ satisfying pt is the identity map on $U \to U$. Evidently this is tantamount to taking t as an element in the Cartesian product. Hence we introduce the presheaf $T(\mathfrak{I}, U) = \prod_{x \in U} P(x)$, where (1.6a)

$$P(x) = \varinjlim_{U(x)} \{P(U), r^{U(x)}{}_{V(x)}\}.$$

Write

$$(TP)(x) = \varinjlim \{T(\mathfrak{I}, U), r^{U(x)}{}_{V(x)}\}.$$

In general $(T\mathfrak{I})(x)$ is not the same as $P(x)$. Let $p^U{}_V$ be the restriction morphism and let $\pi^U{}_x$ be the projection morphism $T(U)$ to $P(x)$. Furthermore let λ be a morphism of presheaves ($\lambda: \mathfrak{I} \to \mathfrak{I}'$).

Lemma 6.2. *T is a functor on $\mathfrak{P}(X, \mathfrak{A})$ to $\mathfrak{P}(X, \mathfrak{A})$.*

That the matching conditions are satisfied, and that T is a functor can be seen from the following commutative diagrams, the second of which defines $T(\lambda)$. Where a single $\mathcal{S}$ enters, we often write $T(U)$ for $T(\mathcal{S}, U)$.

(6.2a)

$$\begin{array}{ccc} T(U) & \xrightarrow{p^U{}_V} & T(V) \\ & \searrow^{\pi^U{}_x} & \downarrow{\scriptstyle \pi^V{}_x} \\ & & P(x) \end{array}$$

$$\begin{array}{ccc} T(\mathcal{S}, U) & \xrightarrow{T(\lambda)_U} & T(\mathcal{S}', U) \\ \downarrow{\scriptstyle \pi^U{}_x} & & \downarrow{\scriptstyle \pi'^U{}_x} \\ P(x) & \xrightarrow{\lambda} & P'(x) \end{array}$$

Let γ be the morphism on $\mathcal{S}$ to $T(\mathcal{S})$ defined by the condition that $\pi^V{}_x \gamma(V) = r^V{}_x$ for every $x \in V$. Then by the device of introducing the identity functor $\boldsymbol{i} = \boldsymbol{i}(\mathcal{S}(X, A))$ on $\mathcal{S}(X)$ we can consider γ as a transformation on $\boldsymbol{i}$ to T.

Lemma 6.3. *γ is a natural transformation.*

The definition of γ implies the commutativity of

(6.3a)

$$\begin{array}{ccccc} P(U) & \xrightarrow{r^U{}_V} & P(V) & \searrow^{r^V{}_x} & \\ \downarrow{\scriptstyle \gamma(U)} & & \downarrow{\scriptstyle \gamma(V)} & & \\ T(U) & \longrightarrow & T(V) & \xrightarrow{\pi^V{}_x} & P(x) \end{array}$$

On taking direct limits in the right hand triangle there results

$$\begin{array}{ccccc} P(U) & \xrightarrow{r^U{}_x} & P(x) & \searrow^{\approx} & \\ \downarrow{\scriptstyle \gamma(U)} & & \downarrow{\scriptstyle \gamma(x)} & & \\ T(U) & \xrightarrow{p^U{}_x} & T(x) & \xrightarrow{\pi^x{}_x} & P(x) \end{array}$$

where $T(x) = (T\mathcal{S})(x)$.

It then follows that the square and the two triangles in (6.3b) are commutative.

(6.3b)

$$\begin{array}{ccccccc} & \nearrow^{\pi^U{}_x} & P(x) & \xrightarrow{\lambda(x)} & P'(x) & \nwarrow^{\pi'^U{}_x} & \\ & & \uparrow{\scriptstyle r^U{}_x} & & \uparrow{\scriptstyle r'^U{}_x} & & \\ T(U) & \xleftarrow{\gamma(U)} & P(U) & \xrightarrow{\lambda(U)} & P'(U) & \xrightarrow{\gamma'(U)} & \Pi_U P'(x) \end{array}$$

Thus

$$\begin{aligned} \pi'^U{}_x \lambda'(U) &= r'^U{}_x \lambda(U) \\ &= \lambda(x) r^U{}_x \\ &= \lambda(x)\pi^U{}_x \gamma(U) = \pi'^U{}_x (T\lambda)(U)\gamma(U), \quad (6.2a). \end{aligned}$$

Hence the term $\pi'^{U}{}_{x}$ can be cancelled. Therefore $\gamma' \lambda = (T\lambda)\gamma$, the naturality condition on γ.

Lemma 6.4 (a). *Let $\mathcal{M}$ be a general sheaf. Then $\mathcal{M}$ is a general subsheaf of* $T(\mathcal{M})$ (1.9).

(b) *T is a functor on $\mathfrak{P}(X, \mathfrak{A})$ to $\mathfrak{S}(X, \mathfrak{A})$.*

This can be inferred from (1.7). In more detail though, we show that *ker* $\gamma(U)$ has just one element of $\mathcal{M}(U, A)$. Suppose in fact that $p(U)$ and $q(U)$ are distinct elements of $\mathcal{M}(U, \mathfrak{A})$, but that $r^{U}{}_{x}\, p(U) = r^{U}{}_{x} q(U)$ for each $x \in U$. Then for each x and some $V(x)$, $r^{U}{}_{V(x)}\, p(U) = r^{U}{}_{V(x)}\, q(U)$. The collection of finite intersections of the $V(x)$ sets constitutes a cover ν of U. Let $V(x) \cap V(y) \neq \varnothing$. Then

$$r^{V(x)}{}_{V(x)\cap V(y)}(r^{U}{}_{V(x)}\, p(U)) = r^{V(y)}{}_{V(x)\cap V(y)}\, r^{U}{}_{V(y)}\, p(U).$$

According to (1.8b), there is a unique element $t(U) \in \mathcal{M}(U)$ such that

$$r^{U}{}_{V(x)}\, t(U) = r^{V(x)}{}_{V(x)\cap V(y)}\, r^{U}{}_{V(x)}\, p(U).$$

However both $p(U)$ and $q(U)$ can be substituted for $t(U)$. Hence $p(U) = q(U)$.

Let $\omega = \{w_j\}$ be a cover of U. Suppose $\{t_i\}$ are morphisms satisfying $p^{i}{}_{ij}\, t_i = p^{j}{}_{ij}\, t_j$ where $t_i\colon X \to \Pi_{w_i} P(x)$ and $p^{i}{}_{ij}$ is the projection on w_i to $w_i \cap w_j$. Thus $t(x) = p^{i}{}_{x}\, t_i = p^{j}{}_{x}\, t_j$ for $x \in w_i \cap w_j$. Hence t exists on $X \to T(\mathfrak{T}, U)$ such that $p^{U}{}_{x}\, t = t(x)$ where $p^{w} w_i\, t = t_i$. Moreover t is unique since if $p^{w} w_i\, t' = t_i$, then $p^{U}{}_{x}\, t' = t(x)$ whence $t' = t$. Hence (1.8a) and (1.8b) are satisfied.

Lemma 6.5. *Let $\mathcal{M}$ and $\mathcal{N}$ be sheaves on X with values in $\mathfrak{A}$. There is a bijection of $Hom(T\mathcal{M}, T\mathcal{N})$ on Π $Hom(M(x), N(x))$.*

Suppose $\lambda \in Hom(T\mathcal{M}, T\mathcal{N})$. The induced $\lambda(x)$ *is on* $(T\mathcal{M})(x)$ *to* $(T\mathcal{N})(x)$. Define $\rho(x)$ by composition in

$$M(x) \to (\Pi M(y))(x) \to (\Pi N(y))(x) \to N(x).$$

On the other hand, if $\rho(x)$ is assigned on $M(x)$ to $N(x)$, then λ' is defined on $T(\mathcal{M})$ to $T(\mathcal{N})$ by $\lambda(U) = \Pi_U\, \rho(x)$. It is easy to see $\lambda\lambda'$ and $\lambda'\lambda$ are identities.

Lemma 6.6. *If $\mathcal{M}$ is a general sheaf, then $T\mathcal{M} = 0$ and $\mathcal{M} = 0$ are equivalent statements.*

If $\mathcal{M} = 0$, then $M(x) = 0$ and so $\Pi M(x) = 0$.
If $\Pi M(x) = 0$, then since $\gamma\colon \mathcal{M} \to \Pi M(x)$ is a monomorphism, $\mathcal{M} = 0$.

Lemma 6.7. *If $\mathcal{M}$ and $\mathcal{N}$ are general sheaves, then $\lambda\colon \mathcal{M} \to \mathcal{N}$ is an isomorphism provided either $T(\lambda)$ is an isomorphism or $\lambda(x)$ is an isomorphism for all x.*

In view of (6.5) we need only show that when $T(\lambda)$ is an isomorphism, then λ is an isomorphism. We make strong use of the fact that our categories are exact. Let us start with the exact sequence,

(6.7a) $$0 \to (\overline{ker}\ \lambda) \to \mathcal{M} \to \mathcal{N} \to (\overline{cok}\ \lambda) \to 0$$

where $\overline{ker}$ and $\overline{cok}$ refer to the general presheaf kernel and cokernel, while *ker* and *cok* refer to the general sheaf entities. Since exactness is preserved by direct limits,

(6.7b) $$0 \to (\overline{ker}\ \lambda)(x) \to M(x) \to N(x) \to (\overline{cok}\ \lambda)(x) \to 0$$

is exact. Since $T(\lambda)$ is an isomorphism on $T(\mathcal{M})$ to $T(\mathcal{N})$, then by (6.5), $\lambda(x)$ is an isomorphism. This implies

$$(\overline{ker}\ \lambda)(x) = ker\ \lambda(x) = 0 \quad \text{and} \quad (cok\ \lambda)(x) = cok\ \lambda(x) = 0.$$

Accordingly $\Pi\ ker\ \lambda = 0 = \Pi\ cok\ \lambda$. Therefore by (6.6) $ker\ \lambda = 0 = cok\ \lambda$.

A useful result is

Lemma 6.8. *If*

(6.8a) $$0 \longrightarrow M'(x) \xrightarrow{i(x)} M(x) \xrightarrow{j(x)} M''(x) \longrightarrow 0$$

is an exact sequence of general sheaves in $\mathfrak{S}(X, \mathfrak{B})$ for all x

$$0 \longrightarrow \mathcal{M}' \xrightarrow{i} \mathcal{M} \xrightarrow{j} \mathcal{M}'' \longrightarrow 0$$

is exact.

We sketch the demonstration using the technique in the proof of (6.7). The functor T is easily seen to be left exact. Hence starting with (6.8a), $T\mathcal{M}' = T\ ker\ j = \Pi\ ker\ j(x)$. Therefore $\mathcal{M}' = ker\ j$ (6.7). Moreover since $cok\ j(x) = (\overline{cok}\ j)(x) = 0$ for all x, $cok\ j = 0$.

A consequence left over from (3.4) is

Lemma 6.9. *The functor ψ^* (3.5) is exact.*

Let

(6.9a) $$0 \to \mathcal{M}' \to \mathcal{M} \to \mathcal{M}'' \to 0$$

be an exact sequence of sheaves in $\mathfrak{S}(Y, \mathfrak{A})$. The functor replacing $\mathcal{M}$ by $\mathcal{M}(y)$ is exact. It is easy to see $\mathcal{M}\psi(x) = (\psi^* \mathcal{M})(x)$. Hence (6.9a) with $\mathcal{M}'$ replaced by $(\psi^* \mathcal{M})(x)$ etc. is still exact. The assertion of the lemma now follows from (6.8).

ψ_* and $\psi_{\#}$, though developed in different ways, are to be identified as are also the functors ψ^* and $\psi^{\#}$. Henceforth we elect the notation $\psi_{\#}$, ψ_F and $\psi^{\#}$ and reserve the asterisk for omology homomorphisms as say in (10.8). The following theorem is manifestly basic. For example it justifies adjointness assertions entering the proof of (3.5).

Theorem 6.10. *The inclusion functor* $I(\mathfrak{S}, \mathfrak{P}) = I(\mathfrak{S}(X, \mathfrak{A}), \mathfrak{P}(X, \mathfrak{A}))$ *has a unique right adjoint, R.*

We are to show that for every $\mathcal{S} \in \mathfrak{P}(X, \mathfrak{A})$ and $\mathcal{Q} \in \mathfrak{S}(X, \mathfrak{A})$

(6.10a) $$Hom(R\mathcal{S}, \mathcal{Q}) \approx Hom(\mathcal{S}, I\mathcal{Q}).$$

Let $\mathcal{F}_i$ be any general subsheaf of $T(\mathcal{S})$ such that if $\mathcal{S} \to T(\mathcal{S})$, then γ is the composition $\beta_j \alpha_j$ in

(6.10b) $$\mathcal{S} \xrightarrow{\alpha_j} \mathcal{F}_j \xrightarrow{\beta_j} T(\mathcal{S}).$$

(Such a factorization exists since F_j can be taken as $T(P)$.) Define $R\mathcal{S} = \bigcap \mathcal{F}_j$. Then $R\mathcal{S}$ can be verified to be a general sheaf (1.9). Let β be the monomorphism $R\mathcal{S} \to T(\mathcal{S})$. Let α be the morphism (induced by α_i) on $\mathcal{S} \to R\mathcal{S}$. Then

$$\gamma = \beta\alpha.$$

These morphisms depend on $\mathcal{S}$.

Let λ be a general presheaf morphism of $\mathcal{S} \to \mathcal{Q}$ where $\mathcal{Q}$ is a general sheaf. Write $T(\lambda)$ for $\Pi\lambda(x)$ (6.5). We construct a sheaf referred to as a "pull back" (reminiscent of the alternative exposition of ψ^* in (3.2)). Thus in $\mathcal{Q} \times T(\mathcal{S})$ consider the pairs $\{q, p \mid \gamma q = T(\lambda)p\}$. Since γ is a monomorphism, the collection yields a well defined subset of $T(\mathcal{S})$ and can be verified to be a general sheaf. We denote this general sheaf by $\lambda^{-1}(\mathcal{Q})$, though perhaps $(T\lambda)^{-1}\mathcal{Q}$ would indicate the situation better. Accordingly the following diagram is commutative.

(6.10c) $$\begin{array}{ccc} \lambda^{-1}(\mathcal{Q}) & \xrightarrow{\lambda^{-1}(\gamma)} & T(\mathcal{S}) \\ \Big\downarrow {\scriptstyle \lambda'} & & \Big\downarrow {\scriptstyle T(\lambda)} \\ \mathcal{Q} & \xrightarrow{\gamma} & T(\mathcal{Q}) \end{array}$$

where λ' and $\lambda^{-1}(\gamma)$ are symbols for the two obvious monomorphisms. We write γ' for the morphism in (6.2) say on $\mathcal{S} \to T(\mathcal{S})$. It then follows that $\mathcal{T} \subset \lambda^{-1}(\mathcal{Q})$, and in fact there is a unique morphism $\delta\colon \mathcal{T} \to \lambda^{-1}\,\mathcal{Q}$ such that with λ, γ', δ added to the above diagram, as indicated by (6.10d)

(6.10d)
$$\begin{array}{ccccc} & & \mathcal{T} & & \\ & \swarrow^{\lambda} & \downarrow^{\delta} & \searrow^{\gamma'} & \\ \mathcal{Q} & \longleftarrow & \lambda^{-1}(\mathcal{Q}) & \longrightarrow & T(\mathcal{Q}) \end{array}$$

commutativity is preserved for all path pairs with the same termini. In particular, $\gamma' = \lambda^{-1}(\gamma)\delta$. Therefore $\lambda^{-1}(\mathcal{Q})$ is an $\mathcal{F}_j$ in (6.10a). Let μ be the inclusion $R\mathcal{T} \to \lambda^{-1}(\mathcal{Q})$ and let $\nu = \lambda'\mu$. Then

(6.10g) $$\lambda = \nu\alpha.$$

In view of the definition of $R(\mathcal{Q})$, it is easily shown that ν is unique.

The correspondence $\lambda \leftrightarrow \nu$ with $\lambda \in hom(\mathcal{T}, I\mathcal{Q})$ and $\nu \in hom(R\mathcal{T}, \mathcal{Q})$ shows R is the right adjoint functor to I.

The notion of fineness or fullness (81.18), (81.20, (5.1) achieves its purpose by guaranteeing the existence of certain extensions. Direct predication of the possibility of the requisite extensions would seem the natural way to weaken restrictions. This we proceed to do.

Definition 6.11. Let $\mathcal{A}$ be a sheaf over X. It is a **flabby** (flasque) sheaf if for every open set, U, in X, any section $s \in S_U(\mathcal{A})$ can be extended to a section, s', over all of X, i.e., $s' \in S(\mathcal{A})$. It is a **soft** (mou) sheaf if for every closed set C in a paracompactifying family, or in particular if X is paracompact, $s \in S_C(\mathcal{A})$ can be extended to $s' \in S(\mathcal{A})$. (The parentheses give the French equivalents.) Accordingly the restriction of a soft sheaf to a closed set yields a soft sheaf. The restriction of a flabby sheaf to an open set is plainly flabby. A sheaf $\mathcal{A}$ is **injective** if for every sheaf $\mathcal{B}$ (of modules over a fixed integral domain and the same space) $Hom(\mathcal{B}, \mathcal{A})$ is exact.

Example 17-12. If ψ is an analytic function with a natural boundary, the section defined by $s(x) = \psi(x)$ for $x \in U$ or $x \in \bar{V} \subset U$ cannot be continued to all X, so that the sheaves in Examples 17-2, 17-3, and 17-4 are neither fine, flabby, nor soft.

Lemma 6.12. *If F is a paracompactifying support family and $\mathcal{A}$ is a fine sheaf, then $\mathcal{A}$ is F-soft.*

The idea of the proof is to show that if $X_0 \in F$, it has a neighborhood N such that ${}_0s \in S(X_0, \mathcal{A})$ extends to $s \in S(\bar{N}, \mathcal{A})$ with $s(x \mid \dot{N}$ (the boundary of N)) $= 0(x)$. Then the definition $s(x \mid x \bar{\in} N) = 0(x)$ yields the extension of ${}_0s$ to $s \in S(X, \mathcal{A})$. By (81.14c) we can replace X by some paracompact closed neighborhood of X_0 in the demonstration, that is to say we can assume X is paracompact. Let $\{V_i\}$ be an open cover of X_0 with $s_i \in S(V_i, \mathcal{A})$ subject to $s_i \mid V_i \cap X_0 = {}_0s \mid V_i \cap X_0$. We may as well suppose $\{V_i\}$ locally finite, since X_0 is paracompact and we write $Y = \bigcup V_i$. Then Y is paracompact and there is a shrinking, (**A**), $\{W_i\}$ of $\{V_i\}$. Let $C = \{x \mid x \in \bar{W}_i \cap \bar{W}_j, s_i(x) = s_j(x)\}$. Define the serration $t \in T(C, A)$ by

$$t \mid \bar{W}_i \cap C = s_i \mid \bar{W}_i \cap C.$$

Local finiteness plus the closure of $\{\bar{W}_i\}$ guarantees the existence of a neighborhood, $N(x)$, meeting only $\{\bar{W}_i \mid i \in \pi\}$ with $x \in \bigcap_\pi \bar{W}_i$. Accordingly there is a section ${}_1s \in S(N(x), \mathcal{A})$ with ${}_1s(x) = s_i(x) = t(x)$, $i \in \pi$. For some neighborhood $U_i(x)$,

$${}_1s \mid U_i(x) \cap \bar{W}_i = s_i \mid U_i(x) \cap \bar{W}_i.$$

Let $N^1(x) = \bigcap U_i(x) \cap \bigcap_\pi \bar{V}_i$. Then

$${}_1s \mid N^1(x) \cap \bigcap_\pi \bar{W}_i = t \mid N^1(x) \cap \bigcap_\pi \bar{W}_i.$$

Since ${}_1s$ is continuous, so is t. Accordingly, $t \in S(C, \mathcal{A})$ and is an extension of ${}_0s$ since $X_0 \subset C$. Since $s_i(x) = s_j(x)$, $i, j \in \pi$ it follows $s_i \mid M_{ij}(x) = s_j \mid M_{ij}(x)$ $i, j \in \pi$, when $M_{ij}(x) \subset N^1(x)$. Since π is a finite set, $M(x) = \bigcap_{i,j\in\pi} M_{ij}(x)$ is open and $s_i \mid M(x) = s_j \mid M(x)$, $i, j \in \pi$. Then $M(x) \subset C$. Accordingly, $X_0 \subset \bigcup_{x\in X_0} M(x) = M$ is an open set in C. We have shown $t \mid M$ is an extension of ${}_0s$ to a neighborhood of X_0.

Let $\dot{M}$ be the boundary of M. Consider the parafine cover M, $X_0^\sim$. There is a shrinking to the cover $\beta = b_1, b_2$, i.e., $b_1 \subset \bar{b}_1 \subset M$, $b_2 \subset \bar{b}_2 \subset X_0^\sim$. Since $b_2 \cap X_0 = \varnothing$, $b_1 \supset X_0$. There are endomorphisms e_1, e_2 with $e_1A(x) = 0$, $x\, b_1 = m$. Define ${}_1s$ a serration by ${}_1s(x) = e_1t(x)$, ${}_1s(x) = 0(x)$, $x \bar{\in} M$. Then, in particular since $\dot{M} \cap b_1 = \varnothing$, ${}_1s(x \mid \dot{N}) = 0(x)$. Accordingly ${}_1s$ is a section in $S(X, \mathcal{A})$ extending s_0.

Lemma 6.13. *Suppose $\mathcal{A}$ is flabby over X. If F and G refer to all closed sets, then $\psi_F\ \mathcal{A}$ is flabby. If G is paracompactifying, and $\mathcal{A}$ is flabby, then $\psi_F\ \mathcal{A}$ is G soft.*

If F and G refer to all closed sets, the proof is immediate.

Let $Y_0 \in G$ and let $s \in S(Y_0, \psi_F(\mathcal{A}))$. Since G is paracompactifying, there is a paracompact closed neighborhood $N(Y_0) \in G$ so by an argument used in (6.4), s is the restriction of some $s' \in S(U, \psi_F(\mathcal{A}))$ for some $U \subset N(Y_0)$. By a normality argument, an open set, W, exists with $Y_0 \subset W \subset \bar{W} \subset U$. Assume $s' \in S_{F(U)}(\psi^{-1}(U), \mathcal{A})$, so $\|s'\| \subset \psi^{-1}(U)$, and hence $\|s'\| \cap \psi^{-1}(\bar{W})$ is closed in X. Therefore $V = (X - (\|s'\| \cap \psi^{-1}(\bar{W})) \cap \psi^{-1}(W) \subset X - \|s'\|$ so $s' \mid V = 0$. Hence there is a section, s'', on $\psi^{-1}(W) \cup (X - (\|s'\| \cap \psi^{-1}(\bar{W})))$ with $s'' = s'$ on $\psi^{-1}(W)$, $s'' = 0$ on $X - (\|s'\| \cap \psi^{-1}(W))$. Since $\mathcal{A}$

is flabby, there is an extension of s'' to $\check{s} \in S(X, \mathcal{A})$. Moreover $\|\check{s}\| \subset \|s''\| \cap \psi^{-1}(W)$ and it is a direct consequence that $\check{s}$ can be considered in $S_G\, \psi_F(\mathcal{A})$ whence by restricting s first to W and then to Y_0, we get successively s' and then s. Paracompactness of $X = Y$ with ψ the identity map is enough to confirm that flabby sheaves are soft.

The sheaves in (6.14) and (6.15) are on a common space, X.

Lemma 6.14. *If* (**a**) $0 \to \mathcal{A}_1 \to \mathcal{A} \xrightarrow{\eta} \mathcal{A}_2 \to 0$ *is an exact sequence of sheaves of Abelian groups, and if $\mathcal{A}_1$ and $\mathcal{A}$ are flabby (or soft), then $\mathcal{A}_2$ is flabby (or soft).*

Let $a_2(x_0)$ be $s_2(x_0)$. Then by (**a**) there is an $a(x_0)$ in $A(x_0)$ such that $\eta a(x_0) = a_2(x_0)$. Let s be a section over an open subset, say X_0, of X, with $s(x_0) = a(x_0)$. Use $\dot{\eta}$ for the induced homomorphism on sections. We get $\dot{\eta}s \in S(X_0, \mathcal{A}_2)$. Therefore since $\dot{\eta}s(x_0) = s_2(x_0)$ there is a $V(x_0)$ on which $\dot{\eta}s = s_2$. Denial that the induced homomorphism $\dot{\eta}$ on $S(\mathcal{A}) \to S(\mathcal{A}_2)$ is onto leads to a contradiction: Suppose then there is an s_2 not covered by any $s \in S(\mathcal{A})$. Hence by the argument above there is a maximal open set $U \neq X$ such that $s \in S(U, \mathcal{A})$ and $\dot{\eta}s = s_2 \mid U(x_0)$ where $\dot{\eta}$ is written in place of the more natural $\dot{\eta}_{U(x_0)}$. Let $x \in X - U$. Let $\check{s} \in S(V(x), \mathcal{A})$ with $\eta\check{s} = s_2$ on $V(x)$. There results by the left exactness of S (1.16).

(6.14b) $$0 \to S(W, \mathcal{A}_1) \to S(W, \mathcal{A}) \to S(W, \mathcal{A}_2)$$

for any open set, W. Hence for $W = V(x) \cap U$, the antecedent of $s_2 \mid W$ consists of sections differing by sections in $iS(W, \mathcal{A}_1)$. In particular then, $t = (s - \check{s}) \mid W \in iS(W, \mathcal{A}_1)$. Since $\mathcal{A}_1$ is flabby, $s - \check{s}$ can be prolonged to $V(x_0)$. On $V(x)$, let $\check{t} = \check{s} + t$. Then, replacing $\check{s}$ by $\check{t}$, $s = \check{t}$ on W whence t extends s to $U \cup V(x_0)$ contradicting maximality. Moreover this argument shows that (6.14b) is exact with $\to 0$ added. Thus for $s_2 \in S(U, \mathcal{A})$ there is an $s \in S(U, \mathcal{A})$ with $\dot{\eta}s = s_2$. Since $\mathcal{A}$ is flabby, s extends to $\bar{s} \in S(X, \mathcal{A})$. Then $\dot{\eta}\bar{s}$ is an extension of s_2 to X.

Lemma 6.15. *If* $0 \to \mathcal{A}^0 \to \mathcal{A}^1 \to \cdots$ *is an exact sequence of flabby sheaves of Abelian groups, then* $0 \to \cdots \to S(\mathcal{A}^i) \to$ *is exact.*

Just as in (72.1)

(6.15a) $$0 \to ker\ d^n \to \mathcal{A}^n \to d^n\, \mathcal{A}^n = ker\ d^{n+1} \to 0.$$

If $n = 0$, $ker\ d^n = 0$ is flabby. Also $\mathcal{A}^0$ is flabby. Hence by (6.14) $ker\ d^1$ is flabby. By induction $ker\ d^n$ is flabby. Then by the exactness of the extended (6.14b) with $W = X$,

$$0 \longrightarrow S(ker\ d^n) \longrightarrow S(\mathcal{A}^n) \xrightarrow{\ \eta\ } S(ker\ d^{n+1}) \longrightarrow 0$$

is exact, which implies the theorem.

Lemma 6.16. *If $\mathcal{A}$ is an injective sheaf of modules over R then $\mathcal{A}$ is flabby.*

For any open set U let $\mathcal{B}_U$ be the sheaf determined by an arbitrary sheaf of modules $\mathcal{B}$, (1.15). Then $\mathcal{B}_U$ is a subsheaf of $\mathcal{B}$ and the injection property of $\mathcal{A}$ implies exactness of

$$Hom(\mathcal{B}, \mathcal{A}) \to Hom(\mathcal{B}_U, \mathcal{A}) \to 0.$$

In particular take for $\mathcal{B}$ the constant sheaf $R \times X$. Let t be the serration defined by $t(x) = {}_0s(x)$ for $x \in U$ where ${}_0s \in S(U, \mathcal{A})$ and by $t(x) = 0(x) \in A(x)$ for $x \in U^{\sim}$. Define h by $r \times x \to rt(x)$ on $\mathcal{B}_U$ to $\mathcal{A}$. Then h has an antecedent h' in $Hom(\mathcal{B}, \mathcal{A})$. Since homomorphisms are continuous (1.11) this means $h'\colon 1 \times X$ is a map to $\mathcal{A}$ coinciding with ${}_0s$ in U, i.e., $h'j = s \in S(\mathcal{A})$ is an extension of ${}_0s$ where $x \xrightarrow{j} 1 \times x$.

PROBLEM

17-11. Show (6.15) is valid with $\mathcal{A}^i$, P soft (where P is a paracompactifying support family).

7. RESOLUTIONS. We meet the notion of a resolution once more. Indeed for spaces not restricted to be locally compact or paracompact, or even T_2, the resolution furnishes a definition of cohomology with respect to a sheaf not equivalent to the Alexander definition (2.2). The natural question is, which definition is preferable? If the criterion is that $H(X, \mathcal{A})$ is to be a cohomology functor, then for the more general spaces only the definition of $H(X, \mathcal{A})$ by suitable resolutions is satisfactory.

Definition 7.1. Let $\mathcal{G}$ be a sheaf over X. Suppose a DG sheaf $\mathcal{G}^* = \{\mathcal{G}^n\}$ exists for which

$$0 \longrightarrow \mathcal{G} \xrightarrow{j} \mathcal{G}^0 \xrightarrow{d^0} \mathcal{G}^1 \xrightarrow{d^1} \mathcal{G}^2 \longrightarrow \tag{7.1a}$$

is exact. Then (7.1a) is a **cohomology resolution** or simply **resolution,** $\mathcal{G}^*$. The resolution is fine or flabby or soft (6.11) if each $\mathcal{G}^i$ satisfies the condition.

Lemma 7.2. *If $\mathcal{G}^*$ yields a resolution of $\mathcal{G}$, then*

$$H^0(\mathcal{G}^*) = \mathcal{G}, H^n(\mathcal{G}^*) = 0, \qquad n > 0.$$

Evidently $$\mathcal{B}^{n-1} = d\mathcal{G}^{n-1} = ker\ d^n = \mathcal{Z}^n.$$

Definition 7.3. We proceed to construct a resolution of $\mathcal{G}$. We replace $\mathcal{G}^i$ by $\mathcal{T}^i$ in (7.1a) and start with the serrations $T(\mathcal{G})$ (6.1), written $\mathcal{T}^0(X, \mathcal{G})$, as $\mathcal{G}^0$. Then (6.2) assures the exactness of $0 \longrightarrow \mathcal{G} \xrightarrow{j} \mathcal{T}^0 \xrightarrow{d}$. Define

d^0 as the natural homomorphism $\mathscr{T}^0 \xrightarrow{d^0} \mathscr{T}^0/j\mathcal{G}$. Thus $0 \longrightarrow \ker d^0 = \mathcal{G} \longrightarrow \mathscr{T}^0 \xrightarrow{d^0} d^0\mathscr{T}^0 \longrightarrow 0$. It is convenient to write $\mathscr{Z}^1$ for $d^0\mathscr{T}^0 \approx \mathscr{T}^0/j\mathcal{G}$. Proceed with $\mathscr{Z}^1$ replacing $\mathcal{G}$. Then with $\mathscr{T}^1 = T(\mathscr{Z}^1)$, we define d^1 by the natural homomorphism

$$\mathscr{T}^1 \xrightarrow{d^1} \mathscr{T}^1/\mathscr{Z}^1$$

and we write $\mathscr{Z}^2$ for $\mathscr{T}^1/\mathscr{Z}^1$ so

$$0 \to \ker d^1 \to \mathscr{T}^1 \to \mathscr{Z}^2 \to 0.$$

By induction

(7.3a) $$\mathscr{T}^n = \mathscr{T}^0(X, \mathscr{Z}^n),$$

$$\mathscr{Z}^n = \mathscr{T}^{n-1}/\mathscr{Z}^{n-1}.$$

The **canonical resolution**

(7.3b) $$0 \longrightarrow \mathcal{G} \xrightarrow{j} \mathscr{T}^0(X, \mathcal{G}) \xrightarrow{d^0} \mathscr{T}^1 \xrightarrow{d^1} \cdots \longrightarrow \mathscr{T}^n \longrightarrow$$

is referred to as $\mathscr{T}^*(\mathcal{G})$ rather than $\mathcal{G}^*$. Denote by $C^*(X, \mathcal{G})$ the *associated grating of sections*, $S(\mathscr{T}^*)$. This notation will be used even if the supports of the sections are in an F family. In particular

(7.3c) $$C^p(X, \mathcal{G}) = S(X, \mathscr{T}^p),\ C^p(X, \mathcal{G}^q) = S(X, \mathscr{T}^p(\mathcal{G}^q)).$$

The injective sheaf is more lavishly endowed with desirable properties than any of the others. We therefore describe the imbedding of a sheaf in an injective sheaf and we construct an injective resolution.

Definition 7.4. Let R be a principal ideal domain and $\mathcal{G}$ a sheaf over X. Imbed the module $\mathcal{G}(x)$ in the injective module $\mathscr{I}\mathcal{G}(x)$ as accomplished in (92.7). The injective sheaves and the injective resolutions arise by replacing $\mathscr{T}$ by $\mathscr{I}$ and $\mathscr{T}^n$ by $\mathscr{I}^n$ in (6.1), (7.3a), and (7.3b). For instance, the presheaf

$$\mathscr{I}(U, \mathcal{G}) = \Pi_{x\in U}\, \mathscr{I}\mathcal{G}(x)$$

leads to the injective sheaf

$$\mathscr{I}(X, \mathcal{G}) = \underrightarrow{\mathrm{L}}_U\{\mathscr{I}(U, \mathcal{G}), r^U{}_V\}.$$

Further, on writing $\mathscr{I}^0(X, \mathcal{G})$ for $\mathscr{I}(X, \mathcal{G})$ and $\mathscr{I}^n = \mathscr{I}^0(X, \mathscr{Z}^n)$ where $\mathscr{Z}^n = \mathscr{I}^{n-1}(\mathscr{Z}^{n-1})$ (Cf. 7.3a) there results the injective resolution

(7.4a) $$0 \longrightarrow \mathcal{G} \longrightarrow \mathscr{I}^0(X, \mathcal{G}) \xrightarrow{d^0} \mathscr{I}^1(X, \mathcal{G}) \longrightarrow$$

denoted by $\mathscr{I}^*(X, \mathcal{G})$.

Lemma 7.5. *$\mathscr{T}^n(X, \mathcal{G})$ is a flabby sheaf.*

Indeed $S(U, \mathscr{T}^0(X, \mathcal{G})$ and $S(X, \mathscr{T}^0\,(X, \mathcal{G}))$ consist of arbitrary functions on U to $\mathcal{G}$ and X to $\mathcal{G}$ respectively. By (7.3) this covers the case of $\mathscr{T}^n$ for $\mathcal{G}$ can be replaced by $\mathscr{Z}^n$.

Lemma 7.6. *If the sheaf sequence*

$$0 \to \mathcal{G}_1 \to \mathcal{G}_2 \to \mathcal{G}_3 \to 0 \tag{7.6a}$$

is exact, then (7.3c)

$$0 \to C^p(X, \mathcal{G}_1) \to C^p(X, \mathcal{G}_2) \to C^p(X, \mathcal{G}_3) \to 0 \tag{7.6b}$$

is exact. In brief, the functor C^p on the category of sheaves on X to the category of modules is exact.

For every open set U

$$0 \to \Pi_{x \epsilon U}\, \mathcal{G}_1(x) \to \Pi_{x \epsilon U}\, \mathcal{G}_2(x) \to \Pi_{x \epsilon U}\, \mathcal{G}_3(x) \to 0$$

is exact whence by taking direct limits with the projections, ${r^{U(x)}}_{V(x)}$, those of restriction, there results the exact sequence (77.15)

$$0 \longrightarrow \mathscr{T}^0(X, \mathcal{G}_1) \xrightarrow{i'} \mathscr{T}^0(X, \mathcal{G}_2) \xrightarrow{\eta'} \mathscr{T}^0(X, \mathcal{G}_3) \longrightarrow 0 \tag{7.6c}$$

Since $\mathscr{T}^0(x, \mathcal{G}_i) \approx \mathcal{G}_i$, we can assume $\mathcal{G}_i$ is a subsheaf of $\mathscr{T}^0(X, \mathcal{G}_i)$ and then (7.6a) and (7.6c) imply the quotient sequence

$$0 \longrightarrow \frac{\mathscr{T}^0\,(X, \mathcal{G}_1)}{\mathcal{G}_1} = \mathscr{Z}^1(X, \mathcal{G}_1) \xrightarrow{i''} \mathscr{Z}^1(X, \mathcal{G}_2) \xrightarrow{\eta''} \mathscr{Z}^1(X, \mathcal{G}_3) \longrightarrow 0$$

is exact. In (7.6a) replace $\mathcal{G}_i$ by $\mathscr{Z}^1(X, \mathcal{G}_i)$ and repeat the argument. Continue by induction. Hence writing i_1, η_1 for the obvious induced homomorphisms

$$0 \longrightarrow \mathscr{T}^p(\mathcal{G}_1) \xrightarrow{i_1} \mathscr{T}^p(\mathcal{G}_2) \xrightarrow{\eta_1} \mathscr{T}^p(\mathcal{G}_3) \longrightarrow 0. \tag{7.6d}$$

Then (7.6b) follows from (7.6d), (6.15), and (7.5).

Corollary 7.7. *If $\mathcal{G}$ is a DG sheaf with $\delta\colon \mathcal{G}^q \to \mathcal{G}^{q+1}$ there is an induced homomorphism, $d'S(\mathscr{T}^n(X, \mathcal{G}^q)) \to S(\mathscr{T}^n(\mathcal{G}^{q+1}))$ with $d'\,d' = 0$.*

Consider

$$\begin{array}{ccccccccc}
 & & \downarrow{\scriptstyle\delta} & & \downarrow & & \downarrow & & \\
0 & \longrightarrow & \mathcal{G}^q & \xrightarrow{j^q} & \mathscr{T}^0(\mathcal{G}^q) & \xrightarrow{d^0} & \mathscr{T}^1(\mathcal{G}^q) & \longrightarrow & \\
 & & \downarrow{\scriptstyle\delta} & \text{I} & \downarrow{\scriptstyle {}_1d^0} & \text{II} & \downarrow{\scriptstyle {}_1d^1} & & \\
0 & \longrightarrow & \mathcal{G}^{q+1} & \xrightarrow{j^{q+1}} & \mathscr{T}^0(\mathcal{G}^{q+1}) & \xrightarrow{d^0} & \mathscr{T}^1(\mathcal{G}^{q+1}) & \longrightarrow & \\
 & & \downarrow & & \downarrow & & \downarrow & &
\end{array}$$

Define ${}_1d^0$ by the condition that the square I be commutative. Then define ${}_1d^1$ by the condition that the square II be commutative. This can be phrased as an induction construction. Each column is exact by (7.6d). Hence (6.7) assures the result. Specifically, d' is defined by

$$(d' s)(x) = {}_1d^n s(x)$$

where $s \in S(\mathscr{T}^n(X, \mathcal{G}^q))$.

Definition 7.8. A cohomology group H over X with coefficients in the sheaf of Abelian groups $\mathcal{G}$ can be defined by going to the associated grating $S(\mathscr{T}^n) = C^n(X, \mathcal{G})$, with d^p defined by $(d^p s^p)(x) = d^p(s^p(x))$ where $s^p \in S(X, \mathscr{T}^p) = C^p(X, \mathcal{G})$ and d^p occurs in (7.3b). Thus

$$H^m(X, \mathcal{G}) = H^m(C^*(X, \mathcal{G})) = ker\, d^m/Im\, d^{m-1}$$

where the supports of elements in C^* lie in an assigned family, F. Of course since flabby resolutions are equivalent up to homotopy $\mathscr{T}^*$ can in particular be replaced by $\mathscr{I}^*$ (7.4).

Remark. For X paracompact, or locally compact, the groups defined in (7.8) and in (2.3) are isomorphic.

The result (2.5) has an analogous formulation with resolutions. Thus

Lemma 7.9. $H^0(X, \mathcal{G}) \approx S(X, \mathcal{G})$.

The exactness of the canonical resolution of $\mathcal{G}$ implies by (6.15)

$$0 \longrightarrow S(X, \mathcal{G}) \xrightarrow{j'} C^0(X, \mathcal{G}) \xrightarrow{d'} C^1(X, \mathcal{G}) \longrightarrow$$

is exact. Since there are no coboundaries in dimension 0,

$$H^0(X, \mathcal{G}) = ker\, d' = Im\, j'.$$

We interpolate a comment about fine resolutions.

Lemma 7.10. *If X is locally compact or paracompact, and $\mathcal{A}$ and $\mathcal{G}$ are sheaves over X with $\mathcal{G}$ fine, and if* (**a**) $\mathcal{A} \xrightarrow{\varphi} \mathcal{A}^1 \longrightarrow 0$ *under the homomorphism φ, then with θ the homomorphism induced by φ,*

$$S(\mathcal{A} \otimes \mathcal{G}) \xrightarrow{\theta} S(\mathcal{A}^1 \otimes \mathcal{G}) \longrightarrow 0. \tag{7.10b}$$

Since $\mathcal{G}$ is fine, so is $\mathcal{A} \otimes \mathcal{G}$. Indeed, if $\beta = \{b^i\}$ is a fine or parafine cover, and the associated endomorphisms of $\mathcal{G}$ are $\{e_i\}$, then $\{1 \otimes e_i\}$ constitute endomorphisms satisfying (5.1). Then (6.12) and (6.15) imply (7.10b).

Lemma 7.11.

(7.11a) *If* $\mathcal{A}$ *is a flabby sheaf of Abelian groups,* $H^n(X, \mathcal{A}) = 0$ *for* $n \geq 1$.

(7.11b) *If* $\mathcal{A}$ *is soft and* P *is paracompactifying,* $H^n_P(X, \mathcal{A}) = 0$ *for* $n \geq 1$.

Consider the canonical resolution

(7.11c) $$0 \to \mathcal{A} \to \mathcal{T}^0 \to \mathcal{T}^1 \to$$

Then

(7.11d) $$0 \longrightarrow S(X, \mathcal{A}) \longrightarrow C^0(X, \mathcal{T}^0) \xrightarrow{d^0}$$

is exact (6.15). Since $ker\ d^n = Im\ d^{n-1}$, it follows that $ker\ d^n/Im\ d^{n-1} \approx 0$.
For (7.11b), all the sheaves in (7.11c) are P soft and again (7.11d) is exact. (Cf. Problem 17-11).

The existence of fine resolutions is easy to verify.

Definition 7.12. Let F be the Alexander pregrating on X with coefficients in J, (86.1). Then F is fine, torsion free, and acyclic (86.2a). Hence the associated graded differential sheaf $\mathcal{F}$ is fine in view of the definition of the associated sheaf. Accordingly $\mathcal{F}$ is a fine resolution of the simple sheaf $\mathcal{J}$ $(= X \times \text{J})$ associated with J, i.e., $0 \to \mathcal{J} \to \mathcal{F}^0 \to \mathcal{F}^1 \to$. Suppose $\mathcal{A}$ is an arbitrary sheaf over X. Then

(7.12a) $$0 \longrightarrow \mathcal{A} \otimes \mathcal{J} \xrightarrow{1 \otimes j} \mathcal{A} \otimes \mathcal{F}^0 \xrightarrow{1 \otimes d^0} \mathcal{A} \otimes \mathcal{F}^1$$

is exact since $\mathcal{F}$ is torsion free. Thus $\mathcal{A} \otimes \mathcal{F}$ is a fine resolution, $\mathcal{A}^*$, of $\mathcal{A} \approx \mathcal{A} \otimes \mathcal{J}$.

The filtration on $S(\mathcal{A} \otimes \mathcal{F})$ will be understood to be

$$S^{(p)}(\mathcal{A} \otimes \mathcal{F}) = \oplus_{p \leq i} \oplus_j S(\mathcal{A}^i \otimes \mathcal{F}^j).$$

Let $\mathcal{G}$ be an arbitrary sheaf over X. We have defined several resolutions, namely $\mathcal{G}^* = \mathcal{T}^*$ (7.3b) the flabby resolution, $\mathcal{G}^* = \mathcal{I}^*$ an injective resolution, and $\mathcal{G}^* = \mathcal{F}^* \times \mathcal{J}$ (7.12) a fine (torsion free) and also soft resolution. If X is paracompact and locally compact, cohomology results stated below are valid with any of these resolutions (cf. (9.3c)).

Definition 7.13. $\mathcal{A}$ is **locally concentrated** on Y if for every x in Y, there is an open neighborhood $U(x)$ such that $\mathcal{A}$ induces 0 on $U(x) - U(x) \cap Y$. If $\mathcal{A}$ induces 0 in $X - Y$, then $\mathcal{A}$ is **concentrated** on Y.

Lemma 7.14. *There is a homomorphism of* $\mathcal{T}^*(\mathcal{A}) \mid Y$ *to* $\mathcal{T}^*(Y, \mathcal{A})$.

Let U be open in Y. Then $\mathcal{T}^0(\mathcal{A})(U = \Pi_{x \in U}\ \mathcal{A}(x)$. The germ of the section of $\mathcal{T}^0(X, \mathcal{A})$ at x is the germ of the serration of $\mathcal{A}$. Hence we have the homomorphism $h_x \mathscr{T}^0(\mathcal{A})(x) \to \mathcal{A}(x)$ and so with U an arbitrary set there is a homomorphism $h(U)\colon S(U, T(\mathcal{A})) \to \Pi_{x\in U}\, \mathcal{A}(x)$. Hence if $s \in S(U, \mathscr{T}^0(\mathcal{A}))$, $h(U)s$ is the element t of $\Pi_{x\in U}\, \mathcal{A}(x)$ with $t(x) = h(x)s(x)$ for $x \in U$. Accordingly a homomorphism h is defined on taking direct limits, with U open in Y

$$h\colon \mathscr{T}^0(X, \mathcal{A}) \mid Y \to \mathscr{T}^0(\mathcal{A}, Y).$$

Since $\mathscr{Z}^1(X, \mathcal{A}) = \mathscr{T}^0(\ \mathcal{A})/j\mathcal{A}$ (7.3a) it follows at once that h induces $\mathscr{Z}^1(X, \mathcal{A}) \mid Y \to \mathscr{Z}^1(Y, \mathcal{A})$. Moreover according to (7.3a) $\mathscr{T}^i(\mathcal{A})$ is merely $\mathscr{T}^0$ with $\mathcal{A}$ replaced by $\mathscr{Z}^i$. Hence the lemma's assertion is demonstrated.

Lemma 7.16. *If $\mathcal{A}$ is locally concentrated on Y, then h as defined above is an isomorphism $\mathscr{T}^*(\mathcal{A}) \mid Y \xrightarrow{h} \mathscr{T}^*(\mathcal{A}, Y)$.*

Again we note that since $\mathscr{T}^i(\mathcal{A}) = \mathscr{T}^0(\mathscr{Z}^i)$ it is sufficient to consider the case $i = 0$. Thus

$$\mathscr{T}^0(\mathcal{A})(x) = \varinjlim \Pi_{y\in U(x)}\, \mathcal{A}(y),$$
$$\mathscr{F}^0(\mathcal{A}, Y)(x) = \varinjlim \Pi_{y\in U(x)}\, \mathcal{A}(y).$$

Since for $x \in Y$ and some $U(x)$, $\mathcal{A}(y) = 0$ in $U(x) - U(x) \cap Y$, the two lines are equal for all $x \in Y$.

We remark on the criteria to be satisfied by a definition of the cohomology modules. (Cf. the comment on 9.3c.) We start with the category of sheaves over a fixed space, X. Then H^m or H^m_F is a graded functor on this category to the category of Abelian groups or modules. The properties demanded are:

(7.16a) H^m is a cohomology functor in the usual sense, (107.3), that exactness of $0 \to \mathcal{A}' \to \mathcal{A} \to \mathcal{A}' \to 0$ carries the exactness of

$$\begin{array}{ccc} H^{m+1}(X, \mathcal{A}') & \longrightarrow & H(X, \mathcal{A}) \\ & {\nwarrow}^{d} \quad \swarrow & \\ & H(X, \mathcal{A}'') & \end{array}$$

(7.16b) $H^m(X, \mathcal{A}) = 0$ for $m < 0$

(7.16c) $H^m_F(X, \mathcal{A}) = S_F(\mathcal{A})$, $m = 0$

(7.16d) $H^m_F(X, \mathcal{A}) = 0$ for $\mathcal{A}$ injective if $m > 0$,

where (7.16d) is for injective sheaves since our earlier resolutions have been injective resolutions. However every injective sheaf is flabby (6.8) and accordingly (7.8) is consistent with these conditions and in particular (7.16c) and (7.16d) are included in (7.9) and (7.12).

8. E_1 AND E_2 FOR A DG SHEAF. Let $\mathcal{G}^*$ be a DG sheaf. Let $C^* = {}_FC^*(X, \mathcal{G}^*)$ be the associated grating with supports in F. In consonance with (166.2) this is a doubly graded grating but we use the notation for complexes. Thus

$$C^* = \oplus_{i,j}\,(C^i(X, \mathcal{G}^j) = A^{ij}).$$

Review 8.1. We review some of our earlier results in Chapter 16. Thus the two filtrations are given by the direct sums,

$$(8.1a) \qquad {}_1K^{(p)} = \oplus_{i\geq p}\oplus_j\, C^i(X, \mathcal{G}^j)$$

$$(8.1b) \qquad {}_2K^{(q)} = \oplus_{j\geq q}\oplus_i\, C^i(X, \mathcal{G}^j),$$

with

$$^nK = {}^n_1K = {}^n_2K = \oplus_{i+j=n}\, C^i(X, \mathcal{G}^j)$$

If $C^i(X, \mathcal{G}^j) = 0$ for $i < 0$ and $\mathcal{G}^n = 0$, $n < 0$ are taken into account, both filtrations are strongly regular. We have

$${}_1d\colon C^p(X, \mathcal{G}^q) \to C^{p+1}(X, \mathcal{G}^q)$$

where ${}_1d$ is the d in (7.1) and ${}_2d$ is induced by the δ: $G^q \to G^{q+1}$ except that $(-1)^p$ is prefixed to the result (7.7). This assures ${}_1d\,{}_2d = -{}_2d\,{}_1d$.

Review 8.2. According to (168.2k) and (168.2l)

$$(8.2a) \qquad {}_1E_1^{pq} = {}_2H^q(A^{p*} = C^p(X, \mathcal{G}^*))$$

$$(8.2b) \qquad {}_1E_2^{pq} = {}_1H^p\,{}_2H^q(C^*).$$

By (7.6), C is an exact functor, so on replacing T by C in (4.2f), (8.2a) becomes

$$(8.2c) \qquad {}_1E_1^{pq} = C^p(X, \mathscr{H}^q(\mathcal{G}^*)).$$

Then from (8.2b) and the definition of $H(X, \mathcal{A})$, (7.8),

$$(8.2d) \qquad {}_1E_2^{pq} = {}_1H^p\, C^p(X, \mathscr{H}^q(\mathcal{G}^*)) = {}_1H^p(X, \mathscr{H}^q(\mathcal{G}^*)).$$

If we had started with the second filtration, (166.3a), the formal effect would have been to switch subscripts 1 and 2 and superscripts q and p on the right hand side of (8.2a) and (8.2b) (166.3b), (166.3c)

$$(8.2e) \qquad {}_2E_1^{qp} = {}_1H^p(C^*(X, \mathcal{G}^q)) = {}_1H^p(X, \mathcal{G}^q)$$

and ${}_1H^p(X, \mathcal{G}^*) = \oplus_q\, {}_1H^p(X, \mathcal{G}^q)$

$$(8.2f) \qquad {}_2E_2^{qp} = {}_2H^q({}_1H^p(X, \mathcal{G}^*)).$$

9. EQUIVALENCES. We shall suppose in this section, that X is locally compact and that there is a support family F consisting of either compact or paracompact sets.

Relations 9.1. Suppose $\mathcal{G}^*$ is a fine, flabby, or injective resolution of $\mathcal{G}$. We can consider also resolutions of $\mathcal{G}^i$. Thus as a parallel to (169.1)

(9.1a) $$0 \longrightarrow \mathcal{G} \xrightarrow{{}_2i} \mathcal{G}^0 \xrightarrow{{}_2d} \mathcal{G}^1 \longrightarrow \cdot \longrightarrow \cdot\, \mathcal{G}^q \longrightarrow$$

(9.1b) $$0 \longrightarrow \mathcal{G}^q \xrightarrow{{}_1i} \mathcal{G}^{0q} \xrightarrow{{}_1d} \mathcal{G}^{1q} \longrightarrow \cdots$$

Here we write $\mathcal{G}^{*q}$ for $\oplus_i \mathcal{G}^{iq}$. We can write $C^*(X, \mathcal{G}^q) = S(X, \mathcal{G}^{*q})$. In particular $C^*(X, \mathcal{G}^q) = S(X, \mathscr{T}^{*q})$ or $S(X, \mathcal{F}^* \otimes \mathcal{G}^q)$. Thus

(9.1c) $$C^*(X, \mathcal{G}^*) = \oplus\, (C^p(X, \mathcal{G}^q) = C^{pq}(X, \mathcal{G}^*)).$$

In view of (9.1a) and (7.6)

(9.1d) $$0 \longrightarrow C^p(X, \mathcal{G}) \xrightarrow{{}_2i'} C^p(X, \mathcal{G}^0) \xrightarrow{{}_2d'} C^p(X, \mathcal{G}^1) \longrightarrow$$

is exact where ${}_2i'$ and ${}_2d'$ are induced by ${}_2i$ and ${}_2d$. The following sequence is exact also:

(9.1e) $$0 \longrightarrow S(X, \mathcal{G}^q) \xrightarrow{{}_1i'} S(X, \mathcal{G}^{0q}) \xrightarrow{{}_1d'} S(X, \mathcal{G}^{1q}) \longrightarrow$$

i.e., $$0 \longrightarrow S(X, \mathcal{G}^q) \xrightarrow{{}_1i'} C^0(X, \mathcal{G}^q) \xrightarrow{{}_1d'} C^1(X, \mathcal{G}^q) \longrightarrow$$

Hence

(9.1f) $$C^{p0} \supset {}_2i'\, C^p(X, \mathcal{G}) = ker\, {}_2d',$$

(9.1g) $$C^{0q} \supset {}_1i'\, S(X, \mathcal{G}^q) = ker\, {}_1d'.$$

Lemma 9.2. *Let $\mathcal{G}^*$ be a DG sheaf over X. Let $H^m_F(X, \mathcal{G}^*) = 0$ for $m > 0$. Then there is a spectral sequence with $E_2^{pq} = H^p(X, \mathscr{H}^q(\mathcal{G}^*))$ and*

$$E_\infty = G\, H(S_F(\mathcal{G}^*)).$$

The hypotheses guarantee

$$\begin{aligned} {}_2E_2^{pq} &= {}_2H^p\, {}_1H^q_F(X, \mathcal{G}^*) = 0 \quad \text{for} \quad q > 0 \\ &= H^p\,(S_F(X, \mathcal{G}^*)) \quad \text{for} \quad q = 0. \end{aligned}$$

Then (167.8a) yields, in view of the regularity of the second filtration,

(9.2a) $$H^p(S_F(X, \mathcal{G}^*)) \approx {}^pH(C^*(X, \mathcal{G}^*)).$$

Then, ${}_1E_r^{pq}$ satisfies the assertions of the lemma. Indeed the first filtration of $C^*(X, \mathcal{G}^*)$ can be used in order to obtain a filtration of $H(S_F(X, \mathcal{G}^*))$ as described in (162.2) and (162.2b). Then

$${}_2E_\infty \approx {}_1E_\infty \approx GH(C^*(X, \mathcal{G}^*)) \approx GH(S_F(X, \mathcal{G}^*))$$

Theorem 9.3. *Let $\mathcal{G}^*$ be a resolution of $\mathcal{G}$* (7.1a). *Then*

(9.3a) $$H^p(X, \mathcal{G}) \approx H^p(C^*(X, \mathcal{G})) \approx H^p\, C^*(X, \mathcal{G}^*).$$

(9.3b) *There is a homomorphism $H\, S(X, \mathcal{G}^*) \to H(X, \mathcal{G})$.*

(9.3c) *If the resolution is flabby, or if the support family is paracompactifying, and $\mathcal{G}^*$ is F soft, then* (9.3b) *represents a bijection, and in particular for locally compact spaces,*

$$H^p(X, \mathcal{G}) \approx H^p(S(X, \mathcal{F}^* \otimes \mathcal{G})).$$

From (8.1a), (7.9), and (8.2*e*) results

$${}_2E_1^{q0} = {}_1H^0(X, \mathcal{G}^q) \approx S_F(\mathcal{G}^q).$$

Hence ${}_2E_2^{q0} = {}_2H\, S_F(\mathcal{G}^q)$. The edge homomorphisms (168.5) apply to give

(9.3d) $${}_2H^q\, S_F(\mathcal{G}^q) \to {}^qH(C^*(X, \mathcal{G}^*)).$$

Since $\mathscr{H}^q(\mathcal{G}^*) = 0$ for $q > 0$ (7.2), ${}_1E_2^{pq} = 0$ for $q > 0$. Hence according to (167.8a)

(9.3e) $$H^p(X, \mathcal{G}) \approx {}_1E_2^{p0} \approx {}^pH(C^*(X, \mathcal{G})).$$

Then (9.3d) and (9.2e) yield the homomorphism

$$H^q(S_F(\mathcal{G}^*)) \to H^q(X, \mathcal{G}).$$

Under the hypothesis (9.3c) we see that (7.12) is enough for (9.2).

The inclusion (9.3c) is an important uniqueness theorem and shows that any flabby resolution and not only the canonical one yields the same definition of the cohomology groups (up to a bijection).

Lemma 9.4. *Let Y be closed in X and let $\mathcal{A}$ be a sheaf over the paracompact space X. Then*

$$\underrightarrow{\mathsf{L}}\, H(U(Y), \mathcal{A}) \to H(Y, \mathcal{A})$$

is bijective.

The first paragraph of the demonstration of (6.12) essentially shows that if Y is closed, and B is a sheaf, any element ${}_0s \in S(Y, \mathcal{B})$, extends to a section, $s \in S(U, \mathcal{B})$, where U is some neighborhood of Y. Remark further that since $\|s_1 - s_2\|$ is closed, if s_1 and s_2 are sections coinciding on Y, they must coincide on an open set containing Y. Accordingly with $\mathcal{B} = \mathscr{T}^*(X, \mathcal{A})$ we have

(9.4a) $$S(Y, \mathscr{T}^*(X, \mathcal{A})) = \underrightarrow{\mathsf{L}}_{U(Y)} \{S(U(Y), \mathscr{T}^*(X, \mathcal{A})), r^{U(Y)}{}_{V(Y)}\}.$$

By (7.15) the right hand side of (9.4a) is the same as

$$\underrightarrow{\mathsf{L}}_{U(Y)}\, C^*(U, \mathcal{A}).$$

Hence by (77.17)

$$H^*S(Y, \mathscr{T}^*(X, \mathcal{A})) = \varinjlim H^*(C^*(U, \mathcal{A})).$$

Now $\mathscr{T}^*(X, \mathcal{A}) \mid Y$ is a resolution of $\mathcal{A} \mid Y$. Since X is paracompact, $\mathscr{T}^*(X, \mathcal{A})$ is a soft sheaf and hence since the restriction of a soft sheaf to a closed set is plainly soft, $\mathscr{T}^*(X, \mathcal{A}) \mid Y$ is soft. By (9.3c) we infer $H(C^*(X, \mathcal{A})) \mid Y = H(S(Y, \mathscr{T}^*(X, \mathcal{A}))Y) = H(Y, \mathcal{A})$.

PROBLEM

17-12. Show that if Y is an arbitrary subset of a metric space, (9.4) is valid. *Hint:* $S(Y, \mathcal{A})$ extends to $S(X, \mathcal{A})$.

We now present our most general form of the exact cohomology sequence for a pair X, Y. The coefficient sheaf, $\mathcal{G}$, is a sheaf of R modules where R is a principal ideal domain and under certain circumstances Y need not be closed in X. We utilize the injective resolution of (7.4a). We require the definition

$$H^p(X, Y, \mathcal{G}) = \varinjlim_{U \supset Y} \{H^p(X, U, \mathcal{G}), r^{U(Y)*}{}_{V(Y)}\}$$

Theorem 9.5. *If X is paracompact and Y is a closed subset, or if X is metric and Y is an arbitrary subset, then*

$$\longrightarrow H^p(X, Y, \mathcal{G}) \longrightarrow H^p(X, \mathcal{G}) \longrightarrow H^p(Y, \mathcal{G}) \xrightarrow{d} H^{p+1}(X, Y, \mathcal{G}) \longrightarrow$$

is exact.

We use injective resolutions (7.4a). Since $\mathscr{I}^*(X, \mathcal{G})$ is flabby (6.16), $S(\mathscr{I}^*(X, \mathcal{G})) \xrightarrow{j} S(\mathscr{I}^*(X, \mathcal{G}) \mid U) \rightarrow 0$, is exact for every open U. The sections of *ker* j are cochains which vanish on U or, alternatively expressed have their supports in $X - U$. Then since any sheaf over X is obviously locally concentrated on any open set, the hypotheses of (7.16) are met and $\mathscr{I}^*(X, \mathcal{G}) \mid U$ can be replaced by $\mathscr{I}^*(U, \mathcal{G})$. We have the exact sequence

(9.5a) $$0 \longrightarrow \ker j \xrightarrow{j} S(\mathscr{I}^*(X, \mathcal{G})) \xrightarrow{j} S(\mathscr{I}^*(U, \mathcal{G})) \longrightarrow 0.$$

We use the notation $S_{X,U}$ $(\mathscr{I}^*(X, \mathcal{G}))$ for *ker* j. There results

(9.5b) $$H^p(X, U, \mathcal{G}) \longrightarrow H^p(X, \mathcal{G}) \longrightarrow H^p(U, \mathcal{G}) \longrightarrow H^{p+1}(X, U, \mathcal{G})$$

If V is open and $V \subset U$, there is a restriction homomorphism of the sequence of (9.5b) into one with V in place of U. Hence the direct limit may be taken in each column. With either of the conditions of the hypotheses on X, Y

we are assured $\underrightarrow{\mathsf{L}}_{U \supset Y}\ H^p(U, \mathcal{G}) = H^p(Y, \mathcal{G})$ since (9.4) and Problem 17-12 cover both cases.

When $\mathcal{G}$ is a constant sheaf with $\mathcal{G} = R \times X$ and X is locally compact also, then the cohomology groups in this sequence are those arising from a full or a complete grating.

Remark. It is not true that the closed sets of U constitute a subfamily of those of X.

We give an indication of possible applications.

EXAMPLE 17-13. Suppose $M = \{x\}$ is a C^∞ manifold (126.1). Let $A(x)$ be the vector space of elements $\{a(x) = [a]_x\}$ where a is a real valued function in C^∞ $(U(x))$, for $U(x)$ a neighborhood of x. Thus $[b]_x = [a]_x$ if, for some $V(x)$, $b \mid V(x) = a \mid V(x)$. The topology in $\mathcal{A}$ is given by a basis of open sets $\{[a]_y \mid a \in C^\infty,\ y \in (U(x)\}$ cf. (5.2). Let T_x be a linear operator on $A(x)$ to $A(x)$, for instance T_x may be an integral or a partial differential operator. For T_x to be a homomorphism on $A(x)$ to $A(x)$ it is necessary that if a' and a'' belong to $[a]_x$, then $T_x a' = T_x a''$. This is ensured by the requirement that if u is a local unit, i.e., $u(y) = 1$, $y \in U(x)$, then

(a) $$T_x ua = T_x a, \quad a \in [b]_x.$$

Assume **(a)** satisfied. Furthermore, if $a \in C^\infty\ U(x)$ assume $T_y a = T_x a$, $y \in U(x)$. Accordingly $T = \{T_x\}$ constitutes a homomorphism of $\mathcal{A}$ to $\mathcal{A}$. In view of **(a)** we can define a sheaf by

$$(\mathit{ker}\ T)(x) = \{[b]_x \mid T_x a = 0,\ a \in [b]_x\}.$$

Define $(\mathit{Im}\ T)$ by

$$(\mathit{Im}\ T)(x) = \{[T_x a]_x \mid a \in [b]_x\}.$$

Then the following sheaf sequence is exact:

$$0 \longrightarrow \mathit{ker}\ T \xrightarrow{\ i\ } \mathcal{A} \longrightarrow \mathit{Im}\ T \longrightarrow 0.$$

The induced cohomology sequence is (1.12), (2.5)

$$0 \longrightarrow S(\mathit{ker}\ T) \longrightarrow S(\mathcal{A}) \longrightarrow S(\mathit{Im}\ T) \longrightarrow H^1(\mathit{ker}\ T) \longrightarrow \cdots$$

The proof that the Alexander grating is fine (86.3) carries over when the cochains are infinitely differentiable on M. In the case of the 0 dimensional cochains, this implies the associated sheaf, namely $\mathcal{A}$, is fine. Hence $H^m(\mathcal{A}) = 0$, $m \geq 1$. Accordingly

$$H^1(\mathit{ker}\ T) \approx S(\mathit{Im}\ T)/S(\mathcal{A})$$

and

$$H^m(\mathit{Im}\ T) \approx H^{m+1}(\mathit{ker}\ T), \quad m \geq 1, \text{ etc.}$$

PROBLEM

17-13. Define the homomorphism T for the example above by considering the presheaves.

10. MAPS. Throughout the present section ψ will denote a map of X to Y. We remark on the rationale governing the utilization of support families. The crucial property of a sheaf $\mathcal{B}$ or a resolution $\mathcal{B}^*$ in applications we have in mind is that it be acyclic, i.e., $H^m(W, \mathcal{B}) = 0$ or $H^m(X, \mathcal{B}^*) = 0$ for $m > 0$. The sheaf $\mathcal{B}$ may enter as $\psi_{\#} \mathcal{A}$ or $\psi_F \mathcal{A}$ or $\psi^{\#} \mathcal{A}$ and W is either X or Y. Specifically for $\psi_{\#} \mathcal{A}$ it is sufficient that $\mathcal{A}$ be flabby (or injective) (6.13). Suppose now that X_0 is locally closed in X. In practice $X_0 = \psi^{-1} Y_0$. To guarantee $\mathcal{A}^* \mid X_0$ is an acyclic resolution of $\mathcal{A} \mid X_0$ it is sufficient that $\mathcal{A}^*$ be soft. If X_0 is open it is obviously sufficient also that $\mathcal{A}^*$ be flabby. If $\mathcal{A}^*$ is an F soft resolution then $\mathcal{A}^* \mid X_0$ is an $F \mid X_0$ soft resolution. However since $\psi_F \mathcal{B}$ is not necessarily G soft when $\mathcal{B}$ is F soft, $\psi_F \mathcal{B}$ may not be G acyclic. Accordingly if $\mathcal{A}^* \mid X_0$ is to be an acyclic resolution of $\mathcal{A} \mid X_0$ by $F \mid X_0$ acyclic sheaves with $\psi_F \mathcal{A}^m$, $G \mid \psi X$ acyclic for all m, it is sufficient to require **(a)** that $\mathcal{A}^*$ be F soft and that F and G be very well adapted where G refers to a paracompactifying family, or **(b)** that X_0 be open and that $\mathcal{A}^*$ be a flabby resolution since $\psi_F \mathcal{A}$ is always G soft for G paracompactifying. (It is true that injective can replace flabby in (b) and that X_0 closed can be handled if X is a special space say metric). We write **Abelian sheaf** for sheaf of Abelian groups.

Remark. Acyclicity with respect to a support family such as G above will not be confused of course with the functor acyclicity defined in (169.3).

Lemma 10.1. *Let W be a covariant functor on an Abelian category $\mathfrak{C}$ to the category of Abelian sheaves over X and suppose there are enough injectives in $\mathfrak{C}$ (so that W^i exists). Let $K^*(C)$ be an injective resolution of $C \in \mathfrak{C}$. Then the sheaf* $\mathrm{W}^i(C) = \underrightarrow{\mathsf{L}} \{H(S(U, WK^*(C))\}$.

Recall the definition

$$\mathrm{W}^q(C) = H^q\, WK(C).$$

Next for a DG sheaf, $\mathcal{A}^*$, the sheaf $Z^m(\mathcal{A}^*)$ is derived from the presheaf $\{Z^m\, S(U, \mathcal{A}^*)\}$ and $\mathcal{B}^m(\mathcal{A}^*)$ from $\{B^m\, S(U, \mathcal{A}^*)\}$. Then by (77.17) and Example 17-8

$$\mathscr{H}^m(\mathcal{A})(x) = \underrightarrow{\mathsf{L}}_{U(x)} \left\{\frac{Z^m\, S(U, \mathcal{A}^*)}{B^m\, S(U, \mathcal{A}^*)}\right\} = \underrightarrow{\mathsf{L}}_{U(x)} \{H^m\, S(U, \mathcal{A}^*)\}$$

$$= H^m \{\underrightarrow{\mathsf{L}}_{U(x)}\, S(U, \mathcal{A}^*)\} = H^m(A(x)).$$

Finally identify $\mathcal{A}^*$ with $WK^*(\mathrm{C})$

Theorem 10.2. *Suppose F and G are support families where either F consists of all closed sets and G is arbitrary or G is paracompactifying. Let $\mathcal{C}$ be a sheaf of Abelian groups on X. Then $\psi^q_F(\mathcal{C})$ can be identified with the sheaf derived from the presheaf $\{H^q_{F(U)}(\psi^{-1}(U), \mathcal{C}), r^U{}_V\}$. There is a spectral sequence with*

(10.2a) $$E_2^{pq} = H^p_G(Y, \psi^q_F(\mathcal{C}))$$

(10.2b) $$E_\infty^{pq} = G^n H_{F'}(X, \mathcal{C}) = \frac{{}^nH^{(pq)}_{F'}(X, \mathcal{C})}{{}^nH^{(p+1\, q-1)}_{F'}(X, \mathcal{C})}$$

where F' is $F(Y)$ (81.15).

Let $\mathcal{K}^*(\mathcal{C})$ be an injective and therefore a flabby resolution (6.16), for instance $\mathcal{K}^*(\mathcal{C}) = \mathcal{I}^*(X, \mathcal{C})$. The definition of $S(U, \psi_F\, \mathcal{K}^*)$ is

$$S_{F(U)}(\psi^{-1}(U), \mathcal{K}^*), \quad (3.2).$$

Then (10.1) yields

(10.2c) $$\psi^q_F(\mathcal{C})(y) = \varinjlim_{U(y)} \{H^q_{F(U)}(\psi^{-1}(U), \mathcal{K}^*(\mathcal{C}))\}$$

when F is the family of closed sets but the argument which is that of (77.16) is the same for a general F. The point to check is that the support family $F(U)$ goes into $\psi(V)$ under $r^U{}_V$ and this is covered by $F(U) \cap \psi^{-1}(V) \subset F(V)$. Of course just as in (10.1), $\mathcal{K}^m(\mathcal{C}) \mid \psi^{-1}(U)$ is flabby since $\mathcal{K}^m(\mathcal{C})$ is. We turn to (169.4) and make the following identification; $\mathfrak{C}$ is the category of Abelian sheaves over X, $\mathfrak{C}'$ the category of Abelian sheaves over Y and $\mathfrak{C}''$ the category of Abelian groups over Y. Also $U = \psi_F$, $V = S_G$. We obtain the group of sections over a support family F' where we write

(10.2d) $$S_{F'}(\mathcal{A}) = S_G(\psi_F\, \mathcal{A}).$$

Here F' consists of the closed sets of X which are in $F(Y)$ (81.15) and $F' = F$ if F and G are very well adapted. For instance this would be the case when F and G consist of all closed sets. The condition, V is left exact in (169.4), is met by S_G. We now verify the other condition, namely $U(\mathcal{A})$ is V acyclic for $\mathcal{A}$ injective. That is to say $\psi_F(\mathcal{A})$ is S_G acyclic for an injective $\mathcal{A} \in \mathfrak{C}$. That this is so is the content of (6.13) and (7.12). Thus depending on which of the two support conditions in the statement of (10.2) we take, $\psi_F(\mathcal{C})$ yields either a flabby or a G-soft sheaf. The acyclicity is then guaranteed by (7.12) in either case. The conclusion of (169.4) is precisely that announced in (10.2), viz

$$\begin{aligned} E_2^{pq} &= \overset{p}{S}_G(\overset{q}{\psi}_F(\mathcal{C})) \\ &= H^p(S_G(Y, \mathcal{K}^*(\overset{q}{\psi}_F(\mathcal{C})))), \end{aligned}$$

where $\mathcal{K}^*$ is an injective or, more generally, a flabby resolution so that (10.2a) now follows by (9.3c)

$$E_2^{pq} = H^p(Y, \overset{q}{\psi}_F(\mathcal{C})).$$

Finally with $VU = S_F$, according to (10.2d) and (169.4)

$$^nE_\infty^{pq} = {}^nH^{(pq)}(S_{F'}(\mathscr{K}^*(\mathfrak{C})))/{}^nH^{(p+1\,q-1)}(S_{F'}(\mathscr{K}^*(\mathfrak{C})))$$

which is equivalent to (10.2b). (Of course if F and G constitute all closed sets then F and F' drop out of (10.2a) and (10.2b) and the result is valid with no restrictions on the spaces X or Y). However the interpretation of (10.2c) will generally introduce special conditions. The sheaf defined by (10.2c) is referred to as the **Leray sheaf** and is often indicated by $\mathscr{H}_F^q(\psi^{-1}(y), \mathfrak{C})$ rather than $\psi_F^q(\mathfrak{C})(y)$.

Theorem 10.3. *For each y and basis $\{U(y)\}$ suppose $\{\psi^{-1}\,U(y)\}$ constitutes a neighborhood basis for $\psi^{-1}(y)$ or suppose ψ is open. Let X be paracompact and let $\mathfrak{C}$ be an arbitrary sheaf over X. There is a bijection $\psi^q(\mathfrak{C})(y) \to H^q(\psi^{-1}(y), \mathfrak{C})$.*

Substantiation comes from (9.4) under the hypotheses on $\{\psi^{-1}(U)\}$

Corollary 10.4. *Let X and Y be locally compact and suppose ψ is proper* (81.12). *Then* (10.3) *is valid.*

It is easy to see $\psi^{-1}(U)$ is a neighborhood basis for $\psi^{-1}(y)$ with $V(y) \subset \bar{V}$ a compact set. Moreover X can be replaced by some compact set containing $\psi^{-1}(y)$, (say $\psi^{-1}\bar{V}(y)$ for a fixed $\bar{V}(y)$).

In application to mapping problems the situations of interest are usually those for which the Leray sheaf is either simple or locally simple. Then in (10.2a) $\mathscr{H}^q(\psi^{-1}(y), \mathfrak{C}) = \psi^q(\mathfrak{C})$ can be replaced by a module in the first case, or by a sum of modules each over one of the sets of a partition of Y. We take up a special case where this is possible.

Lemma 10.5. *Let Y be connected and compact and let W be locally compact. Let $i(y)$ be the inclusion map of $W \times y \to W \times Y$. Then $i^*(y)$ is a module isomorphism of $H^*(W \times Y, R) \to H^*(W \times y, R)$ which is independent of y. (The cohomology modules can be those for a full or for a singular grating.)*

Let $r(y_0)$ map Y onto y_0. Then $(r(y_0) \times 1) \cdot i(y_0)$ is the identity map whence $((r(y_0) \times 1) \cdot i(y_0)$ is the identity isomorphism. Hence $i(y_0)^*$ is an epimorphism.

Let $h(y_0)$: $W \to W \times y_0$ where $h(y_0)(w) = w \times y_0$. Define ψ by $\psi(w, y_0) = i(y_0)h(y_0)$. Then ψ is proper and is a homotopy (where Y is identified with T in (95.3)). Hence by (95.3) or (95.7), $\psi^* = h(y_0)^*\, i(y_0)^*$ is independent of y_0 on $H^*(W \times Y)$ to $H^*(W)$ and since $h(y_0)^*$ is plainly the identity isomorphism, $ker\ i(y)^* = ker\ \psi^*$.

Let X, Y, p be a mapping triple with $p^{-1}(y)$ homeomorphic to $p^{-1}(y_0) = W \subset X$ (homotopy equivalence would be enough). We require of a fiber space in the following theorem merely that it be such a mapping triple with $p^{-1}\,\bar{U}(y)$ homeomorphic to $\bar{U}(y) \times W$ for each y and some neighborhood $U(y)$.

Theorem 10.6. *Let X, Y, p be a fiber space with X and Y locally compact and with Y locally connected. Let $\mathfrak{C}$ be a constant sheaf $Y \times R$. Then the Leray sheaf $\mathscr{H}^*(p^{-1}(y), \mathfrak{C})$ is locally simple and is locally isomorphic to $H^*(W, R)$. (Either full or singular gratings can be used for the cohomology modules.)*

Since a fiber bundle is locally a product space for each $y_0 \in Y$, there are neighborhoods $V(y_0) \subset \bar{V}(y_0) \subset U(y_0)$ such that $\bar{V}(y_0)$ is compact and connected and $p^{-1}\,\bar{V}(y_0)$ is homeomorphic to $\bar{V}(y_0) \times W$. Then by (10.5) there is an isomorphism of $H^*(W \times \bar{V}(y_0))$ and $H^*(W \times y_0)$ which is independent of the choice of y in $V(y_0)$. Accordingly in view of (10.3) there is a bijection of the Leray sheaf and the constant sheaf $H^q(\psi^{-1}(\bar{V}(y_0)), R) \times \bar{V}(y_0)$.

Remark. The conclusion that the Leray sheaf is simple is available, for instance, if in (10.6) Y is arcwise connected and locally connected, and $\pi(Y, y_0) = 0$, or if G is compact and connected and X is locally connected and $\boldsymbol{P} = (X, B, G, p)$ is a principal fiber bundle.

The power of theorems like (9.4) and (10.3) or (10.6) can be tested immediately by applying them to the proof of the following fundamental result.

Theorem 10.7 (Vietoris-Begle). *Let X and Y be paracompact and locally compact and suppose F and G are well adapted support families on X and Y respectively, or that ψ is open. Let $\mathcal{A}$ be the constant sheaf R on X. Suppose $\psi^{-1}(x)$ is acyclic in dimensions $\leq N$. Then*

$$H^i_G(Y, R) \xrightarrow[\approx]{\psi^*} H^i_F(X, R), \quad i \leq N.$$

According to (10.2)

(10.7a) $$E_2^{p0} = H^p_G(Y, R),$$

$$E_2^{pq} = 0, \quad 0 < q < N + 1.$$

These are the hypotheses of (167.8), whence by (167.8a)

(10.7b) $$E_2^{p0} \approx H^p_F(X, R), \quad p < N + 1$$

Remark. If $\psi^{-1}(y)$ consists of n acyclic components, $n > 1$, then (10.2a) and (167.8) apply but even for $n = 2$ and R a field one *cannot* conclude from (105.8) that

$$H^p(Y, R) \oplus H^p(Y, R) \approx H^p(X, R). \tag{10.7c}$$

A counter instance is $X, Y = S^m, P^m$. The rub is that just as the bundle S^m, P^m, T_2, p is nontrivial so too the Leray sheaf $\bigcup H^0(\psi^{-1}(y), R)$ is here nonsimple. (If the Leray sheaf is simple then (10.7c) holds for general n as well and torsion in R is included under (105.8).)

Relations 10.8. Let $\mathcal{A}$ and $\mathcal{B}$ be sheaves on X and on Y respectively. Suppose that $\psi: X \to Y$ and that λ on $\mathcal{B}$ to $\mathcal{A}$ is a ψ-sheaf homomorphism Let us suppose also that $\psi^{-1}(G) \subset F$ where F and G are support families over X and Y respectively. Since $\psi^{\#}$ is an exact functor, (6.9), a flabby resolution of $\mathcal{B}$, say $\mathscr{T}^*(Y, \mathcal{B})$, is taken into a resolution, $\psi^{\#} \mathscr{T}^*(Y, \mathcal{B})$, of $\psi^{\#} \mathcal{B}$. Combining (9.1b) and (9.3b) we have

$$H^* (S_F(\psi^{\#} \mathscr{T}^*(Y, \mathcal{B}))) \xrightarrow{\Phi^*} H^*_F(X, \psi^{\#} \mathcal{B}).$$

Observe further that $\mathscr{T}^*(Y, \mathcal{B}) \to \psi^{\#} \mathscr{T}^*(Y, \mathcal{B})$ implies $S_G \mathscr{T}^*(Y, \mathcal{B}) \to S_F \psi^{\#} \mathscr{T}^*(Y, \mathcal{B})$ (since $\psi^{-1}(G) \subset F$) whence

$$H_G (Y, \mathcal{B}) \xrightarrow{\psi^*} H(S_F(\psi^{\#} \mathscr{T}^*(Y, \mathcal{B}))).$$

Accordingly, $H^*_G(Y, \mathcal{B}) \xrightarrow{\Phi^*\psi^*} H^*_F(X, \psi^{\#} \mathcal{B})$.

We can combine $\psi^{\#}$ with the homomorphism induced by ρ in Problem 17-5, namely

$$H^*_F(X, \psi^{\#} \mathcal{B}) \xrightarrow{\rho^*} H^*_F(X, \mathcal{A}), \tag{10.8a}$$

to get the fundamental relation

$$\theta^* = \rho^* \Phi^* \psi^*$$

$$H^*_G(Y, \mathcal{B}) \xrightarrow{\theta^*} H^*_F(X, \mathcal{A}). \tag{10.8b}$$

A special important case is that of constant sheaves, $\mathcal{B} = R \times Y$ and $\mathcal{A} = R' \times X$. Then, writing for instance $H(X, R' \times X)$ as $H(X, R')$, one obtains the conventional homomorphism, slightly generalized to include changes of coefficient ring, and if $R = R'$, one winds up with $H^*(Y, R) \to H^*(X, R)$.

Since so many sphere mapping conclusions follow from it we include the cup product in the formulation of the Gysin sequence.

Theorem 10.9. Gysin. *Let X be compact, and suppose R is either* J *or* Q. *Let $F = S^k$, $k > 0$ and suppose $\mathscr{H}(S^k)$ is the constant sheaf* (10.6). *Then, for some $\mathbf{c}^{k+1} \in H^{k+1}(B)$, there is an exact sequence*

(10.9a) $$\longrightarrow H^{n-k}(B) \xrightarrow{\cup \mathbf{c}} H^{n+1}(B) \xrightarrow{p^*} {}^{n+1}H(X) \xrightarrow{\alpha} H^{n+1-k}(B) \longrightarrow$$

(If $\mathscr{H}(S^k)$ is not the constant sheaf, replace $H^{n-k}(B)$ by $H^{n-k}(B, \mathscr{H}^k(S^k))$, etc.)

Let $\mathbf{u}$ and $\mathbf{f}$ be the generators of $H^0(S^k)$ and of $H^k(S^k)$ respectively. Write $\mathbf{v}$ for the generator of $H^0(B)$ and $\mathbf{b}$ for an arbitrary element of $H(B)$. We start with the exact sequence of (167.7) and make use of (105.8). Thus bearing in mind $H(S^k, R)$ is torsion free, $E_2^{pq} = H^p(B) \otimes H^q(F)$ and

(10.9b) $$E_2^{p0} = E_{k+1}^{p0} = H^p(B) \otimes \mathbf{u}$$

$$E_2^{p-k,\,k} = E_{k+1}^{p-k,k} = H^{p-k}(B) \otimes \mathbf{f}^k$$

Since ${}^nE_r^{pq} = 0$ for $q \neq 0, k$ when $r \geq 0$ and $d_r\colon E_r^{pq} \to E_r^{p+r,\,q-r+1}$ it follows d_r is trivial for $r \neq k+1$. Accordingly we can state

(10.9c) $$d_{k+1}(\mathbf{b} \otimes \mathbf{u}) = 0,\ d_{k+1}(\mathbf{v} \otimes \mathbf{f}^k) = \mathbf{c}^{k+1} \otimes \mathbf{u} \in E_{k+1}^{k+1\,0}$$

Consider

(10.9d) $$\begin{aligned} d(\mathbf{b} \otimes \mathbf{f}^k) &= d((\mathbf{b} \otimes \mathbf{u}) \cup (\mathbf{v} \otimes \mathbf{f}^k)) \\ &= 0 \pm (\mathbf{b} \otimes \mathbf{u}) \cup d(\mathbf{v} \otimes \mathbf{f}^k) \\ &= \pm(\mathbf{b} \otimes \mathbf{u}) \cup (\mathbf{c}^{k+1} \otimes \mathbf{u}) = \pm\,(\mathbf{b} \cup \mathbf{c}^{k+1}) \otimes \mathbf{u}. \end{aligned}$$

Hence if $(\mathbf{b} \cup \mathbf{c}^{k+1}) = 0$ indicated by $\mathbf{b} \in Ann\,\mathbf{c}$ (the annihilator of $\mathbf{c}^{k+1}$) then $\mathbf{b} \otimes \mathbf{f}^k \in Z(E_{k+1}^{p-k\,k})$. Another conclusion from (10.9d) is that $(H^{p-k-1}(B) \cup \mathbf{c}^{k+1}) \otimes \mathbf{u} = B(E_{k+1}^{p0})$. From (10.9c) follows $H^p(B) \otimes \mathbf{u} = Z(E^{p0})$ while $B(E_{k+1}^{p-k\,k})$ is manifestly 0. We make use of these facts by presently substituting in

(10.9f) $$GH(X) = E_\infty^{pq} = E_{k+2}^{pq} = Z(E_{k+1}^{pq})/B(E_{k+1}^{pq}).$$

Since ${}^nH^{(pq)} = 0$ for $q < 0$, ${}^nE_\infty^{n0} = {}^nH^{(n)}(X, R)$. Moreover the fact that ${}^nE_\infty^{n-k+i\,k-1} = 0$, $i \neq 0, k$ implies ${}^nH^{(n0)}(X, R) \approx {}^nH^{(n-k+1\,k-1)}(X, R)$. Finally (167.1b) (with $P = n - k$) guarantees ${}^nH(X, R) \approx {}^nH^{(n-k\,k)}(X, R)$. Accordingly

(10.9g) $$\begin{aligned} {}^nE_\infty^{n-k\,k} &= {}^nH^{(n-k\,k)}(X, R)/{}^nH^{(n-k+1\,k-1)}(X, R) \\ &\approx {}^nH(X, R)/{}^nH^{(n0)}(X, R) \end{aligned}$$

Also

$$ {}^nE_\infty^{n-k\,k} = (Ann\,\mathbf{c})^{n-k} \otimes \mathbf{f}^k \quad (10.9\text{f}).$$

(10.9h) $$\begin{aligned} {}^nE_\infty^{n0} &\approx {}^nH^{(n0)}(X, R) \\ &\approx {}^nH(B, R)/({}^{n-k-1}H(B, R) \cup \mathbf{c}^{k+1}) = p^*H^n(B, R) \end{aligned}$$

The following diagram elucidates the conclusion of the argument: and in particular ρ: $\mathbf{b} \otimes \mathbf{f} = \mathbf{b}$.

(10.9i)

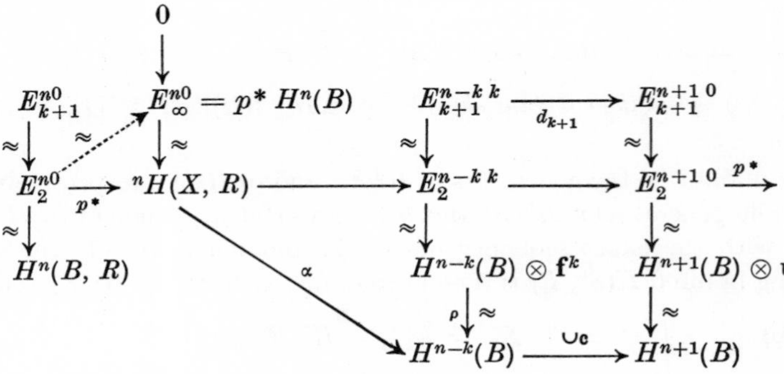

Here the horizontal sequence is exact by (167.7). Then (10.9d) indicates d_{k+1} can be replaced by $\cup\mathbf{c}$ in (10.9i). The isomorphisms listed in (10.9i) lead to (10.9a). The results of (10.9g) and (10.9h) are gratuitous.

Theorem 10.10. *If R is a field and $H^p(B) = 0$, $p > P$, $H^q(F) = 0$, $q > Q$ then*

(10.10a) $${}^nH(X) = 0, \quad n > P + Q = N$$

(10.10b) $${}^NH(X) \approx H^P(B) \otimes H^Q(Y).$$

From

$$E^{pq}_r \approx H^p(B) \otimes H^q(F)$$

we infer $E^{pq}_r = 0$ for $p > P$ or $q > Q$. Hence $E^{pq}_{\infty} = 0$ for $n > P + Q$. This establishes (10.10a) since

$$H^n(X) = \Sigma_{p+q=n}\; {}^nE^{pq}_{\infty}.$$

For (10.10b) note $E^{PQ}_2 \xrightarrow{d_3} 0$ and $d^{-1} E^{PQ}_2 \subset E^{P-2\,Q+1}_2 = 0$. Hence $E^{PQ}_2 = E^{PQ}_3 = \cdots = E^{PQ}_{\infty}$.

The following corollary is more important in applications than the theorem.

Corollary 10.11. *If R is a field and $H^i(X) = 0$ for all $i > 0$, then either $H^p(B) = H^q(F) = 0$, $p > 0$, $q > 0$ or $H^p(B) \neq 0$ for an infinite number of p values or $H^q(F) \neq 0$ for an infinite number of q values.*

A typical implication for the loop space over an arcwise connected space X, bearing in mind (146.1) and (156.3) occurs in Problem 17-14.

PROBLEM

17-14. If R is a field and $H^i(X) = 0$ for $i > N \geq 2$ while $H^N(X) \neq 0$, then $H^i(\Lambda) \neq 0$ for an infinite number of values of i. *Hint:* In the corollary make the replacements, $\Omega(x_0, X)$ for X, X for B and Λ for F.

For the remainder of this chapter in reference to fibrations the superspace is understood to be at least locally compact. Accordingly, to guarantee the existence of a principal rather than general principal bundle, we can assume from now on that the group G is a compact, Lie group. (That this does indeed ensure local triviality is a fact not proved in this book.) A **Lie group** G is a class C^∞, n manifold (96.1) admitting a group structure such that $(x, y) \to xy^{-1}$ is real analytic on $G \times G$ to G.

Definition 10.12. Let G be a compact topological group. In the principal bundle $\boldsymbol{P} = (X, B, G, p)$ suppose $H^i(X, \mathrm{J}) = 0$ for $i < n$. Then X is denoted by $E(n, G)$ and is **universal** for G in dimension n. The base space $B = E(n, G)/G$ is written $B(n, G)$ and is the **classifying** space in dimension n.

The applicability of classifying spaces rests in large part on the following lemma.

Lemma 10.13. *If B and B' are classifying spaces in dimension n for G, then*

$$H^i(B, \mathrm{J}) \approx H^i(B', \mathrm{J}), \quad i \leq n.$$

Let $X = E(n, G)$ and $Y = E'(n', G)$ be bundle spaces whose base spaces are B and B' respectively. There are two fiber bundles $[X \times Y]_G$, X/G, Y, p_1 and $[X \times Y]_G$, Y/G, X, p_2. Then $p_1^{-1}[x]_G = E'(n', G)$ is acyclic up through dimension n. Hence by (10.7), $H^i(B, \mathrm{J}) \approx H^i([X \times Y]_G, \mathrm{J}) \approx H^i(B', \mathrm{J})$ for $1 \leq n$.

Remark. Accordingly when $i < n$, $B(n, G)$ is often written B_G. We may remark that introduction of a suitable direct limit of $E(n, G)$ spaces or $B(n, G)$ spaces would allow us to drop n and to write E_G and B_G but then local compactness may be lost.

EXAMPLE 17-14. For the cyclic group of prime order p, indicated by J_p,

$$E_{J_p} = \bigcup S^{2n+1}$$

$$B_{J_p} = \bigcup (S^{2n+1}/J_p)$$

where the action of J_p is consistent with the inclusions $S^1 \subset S^3 \subset S^5 \subset$. (Neither of these spaces is locally compact.)

We take account of two homomorphisms involving classifying spaces.

Definition 10.14. If W is a closed subgroup of G, then since E_G is universal for W, there is a map $\rho(G, W)$: $B_W = E_G/W \to E_G/G = B_G$ which yields $\rho^*(G, W)$: $H^*(B_G, R) \to H^*(B_W, R)$. Transitivity is obvious. Thus if U is a closed subgroup of W, then $\rho^*(G, U) = \rho^*(W, U)\,\rho^*(G, W)$.

Remark. The interest of this definition lies in the fact that the study of quotient groups and homogeneous spaces of compact Lie groups makes essential use of ρ^* applied to maximal torus groups contained in the Lie group. For instance

$$\rho^*(SO(n), SO(n-k)) = \rho^*(T, SO(n-k))\,\rho^*(SO(n), T)$$

where T is a maximal torus group in $SO(n)$, the rotation group on R^n.

Remark. Similar developments enter with homotopy replacing omology. Thus a principal bundle $\boldsymbol{P}^n$ with group G is **homotopy** ***n*-universal** *hnu*, if X is arcwise connected and $\pi_i(X, x_0) = 0$, $i < n$. Here too, a key property reminiscent of the existence of ρ^* is: If $\boldsymbol{Q}^n$ is any bundle over a finite simplicial n-complex with structure group G, there is a bundle map on $\boldsymbol{Q}^n$ to $\boldsymbol{P}^n$. If G is a compact Lie group an *hnu* bundle exists for each n. In a slightly different direction, the counterpart for homotopy of the sphere for augmented omology is the **Eilenberg Maclane** space, $X = K(G, n)$. This is arcwise connected and satisfies: $\pi_m(K(G, n)) \approx G$ if $m = n$ and is otherwise trivial. The analogue of (10.13) is that any two such spaces are of the same homotopy type (and actually $K(G, n)$ refers to a realization by a complex).

Definition 10.15. Let $\boldsymbol{P} = (X, B, G, p)$ be a principal fiber bundle with X locally compact and connected while G is compact. Then from

$$B \xleftarrow{q} [(X \times E(n, G)]_G \xrightarrow{p} B_G$$

we infer $q^{-1}(b) = E(n, G)$ so (10.7) applies. In particular q^{*-1} is defined. Then $\sigma^* = q^{*-1}\,p^*$: $H^i(B(n, G), R) \to H^i(B, R)$. σ^* is the **characteristic map** up to dimension n and $Im\ \sigma^*$ is the **characteristic ring** of $\boldsymbol{P}$.

Remark. Various characteristic classes of recent definition are of this type. For instance with $G = O(n)$, $SO(n)$ and $U(n)$ respectively, one gets the Stiefel-Whitney, Pontrjagin and the Chern classes.

Lemma 10.16. *If X, B, G is a principal fiber bundle, there is a spectral sequence*

$$E_2^{pq} = H^p(B_G, \mathscr{H}^q(X, R)), \quad p + q \leq N$$

$$E_\infty = G\,H(X/G, R).$$

Consider the fiber bundle $[X \times E_G]_G, B_G, X, p$. Then $p^{-1}b = X$ for $b \in B_G$. Since X, B, G is a principal bundle, $G_x = e$. Hence the projection $q: [X \times E_G]_G \to X/G$ yields $q^{-1}[x] = E_G$ for $[x] \in X/G$. Since E_G is acyclic, (10.7) applies.

We give a second definition of the cohomology group of a finite group.

Definition 10.17. Let G be a finite group. Let A be a left $J(G)$ module. Then $H^*(G, A)$ is defined as $H^*(B_G, A)$. (This is consistent with (102.11) though we do not prove this.) In particular $H^0(G, A) = F(A)$ the invariant elements of A under G.

Example 17-15. $H^*(\mathrm{J}_p, \mathrm{J}_p) = P(a) \times J_p(b)$, p an odd prime where $P(a)$ is the exterior algebra generated by a and $J_p(a)$ is the truncated polynomial ring generated by b. Here dim $a = 1$, dim $b = 2$.

Definition 10.18. Let G be a finite transformation group acting freely on the left on the arcwise connected, compact space X, i.e., if $gx = x$ for any x, then $g = e$. For every x, compactness assures there is a $U = U(x)$ such that independently of $g \in G$, $U \cap gU = \varnothing$. For our purpose below any of the usual omology groups can be chosen. The important observation is that the chain or cochain groups are "G free". Thus for instance the singular chain group $C_S(X, \mathrm{J})$ obviously admits G on the left. For each singular simplex u let $G(u) = \{gu \mid g \in G\}$ be the orbit of u (132.5). Every singular simplex v is in a unique $G(u)$. Select a representative from each $G(u)$. This yields a $\mathrm{J}(G)$ basis for $C_S(X, \mathrm{J})$ and this is the sense of the term, G free, here. (The action of G on the cochains is given by $(gf)u = g(f(g^{-1}u))$. Let Y be the orbit space of X, namely X/G. Assume the Leray sheaf is simple. Then (10.15) and (10.16) yield

$$E_2^{pq} = H^p(B_G, H^q(X, \mathrm{J})) = H^p(G, H^q(X, \mathrm{J})) \tag{10.18a}$$

$$E_\infty = GH(Y, \mathrm{J}). \tag{10.18b}$$

The next two theorems bring out the limitations imposed on the possible choices of a freely acting group. Here (10.18) is understood to hold.

Theorem 10.19. (a) *If* $H^q(X, \mathrm{J}) = 0$, $0 < q < n$, *then* $H^q(Y, \mathrm{J}) \approx H^q(G, \mathrm{J})$, $q < n$ *and*

$$0 \to H^n(G, \mathrm{J}) \to H^n(Y, \mathrm{J}) \to F(H^n(X, \mathrm{J})) \to H^{n+1}(G, \mathrm{J}) \to H^{n+1}(Y, \mathrm{J})$$

is exact.

The conclusions follow from (10.17), (10.18), (167.8a), and (167.8b) since $H^0(B_G, H^n(X, J)) = F(H^n(X, J))$.

Theorem 10.20. *Let $X = S^n$. Then if $n = 2m$, G is either trivial or* J_2. *If* $n = 2m + 1$

(10.20a) $$H^m(S^n/G, \mathrm{J}) \approx H^m(G, \mathrm{J}), \qquad 0 \le m < n,$$

(10.20b) $$H^m(G, \mathrm{J}) \approx H^{m+n+1}(G, \mathrm{J}), \qquad m > 0.$$

For $n = 2m$, if $g \neq e$, g must reverse orientation if G is to act freely. Since $H^q(S^n, \mathrm{J})$ is trivial for $q \neq 0, n$, (10.18a) and (167.7a) imply

(10.20c) $$0 \to H^m(G, \mathrm{J}) \to H^m(S^n/G, \mathrm{J}) \to H^{m-n}(G, \mathrm{J}) \to H^{m+1}(G, \mathrm{J}) \to$$

is exact. Since S^n/G is an n dimensional manifold, $H^m(S^n/G, \mathrm{J}) = 0$ for $m > n$. Then (10.20a) and (10.20b) follow from (10.20c) by taking $m - n < 0$ or $m - n > 0$ respectively. The universal coefficient theorem shows J can be replaced by arbitrary coefficient groups in the demonstration.

In many applications of spectral sequences, for instance to the cohomology rings of topological (Lie) groups, the notion of transgression (without sin) plays a central role. We proceed to the underlying idea.

Evidently

$$E_2^{0s} \to H(E_2^{0s}) \approx \frac{Z(E^{0s})}{0} \approx E_3^{0s} \subset E_2^{0s}.$$

On continuing we arrive at

$$E_\infty^{0s} \approx E_{s+1}^{0s} \subset E_2^{0s} \approx H^0(B, \mathscr{H}(F_b, R)).$$

On the other hand

$$E_2^{s+1\ 0} \to H(E_2^{s+1\ 0}) = \frac{E_2^{s+1\ 0}}{B(E_2^{s+1\ 0})}$$

so for a certain subgroup L identified as *ker* q^* in (10.21a),

$$p_{s+1}^2 \colon E_2^{s+1\ 0} \to E_{s+1}^{s+1\ 0} \approx H^{s+1}(B, R)/L.$$

Suppose now that X is connected and locally connected and that the Leray sheaf is simple.

Definition 10.21. Consider the diagram

(10.21a) $$\begin{array}{ccccc} H^s(F_b, \mathrm{J}) & \xrightarrow{\ \delta\ } & H^{s+1}(X, F_b) & \xleftarrow{\ q^*\ } & H^{s+1}(B) \\ & & p^* \uparrow & & \downarrow \eta^* \\ & & & H^{s+1}(B, b) & \end{array}$$

Define $T^s(F_b)$ as $\{t \mid t \in H^s(F_b), \delta t = q^*(u + ker\, q^*)$. The elements of $T(F_b)$ are **transgressive**. The restriction $\delta \mid T(F_b)$ is referred to as the **transgression** and is designated by τ.

The commutative diagram below describes the relationships.

(10.21b)

$$\begin{array}{ccccc}
E_2^{0s} \approx H^s(F_b, \mathrm{J}) & & & & \\
\uparrow & & & & \\
T^s(F_b) & \xrightarrow{\tau} & H^{s+1}(B)/ker\, q^* & \longleftarrow & H^{s+1}(B) \\
\approx \uparrow i_b^* & & \approx \uparrow \pi^* & & \approx \uparrow \pi^* \\
E_{s+1}^{0s} & \xrightarrow{d_{s+1}} & E_{s+1}^{s+1\,0} & \xrightarrow{p^2{}_{s+1}} & E_2^{s+1\,0}
\end{array}$$

EXAMPLE 17-16. Let T^1 be the circle group, i.e., $T \approx R\, mod\, 1$ or $T^1 \approx S^1$. More generally, let T^m be the torus group of order m, i.e., $T^m \approx R \times R \times \cdots R\, mod\, 1$ or $S^1 \times S^1 \times \cdots \times S^1$. Then

$$H^1(T^m, \mathrm{J}_k) \approx P(x_1, \ldots, x_m), \dim x_i = 1$$

$$H^2(B_T, \mathrm{J}_k) \approx J_k(y_1, \ldots, y_n), \dim y_i = 2$$

where P is the exterior algebra and J_k is the truncated polynomial ring over J_k. Then y_i is the map by transgression of x_i, i.e., $y_i = \tau x_i$.

PROBLEM

17-15. Let G be a compact, connected group. Let $\langle z\rangle \in H^*(G, R)$ be a transgressive element in the fiber bundle $E(n, G)$, B_G, G, p. Show that $\langle z\rangle$ is transgressive in any principal fiber bundle X, B, G with X compact connected and locally connected. (By reason of this result $\langle z\rangle$ is called a universally transgressive element.)

Theorem 10.22. *Let the coefficient ring which we generally omit refer either to* J *or to a field. Suppose* $H^u(B, R) = H^u(B) = 0$ *for* $0 < u < P$ *and suppose* $H^v(F, R) = 0$ *for* $0 < v < Q$. *Let* $N = P + Q$. *Assume that* $\pi_1(B, b_0)$ *acts simply on* $H(F, b_0)$ *or that* $\pi_1(B, b_0) = 0$. *Then there is an exact sequence*

(10.22a) $$\longrightarrow H^{n-1}(X, R) \longrightarrow H^{n-1}(F, R) \xrightarrow{\tau} H^n(B, R) \xrightarrow{p^*} H^n(X, R) \xrightarrow{i^*} H^n(F, R)$$

where τ *is the transgression and*

(10.22b) $$H^n(B) \approx H^n(X, F), \qquad 1 \leq n \leq N - 1.$$

From the Kunneth theorem (105.8), (105.9) and (105.13) with J as the coefficient group

(10.22c) $${}^mE_2^{pq} = H^p(B, H^q(F)) \approx H^p(B) \otimes H^q(F).$$

Then ${}^nE_2^{n0} = H^n(B)$ and ${}^nE_2^{0n} = H^n(F)$ are the only members of ${}^nE_2^{pq}$ which are not 0, for $0 < n < N$. Substitute $p = 0$, $a = n - 1$, $r = 2$ in (167.6a) to get the exact sequence

$$(10.22\text{d}) \qquad {}^nH(X) \xrightarrow{\delta} {}^nE_2^{0n} \to {}^{n+1}E_2^{n+1\,0}.$$

In (167.6b) take $p = n$, $a = n - 1$, $r = 2$ and get the exact sequence.

$$(10.22\text{e}) \qquad {}^{n-1}E_2^{0\,n-1} \xrightarrow{\delta} {}^nE_2^{n0} \to {}^nH(X).$$

We infer from (167.5c) the exactness of

$$(10.22\text{f}) \qquad {}^nE_2^{n0} \to {}^nH(X) \to {}^nE_2^{0n}.$$

It may be verified that the first homomorphism of (10.22f) is the last in (10.22e) and the second homomorphism in (10.22f) is the first in (10.22d). Accordingly there is exactness in

$$(10.22\text{g}) \qquad \to {}^nE_2^{n0} \to {}^nH(X) \to {}^nE_2^{0n} \xrightarrow{\delta} {}^{n+1}E_2^{n+1\,0} \to {}^{n+1}H \to$$

Then (10.22c) yields the form asserted in the theorem. Note the hypotheses imply for $n < N - 1$

$$d_2\colon E_2^{n0} \to E_2^{n+2\,-1} = 0,\ d_2\, E_2^{0n} \to E_2^{2\,n-1} = 0$$
$$d_2^{-1}\, E_2^{n0} = E_2^{n-2\,1} = 0,\ d_2^{-1}\, E_2^{0n} = E_2^{-2\,n+1} = 0.$$

Accordingly ${}^nE_2^{0n} \approx {}^nE_{n+1}^{0n}$, $E_2^{n+1\,0} \approx E_{n+1}^{n+1\,0}$. This indicates that $T^n(F_b)$ is here $H^n(F_b)$. The following diagram is commutative

$$\begin{array}{ccc} E_{n+1}^{n+1\,0} & \xleftarrow{d_n} & E_n^{0n} \\ \uparrow{\scriptstyle p^2{}_{n+1}} & & \downarrow{\scriptstyle i_{b*}\ \approx} \\ E_2^{n+1\,0} & \xleftarrow{d_2} & E_2^{0n} \end{array}$$

where the notation is that of (10.21). Accordingly (10.21) makes clear that τ in (10.22a)) is the transgression.

To establish (10.22b) place the cohomology sequence for the pair X, F under that of (10.13a) with $H(X, F)$ under $H(B)$. Then apply the 5-lemma (101.2).

APPENDIX

1. NOTATION. We employ the following conventions: $\{x \mid P\}$ is the collection of elements x with property P. If A is a collection of indices then $\{x_a \mid A\}$ is the totality of elements x_a where a varies over A. The common part of the sets S and T is called their **intersection** and indicated by writing $T \cap S$, or in the case of the sets $\{S_a \mid A\}$ we write $\bigcap_A S_a$. The points in either S or T or in at least one member of $\{S_a \mid A\}$ are indicated by $S \cup T$ or $\bigcup_A S_a$. Set inclusion is indicated by $A \subset B$. The **power** or **cardinal number** of elements in the set A is denoted by $|A|$. Set complementation will be indicated by $A^\sim$ or $-A$. Thus the set of points of B which are not in A is written $B \cap A^\sim$ or $B - A$. The empty set is denoted by the Scandinavian $\varnothing$. **Denumerable** precludes **finite. Countable** is used in the sense of either finite or denumerable. A **partition** of A, $P(A)$, is a sectioning of A into mutually exclusive sets whose union is A. A deviation from current practice is our use of $\{x\}$ to denote a collection and not a singleton. In the absence of indications on Σ, the index summed will appear both as a subscript and as a superscript.

The following notations are invariable: δ_{ab} or δ_a^b is a Kronecker delta, i.e., $\delta_{aa} = \delta_a^a = 1$, $\delta_a^b = 0$ for $a \neq b$. In the context of sets π denotes a finite subset.

2. ORDER. Definition 2.1. A set A is **ordered** if there is a **transitive** relation indicated by $<$ (or $>$) between some of the elements of A, i.e., if $a_1 < a_2$, $a_2 < a_3$ then $a_1 < a_3$. We assume there is at least one pair a_1, a_2 in the correspondence $<$. We say a_2 **follows** a_1 if $a_1 < a_2$. We refer to A as an ordered system. A is **reflexively** ordered if $a < a$ and is **properly** ordered if $a < b < a$ implies $a = b$. The order relation $<$ is **symmetric** if $a < b$ implies $b < a$. An order relation which is symmetric and reflexive (and transitive) is called an **equivalence** and is often denoted by R.

Definition 2.2. B is an ordered subsystem of A if $B \subset A$ and $b < b'$ for elements of $B \Leftrightarrow b < b'$ considered as elements of A.

Definition 2.3. An ordered set A is a **directed** set if it is reflexively ordered and for each pair a_1, a_2 in A there is an a_3 which follows both a_1 and a_2. A directed set is often indicated by writing $\{A, <\}$.

Definition 2.4. A system of subsets of a set A is **ordered by inclusion** if, for A' and A'' in A, $A' \subset A'' \Leftrightarrow A' < A''$. The ordering is proper and reflexive.

Definition 2.5. The directed set $\{A_1, <_1\}$ is a **subset** of the directed set $\{A, <\}$ if it is an ordered subsystem of $\{A, <\}$. Accordingly if A_1 is a subset of A we shall not distinguish the order symbols (thus we write $<$ in place of $<_1$).

Definition 2.6. $\{A', <\}$ is **cofinal** in the directed set $\{A, <\}$ if $a \in A \Rightarrow$ there is an element a' in A' with $a < a'$.

Definition 2.7. $\{A', <\}$ is the **residual** set determined by a in $\{A, <\}$ if $A' = \{a' \mid a < a'\}$.

3. TOPOLOGICAL SPACES. Definition 3.1. A point set S is a **topological space** or **space** if to every point s there correspond subsets of S called **neighborhoods** and denoted by $U(s)$ subject to the following restrictions.

N 1. For every s there is at least one $U(s)$ and $s \in U(s)$.
N 2. For any pair $U(s)$, $U'(s)$ there is a $U''(s)$ contained in their intersection.
N 3. For every $s \in U(s_0)$ and some $U'(s)$, $U'(s) \subset U(s_0)$. We shall understand that $U(s)$ is a neighborhood of every point contained in it, and refer to $\mu = \{U(s) \mid S\}$ as a **neighborhood base** for S. More generally, N3′, we require the existence of $U'(s) \subset U(s_0)$ for every s in some $U''(s_0) \subset U(s_0)$, only.

Definition 3.2. A point $s \in S'$, $S' \subset S$ is an **inner** or **interior point** of S' if for some $U(s)$, $U(s) \subset S'$. $A_- = \{s \mid s \text{ is an inner point of } A\}$ is the **open kernel** of A. A is an **open set** if $A = A_-$.

Definition 3.3. A is **closed** if $A^\sim$ is open. A is **locally closed** if $A = G \cap F$ where G is open and F is closed. $\bar{A}$ is the minimal closed set containing $\bar{A}$ and is called the **closure** of A.

Definition 3.4. B is the **boundary** or **frontier** of A if $B = \bar{A} \cap \overline{A^\sim}$ and is then often written $\dot{A}$.

Definition 3.5. A **topology** for a topological space is constituted by the assignment of all the open sets (or closed sets) of the space. The topology is said to be **induced** by the neighborhood base $\mu = \{U(s)\}$ and is indicated by the notation $T(\mu)$.

Definition 3.6. A topology in which every set is open (and therefore closed) is called **discrete** and a space with this topology is a **discrete space.**

Definition 3.7. If μ and ν represent neighborhood bases for S, then $T(\mu)$ is **stronger** or **coarser** than $T(\nu)$ or equivalently $T(\nu)$ is **weaker** or **finer** than $T(\mu)$, indicated by $T(\mu) < T(\nu)$, if every set open under $T(\mu)$ is open under $T(\nu)$. Thus the discrete topology is the weakest or finest. $T(\mu)$ is **equivalent** to $T(\nu)$ if $T(\mu) < T(\nu) < T(\mu)$.

Definition 3.8. The sets in $\mu_0 = \{U(s_0)\}$ constitute a **base at the point** s_0 if every open set containing s_0 includes a $U(s_0)$ in μ_0. *A* collection $\nu = \{V(s_0)\}$ of open sets each containing s_0 is an **equivalent base** at s_0 if every $U(s_0)$ contains some $V(s_0)$ in ν and conversely.

Definition 3.9. The space S is **regular** if every neighborhood $U(s_0)$ contains the closure of a neighborhood $U'(s_0)$.

Lemma 3.10. *Let* $\{G_a \mid A\}$ *be a collection of open subsets and let* $\{F_a \mid A\}$ *be a collection of closed subsets of a topological space and let* π *be a finite subset of* A. *Then* $\bigcap_\pi G_a$ *and* $\bigcup_A G_a$ *are open sets while* $\bigcap_A F_a$ *and* $\bigcup_\pi F_a$ *are closed sets.*

Definition 3.11. If S' is a subset of a space S then the **relative topology** of S' or the topology **induced** in S' is that determined by selecting $\{U(s') \cap S')$ as the neighborhood base where $\{U(s)\} = \mu$ is a neighborhood base of S. Equivalently, open (closed) sets in S' are the intersections with S' of sets open (closed) in S. We then refer to S' as a topological **subspace** of S.

Definition 3.12. A space satisfies:

(a) the **first countability axiom** if a countable neighborhood base exists at every point;

(b) the **second countability axiom** if a countable neighborhood base exists for the space.

4. TRANSFORMATIONS. **Definition 4.1.** Let S and T be point sets whose generic points are denoted by s and t respectively. For each s in S' let f determine a point, set denoted by $f(s)$, in T. The subset S' is the **domain** of f and is indicated by $D(f)$ or D_f. The set $\bigcup_s f(s)$ is referred to as the **range** of f and is indicated by $R(f)$ or R_f. f is said to be **on** $D(f)$ **to**, or **into**, T or

onto $R(f)$. If $f(s \mid S')$ is a point of T then f is **single valued** on S'. If $f(s_0)$ is not a single point f is **multivalued** at s_0 or **on** any set in $D(f)$ which contains s_0. f^{-1} is the transformation on $R(f)$ into T or onto $D(f)$ defined by $f^{-1}(t \mid R(f)) = \{s \mid f(s) \supset t\}$. f^{-1} is referred to as the **inverse transformation** to f.

If S is a directed set then the single valued functions are sometimes referred to as **generalized sequences** or **hypersequences** and are written $\{f_x \mid S\}$ as well as $f(-)$. When S is the directed set $\{n \mid n = 1, 2 \cdots\}$ ordered by size, the function with function values $\{f_n\}$ is called a **sequence**.

Definition 4.2. Let $\{x(a \mid A)\}$ be a generalized sequence on A to S. Then $\bar{x}$ is a **limit** if for every neighborhood of $\bar{x}$, $U(\bar{x})$, there is a set $A' = \{a' \mid a < a'\}$ for which $\{x(a' \mid A')\} \subset U(\bar{x})$ and then $\{x(a \mid A)\}$ **converges** to $\bar{x}$.

The point $\bar{x}$ is a **cluster point** if for every neighborhood of $\bar{x}$, $U(\bar{x})$, there is a cofinal set A'' for which $\{x(a \mid A'')\} \subset U(\bar{x})$.

Definition 4.3. The point x is a **limit point** of a subspace S' if every neighborhood of x contains at least two points of S'.

Definition 4.4. If S and T are topological spaces the transformation f on S onto $R(f) \subset T$ is $\begin{matrix}\textbf{closed}\\ \textbf{open}\end{matrix}$ if $\begin{matrix}\text{closed}\\ \text{open}\end{matrix}$ sets in S are taken into sets $\begin{matrix}\text{closed}\\ \text{open}\end{matrix}$ in the relative topology of $R(f)$ $\left(\text{though not necessarily } \begin{matrix}\text{closed}\\ \text{open}\end{matrix} \text{ in } T\right)$.

Definition 4.5. If S and T are topological spaces the single valued transformation f on S onto $R(f)$ is **continuous** at s_0 if the transformation f^{-1} takes a neighborhood of $f(s_0)$ into a set containing a neighborhood of s_0 and is **continuous** *on* S if f^{-1} is an open transformation on $R(f)$ onto $D(f)$. A continuous transformation is referred to as a **map** (or mapping) *and so is the image*. If f is 1–1 and f is continuous and open on S onto T then f is a **homeomorphism** or a **topological transformation** of S onto T. Then S and T are **homeomorphic spaces**.

The statement "f is a map of S into T" implies both S and T are topological spaces. However one has essentially the untopologized situation in assigning the discrete topology to S and T for then all single valued functions are maps.

Lemma 4.6. *The transformation f on S into T is continuous at $s \Leftrightarrow$ every generalized sequence $\{s(a) \mid A\}$ which converges to s is transformed into a generalized sequence $\{f(s(a)) \mid A\}$ which converges to $f(s)$.*

Definition 4.7. If A and B are disjunct in S then the **Urysohn function** $u(s; A, B; a, b)$ is continuous on S to the real line, with values in the range

$a \leq t \leq b$ and $u \mid A = a$, $u \mid B = b$. If $a = 0$ and $b = 1$ we write $u(s; A, B)$ or $u(A, B)$.

Definition 4.8. A subset $A \subset S$ is **dense in** S if $\bar{A} = \bar{S}$.

5. PRODUCT SPACES. Definition 5.1. The **Cartesian product** of the sets $S = \{s\}$ and $T = \{t\}$ is the set whose points are the pairs $\{(s, t)\}$. This set is indicated by $S \times T$. More generally if $\{S_a \mid A\}$ is a collection of point sets the Cartesian product $\prod_A S_a$ is the set whose elements are the single valued functions $s \sim \{s(a \mid A)\}$ with $s(a) \in S_a$ for each $a \in A$. $s(a)$ is the a **coordinate** or a **projection** of s.

Definition 5.2. If $\{S_a \mid A\}$ is a collection of topological spaces with neighborhood base $\{U_a^b(s^0) \mid B\}$ for S_a, the **topological product** $\mathbf{P}_A(S_a)$ (often written $\Pi_A S_a$ also) is the space whose points are those of the Cartesian product (definition 5.1) i.e., $s \sim (s(a \mid A))$. A neighborhood base at $s^0 = \{s^0(a)\}$ is constituted by the sets $U(s, \pi) = \{s \mid s(a) \in U_a^b(s^0(a), a$ is in the subset π of $A\}$. Thus the set $U(s, \pi)$ arises from pinching, or rather introducing constrictions at a of size $U_a^b(S^0(a))$ for a finite number of a's. The **uniform** or **full topology** refers to the neighborhood assignments $U(s) = \{s \mid s(a) \in U_a^b(s^0(a))\}$.

If the number of elements in A is n, $\mathbf{P}_A I_i$ is the n-**dimensional parallelotope** where I_i is the unit segment. If $|A| = \aleph_0$ we write P^ω and this is called the **Hilbert parallelotope** where the product topology is taken.

Definition 5.4. If $S_a = S$ then $\mathbf{P}_A S_a$ is written also $S^{|A|}$ and the point set $\{s_a \mid s_a = s$ independently of $a\}$ is called the **diagonal** Δ. An open set V in $S^{|A|}$ containing Δ is called a **vicinity** of Δ.

EXAMPLE 1. If S^1 is the unit circle then $I \times S^1$ is a hollow cylinder with roof and floor circles. $S^1 \times S^1$ is a torus.

6. PROJECTIONS AND GRAPHS. Definition 6.1. The transformation $p_a(s)$ which assigns to each point s in the Cartesian product space $\Pi_A S_a$ it's a coordinate is called a **projection** of S onto S_a.

Lemma 6.2. *A projection $p_a(s)$ of the topological product $\mathbf{P}(S_a)$ onto S_a is open and continuous.*

Openness follows from p_a: $\Pi_\pi N_a \times \Pi_{\pi\sim} S_a$ is N_a for $a \in \pi$ and is S_a for $a \bar{\in} \pi$. Continuity is established by $p_b^{-1} N_b = N_b \times \Pi_{\cdot b \sim} S_a$.

Definition 6.3. Let f be a transformation of the set S into the set T. Then the **graph** of f, denoted by $\Gamma(f)$, is $\{(s, t) \mid s \in S, t \in f(s)\} \subset S \times T$. Every subset A of $S \times T$ can be considered the graph of a (multi-valued) function f on $p_S(A) = D_f$ to $p_T(A) = R_f$ with $f(s) = p_T\, p_S^{-1}\, s$.

Lemma 6.4. *If f is continuous on S to T then the projection p on $S \times T$ onto S induces a homeomorphism on $\Gamma(f)$ onto S.*

Lemma 6.5.

(a) *If f_a is $\begin{matrix}\text{continuous}\\ \text{open}\end{matrix}$ on the space S_a onto the space T_a then f on $\mathbf{P}_A S_a$ to $\mathbf{P}_A T_a$ defined by $f\{s(a)\} = \{f_a(s(a))\}$ is $\begin{matrix}\text{continuous}\\ \text{open}\end{matrix}$.*

(b) *If f_a maps S onto T_a then $f(s) = \{f_a(s)\}$ maps S onto $\mathbf{P}_A T_a$.*

Let N_a, M_a be neighborhoods in S_a and T_a respectively. The continuity assertion follows from the observation $\mathbf{P}_\pi f_a^{-1} M_a \times \mathbf{P}_{\pi\sim} S_a$ contains a neighborhood in $\mathbf{P}S_a$ which is taken by f into $\mathbf{P}_\pi N_a \times \mathbf{P}_{\pi\sim} T_a$. The openness of f is consequent on

$$f(\mathbf{P}_\pi N_a \times \mathbf{P}_{\pi\sim} S_a) = (\mathbf{P}_\pi f_a(N_a) \times \mathbf{P}_{\pi\sim} T_a).$$

For (b) note $f^{-1}(\mathbf{P}_\pi N_a \times \mathbf{P}_{\pi\sim} T_a) = \bigcap_\pi f_a^{-1}(N_a)$ an open set by virtue of the continuity of f_a.

7. COVERINGS. **Definition 7.1.** A collection of subsets, $\boldsymbol{S} = \{X_a \mid A\}$ of a set S whose union contains S is a **cover** or **covering** of S. It is irreducible if it fails to be a cover when any set is removed. The cover $\boldsymbol{S}' = \{X_b' \mid B\}$ is a **refinement** of the cover $\boldsymbol{S} = \{X_a \mid A\}$ if for every X_b' there is an X_a containing it. We write $\boldsymbol{S} < \boldsymbol{S}'$ and observe this yields a (transitive) ordering of coverings. A **subcover** of a cover $\boldsymbol{S}$ is a cover by a subcollection of the elements of $\boldsymbol{S}$.

Definition 7.2. If $\boldsymbol{S} = \{X_a \mid A\}$ is a covering of S and X is a subset of S then the **star of** X **in** $\boldsymbol{S}$ is $St(X, \boldsymbol{S}) = \bigcup\{X_a \mid X \cap X_a \neq \varnothing\}$. We denote $St(St(X, \boldsymbol{S}), \boldsymbol{S})$ by $St^2(X, \boldsymbol{S})$. Similarly by induction

$$St^m(X, \boldsymbol{S}) = St(St^{m-1}(X, \boldsymbol{S})).$$

Lemma 7.3. *The star operation with respect to a covering $\boldsymbol{S} = \{X_a \mid A\}$ is monotone, i.e., $X \subset Y \Rightarrow St(X, \boldsymbol{S}) \subset St(Y, \boldsymbol{S})$.*

Definition 7.4. If $\boldsymbol{S} = \{X_a \mid A\}$ then $\boldsymbol{S}^* = \{St(X_a, \boldsymbol{S})\}$ and

$$\boldsymbol{S}^\Delta = \{St(s, \boldsymbol{S}),\ s \in S\}.$$

The meaning of $\boldsymbol{S}^{**}$, $\boldsymbol{S}^{*\Delta}$, $\boldsymbol{S}^{\Delta *}$, etc., is clear.

Lemma 7.5. *A single set, X_a, of a cover S contains both s_1 and $s_2 \Leftrightarrow s_1 \in St(s_2, \boldsymbol{S})$ and $s_2 \in St(s_1, \boldsymbol{S})$.*

Lemma 7.6. *For the cover $\boldsymbol{S} = \{X_a \mid A\}$, $\boldsymbol{S}^{\Delta\Delta} < \boldsymbol{S}^* < \boldsymbol{S}^{\Delta}$.*

Indeed $s_0 \in X_a \Rightarrow St(s_0, \boldsymbol{S}) \subset St(X_a, \boldsymbol{S})$. Hence $S^{\Delta} > S^*$. For any X_a select an arbitrary point $s_0 \in X_a$. Then $St(X_a, \boldsymbol{S}) \subset St^2(s_0, \boldsymbol{S})$ whence $\boldsymbol{S}^* > \boldsymbol{S}^{\Delta\Delta}$.

Definition 7.7. The cover $\boldsymbol{S}' = \{X_a \mid A\}$ is *a* $\overset{\Delta}{*}$ *refinement*, read $\begin{matrix}\textbf{triangle}\\ \textbf{star}\end{matrix}$ **refinement**, of the cover $\boldsymbol{S} = \{Y_b \mid B\}$ if $\begin{matrix} \boldsymbol{S} < \boldsymbol{S}'^{\Delta} \\ \boldsymbol{S} < \boldsymbol{S}'^{*}\end{matrix}$. This is denoted by

$$\boldsymbol{S} \overset{\Delta}{<} \boldsymbol{S}'$$
$$\boldsymbol{S} \overset{*}{<} \boldsymbol{S}'.$$

In view of lemma 7.6 assertions in the sequel, of the existence of star refinements, are equivalent with assertions of the existence of $\triangle$ refinements.

Definition 7.8. A cover $\boldsymbol{S} = \{X_a \mid A\}$ is: **(a)** $\begin{matrix}\textbf{open}\\ \textbf{closed}\end{matrix}$ if each X_a is $\begin{matrix}\text{open}\\ \text{closed}\end{matrix}$; is **(b)** a **finite** cover if $|A|$ is finite; **(c)** a **point finite** cover, if every point is common to at most a finite number of members of S; **(d) star finite** if each X_a intersects at most a finite number of other members of $\boldsymbol{S}$; **(e) neighborhood** or **locally finite** if for each $s \in S$ there is a neighborhood containing s which intersects at most a finite number of members of $\boldsymbol{S}$.

8. COMPACTNESS. Definition 8.1. A space S is **compact** if every open cover admits a finite subcover. S is **countably compact** if every countable open cover admits a finite subcover. S is **paracompact** if every open cover has an open neighborhood finite refinement. It is **countably paracompact** if every countable open cover has an open neighborhood finite refinement.

Definition 8.2. A family of sets $\{S_a \mid A\}$ has the F.I.P., i.e., has the **finite intersection property**, if $\bigcap_\pi S_a \neq \varnothing$ for any finite subset, π, of A.

Lemma 8.3. *S is compact if and only if any collection of closed sets with F.I.P. has a common point.*

Necessity follows from the observation that if $\bigcap_\Lambda F_\lambda = \varnothing$ then $\{G_\lambda \mid G_\lambda = F_\lambda^{\sim}\}$ is an open cover and so admits a finite subset which is a cover i.e., $\{G_\lambda \mid G_y = F_\lambda^{\sim}\}$ is a cover or $\bigcap_\pi F_\lambda = \varnothing$ in contradiction with the assumed F.I.P. The sufficiency proof is equally simple.

This lemma yields an equivalent definition of compactness of S, namely that any family of closed sets with the F.I.P. has a common point.

Definition 8.4. The topological space S is **sequentially compact** if every sequence includes a subsequence which converges to a point in S.

Lemma 8.5. *If F is closed in S and S is* **(a)** *compact, countably compact, or sequentially compact, or* **(b)** *paracompact, or countably paracompact, then so is F.*

Let $\boldsymbol{S} = \{G_a \mid A\}$ be an open cover of F. Then $G_a = Q_a \cap F$, where Q_a is open in S (Definition 3.11). Accordingly $\boldsymbol{S}' = \{Q_a \mid A\} \cup F^{\sim}$ is a cover of S and $|A|$ is either unrestricted or countable. $\boldsymbol{S}'$ admits a finite subcover in case **(a)** and a neighborhood finite refinement in case **(b)**. Let $\boldsymbol{S}'' = \{K_b \mid B, |B| \leq |C|\}$ be the refinement in question where $|C|$ is either unrestricted or $\aleph_0$. If $K_b \cap F \neq \varnothing$ then $K_b \cap F \subset G_a$ for some a. Accordingly $\{K_b \cap F \mid B, b \in B \Rightarrow K_b \cap F \neq \varnothing\}$ is a neighborhood finite refinement of F in either of the cases in **(b)**. (The sequential compactness in F follows from the trivial observation that limits of sequences in F must be in F.)

Lemma 8.6. *If points are closed sets then the space S is countably compact $\Leftrightarrow$ every nonfinite set has a limit point.*

If S_0 is nonfinite let S_1 be a denumerable subset. Let π denote a finite subset of S_1. Suppose S_1 admits no limit points. Then S_1 is closed and so is $S_1(\pi) = S_1 \cap \pi^{\sim}$. Then the sets $\{S_1(\pi)\}$ have the F.I.P. and so Lemma 8.5 and the countable compactness of S imply $\{S_1(\pi)\}$ have a common point say s_1. This contradicts the fact that $S_1(\pi)$ does not contain s_1 if $s_1 \in \pi$.

The reverse implication is established by noting that if the closed sets $\{F_i\}$ have the F.I.P. then the sets $\bigcap_{j=1}^{j=k} F_j = T_k$ have the F.I.P. Then $\bigcap F_n = \varnothing$ implies $\bigcap T_n = \varnothing$. On the other hand select arbitrarily $t_i \in T_i$. Then $\{t_i\}$ has a limit point t. Since T_j contains all but the first $j - 1$ terms of $\{t_i\}$, and is closed, $t \in T_j$.

Lemma 8.7. *If points are closed sets S is sequentially compact $\Rightarrow$ S is countably compact.*

Sequential compactness implies the existence of a limit point for every nonfinite set whence the result follows by Lemma 8.6. The converse is not generally true.

Lemma 8.8. *If the neighborhood basis at every point is countable then S is sequentially compact when S is countably compact.*

Let s be a limit point of S'. Replace the basis $\{U^n(s) \mid n = 1, \ldots\}$ by the equivalent basis $\{V^n(s) \mid \bigcap_{j=1}^{j=n} U^j(s)\}$. The sequence $\{s^n \mid s^n \in S' \cap V^n(s)\}$ converges to s.

Lemma 8.9. **(a)** *A map f of a compact space S is compact;* **(b)** *S compact T_2* (10.1c) *under T, T properly finer than $T' \Rightarrow S$ is not compact under T'.*

The line of proof is to consider the open cover U of S obtained from the inverse map by f^{-1} of the open cover V of $f(S)$. Our hypotheses allow a finite subcover in **(a)** and the correspondent under f of this finite subcover is a finite subcover of U.

For **(b)**: Let i be the identity transformation, $s \to s$ of $S' = S$ under T' onto S under T. Evidently i is a map. If S' were compact then i would be a homeomorphism (10.8b) or $T \sim T'$ (5.15).

Theorem 8.10. (Tychonoff). *If $\{C_a \mid A\}$ are compact spaces then the topological product is compact.*

It is this theorem which in a large sense has given the preferred position to the usual product topology, for it is no longer true, when $|A|$ is nonfinite, when other topologies are imposed on the product as say the full topology. Since (8.10) is rapidly becoming one of the most frequently proved theorems in mathematics, we forego a proof here. The key is Zorn's lemma and in fact the assertion of Theorem 8.10 is tantamount to Zorn's lemma.

(We may remark on the close relationship of two procedures for establishing the existence of a common point for a prescribed collection of sets. The presence of a common point is of course not affected by the topology assigned these sets. One may demonstrate the F.I.P. and then appeal to the choice axiom or Zorn's lemma. An alternate attack is to show the sets are closed in some compact containing set.)

EXAMPLE 2. The closed interval I is compact, sequentially compact, countably compact.

All parallelotopes are compact and so in particular P^ω is compact.

Closed bounded subsets of an Euclidean space are compact.

Remark. Theorem 8.10 is untrue in general if paracompact replaces compact even in the case A has just two elements.

9. CONNECTEDNESS. **Definition 9.1.** The subsets A and B of the topological space S are **separated** if

$$(\bar{A} \cap B) \cup (A \cap \bar{B}) = \varnothing;$$

i.e., A is disjunct from the closure of B and B from the closure of A.

Definition 9.2. The space S is **connected** if it cannot be expressed as the union of two separated non-void subspaces A and B.

Lemma 9.3. *The space S is connected$\Leftrightarrow$if $S = A \cup B$ with A and B disjunct then A and B cannot both be open or both be closed (neither empty).*

Example 3. All parallelotopes are connected.

Lemma 9.4.

(a) *$\bar{S}$ is connected if S is a connected subset of a space T.*

(b) *The topological product $S_1 \times S_2$ is connected if S_i is connected $i = 1, 2$ and conversely.*

Lemma 9.5. *A map of a connected set is connected.*

Definition 9.6. A **component** is a maximal connected set K in the space S; i.e., $K \cup s$ is not connected if $s \bar{\epsilon} K$.

Definition 9.7. The subspace S' of S is **totally disconnected** if every component of S' is a single point. (This property is independent of the containing space S.)

Definition 9.8. The subspace S' of S is **discontinuous** if every connected set in S' which is **closed in** S is a single point. This property depends on the containing space. Indeed since S' may be discontinuous and yet connected such an S' cannot be discontinuous in itself.

Example 4. The Cantor set is totally disconnected as are also all discrete spaces with more than one point.

Example 5. Let $x(t) = \Sigma\, a_n\, (\sin\, (\pi(t - r_n)^{-1})$ or 0 according as $t \neq r_n$ or $t = r_n$ respectively). Here $a_n > 0$, $\Sigma\, a_n < \infty$ and r_n is the nth rational in the standard ordering. Then the graph $\Gamma(x) = \{(t, x(t)) \mid 0 < t \leq 1\} \cup \{(0, 0)\}$ is a connected set which is discontinuous in $I \times I$ but not discontinuous of course in $\Gamma(x)$.

10. SEPARATION. Definition 10.1. If for each pair of distinct points of the topological space S there is

(a) a neighborhood of one of them which does not contain the other then S is a T_0 space;

(b) a neighborhood of each of them which does not contain the other then S is a T_1 space;

(c) a neighborhood of each of them such that the pair of neighborhoods are disjunct then S is a T_2, or **Hausdorff space**. Throughout the book *space* *is tacitly understood to refer to* T_2 *space and* neighborhoods are *open* (3.1 N3) except when otherwise stipulated.

Definition 10.2. The topological space S is **completely regular**, or is a **Tychonoff space**, if it is T_2 and for each point s_0 and disjunct closed set F there is a Urysohn function $u(s; s_0, F)$.

Definition 10.3. The topological space S is

(a) **normal** if for every pair of disjunct closed sets F_i, $i = 1, 2$ there is a pair of disjunct open sets $\{G_i \mid i = 1, 2\}$ with $F_i \subset G_i$;

(b) **fully normal** if every open covering S admits an open Δ refinement (or an open star refinement);

(c) **completely normal** if $(\bar{A}_1 \cap A_2) \cup (A_1 \cap \bar{A}_2) = \varnothing$ implies there exist a pair of disjunct open sets G_i with $A_i \subset G_i$, $i = 1, 2$.

Lemma 10.4. *X normal* $\Leftrightarrow$ *if* $\boldsymbol{S}$ *is the binary open cover* U_1, U_2 *then there is an open* Δ *refinement* $\boldsymbol{S}'$.

Remark. For sufficiency $\boldsymbol{S}'$ need not be finite though an obvious consequence is that there must exist some open refinement with just three members.

For necessity note that with $F_i = U_i^{\sim}$ and G_i as in (10.3a) there is a cover $\boldsymbol{S}' = (G_1, G_2, U_1 \cap U_2)$ with $\boldsymbol{S}'^{\Delta} = G_1, G_2, U_1, U_2, U_1 \cap U_2$. Since $G_1 \cap F_2 = \varnothing$ implies $G_1 \subset U_2$ we have $\boldsymbol{S}'^{\Delta} > \boldsymbol{S}$.

For sufficiency suppose F_1 and F_2 disjunct and closed and let $\boldsymbol{S}' = \{V_a \mid A\}$ be an open Δ refinement of $\boldsymbol{S} = \{U_i \mid U_i = -F_i, i = 1, 2\}$. Then $F_i \subset G_i = \bigcup_{s \in F_i} St(s, \boldsymbol{S}') \subset U_j$ for $i \neq j$. Now G_i is open and if $G_1 \cap G_2 \neq \varnothing$ for some x, $St(x, \boldsymbol{S}')$ would contain points in both F_1 and F_2 and so $\boldsymbol{S}'$ could not refine $\boldsymbol{S}$.

Lemma 10.5. *If* S' *is* T_2 *and compact then*

(a) S' *is closed in any containing* T_2 *space* S.

(b) S' *is normal.*

If $s_0 \bar{\in} S'$ take disjunct pairs $U(s_0)$, $V(s')$ for every $s' \in S'$. By compactness there is a finite cover of S' by $\{V(s_i') \mid i = 1, \ldots, N\}$. Let $U^i(s_0)$ be the set associated with $V(s_i')$. Then $\bigcap_{i=1}^{i=N} U^i(s_0)$ is disjunct from $\bigcup V(s_i')$ and therefore from S'.

If F_0 and F_1 are closed and disjunct in S', the argument for **(a)** shows for each $s_0 \in F_0$ there is an open set $W(s_0)$ disjunct from an open set denoted above by $\bigcup V(s_i')$ or Q. Compactness yields a finite cover of F_0 by $\{W(s_1^i) \mid i = 1, \ldots, M\}$ with each $W(s_1^i)$ disjunct from an open set Q_i containing F_1. Hence $G_0 = \bigcup_{i=1}^{i=M} W(s_1^i)$ and $G_1 = \bigcap Q_i$ are disjunct open sets containing F_0 and F_1 respectively.

Theorem 10.6. *If S is T_2, limits of generalized sequences are unique.*

If x and x' are limits of $X(a|\, A)$ choose $U(x)$ and $U'(x')$ disjunct open sets. It is impossible for both sets to contain a residual set.

Lemma 10.7. *If S and T are T_2 and f maps S into T then the graph of f is closed in $S \times T$.*

Theorem 10.8. *If S is compact and T_2*

(a) *any map is a closed transformation*

(b) *any onto 1–1 map is a homeomorphism.*

We content ourselves with mere statement of the following important result.

Theorem 10.9. *If S is T_2 then paracompactness is equivalent to full normality.*

The theorem is not valid if S is merely T_1.

11. METRICS. Definition 11.1. A real-valued nonnegative function $d(s, s')$ of point pairs is a **metric** (yielding sphere neighborhoods) if

(1) $d(s, s) = 0$.

(2) $d(s, t) = d(t, s) \geq 0$, $d(s, t) = 0$ implies $s = t$.

(3) $d(s, t) \leq d(s, u) + d(u, t)$.

Lemma 11.2. *A metric space has a countable base at each point. The metric spheres $\{s \mid d(s, s_0) < 1/n\}$ form an equivalent base. If s_0 is isolated then s_0 is itself a base. (The point s_0 is isolated in S if s_0 is an open set.)*

Definition 11.3. A space is **separable** if it contains a dense denumerable set.

Lemma 11.4. *For metric spaces separability is equivalent to satisfaction of the second countability axiom.*

If a point is chosen in each neighborhood a dense set arises. If at each point of a dense set the denumerable base of spheres of rational radius is taken, the totality of neighborhoods thus obtained is denumerable and is a base.

EXAMPLE 6. P^w is the homeomorph of the set $\{t = t_1, t_2, \ldots$ where $0 \leq t_n \leq 1/n\}$. It is metric with $d(s, t) = (\Sigma\, (s_i - t_i)^2)^{\frac{1}{2}}$ and is separable.

Remark. Any open set of a separable space is separable. However paradoxically there may be closed subsets which are not separable.

Definition 11.5. If S_1 and S_2 are subsets of the metric space S the distance from S_1 to S_2, $d(S_1, S_2)$, is defined by $inf_{s \in S_1, t \in S_2} d(s, t)$.

The distance may be 0 for two closed disjunct sets. An example is the real line with one point removed with S_1 and S_2 the ensuing half rays.

Theorem 11.6. *A metric space is T_2 and normal.*

Only the normality needs attention. Let F_1 and F_2 be disjunct closed sets. Then $\{s \mid d(s, F_1) < 2^{-2} d(s, F_2)\}$ and $\{s \mid d(s, F_2) < 2^{-2} d(s, F_1)\}$ are disjunct open sets containing F_1 and F_2 respectively.

Lemma 11.7. *A separable metric space is the homeomorph of a subset of P^ω.*

The next theorem is a partial converse of Theorem 11.6.

Theorem 11.8. *If S is normal, T_2 and satisfies the second countability axiom, S is metrisable that is to say there is an equivalent metric topology for S.*

Definition 11.9. The sequence $\{s^n\}$ with $d(s^n, s^m) \to 0$ as n and $m \to \infty$ is a **Cauchy sequence**. It is convergent (to s) if $d(s^n, s) \to 0$.

Definition 11.10. If every Cauchy sequence is a convergent sequence, the metric space S is **complete**.

Definition 11.11. If S is not complete but is a dense subset of the complete space S' then S' is the **completion** of S and S is completed (to S').

Theorem 11.12. Cauchy-Meray. *Every metric space can be completed.*

Definition 11.13. A compact metric space is a **compactum**.

Definition 11.14. If A is a subset of a compactum, then A is **conditionally compact**.

Theorem 11.15. Lebesgue. *Let $\alpha = \{a_i\}$ be an arbitrary open cover of the compactum X. There exists a positive real number $d(\alpha)$, referred to henceforth as a Lebesgue number for α, such that every subset of diameter inferior to $d(\alpha)$ is contained in some element, a_i, of α.*

Let $\beta = \{b_j\}$ be a finite subcover of α: If the theorem is false, for every n there is a subset A_n, of diameter $<1/n$, not in any b_j. Choose $x_n \in A_n$. Then

$\bar{x}$, a cluster point of $\{x_n\}$ is in b_k, say. Then $d(\bar{x}, X - b_k) = 2e > 0$. Hence for $n > 2/e$,

$$sup_{A_n}(d(x_n, x'_n) \mid x_n, x'_n \in A_n) \leq sup\, d(x_n, \bar{x}) + d(\bar{x}, x'_n) \leq e.$$

Hence for $n > 2/e$, $d(x_n, \bar{x}) < e/2$. Accordingly for all y in A_n, $d(\bar{x}, y) \leq d(\bar{x}, x_n) + d(x_n, y) \leq e$ or $A_n \subset b_k$, a contradiction.

Definition 11.16. A real (complex) **Banach** space X is a complete vector space over R, (C), where $d(x, y)$ depends only on $x - y$ and is written $\|x - y\|$, $\|rx\| = |r|\,\|x\|$ and $\|x\| = 0$ is equivalent to $x = 0$.

12. LOCAL COMPACTNESS AND PARACOMPACTNESS. Definition 12.1. A space is **locally compact** if every point admits a neighborhood with compact closure.

Lemma 12.1. *If S is locally compact and T_2 then: S is paracompact $\Leftrightarrow$ every open cover has a star finite refinement.*

Let μ be an open cover of S. This can be replaced by a refinement μ' consisting of open sets with compact closures. There is a neighborhood finite refinement $\nu = \{V_a\}$ of μ'. For each $s \in V_a$ there is a neighborhood $N(s)$ whose star with respect to ν is composed of a finite number of sets. A finite collection $\{N(s_i) \mid s_i \in V_a, i = 1, \ldots, M\}$ covers the compact set $\bar{V}_a$, and hence $\bigcup_{i=1}^{i=M} St(N(s_i), \nu\}$ is composed of a finite number of sets of ν. Thus $St(V_a, \nu)$ consists of a finite number of sets of ν. In short, ν must be a star finite covering refining μ.

Theorem 12.2. *If S is locally compact, T_2 and connected then S is paracompact implies S is σ-compact (that is to say S is the union of a countable number of open sets with compact closures).*

There is a cover by open sets with compact closures $\mu = \{u_a \mid A\}$. Paracompactness implies μ can be supposed star finite. Then

$$G_1 = \bigcup \{u_a \mid u_a \cap u_1 \neq \varnothing\}, \quad G_n = \bigcup \{u_a \mid u_a \cap G_{n-1} \neq \varnothing\}$$

are finite unions. Then $E = \bigcup G_n$ is open as a union of open sets. Also E is closed for if $s_0 \in \bar{E}$ then $s_0 \in u'$ for some $u' \in \mu$ and $u' \cap \bigcup G_n \neq \varnothing$. Hence $u' \subset G_n$ for some n. Hence $E = \bar{E}$. Thus since S is connected, $E = S = \bigcup \bar{G}_n$ where $\bar{G}_n$ is compact since $\bar{G}_j$ is the union of a finite number of the compact sets in $\{\bar{u}_a\}$.

Lemma 12.3. *If X is locally compact, T_2, connected and paracompact there is a countable open cover $\nu = \{v_i \mid \bar{v}_i$ compact$\}$ such that $\bar{v}_i$ meets at most $\bar{v}_{i-1}$ and $\bar{v}_{i+1}$.*

The existence of a denumerable star finite open cover, $\omega = \{w_i \mid \bar{w}_i$ compact$\}$ is a consequence of (12.1) and of (12.2). Shrink the cover (cf. Section 13) to $\tau = \{t_i \mid t_i \subset \bar{t}_i \subset w_i\}$ (13.2b). Let $\pi_i = \{j \mid t_j \cap t_i \neq \phi\}$. Define v_i by

$$v_i = \bigcup \{t_m \mid m \in \pi_i - \textstyle\bigcup_{k=1}^{i-1} \pi_k\}.$$

This fills the bill.

13. SHRINKABLE COVERS. Definition 13.1. An open cover $\mu = \{U_a \mid A\}$ is **shrinkable** if there is an open cover $\nu = \{V_a \mid A\}$ with $V_a \subset \bar{V}_a \subset U_a$. μ is a **swelling** of ν.

Theorem 13.2. **(a)** *A point finite cover of a normal space S is shrinkable;* **(b)** *a point finite cover whose elements have compact closures is shrinkable if S is locally compact and T_2.*

Let $\mu = \{U_a \mid A\}$ be the cover. Suppose $W_a = (\bigcup_{b \neq a} U_b)^\sim \neq \varnothing$. Then in case **(a)**, normality guarantees the existence of a Urysohn function $u(s, U_a^\sim, W_a)$ In case **(b)** since $\bar{U}_a$ is compact it is normal and so there is a Urysohn function on $\bar{U}_a$ given by $u(s, \bar{U}_a \cap U_a^\sim\ W_a)$. This can be extended to a Urysohn function $u(s, U_a^\sim, W_a)$ by assigning the value 0 for $s \in U_a^\sim$. For both cases **(a)** and **(b)** let $V_a = \{s \mid u(s, U_a^\sim, W_a) > 0\}$. This satisfies the conditions **(c)** $V_a \subset \bar{V}_a \subset U_a$ and **(d)** $V_a \cup (\mu - U_a)$ is a cover of S. (Evidently V_a is not unique.) If $W_a = \varnothing$, the choice of V_a to satisfy **(c)** is trivial for **(d)** imposes no restriction. Throughout, the notation V_a will imply satisfaction of **(c)**.

Let $Q = \{Q_a \mid Q_a = V_a$ or $Q_a = U_a\}$ be required to be a cover. Order such covers Q, Q' by the requirement that $Q' < Q$ if $Q'_a = V_a \Rightarrow Q_a = V_a$. Let $\{Q^\rho\}$ be simply ordered. Then $Q = \{Q_a \mid Q_a = \bigcap_\rho Q_a^\rho\}$ is an upper bound. One need only check that Q is a cover. This follows from the point finiteness of μ for if $\{U_a \mid \pi\}$ comprise the set over s then for some ρ_0 and all $a \in \pi$, Q_a^ρ remains constant for $\rho_0 < \rho$ so the covering property for Q^ρ implies s is covered by Q.

By Zorn's lemma there must be a maximal Q, say ${}_mQ = \{{}_mQ_a\}$ in the collection of all Q's. Suppose for some a, ${}_mQ_a = U_a$. Then application of the argument at the beginning of this proof exhibits a V_a which substituted for U_a in ${}_mQ_a$ yields a Q' satisfying ${}_mQ < Q'$, ${}_mQ \neq Q'$ contradicting the maximality of ${}_mQ$.

Theorem 13.3. *If S is T_2 and paracompact any open cover has a subcover that is shrinkable to an open neighborhood finite cover.*

14. COUNTABLE PARACOMPACTNESS (8.1)

Lemma 14.1. *If S is countably paracompact and normal and T is a compactum, then $S \times T$ is normal.*

Let F^1 and F^2 be closed disjunct sets of $S \times T$. The section $F^i(s_0)$ is defined by $F^i(s_0) = \{t \mid (s_0, t) \in F^i\} \subset T$. For each s there is an open set G in T such that **(a)** $F^1(s) \subset G$ and **(b)** $\bar{G} \subset F^2(s)^\sim$. The compactness of $\bar{G}$ implies that if s_0 satisfies **(a)** then $F^1(s) \subset G$ for all s in a neighborhood of s_0 in S. Thus for fixed G the set *in* S defined by **(a)** is open. Similarly the S set defined by **(b)** is open also so that their intersection U is also open. Since T has a countable base for the open sets and $F^1(s)$ is compact it follows that for each s, a G satisfying **(a)** and **(b)** is a finite sum of sets of the base. The collection of finite subsets of the integers is denumerable. Thus some G_i of a countable collection $\{G_n\}$ of open sets of T, satisfies **(a)** and **(b)** for each choice of s. Let U_n correspond to G_n so $\mu = \{U_n\}$ is a countable cover of S. Let $\nu = \{V_m\}$ be a locally finite refinement of μ. Let $j(n)$ be the first index for which $V_n \subset U_j$. Let $Q_m = \bigcup \{V_n \mid j(n) = m\}$. Since S is normal $\{Q_m\}$ is an open cover with an open refinement $\omega = \{W_r\}$ satisfying $W_m \subset \bar{W}_m \subset Q_m \subset U_m$ for every m in view of Theorem 13.2(b). Evidently ω is a locally finite refinement of μ. The set $O = \bigcup W_n \times G_n$ is open. Since $(s, t) \in F^1$ implies $s \in W_m \subset Q_m, t \in F^1(s) \subset G_m$. Hence $O \supset F^1$. For each s let $N(s)$ be the neighborhood which meets at most a finite number of the members of ω. Then $N(s) \times T$ meets at most a finite number of the sets $W_n \times G_n$. Hence $\bar{O} = \bigcup \overline{W_n \times G_n} = \bigcup \bar{W}_n \times \bar{G}_n$. Since $U_n \times \bar{G}_n$ is disjunct from F^2 for all n, $\bar{O} \cap F^2 = \varnothing$. Thus $F^1 \subset O \subset \bar{O} \subset F^{2\sim}$ or $S \times T$ is normal.

15. COMPACTIFICATION. If the topological space S has the relative topology of a compact space C in which S is dense, then C is referred to as the compactification of S. There are two main lines of compactification of S. In the first, points are considered maximal families of closed sets with the F.I.P. In the second a point is identified with a map to the real line. Accordingly the first is expected to be of utility when problems involving coverings are considered, the second when problems concerned with extending the domain of real valued functions are considered.

Theorem 15.1. **(a)** *If S is a T_1 space, there is a compactification which is a T_1 space.* **(b)** *If S is normal the compactification is a T_2 normal space.*

We sketch a proof. Consider a family $\{F'_a \mid A\}$ of sets closed in S with the F.I.P. By Zorn's lemma this family has a maximal extension: $\{F_b \mid B\}$. Denote such a maximal family by the generic symbol x. Refer to F_b as the b coordinate of x. To every $s \in S$ there is a corresponding x, which we write $x(s)$, denoting the maximal family of closed sets containing s, and since $s_1 \neq s_2 \Rightarrow x(s_1) \neq x(s_2)$ the correspondence f: $s \to x(s)$ is 1–1. However there may be some elements x for which no antecedent s exists. Let $C = \{x\}$ with the topology specified by finite unions of sets $F = \{x \mid F$ a coordinate of $x\}$ as a basis for the closed sets. The properties in 3.1 (using $F^{\sim}$) may be verified so C is a topological space. To demonstrate compactness we need merely observe that $\{F_a \mid A\}$ with the F.I.P. must be contained in at least one maximal set, say x. This is to say $\bigcap_A F_a \supset x$.

(b). Suppose then $x_1 \neq x_2$ in C. Accordingly some coordinate F_1 of x_1 is disjunct from the coordinate F_2 of x_2. The normality of S carries the existence of disjunct open sets G_j, containing F_j, $j = 1, 2$. Let H_i be the closed set in C determined by $\tilde{G}_i$ in S. Then the sets $G_i = C - H_i$, $i = 1, 2$ are disjunct open sets containing x_1 and x_2 respectively and so C is T_2. It is furthermore normal by Lemma 10.5.

The compactification just achieved is the significant one for the usual Cech Homology Theory. In the case that S is normal and T_2 the compactification achievement is maximal in the sense that if S has homeomorphs dense in C and (compact) C' under ψ and θ there is a map λ of C onto C' with $\lambda\psi = \theta$ (Cf 15.4). This remark is not valid if S is T_1 and not T_2.

Lemma 15.2. *If S is completely regular then for every point s and assigned neighborhood $U(s_0)$ there is an open set $V(s_0) \subset \bar{V}(s_0) \subset U(s_0)$ for which a Urysohn function $u(s;\, \bar{V}(s_0),\, U(s_0)^{\sim})$ exists.*

Let $V(s_0)$ be $\{s \mid u(s;\, U(s_0)^{\sim},\, s_0) > \frac{1}{2}\}$. Define $u(s;\, U(s_0)^{\sim},\, \bar{V}(s_0))$ as $u(s;\, U(s_0)^{\sim},\, s_0)$ for $s \in U(s_0)^{\sim}$, as $= 1$ for $s \in \bar{V}(s_0)$, and as $2u(s)$ elsewhere.

Definition 15.3. Let S be completely regular. A **canonical pair** of neighborhoods (U^a, V^a) is any pair in the relation of Lemma 15.2. Denote the canonical pair by W^a and let W be the collection of distinct canonical pairs; i.e., $W^a \neq W^b \Rightarrow$ either $U^a \neq U^b$ or $V^a \neq V^b$ and $\{U^a\}$ is a neighborhood basis of S.

Theorem 15.4. *S completely regular implies S may be imbedded in $\mathbf{P}_A\, I_a = P^\alpha$ where $|A| = \alpha$ is the power of a neighborhood basis of S and the compactification of S is written $\beta(S) = \bar{S}$ where the closure is taken in P^α.*

We restrict ourselves to spaces with nonfinite α. Then the power $W = \{U^a, V^a\} = \alpha$ also. Let u_a be the function of Lemma 15.2 for $W^a = (U^a, V^a)$. Let $T_s(a) = u_a(s)$. Then $\psi(s) = T_s$ transforms S into $\mathbf{P}_A\, I_a$ for T_s is the point $\{T_s(a) \mid A\}$. Since $u_a(s)$ is continuous for each a, $\psi(s)$ is continuous, Lemma 6.5b. Furthermore ψ is 1–1 since $s \neq s'$ implies $s' \bar{\in} U(s)$ for some $U(s)$ since S is T_2. Hence there is a canonical pair (U^a, V^a) with $s \in V^a$ and so $T_s(a) \neq T_{s'}(a)$. Finally $\psi(s)$ is open. Consider $U = U(s_0)$. Then let W^{a_0} be a canonical pair with $s_0 \subset V^{a_0}$ and $U^{a_0} \subset U(s_0)$. For this fixed a_0, $\{s \mid u_{a_0}(s) < 1\} = Q \subset U$ yields an open set $N(s_0) = \{T_s \mid T_s(a_0) \in Q\}$ such that $\psi(U) \supset N$. Thus the points of S may be identified with the functions on A. Since I_a is compact $\bar{S} = \beta(S)$ is compact.

Evidently if $f(s)$ is continuous and bounded on S to R then *f can be uniquely* extended to $\beta(S)$. In fact $\beta(S)$ is the largest compact space in which S is dense for which this extension property is valid.

We give one other compactification useful in grating theory.

Definition 15.5. If S is locally compact but not compact let the neighborhoods of the ideal point ∞ be the complements of compact sets in S. Thus F closed and not compact in S yields $\bar{F} = F \cup \infty$.

Theorem 15.6. *If S is locally compact, $S \cup \infty$ is compact.*

Thus the real line with the 1-point compactification becomes the circle; the plane becomes the sphere, etc.

If E is a T_2 locally compact connected space, but not σ-locally compact, then $E \cup \infty$ is a paracompact space such that elision of one point, ∞, destroys paracompactness; cf. Theorem 12.2.

Theorem 15.7. *If S is compact Hausdorff and K is the family of all closed and open sets K_a containing s_0 then $\bigcap K_a$ is connected.*

If not, $\bigcap K_a = F^1 \cup F^2$ for two disjunct closed nonvacuous sets. Normality guarantees the existence of open sets G^1 and G^2 with (1) $\bar{G}^1 \cap \bar{G}^2 = \varnothing$ and $F^1 \subset G^i \subset \bar{G}^i$. The complement, E, of $G^1 \cup G^2$ is compact. Suppose $K_a \cap E = \varnothing$. Then $K_a = K_a^1 \cup K_a^2$ where $K_a^i \subset G^i$, $i = 1, 2$. Now $K_a^i = K_a \cap G^i$ is open in G^i and therefore in S. Since K_a is closed it is also given by $\bar{K}_a^1 \cup K_a^2$. If K_a^1 were properly contained in $\bar{K}_a^1$ we should have $\bar{K}_a^1 \cap K_a^2 \neq \varnothing$ in contradiction with (1). In short K_a^1 is both open and closed and is disjunct from F^2 whence we derive the contradiction $\bigcap K_a = F^1$. We have therefore shown $K_a \cap E \neq \varnothing$. Observe $\bigcap_{i=1}^{i=N} K_{a_i}$ is open and closed and is a member of K so $\{K_a \cap E\}$ is a family of closed sets with the F.I.P. Accordingly $\varnothing \neq E \cap \bigcap K_a$ which is inconsistent with the definition of E. The compactness of S is necessary for the validity of the theorem.

EXAMPLE 7. A case where S is metric (and therefore normal) but not compact and the theorem above fails to hold is

$$S = \bigcup \left\{ \left(\frac{1}{n}, y \right) \middle| \, |y| \leq 1 \right\} \cup (0, 1) \cup (0, -1).$$

$K_n = \left\{ \left(\frac{1}{m}, y \right) \middle| \, n \leq m, |y| \leq 1 \right\}$. $\bar{K}_n$ is open and closed and so are (0, 1) and (0, -1). Yet $\bigcap \bar{K}_n = (0, 1) \cup (0, -1)$ in contradiction to the assertion of the theorem.

16. PARTITION OF UNITY **Theorem 16.1.** *Let S be either* **(a)** *normal or* **(b)** *locally compact. Let $\mu = \{U_a \mid a \in A\}$ be a locally finite cover and let the elements of μ have compact closures in case* **(b)**. *Then there exist continuous functions $\{f_a(s) \mid A\}$ on S to $0 \leq t \leq 1$, such that* (16.1a) $\{s \mid f_a(s) > 0\} \subset U_a$ *and* (16.1b) $\Sigma\, f_a(s) = 1$.

In either case we can shrink μ onto $\nu = \{V_a \mid \bar{V}_a \subset U_a\}$. In **(a)** let $u_a(s)$ be the Urysohn function $u(s, U_a^{\sim}, V_a^{\sim})$ shown to exist in the course of the proof of Theorem 13.2. The local finiteness of μ implies that for each s, $\{a \mid u_a(s) > 0\}$ is a finite set. Hence we can write $\Sigma_A\, u_a(s)$. Define $f_a(s)$ by $f_a(s) = u_a(s)/\Sigma_A\, u_a(s)$. These functions satisfy the conditions of the theorem.

Definition 16.2. The collection $\{f_a(s)\}$ occurring in the preceeding theorem is referred to as a **partition of unity** associated with the open cover μ.

Theorem 16.3. *S, T compact Hausdorff, f maps $S \times T$ into the real line $R \Rightarrow$ for $\delta > 0$ there is a positive integer $M(\delta)$ and maps $f^i(-)$, $h^i(-)$, $i = 1, \ldots, M(\delta)$ continuous on S and T to the real line such that*

$$|f(s, t) - \Sigma f^i(s) h^i(t)| < \delta.$$

Observe $f(-, -)$ is uniformly continuous. For (s_0, t_0) let $U(s_0) \times V(t_0) = \{(s, t) \mid |f(s, t) - f(s_0, t_0)| < \delta\}$. By the compactness a finite number of such sets span $S \times T$. That is to say for $\varepsilon > 0$ there is an open cover $\mu = \{U_j \mid j = 1, \ldots, M(\varepsilon)\}$ of S and an open cover $\nu = \{V_h \mid h = 1, \ldots, N(\varepsilon)\}$ of T such that

(16.3a) $\quad |f(s, t) - f(s', t')| < \delta, (s, t) \cup (s', t') \in U_j \times V_j.$

Let $\{f^i(s) \mid i = 1, \ldots, M(\delta)\}$ be the functions related to $\{U_i\}$ with the properties (16.1a) and (16.1b). Let $\{g^i(t) \mid i = 1, \ldots, N(\delta)\}$ be the similar functions related to $\{V_i\}$. Let s^i satisfy $f^i(s^i) > 0$ and let t^j satisfy $g^j(t^j) > 0$. Then

(16.3b) $\quad f(s, t) - \Sigma_1^{M(\delta)} \Sigma_1^{N(\delta)} f(s^i, t^j) f^i(s) g^j(t)$

$$= \Sigma_1^{M(\delta)} \Sigma_1^{N(\delta)} f^i(s) g^j(t)(f(s, t) - f(s^i, t^j)).$$

on utilizing property (16.1b) for $\{f^i(s)\}$ and $\{g^j(t)\}$. When $(s, t) \in U_i \times V_j$, (16.3a) applies. Otherwise $f^i(s) g^j(t) = 0$. Write $h^i(t) = \Sigma_{j=1}^{j=N(\delta)} f(s^i, t^j) g^j(t)$. Then (16.3b) takes the form of the assertion of the theorem.

17. TOPOLOGIES ON SPACES OF MAPPINGS. **Definition 17.1.** A topological space whose elements are maps on X to B is denoted by $B^X = \{f\}$. The following are some of the topologies on B^X in use.

The **compact-open** or **co-open topology**, or ***k*-topology**, is defined by a subbasis (defined by (17.1b)) of open neighborhoods.

(17.1a) $M(C; O) = \{f \mid f(C) \subset O, C \text{ a compact set of } X, O \text{ an open set of } B\}$.

The **point open topology** has the subbasis of open neighborhoods

$$M(x; O) = \{f \mid f(x) \subset O, x \in X, O \text{ open in } B\}.$$

Thus the general neighborhood is given by unions of

(17.1b) $$\bigcap_{i=1}^{i=N} M(C_i, O_i)$$

or of

(17.1c) $$\bigcap_{i=1}^{i=N} M(x_i, O_i).$$

If B is a metric space with metric ρ, the **metric topology** of B^X or ***d*-topology** is defined by the neighborhood system

$$N(f_0) = \{f \mid sup_B\, \rho(f_0(x), f(x)) < \delta\}.$$

The metric topology is not completely determined by the topologies of X and B as is the co-open topology, but may vary with change of metric from one metric to an equivalent one (unless suitable conditions like compactness are introduced).

Example 8. $X =$ positive integers $B = 0, 1, B^X = \{\text{sequences of } 0, 1\text{'s}\}$. In the k-topology B^X is separable. In the d-topology it is discrete but the number of sequences is $\aleph$ and this is the power of a neighborhood basis.

Theorem 17.2. *If X, Y is locally compact and if W^X has the k-topology then $(W^X)^Z$ is homeomorphic to $W^{X \times Z}$.*

Definition 17.3. Let f transform X to Y. Suppose $A \subset X$, then A is **saturated** with respect to f if $f^{-1}f(A) = A$

Example 9. $X = Y =$ real numbers, $A = 1 \leq y \leq 2$. Then, if $f(x) = x^2$, A is not saturated since $f^{-1}f(A) = A \cup \{x \mid -2 \leq x \leq -1\}$

A topology of wide utility in mapping triples is the **identification topology** or **quotient topology** under f defined by taking, as open (closed) sets in Y, the maps of open (closed) saturated sets in X.

Theorem 17.4. *The finest topology for Y under which f is continuous is the identification topology.*

Thus if f is continuous and O is open in Y then $f^{-1}(O) = W$ is saturated and is open and so O is open in the identification topology of Y.

Definition 17.5. Let X be a space and let R be an equivalence relation between its points. In particular a transformation $f: X \to Y$ defines an equivalence relation by $x \sim x^1$ if $f(x) = f(x^1)$. The graph $\Gamma(R)$ of R is defined by

$$\Gamma(R) = \{(x, x') \mid x' \sim x\} \subset X \times X$$

Denote by X/R, the space of elements, $\{[x] = \{x' \mid x' \sim x\}\}$, under the identification topology. Generally the notation p is used for the projection (or natural projection)

$$X \xrightarrow{p} X/R,$$

where

$$px = [x].$$

Definition 17.6. The equivalence relation R is **open**, or **closed**, provided the associated projection p is open, or closed. (cf. Definition 4.4)

EXAMPLE 10. **(a)** A nonopen relation is defined by identifying 1 and $\frac{1}{2}$ in I. Then the map by p of the open set $\frac{1}{2} < t \leq 1$ is not an open set. **(b)** Let X be the Euclidean plane with coordinates x_1, x_2 and let Y be the unit square. Let $p(x_1, x_2) = x_1 \bmod 1, x_2 \bmod 1$. Then, the line $x_2 = \alpha x_1$, with α irrational maps into a dense proper subset of Y so p is not closed. It is open however.

By combining **(a)** and **(b)** an example of a relation which is neither open nor closed is obtained.

NOTATION. I or $I_t = \{t \mid 0 \leq t \leq 1\}$.

Definition 17.7. The map $h: Y \times I \to X$ is a **homotopy** of Y **over** X **relative** to A if $h(A, t)$ is independent of $t \in I_t$. The map

$$h: (Y, A) \times I \to X, B$$

is a homotopy of the pair Y, A into X, B if $h(A, t) \subset B$.
The homotopy h is **weak** if $h(a, 0) \cup h(a, 1) \subset B$ though $h(a, t)$ need not be in B for $t \neq 0, 1$.

We say $h(-, 0) = f_0$ and $h(-, 1) = f_1$ are **homotopic**. If $Y = X$ and $h(-, 0)$ is the identity, h is a **deformation** though sometimes merely the end result, namely $h(-, 1)$, is called a deformation.

EXAMPLE 11. Let Y be the unit circle about 0 in the plane X. Let (y, r) be polar coordinates, $0 \leq y < 2\pi$. Then Y can be deformed into 0 by a deformation h given by

$$h(y, t) = (y, t), \qquad 0 \leq t \leq 1.$$

Definition 17.8. Let ψ map X onto Y. In the disjoint union $Z = X \times I \cup Y$ identify $x \times 1$ and $y = \psi(x)$ to get an identification space C_ψ called the **mapping cylinder**. (If X and Y are replaced by X, x_0 and Y, y_0 the further identification of $x_0 \times I$ and y_0 is made.) The natural projection of Z onto C_φ is denoted by p.

Lemma 17.9. (a) *If* $i(x) = p(x \times 0)$, *i imbeds* X *in* $p(X \times 0) \subset C_\varphi$.

(b) p *is a homeomorphism on* Y *into* C_φ.

(c) Y *is a deformation of* C_φ.

For (c) define the deformation h on $C_\varphi \times I$ to Y by

$$h(x \times t, u) = p(x, t + u(1 - t)), \qquad h(y, u) = y$$

for $0 \leq t \leq 1, \quad 0 \leq u \leq 1.$

SPECIAL SYMBOLS

HOMOLOGY AND HOMOTOPY SYMBOLS

BIBLIOGRAPHY

The bibliography lists some of the articles that have influenced this book. Many innovators are either not listed or are inadequately listed if their contributions occur in cited articles or books. Besides, an arbitrary cut-off has been applied of two papers typical for our applications per author.

BOOKS

Alexandroff, P., and Hopf, H. *Topologie*. Berlin: Springer (1935).

Borel, A. "Cohomologie des espaces localement compacts d'après J. Leray." *Notes*. Zurich (1957).

———, *Seminar on Transformation Groups*. Princeton: The University Press (1960).

Cairns, S. S. *Introductory Topology*. New York: Ronald (1962).

Cartan, H., and Eilenberg S. *Homological Algebra*. Princeton: The University Press (1956).

Eilenberg, S., and Steenrod, N. *Foundations of Algebraic Topology*. Princeton: The University Press (1952).

Godement, R. *Topologie algébrique et théorie des faisceaux*. Paris: Hermann (1958).

Hilton, P. J., and Wiley, S. *Homology Theory*. Cambridge: The University Press (1960).

Hirzebuch, F. *Neue topologische Methoden in der algebraicschen Geometrie*. Berlin: Springer (1956).

Hocking, J. G., and Young, G. S. *Topology*. Reading, Mass.: Addison-Wesley (1961).

Hu, S. T. *Homotopy Theory*. New York: Academic Press (1959).

Lefschetz, S. *Algebraic Topology*. AMS Colloquium Publications, Vol. 27. New York (1930).

Seifert, H., and Threlfall, W. *Lehrbuch der Topologie*. Leipzig: Teubner (1934).

Steenrod, N. *The Topology of Fibre Bundles*. Princeton: The University Press (1951).

Wallace, A. H. *Homology Theory on Algebraic Varieties*. New York: Pergamon Press (1958).

Wilder, R. L. *Topology of Manifolds*. AMS Colloquium Publications, Vol. 32. New York (1949).

ARTICLES

Borel, A. "Sur la Cohomologie des espaces fibrés principaux et des espaces homogènes de groupes de Lie compacts," *Annals of Mathematics*, **57** (1953), 115–207.

Borsuk, K. "Drei Sätze über die n-dimensionale Euklidische Sphare," *Fundamenta Mathematicae*, **20** (1932), 177–190.

Bourgin, D. G. "Deformation and mapping theorems," *Fundamenta Mathematicae*, **46** (1959), 285–303.

———, "Some separation and mapping theorems," *Commentarii Mathematici Helvetici*, **29** (1955), 199–214.

Browder, F. E. "On the fixed point index for continuous mappings of locally connected spaces," *Summa Brasiliensis Mathematicae*, **4** (1960), 253–293.

Buchsbaum, D. "Exact categories and duality," *Transactions American Mathematical Society*, **80** (1955), 1–34.

Chogosvili, C. "On homology theory of non-closed sets," Prague Conference (1961).

Dowker, D. H. "Mapping theorems for non-compact spaces," *American Journal of Mathematics*, **49** (1947), 200–242.

Dugundji, J. "A generalization of Tietze's theorem," *Pacific Journal of Mathematics*, **1** (1951), 353–367.

Eckman, B., and Hilton, P. J. "Operators and cooperators in homotopy theory," *Mathematische Annalen*, **141** (1960), 1–21.

Eilenberg, S. "On the problems of topology," *Annals of Mathematics*, **50** (1949), 247–260.

Eilenberg, S., and MacLane, S. "Acyclic models," *American Journal of Mathematics*, **75** (1953), 180–199.

Fary, I. "Sur une nouvelle démonstration de l'unicité de l'algèbre de cohomologie à supports compacte d'un espace localement compact," *Comptes Rendus de l'Académie* (Paris), **237** (1953), 582–554.

Floyd, E. E. "On periodic maps and the Euler characteristic of associated spaces," *Transactions of the American Mathematical Society*, **72** (1952), 138–147.

Fox, R. H. "Homotopy groups and torus homotopy groups," *Annals of Mathematics*, **49** (1948), 471–510.

Fuller, F. B. "The homotopy theory of coincidences," *Annals of Mathematics*, **59** (1954), 219–226.

Gray, J. W. "Sheaves with values in a category," *NSF Report G 1 9022*.

Grothendieck, A. "Sur quelques points d'algèbre homologique," *Tohoku Mathematical Journal*, **9** (1957), 119–221.

Heller, A. "On equivariant maps of spaces with operators," *Annals of Mathematics*, **55** (1952), 223–231.

Higman, G., and Stone, A. H. "On inverse systems with trivial limits," *London Mathematical Society Journal*, **29** (1954), 233–236.

Hirsch, G. "Quelques théorèmes sur les points fixes des groupes de représentations," *Société Royale des Sciences de Liége*, **6** (1943), 392–407.

Hopf, H. "Über du Topologie der gruppen-mannig Faltigkerten und ihre Verallgemeinerungen," *Annals of Mathematics*, **42** (1941), 22–52.

———, "Eine Verallgemeinerung Bekannter Abbildungs und Uberdeckungs satze," *Portugalise Mathematica*, **4** (1943), 129–139.

Hu, S. T. "On fiberings with singularities," *Michigan Mathematical Journal*, **6** (1959), 131–149.

Kan, D. M. "Adjoint functors," *Transactions American Mathematical Society*, **87** (1958), 295–329.

Leray, J. "Sur les équations et les transformations," *Journal Mathematiques Pures et Appliquées*, **24** (1945), 201–248.

———, "L'anneau spectral et l'anneau filtre d'homologie d'un espace localement compact et d'une application continue," *ibid.*, **29** (1950), 1–139, 169–213.

Livesay, G. "On a theorem of F. J. Dyson," *Annals of Mathematics*, **59** (1954), 227–229.

———, "Fixed point free involutions on the 3-sphere," *ibid.*, **72** (1960), 603–611.

Milnor, J. W., and Moore, J. C., "On the structure of Hopf algebras," Air Force Report.

O'Neill, B. "Essential sets and fixed points," *American Journal of Mathematics*, **75** (1953), 497–509.

O'Neill, B., and Strauss, E. G. "A fixed point theorem," *Proceedings of the American Mathematical Society*, **8** (1957), 1148–1151.

Raymond, F. "The end point compactification of manifolds," *Pacific Journal*, **10** (1960), 947–963.

———, "Local cohomology groups with closed support," *Mathematische Zeitschrift* (1960).

Smith, P. A. Appendix to Lefschetz, S. *Algebraic Topology*. AMS Colloquium Publications, Vol. 27. New York (1930).

———, "Fixed point theorems for periodic transformations," *American Journal of Mathematics*, **63** (1941), 1–8.

Spanier, E. H. "Cohomology theory for general spaces," *Annals of Mathematics*, **49** (1948), 407–427.

Steenrod, N. "Cohomology operations and obstructions to extending continuous functions," *AFOSR TN 57-548*.

Swan, R. G. "A new method in fixed point theory," *Commentarii Mathematici Helvetici*, **34** (1960), 1–16.

Yang, C. T. "On theorems of Borsuk-Ulam, Kakutani-Yamabe-Yujobô and Dyson," *Annals of Mathematics* (I) **60** (1954), 262–282; (II) **62** (1955), 271–283.

Wu Wen-Tsün. "On the relations between Smith operations and Steenrod powers," *Fundamenta Mathematicae*, **44** (1957), 262–269.

Zeeman, E. C. "On the filtered differential group," *Annals of Mathematics*, **66** (1957), 557.

INDEX